About the editors—

EMIL THOMAS KAISER is currently an Associate Professor of Chemistry at the University of Chicago.

He received the B.S. degree from the University of Chicago, and the M.A. and Ph.D. degrees from Harvard University. A member of Phi Beta Kappa, Dr. Kaiser's academic honors have included: a Ford Foundation scholarship, National Science Foundation predoctoral fellowships and National Institute of Health predoctoral and postdoctoral fellowships. He was recently awarded an Alfred P. Sloan Foundation Fellowship.

He was an Associate Director of the Princeton University Conference on the Chemistry of Sulfur (1966), and is a member of the Advisory Council on College Chemistry.

Dr. Kaiser has published more than 35 papers in the areas of electron spin resonance of radical anions and mechanistic, organic, and biological chemistry.

LARRY KEVAN is an Associate Professor of Chemistry at the University of Kansas.

He received the B.S. degree from the University of Kansas, and the Ph.D. degree from the University of California, Los Angeles.

Dr. Kevan is a member of Phi Beta Kappa, and has received a Summerfield Scholarship, a Woodrow Wilson Fellowship, and National Science Foundation Fellowships (1960-1963).

He has published more than 30 papers in areas of ionic reactions in condensed phases, electron spin resonance of trapped electrons, and in radiation chemistry.

RADICAL IONS

REACTIVE INTERMEDIATES IN ORGANIC CHEMISTRY

Edited by GEORGE A. OLAH and LESTER FRIEDMAN
Case Western Reserve University

A series of collective volumes and monographs on the chemistry of all the important species of organic reaction intermediates:

CARBONIUM IONS 4 vols.

Edited by George A. Olah of Case Western Reserve University and Paul v. R. Schleyer of Princeton University (1968–)

RADICAL IONS

Edited by E. T. Kaiser of the University of Chicago and L. Kevan of the University of Kansas (1968)

Planned for the Series

NITRENES

Edited by W. Lwowski of New Mexico State University

CARBANIONS

Edited by R. Waack of the Dow Chemical Company

CARBENES

Edited by L. Friedman of Case Western Reserve University

FREE RADICALS

Edited by J. K. Kochi of Case Western Reserve University

ARYNES

Edited by R. M. Stiles of The University of Michigan

RADICAL IONS

Edited by

E. T. KAISER

Department of Chemistry
University of Chicago
Chicago, Illinois

L. KEVAN

Department of Chemistry
University of Kansas
Lawrence, Kansas

INTERSCIENCE PUBLISHERS

a division of John Wiley & Sons, New York · London · Sydney

Copyright © 1968 by John Wiley & Sons, Inc.
Library of Congress Catalog Card Number: 67-20263
Printed in the United States of America

Preface

Progress has been rapid in radical ion chemistry during the past several years. Radical ions have been studied in a variety of contexts by both organic and physical chemists. We have construed the definition of radical ion to include not only relatively stable aromatic systems that can exist in solution, but also transition metal complex ions as well as unstable organic and inorganic species that are stabilized in solids. This book draws together much that is relevant within these areas. More attention has been paid to recent developments than to older and previously reviewed work such as that on aromatic radical anions. In particular, the complementary aspects of the characterization of radical ions in solids and in solution have been stressed.

The investigation of radical ions involves their generation, identification, spin density determination, and reactivity. All of these aspects are treated in the present book. In addition to the conventional methods of generation by chemical reduction and oxidation in solution, and by electrochemical means, several chapters describe how gamma radiation can be used to produce new types of radical ions.

Identification has largely been performed by EPR, but optical methods are also often useful. Consequently, although most of the chapters deal with EPR methods, the power of optical techniques is discussed for organic and inorganic glasses.

The determination of spin densities from experimental data on radical ions and the concomitant testing of molecular orbital theory has been of major importance. The present situation is summarized in the book for organic and inorganic systems.

Reactivity of radical ions is a new and exciting area, as is illustrated by a number of the contributions. Russell has utilized their reactivity in an elegant fashion to generate new radical ions. Hirota has thoroughly examined the complex equilibria which are found for ketyl radical ions, species which are of great interest in organic and biological chemistry. Hamill has developed an outline of radical ion chemistry in the organic solid state involving selective electron and positive ion transfer.

This book should be useful to a wide spectrum of readers, both novitiates and experts. By cutting across diverse fields of chemistry the authors hope to set the stage for catalysis of innovative ideas in radical ion chemistry.

v

We wish to express our appreciation to our secretaries, Hanna Posner and Naida Jimenez, for their invaluable aid and patience. We would like also to thank all the contributors to this book, who made it possible.

E. T. KAISER
LARRY KEVAN

January 1968

Authors

JAMES R. BOLTON, *Department of Chemistry, University of Minnesota, Minneapolis, Minnesota*

HILARY J. BOWER, *Department of Chemistry, The University, Leicester, England*

KERRY W. BOWERS, *Department of Chemistry and Research Laboratory of Electronics, Massachusetts Institute of Technology, Cambridge, Massachusetts*

JOSEPH CUNNINGHAM, *Chemistry Department, University College, Dublin, Ireland*

WILLIAM H. HAMILL, *Department of Chemistry and the Radiation Laboratory, University of Notre Dame, Notre Dame, Indiana*

NOBORU HIROTA, *Department of Chemistry, State University of New York at Stony Brook, Stony Brook, New York*

M. THOMAS JONES, *Department of Chemistry, St. Louis University, St. Louis, Missouri*

E. T. KAISER, *Department of Chemistry, University of Chicago, Chicago, Illinois*

H. A. KUSKA, *Department of Chemistry, University of Akron, Akron, Ohio*

MAX T. ROGERS, *Department of Chemistry, Michigan State University, East Lansing, Michigan*

GLEN A. RUSSELL, *Department of Chemistry, Iowa State University, Ames, Iowa*

M. C. R. SYMONS, *Department of Chemistry, The University, Leicester, England*

D. J. A. TINLING, *Department of Chemistry, The University, Leicester, England*

A. TREININ, *Department of Physical Chemistry, The Hebrew University, Jerusalem, Israel*

M. M. URBERG, *Department of Chemistry, University of Chicago, Chicago, Illinois*

GRANT URRY, *Department of Chemistry, Purdue University, Lafayette, Indiana*

GERSHON VINCOW, *Department of Chemistry, University of Washington, Seattle, Washington*

Contents

CHAPTER 1

Electron Spin Densities

JAMES R. BOLTON*

Department of Chemistry, University of Minnesota, Minneapolis, Minnesota

I. INTRODUCTION

A. Scope of the Article

The technique of electron spin resonance spectroscopy is obviously of central importance to the study of radical ions. The paramagnetism of these molecules provides a very sensitive probe into their detailed electronic structure. Specifically, it is possible in many cases to obtain a picture of the distribution of the unpaired electron (or more generally the distribution of the unpaired electron spin) over the molecule. Thus, it is appropriate that this treatise concerning radical ions begin with a discussion of what is meant by the term "electron spin density," and how spin densities (unless

* Alfred P. Sloan Foundation Research Fellow.

stated otherwise, the term "spin density" will imply "electron spin density") can be elucidated from experimental observables. This is not an easy task because, like many physical concepts of molecular structure, spin density is a theoretical concept which must be related to experimental observables (such as hyperfine couplings, g values, chemical shifts, etc.) by relations usually theoretically derived and tested by correlations with experimental data. Therefore, most of this article will be devoted to an exposition of the various relations which have been used to connect spin densities with experimental observables.

The importance of obtaining experimental estimates of spin densities lies in the fact that spin densities can be calculated with ease from approximate wave functions. Thus, "experimental" spin densities provide a sensitive test of the validity of the approximations which are inherent in molecular wave functions for any but the simplest molecules. We shall indicate how spin densities can be calculated from molecular wave functions, but the actual calculation of these wave functions is beyond the scope of this article.

B. Definitions

A density function implies units of something per unit volume—where the something could be grams, electrons, spin angular momentum, etc. Thus, when using the term spin density, care must be taken to specify the volume in which the spin density is to be determined. This volume could be a point in space defined by $d\tau = (dxdydz)$ at (x, y, z) or a finite volume such as an atomic orbital. To formulate a definition of spin density, we must introduce the complete wave function, Ψ, of a molecule. We shall consider a normalized spin density function $\rho(x, y, z)$ at the point (x, y, z) to be defined by:

$$\rho(x, y, z) = S_z^{-1} \langle \Psi | \sum_k \hat{S}_{kz} \, \delta(r_k) \, | \Psi \rangle \tag{1}$$

where S_z is the eigenvalue of the z component of the total spin angular momentum operator, $\hat{S}_{kz}$ is the operator for the z component of electron spin for electron k, and $\delta(r_k)$ is the Dirac delta function of the distance r_k between the electron k and the point (x, y, z) (1).

Since the operation of $\hat{S}_{kz}$ on Ψ can have only two eigenvalues ($\pm \frac{1}{2}$) corresponding to whether the electron has α or β spin, it would perhaps be easier to visualize the spin density concept by reformulating equation 1 in the following manner (2):

$$\rho(x, y, z) = P(x, y, z, \alpha) - P(x, y, z, \beta) \tag{2}$$

Here $P(x, y, z, \alpha)$ represents the probability density of α spin at the point (x, y, z) and $P(x, y, z, \beta)$ the probability density of β spin at (x, y, z). It is easily seen that the absolute value of each of the terms of the summation in equation 1 represents the electron density of the electron k. Thus, the total electron density, $q(x, y, z)$, will be given by:

$$q(x, y, z) = P(x, y, z, \alpha) + P(x, y, z, \beta) \tag{3}$$

The spin density then is simply the difference in electron density between electrons of α spin and electrons of β spin at the point (x, y, z). By convention, for purposes of calculating spin densities, the overall orientation of spin in a free radical is taken to be α, although there may be regions in the molecule where the spin density may be negative (3) (i.e., electrons of β spin predominating over electrons of α spin).

The foregoing definition implies that spin density is a many-electron function. How is this possible when a free radical contains only one unpaired electron? It is true that the *unpaired-electron density* usually closely parallels the *spin density* in a given region of the molecule, but due to electron correlation effects the distributions of the paired electrons become "polarized" so that local unpairing of spins results. Consequently, in some regions of the molecule, the spin density can differ markedly in both sign and magnitude from the unpaired-electron density, which must be positive everywhere since it is a one-electron function. Interchange of the terms "spin density" and "unpaired-electron density" has led to much confusion in the past.

Usually we are interested in the spin density around a given atom, i, in a molecule and, in particular, the spin density in a given atomic orbital, φ, on that atom. Thus, we shall define an *atomic orbital spin density*, ρ_i^φ, by:

$$\rho_i^\varphi = P_i^\varphi(\alpha) - P_i^\varphi(\beta) \tag{4}$$

where now the region of interest for the probabilities $P_i^\varphi(\alpha)$ and $P_i^\varphi(\beta)$ is the atomic orbital, φ, on the atom i.

Up to this point the complete molecular wave function, Ψ, has not been specified. It is usual to express Ψ as an antisymmetrized product of orthonormal molecular orbitals, Φ. In this case, the spin density, ρ, must be formulated in terms of the elements, $\bar{\rho}_{ij}$, of a molecular orbital spin density matrix, $\bar{\rho}$, defined by:

$$\rho = \sum_{ij} \bar{\rho}_{ij} \Phi_i^* \Phi_j \tag{5}$$

where ρ and $\bar{\rho}_{ij}$ refer to the same volume element (1). Since the Φ_i are orthogonal, $\bar{\rho}$ is a diagonal matrix with a trace of unity.

Ψ may also be expressed in terms of a set of normalized atomic orbitals, φ_λ, which will, in general, not be orthogonal. ρ must then be formulated in terms of the elements, $\rho_{\lambda\mu}$, of an *atomic orbital spin density matrix*, ρ, defined by:

$$\rho = \sum_{\lambda\mu} \rho_{\lambda\mu} \varphi_\mu^* \varphi_\lambda \tag{6}$$

In the linear combination of atomic orbitals (LCAO) approximation for the molecular orbitals, $\bar{\rho}_{ij}$, $\rho_{\lambda\mu}$, and Φ_i are related by:

$$\rho_{\lambda\mu} = \sum_{ij} \bar{\rho}_{ij} a_{\mu j}^* a_{\lambda i} \qquad (7)$$

where

$$\Phi_i = \sum_{\lambda} a_{\lambda i} \varphi_\lambda \qquad (8)$$

Since the φ_λ are not orthogonal, there will be nondiagonal elements in the matrix, ρ, which may be interpreted as measuring spin angular momentum that is concentrated between atoms and cannot be assigned uniquely to any particular atom. The diagonal elements $\rho_{\lambda\lambda}$ of the atomic orbital spin density matrix are just the atomic orbital spin densities defined by equation 4. However, due to the nonorthogonality of the atomic orbitals, the trace of ρ will not be unity.

As an example of a spin density matrix, consider that for the allyl radical:

$$\overset{1}{H_2C}-\overset{2}{CH}-\overset{3}{CH_2}$$

McConnell (1) has calculated the following spin density matrix for this molecule using molecular orbital wave functions calculated by Chalvet and Daudel (4):

$$\rho = \begin{bmatrix} 0.5694 & -0.0063 & -0.3349 \\ -0.0063 & -0.1055 & -0.0063 \\ -0.3349 & -0.0063 & 0.5694 \end{bmatrix} \qquad (9)$$

The diagonal elements are the atomic orbital spin densities. These sum to 1.0334, which implies that the spin density in the π bonds must be -0.0334. The spin density in each overlap region is obtained by multiplying the appropriate off-diagonal element in ρ by the overlap integral for that region. Note that the approximation of placing all the spin density on the individual atomic orbitals is quite good, since, at least in this case, only 3% of the spin density is in the overlap regions. In the discussion that follows, we shall ignore, for the most part, spin densities in overlap regions between atoms and consider only the diagonal elements of the spin density matrix. We shall also approximate the trace of the atomic orbital spin density matrix, ρ, as unity.

When wave functions are calculated using the Hückel LCAO-MO method (5), then the spin density is the same as the unpaired electron density, namely, $\rho_\lambda = |a_{\lambda i}|^2$ where the unpaired electron is located in the molecular orbital, Φ_i, and the spin density is being evaluated for the atomic orbital φ_λ. The $a_{\lambda i}$ is the coefficient of φ_λ in the molecular orbital, Φ_i.

II. RELATIONS BETWEEN SPIN DENSITIES AND EXPERIMENTAL OBSERVABLES

A. Proton Hyperfine Splittings in Planar Radicals

1. The McConnell Relation

Proton hyperfine splittings in the electron spin resonance spectra of radical ions have provided a wealth of information concerning the spin density distributions in these molecules (6). In order to obtain these "experimental" spin densities, a relation must be found to connect the observed hyperfine splittings with the individual spin densities.

When the first electron spin resonance spectrum of an organic radical ion, the naphthalene negative ion, was observed by Weissman et al. (7), it was somewhat of a surprise that proton hyperfine splittings were observed at all. Isotropic proton hyperfine splittings can arise only from a net spin density at the proton and since the protons in naphthalene lie in the nodal plane of the π orbitals in which the unpaired electron was expected to reside, no proton hyperfine splittings are possible in zero order. However, this apparent paradox was resolved when McConnell, utilizing a valence bond calculation (8), and Weissman, using a molecular orbital calculation (9), showed that spin density could be induced at the proton via a mechanism called "spin polarization." Because of the importance of this McConnell relation in the interpretation of ESR hyperfine splittings, a full derivation will be given. The derivation to follow will use the valence bond method (3) although virtually the identical result is obtained using the molecular orbital method (3,9).

We shall consider a three-electron system comprising a CH radical fragment in a conjugated hydrocarbon:

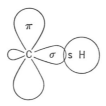

Here π is a $2p_z$ atomic orbital on carbon, σ is an sp^2 hybrid orbital on carbon pointing to the hydrogen atom, and s is a $1s$ orbital on hydrogen. In a valence bond description retaining all neutral structures with one electron in each orbital there would be eight different structures corresponding to the eight ways of specifying the electron spins. These eight spin functions would be:

$$\alpha\alpha\alpha, \quad \alpha\alpha\beta, \quad \alpha\beta\alpha, \quad \beta\alpha\alpha, \quad \beta\beta\alpha, \quad \beta\alpha\beta, \quad \alpha\beta\beta, \quad \beta\beta\beta$$

These functions fall into four classes according to whether the eigenvalue, M_S, of the z component, $\hat{S}_z$, of the total spin is $+^3/_2$, $+^1/_2$, $-^1/_2$, or $-^3/_2$. There must be one set of four functions which corresponds to an eigenvalue of $\hat{S}^2$ equal to $^{15}/_4$ (i.e., $S = ^3/_2$). This leaves two sets of two functions with eigenvalue of $\hat{S}^2$ equal to $^3/_4$ (i.e., $S = ^1/_2$). In order to obtain these spin eigenfunctions, the functions with a given eigenvalue of S_z must be orthogonalized. The resulting spin eigenfunctions are (10,11):

$$
\begin{array}{ll}
 & M_S \\
\alpha\alpha\alpha & +^3/_2 \\
(1/\sqrt{3})(\alpha\alpha\beta + \alpha\beta\alpha + \beta\alpha\alpha) & +^1/_2 \\
(1/\sqrt{3})(\beta\beta\alpha + \beta\alpha\beta + \alpha\beta\beta) & -^1/_2 \\
\beta\beta\beta & -^3/_2
\end{array} \Bigg\} \; S = ^3/_2
$$

$$
\begin{array}{ll}
(1/\sqrt{6})(\alpha\alpha\beta + \alpha\beta\alpha - 2\beta\alpha\alpha) & +^1/_2 \\
(1/\sqrt{6})(\beta\beta\alpha + \beta\alpha\beta - 2\alpha\beta\beta) & -^1/_2
\end{array} \Bigg\} \; S = ^1/_2
$$

$$
\begin{array}{ll}
(1/\sqrt{2})(\alpha\beta\alpha - \alpha\alpha\beta) & +^1/_2 \\
(1/\sqrt{2})(\beta\alpha\beta - \beta\beta\alpha) & -^1/_2
\end{array} \Bigg\} \; S = ^1/_2
$$

$$(10)$$

In the CH fragment we are dealing with a doublet state ($S = ^1/_2$); therefore, we need to consider only the doublet spin functions. Furthermore, by convention we are assigning $M_S = +^1/_2$ for the whole fragment, so there are only two functions remaining:

$$(1/\sqrt{2})(\alpha\beta\alpha - \alpha\alpha\beta) \tag{11a}$$

$$(1/\sqrt{6})(\alpha\alpha\beta + \alpha\beta\alpha - 2\beta\alpha\alpha) \tag{11b}$$

The first of these obviously corresponds to the ground state, since it represents a valence bond between σ and s. The ground state wave function will thus be written:

$$\psi_1 = \frac{1}{(1 + S_0^2)^{1/2}} \frac{1}{\sqrt{6}} \|\pi(1)\sigma(2)s(3)\| \frac{1}{\sqrt{2}} (\alpha\beta\alpha - \alpha\alpha\beta) \tag{12}$$

where S_0 is the overlap integral between σ and s and the double lines represent a determinantal wave function. The spin values refer sequentially to electrons 1, 2, and 3.

It can be seen that ψ_1 represents perfect pairing of spins between σ and s. This means that there will be no spin density in the hydrogen $1s$ orbital in the ground state. In order to introduce the required electron correlation, we must invoke configuration interaction with an excited state. It has already been shown that the only excited state which can mix with the ground state corresponds to the spin function (eq. 11b). The resulting wave function will be:

$$\psi_2 = \frac{1}{(1 - S_0^2)^{1/2}} \frac{1}{\sqrt{6}} \|\pi(1)\sigma(2)s(3)\| \frac{1}{\sqrt{6}} (\alpha\alpha\beta + \alpha\beta\alpha - 2\beta\alpha\alpha) \quad (13)$$

It is evident that this excited state contains considerable antibonding between σ and s and furthermore there will be a net spin density in the hydrogen $1s$ orbital. An improved wave function, Ψ, for the CH fragment will be a linear combination of ψ_1 and ψ_2:

$$\Psi = \psi_1 + \lambda\psi_2 \quad (14)$$

where $\lambda \ll 1$. We can write the three-electron Hamiltonian for this system as

$$\mathscr{H} = \sum_i \mathscr{H}_i + \sum_{i<j} \frac{e^2}{r_{ij}} \quad (15)$$

where $\mathscr{H}_i$ includes the electronic kinetic energy terms, nuclear potential energy repulsion terms, and electron–nuclear attraction terms.

Since $\lambda \ll 1$, we can use first-order perturbation theory to solve for λ. Taking as the perturbation Hamiltonian the second term of equation 15, the wave function, to first-order, becomes:

$$\Psi = \psi_1 - \frac{H_{21}}{\Delta E_{21}} \psi_2 \quad (16)$$

Hence

$$\lambda = -\frac{H_{21}}{\Delta E_{21}} \quad (17)$$

where

$$H_{kl} = \langle \psi_k | \sum_{i<j} \frac{e^2}{r_{ij}} |\psi_l\rangle$$

and

$$\Delta E_{21} = E_2^0 - E_1^0$$

where E_2^0 and E_1^0 are the zero-order energies of ψ_1 and ψ_2, respectively.

Substitution of equations 12 and 13 in the expression for H_{21} yields:

$$H_{21} = \frac{-\sqrt{3}}{2(1 - S_0^4)^{1/2}} \{[\pi\sigma|\pi\sigma] - [\pi s|\pi s]\} \quad (18)$$

where

$$[\pi\sigma|\pi\sigma] = \langle \pi(1)\sigma(2)| \frac{e^2}{r_{12}} |\sigma(1)\pi(2)\rangle$$

$$[\pi s|\pi s] = \langle \pi(1)s(2)| \frac{e^2}{r_{12}} |s(1)\pi(2)\rangle$$

Now that we have an expression for the wave function, Ψ, of the CH fragment, we must compute the spin density, $\rho^H(0)$, at the proton since the isotropic proton hyperfine splitting can only arise from this spin density. Let us designate the proton hyperfine splitting for a unit spin density in π as Q_{CH}^H. [The notation for these Q factors (12) requires some explanation. The superscript will always refer to the nucleus giving rise to the hyperfine splitting. The subscript closest to the Q will denote the atom containing the π spin density, which is related to the hyperfine splitting by the Q factor. The two subscripts together indicate the σ bond which is being polarized by the π spin density.] Then Q_{CH}^H is directly related to $\rho^H(0)$ by the Fermi contact hyperfine interaction (13,14):

$$Q_{CH}^H = \frac{8\pi}{3} \frac{\mu_H}{I} \rho^H(0) \quad \text{(gauss)} \tag{19}$$

where μ_H and I are the magnetic moment and spin of the proton. Using equations 1 and 14, we obtain the following expression for $\rho^H(0)$:

$$\rho^H(0) = -\frac{2\lambda}{\sqrt{3}(1 - S_0^4)^{1/2}} |s(0)|^2 \tag{20}$$

where $|s(0)|^2$ is the probability density of the hydrogen $1s$ orbital at the proton.

With the use of equations 17, 18, and 19, the following expression for Q_{CH}^H is obtained:

$$Q_{CH}^H = \frac{-8\pi}{3} \frac{\mu_H}{I} \frac{1}{(1 - S_0^4)} \left\{ \frac{[\pi\sigma|\pi\sigma] - [\pi s|\pi s]}{\Delta E_{21}} \right\} |s(0)|^2 \tag{21}$$

If we assume that the hydrogen atom is in a state not much perturbed from that of a free hydrogen atom, we may use the value of the hyperfine splitting, a_H^H, in the hydrogen atom to obtain an estimate of $|s(0)|^2$.

In the hydrogen atom,

$$a_H^H = \frac{8\pi}{3} \frac{\mu_H}{I} |s(0)|^2 \tag{22}$$

The final result for Q_{CH}^H is:

$$Q_{CH}^H = -\frac{1}{(1 - S_0^4)} \left\{ \frac{[\pi\sigma|\pi\sigma] - [\pi s|\pi s]}{\Delta E_{21}} \right\} a_H^H \tag{23}$$

Equation 23 has been derived assuming a unit spin density in π. McConnell (1,3,8) and also McLachlan et al. (8a) have shown that the proton hyperfine splitting a_i^H at carbon atom i will vary linearly with the spin density in

π for situations where the π spin density is distributed over more than one center. The relation which results is commonly called the McConnell relation:

$$a_i^H = Q_{CH}^H \rho_i^\pi \tag{24}$$

2. What Value of Q?

The introduction of the McConnell relation made possible detailed comparisons of experimental and theoretical spin densities (6). However, in order to do this, the magnitude of Q_{CH}^H had to be fixed. Many attempts have yielded values of the order of -20 to -30 G. Jarrett (15) has attempted to evaluate all the quantities in equation 23 and arrived at a value of -28 G. The negative sign of Q_{CH}^H has been confirmed experimentally by Gutowsky et al. (16), using broad-line NMR. There are some situations where ρ_i^π is fixed by symmetry or can be reliably estimated. For instance, in the methyl radical (17) $a^H = -23.03$ G; since $\rho_i^\pi = 1$, this gives one a value of Q_{CH}^H. Also, in the benzene negative ion (18) $a^H \simeq -3.75$ G [temperature dependent (19)]; since $\rho_i^\pi = \frac{1}{6}$, this yields $Q_{CH}^H = -22.5$ G. However, similar considerations in other molecules provide quite different values: e.g., cyclooctatetraene anion (20) ($Q_{CH}^H = -25.68$ G), cycloheptatrienyl radical (19,21) ($Q_{CH}^H = -27.7$ G), cyclopentadienyl radical (19,22) ($Q_{CH}^H = -30.0$ G), and butadiene negative ion (23) ($Q_{CH}^H = -20.81$ G). It thus appears that although the McConnell relation holds approximately, Q_{CH}^H is by no means a fixed constant but does vary somewhat from one molecule to another. We shall consider various treatments which extend the McConnell relation in the next section, but it will suffice at this point to say that Q_{CH}^H should be a constant only for neutral radicals.

In the literature there are many cases where Q_{CH}^H has been fixed by comparing experimental hyperfine splittings with spin densities calculated from various valence theories. This procedure has limited value if the resulting value of Q_{CH}^H is then used to test the validity of the theoretical spin densities calculated from the same valence theory. Such a procedure only indicates that there is a significant correlation between proton hyperfine splittings and theoretical spin densities. In spite of the wide range of values proposed for Q_{CH}^H, there appears to be good evidence that a fairly constant value of Q_{CH}^H is applicable under certain specific conditions. The following argument is almost entirely based on situations where spin densities are known or can be reliably estimated with a minimum use of theoretically derived quantities. As noted before, only neutral radicals will be considered at this point.

The simplest neutral radicals are the alkyl radicals which were studied in elegant detail by the pioneering work of Fessenden and Schuler (17).

Some of the results they obtained are listed in Table I. The only assumption in obtaining the Q_{CH}^H values listed in Table I is that the spin density on

TABLE I

Radical	ρ^π	a_α^H (G)	Q_{CH}^H (G)	a_β^H (G)	$Q_{CCH_3}^H$ (G)
$\dot{C}H_3$	1.000	23.04	23.04	—	—
$CH_3\dot{C}H_2$	0.919	22.38	24.35	26.87	29.25
$(CH_3)_2\dot{C}H$	0.844	22.11	26.20	24.68	29.25
$(CH_3)_3\dot{C}$	0.776	—	—	22.72	29.30

the central trigonal carbon atom will be given by the empirical relation:

$$\rho^\pi = (1 - 0.081)^n \tag{25}$$

where n is the number of methyl groups attached. This assumption is supported by several considerations. First, the values of $Q_{CCH_3}^H$ obtained with these spin densities and the experimental values of the methyl hyperfine splittings are nearly constant. Second, the value of ρ^π for the ethyl radical (0.919) agrees very well with a very extensive molecular orbital calculation by Lazdins and Karplus (24) and also by Nordio, Pavan, and Giacometti (24a) (their value for ρ^π is 0.911). Finally, some recent work by Fessenden (25) shows that substitution of a methyl group must affect Q_{CH}^H. He studied the *trans*-1-methyl allyl radical:

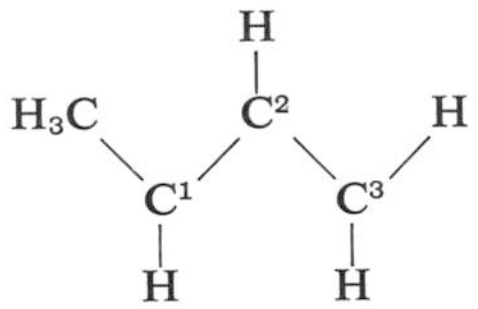

for which he quotes $a^H(CH_3) = 16.23$ G, $a_1^H = a_3^H = 13.72$ G (two protons), $a_{3'}^H = 14.77$ G (one proton), and $a_2^H = 3.78$ G. The allyl radical results (17) are $a_1^H = a_3^H = 13.93$ G, $a_{1'}^H = a_{3'}^H = 14.83$ G, and $a_2^H = 4.06$ G. Thus, the methyl substitution does not greatly change the spin distribution. Using $Q_{CCH_3}^H = 29.25$ G, one gets $\rho_3 = 0.555$ G, while the average of the two splittings, 13.72 and 14.77 G, with $Q_{CH}^H = -24.7$ G gives $\rho_1 = 0.576$ G. From ρ_3 and a_3^H we compute $Q_{CH}^H = 26.6$ G, in excellent agreement with the value expected for a $CC_2'H$ fragment. (It is not clear yet as to why the two end proton splittings in allyl should be different.)

Thus, it would appear that Q_{CH}^H changes slightly according to which atoms or groups are bonded to the central trigonal carbon atom. An extension of Fessenden's and Schuler's argument by Fischer (26) to other alkyl-substituted radicals detected in aqueous solutions seems to indicate that Q_{CH}^H may vary considerably. For a series of radicals of the type CH_3—CH—X, Fischer obtains the Q_{CH}^H values listed in Table II. A

TABLE II

Variation of Q_{CH}^H with Substituent in Radicals of the Type CH_3—CH—X (26)

X	a_α^H (G)	$a_{CH_3}^H$ (G)	Q_{CH}^H (G)
CH_3	21.11	24.68	26.2
H	22.38	26.87	24.4
$CO-CH_2CH_3$	18.45	22.59	23.9
COOH	20.18	24.98	23.7
OH	15.04	22.61	19.5
$O-CH_2CH_3$	13.96	22.28	18.3

constant value (29.30 G) was assumed for $Q_{CCH_3}^H$ and the methyl splittings were used to obtain ρ_C^π. Then from the a_α^H values, the Q_{CH}^H values were computed. It is not clear what causes the variation in Q_{CH}^H, although Fessenden (27) and Hausser (28) have suggested that the variation may be due to these radicals being nonplanar. A nonplanar structure has been confirmed in the CF_3 and CF_2H radicals (29). Whatever the cause of the changes in Q_{CH}^H, it is clear that one must exercise care in the choice of Q_{CH}^H in a given case. Nevertheless, if the free radicals to be considered are restricted to neutral hydrocarbon free radicals, the values of Q_{CH}^H given in Table I are reasonably consistent, if one uses the value of Q_{CH}^H appropriate to whether the radical has zero, one, or two carbons bonded to the trigonal carbon atom. Let us examine some cases where these values of Q_{CH}^H can be tested. The allyl radical which was mentioned previously has been studied by Fessenden and Schuler (17). The signs of the hyperfine splittings in the unsubstituted radical have not been determined (the signs have been determined in a substituted allyl radical (30) and agree with predictions), but a_2^H is almost certainly positive corresponding to ρ_2^π which is negative. According to Table I, the appropriate values of Q_{CH}^H for the 1- and 2-position carbon atoms are -24.4 and -26.2 G, respectively. Taking the average of a_1^H and $a_{1'}^H$, the following "experimental" spin densities are computed:

$$\rho_1^\pi = \rho_3^\pi = 0.589; \qquad \rho_2^\pi = -0.155$$

These sum to 1.023, which is very close to the value of unity required by the definition of spin densities.

Another example is provided by the anthracene positive and negative ions. Based on consistency of proton and carbon-13 hyperfine splittings, Bolton and Fraenkel (31) conclude that the average Q_{CH}^H for corresponding positions in the positive and negative ion (i.e., appropriate for neutral radicals) should be in the range -26 to -28 G. Thus, again this value of Q_{CH}^H is in agreement with that for the isopropyl radical.

In light of the evidence presented, the value of Q_{CH}^H will be fixed at 27.0 G for neutral hydrocarbon free radicals at positions where two carbon atoms and a hydrogen atom are bonded to the trigonal carbon atom of interest. It is not expected that this value will be in error by more than ± 1.0 G for the above conditions.

3. Extensions of the McConnell Relation

Up to now it has been stressed that Q_{CH}^H may only be taken as a constant for a restricted group of neutral free radicals. Since the primary concern in this book will be charged radicals, it is important to seek an extension of the McConnell relation which will apply to charged radicals. The even alternant aromatic hydrocarbon radical ions provide an excellent group of compounds to test whether or not Q_{CH}^H depends on the excess charge (we shall define the excess charge, ϵ_i^π, by $\epsilon_i^\pi = (1 - q_i^\pi)$ where q_i^π is defined by equation 3). For these molecules the pairing theorem (32) predicts that the spin density distribution should be identical for the positive and negative ions of a given even alternant aromatic hydrocarbon. In Table III experimental hyperfine splittings are listed for a representative group of such hydrocarbons. This group of linear polyacenes has been chosen because it is expected that they will form a structurally homologous group.

It is apparent that, especially at positions with large hyperfine splittings, the positive ion hyperfine splittings are larger than those at the corresponding positions in the negative ion. This can either be interpreted as a breakdown of the pairing theorem (i.e., spin density distribution different for positive and negative ions) or a variation of Q_{CH}^H with excess charge. Bolton and Fraenkel (31) found that the ^{13}C hyperfine splittings in the anthracene positive and negative ions were almost identical for corresponding carbon positions. This and other evidence (36) seems to rule out a major breakdown of the pairing theorem and lays the blame for the difference in the hyperfine splittings on variations in Q_{CH}^H. Further evidence for an excess charge effect can be obtained from the extensive investigation of positive and negative ions by Lewis and Singer (37).

Colpa and Bolton (2) were the first to propose an extension to the McConnell relation to account for excess charge effects. Based on a

TABLE III
Experimental Hyperfine Splittings for a Group of Polyacene Positive and Negative Ions

Hydrocarbon	Position	a_+^H	a_-^H	$\bar{a}^H$	Δa^H
Anthracene					
9	9	6.533[a]	5.337[a]	5.935	+0.598
	1	3.061	2.740	2.901	+0.161
	2	1.379	1.509	1.444	−0.065
Tetracene					
	5	5.061[b,c]	4.226[c]	4.644	+0.418
	1	1.694	1.541	1.618	+0.077
	2	1.030	1.162	1.096	−0.066
Pentacene					
	6	5.083[d]	4.263[d]	4.673	+0.410
	5	3.554	3.032	3.293	+0.261
	1	(0.975)[e]	(0.915)[e]	0.945	+0.030
	2	(0.757)[e]	(0.870)[e]	0.814	−0.057

[a] Reference 31.   [b] Reference 33.   [c] Reference 34.
[d] Reference 35.   [e] Assignment uncertain.

second-order perturbation theory molecular orbital treatment, they proposed the following relation:

$$a_i^H = [Q_{CH}^H(0) + K_{CH}^H \epsilon_i^\pi]\rho_i^\pi \qquad (26)$$

where $Q_{CH}^H(0)$ is the value of Q_{CH}^H appropriate for neutral radicals and K_{CH}^H is a constant. Unfortunately, their calculation contained a serious sign error (38) and the corrected calculation predicts that K_{CH}^H and $Q_{CH}^H(0)$ should be opposite in sign. The experimental data dictate that $Q_{CH}^H(0)$ and K_{CH}^H must both be negative if an equation, such as equation 26, is to be applied. Higuchi (39) has carried out a very extensive molecular orbital calculation pertaining to a CH fragment; however, he also predicts that K_{CH}^H should be positive. Recently, Bolton (40) presented a calculation of the exchange integrals in equation 21 including the effect of the excess charge in changing the orbital screening exponents on the carbon atom. The result predicts an equation of the form of equation 26 with a *negative* value of K_{CH}^H. Also, quantitative estimates (40) indicate that this effect is of the correct magnitude to account for the variation. At this stage it would be premature to say that this "excess charge effect" is fully explained, but it is clear from an analysis to follow that equation 26 with negative values of $Q_{CH}^H(0)$ and K_{CH}^H accounts for a major part of the variation in proton hyperfine splittings for even alternant hydrocarbons.

One other extension of the McConnell relation has been proposed by Giacometti, Nordio, and Pavan (41). They included the effect of spin density in the bonds and proposed the following relation:

$$a_i^H = Q_1\rho_{ii}^\pi + Q_2 \sum_j \rho_{ij}^\pi \qquad (27)$$

where ρ_{ij}^π is an element in the π-atomic orbital spin density matrix and Q_1 and Q_2 are constants. Atom j is assumed to be bonded to atom i. If Hückel LCAO-MO coefficients are used, equation 27 reduces to:

$$a_i^H = Q_1 c_i^2 + Q_2 \sum_j c_i c_j \qquad (28)$$

where the c_i and c_j are atomic orbital coefficients in the Hückel molecular orbital containing the odd electron. Snyder and Amos (42), using spin densities calculated by use of an unrestricted Hartree-Fock method, have carried out an extensive test of equations 26 and 27. They concluded that both were an improvement over the simple McConnell relation but that one did not give any better agreement than the other. However, recently, in an analysis of the positive and negative ions of benzene, Vincow (43) concluded that the excess charge correction gives much better agreement than the bond spin density correction. Also, Lefebvre (44) has pointed out that both in the Hückel and more elaborate Pariser-Parr-Pople molecular orbital treatments, the π-atomic orbitals are only defined insofar as they obey certain integral properties. In particular, they certainly obey the Mulliken approximation for coulomb integrals, which states that:

$$\pi_l(1)\pi_k(1) = \tfrac{1}{2}S_{kl}\{\pi_l^2(1) + \pi_k^2(1)\}$$

where $\pi_l(1)$ and $\pi_k(1)$ represent π-atomic orbital wave functions and S_{kl} represents the π-overlap integral between atoms l and k. It is not unreasonable that they also obey the Mulliken approximation for exchange integrals which states that:

$$\pi_l(1)\pi_k(2) = \tfrac{1}{2}S_{kl}\{\pi_l(1)\pi_l(2) + \pi_k(1)\pi_k(2)\}$$

If such is the case, no departure from the equality in the coupling constants of the positive and negative ions of even alternant hydrocarbons can be obtained within the Giacometti-Nordio-Pavan scheme. Any such departure would represent a breakdown of the Mulliken approximation *and* the pairing theorem. It is too early yet to say definitely what is the origin of the change in Q_{CH}^H. More theoretical work is needed and it may turn out that the end result is a combination of many factors. For instance, all calculations [except that of Higuchi (39)] have assumed no polarity in the CH bond.

Equation 27 also has the disadvantage that two or more theoretical quantities (ρ_{ii}^π and the ρ_{ij}^π's) need to be evaluated for each experimental proton hyperfine splitting. Clearly, it is impossible to estimate "experimental" spin densities using equation 27, although it is possible to compute theoretical proton hyperfine splittings for a given theoretical calculation of spin densities.

Equation 26 (involving the excess charge correction), also involves two theoretical quantities, ϵ_i^π and ρ_i^π. However, in this case a very reasonable approximation reduces this number to one. Most calculations of spin densities and charge densities in alternant aromatic hydrocarbons (45,47) indicate that the approximation, $|\epsilon_i^\pi| = \rho_i^\pi$ is valid, especially at positions of large spin density. Making this substitution, equation 26 reduces to a quadratic in ρ_i^π:

$$a_i^H = Q_{CH}^H(0)\rho_i^\pi \pm K_{CH}^H[\rho_i^\pi]^2 \qquad (29)$$

with the $+$ sign applicable to positive ions and the $-$ sign to negative ions. Thus, given a value of a_i^H, an "experimental" spin density can be calculated.

The question still remains as to how well an equation like equation 29 accounts for the variations in proton hyperfine splittings for corresponding positions in the positive and negative ions of the same aromatic hydrocarbon. Assuming that the pairing theorem holds exactly (i.e., that the spin density distribution for the positive and negative ions of the same alternant aromatic hydrocarbon will be identical), the average hyperfine splitting, $\bar{a}^H$, and the deviation Δa^H can be defined by:

$$\bar{a}^H = \frac{a_+^H + a_-^H}{2} = Q_{CH}^H(0)\rho^\pi \qquad (30)$$

$$\Delta a^H = \frac{a_+^H - a_-^H}{2} = K_{CH}^H[\rho^\pi]^2 \qquad (31)$$

Substituting for ρ^π in equation 31 the following relation is obtained:

$$\Delta a^H = \frac{K_{CH}^H}{[Q_{CH}^H(0)]^2}[\bar{a}^H]^2 \qquad (32)$$

Thus, a plot of Δa^H vs. $[\bar{a}^H]^2$ (both experimental quantities) should be a straight line. Figure 1 shows such a plot using the data from Table III. (Some of the positions have a negative Δa^H. These all involve small hyperfine splittings where the excess charge effect should be negligible. Presumably, other effects are causing Δa^H to be negative, possibly a neighbor effect, since these positions are all adjacent to large spin density positions.) The data points do indeed fit closely to a straight line. Using the value of $Q_{CH}^H(0) = -27$ G proposed earlier, the value of K_{CH}^H obtained from the slope and equation 32, is -12 G.

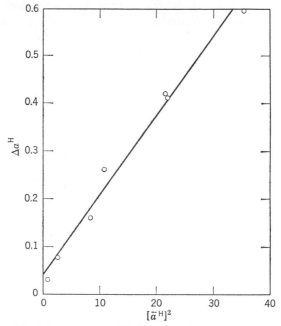

Fig. 1. Plot of Δa^H (in gauss) vs. $[\bar{a}^H]^2$ (in gauss^2) for the proton hyperfine splittings of the positive and negative ions of anthracene, tetracene, and pentacene (see Table III). The solid line is a fitted least squares regression line including all seven points with equal weight.

The following example is included to indicate how equation 29 might be applied. The 1,3-butadiene negative ion has been studied by Levy and Myers (23). They report the following proton hyperfine splittings:

$$\overset{1}{CH_2} \quad \overset{3}{CH}$$
$$\underset{2}{\diagdown} \underset{CH}{\diagup} \underset{CH_2}{\diagdown}^4$$

$$a_1^H = a_4^H = -7.617 \text{ G}$$

$$a_2^H = a_3^H = -2.791 \text{ G}$$

(The signs have been chosen to conform with theoretical predictions.) The following two equations should apply:

$$-\{24.4\rho_1^\pi - 12.0[\rho_1^\pi]^2\} = -7.617 \tag{33}$$

$$-\{26.2\rho_2^\pi - 12.0[\rho_2^\pi]^2\} = -2.791 \tag{34}$$

(Note: The negative sign in front of the 12.0 appears because we are dealing with a negative ion.) The values of $Q_{CH}^H(0)$ are those from the ethyl and isopropyl radicals, respectively (see Table I). Solving these quadratic equations, one obtains the "experimental" spin densities as $\rho_1^\pi = 0.385$, $\rho_2^\pi = 0.112$; these sum to 0.994, which is almost exactly the expected value of unity. Note that the ratio of these spin densities is 3.44, whereas the ratio of the hyperfine splittings is only 2.73. It is interesting that the ratio of Hückel spin densities is 2.62, whereas in more advanced calculations (42), the ratio is about 3.50. Thus, although it may often appear that experimental hyperfine splittings agree very well with Hückel spin densities, this apparent agreement may be the result of two nearly cancelling effects (2).

For a second example, consider the naphthalene negative ion proton hyperfine splittings (46):

$$a_1^H = -4.95 \text{ G}$$
$$a_2^H = -1.87 \text{ G}$$

Using equation 29 with $Q_{CH}^H = -27.0$ G and $K_{CH}^H = -12.0$ G, the spin densities are computed to be $\rho_1^\pi = 0.201$ and $\rho_2^\pi = 0.072$, which are in reasonable agreement with theoretical predictions (42).

A prediction can now be made concerning the naphthalene positive ion which has not yet been observed in its monomeric form. Using equation 29 to calculate the hyperfine splittings, we obtain $a_1^H = -5.92$ G and $a_2^H = -1.99$ G. The naphthalene positive ion in a dimeric form (one positive hole distributed over two naphthalene molecules) has been observed by Lewis and Singer (37). They report $a_1^H = -2.77$ G and $a_2^H = -1.03$ G. From equation 29 we obtain $\rho_1^\pi = 0.108$ and $\rho_2^\pi = 0.039$, which when doubled are 0.216 and 0.078, respectively. Although it is perhaps a rash assumption that the dimer spin distribution should be just one-half the monomer spin distribution, the agreement of the doubled dimer spin densities with those calculated from the negative ion is interesting.

4. Anisotropic Proton Hyperfine Splittings

We have shown how isotropic proton hyperfine splittings arise for free radicals. Where radicals or radical ions can be produced or trapped in a diamagnetic host single crystal, anisotropic proton hyperfine splittings can often be detected. McConnell and Strathdee (47) were the first to consider quantitatively the relation between the anisotropic proton hyperfine splitting and electron spin densities in planar π-electron radicals, although Ghosh and Whiffen (48) presented a qualitative argument. McConnell and Strathdee showed that the interaction arises primarily through electron–nuclear dipole–dipole coupling. For a CH fragment, they derived an expression for the complete hyperfine term in the spin Hamiltonian:

$$\mathscr{H}_{HF} = h^{-1}\hat{S}\cdot\mathbf{A}\cdot\hat{I} \tag{35}$$

Here **A** is a diagonal hyperfine tensor:

$$\mathbf{A} = \begin{pmatrix} A_{xx} & 0 & 0 \\ 0 & A_{yy} & 0 \\ 0 & 0 & A_{zz} \end{pmatrix} \tag{36}$$

when defined for the principal axis system of the hyperfine coupling. The x axis is taken to be along the CH bond and the z axis along the carbon $2p^\pi$ orbital. If A_0, the isotropic hyperfine coupling, is subtracted from each element of **A**, the anisotropic hyperfine tensor, **T**, is obtained:

$$\mathbf{T} = \begin{pmatrix} T_{xx} & 0 & 0 \\ 0 & T_{yy} & 0 \\ 0 & 0 & T_{zz} \end{pmatrix} \tag{37}$$

Here $(T_{xx} + T_{yy} + T_{zz}) = 0$. McConnell and Strathdee (47) give the following expressions (in MHz) for the elements of **T**:

$$T_{xx} = 43.1\rho^\pi + 338\rho^\sigma \tag{38a}$$

$$T_{yy} = -38.2\rho^\pi - 152\rho^\sigma \tag{38b}$$

$$T_{zz} = -4.9\rho^\pi - 186\rho^\sigma \tag{38c}$$

where ρ^π is the spin density in the $2p^\pi$ orbital on carbon and ρ^σ is the spin density in the CH σ molecular orbital. Since the σ spin density is negative near the hydrogen atom and positive near the carbon atom, it is expected that ρ^σ will be very small and can be neglected. (Of course, ρ^σ cannot be neglected for the isotropic hyperfine splitting!) For comparison, consider the radical obtained from the γ irradiation of a single crystal of malonic acid (49):

$$\begin{matrix} \text{H} \\ | \\ \text{C} \\ {}^{\cdot} \\ \text{HOOC} \quad \text{COOH} \end{matrix}$$

The CH proton anisotropic hyperfine tensor is:

$$\begin{pmatrix} +31 & 0 & 0 \\ 0 & -32 & 0 \\ 0 & 0 & +1 \end{pmatrix} \text{(MHz)} \tag{39}$$

ρ^π is probably reduced from unity due to some delocalization into the carboxyl groups, so the agreement with equations 38a, 38b, and 38c can be considered satisfactory.

Unfortunately, in situations where there is significant π-electron spin density on nearby positions (e.g., in oriented aromatic radicals), these spin densities can make a significant contribution to T. McConnell's and Strathdee's equations (47) can be used to calculate the effect of these neighboring spin densities, but in order to carry out these calculations some other estimate of the magnitude of these spin densities must be available.

5. Hyperfine Splitting from Protons Bonded to Atoms Other than Carbon

Both isotropic and anisotropic hyperfine splittings have been observed for protons bonded to nitrogen and oxygen. In the derivation of the McConnell relation, no assumption was made concerning the particular atom to which the hydrogen was bonded. Hence, we would expect that a relation of the form of equation 24 would be applicable, i.e.,

$$a_{NH}^H = Q_{NH}^H \rho_N^\pi \tag{40}$$

$$a_{OH}^H = Q_{OH}^H \rho_O^\pi \tag{41}$$

Equation 26, containing the excess charge correction, may be applicable, but one must be careful about the values of ϵ_i^π to use. Since $\epsilon_i^\pi = (1 - q_i^\pi)$ and $q_i^\pi = 1$ for $NH_{3,}^+$, a *negative* value of ϵ_i^π should be used for a radical cation, such as the dihydropyrazinium cation (1) (note that ϵ_i^π is *not* the

(1)

actual charge). Also, the approximation that $|\epsilon_i^\pi| \simeq \rho_i^\pi$ is no longer valid, since the π-electron charge density at the nitrogen or oxygen will not be unity in the diamagnetic precursor to the radical. One should also consider the fact that the NH and OH bonds would be expected to be much more polar than the CH bond. This effect has not been included in the theoretical treatments, so any application of equation 26 to NH or OH proton hyperfine splittings may be hazardous.

Data are still rather sketchy on the appropriate values to use for Q_{NH}^H and Q_{OH}^H in equations 40 and 41. A negative value for Q_{NH}^H has been predicted (50) and confirmed experimentally (51). The NH_3^+ radical ion has been detected in irradiated NH_4ClO_4 single crystals by Cole (52) and also by Hyde and Freeman (53). They report the isotropic proton hyperfine splitting to be -25.8 G. Analogous to the carbon case, one might expect that $|Q_{NH}^H|$ would increase slightly for cases where one or two carbon atoms are bonded to the nitrogen. In a study of dihydropyrazine cations, Barton and Fraenkel (54) find that with $Q_{CH}^H = -23.7$ G, Q_{NH}^H is -33.7 G. If the value of Q_{CH}^H is taken to be -27.0 G, then Q_{NH}^H becomes -29.6 G. However, in the hydrazine positive ion radical, a_{NH}^H is found to be 11.0 G (55) from which we induce $|Q_{NH}^H| = 22.0$ G. Also, in the NH_2 radical (56), $|Q_{NH}^H| = 23.9$ G. It thus appears that, analogous to Q_{CH}^H, Q_{NH}^H may vary considerably in different bonding situations.

In the case of OH hyperfine splittings, no clear case is available where some independent estimates of the π-electron spin density on the oxygen atom is available, although an estimate of $Q_{OH}^H \approx -7$ G has been made by Rabold et al. (57) from a study of the hydroxyperinaphthenyl radical (2). Indeed the validity of equation 41 seems to be in some doubt, as

(2)

Bolton, Carrington, and Veiga (58) found that the OH proton splittings in acid semiquinones were not linearly correlated with calculated Hückel odd-electron densities on the oxygen atoms. Clearly, further work on these systems is required before reliable values of Q_{NH}^H and Q_{OH}^H can be quoted.

6. Methyl Proton Hyperfine Splittings

We have already implied that methyl proton splittings can be related to the π-electron spin density on the adjacent carbon atom by the relation:

$$a^H(CH_3) = Q_{CCH_3}^H \rho_C^\pi \tag{42}$$

However, both theoretical (59–61) and experimental (59,60,62) results indicate that $Q_{CCH_3}^H$ should be a constant only for neutral odd-alternant hydrocarbons (this would include the alkyl radicals). For this restricted group of radicals, Fessenden and Schuler (17) give a value of $+29.3$ G. However, for radical ions, $Q_{CCH_3}^H$ has been given values as low as 18.4 G (54) and as high as ~ 38 G (59). Hence, considerable care must be exercised in utilizing equation 42 to probe π-electron spin densities.

The mechanism of hyperfine splittings by methyl protons is quite different from that for ring proton splittings. The problem has been treated theoretically by many authors (24,59,60,62,63), and it appears that a hyperconjugative (i.e., π-electron transfer) mechanism plays a significant role, although a recent extensive molecular orbital calculation on the ethyl and allyl radicals by Lazdins and Karplus (24) would indicate that the hyperconjugative electron transfer mechanism contributes only $\sim 40\%$ to the proton splitting, the remaining 60% being accounted for by an exchange polarization mechanism. This mechanism is essentially the same as the π–σ spin polarization mechanism leading to ring proton splittings; however, in this case the polarization is essentially π–π rather than π–σ (24).

B. Hyperfine Splitting from Nuclei Other than Protons

1. Isotropic Hyperfine Splitting from Atoms with a Net π Electron Spin Density

a. The General Model. In the case of the isotropic proton hyperfine splittings, we only had to consider the interaction of the unpaired π electron with the σ electrons in one bond (i.e., the CH bond). However, in the case of nuclei, which form part of the framework of an aromatic molecule, interactions with many bonds must be considered. As a general model for such systems, we shall follow the treatment and notation of Karplus and Fraenkel (12). Their calculation was developed for ^{13}C hyperfine splittings, but the model should be generally applicable to other nuclei, such as ^{14}N, ^{17}O, ^{19}F, etc. The treatment is essentially an extension of the valence bond calculation on the CH fragment. In that calculation we could have calculated the spin density induced at the carbon nucleus by the same spin polarization mechanism which produced spin density at the hydrogen atom. We would have found that this spin density would be positive, while the spin density at the proton is negative. However, it is found experimentally that ^{13}C splittings are not correlated in a linear manner with the π electron spin density on the same carbon atom (12,64,65). Clearly, we must consider other contributions to the spin density at the ^{13}C nucleus. Let us consider the general case of a four-atom fragment from an aromatic system,

where the nucleus of the atom Y is producing an isotropic hyperfine splitting. Let the π spin density on Y be ρ_Y^π and the π spin densities on the

X_i atoms be $\rho_{X_i}^\pi$ ($i = 1, 2, 3$). (One, two, or three of the X_i may be hydrogen atoms, in which case $\rho_{X_i}^\pi$ would be zero.) First consider the possible π–σ interactions of the π electrons on Y with the σ electrons around Y. Karplus and Fraenkel show that there will be four such interactions—spin polarization of the $1s$ electrons on Y, and spin polarization of $2s$ electrons on the atom Y in the Y—X_1, Y—X_2, and Y—X_3 σ bonds. For $\rho_Y^\pi = 1$ and $\rho_{X_i}^\pi = 0$, the contribution to a^Y from the $1s$ electrons is designated S^Y. The contributions from the $2s$ electrons are designated $Q_{YX_i}^Y$. There will also be a contribution to a^Y from the π spin densities on the X_i (in the same sense as the proton splitting in the CH fragment). For $\rho_{X_1}^\pi = \rho_{X_2}^\pi = \rho_{X_3}^\pi = 0$ and $\rho_{X_1}^\pi = 1$, the contribution to a^Y from the $2s$ electrons on Y will be designated $Q_{X_1Y}^Y$, with similar expressions for $\rho_{X_2}^\pi$ and $\rho_{X_3}^\pi$ equal to unity, respectively. Thus, we can write the following expression relating a^Y to the π electron spin densities:

$$a^Y = [S^Y + \sum_i Q_{YX_i}^Y]\rho_Y^\pi + \sum_i Q_{X_iY}^Y \rho_{X_i}^\pi \qquad (43)$$

where the coefficient of ρ_Y^π represents spin polarization due to π spin density on Y, and the coefficients of $\rho_{X_i}^\pi$ arise from spin polarization due to π spin density on the X_i. This is commonly referred to as the Karplus-Fraenkel relationship. Karplus and Fraenkel indicate that in general S^Y should be negative. We have already indicated that the $Q_{YX_i}^Y$ should be positive while, analogous to Q_{CH}^H, the $Q_{X_iY}^Y$ should be negative. We shall now consider the values of the various parameters which have been proposed for ^{13}C, ^{14}N, and ^{19}F.

b. ^{13}C Hyperfine Splittings. Karplus and Fraenkel were able to make quantitative calculations of the spin polarization constants in equation 43 for a carbon atom, with the X_i being either carbon or hydrogen atoms. Their values are $S^C = -12.7$ G, $Q_{CH}^C = +19.5$ G, $Q_{CC'}^C = 14.4$ G and $Q_{C'C}^C = -13.9$ G. Inserting these values into equation 43, we obtain

$$a^C = 35.6\rho_C^\pi - 13.9 \sum_i \rho_{C_i}^\pi \qquad (44)$$

$$a^C = 30.5\rho_C^\pi - 13.9 \sum_i \rho_{C_i}^\pi \qquad (45)$$

for a $CC_2'H$ and a CC_3' fragment, respectively. (The C_i must be bonded to C.) Sometimes an independent estimate of the ρ^π's can be obtained from proton hyperfine splittings using equation 24 or equation 26. This has been done in the case of the anthracene positive and negative ions (31). With $Q_{CH}^H(0) = -27.0$ G and the normalization condition, $\sum_i \rho_i^\pi = 1$, the spin densities and ^{13}C hyperfine splittings were calculated and are listed in Table IV. The agreement is extremely good considering that the ^{13}C parameters were calculated from an approximate theory. In fact the only

TABLE IV

Calculated and Experimental ^{13}C Splittings and Spin Densities in the Anthracene Positive and Negative Ions

Position	^{13}C Splittings, a_i^C(G)			Exp. spin Densities[a]
	Neg. ion	Pos. ion	Calc.	
9	8.76	8.48	8.42	0.220
11	−4.59	−4.50	−4.90	−0.021
1	3.57	—	3.37	0.107
2	−0.25	±0.37	−0.33	0.054

[a] Calculated from proton hyperfine splittings using $\bar{Q}_{CH}^H = -27.0$ G.

indication of a slight discrepancy is for position 11. This splitting is determined largely by $Q_{C'C}^C$ and a slight decrease (no more than 0.5–1.0 G) in the magnitude of this constant might be in order. Similar comparisons for the perinaphthenyl radical, the naphthalene negative ion, and the biphenyl negative ion show that equations 44 and 45 are widely applicable for aromatic hydrocarbons.

It should be noted that the Q spin polarization constants depend on the hybridization around the central carbon and around the atoms to which the carbon is bonded. For instance, Rieger and Fraenkel (66) calculated Q's for an sp^2 hybridized carbon (C) bonded to an sp hybridized carbon (C') (e.g., a cyano carbon). Their results are $Q_{CC'}^C = +13.63$ G, $Q_{CC'}^{C'} = -19.76$ G, $Q_{C'C}^C = +36.44$ G, and $Q_{C'C}^C = -22.89$ G. Also, Strauss and Fraenkel (67) computed Q's for an sp^2 hybridized carbon bonded to an sp^3 hybridized carbon (e.g., $-CH_3$) and quote $Q_{CC'}^C = 30.0$ G and $Q_{CC'}^{C'} = -20.9$ G, no spin density being assumed on the sp^3 hybridized carbon. The ^{13}C splitting in $CH_2{}^{13}CH_3$ ($|a^C| = 13.57$ G) (68) shows that $Q_{CC'}^C$, in this case, may be an overestimate.

In cases where one of the X_i is an atom other than carbon or hydrogen, some information is available. Das and Fraenkel (69) have carried out an extensive investigation of ^{13}C splittings in semiquinones. Again using $Q_{CH}^H = -27.0$ G, they infer that the parameters for a CC_2O fragment should be: $Q_{CO}^C = 17.7$ G and $Q_{OC}^C = -27.1$ G. For nitrogen bonded to carbon, some estimates have been made, mostly based on theoretical spin densities. Rieger and Fraenkel (66) have studied a number of nitrile anion radicals. Based on spin densities calculated using the McLachlan method (70), they propose $Q_{CN}^C = +14.7$ G and $Q_{NC}^C = -47.5$ G for the nitrile carbon atom. However, for nitrogen in an aromatic ring, Stone and Maki (71) propose that $Q_{CN}^C \cong +4$ G. It should be pointed out that when the spin densities, used to calculate these constants, are obtained from a calculation with a number of adjustable parameters (e.g., Hückel or McLachlan calculations) the Q's obtained can be considered only rough estimates subject to change when more data are available.

c. ^{14}N Hyperfine Splittings.   Analogous to the ^{13}C splittings, we can write a relationship for ^{14}N hyperfine splittings for a nitrogen in an aromatic ring. Two situations are most commonly encountered. First, a nitrogen atom bonded to two carbon atoms (e.g., in pyridine)

and second, a nitrogen atom bonded to two carbon atoms and a hydrogen atom (e.g., in N,N'-dihydropyrazine):

$$a^N = (P^N + 2Q_{NC'}^N)\rho_N^\pi + Q_{C'N}^N \sum_i \rho_i^\pi \tag{46}$$

$$a^N = (S^N + Q_{NH}^N + 2Q_{NC'}^N)\rho_N^\pi + Q_{C'N}^N \sum_i \rho_i^\pi \tag{47}$$

where P^N includes the spin polarization of the nitrogen $1s$ electrons and the lone pair electrons. Equations 46 and 47 apply to

$$\begin{array}{ccc} & & H \\ & & | \\ N & \text{and} & N \\ \diagup\ \diagdown & & \diagup\ \diagdown \\ C\quad C & & C\quad C \end{array}$$

fragments, respectively.

No attempts have been made to calculate the Q's, mainly because many of the required exchange integrals are not available. However, it is possible in some cases to estimate the Q's from experimental nitrogen hyperfine splittings. The s-tetrazine negative ion (71) has a very small proton hyperfine splitting (0.212 G). Thus, almost all the spin density is on the nitrogens (i.e., $\rho_N^\pi \cong 0.250$). Since $Q_{NN'}^N \cong -Q_{N'N}^N$, the observed nitrogen hyperfine splitting (5.275 G) provides an estimate of $(P^N + Q_{NC}^N) = 21.1 \pm 0.4$ G (71), which is independent of any assumption as to the value of Q_{CH}^H.

Although to be complete an equation such as equation 43 should apply to ^{14}N splittings, most experimental studies have found that a simple proportionality between a^N and ρ_N^π works quite well for nitrogen heterocyclic radical ions. This implies that $Q_{C'N}^N$ must be small. Indeed in a study of methyl-substituted dihydropyrazine cations, Barton and Fraenkel (54) obtained $Q_{C'N}^N = +2.62$ G without making any assumptions about the magnitudes of other spin polarization constants and without using theoretically calculated spin densities. In a similar study of the pyrazine and 3,5-lutidine anions, Atherton, Gerson, and Murrell (72) found that $Q_{C'N}^N = -1.5$ G.

Many other attempts have been made to estimate $Q_{C'N}^N$, with results varying from -4 G to $+9$ G (73). Since these estimates were made on the basis of calculated spin densities (which can be very uncertain for heterocyclic compounds), we would tend to put more faith in the Q's obtained without recourse to calculated spin densities.

Since $Q_{C'N}^N$ appears to be small, simplified equations, similar to the McConnell relation, seem appropriate for ^{14}N splittings in nitrogen heterocyclic radicals (74):

$$a^N = Q_{N(C_2 H)}^N \rho_N^\pi \tag{48}$$

$$a^N = Q_{N(C_2 P)}^N \rho_N^\pi \tag{49}$$

where equation 48 applies to a nitrogen bonded to two carbons and a proton, and equation 49 applies to nitrogen bonded only to two carbons, with P representing the lone pair electrons. Barton and Fraenkel (54) estimate that

$$Q_{N(C_2 H)}^N = -0.94 Q_{NH}^H \tag{50}$$

With a value of $Q_{NH}^H = -29.6$ G, we estimate $Q_{N(C_2 H)}^N = +27.8$ G. (These values are slightly different from those given by Barton and Fraenkel because we have used $Q_{CH}^H = -27.0$ G to be consistent throughout.) A similar treatment for the pyrazine anion (54,74) with $Q_{CH}^H = -27.0$ G gives $Q_{N(C_2 P)}^N = +23.8$ G. It should be noted that equations 48 and 49 will only apply when $\rho_N^\pi \gg \sum_i \rho_i^\pi$, where the summation is taken over neighbors. When $\rho_N^\pi \ll \sum_i \rho_i^\pi$, the nonzero value of $Q_{C'N}^N$ is expected to contribute significantly to a^N.

It should be pointed out that the Q parameters will not necessarily be the same when the bonding situation is changed. For instance, it would not be valid to use equations 48 or 49 for a nitrogen with another adjacent nitrogen. For situations where the same or similar bonding can be assumed, the following useful relationship can be used to obtain some of the Q's (12,66,71,75):

$$Q_{AB}^A \simeq -\frac{|2s_A(0)|^2}{|2s_B(0)|^2} \frac{\gamma_A}{\gamma_B} Q_{AB}^B \tag{51}$$

When A = carbon and B = nitrogen, Rieger and Fraenkel (66) calculate the coefficient in equation 51 to be -0.460, i.e.,

$$\frac{Q_{CN}^N}{Q_{CN}^C} \simeq \frac{Q_{NC}^N}{Q_{NC}^C} \simeq -0.460 \tag{52}$$

d. ^{19}F Hyperfine Splittings. It might be expected that since fluorine substitutes for hydrogen in aromatic compounds, the McConnell relation will also hold for fluorine hyperfine splittings. That is, if ρ_C^π is positive, we would expect that a^F would be negative. To test this hypothesis consider the radical:

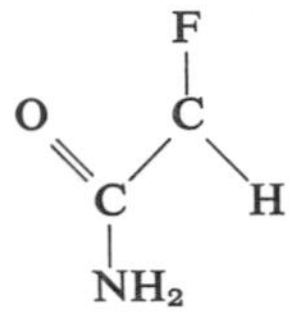

which has been studied in a single crystal by Cook, Rowlands, and Whiffen (76). They report the following principal values of the hyperfine tensors:

$$^{19}F: \quad +530, \; -11, \; -45 \text{ MHz}$$

$$^{1}H: \quad -96, \; -63, \; -31 \text{ MHz}$$

for the fluorine and hydrogen atoms, respectively, attached to the radical carbon. The isotropic fluorine hyperfine coupling is thus *positive* ($+158$ MHz); the anisotropic hyperfine tensor components are then (372, -169, and -203) MHz. Here, the 372 MHz value corresponds to a direction perpendicular to the radical plane and the tensor is almost axial. This indicates that the predominant contribution to the anisotropic fluorine coupling arises from spin density in a $2p^\pi$ orbital on fluorine. We can use the method to be described in the next section to evaluate ρ_F^π and obtain $+0.119$. From the isotropic hydrogen hyperfine coupling (63.3 MHz) with $Q_{CH}^H = -75.6$ MHz (-27.0 G) we calculate $\rho_C^\pi = 0.837$. Thus although most of the spin density is still on the carbon, there is enough spin density on the fluorine to make it the major contributor to the isotropic fluorine coupling (presumably through the same $\pi-\sigma$ spin polarization mechanism which has been shown to operate for ^{13}C and ^{14}N splittings). In view of these considerations, a relationship for the fluorine hyperfine splitting (or coupling) should be based on equation 43 and not equation 26, (76–78), i.e.:

$$a^F = (P^F + Q_{FC}^F)\rho_F^\pi + Q_{CF}^F\rho_C^\pi \tag{53a}$$

$$= Q_{F(FC)}^F\rho_F^\pi + Q_{CF}^F\rho_C^\pi \tag{53b}$$

where P^F includes the polarization of the fluorine $1s$ and lone pair electrons, and the other Q's have their usual significance. Data are still sketchy concerning appropriate values to use for the parameters, mainly since it is difficult to estimate ρ_F^π. $Q_{F(FC)}^F$ must be positive and is probably in the range 700–1500 G (78). Since ρ_C^π and ρ_F^π are known for the monofluoroacetamide radical, we have at least the relationship:

$$Q_{CF}^F = 67.4 - 0.142\, Q_{F(FC)}^F \tag{54}$$

which implies that Q_{CF}^F must lie in the range -32 to -145 G. These values agree with those proposed by Eaton et al. (77,79).

2. Anisotropic Hyperfine Splitting from Atoms with a Net π Electron Spin Density

In contrast to the isotropic hyperfine couplings, which usually arise through an indirect π–σ interaction, anisotropic hyperfine couplings result from a dipole-dipole coupling of the nuclear spin with a nonspherically symmetric electron spin distribution (i.e., an electron in a p, d, etc. orbital). Consider an electron in a p orbital interacting with the nucleus of the same atom. The dipole–dipole term in the spin Hamiltonian will be:

$$\mathscr{H}_D = -h^{-1}g_e\beta_e g_N\beta_N\left[\frac{\hat{S}\cdot\hat{I}}{r^3} - 3\frac{(\hat{S}\cdot\mathbf{r})(\hat{I}\cdot\mathbf{r})}{r^5}\right] \tag{55}$$

where g_e and g_N are the g values of the electron and nucleus, respectively; β_e is the Bohr magneton; β_N is the nuclear magneton; $\hat{S}$ and $\hat{I}$ are the spin operators for the electron and nucleus, respectively; $\mathbf{r}$ is the radius vector between the electron and the nucleus. Equation 55 when applied to the spin wave functions results in the following anisotropic hyperfine energy (80):

$$W'_{M_S M_I} = h^{-1}\frac{g_e\beta_e g_N\beta_N M_I M_S}{2}\left\langle\frac{1 - 3\cos^2\alpha}{r^3}\right\rangle_{av}(1 - 3\cos^2\theta) \quad (\text{MHz}) \tag{56}$$

Here α is the angle between $\mathbf{r}$ and a principal axis of the anisotropic hyperfine tensor and θ is the angle between $\mathbf{H}_0$ and the same axis. (Note $\langle 3\cos^2\theta\rangle_{av} = 1$ when averaged over a sphere and thus $W'_{M_S M_I}$ is truly anisotropic.) Consider $\mathbf{H}_0$ along the z axis which we take to be the major axis of the p orbital. $\theta = 0$, so the last factor in equation 56 will be -2. For a p orbital, the average value of $\cos^2\alpha$ is $3/5$. The anisotropic hyperfine energy or coupling with $\mathbf{H}_0$ along the z axis will then be $2B_0$, where:

$$B_0 = \tfrac{2}{5}h^{-1}g_e\beta_e g_N\beta_N\langle r^{-3}\rangle_{av} \quad (\text{MHz}) \tag{57}$$

$\langle r^{-3}\rangle_{av}$ can be calculated from SCF wave functions or from a Slater wave function. Morton (80) presents a useful table of values of A_0 (the isotropic hyperfine coupling) and B_0 (the anisotropic hyperfine coupling) computed from atomic wave functions.

As an example of the calculation of a spin density using this method, consider the malonic acid radical enriched in ^{13}C (81):

$$\begin{array}{c} \text{H} \\ | \\ ^{13}\text{C} \\ \diagup \quad \diagdown \\ \text{HOOC} \qquad \text{COOH} \end{array}$$

The isotropic ^{13}C hyperfine coupling is 93 MHz and the anisotropic coupling tensor components are (120, -70, -50) MHz, with the 120 MHz component oriented perpendicular to the radical plane. This anisotropic coupling can thus be identified with the $2B_0$ term in the $2p_z$ atomic anisotropic hyperfine coupling tensor. For ^{13}C the value of $2B_0$ is calculated to be 182 MHz (80). We thus compute $\rho_C^\pi = {}^{120}/_{182} = 0.66$. This value can be checked from the isotropic proton hyperfine coupling (-59 MHz) and $Q_{CH}^H = -75.6$ MHz, which gives $\rho_C^\pi = 0.78$. The discrepancy may be due to spin density on the carboxyl groups affecting the anisotropic hyperfine couplings, or to σ spin density in the bonds, or perhaps to an overestimate of $2B_0$ in the atomic carbon $2p^\pi$ orbital. One other indication of ρ_C^π can be obtained from the isotropic ^{13}C hyperfine coupling. If we assume no spin density on the carboxyl carbons, then the ^{13}C isotropic hyperfine coupling should be 35.6 G $= 99.7$ MHz for $\rho_C^\pi = 1$. From the observed value of 93 MHz, we compute $\rho_C^\pi = 0.93$. This seems rather high and may indicate some *negative* spin density on the carboxyl carbon atoms. (Simple molecular orbital calculations indicate that this may be true.) This example points out the fact that our knowledge of the relations between spin densities and the experimental observables is still rather crude.

This method of obtaining spin densities from anisotropic hyperfine couplings has also been used to estimate the extent of delocalization of electron spin into the ligands of transition metal ion complexes. For instance consider the $IrCl_6^{2-}$ ion, studied as the ammonium salt diluted in

$$\left[\begin{array}{c} \text{Cl} \\ | \quad \text{Cl} \\ | \diagup \\ \text{Cl}\!-\!\!-\!\!-\!\text{Ir}\!-\!\!-\!\!-\!\text{Cl} \\ \diagup | \\ \text{Cl} \quad | \\ \text{Cl} \end{array}\right]^{2-}$$

a single crystal of $Na_2PtCl_6 \cdot 6H_2O$ (82). The crystal field is essentially cubic and thus the spectrum is the same along any principal axis. Hyperfine splitting was observed from ^{191}Ir and ^{193}Ir superimposed (both with spin $3/2$ and nearly the same magnetic moment) and from the six chlorine atoms (^{35}Cl and ^{37}Cl both have spin $\frac{3}{2}$ and similar magnetic moments). Griffiths and Owen show that the chlorine hyperfine splitting should be given by:

$$a^{Cl} = \frac{8h^{-1}}{5} g_e \beta_e g_N \beta_N \langle r^{-3} \rangle \rho_{Cl} \quad (MHz) \tag{58}$$

where ρ_{Cl} is the spin density in $3p$ orbitals on a chlorine atom. From the value of $B_0 = 137$ MHz (80) for ^{35}Cl and $a^{Cl} = 26.4$ MHz (82), we compute $\rho_{Cl} = 0.048$. Since there are six chlorine atoms, this means that the unpaired electron is about 30% on the ligands.

C. Spin Densities from g Values

For transition metal ions, it is often possible to calculate g values with some accuracy in those cases where bonding to the surrounding lattice is purely ionic. [For methods of computing these g values, see Abragam and Pryce (83) or Pake (84).] For example, consider again the IrCl$_6^{2-}$ ion (82). If the unpaired electron resides entirely on the Ir atom, then the g value is expected to be 2.000 for cubic symmetry. However, if some spin density is on the Cl atoms, some orbital angular momentum is introduced which tends to decrease the g value. Griffiths and Owen (82) show that the g value should be decreased 2–4 ρ_{Cl} where ρ_{Cl} is the spin density on a chlorine atom. The observed g value is 1.775, hence ρ_{Cl} is 0.056, in good agreement with the value calculated from the chlorine hyperfine splittings.

D. Spin Densities from Chemical Shifts in the NMR of Paramagnetic Molecules

Only a brief outline of this method will be presented here, as an excellent review on the subject by Eaton and Phillips (79) has appeared to which the reader is referred for more details.

Under certain conditions (i.e., when the electron spin lattice relaxation time T_1 or the intermolecular electron exchange time T_e is very short compared to the inverse of the hyperfine coupling frequency, A_N^{-1}) hyperfine splitting cannot be observed in the ESR spectrum due to lifetime broadening. However, either or both of these conditions means that the nucleus N will see a time average, $\langle S_z \rangle$, of the z component of the electron spin. This produces a net magnetic field at the nucleus of a magnitude:

$$H' = \frac{-2\pi A_N}{\gamma_N} \langle S_z \rangle \tag{59}$$

where A_N is the isotropic hyperfine coupling constant between the electron and the nucleus N and γ_N is the magnetogyric ratio for the nucleus N. For a ground state paramagnetic molecule it can be shown that H' results in a chemical shift (relative to a reference diamagnetic molecule) of the form:

$$\sigma_i = \left(\frac{\Delta H}{H_o}\right)_i = -A_i \frac{\gamma_e}{\gamma_N} \frac{g_e \beta_e S(S+1)}{3kT} \tag{60}$$

Thus if these chemical shifts can be measured, the *sign* and *magnitude* of isotropic hyperfine splittings can be obtained. These hyperfine splittings can then be used to obtain spin densities using the methods we have already described.

To illustrate the sensitivity of this method, consider the nickel complex (79) shown in structure **3**, where peaks in the NMR were observed for all

(3)

the ligand protons with shifts as low as -300 Hz and as high as $+450$ Hz (at 60 MHz) with respect to the reference tetramethylsilane. π Spin densities in the ligands as low as ± 0.0001 can be measured with ease. In this compound spin densities were measured for all carbon atoms with attached protons in the π system of the ligand.

Acknowledgments

Support from the National Science Foundation Grant No. GP-5847 during the writing of this article is gratefully acknowledged. It is a pleasure to thank my colleague, John E. Wertz, for his many helpful comments in reading the manuscript. Mr. William Knolle and Miss Pamela Wormington kindly checked the manuscript and references. I would also like to thank Dr. R. Lefebvre, Dr. R. W. Fessenden, and Dr. G. Vincow for their permission to quote their unpublished work and for their helpful comments.

References

1. H. M. McConnell, *J. Chem. Phys.*, **28**, 1188 (1958).
2. J. P. Colpa and J. R. Bolton, *Mol. Phys.*, **6**, 273 (1963).
3. H. M. McConnell and D. B. Chesnut, *J. Chem. Phys.*, **28**, 107 (1958); P. Brovetto and S. Ferroni, *Nuovo Cimento*, **5**, 142 (1957).
4. O. Chalvet and R. Daudel, *J. Chim. Phys.*, **49**, 629 (1952).
5. E. Hückel, *Z. Physik*, **76**, 628 (1932); C. A. Coulson and H. C. Longuet-Higgins, *Proc. Roy. Soc. (London), Ser. A*, **192**, 16 (1947); C. A. Coulson, *Proc. Roy. Soc. (London), Ser. A*, **164**, 383 (1938).
6. A. Carrington, *Quart. Rev. (London)*, **17**, 67 (1963).
7. S. I. Weissman, J. Townsend, D. E. Paul, and G. E. Pake, *J. Chem. Phys.*, **21**, 2227 (1953).
8. H. M. McConnell, *J. Chem. Phys.*, **24**, 632, 764 (1956).
8a. A. D. McLachlan, H. H. Dearman, and R. Lefebvre, *J. Chem. Phys.*, **33**, 65, (1960).
9. S. I. Weissman, *J. Chem. Phys.*, **25**, 890 (1956).
10. J. C. Slater, *Phys. Rev.*, **38**, 1109 (1931).
11. L. Pauling, *J. Chem. Phys.*, **1**, 280 (1933).
12. M. Karplus and G. K. Fraenkel, **35**, 1312 (1961).
13. E. Fermi, *Z. Physik*, **60**, 320 (1930).
14. R. A. Ferrell, *Am. J. Phys.*, **28**, 484 (1960); F. J. Milford, *ibid.*, **28**, 521 (1960).
15. H. S. Jarrett, *J. Chem. Phys.*, **25**, 1289 (1956).
16. H. S. Gutowsky, H. Kusumoto, T. H. Brown, and D. H. Anderson, *J. Chem. Phys.*, **30**, 860 (1959); T. H. Brown, D. H. Anderson, and H. S. Gutowsky, *ibid.*, **33**, 720 (1960); M. E. Anderson, G. E. Pake, and T. R. Tuttle, Jr., *ibid.*, **33**, 1581 (1960); M. E. Anderson, P. J. Zandstra, and T. R. Tuttle, Jr., *ibid.*, **33**, 1591 (1960).
17. R. W. Fessenden and R. H. Schuler, *J. Chem. Phys.*, **39**, 2147 (1963).
18. T. R. Tuttle, Jr. and S. I. Weissman, *J. Am. Chem. Soc.*, **80**, 5342 (1958); J. R. Bolton, *Mol. Phys.*, **6**, 219 (1963).
19. R. W. Fessenden and S. Ogawa, *J. Am. Chem. Soc.*, **86**, 3591 (1964).
20. T. J. Katz and H. L. Stevens, *J. Chem. Phys.*, **32**, 1873 (1960).
21. S. Arai, S. Shida, K. Vomazaki, and Z. Kuri, *J. Chem. Phys.*, **37**, 1885 (1962); A. Carrington and I. C. P. Smith, *Mol. Phys.*, **7**, 99 (1963); G. Vincow, M. L. Morrell, W. V. Volland, H. J. Dauben, Jr., and F. R. Hunter, *J. Am. Chem. Soc.*, **87**, 3527 (1965); D. E. Wood and H. M. McConnell, *J. Chem. Phys.*, **37**, 1150 (1962).
22. S. Ohnishi and I. Nitta, *J. Chem. Phys.*, **39**, 2848 (1963); P. Zandstra, *ibid.*, **40**, 612 (1964).
23. D. H. Levy and R. J. Myers, *J. Chem. Phys.*, **41**, 1062 (1964).
24. D. Lazdins and M. Karplus, *J. Chem. Phys.*, **44**, 1600 (1966).
24a. P. Nordio, M. V. Pavan, and G. Giacometti, *Theoret. Chim. Acta (Berlin)*, **1**, 302 (1963).
25. R. W. Fessenden, private communication.
26. H. Fischer, *Z. Naturforsch.*, **20A**, 428 (1965).
27. R. W. Fessenden, *J. Chem. Phys.* (in press).
28. K. H. Hausser, private communication from H. Fischer.
29. R. W. Fessenden and R. H. Schuler, *J. Chem. Phys.*, **43**, 2704 (1965).
30. C. Heller and T. Cole, *J. Chem. Phys.*, **37**, 243 (1962).
31. J. R. Bolton and G. K. Fraenkel, *J. Chem. Phys.*, **40**, 3307 (1964).

32. A. D. McLachlan, *Mol. Phys.*, **2**, 271 (1959); H. M. McConnell and R. E. Robertson, *J. Chem. Phys.*, **28**, 991 (1958).
33. J. S. Hyde and H. W. Brown, *J. Chem. Phys.*, **37**, 368 (1962).
34. J. R. Bolton, unpublished work.
35. J. R. Bolton, *J. Chem. Phys.*, **46**, 408 (1967).
36. G. J. Hoijtink and W. P. Weizland, *Rec. Trav. Chim.*, **76**, 836 (1957).
37. I. C. Lewis and L. S. Singer, *J. Chem. Phys.*, **43**, 2712 (1965).
38. R. Lefebvre, private communication.
39. J. Higuchi, *J. Chem. Phys.*, **39**, 3455 (1963).
40. J. R. Bolton, *J. Chem. Phys.*, **43**, 309 (1965).
41. G. Giacometti, P. L. Nordio, and M. V. Pavan, *Theoret. Chim. Acta (Berlin)*, **1**, 404 (1963).
42. L. C. Snyder and T. Amos, *J. Chem. Phys.*, **42**, 3670 (1965).
43. G. Vincow, private communication.
44. R. Lefebvre, private communication.
45. T. C. Sayetta and J. D. Memory, *J. Chem. Phys.*, **40**, 2748 (1964).
46. N. M. Atherton and S. I. Weissman, *J. Am. Chem. Soc.*, **83**, 1330 (1961).
47. H. M. McConnell and J. Strathdee, *Mol. Phys.*, **2**, 129 (1959).
48. D. K. Ghosh and D. H. Whiffen, *Mol. Phys.*, **2**, 285 (1959).
49. T. Cole and C. Heller, *J. Chem. Phys.*, **34**, 1085 (1961); T. Cole, C. Heller and H. M. McConnell, *Proc. Natl. Acad. Sci. U.S.*, **45**, 525 (1959); H. M. McConnell, C. Heller, T. Cole, and R. W. Fessenden, *J. Am. Chem. Soc.*, **82**, 766 (1960).
50. J. C. Schug, T. H. Brown, and M. Karplus, *J. Chem. Phys.*, **37**, 330 (1962).
51. B. L. Barton and G. K. Fraenkel, *J. Chem. Phys.*, **41**, 695 (1964).
52. T. Cole, *J. Chem. Phys.*, **35**, 1169 (1961).
53. J. S. Hyde and E. S. Freeman, *J. Phys. Chem.*, **65**, 1636 (1961).
54. B. L. Barton and G. K. Fraenkel, *J. Chem. Phys.*, **41**, 1455 (1964).
55. J. Q. Adams and J. R. Thomas, *J. Chem. Phys.*, **39**, 1904 (1963).
56. S. N. Foner, E. L. Cochran, V. A. Bowers, and C. K. Jen, *Phys. Rev. Letters*, **1**, 91 (1958).
57. G. P. Rabold, K. H. Bar-Eli, E. Reid, and K. Weiss, *J. Chem. Phys.*, **42**, 2438 (1965).
58. J. R. Bolton, A. Carrington, and J. dos Santos Veiga, *Mol. Phys.*, **5**, 465 (1962).
59. J. R. Bolton, A. Carrington, and A. D. McLachlan, *Mol. Phys.*, **5**, 31 (1962).
60. P. Nordio, M. V. Pavan, and G. Giacometti, *Theoret. Chim. Acta (Berlin)*, **1**, 302 (1963).
61. J. P. Colpa and E. deBoer, *Mol. Phys.*, **7**, 333 (1964).
62. E. deBoer and E. L. Mackor, *Mol. Phys.*, **5**, 493 (1962).
63. R. Bersohn, *J. Chem. Phys.*, **24**, 1066 (1956); D. B. Chesnut, *J. Chem. Phys.*, **29**, 43 (1958).
64. F. C. Adam and S. I. Weissman, *J. Am. Chem. Soc.*, **80**, 2057 (1958).
65. A. D. McLachlan, H. H. Dearman, and R. Lefebvre, *J. Chem. Phys.*, **33**, 65 (1960).
66. P. H. Rieger and G. K. Fraenkel, *J. Chem. Phys.*, **37**, 2795 (1962).
67. H. L. Strauss and G. K. Fraenkel, *J. Chem. Phys.*, **35**, 1738 (1961).
68. R. W. Fessenden, *J. Phys. Chem.*, **71**, 74 (1967).
69. M. R. Das and G. K. Fraenkel, *J. Chem. Phys.*, **42**, 1350 (1965).
70. A. D. McLachlan, *Mol. Phys.*, **3**, 233 (1960).
71. E. W. Stone and A. H. Maki, *J. Chem. Phys.*, **39**, 1635 (1963).
72. N. M. Atherton, F. Gerson, and J. N. Murrell, *Mol. Phys.*, **5**, 509 (1962).

73. R. L. Ward, *J. Am. Chem. Soc.*, **84**, 332 (1962); J. C. M. Henning and C. deWaard, *Phys. Letters*, **3**, 139 (1962); D. H. Geske and G. R. Padmanabhan, *J. Am. Chem. Soc.*, **87**, 1651 (1965); J. C. M. Henning, *J. Chem. Phys.*, **44**, 2139 (1966).

74. A. Carrington and J. dos Santos Veiga, *Mol. Phys.*, **5**, 21 (1962); C. A. McDowell and K. F. G. Paulus, *ibid.*, **7**, 541 (1964).

75. H. L. Strauss and G. K. Fraenkel, *J. Chem. Phys.*, **35**, 1738 (1961).

76. R. J. Cook, J. R. Rowlands, and D. H. Whiffen, *Mol. Phys.*, **7**, 31 (1963).

77. D. R. Eaton, A. D. Josey, R. E. Benson, W. D. Phillips, and T. L. Cairns, *J. Am. Chem. Soc.*, **84**, 4100 (1962); D. R. Eaton, A. D. Josey, W. D. Phillips, and R. E. Benson, *Mol. Phys.*, **5**, 407 (1962).

78. M. Kaplan, J. R. Bolton, and G. K. Fraenkel, *J. Chem. Phys.*, **42**, 955 (1965).

79. D. R. Eaton and W. D. Phillips, in *Advances in Magnetic Resonance*, Vol. 1, J. S. Waugh, Ed., Academic Press, New York, 1965.

80. J. R. Morton, *Chem. Rev.*, **64**, 453 (1964).

81. T. Cole and C. Heller, *J. Chem. Phys.*, **34**, 1085 (1961); H. M. McConnell and R. W. Fessenden, *ibid.*, **31**, 1688 (1959).

82. J. H. E. Griffiths and J. Owen, *Proc. Roy. Soc. (London), Ser. A*, **213**, 459 (1952); *Proc. Phys. Soc.*, **A65**, 951 (1952); *Proc. Roy. Soc. (London), Ser. A*, **226**, 96 (1954).

83. A. Abragam and M. H. L. Pryce, *Proc. Roy. Soc. (London), Ser. A*, **205**, 135 (1950).

84. G. E. Pake, *Paramagnetic Resonance*, Benjamin, New York, 1962.

CHAPTER 2

Metal Ketyls and Related Radical Ions—
Electronic Structures and Ion Pair Equilibria

Noboru Hirota

Department of Chemistry, State University of New York at Stony Brook, Stony Brook, New York

I. INTRODUCTION

In the last 15 years, since EPR began to be applied to free radical studies, a large number of radical anions have been investigated. Radical anions are usually prepared by either chemical reduction with alkali metal in ethereal solvents (1) or by electrolytic reduction in acetonitrile or in N,N-dimethylformamide (2). The scheme is given by

$$R + M \longrightarrow R^- + M^+ \qquad \text{Chemical reduction}$$

$$R + e^- \longrightarrow R^- \qquad \text{Electrolytic reduction}$$

Perhaps the most vigorously pursued area in the radical anion field has been the study of spin distributions in radicals in connection with the theoretical calculation of the spin distribution by molecular orbital (MO) or valence bond methods. The successful preparation of a great many radical anions by electrolytic reduction (2) facilitated such studies in a variety of systems. This problem, however, is treated elsewhere in this volume and is not treated here except for some special purposes.

The preparation of radical anions by chemical reduction (3) is somewhat more limited than that by electrolytic reduction because of the high reactivity of alkali metals toward many organic molecules. Furthermore reduction in ethereal solvents such as tetrahydrofuran (THF) or 1,2-dimethoxyethane (DME) often leads to the association of the anion with the alkali metal ions. The presence of hyperfine splittings due to the associated positive ions makes EPR spectra very complicated and the complete analysis of the spectra often becomes very difficult. However, the fact that these radical ions form associated ion pairs in solution provides unique opportunities to investigate the processes involving association, dissociation, and ion cluster formation of ionic species in such solutions on the microscopic level.

Recent investigations have revealed detailed structural and kinetic aspects of ion pairs in solution. Furthermore, ion pair formation and differences in the ion pair structures play important roles in determining the rates and mechanisms of reaction in many systems. Therefore, it is hoped that the understanding of the detailed natures of the ion pair equilibria would lead to the better understanding of the complex reaction processes in solution

In the following discussion, metal ketyls and the related radical anions are taken as examples, and the following topics are discussed in detail: (1) electronic structure and spin distribution in radical anions and the perturbation due to ion pair formation, (2) ion pair equilibria in solution, (3) structure of ion pairs, and (4) rapid electron and atom transfer reactions and their connection with the structures of ion pairs. Comparisons between ketyls and other radical ions such as hydrocarbon negative ions are given as often as possible. Although special examples are discussed here, the phenomena described in this chapter have wide implications for the consideration of the properties of many other radical ions in solution.

This discussion is not intended to be a complete review of the wide variety of investigations of radical anions or even metal ketyls which have been reported. The emphasis is placed on the various aspects of the behavior of ion pairs of radical anions in solution. The main objective of the discussion is to show how spectroscopic (particularly EPR) studies of these systems can provide detailed information concerning the rather complicated processes involving ion pairs in solution.

Several important aspects of the properties of radical anions, such as their behavior in polymerization reactions and the disproportionation reactions between mono- and dinegative ions are not treated here in detail. These aspects are discussed in more detail in other existing review articles (4,5).

A. Historical Background

In 1891 Bechman found the appearance of a strong blue color when he treated benzophenone with sodium in an inert atmosphere of nitrogen (6). This was probably the first discovery of a radical anion, although the nature of the reaction product was not well understood. Before 1935 many investigators carried out extensive studies of chemical properties of metal ketyls and their free radical characters were recognized. For example, Schlenk suggested the molecular structure $(C_6H_5)_2\dot{C}$—ONa for benzophenone ketyl (7). Although free radical structures were suggested for ketyls, the presence of the dimeric forms of ketyls, the pinacolates, was suspected to exist in view of the easy transformation of sodium benzophenone to pinacol (7b,8).

In order to confirm the presence of such species, boiling point measurements were made (9). However, conflicting observations were made by different investigators and no conclusive information was obtained. Conductivity measurements of sodium benzophenone in liquid ammonia by Wooster indicated that the sodium ion and the benzophenone negative ion were combined ionically to form ion pair ketyls and that they were largely dissociated in this solvent (10). Therefore, by 1935 the complexity of the system and the presence of at least three different species—dissociated ion, ion pair ketyl, and pinacolate—were realized.

Magnetic susceptibility measurements in the 1930's confirmed the free radical character of the system, but at the same time it was shown that the paramagnetic susceptibilities of ketyls in solution and in solids were appreciably lower than expected from pure free radical formation (11–13). Thus, it was thought that the ketyl radical was in equilibrium with diamagnetic pinacolate.

The equilibrium was written as

$$
2 \quad \overset{Ar}{\underset{Ar}{\diagdown}} \dot{C}\!-\!O^-Na^+ \rightleftharpoons \overset{Ar}{\underset{Ar}{\diagdown}} C\!-\!O^-Na^+ \\
\begin{array}{c}
\overset{Ar}{\underset{Ar}{\diagdown}} C\!-\!O^-Na^+
\end{array}
$$

A similar type of reaction was also found in certain aliphatic ketyls, such as hexamethylacetone for which the structure

$$(CH_3)_3C \diagdown \\ \overset{\cdot}{C}-O^-Na^+ \\ (CH_3)_3C \diagup$$

was suggested by Favorsky and Nazarow (14).

These descriptions summarize the major investigations of the pre-EPR age. None of these classical experiments, however, gave decisive information concerning the real structures of ketyls in solution and various authors disagreed about the structures of ketyls.

Radical anions of simple aromatic hydrocarbons, such as naphthalene, anthracene, etc., in ethereal solvents were prepared similarly (15,16). It was noted that the ease of the reduction depended strongly on the solvent. For example, naphthalene was reduced very easily with sodium in dimethyl ether, but not in diethyl ether (DEE) at room temperature (16).

B. Recent Investigations

In the last 10 years ketyls and other radical anions have been investigated extensively. The primary tools for these investigations have been (*1*) EPR, (*2*) visible and UV spectra, and (*3*) electrical conductivity measurements. Although many unsolved problems remain, the details of the electronic structures of some radicals are understood and we now are beginning to understand the detailed nature of ion pairs in solution. In the following discussion results obtained in recent investigations are given. EPR investigations are described in more detail than are other studies, partly because of the author's familiarity with this area and partly because of the author's belief that this technique can give very detailed information concerning the problems of present concern.

II. EPR AND VISIBLE-UV SPECTRA OF KETYLS AND THEIR ELECTRONIC STRUCTURES

A. EPR Spectra and Electronic Structures

1. Hyperfine Splittings and Spin Distributions in Radical Anions

The interpretation of the proton hyperfine splittings of the EPR spectra of radical anions is based on the so-called "McConnell relation" (17–19)

$$a_i = Q\rho_i \tag{1}$$

where a_i is the observed hyperfine splitting of the proton attached to the ith carbon atom and ρ_i is the unpaired electron density at the ith carbon atom in the conjugated system. Q is usually around 23 G, but it depends on the particular system.

The relationship between spin density and hyperfine splitting due to other nuclei also has been studied theoretically and experimentally. For example, a theoretical formulation for the relationship between ^{13}C splitting and spin density was given by Karplus and Fraenkel (20) and was tested for a number of experimental values.

The expression is given as

$$a^{^{13}C} = \left(S_C + \sum_X Q_{CX}\right)\rho_C + \sum_X Q_{XC}\,\rho_X \qquad (2)$$

where $a^{^{13}C}$ is the ^{13}C splitting and ρ_C is the spin density on the ^{13}C carbon, ρ_X are the spin densities on the adjacent atom X. Proportionality constants S_C, Q_{CX}, and Q_{XC} were estimated by Karplus and Fraenkel. Similar formulas are known to be applicable to other nuclei, such as nitrogen.

Using these relationships, experimental spin distributions have been determined for many systems. The interpretation of the spin distributions in radicals has been made mostly in terms of the MO theory. The simple Hückel MO treatment has been applied to many systems and good agreement between the observed and the estimated spin densities was found in certain systems, such as even alternant hydrocarbon negative ions, with proper choice of the Coulomb and resonance integrals (21). However, Hückel MO treatments were found to be unsatisfactory in explaining the observed EPR spectra in many systems including most of the ketyls. One fundamental fault of the Hückel MO is its inability to predict negative spin densities which were found to be important in many systems, such as ketyls. Among the refined theoretical treatments McLachlan's self-consistent field MO treatment (22) has been used widely and successfully.

We will now discuss EPR spectra and spin distributions in ketyls. The EPR spectra of electrolytically produced ketyl ions represent the spectra of the free ions. The usual electrolytic reduction is carried out in solvents of high dielectric constant, such as N,N-dimethylformamide (DMF) or acetonitrile, and the radical ions produced are considered to be free ions. EPR spectra of a great many ketyl radical ions have been reported by Fraenkel and his co-workers (23–25). They made extensive MO calculations for ketyls using McLachlan's method as well as the Hückel MO treatment. With suitable choices of the parameters, the Coulomb integral $\alpha_0 = \alpha + \delta_0\beta$ and the resonance integral $\beta_{CO} = \gamma_{CO}\beta$, generally good agreement between experimental results and calculations was obtained. Here α_0 and α are the Coulomb integrals for oxygen and an aromatic carbon atom. β_{CO} and β are the resonance integrals for the carbonyl C—O bond and the aromatic C—C bond.

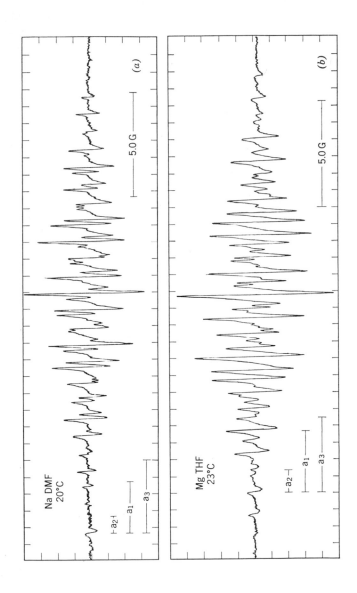

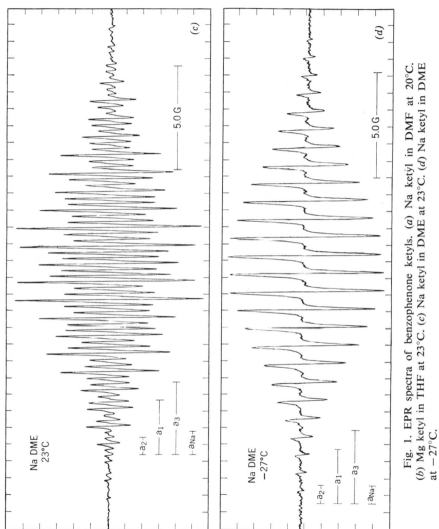

Fig. 1. EPR spectra of benzophenone ketyls. (a) Na ketyl in DMF at 20°C. (b) Mg ketyl in THF at 23°C. (c) Na ketyl in DME at 23°C. (d) Na ketyl in DME at −27°C.

The parameters which give the best fits between the observed and estimated values depend on the individual system, but Rieger and Fraenkel (23) found that the best parameters for many ketyl radical ions are somewhere around $\delta_0 \sim 1.6$ and $\gamma_{CO} \sim 1.5$. A number of radical anions containing carbonyl groups have been investigated by Rieger and Fraenkel (23) and Dehl and Fraenkel (24). Some examples of the hyperfine splittings found and the experimental and calculated spin densities are given in Table I.

The EPR spectra of a number of aromatic metal ketyls have been studied by various groups (26–34). The proton hyperfine splittings are usually slightly perturbed by the presence of the associated metal ions. Measurements of the hyperfine splittings observed in the EPR spectra of metal ketyls (including benzophenone ketyls) produced by reduction with alkali and alkaline earth metals have been made by Hirota (26,42). The alkali metal ketyls produced by the photolytic reduction of ketones with sodium methoxide or ethoxide have been studied by Ayscough and Wilson (27), the photolytically produced fluorenone ketyl by Luckhurst and Orgel (28), and the metal ketyls of substituted benzophenones by Maruyama and co-workers (29). In Figure 1 the EPR spectra of some benzophenone ketyls are given as examples. Hyperfine splittings of some representative metal ketyls are given in the table together with those of the corresponding free ions electrolytically produced in DMF or in acetonitrile. As noted by Favorsky and Nazarow as early as 1938 (14), certain aliphatic ketones produce stable ketyls, and the EPR spectra of several aliphatic ketyls have been reported (32–38). These include the ketyls of hexamethylacetone and pentamethylacetone, which were reported by Hirota and Weissman (32) and by Luckhurst (33) 2,2,5,5-tetramethyl-hexane-3,4-dione, which was described by Luckhurst and Orgel (34), and various alicyclic ketyls which were prepared by Lown (35).

Ketyl analogs of other radical anions, such as thioxanthone, thianthrene-5,10-tetroxide, and other sulfur-containing radical anions were studied in the same way. Special interest in these radicals has been focused on the participation of the d orbitals in conjugation with the π electron system and the delocalization of the unpaired electron into the d orbitals. EPR investigations seem to support the postulation of d-orbital participation in conjugation with π electron systems (36,37).

EPR spectra of chemically produced ketyls usually show additional hyperfine splittings due to metal ions (potassium splittings are often too small to be observed). As is easily seen from Table I, there are systematic differences in the proton and ^{13}C hyperfine splittings between electrolytically reduced free ketyl ions and chemically reduced ketyls. The difference originates mainly from the electrostatic perturbation due to the

TABLE I
Hyperfine Splittings[a] and Spin Densities[b] in Some Ketyls

1. Benzophenone

	^{13}C (Carbonyl)	H_1	H_2	H_3	Ref.
Hyperfine splittings					
Free ion (1)		2.52	0.82	3.50	—c
(2)		2.55	0.86	3.38	—d
K	9.3	2.58	0.86	3.44	—e
		2.53	0.84	3.45	—d
Na		2.60	0.87	3.45	—e
		2.58	0.86	3.44	—d
Ba	12.1	2.64	0.93	3.44	—e
Ca	13.2	2.76	0.98	3.46	—e
Mg	15.8	2.87	1.06	3.46	—e
Spin densities					
Experimental (free ion)		0.106	0.036	0.148	—c
Calculated (Hückel)		0.0746	0.0060	0.0971	—c
(McLachlan)		0.0976	−0.0319	0.1330	—c

2. Fluorenone

	^{13}C (Carbonyl)	$H_{1,8}$	$H_{2,7}$	$H_{3,6}$	$H_{4,5}$	Ref.
Hyperfine splittings						
Free ion (1)		1.96	0.03	3.08	0.65	—f
(2)	2.75	1.88	—	3.07	0.64	—e,g
K	4.20	2.03	0.1	3.12	0.66	—e,g
Na	4.85	2.08	0.11	3.15	0.66	—e,g
Li	6.20	—	—	—	—	—g
Ca	—	2.53	0.35	3.25	0.73	—e
Mg	—	2.62	0.42	3.33	—	—e
Spin densities						
Experimental (free ion)		0.083	0.001	0.130	0.027	—f
Calculated (McLachlan)		0.084	−0.006	0.110	−0.027	—f

(*continued*)

TABLE I (*continued*)

3. Benzil

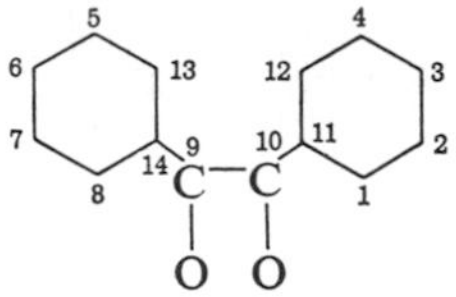

	$H_{1,8,12,13}$	$H_{2,4,5,7}$	$H_{3,6}$	Ref.
Hyperfine splittings				
Free ion	0.99	0.36	1.12	—[f]
K	0.91	0.36	0.91	—[e]
Na	0.96	0.36	0.96	—[e]
Spin densities				
Experimental (free ion)	0.042	0.015	0.047	—[f]
Calculated (McLachlan)	0.040	−0.015	0.045	—[f]

4. Acenaphthenequinone

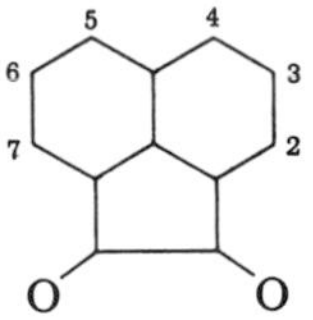

	$H_{2,7}$	$H_{3,6}$	$H_{4,5}$	Ref.
Hyperfine splittings				
Free ion	1.17	0.27	1.27	—[f]
K	1.28	0.28	1.28	—[e]
Na	1.28	0.30	1.28	—[e]
Spin densities				
Experimental (free ion)	0.050	0.011	0.054	—[f]
Calculated (McLachlan)	0.036	−0.022	0.040	—[f]

5a. Terephthalaldehyde (*cis*)

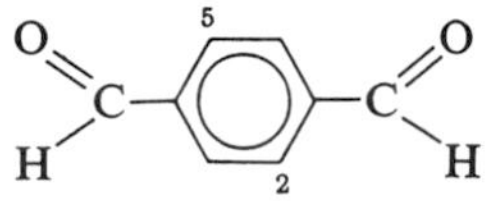

	H_2	H_5	H_{ald}	Ref.
Hyperfine splittings				
Free ion	1.16	1.54	3.81	—[c]
Spin densities				
Experimental (free ion)	0.0489	0.0650	0.1607	—[c]
Calculated (McLachlan)	0.0451	0.0641	0.1602	—[c]

(*continued*)

TABLE I (*continued*)

5b. Terephthalaldehyde (*trans*)

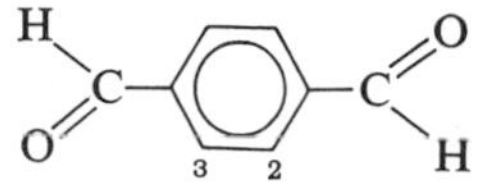

	H$_2$	H$_3$	H$_{ald}$	Ref.
Hyperfine splittings				
Experimental (free ion)	2.08	0.70	3.89	—^{c}
Spin densities				
Experimental (free ion)	0.0878	0.0295	0.154	—^{c}
Calculated (McLachlan)	0.0799	0.0298	0.1590	—^{c}

6. Benzaldehyde

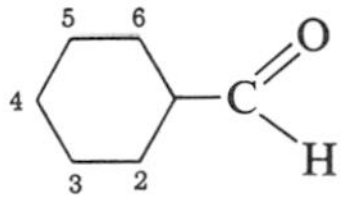

	H$_2$	H$_3$	H$_4$	H$_5$	H$_6$	Ref.
Hyperfine splittings						
Free ion	4.685	1.307	6.471	0.750	3.393	—^{h}
Spin densities						
Experimental (free ion)	0.198	0.055	0.273	0.032	0.143	—^{h}
Calculated (McLachlan)	0.190	−0.063	0.242	0.037	0.143	—^{h}

7. Hexamethylacetone

	^{13}C (Carbonyl)	^{13}C (Methyl)	H	Ref.
K	49.6	7.2	0.12	—^{e}
Na	53.1	7.6	0.12	—^{e}

^{a} Splittings are measured in gauss.
^{b} Spin densities are calculated using $a_i = Q_i\rho_i$ for aromatic hydrogen $Q_i = 27.3$ G is assumed.
^{c} P. II. Rieger and G. H. Fraenkel, *J. Chem. Phys.*, **37**, 2811 (1962).
^{d} R. Wilson and R. R. Ayscough, *J. Chem. Soc.*, **1963**, 5412.
^{e} N. Hirota, Thesis, Washington University, 1963.
^{f} R. Dehl and G. K. Fraenkel, *J. Chem. Phys.*, **39**, 1793 (1963).
^{g} N. Hirota, *J. Am. Chem. Soc.*, **89**, 32 (1967).
^{h} N. Steinberger and G. K. Fraenkel, *J. Chem Phys.*, **40**, 723 (1964).

positive counterions associated with the negative ions. Such perturbations of the spin densities are found in many ion pair systems and usually give good evidence for the presence of ion pair association in solution.

Perhaps the most drastic perturbations in the ion pair radical ions are seen in m-dinitrobenzene radical anions (38) in which the large nitrogen hyperfine splitting comes only from one nitrogen atom in the chemically reduced radical anion in DME, whereas the hyperfine splittings due to two equivalent nitrogen atoms are observed in the electrolytically produced radical ions (2) in acetonitrile. Conclusive evidence for the fact that ion pair formation is responsible for this change in hyperfine splittings was given recently by an experiment in which hyperfine splittings due to two nitrogen atoms were observed even in chemically reduced ions when a solvent of high dielectric constant, such as a mixture of acetonitrile and DME, was used (39).

Small perturbations in hyperfine splittings due to positive ions are observed quite generally in radical ions including hydrocarbon negative ions (40,41). As shown in Table I, changes in proton hyperfine splittings are not very large in ketyls, but quite large changes in the carbonyl ^{13}C splittings were observed in going from the free ions to the metal ketyls. The general trend is that larger ^{13}C and proton hyperfine splittings are observed when ions of small size and higher charge are associated. The observed effects of the positive ions on the hyperfine splittings and the spin distributions are easily understood at least qualitatively in terms of valence bond pictures (26) or simple MO treatments (42).

Let us take the case of benzophenone and consider it in the valence bond framework. The ground state of the ketyl ion is approximately represented by a linear combination of wave functions corresponding to

(1)   (2)   (3)

(4)   (5)   (6)

structures **1–6**. As the strength of the electrostatic interactions increases, structures **1**, **3**, and **4** become more favored relative to the others. Larger spin densities at the carbon atoms la, 2, and 4, particularly at la, are expected in the metal ketyls with the metal ions of smaller size or higher charge. From equations 1 and 2 it is expected that the proton hyperfine splittings and particularly the ^{13}C hyperfine splitting of the carbonyl carbon will increase in metal ketyls relative to the corresponding splittings of free ketyl ions.

The observed perturbation of spin densities in ketyls also can be explained in terms of the MO treatment. As discussed by several authors for similar problems (40,43,44), this is done in the following way. Suppose that the Hamiltonian for a free ion is $\mathcal{H}^0$. Then the Hamiltonian for an ion pair is given by

$$\mathcal{H} = \mathcal{H}^0 + \sum_i \frac{ne^2}{r_i} \qquad (3)$$

where r_i is the separation from the positive ion to the ith electron. Summation is taken for all electrons. The value of n represents the number of charges on the positive ion. In the free ion the wave function, ψ^0, for a molecular orbital is given by a linear combination of atomic orbitals

$$\psi_k^0 = \sum_\mu a_{k\mu} \varphi_\mu$$

by solving the usual secular equations with matrix elements $H_{\mu\nu}^0$. $H_{\mu\nu}^0$ is given by

$$H_{\mu\nu}^0 = \int \varphi_\mu^* \mathcal{H}^0 \varphi_\nu \, d\tau$$

φ_μ and φ_ν are the $2p\pi$ orbitals of the atoms μ and ν.

In the ion pair the second term of the Hamiltonian (3) is expanded in terms of spherical harmonics, and new matrix elements $H_{\mu\nu}$ for ion pairs are calculated. In many cases, as pointed out by McClelland (43),

$$\int (\varphi_\mu^* \varphi_\nu / r_i) \, d\tau \cong 2 S_{\mu\nu} / (r_\mu + r_\nu)$$

is sufficiently good approximation where r_μ and r_ν are the distances of the center of the cation from the nuclei μ and ν. $S_{\mu\nu}$ is the overlap integral between φ_μ and φ_ν. Then, $H_{\mu\nu}$ in the ion pair is given by

$$H_{\mu\nu} \cong H_{\mu\nu}^0 + \frac{2ne^2 S_{\mu\nu}}{r_\mu + r_\nu} \qquad (4)$$

Therefore, the effect of the perturbation may be treated by simply adjusting the Coulomb and resonance parameters for each atom. In the simplest approximation $S_{\mu\nu}$ may be taken to be zero for $\mu \neq \nu$. Then the new Coulomb integral for the ion pair is given by

$$\alpha_\mu = \alpha_\mu^0 + ne^2 / r_\mu \qquad (5)$$

Such adjustments of the parameters indeed predict the observed trend in the spin densities and the qualitative features of the counterion effect are explained within the limits of the simple MO treatment (42). However, one has to perform more refined calculations including configuration interaction among different orbitals in order to obtain quantitative agreement. No such detailed calculations of the counterion effect in ketyls have appeared yet in the literature.

The effect of the counterion charge on the spin distribution bears a close similarity to the solvent effect on the spin distribution if the origin of the solvent effect is primarily electrostatic interaction. The solvent effect on the spectra of ketyls has been studied in detail by Luckhurst and Orgel (28) in fluorenone ketyls in a mixture of methanol and N,N-dimethylformamide. Their results were interpreted in terms of an equilibrium between solvated ketyl molecules and hydrogen-bonded ketyl–alcohol complexes. The changes in the spin densities in fluorenone ketyl, however, could not be quantitatively interpreted by adjusting only the Coulomb parameters of the carbonyl oxygen in the Hückel treatment. On the other hand, Gendall, Freed, and Fraenkel (45) treated the solvent effect in the semiquinone case by using the Hückel MO method and adjusting the Coulomb integral of the oxygen atom. They obtained good agreement between the experimental splittings and the calculated splittings, although the choice of parameters was somewhat arbitrary.

Although no detailed analyses of the perturbations due to the counterion or to solvation have been made, the perturbations in certain systems are fairly large as in the case of the ^{13}C splitting in benzophenone. Since different degrees of interaction between ions and between the ions and the solvent are reflected in the different magnitudes of perturbation, detailed analyses of such perturbations would be potentially useful in obtaining the details of ion–ion and ion–solvent interactions.

B. EPR Spectra and Molecular Structures

Several interesting structural problems have been studied by EPR in ketyl-type radical ions. Some of these examples are given here. EPR has been useful in studying hindered rotation and rotational isomerism. In ketyl-type radical anions, hindered rotation of the carbonyl groups with respect to the ring can be studied by EPR. If the rotational frequencies are much faster than the difference in the hyperfine frequencies of the two rotational isomers, we only see the average of the two isomers. When the rate of rotation is approaching the difference in the hyperfine frequencies of the two rotational isomers, broadening of the line starts to occur. When the rotational frequency is much slower than the difference in the hyperfine frequencies, the superposition of different spectra due to two different isomers is obtained. In this case one can say that the carbonyl group is "locked" in the EPR sense.

Maki was the first to note the effects of such rotational isomerism in EPR spectra (46). It was noted that the rotation of the carbonyl group with respect to the aromatic ring is slow in the terephthalaldehyde anion. Thus, the superposition of the spectra due to the *cis* and *trans* forms which are shown here, was obtained.

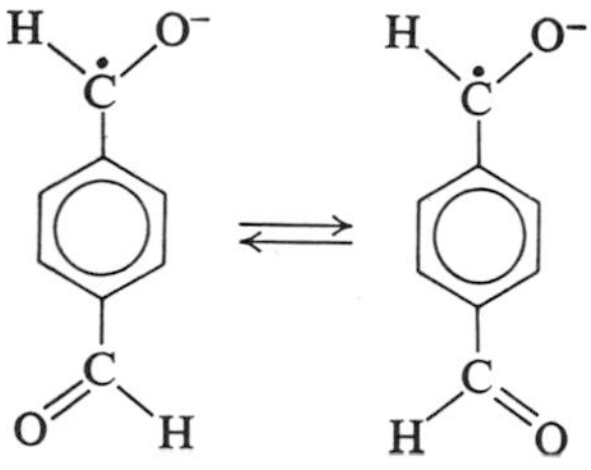

Rieger and Fraenkel (23) subsequently found many other examples of slow rotational isomerism in similar systems. Hyperfine splittings due to the ring protons are substantially different in the *cis* and *trans* forms of these ketyls. MO calculations gave reasonably good estimates of the spin densities in both forms (Table I). Steinberger and Fraenkel (25) found later that the carbonyl groups are locked into the plane of the aromatic rings in benzaldehyde and acetophenone ketyls.

The effects of *ortho*-methyl substituents on the structure of benzophenone ketyl and on the spin distributions in the molecule have been noted by Maruyama and co-workers (29). In 2-methylbenzophenone and 2,6-dimethylbenzophenone they observed only very broad spectra which seem to indicate that the unpaired electron stays almost exclusively on the unsubstituted phenyl group. Thus, the methyl groups interfere with the carbonyl group and the *ortho*-methyl substituted ring appears to be perpendicular to the rest of the molecule, and the conjugation of the π system to the *ortho*-methyl substituted ring is disrupted.

The effect of the metal ion on the structure of the ketyl radicals has been noted in several systems. The free benzil ketyl ion seems to be in the *trans* form, but in the metal ketyls the *cis* form is more stabilized by the association of the metal ion with the two carbonyl groups. In benzil a 0.6 G sodium splitting was observed, but in 2,2,5,5-tetramethylhexane-3,4-dione no sodium splittings were observed in THF. This difference was attributed to the fact that benzil can take the *cis* form, but the *cis* form of 2,2,5,5-tetramethylhexane-3,4-dione is sterically difficultly accessible (34). The *cis–trans* isomerization of benzil negative anions and the effects of metal ions and solvents have been further discussed by Bauld (47).

C. Electronic Spectra of Ketyls

Almost all ketyls have characteristic visible and UV absorptions and are characterized by their color. The visible and UV spectra of these species have been investigated by several groups of investigators (48–52). Warhurst and co-workers studied the visible spectra systematically and found that the position of the absorption maximum shifts toward longer wavelength as the size of the positive ion becomes larger for a series of alkali metal ketyls in the same solvent (48,49). Observations of similar systematic shifts of the absorption maxima with variations in the size and the charge of the positive ion were extended to systems which include alkaline earth and rare earth metal ketyls (52). These systematic perturbations of the spectra indicate that the ketyls form ion pairs. The crude formula for these species is

$$\left(\begin{array}{c} Ar \\ \searrow \\ \dot{C}-O^- \\ \nearrow \\ Ar \end{array} \right)_n M^{n+}$$

The solvent dependence of the absorption maxima of some ketyls has also been reported (51,52). Some of the representative examples of the metal and solvent dependence of the spectra are summarized in Table II. The spectra arise through π–π^* transitions. Calculations of the energies of the π molecular orbitals and assignments of the electronic spectra were made by McClelland using the Hückel MO and the more detailed self-consistent field treatment (43,54).

In the Hückel approximation calculations of the electronic levels were made in the same way as has been done for the interpretation of the electronic spectra of aromatic hydrocarbon negative ions (43,54,55). The energies of the molecular orbitals of a free ion are determined by solving secular equations, such as

$$\det \left| H_{\mu\nu}^0 - E S_{\mu\nu} \right| = O \tag{6}$$

with $S_{\mu\nu} = \int \varphi_\mu^* \varphi_\nu \, d\tau$. The systematic shifts due to the associated positive ions are explained by including the electrostatic interaction term in the Hamiltonian as in the case of the perturbation of spin distribution. In an approximation similar to that described in the previous section the new secular equation to be solved is

$$\det \left| \mathscr{H}_{\mu\nu}^0 + \left(\frac{2ne^2}{r_\mu + r_\nu} - E \right) S_{\mu\nu} \right| = O \tag{7}$$

The energies of the molecular orbitals of an ion pair are obtained by solving the above equation. McClelland explained the systematic shifts

TABLE II
Electronic Spectra of Ketyls—Metal and Solvent Dependence of the Absorption Maximum

Metal dependence[a]			
Benzophenone (THF, $10^{-3}M$)		Fluorenone (THF, $2 \times 10^{-3}M$)	
K	681 mμ	Na	520 mμ
Na	660		450
Ba	637	Ba	451
Ca	620	Ca	449
Mg	605	Mg	446
La	595		
Sm	592		

Solvent dependence[b]	
Na benzophenone ($10^{-4}M$)	
1,2-Dimethoxyethene	698 mμ
Tetrahydrofurane	674
1,4-Dioxane	646
1,1-Dimethoxyethane	644
Diethylether	634
Di-n-butyl ether	628

[a] N. Hirota and S. I. Weissman, *J. Am. Chem. Soc.*, **86**, 2538 (1964).

[b] J. F. Garst, R. A. Klein, O. Walmsky, and E. R. Zabolotny, *J. Am. Chem. Soc.*, **87**, 4080 (1965).

from such calculations and the predictions from the calculations seemed to agree with the observations reasonably well. However, it should be noted that the choice of α_O and β_{CO} in McClelland's calculation is quite different from what Fraenkel and co-workers recommended for ketyls. Quantitative comparisons between the observed and calculated values are also in question because of the complexity of the ion pair structures which will be discussed in the following sections. More detailed discussions of the experimental observations of the electronic spectra of ketyls are given in later sections in connection with the ion pair structures.

D. Di- and Trinegative Ions

Many aromatic ketones and aromatic hydrocarbons can accept two electrons very easily to form dinegative ions when the molecules are brought into contact with alkali metals for a prolonged time. The electronic structures of the dinegative ions have been studied from their optical absorption (55). The ground states of most dinegative ions are singlet states, but triphenylbenzene and decacyclene dinegative ions are known to be in triplet states at the ground state from their characteristic EPR spectra (56). The electronic structures of most dinegative ions cannot be studied by EPR and there have been relatively few investigations of dinegative ions.

Some molecules appear to accept three electrons to form trinegative ions. For example, Bauld has succeeded in obtaining trinegative ions from benzil and phenanthrenequinone (57). Further reduction of the dinegative ions of these compounds gave new optical absorption peaks and EPR absorption. Since both molecules gave the same EPR spectra and absorption spectra, it was suggested that benzil trianion had cyclized to form phenanthrenequinone trianion.

III. IONIC EQUILIBRIA IN KETYLS AND RELATED SYSTEMS

In ethereal solutions of ketyls there are ion pair equilibria between monomers and dimers (or ion clusters). EPR spectra combined with visible absorption spectra give very detailed pictures of such processes in solution. We will first describe the visible absorption spectra.

A. Concentration and Solvent Dependence of Visible UV Spectra and the Monomer–Dimer Equilibria among Paramagnetic Species

The visible spectra of many ketyls were found to show a concentration dependence (52). The concentration dependence of the absorption maxima is most clearly demonstrated in the case of the fluorenone ketyls in which two distinct absorption peaks appear at the high and low concentration limits. A representative example is given in Figure 2.

Analysis of the concentration dependence of the absorption spectra shows that the changes in the spectra come from the monomer–dimer equilibrium. The peak at 450 mμ is assigned to the dimer and the other at 525 mμ is assigned to the monomer from the concentration dependence. Since the difference in the absorption peaks is only 70 mμ, the electronic structures of the monomer and the dimer are considered to be similar. This indicates that both species are probably paramagnetic. The equilibrium is given by the following scheme.

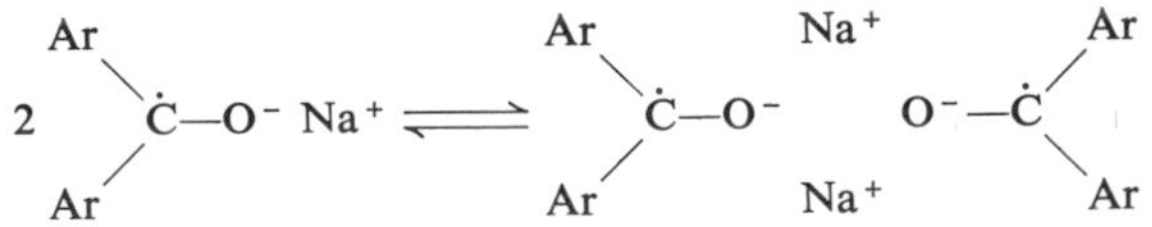

$$2 \; \begin{array}{c} Ar \\ \diagdown \\ \dot{C}-O^- \, Na^+ \\ \diagup \\ Ar \end{array} \rightleftharpoons \begin{array}{c} Ar \\ \diagdown \\ \dot{C}-O^- \\ \diagup \\ Ar \end{array} \begin{array}{c} Na^+ \\ \\ Na^+ \end{array} \begin{array}{c} Ar \\ \diagup \\ O^-\!-\dot{C} \\ \diagdown \\ Ar \end{array}$$

The paramagnetism of the dimeric species is most conclusively demonstrated by EPR as discussed in later sections. The primary cause of the

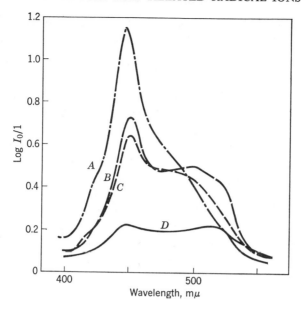

Fig. 2. Concentration dependence of optical absorption of sodium fluorenone in MTHF. $(A)\,2.8 \times 10^{-2}\,M$. $(B)\,3.5 \times 10^{-4}\,M$. $(C)\,2.2 \times 10^{-4}\,M$. $(D)\,5.8 \times 10^{-5}\,M$.

shifts in the absorption spectra probably comes from the stronger electrostatic interactions due to the two positive ions in the dimers.

The concentration dependence of the visible spectra in other ketyls, such as sodium benzophenone and sodium xanthone in THF and MTHF, is not so clear as in fluorenone ketyls. Nevertheless, the position of the maximum absorption depends on concentration and shifts considerably toward longer wavelength upon dilution. Therefore, similar monomer–dimer equilibria seem to exist quite generally in other systems.

Detailed studies of the concentration and temperature dependence of the absorption spectra of sodium fluorenone gave approximate estimates of the dissociation constant K and the thermodynamic quantities, ΔF°, ΔH°, and ΔS° for the dissociation of the paramagnetic dimers into monomers. $K \simeq 10^{-4}\,M$, ΔH° of $\sim -2\,kcal$ and ΔS° of $-30\,eu$ were found for sodium fluorenone in DME and THF. The large negative entropy changes are apparently due to increased solvation in the monomers. The positive ions are surrounded by two large negative ions in the dimer and more space is available for the solvent molecules to solvate the positive ion in the monomer.

The solvent dependence of the visible spectra of various ketyls was studied by Garst and co-workers (51) and Hirota and Weissman (52).

Garst and co-workers found that the maximum peak positions of benzo-phenone ketyls shift toward longer wavelength in the following order:

DMF > DME > THF > DEE (diethyl ether) > NBE (n-dibutyl ether)

The solvent dependence of the spectra could be due to structural changes in the ion pairs and the equilibrium between monomer and dimer. Different solvents have different degrees of solvation toward positive ions and the structure of the ion pair is expected to depend on the solvent. However, the concentration dependence of the monomer in sodium fluorenone follows the same order and the EPR results show the predominant existence of the dimer in the solvent such as DEE and NBE. Therefore, the main cause of the solvent dependence in ketyls seems to be the mono-mer–dimer equilibrium. Different structures of ion pairs, such as contact and solvent shared ion pairs in monomer and dimer ketyls, must be considered, however, in order to understand fully the solvent dependence.

Such different structures of ion pairs will be discussed in detail in later sections. (Fig. 3).

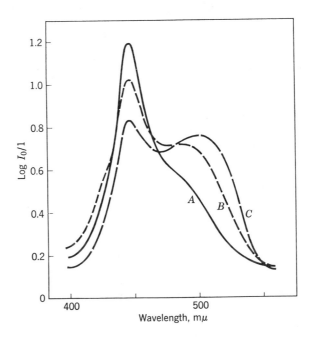

Fig. 3. Solvent dependence of optical absorption of sodium fluorenone. (A) MTHF 4.1 × 10^{-2} M. (B) THF 3.5 × 10^{-2} M. (C) DME 3.0 × 10^{-2} M.

B. Equilibria between Paramagnetic and Diamagnetic Species

As the early susceptibility measurements indicated, ketyls do not exist as pure paramagnetic species in many systems. This is also demonstrated very easily spectroscopically (52).

The intensities of the characteristic colors of benzophenone and fluorenone ketyls are reduced in nonpolar solvents, such as toluene and cyclohexane. Therefore, the paramagnetic substances seem to be converted into colorless compounds in these solutions. The color is recovered if the nonpolar solvent is removed and the ethereal solvent is introduced again. Comparison of the spectral changes and the susceptibility changes suggests that an equilibrium between the dimeric paramagnetic species and diamagnetic molecules such as pinacolate exists. If this equilibrium is included, the equilibria in solution are now given by

$$2Na^+ + 2Ar_2\dot{C}O^- \rightleftharpoons 2Ar_2\dot{C}O^- Na^+ \rightleftharpoons$$

$$\text{Free Ion} \qquad\qquad \text{Ion pair}$$

$$Ar_2\dot{C}O^- \overset{Na^+}{\underset{Na^+}{}} {}^-O\dot{C}Ar_2 \rightleftharpoons Ar_2\underset{|}{C}{-}O^-Na^+$$

$$Ar_2C{-}O^-Na^+$$

$$\text{Paramagnetic dimer} \qquad \text{Diamagnetic dimer}$$

The complete reversibility of this equilibrium was demonstrated in the cases of benzophenone and fluorenone. The extent of formation of the diamagnetic dimer depends on the nature of solvent and increases in nonpolar solvents (Fig. 4).

The assumption that the diamagnetic species is pinacolate is widely accepted. It certainly seems to be correct for benzophenone, fluorenone, and many other ketyls. However, it is quite doubtful whether or not the same type of diamagnetic species is in equilibrium with a paramagnetic dimer in the α-diketone ketyls, such as benzil and phenanthrenequinone. The diamagnetic substances in benzophenone and fluorenone ketyls do not have visible absorption and probably result from covalent bond formation as shown in the pinacolate form. Although the paramagnetism of some α-diketone ketyls, such as acenaphthoquinone, naphthoquinone, and phenanthrenequinone, is very weak under certain conditions and these ketyls must be mixed with diamagnetic species, they are highly colored (58).

Interesting temperature, solvent, and concentration dependent color changes are observed in phenanthrenequinone and naphthoquinone ketyls. The phenanthrenequinone ketyls studied by Maruyama (30) show dichroism. It was found that ketyls with larger ions are red at higher temperatures, but they turn to green at low temperatures. The red form was found to be paramagnetic, but the green form was found to be

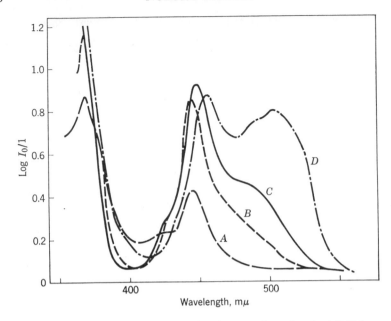

Fig. 4. Spectra of sodium fluorenone ion in nonpolar solvents. (*A*) Toluene. (*B*) 1:1 MTHF and toluene. (*C*) MTHF. (*D*) DME. Different solvents were introduced following the order shown by the above.

diamagnetic. In more polar solvents more red form was detected and the concentration and temperature dependence of the optical and EPR spectra seem to show that the red form is a paramagnetic monomer, but the green form is the diamagnetic dimer. Similar dichroism was also observed in naphthoquinone (58). In these colored diamagnetic dimers two radical ions may be close to each other and interact strongly. Then the singlet–triplet separation is large and the dimeric species may exist predominantly in a singlet state at room temperature although it does not form an ordinary covalent chemical bond. Murrell and Hausser discussed the possibility of the presence of such colored diamagnetic species and the formation of the diamagnetic complexes previously in connection with the temperature dependence of the optical spectra and the susceptibility changes in phenazine radicals (59). An increasing number of references have documented the existence of such diamagnetic species (59–61).

C. Ion Pair Equilibria in Related Systems

The ion pair equilibria described in the preceding two sections are not unique to ketyl systems. In several other systems, such as the triarylboron negative ions studied by Van Willigen and Weissman (62), very similar ion pair equilibria are apparently taking place. In the trimesitylboron radical anion the following equilibria in solution were proposed by Van Willigen (63)

$$n\text{Me}^+ + n\text{TMB}^- \rightleftarrows n\text{TMB}^-\text{Me}^+ \rightleftarrows (\text{TMB}^-\text{Me}^+)_n \rightleftarrows (\text{TMB}^-\text{Me}^+)_n$$

$$\text{Free ion} \qquad \text{Ion pair} \qquad \text{Ion cluster} \qquad \text{Polymer}$$

There seem to be equilibria among monomeric and dimeric paramagnetic species in the case of the α,α-dipyridyl radical anions also (64). In these systems the changes from monomeric ion pairs to paramagnetic dimers (or ion clusters) and to diamagnetic dimers (polymers) are similar to those observed for the ketyls and depend on the nature of the solvent as described in the previous section. In many other radical anions similar equilibria involving monomers and ion clusters probably exist under favorable conditions. Further studies in this area are desirable in order to understand fully the equilibrium processes involving ion pairs in solution.

A brief account of other equilibrium processes involving radical anions is given below. More complete discussions on these topics are given in several other existing articles (4,5). Interested readers should refer to these articles or to the original papers.

The dimerization of hydrocarbon radical ions, such as diphenylethylene anion, is, of course, very similar to the dimerization of ketyls to form pinacolate. The free energy changes for the dimerization of such radical anions are correlated to the changes in π electron energies caused by dimerization as well as to the solvation effects. The calculation of the free energy changes and the equilibrium constants for dimerization has been undertaken by means of the Hückel MO method. Qualitative agreements between the observed equilibrium constants and the predicted values were found in a series of negative ions (4,5,65). Similar arguments can be extended to the polymerization reaction of radical anions in hydrocarbons containing vinyl groups. However, these problems are treated in other review articles and are not treated further here.

Another important type of equilibrium involving radical ions is a disproportionation reaction involving the neutral molecule, mononegative ion, and dinegative ion, such as $2\text{R}^- = \text{R} + \text{R}^{2-}$. In most ketyls the equilibrium constants for the formations of dinegative ions and neutral molecules from mononegative ions are very small.

In certain hydrocarbon radical anions, such as tetraphenylethylene radical anion, the disproportionation reaction to form a dinegative ion is known to take place to a very large extent (66). The equilibrium constants, however, are known to depend on the nature of the solvent and possibly depend on the structures of the ion pairs in the mono- and dinegative ions, respectively.

IV. STRUCTURES AND EQUILIBRIA OF ION PAIRS: MONOMER KETYLS

In the last section optical evidence for the presence of the various ionic equilibrium processes in solution was given. In the following two sections, more confirmative EPR evidence for the presence of such equilibrium processes and detailed discussions on the structures of each entity are given. We will first discuss the structure of monomer ion pairs.

A. Ion Pair Equilibria and the Structures of Ion Pairs

The EPR spectra of metal ketyls in ethereal solvents show additional hyperfine splittings due to alkali metal ions. The presence of such hyperfine splittings in EPR spectra gives confirmatory evidence for the formation of ion pairs, although the absence of the alkali metal splitting does not necessarily mean that free ions are present.

Although the exact mechanism producing spin densities at the metal ions is not well established and it appears that there are a variety of mechanisms, we simply assume here that a particular ion pair has a definite magnitude of alkali metal splitting.

Many aromatic hydrocarbon negative ions produced by alkali metal reduction also form ion pairs in ethereal solution. The ion pairs in ketyls and aromatic hydrocarbon negative ions behave similarly in some respects, but differently in others. One should note that the negative charge is more localized in the carbonyl group in ketyls, but is dispersed over the entire system in many aromatic hydrocarbon negative ions. We will compare the behavior of ion pairs in both systems as much as possible.

First, several relevant observations concerning the structures of ion pairs are described.

1. Temperature and Solvent Dependence of the Alkali Metal Splittings. The temperature dependence of the alkali metal splittings in ion pairs of radical anions was first observed by Atherton and Weissman (3). The temperature dependence of the alkali metal splittings of several ketyls has been reported by Ayscough and Wilson (27) and Hirota and Weissman (67). Similar temperature dependence of the alkali metal splittings was also observed in many other ketyls and hydrocarbon negative ions. Some examples are shown in Figure 5. As seen from the figure metal splittings usually decrease at lower temperatures. They also depend on the nature of the solvent. Although there are close resemblances in the temperature dependence of the splittings of the ketyls and hydrocarbon negative ions, there are some differences between the two types of systems. The alkali metal splittings are usually not very sensitive to the change of solvent in ketyls, whereas they are extremely sensitive to the nature of solvent in

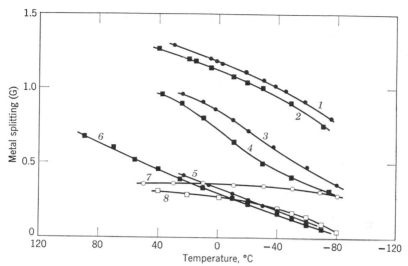

Fig. 5. Temperature dependence of alkali metal splittings in ketyls. (*1*) Sodium benzophenone in THF. (*2*) Sodium benzophenone in DME. (*3*) Sodium xanthone in THF. (*4*) Sodium xanthone in DME. (*5*) Sodium fluorenone in THF. (*6*) Sodium fluorenone in DME. (*7*) Cesium fluorenone in THF. (*8*) Cesium fluorenone in DME.

hydrocarbon radical ions. (For example, the sodium splittings of fluorenone ketyl are very similar in THF and DME. The sodium splitting of the naphthalene negative ion in THF is about 1 G at room temperature, but no sodium splitting is observed for sodium naphthalene in DME.) The magnitudes of sodium splittings usually increase in the following order: MTHF > THF > DME. No alkali metal splittings were observed in solvents of high dielectric constant, such as liquid ammonia and DMF.

2. Temperature Dependence of ^{13}C Splitting. ^{13}C splittings of the carbonyl carbon atom in various fluorenone ketyls were found to be very temperature dependent (68). Carbonyl ^{13}C splittings in all alkali metal fluorenone ketyls decrease considerably at lower temperature. In the case of sodium fluorenone in DME the decrease is nearly 20% in going from +60 to −90°C. As discussed earlier (Section II-A-1) the carbonyl ^{13}C splittings strongly depend on the electrostatic interaction between positive and negative ions. Smaller ^{13}C splittings at lower temperatures suggest that there are weaker electrostatic interactions between the ions at lower temperatures (see Fig. 6).

These observations of the temperature dependence of the hyperfine splittings indicate the dynamic character of ketyl ion pairs. If the ion pair had a rigidly fixed structure, we would expect that alkali metal splittings as well as the ^{13}C splittings would be temperature insensitive. Actually,

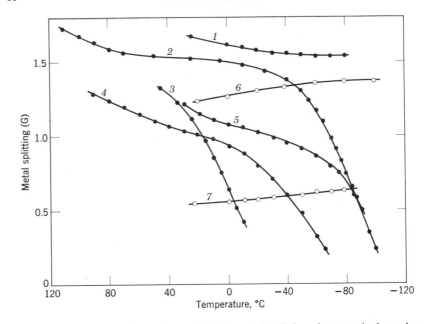

Fig. 6. Temperature dependence of alkali metal splittings in some hydrocarbon negative ions. (*1*) Sodium anthracene in MTHF–DEE mixture (0.41:0.59). (*2*) Sodium anthracene in MTHF. (*3*) Sodium anthracene in MTHF–THF mixture (0.30:0.70). (*4*) Sodium naphthalene in THF. (*5*) Sodium naphthalene in THF–DEE mixture (0.25:0.75). (*6*) Cesium naphthalene in MTHF. (*7*) Cesium anthracene in MTHF.

metal splittings in certain α-diketone ketyls, such as sodium benzil, do not change much with temperature, suggesting that in these instances, the ion pair structures are more rigid. The alkali metal splittings in hydrocarbon ion pairs also do not change much with temperature in certain cases. A possible explanation for the temperature dependence of the alkali metal splitting is given in the following way.

The observed splitting, a, is given by the average over the splittings at different states, $a = \sum_i p_i a_i$, if the averaging process is rapid. a_i is the splitting in the ith state and p_i is the probability of finding the ith state. The different states in this expression can be: (*1*) different vibrational states in one extreme case and (*2*) distinct ion pair structures in equilibrium in which the relative positions of positive and negative ions are different, in the other extreme. The distinctions between these cases are, of course, not very clean-cut in many instances.

In the case of the ketyls one may explain the temperature dependence of the alkali metal splittings from both points of view. Suppose that the positive ion sits next to the oxygen atom and lies in the nodal plane of $2p\pi$ orbital of the ketyls. One expects a small splitting because of the small overlap integrals between the $2p\pi$ orbital of the ketyls and s orbitals of the metal ion. Vibration around this position can give larger alkali metal splittings. Alternatively, the equilibrium model can explain the changes in the alkali metal splitting, if there are rapid equilibria among various ion pair structures with different magnitudes of alkali metal splittings.

The observation of the temperature dependence of the ^{13}C splittings appears to lend support to the equilibrium model. The smaller values of the ^{13}C splittings in fluorenone ketyls at lower temperatures seem to indicate that there is weaker electrostatic interaction between positive and negative ions and that positive and negative ions are actually more separated at lower temperatures. If we make the hypothesis that the ion pair can assume different structures with varying degrees of solvation, which range from the contact ion pair to the solvent shared ion pair, the observed changes of ^{13}C splittings can be interpreted as due to changes from structures of the contact type to the more solvated structures at lower temperatures. Since ^{13}C splittings in fluorenone strongly depend on the nature of the alkali metal, the structure of the ion pair is considered to be close to that of a contact ion pair at room temperature.

The position of the equilibrium, of course, depends on the nature of the solvent. The observation that the equilibrium shifts more toward the solvent shared ion pair and that the average separation between the positive and negative ions increases at lower temperatures is quite common in many ion pairs formed between aromatic negative ions and alkali metal ions (69–71). From the observed line width in ketyl systems, the conversion rates between different ion pairs must be very rapid ($k \sim 10^9$ sec^{-1}) at temperatures from $+50$ to $-90°C$, if such equilibria exist. A detailed discussion of the temperature dependence of the metal and ^{13}C splittings is given in reference 68.

Although the observed temperature dependence of the metal and ^{13}C splittings can be explained by the above mechanism, the decisive evidence for the existence of such a dynamic process is still lacking for ketyls and the above model should be taken as a hypothesis at this time. However, a number of examples of the dynamic equilibria between different ion pairs have now accumulated in the case of hydrocarbon ion pairs (69–71). Therefore, a brief description of these equilibrium processes is worthwhile.

1. Hydrocarbon Negative Ions

In many cases the temperature dependence of the alkali metal splittings in hydrocarbon negative ions seems to be explained by the rapid equilibria among different ion pairs (69,70). The most convincing evidence for the existence of such equilibrium processes is given by the dependence of the line width on the alkali metal nucleus magnetic quantum number (M_Z^M).

Let us consider the simplest case in which there is a rapid equilibrium between two ion pairs A and B. A and B now have different alkali metal splittings a_A and a_B, respectively.

$$A \underset{k_{-1}}{\overset{k_1}{\rightleftharpoons}} B$$

$$K = \frac{[B]}{[A]} = \frac{P_B}{P_A} = \frac{k_1}{k_{-1}} = \frac{\tau_B}{\tau_A} \tag{8}$$

Here P_A and P_B represent the probability of finding the forms A and B, and τ_A and τ_B are the lifetimes of A and B, respectively.

In the limit of rapid exchange the observed metal hyperfine splitting is given by

$$a = P_A a_A + P_B a_B = \frac{a_A + K a_B}{1 + K} \tag{9}$$

where a_A and a_B are the metal splittings in the ion pairs A and B, respectively. In the region of rapid interconversion the total line width of the spectra including the contribution due to the interconversion process is given by (72,73)

$$\frac{1}{T_2} = \frac{P_A}{T_{2A}} + \frac{P_B}{T_{2B}} + P_A^2 P_B^2 (\omega_A - \omega_B)^2 \tau_A (1 + K) \tag{10}$$

where ω_A and ω_B are the resonant frequencies for the ion pairs A and B. $1/T_{2A}$ and $1/T_{2B}$ are the line widths for the ion pairs A and B in the absence of their mutual interconversion. If the proton hyperfine splittings do not change much from one ion pair to the other $\omega_A - \omega_B$ can be approximately replaced by*

$$\omega_A - \omega_B \cong M_Z^M \gamma(a_A - a_B)$$

where, M_Z^M is the magnetic quantum number of the metal nucleus spin. When the interconversion rate approaches the difference in hyperfine frequency, $\omega_A - \omega_B$, broadening due to the interconversion becomes appreciable. From equation 10 the broadening due to this process is approximately proportional to the square of M_Z^M. Hence, in sodium ion pairs hyperfine lines corresponding to $M_Z^{Na} = \pm \frac{3}{2}$ are expected to be much broader than the lines corresponding to $M_Z^{Na} = \pm \frac{1}{2}$. In the extreme case the lines corresponding $M_Z^{Na} = \pm \frac{3}{2}$ are completely broadened and cannot be seen. There are a number of systems in which the sodium hyperfine lines observed depend on M_Z^{Na}. The clearest examples known are

* This is not true in many examples. In many radical ions the perturbation of hyperfine splittings by positive ions are large and they show different proton hyperfine splittings in different ion pairs.

seen in the case of sodium anthracenide in MTHF, sodium 2,6-di-*t*-butyl naphthalenide in THF and sodium naphthalenide in a solvent mixture of THF and DEE (74). The latter example is shown in Figure 7.

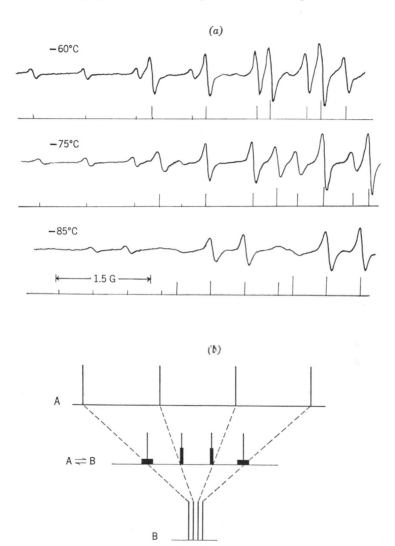

Fig. 7. Change of line widths with temperature (broadening due to ion pair equilibrium). (*a*) Sodium naphthalene in THF–DEE mixture (0.25:0.75) at various temperatures. Broadening of the outside lines is seen. (*b*) Schematic illustration of the line width and splitting in rapid equilibrium situation. A, Sodium splittings of ion pair A. B, Sodium splittings of ion pair B. A ⇌ B, Sodium splittings in case of rapid equilibrium between A and B. Broadening of the outside lines is indicated.

The expression for the calculation of rate constant is obtaiñed directly from equations 8 and 10 to be

$$k_1 = 2.03 \times 10^7 \frac{P_A^2 P_B^2 (1 + K)(H_A - H_B)^2}{\Delta H} \text{ sec}^{-1}$$

Here ΔH (gauss) is the line broadening due to the interconversion process and $H_A - H_B$ is the difference in the hyperfine lines (gauss) in the two ion pairs.

The analysis of the alkali metal splittings and their line widths give valuable information concerning the nature of the ion pair equilibria. In the case of sodium anthracenide in MTHF (see Fig. 6, Curve 2), the ion pair equilibria can be written as

$$R^-Na^+ \underset{k_{-1}}{\overset{k_1}{\rightleftarrows}} R^- \quad Na^+ \rightleftarrows R^- + Na^+$$

$$\text{A} \qquad (1) \qquad \text{B} \qquad (2)$$
$$\text{Tight ion pair} \qquad \text{Loose ion pair}$$

Analysis of the observed splitting through the use of equation 9 with $a_A = 1.55$ G and $a_B \cong 0$ gives an estimate of the thermodynamic quantities. The broadening in the $M_Z^{Na} \pm \frac{3}{2}$ lines is $\sim 4 \times 10^{-2}$ G at $-55°C$. The values of $P_A = 0.78$, $P_B = 0.22$, $K = 0.28$, and $H_A - H_B = 2.33$ G lead to an estimate of $k_1 \cong 1 \times 10^8$ sec^{-1} at $-55°C$. The thermodynamic and kinetic data obtained for the above equilibrium are summarized as the following:

$K = 1.0$ at $-80°C$	$k_1 = 1 \times 10^8$ sec^{-1} at $-55°C$
$\Delta H_1^0 = -4.5$ kcal	$k_{-1} = 4 \times 10^8$ sec^{-1} at $-55°C$
$\Delta S_1^0 = -23$ eu	$\Delta H_1^\ddagger = \sim 3$ kcal
$\Delta H_2^0 = \sim -2$ kcal	$\Delta H_{-1}^\ddagger = \sim 7.5$ kcal

The large value of ΔS^0 observed here indicates that a large rearrangement of the solvent sphere has taken place. The structure of the species A is a tight ion pair, but A is not a real contact ion pair in which the positive and negative ions are separated by ionic and van der Waals radii. The two ions are pushed away from each other by solvated solvent molecules.* The tight ion pair also seems to change structure as the temperature increases. In the ion pair B the ions are separated by solvent molecules so that the alkali metal splittings are almost zero. In solvents whose solvating power is poorer than MTHF, equilibrium between two or more different tight ion pairs appears to be taking place. At higher

---

* Detailed discussions concerning the structures and equilibria in hydrocarbon ion pairs are given in reference 70.

temperatures the two ions approach each other more closely. Sodium anthracenide in diethyl ether is an example of this phenomenon.

One other very interesting and important observation with respect to the dynamic character of ion pairs is that of alternating line widths.* The alternation in line width is caused by the jumping of the positive ion between equivalent sites in the anion, when the rate of jumping is comparable with the induced difference in the hyperfine frequencies of the nuclei at equivalent sites in the ion pair. The line width alternation in ion pairs was first found by de Boer and Mackor (75) in pyracene radical anion. They proposed that the cation is jumping between the equivalent sites A and B. When the cation associates at a particular site (let us say A)

the hyperfine splittings of the protons at the site A are significantly different from those of protons at the site B. When the rate of jumping between A and B approaches this difference in the hyperfine frequencies alternation of the line widths takes place.

Similar line width alternation due to the migration of the counterions has been observed subsequently in several other systems, such as the pyrazine anions studied by Atherton and Goggins (76) and the m-dinitrobenzene anion radical studied by Symons and co-workers (77).

The examples described in this section clearly demonstrate the power of EPR technique in elucidating the dynamic aspects of ion pairs. It is hoped that further studies along these lines will lead to new knowledge of the detailed nature of ion-pair and ion–solvent interactions.

2. Comparison between Ketyls and Aromatic Hydrocarbons

In ketyl ions there is considerable localization of the negative charge on the carbonyl groups and ketyls appear to form contact ion pairs more easily than hydrocarbons. From another viewpoint one may consider that the ketyl ions are competing with solvent molecules in solvating positive ions.

There are many similarities between ketyls and aromatic hydrocarbon negative ions in the temperature dependence of the metal splittings.

---

* For a complete and general discussion of the line width alternation in EPR spectra, reference 73 is recommended. This reference describes the theoretical basis of the line width effect and the actual chemical examples known to the date.

However, the temperature dependence of the sodium splittings in ketyls are much less marked than those found in sodium naphthalenide in THF and sodium anthracenide in MTHF. This may indicate that changes in the ion pair structure with temperature in ketyls are more gradual than those found in hydrocarbon negative ions. In the ketyl systems so far studied the four sodium hyperfine splittings have equal intensities. This implies that the rate of interconversion between different ion pairs must be on the order of 10^9 sec $^{-1}$ at temperatures as low as $-80°C$. Therefore, this rate is faster than the rate of interconversion between tight and loose ion pairs in sodium naphthalenide ion pairs ($k \sim 10^8$ sec^{-1} at $-80°C$). Since the change in the structure of the anthracenide ion pair requires a large change in the solvation sphere, the very fast rate for ion pair interconversion required to interpret the ketyl's spectra may not be very surprising, if the structural differences between different ion pairs are relatively small in the case of the ketyls.

Although they cannot be taken too literally, structures **1–4** are suggested to illustrate the possible structures of monomer ion pairs.

(1)   (2)   (3)   (4)

B. Alkali Metal Splittings and the Structures of Ion Pairs

The exact mechanism which gives rise to the alkali metal splittings in the EPR spectra of radical anions is not yet well established, although several attempts at theoretical calculations have been made and several different mechanisms have been proposed (3,81,82). These include direct occupancy of s orbitals of the metal ion by the unpaired electron and indirect spin polarization of the s electrons of the metal ion. A charge transfer mechanism is probably the most important mechanism producing the alkali metal splittings. Thus, the correct wave function for the singly occupied molecular orbital must be given by a proper linear combination of the wave function for the molecular orbital of the negative ion and the s orbitals of the positive ion.

$$\Phi = \psi + \sum_i \lambda_i \varphi_i \tag{10}$$

Here, ψ represents the molecular orbital of the anion and φ_i designates the s orbitals of the alkali metal ion.

The charge transfer mechanism gives rise to positive spin density at the alkali metal nucleus. However, there are some experimental observations which suggest that the spin density at the alkali metal could be negative (68,79). If this is the case, there must be another important mechanism. In fact, de Boer has suggested that the spin polarization due to the configuration interaction involving an excitation from the lowest occupied $(n - 1)s$ orbital to ns can lead to negative spin density (79).

The magnitude of the alkali metal splitting is sensitive to the separation between the positive and the negative ions and the relative position of the positive ion with respect to the negative ion. Therefore, a better understanding of the origin of the alkali metal splittings and their magnitudes should lead to a clearer picture of the structure of ion pairs in radical ions and possibly to the nature of the bonding between the positive and negative ions.

In most ketyls, metal splittings increase further at higher temperature and we do not know the maximum value. In the usual model of the ion pair the negative and positive ions are considered to be associated primarily by electrostatic interaction. In almost all cases studied so far the magnitudes of the metal splittings are very small compared to the free atom values and this assumption seems to be right. However, if two ions are closely associated and the appreciable admixture of s orbitals of the metal ion is needed to explain the observed alkali metal splittings, a model involving the association of two purely ionic species is not strictly valid and the covalency of the bonding must be considered. At least one example seems to fall in this category. Herold and co-workers observed relatively large alkali metal splittings (Li, 3.25 G; Na, 6.25 G; and Cs, 10.1 G) in *ortho*-dimesitoylbenzene ketyls (80). It was noted that the spin density at the nucleus decreases regularly in going from lithium to cesium. This was attributed to the decrease in the covalency of metal oxygen bonding.

C. Optical and Conductometric Studies for the Determination of the Presence of Different Ion Pairs

Although there are no direct optical and conductivity measurements to support the model of rapid ion pair equilibria in ketyls, there is considerable optical and conductometric evidence for the presence of structurally different ion pairs in other systems.

Hogen-Esch and Smid (82) observed separate absorption peaks for two different ion pairs for many hydrocarbon anion radicals, including sodium naphthalenide in THF. The conclusions obtained from the temperature dependence of the optical absorption of sodium naphthalenide in THF are quite consistent with the conclusions obtained from the temperature dependence of the sodium splittings of the EPR spectra. Conductivity measurements on ethereal solutions of hydrocarbon radical ions have been made by several investigators. Buschow, Dielman, and Hoijtink (81) made measurements on a number of solutions of simple hydrocarbon radical ions and showed that the systems involve complicated ion pair equilibria. Hogen-Esch and Smid (82) also studied the conductivity of ethereal solutions of alkali metal fluorenides. Their data again demonstrate the co-existence of two different ion pairs.

Szwarc and co-workers (83) and Hogen-Esch and Smid (82) analyzed in detail their conductivity measurements on several radical anion solutions. Their analyses were based on the simple "sphere in continuous model," which assumes that the ions are spheres distributed in a continuum characterized by its macroscopic dielectric constant and viscosity. The analysis based on such a simple theory may give reasonable values for the dissociation constant, enthalpy, and entropy for the dissociation of solvent shared ion pairs. However, it would fail to give good values for the contact ion pairs in which positive and negative ions are strongly interacting and specific solvent–ion interactions are important. Details of the optical spectra and the conductivity measurements are not given here, but it should be noted that these measurements support the pictures described in the last section. Readers interested in this area should refer to the references cited here.

V. STRUCTURES AND EQUILIBRIA OF ION CLUSTERS: DIMERIC KETYLS

The existence of monomer–dimer (or monomer–ion cluster) ion pair equilibria in ketyls was demonstrated by the concentration dependence of the optical spectra described in Section II-B. The paramagnetic nature of the dimeric species is most clearly demonstrated by observation of the EPR spectra in rigid media. Then the dimeric species can be considered as a kind of biradical system. A brief account of the EPR spectra of biradical systems is given first and the structures of the dimeric ion pairs in ketyls and other radical ions are discussed. The analysis given here is, of course, valid for any biradical systems.

A. EPR Spectra of Biradicals

A characteristic feature of the EPR spectra of biradical systems is the presence of magnetic dipole–dipole interaction between two unpaired electrons. This term is given by

$$\mathscr{H}_d = g^2\beta^2 \left\{ \frac{(\mathbf{S}_1 \cdot \mathbf{S}_2)}{r_{12}^3} - \frac{3(\mathbf{r}_{12} \cdot \mathbf{S}_1)(\mathbf{r}_{12} \cdot \mathbf{S}_2)}{r_{12}^5} \right\} \tag{11}$$

where S_1 and S_2 are the spin operators for the unpaired electrons 1 and 2. r_{12} is the distance between the two electrons. After an appropriate transformation (84,85) the spin Hamiltonian of the biradical system is given by

$$\mathscr{H} = \beta \mathbf{H} \cdot g \cdot \mathbf{S} + DS_Z^2 + E(S_X^2 - S_Y^2) + \mathbf{I} \cdot A \cdot \mathbf{S} \qquad (12)$$

with

$$D = \tfrac{3}{4}g^2 \cdot \beta^2 \langle \Phi(1.2)| \frac{r_{12}^2 - 3z_{12}^2}{r_{12}^5} |\Phi(1.2)\rangle$$

$$E = \tfrac{3}{4}g^2 \cdot \beta^2 \langle \Phi(1.2)| \frac{x_{12}^2 - y_{12}^2}{r_{12}^5} |\Phi(1.2)\rangle$$

where $\Phi(1.2)$ is the antisymmetrized spatial portion of the wave function for the unpaired electron. This spin Hamiltonian is, of course, the same as the one used to describe the EPR spectra of triplet states. The EPR spectra of randomly oriented biradical species are particularly useful for our purpose. A detailed analysis of the shape of such EPR spectra has been given in the papers by Wasserman, Snyder, and Yager (86) and Kottis and Lefebvre (87). D and E parameters in the present biradical systems are usually approximately one-tenth of the D and E observed in the photo-excited triplet state of naphthalene.

Through equation 11 the observable quantity D is directly related to the separation between two unpaired electrons. In most biradical systems the distance between two electrons r_{12} is relatively large and D can be approximated by a more convenient form (68)

$$D = \tfrac{3}{4}g^2\beta^2 \sum_{ij} \rho_{ai}\rho_{bj} \left\langle \frac{r_{12}^2 - 3z_{12}^2}{r_{12}^5} \right\rangle_{ij} \qquad (13)$$

where the notation $\langle \ \rangle_{ij}$ means the Coulomb integral between the i and j atomic orbitals. ρ_{ai} and ρ_{bj} are the spin densities on the i and j atoms of the molecules a and b of the dimer.

In many biradical systems the separation between unpaired electrons is relatively small and one may use the further approximation that $r_{12} \cong z_{12}$. With this assumption $D = -\tfrac{3}{2}g^2\beta^2\langle 1/r_{12}^3\rangle$ or we can write

$$\bar{r}_{12} = \left(\frac{2|D|}{3g^2\beta^2}\right)^{1/3}$$

as an average separation of two unpaired electrons. $\bar{r}_{12}$ is useful in giving an indication of how far two unpaired electrons are separated.

The EPR spectra of biradicals in solution are expected to be broadened because of the anisotropy of the dipole interaction term when the magnitude of D is relatively large. The effect of the term, $DS^2 + E(S_x^2 - S_y^2)$

on $1/T_1$ and $1/T_2$ has been discussed in detail by Luckhurst and Carrington (88) and it is sufficient to say here that the hyperfine splittings of the solution spectra of most biradical systems with about 100 G dipole interaction are usually broadened and give broad solution spectra.

B. Spectra of Paramagnetic Dimers and Their Structures

1. Rigid Media EPR Spectra

Rigid media EPR spectra of aromatic and aliphatic ketyls were studied by Hirota and Weissman (52,89) and Hirota (68). Some representative examples are shown in Figure 8. It is clear that these spectra consist of the

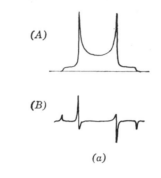

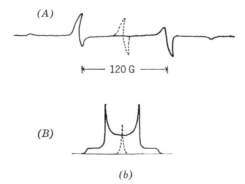

Fig. 8. EPR spectra of two spin systems in rigid medium. (a) A: Integrated curve of the theoretically predicted spectrum ($E = 0$). B: Derivative curve of the theoretically predicted spectrum ($E = 0$) (86). (b) Observed spectra. (A) Derivative curve of lithium fluorenone in MTHF. Dotted curve indicates the monomer spectrum. (B) Integrated curve of the above curve (89).

superposition of two spectra. One spectrum corresponds to the species with large dipole interaction (~ 100 G) and characterized by the spin Hamiltonian (12); the other corresponds to the species with small or zero dipole interaction. One can see that the spectrum with the large dipole interaction agrees very well with the predicted spectrum given in reference 86.

Most of the rigid media spectra were taken at $77°K$ in MTHF solvent. Therefore, we have to be careful in extending the results of the observations under these conditions to systems at higher temperature or systems in other solvents. Nevertheless, careful comparison between EPR spectra and optical spectra at various temperatures identifies the species with the 450 mμ absorption in fluorenone ketyls in MTHF as the paramagnetic dimeric species with a large dipole interaction in rigid media at $77°K$.

The central narrow peak originates from either the dissociated monomer or the dimer with the small dipole interaction. From the existence of the monomer–dimer equilibrium it is clear that the monomer contributes to the central narrow peak, but the solvent shared dimer with small dipole interaction also seems to contribute to this peak. The clearest examples of dimeric species with small dipole interaction are discussed below.

1. Divalent ketyls: alkaline earth metal ketyls of benzophenone, xanthone, and fluorenone, for example. These species form ion pairs of the structure $(Ar_2\dot{C}—O^-)_2M^{2+}$, but the line widths of the hyperfine splittings of the solution EPR spectra are generally narrow, indicating that the dipole interaction is small. The rigid media EPR spectra also show one peak with a half-width of 15 or 20 G again indicating that the dipole interaction is small.

2. Aliphatic metal ketyls: sodium hexamethyl acetone or pentamethyl acetone, for example. These show hyperfine splittings due to two sodium ions. Detailed EPR studies support a dimeric structure $(R_2\dot{C}O^-)_2M_2^+$, rather than the triple ion, $(R_2\dot{C}O^-)M_2^+$, but the dipole interaction between the two spins is small.

The dimeric structure with small dipole interaction can be attributed to the solvent shared dimer ion pair. The two negative ions are pushed away by solvent molecules and the dipole interaction between the two unpaired electrons is expected to be small. The reason for the preferential formation of the solvent shared ion pair in most divalent ketyls could be due to the stronger solvation of solvent molecules by divalent metal ions.

Rigid media EPR spectra of most alkali metal ketyls in MTHF can be interpreted by postulating the presence of at least three species: (*1*) contact dimer, (*2*) solvent shared dimer, and (*3*) monomer. In the aliphatic ketyls cited above, the EPR spectra seem to be best understood by the presence of an equilibrium between a contact ion pair dimer and a solvent shared dimer. Postulation of the solvent shared structure (**2**) was also

supported by the experiments by Luckhurst (33). He studied the temperature dependence of the sodium splittings in sodium hexamethyl acetone in MTHF and THF and mixed THF–MTHF. From the observed changes of the sodium splittings with the change in relative ratio of the two solvents, he concluded that the ketyls responsible for the solution spectra at room temperature are solvent shared dimer ion pairs.

In MTHF solutions of aromatic ketyls the predominant species is a contact dimer ion pair, but there are several examples, such as sodium benzophenone in MTHF and the lithium benzophenone in THF and DME, in which there appears to be a considerable concentration of the solvent shared dimer ion pair (67,90). In these cases, species with splittings due to two alkali metal ions are observed as in the case of hexamethyl acetone. The solution containing these ketyls is apparently an equilibrium mixture of monomer, contact, and solvent shared dimers.

Analogous phenomena involving the formation of paramagnetic dimers or ion cluster formation and the observation of characteristic biradical rigid media EPR spectra have been observed in several other systems. Brown, Weissman, and Snyder (64) found that α,α-dipyridil radical anion produced by alkali metal and alkaline earth metal reduction give characteristic rigid media EPR spectra in MTHF. Contrary to the observations made on ketyls, the dipyridil radical anion formed by alkaline earth metal reduction shows a large dipole interaction.

Van Willigen and Weissman (62,63) observed similar biradical spectra in trimesitylboron anion and dibenzoylmethane radical anions. It appears that equilibrium processes very similar to those described for ketyls are also taking place in these systems.

C. Structure of Contact Ion Clusters

Rigid media EPR spectra of contact dimer ion pairs give structural information about these ions. Except for some ketyls with large positive ions most of the EPR spectra observed in this series are characterized by

$E \cong 0$. The symmetry requirement for $E \cong 0$ is satisfied by the perpendicular structure **1** as shown in Figure 9 and it seems reasonable to assume that most ion pairs have this rigid structure.

The magnitude of the parameter D depends on the negative ion as well as the positive ion. In principle the values of D could be calculated from the ion pair structures. Although no detailed calculations have been undertaken, some approximate estimates of D were made for ketyls by assuming the contact ion pair structure **1** shown in Figure 9. In aliphatic ketyls most of the spin density is located on the carbonyl group and it is easier to estimate D. Estimates made on the structure assumed in the figure gave reasonably close values to the experimental values and the assumed structures are considered to be essentially correct. D values and the estimated $\bar{r}_{12}$ for various dimeric ion pairs are given in Table III. Similarly α,α-dipyridil negative ions produced with alkaline earth metal reduction show $E \cong 0$ and structure **2** shown in Figure 9 was suggested by Brown, Weissman and Snyder (64).

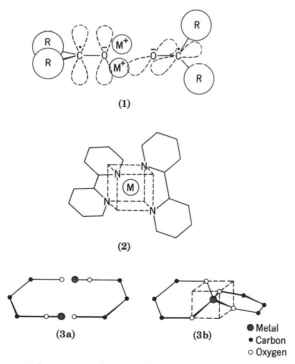

Fig. 9. Suggested structures for some ion clusters. (**1**) Alkali metal hexamethylacetone ketyl (68). (**2**) Alkaline earth metal 2,2′bipyridine (64). (**3**) Alkali metal dibenzoylmethane ketyl (63).

TABLE III
Zero Field Parameters and Average Separation in Some Dimers or Ion Clusters

System	D (G)	D/hc (cm^{-1})	$\bar{r}_{12}$ ($\times 10^8$ cm)	Ref.
Hexamethylacetone				
Li	225	0.0210	5.0	—[a]
Na	167	0.0155	5.6	—[a]
K	179	0.0167	5.4	—[a]
Pentamethylacetone				
Na	161	0.0150	5.6	—[a]
K	150	0.0140	5.7	—[a]
Benzophenone				
Li	137	0.0127	5.9	—[a]
Na	103	0.0096	6.5	—[a]
Fluorenone				
Li	120	0.0110	6.2	—[b]
Na	99	0.0092	6.6	—[b]
K	78	0.0073	7.1	—[b]
Xanthone				
Li	90	0.0084	6.8	—[b]
Na	79	0.0074	7.1	—[b]
2,2′-Bipyridine				
Be	119	0.0111	6.2	—[c]
Mg	120	0.0112	6.2	—[c]
K	80	0.0075	7.0	—[c]
Dibenzoylmethane				
Li	97	0.0090	6.6	—[d]
Na	74	0.0069	7.2	—[d]
K	67.5	0.0063	7.4	—[d]

[a] N. Hirota, *J. Am. Chem. Soc.*, **89**, 32 (1967).
[b] N. Hirota and S. I. Weissman, *J. Am. Chem. Soc.*, **86**, 2538 (1964).
[c] I. M. Brown, S. I. Weissman, and L. C. Snyder, *J. Chem. Phys.*, **42**, 1105 (1965).
[d] H. Van Willigen, *Thesis*, Amsterdam (1965).

One interesting application of rigid media EPR spectra to the structural problem was given by Van Willigen (63). He showed that there are two types of biradicals for dibenzoylmethane dinegative ions **3a** and **3b** in Figure 9 and that structure **3b** became predominant over structure **3a** as the reduction proceeds further. Structure **3b** is characterized by $E = 0$, but structure **3a** has a nonzero E.

As the above examples indicate, it is clear that rigid media EPR spectra are very useful in showing the existence of dimer (or ion cluster) formation and in obtaining information about their structures.

VI. RAPID ELECTRON TRANSFER REACTIONS IN KETYLS AND RELATED RADICAL IONS

Following the pioneering work of Ward and Weissman (91), the EPR technique was successfully applied to studies of rapid electron transfer reactions between radical anions and neutral molecules, such as $R^- + R \rightleftharpoons R + R^-$.

The physical basis of the measurements is the following. The electronic states of an unpaired electron are described by a set of nuclear quantum numbers (m_i) of protons because of the electron and nuclear spin hyperfine interactions. When an unpaired electron is transferred from R^- to R, a transition from a hyperfine state m_i to another hyperfine state m_j takes place (of course, some of the transition is from m_i to m_i). Different hyperfine states have different resonant frequencies corresponding to different hyperfine splittings and the electron transfer process produces uncertainties in the hyperfine frequencies. These uncertainties produce the broadening of each hyperfine line width depending on the transfer rate.

There are now a number of theoretical treatments which discuss the relationship between the transfer rate (or the lifetimes τ_i of the ith hyperfine state) and the line widths of hyperfine lines (92–101).

Theoretical treatments were formulated either by using the classical Bloch equation, and modifying it by adding a term to represent the electron transfer process, or by performing more detailed quantum mechanical calculations. Formulation using the density matrix formalism was found to be useful in many cases (99–101). All these detailed theories predict rather simple relationships between the reaction rates and the line width in two limiting cases: (1) The slow exchange case in which $1/\tau_i$ is much smaller than the hyperfine frequencies. (2) The fast exchange case in which $1/\tau_i$ is much larger than the hyperfine frequencies.

Suppose that the line width of each hyperfine line is represented by a line width parameter $1/T_{2i}$ in the absence of electron transfer. In the slow exchange case the theories show that the total line width observed in the presence of electron transfer $1/T_{2i}^*$ is given by a relationship $1/T_{2i}^* = 1/T_{2i} + 1/\tau_i = \pi\Delta\nu_i$ and the additional broadening is directly related to the lifetime of the unpaired electrons at a particular site. $\Delta\nu_i$ is the full line width of the ith hyperfine component.

For kinetic studies the slow exchange region is most useful, although the use of the fast exchange region is recommended in certain cases (102).

Broadening is related to the transfer rate in the following way

$$\text{Rate} = k[R][R^-] = [R^-]/\tau \tag{14}$$

assuming that the lifetime of the radical is controlled by the electron transfer process. From this equation we obtain a bimolecular rate constant, k by

$$k = \frac{\pi \delta \nu}{[R]} = 1.52 \times 10^7 \frac{\Delta H_{\text{e.s.}}}{[R]} \ (M^{-1} \sec^{-1}) \tag{15}$$

Here $\delta \nu$ is the broadening due to electron transfer and $\Delta H_{\text{e.s.}}$ is the increase in the line width due to electron transfer as measured from the points of extreme slope on the derivative curve.

Rates of rapid electron transfer reaction in many systems have been determined in this way after Ward and Weissman's original work (91).

Besides the intrinsic interest in determining fast electron transfer rates by EPR, additional insight about ion pair equilibria can often be obtained from the application of rate studies. In the discussion that follows, examples of the studies of electron transfer rates are described.

The simple type of electron transfer reaction is given by

$$R^- + R \rightleftharpoons R + R^-$$

However, ketyls form ion pairs in ethereal solutions. Therefore, it is expected that the associated positive ion will be transferred from the radical anion to the neutral molecule at the same time as the unpaired electron transfers. Then the electron transfer reaction is expected to be a sodium atom transfer reaction. The reaction is given by

$$R^- M^+ + R \rightleftharpoons R + M^+ R^-$$

Adam and Weissman (103) first demonstrated the occurrence of very fast electron transfer reactions and the atom transfer mechanism. They showed that the addition of $\sim 1M$ benzophenone to a solution of the ketyl completely washed out the proton hyperfine splittings, but not the sodium splittings. This confirms that the sodium atom is transferred to the neutral molecules when the electron is transferred. Similar phenomena were later observed in other ketyl systems. The case of fluorenone is shown in Figure 10.

More detailed studies of the electron transfer reactions in various ketyls were made by Hirota and Weissman (67). Bimolecular rate constants for the electron transfer reaction for sodium benzophenone, fluorenone, and xanthone monomer ketyls were in the order of $10^8 \ M^{-1} \sec^{-1}$ in DME and THF at room temperature. Apparent activation energies determined from the slopes of the Arrhenius plots were found to be around 5–6 kcal.

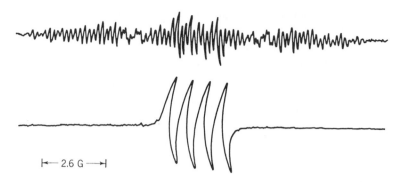

Fig. 10. Exchange broadening and narrowing. (Top) EPR spectra of sodium fluorenone in THF at 23°C. (Bottom) EPR spectra of the same sample after the addition of 1.2*M* fluorenone.

These activation energies are somewhat higher than those for diffusion-controlled reactions which should approach $\Delta Ea = 2\sim3$ kcal in these ethereal solvents. Transfer rates for benzil and acenaphthenequinone ketyls were found to be much slower than for benzophenone ketyls. It was also found that the rate constants for similar transfer reactions in dimeric ketyls were too slow to be measured by EPR. It was found that there exists a 1-to-1 correspondence between the magnitudes of the alkali metal splittings and the reaction rates in xanthone ketyls. Since the alkali metal splittings reflect the ion pair structure, this observation seems to indicate that the reaction rates are determined primarily by the ion pair structure.

The rates of electron transfer reactions have been studied in many aromatic hydrocarbons following the original work of Ward and Weissman (91). It is commonly believed that ion pair formation in hydrocarbon negative ions slows down the transfer rate by a factor of 10^2 or so (104). However, since the structure of the tight ion pair can be different from one system to another, the rate for a very tightly bound ion pair could be very slow. On the other hand, the rate for a loose ion pair could be very fast— not much different from the rate of a free ion.

Zandstra and Weissman studied the rates of electron transfer for ion pairs and species without sodium splittings in sodium naphthalene in THF (105). At most temperatures reaction rates for the species without the sodium splitting are faster than for the species with sodium splitting. The apparent activation energies for the ion pair species were found to change sign from positive to negative. Positive activation energies for ion pairs appeared to be about 16 kcal. The apparent activation energies for the other species was about 12 kcal, which is still much higher than the activation energies for diffusion processes. This fact casts some doubts upon the assignment of a free ion structure to the species without the sodium splitting.

Recent studies of the ion pair structure indicate that the ion pair species in sodium naphthalene in THF is actually a rapid equilibrium mixture of tight and loose ion pairs as discussed in the previous sections. Since the reaction rates for the tight ion pair would be much slower than for the loose ion pair and the fraction of loose ion pairs increases at lower temperatures, it is quite conceivable that the overall electron transfer rates can be faster at low temperatures with negative apparent activation energies. In fact, in sodium anthracenide in a mixture of MTHF and THF, apparent activation energies change sign from positive to negative in the temperature region where the magnitude of sodium splitting changes rapidly (70). In MTHF at room temperature the bimolecular rate constant, $k \sim 10^7 M^{-1} \sec^{-1}$, was observed for the tight ion pair. Since the rate constant becomes large at lower temperatures the transfer rate for a loose ion pair must be very fast.

Also, there seems to be a good correlation between the electron transfer rates and the magnitude of the sodium splitting. Generally, faster rates were observed when the sodium splitting was small in hydrocarbon negative ion systems. This correlation, however, is opposite to the correlation in ketyls. In ketyls faster rates were observed in systems where the sodium splitting is larger. The bimolecular rate constants for electron transfer between ketyls and ketones were found to be the order of $\sim 10^8 M^{-1} \sec^{-1}$ for monomer ketyls at 25°C in most ethereal solvents. This rate is much faster than for sodium anthracenide and the naphthalenide tight ion pair.

The differences in the two systems possibly may be due to the fact that a ketone is more polar than a hydrocarbon and it is easier to form a bridged intermediate in the former case through which the electron is transferred. The rates of electron transfer between paramagnetic dimer ketyls and ketones were found to be too slow to be measured by EPR $(< 10^7 \ M^{-1} \sec^{-1})$.

These experimental observations suggest a close relationship between reaction rates and ion pair structures. Further detailed studies of fast electron transfer rates in connection with ion pair structures would be very fruitful in order to learn more about complex reaction processes in solution.

Atom exchange reactions, such as

$$M^+R^- + M^+ \rightleftharpoons M^+ + R^-M^+$$

may also give some insight to the nature of ion pairs and the reaction mechanisms. Very little attention has been paid to this type of reaction compared to the electron transfer reaction, but the rate of sodium atom exchange between sodium ions associated with ketyls and sodium iodide was found to be rapid with bimolecular rate constants of the order of $10^8 \ M^{-1} \ sec^{-1}$ (67).

The close connection between electron transfer rates and ion pair structures has been emphasized already. If electron transfer rates differ substantially from one type of ion pair to another, one may use rate data in order to distinguish different ion pairs and also to obtain structural information. At least two examples of such studies have been reported.

The addition of benzophenone to the sodium benzophenone in MTHF simplifies the spectrum. With the addition of $1M$ benzophenone to solution, one observes the superposition of two spectra, one species which transfers the electron slowly ($k < 10^7 \ M^{-1} \ sec^{-1}$) and the other species which transfers the electron rapidly ($k > 10^8 \ M^{-1} \ sec^{-1}$). Thus, from data on the electron transfer reaction it can be shown that sodium benzophenone exists as an equilibrium mixture of at least two species (67) (Fig. 11).

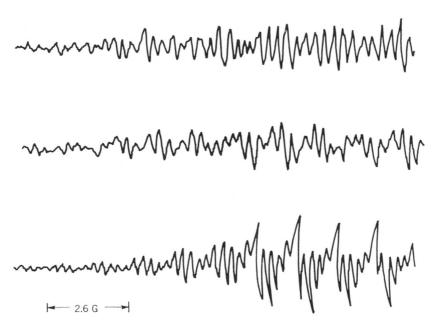

Fig. 11. Demonstration of the existence of two different ion pairs by use of the exchange process. (Top) Sodium benzophenone in MTH. (Middle) After the addition of $10^{-2}M$ benzophenone. (Bottom) After the addition of $1.2M$ benzophenone. Superposition of the dimer spectrum and exchange narrowed monomer spectrum (four strong peaks) are seen.

TABLE IV

Rate Constants for Rapid Electron Transfer Reactions

Molecule	Metal	Temp. (°C)	Solvent	Metal splitting (G)	k (M^{-1} sec^{-1})	Activation energy (kcal)	Ref.	Remark
					Ketyl			
Benzophenone	Na	25	DME	1.18	$(1.10 \pm 0.04) \times 10^8$	6.3	—[a]	Monomer ion pair
	Na	12	THF	1.18	$(1.14 \pm 0.06) \times 10^8$	~6	—[a]	Monomer ion pair
	K	25	THF	?	$\sim 2.5 \times 10^8$		—[a]	Monomer ion pair
	Na	24	MTHF	?	$<10^6$		—[a]	Possibly dimer
	Na	25	Dioxane	?	7.5×10^5		—[b]	With 1.07 M ketone determined by NMR
	Na	25	Dioxane	?	5.2×10^5		—[b]	With 2.7 M ketone determined by NMR
	Mg	24	DME	—	$<10^6$		—[a]	Dimer
	Ca	24	THF	—	$<10^6$		—[a]	Dimer
Xanthone	Na	37	DME	0.95	$(4.56 \pm 0.25) \times 10^8$	5.1	—[a]	Monomer ion pair
	Na	25	THF	0.95	$(4.48 \pm 0.34) \times 10^8$	4.3	—[a]	Monomer ion pair
	Na	7	THP	0.95	$(4.68 \pm 0.46) \times 10^8$		—[a]	Monomer ion pair
	Na	0	MTHF	0.95	$(4.35 \pm 0.18) \times 10^8$		—[a]	Monomer ion pair
Fluorenone	Na	25	DME	0.40	$10^8 < k < 10^9$		—[a]	Monomer ion pair
	Na	25	THF	0.42	$10^8 < k < 10^9$		—[a]	Monomer ion pair
Benzil	Na	24	THF	0.60	$<10^7$		—[a]	Monomer ion pair
Acenaphthoquinone	Na	24	THF	?	$<10^7$		—[a]	Monomer ion pair

Compound			Solvent		*Hydrocarbon negative ions*			Description
						$(1.24 \pm 0.09) \times 10^9$		
Anthracene	Na	23	DME	0		3.0	—[c]	Predominantly loose ion pair
	Na	25	MTHF THF	1.40	1×10^8		—[c]	Equilibrium mixture of loose and tight ion pair
Naphthalene	Na	23	MTHF	1.53	1×10^7		—[c]	Tight ion pair
	Na	25	DME	0	$\sim 1 \times 10^9$		—[d]	Possibly loose ion pair
	Na	25	THF	1.05	2×10^7	4.6	—[e]	Predominantly tight ion pair
	Na	24	MTHF	1.12	4.5×10^6	12.4	—[e]	Tight ion pair
	Na	15	DMTHF	1.5	3×10^6		—[c]	Tight ion pair
Biphenyl	Na	23	DME	0	$\sim 1 \times 10^8$	2.3	—[a]	—
Pyrene	Na	23	DME	0	1.4×10^9		—[a]	Free ion or loose ion pair

[a] N. Hirota, Thesis, Washington University, 1963. Partly published by N. Hirota and S. I. Weissman, *J. Am. Chem. Soc.*, **86**, 2537 (1964).

[b] Determined by A. A. Bothner-By, A. P. Krapcho, and J. M. Van der Veen. Private communication from Bothner-By to S. I. Weissman.

[c] N. Hirota, unpublished results.

[d] R. Ward and S. I. Weissman, *J. Am. Chem. Soc.*, **79**, 2086 (1957).

[e] P. J. Zandstra and S. I. Weissman, *J. Am. Chem. Soc.*, **84**, 4408 (1962).

Similarly, Chang and Johnson (102) applied electron transfer reactions in order to demonstrate the presence of two different species in alkali metal naphthalenides in THF. One species transfers the electron very rapidly (10^9 M^{-1} sec^{-1}) and the other species transfers the electron rather slowly (10^7 M^{-1} sec^{-1}) (102). This indicates that besides the species reported by Zandstra and Weissman (105) there is another species which tranfers electrons very rapidly. Considering the fast electron transfer rates and the small activation energy, the species may be a true free ion.

Kinetic data can be used in differentiating the various types of ion pair. In the previous sections it was indicated that aliphatic and some aromatic ketyls show interactions with two equivalent sodium ions but failed to show large dipole interactions.

The structure assigned to this species was that of a solvent shared dimeric ion pair. However, the solution EPR by themselves cannot exclude the possibility that the species is the triple ion $M^+R^-M^+$ rather than the quadruplets $R^-\ \begin{matrix} M^+ \\ \\ M^+ \end{matrix}\ R^-$. The kinetic data showing that the

TABLE V

Equilibrium Processes for Ketyls

---

1. Aromatic ketyls (alkali metal)

$$R^- + Na^+ \rightleftarrows R^-|Na^+ \rightleftarrows R^-Na^+$$

$$\begin{matrix} \searrow Na^+ \nearrow \\ R^- \quad R^- \\ \nearrow Na^+ \searrow \end{matrix} \rightleftarrows R^- \begin{matrix} Na^+ \\ \\ Na^+ \end{matrix} R^- \rightleftarrows \begin{matrix} R^-Na^+ \\ | \\ R^-Na^+ \end{matrix}$$

⟵ polar solvent   nonpolar solvent ⟶

NH$_3$ DMF   DME   THF   MTHF   DEE   toluene

2. Aliphatic ketyls

$$\begin{matrix} R \\ \diagdown \\ \quad C{=}O + Na \rightleftarrows R_2\dot{C}{-}O^- \\ \diagup \\ R \end{matrix} \qquad \begin{matrix} Na^+ \\ \\ {}^-O{-}\dot{C}{-}R_2 \\ \\ Na^+ \end{matrix} \rightleftarrows \begin{matrix} R_2{-}C{-}O\ Na^+ \\ | \\ R_2{-}C{-}O\ Na^+ \end{matrix}$$

$$R_2\dot{C}{-}O^- \begin{matrix} \searrow Na^+ \nearrow \\ \\ \nearrow Na^+ \searrow \end{matrix} {}^-O{-}\dot{C}{-}R_2$$

3. Aromatic ketyls (alkaline earth)

$$R^-M^{2+}R^- \rightleftarrows R^-|M^{2+}|R^-$$

---

sodium atom exchange reaction as well as the electron exchange reaction are slow in this system favor the quadruplet structure rather than the triple ion structure, because we expect a faster sodium ion exchange rate for triple ions as in the case of the ion pair $R^- M^+$.

The various equilibrium processes for ketyls discussed in this chapter are summarized in Table V.

Acknowledgments

The author would like to express his deep gratitude to Professor S. I Weissman of Washington University for the very instructive and pleasant years which the author spent in his laboratory, for his continual encouragement, and for the many stimulating discussions which the author had with him.

This chapter was written in the summer of 1966. The financial support of the National Science Foundation during this period (GP-5040) is greatly appreciated.

References

1. D. E. Paul, D. Lipkin, and S. I. Weissman, *J. Am. Chem. Soc.*, **78**, 116 (1956).
2. A. H. Maki and D. H. Geske, *J. Am. Chem. Soc.*, **83**, 1852 (1961).
3. N. M. Atherton and S. I. Weissman, *J. Am. Chem. Soc.*, **83**, 1330 (1961).
4. B. J. McClelland, *Chem. Rev.*, **64**, 302 (1964).
5. K. Higashi, H. Baba, and A. Rembaum, *Quantum Organic Chemistry*, Wiley, New York, 1965, Chapter 12.
6. E. Bechman and T. Paul, *Ann. Chem.*, **266**, 1 (1891).
7. (a) W. Schlenk and T. Weickel, *Chem. Ber.*, **44**, 1182 (1911). (b) W. Schlenk and A. Thal, *Chem. Ber.*, **46**, 1840 (1913).
8. W. E. Bachman, *J. Am. Chem. Soc.*, **55**, 1179 (1933).
9. G. W. Wheland and R. N. Doescher, *J. Am. Chem. Soc.*, **56**, 2011 (1934).
10. C. B. Wooster, *J. Am. Chem. Soc.*, **56**, 2436 (1934).
11. S. Sugden, *Trans. Faraday Soc.*, **30**, 11 (1934).
12. G. W. Wheland, *J. Am. Chem. Soc.*, **56**, 2011 (1934).
13. (a) E. Müller and W. Janke, *Z. Electrochem.*, **45**, 380 (1939). (b) E. Müller and W. Wieseman, *Z. Angew. Chem.*, **51**, 661 (1938).
14. A. E. Favorsky and I. I. Nazarow, *Bull. Soc. Chem. Ser. 5*, **1**, 46 (1934); *Chem. Zentr.*, *1937*, **1**, 3127.
15. (a) W. Schlenk, J. Appenrodt, and A. Thal, *Chem. Ber.*, **47**, 479 (1914). (b) W. Schlenk and E. Bergman, *Ann. Chem.*, **463**, 91 (1928).
16. N. D. Scott, J. F. Walker and V. L. Hansley, *J. Am. Chem. Soc.*, **58**, 2442 (1936).
17. H. M. McConnell, *J. Chem. Phys.*, **24**, 764 (1956).
18. S. I. Weissman, *J. Chem. Phys.*, **25**, 890 (1956).
19. D. B. Chesnut and H. M. McConnell, *J. Chem. Phys.*, **28**, 107 (1958).
20. M. Karplus and G. K. Fraenkel, *J. Chem. Phys.*, **35**, 1312 (1961).
21. (a) L. Salem, in *Molecular Orbital Theory of Conjugated Systems*, Benjamin, New York, 1966; (b) A. Streitwieser, in *Molecular Orbital Theory*, Wiley, New York, 1962.
22. A. D. McLachlan, *Mol. Phys.*, **3**, 233 (1960).
23. P. H. Rieger and G. K. Fraenkel, *J. Chem. Phys.*, **37**, 2811 (1962).
24. R. Dehl and G. K. Fraenkel, *J. Chem. Phys.*, **38**, 1793 (1963).
25. N. Steinberger and G. K. Fraenkel, *J. Chem. Phys.*, **40**, 723 (1964).
26. N. Hirota, *J. Chem. Phys.*, **37**, 1881 (1962).

27. R. Wilson and P. B. Ayscough, *J. Chem. Soc.*, **1963**, 5412.
28. G. R. Luckhurst and L. E. Orgel, *Mol. Phys.*, **8**, 117 (1964).
29. K. Maruyama, R. Tanikaga, and R. Goto, *Bull. Chem. Soc. (Japan)*, **36**, 1141 (1963).
30. K. Maruyama, *Bull. Chem. Soc. (Japan)*, **37**, 553 (1964).
31. R. Tanikaga, K. Maruyama, and R. Goto, *Bull. Chem. Soc. (Japan)*, **38**, 144 (1965).
32. N. Hirota and S. I. Weissman, *J. Am. Chem. Soc.*, **82**, 4424 (1960).
33. G. R. Luckhurst, *Mol. Phys.*, **9**, 179 (1965).
34. G. R. Luckhurst and L. E. Orgel, *Mol. Phys.*, **7**, 297 (1964).
35. J. W. Lown, *Can. J. Chem.*, **45**, 2571, 3244 (1965).
36. (a) E. T. Kaiser and D. H. Eargle, *J. Am. Chem. Soc.*, **85**, 1821 (1963); *J. Chem. Phys.*, **39**, 1353 (1963). (b) E. T. Kaiser, M. M. Urberg, and D. H. Eargle, *J. Am. Chem. Soc.*, **88**, 1037 (1966).
37. G. Vincow, *J. Chem. Phys.*, **37**, 2484 (1962).
38. R. L. Ward, *J. Am. Chem. Soc.*, **83**, 1996 (1961); *J. Chem. Phys.*, **36**, 1405 (1962).
39. M. J. Blandamer, T. E. Gough, J. M. Grois, and M. C. R. Symons, *J. Chem. Soc.*, **1964**, 536.
40. A. H. Reddoch, *J. Chem. Phys.*, **43**, 225 (1965).
41. N. Hirota, to be published.
42. N. Hirota, Thesis, Washington University, 1963.
43. B. J. McClelland, *Trans. Faraday Soc.*, **57**, 1458 (1961).
44. N. S. Hush and J. R. Rowland, *Mol. Phys.*, **6**, 201 (1963).
45. J. Gendall, J. Freed, and G. K. Fraenkel, *J. Chem. Phys.*, **37**, 2832 (1962).
46. A. H. Maki, *J. Chem. Phys.*, **35**, 721 (1961).
47. N. L. Bauld, *J. Am. Chem. Soc.*, **87**, 4788 (1965).
48. D. J. Morantz and E. Warhurst, *Trans. Faraday Soc.*, **51**, 1375 (1955).
49. H. V. Carter, B. J. McClelland, and E. Warhurst, *Trans. Faraday Soc.*, **56**, 455 (1960).
50. H. E. Bent and A. J. Harrison, *J. Am. Chem. Soc.*, **66**, 969 (1944).
51. (a) J. F. Garst, C. Hewitt, D. Walmsley, and W. Richards, *J. Am. Chem. Soc.*, **83**, 5034 (1961). (b) J. F. Garst, D. Walmsley, C. Hewitt, W. R. Richards, and E. R. Zabolotny, *J. Am. Chem. Soc.*, **86**, 412 (1964). (c) J. F. Garst, R. A. Klein, D. Walmsley, and E. R. Zabolotny, *J. Am. Chem. Soc.*, **87**, 4080 (1965).
52. N. Hirota and S. I. Weissman, *J. Am. Chem. Soc.*, **86**, 2538 (1964).
53. B. J. McClelland, *Trans. Faraday Soc.*, **57**, 2073 (1961).
54. P. Balk, S. de Bruijn, and G. J. Hoijtink, *Rec. Trav. Chim.*, **76**, 860 (1957); **76**, 907 (1957).
55. P. Balk, S. de Bruijn, and G. J. Hoijtink, *Mol. Phys.*, **1**, 151 (1958).
56. R. E. Jesse, P. Biloen, R. Prins, J. D. W. Van Voorst, and G. J. Hoijtink, *Mol. Phys.*, **6**, 633 (1963).
57. N. L. Bauld, *J. Am. Chem. Soc.*, **86**, 3894 (1964).
58. N. Hirota, unpublished observation.
59. K. H. Hausser and J. N. Murrell, *J. Chem. Phys.*, **27**, 500 (1957).
60. R. H. Boyd and W. D. Philips, *J. Chem. Phys.*, **43**, 2927 (1965).
61. M. Itoh and S. Nagakura, *Tetrahedron Letters*, **1966**, 227.
62. H. Van Willigen and S. I. Weissman, private communication.
63. H. Van Willigen, Thesis, Amsterdam, 1965.
64. I. M. Brown, S. I. Weissman, and L. C. Snyder, *J. Chem. Phys.*, **42**, 1105 (1965).
65. (a) J. Jager, M. Levy, M. Feld, and M. Szwarc, *Trans. Faraday Soc.*, **58**, 2168 (1962). (b) G. Spach, H. Monteiro, M. Levy, and M. Szwarc, *Trans. Faraday Soc.*, **58**, 1809 (1962).

66. (a) J. F. Garst and R. S. Cole, *J. Am. Chem. Soc.*, **84**, 4352 (1962). (b) J. F. Garst, E. R. Zabolotny, and R. S. Cole, *J. Am. Chem. Soc.*, **86**, 2257 (1964). (c) J. F. Garst and E. R. Zabolotny, *J. Am. Chem. Soc.*, **86** 1645 (1964); **87**, 495 (1965).
67. N. Hirota and S. I. Weissman, *J. Am. Chem. Soc.*, **86**, 2537 (1964).
68. N. Hirota, *J. Am. Chem. Soc.*, **89**, 32 (1967).
69. N. Hirota and R. Kreilick, *J. Am. Chem. Soc.*, **88**, 614 (1966).
70. N. Hirota, *J. Phys. Chem.*, **71**, 139 (1967).
71. T. E. Hogen-Esch and J. Smid, *J. Am. Chem. Soc.*, **87**, 669 (1965); **88**, 307 (1966).
72. J. Pople, W. G. Schneider, and H. J. Bernstein, in *High Resolution Nuclear Magnetic Resonance*, McGraw-Hill, New York, 1959, p. 222.
73. G. K. Fraenkel, *J. Phys. Chem.*, **71**, 139 (1967).
74. A. H. Crowley, N. Hirota, and R. Kreilick, to be published.
75. E. de Boer and E. L. Mackor, *Proc. Chem. Soc.*, **1963**, 23; *J. Am. Chem. Soc.*, **86**, 1513 (1964).
76. N. M. Atherton and A. E. Goggins, *Trans. Faraday Soc.*, **61**, 1399 (1965).
77. M. C. R. Symons, *J. Phys. Chem.*, **71**, 172 (1967).
78. S. Aono and K. Oohashi, *Progr. Theoret. Phys. (Kyoto)*, **30**, 162 (1963).
79. E. de Boer, *Rec. Trav. Chim.*, **84**, 609 (1965).
80. B. J. Herold, A. F. N. Correia, and J. dos Santos Veiga, *J. Am. Chem. Soc.*, **87**, 2661 (1965).
81. K. H. J. Buschow, J. Dielman, and G. J. Hoijtink, *J. Chem. Phys.*, **42**, 1993 (1965).
82. T. E. Hogen-Esch and J. Smid, *J. Am. Chem. Soc.*, **88**, 318 (1966).
83. (a) C. Carvajal, J. K. Tölle, J. Smid, and M. Szwarc, *J. Am. Chem. Soc.*, **87**, 5548 (1965). (b) R. V. Slates and M. Szwarc, *J. Phys. Chem.*, **69**, 4124 (1965).
84. K. W. H. Stevens, *Proc. Roy. Soc. (London)*, **A214**, 237 (1952).
85. A. D. McLachlan, *Mol. Phys.*, **6**, 441 (1963).
86. E. Wasserman, L. C. Snyder, and W. A. Yager, *J. Chem. Phys.*, **41**, 1763 (1964).
87. P. Kottis and R. Lefebvre, *J. Chem. Phys.*, **41**, 379 (1964).
88. A. Carrington and G. R. Luckhurst, *Mol. Phys.*, **8**, 125 (1964).
89. N. Hirota and S. I. Weissman, *Mol. Phys.*, **5**, 537 (1962).
90. A. H. Reddoch, *J. Chem. Phys.*, **43**, 3411 (1965).
91. R. L. Ward and S. I. Weissman, *J. Am. Chem. Soc.*, **78**, 2086 (1957).
92. (a) H. S. Gutowsky, D. W. McCall, and C. P. Slichter, *J. Chem. Phys.*, **21**, 279 (1953). (b) H. S. Gutowsky and A. Saika, *J. Chem. Phys.*, **21**, 1688 (1953). (c) H. S. Gutowsky and C. H. Holm, *J. Chem. Phys.*, **25**, 1228 (1956).
93. (a) H. M. McConnell and B. S. Berger, *J. Chem. Phys.*, **27**, 230 (1957). (b) H. M. McConnell, *J. Chem. Phys.*, **28**, 430 (1958).
94. S. Meiboom, *J. Chem. Phys.*, **34**, 375 (1961).
95. L. H. Piette and W. A. Anderson, *J. Chem. Phys.*, **30**, 899 (1959).
96. P. W. Anderson, *J. Phys. Soc. (Japan)*, **9**, 316 (1954).
97. R. Kubo, *J. Phys. Soc. (Japan)*, **9**, 935 (1954).
98. A. Sack, *Mol. Phys.*, **1**, 163 (1958).
99. J. Kaplan, *J. Chem. Phys.*, **28**, 278 (1958).
100. (a) S. Alexander, *J. Chem. Phys.*, **37**, 967 (1962). (b) *ibid.*, **37**, 974 (1962).
101. C. S. Johnson, *J. Chem. Phys.*, **39**, 2111 (1963).
102. R. Chang and C. S. Johnson, *J. Am. Chem. Soc.*, **88**, 2338 (1966).
103. F. C. Adam and S. I. Weissman, *J. Am. Chem. Soc.*, **80**, 1518 (1958).
104. A. C. Aten, J. Dielman, and G. J. Hoijtink, *Discussions Faraday Soc.*, **29**, 182 (1960).
105. P. J. Zandstra and S. I. Weissman, *J. Am. Chem. Soc.*, **84**, 4408 (1962).

CHAPTER 3

Semidione Radical Anions

GLEN A. RUSSELL

Department of Chemistry, Iowa State University, Ames, Iowa

I. INTRODUCTION

One-electron reduction products of conjugated diketones will be referred to as semidiones. Conjugated tri- and tetraketones can give rise to the semitriones and semitetraones. This terminology is suggested by the well-accepted nomenclature of semiquinones. We will consider semiquinone radical anions to be radical anions containing two or more oxygen atoms situated in a conjugated fashion and attached to carbon atoms of a benzenoid system. In both the semidiones and semiquinones the conjugation can involve atoms in a 1,2-, 1,4-, 1,6-, etc., arrangement. Both the semidiones and semiquinones can take part in acid–base reactions to yield neutral semidione or semiquinone radicals, or the semidione or semiquinone radical cations (1,2) (see eqs. 1 and 2).

$$RC(O\cdot)\!=\!C(O^-)R \xrightarrow{H^+} RC(O\cdot)\!=\!C(OH)R \xrightarrow{H^+} R\dot{C}(OH)\!-\!C^+(OH)R \quad (1)$$

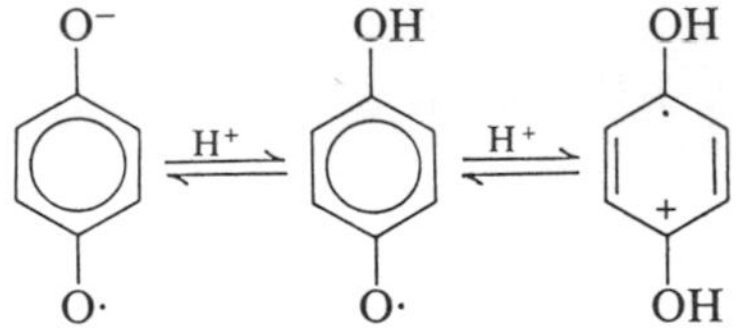

$$(2)$$

Radical anions with two oxy substitutents attached to an aromatic nonbenzenoid ring system should be considered more properly as semiquinones. The radical anion (1) formed by oxidation of ascorbic acid in basic solution (3,4) is now recognized as a furan derivative (5) and hence fits the semiquinone definition.

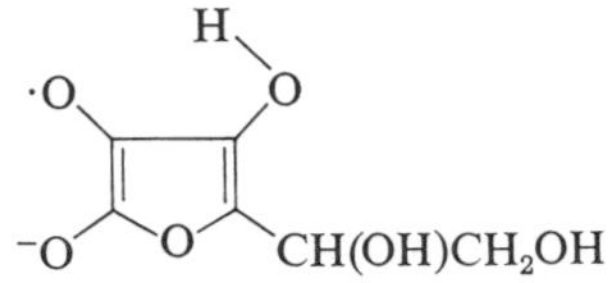

(1)   (Position of enolic proton uncertain)

One-electron reduction products of α-diketones, poorly named as quinones, will not be considered as semiquinones, but as semidiones. Thus, the radical anion produced by reduction of camphorquinone (2) will be referred to as camphor-2,3-semidione (3) or 1,7,7-trimethylbicyclo-[2.2.1]heptane-2,3-semidione (6) (eq. 3).

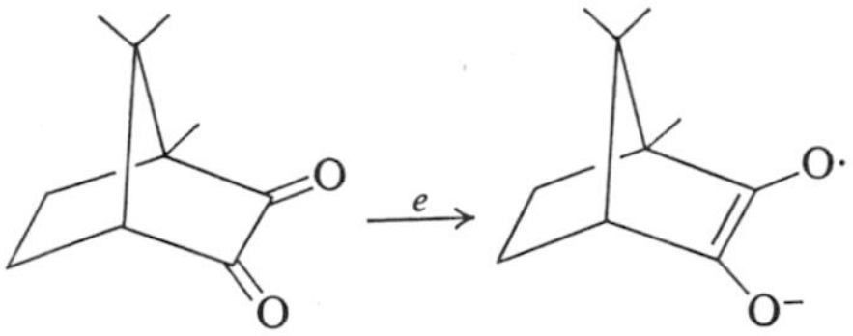

$$(3)$$

(2)   (3)

It is of interest that both the semiquinones and semidiones can be considered to be organic derivatives of the stable inorganic radical anion, the superoxide ion (4). Semidiones are vinylogs of the superoxide ion while semiquinones can be considered to be o- or p-phenylogs.

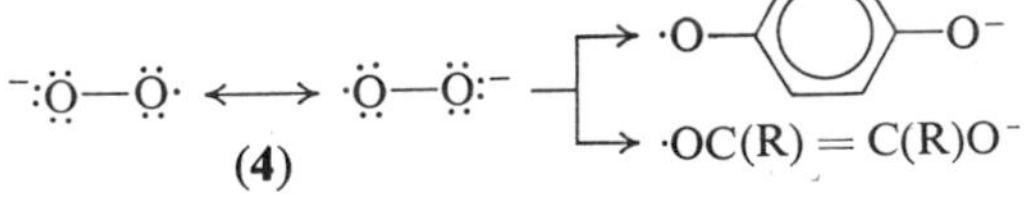

(4)

Semidiones, semitriones, etc., can be considered to be part of a homologous-type series starting with the ketyls. This suggests another approach to the naming of semidiones as a class. By analogy with ketone—ketyl the

$R_2\overset{\cdot}{C}$—O^- $RC(O\cdot)$=$C(O^-)R$ $RC(O\cdot)$=$C(O^-)COR$

Ketyl   Semidione $\updownarrow$

$RCOC(O^-)$=$C(O\cdot)R$

Semitrione

term acylyl can be employed to indicate a paramagnetic substance with a free valency and with an oxidation state intermediate between the acylil and the acyloin.

$$R_2CO \underset{-e}{\overset{+e}{\rightleftharpoons}} R_2\overset{\cdot}{C}\text{—}O^-$$

$$RCOCOR \underset{-e}{\overset{+e}{\rightleftharpoons}} RC(O\cdot)\text{=}C(O^-)R \underset{-e}{\overset{+e}{\rightleftharpoons}}$$
Acylil   Acylyl

$$RC(O^-)\text{=}C(O^-)R \rightleftharpoons RCOCH(OH)R$$
Acyloin

Simple canonical structures for ketyls, acylyls, and semiquinones will be employed. Of course, the unpaired electron occupies the unfilled molecular orbital of lowest energy in the parent ketone. In the case of a 1,2-semidione with R = aliphatic groups or hydrogen, the electron is centered mainly on the four atoms of the original dicarbonyl grouping in a molecular orbital that is bonding between atoms 2–3 and 1–4.

(5)   (6)

Elementary considerations predict the independent existence of *cis* and *trans* forms for the acyclic semidiones (**5** and **6**). This has indeed been observed when R is not too bulky, e.g., R = CH$_3$, CH$_3$CH$_2$ (7). Structure **6** may be stabilized by some overlap between the 1–4 positions.

The electron in the π system of the semidione can interact with other p or π electrons, particularly those on an atom alpha to the dicarbonyl system. However, longer range π–π interactions are also recognized in rigid bicyclic systems (8,9). The unpaired electron can interact with σ bonds attached to the α carbon atom (hyperconjugation),

$$RC(O^-)\text{=}C(O\cdot)CR_2H \longleftrightarrow RCO\text{—}C(O^-)\text{=}CR_2 \text{ H}\cdot$$

as well as with carbon–hydrogen bonds more remotely situated in the molecule. Such long-range interactions are most pronounced in the bridged bicyclic semidiones (6,7,9) and fit the pattern of W-plan couplings well recognized in NMR spectra (10–12). The unpaired electron in the π system can also cause a polarization of the spin in electrons forming a

σ bond between the carbonyl group and another group, particularly hydrogen (eq. 4). The π–σ hyperconjugative or π–π (or p) conjugative

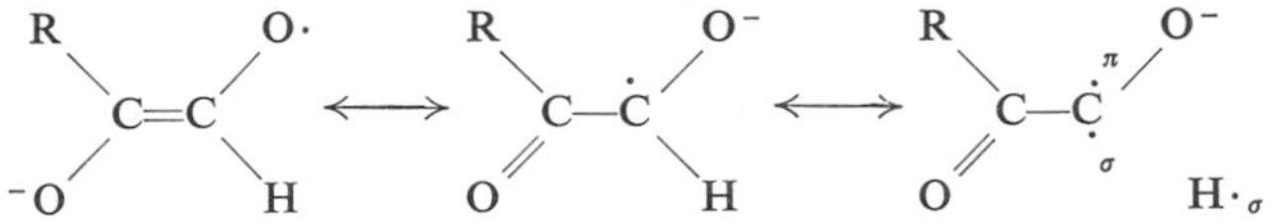

$$(4)$$

interactions will decrease the total spin density on the four major atoms in the π systems while the π–σ spin polarization mechanism will not affect the total π-electron density. The hyperconjugation mechanism introduces a spin on an atom of the same sign as in the π system (eq. 5). On the

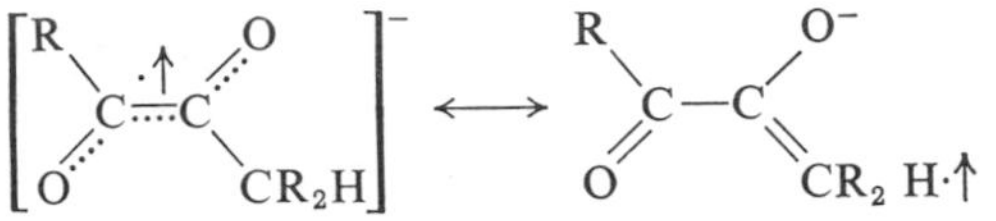

$$(5)$$

other hand, the π–σ polarization mechanism leads to a spin on the adjacent atom opposite in sign to the spin in the π system (eq. 6).

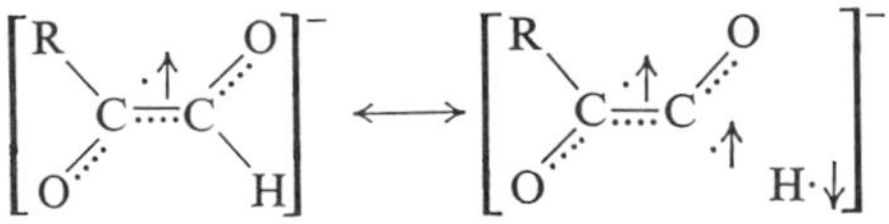

$$(6)$$

Spin densities (ρ) at the various atoms in the semidiones can be empirically estimated from electron spin resonance (ESR) hyperfine splitting constants (a). For example, it is well known that

$$\rho_H = a^H \text{ (gauss)}/508$$

and that for a planar radical with sp^2 hybridization ($R_2\dot{C}H$),

$$\rho_C = a^H \text{ (gauss)}/-22.5$$

Applying these equations to the glyoxal radical anion ($a^H = 7.7$ G in dimethyl sulfoxide solution) yields the spin densities shown here.

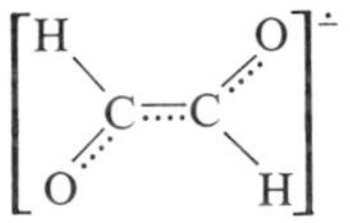

$$\rho_H = -7.7/508 = -0.015$$
$$\rho_{C_\pi} = -7.7/-22.5 = +0.342$$
$$\rho_O = (1 - 2(0.34))/2 = +0.16$$

Glyoxal

For an alkyl group attached to a carbon atom with unpaired spin density the hyperfine splitting constant (hfsc) of α-hydrogen atoms is given by

$$a^H \text{ (gauss)} = +40\rho_{C_\pi-\text{CH}<} \cos^2 \theta$$

wherein θ is the dihedral angle between the p_z orbital containing the unpaired electron and the carbon–hydrogen bond involved in hyperconjugation (13). For a freely rotating methyl group this reduces to

$$\rho_{C_\pi - CH_3} = +20 a^H_{CH_3} \text{ (gauss)}$$

Applying these equations to *trans*-biacetyl radical anion in which only a single ^{13}C hyperfine structure has been noted (and this assigned to the carbonyl carbon atom) (14) yields the spin densities shown (dimethyl sulfoxide solution).

$$\begin{bmatrix} \begin{array}{c} O \diagdown \quad \diagup CH_3 \\ \quad C_\pi \cdots C_\pi \\ H_3C \diagup \quad \diagdown O \end{array} \end{bmatrix}^{\cdot -} \quad \begin{array}{l} a^H = +5.7\text{ G}; \quad \rho_H = +0.011 \\ a^C_{CH_3} = 0, \quad \rho_{CH_3} = 3(0.011) = +0.033 \\ a^C_{C_\pi} = +4.4\text{ G}; \quad \rho_{C_\pi CH_3} = +0.285; \quad \rho_{C_\pi} = +0.25 \\ \rho_O = (1.00 - 6(0.011) - 2(0.252))/2 = +0.215 \end{array}$$

trans-Biacetyl

From the empirical spin densities it is obvious that ketyl-type structures are very important in the semidiones (see eq. 7).

$$(7)$$

| 6 Structures | 2 Structures | 2 Structures |
| 7% of total | 43% of total | 50% of total |

Spin densities of the *trans*-biacetyl radical anion as calculated by the modified Hückel treatment of McLachlan (15) in which the methyl group is treated by a conjugation model are given in Table I.

TABLE I
Spin Densities in Biacetyl Radical Anion

	Carbonyl carbon	Methyl carbon	Oxygen	Hydrogen
Found	0.25	~ 0	0.22	0.011
Calc'd.[a]	0.289	-0.003	0.186	0.009

[a] $h_O = 1.5$, $k_{CO} = 1.6$, $h_{CH_3} = -0.1$, $h_H = -0.5$, $k_{CCH_3} = 0.93$, $k_{CH} = 2.5$. Parameters are those suggested by C. A. Coulson and V. A. Crawford, *J. Chem. Soc.*, **1953**, 2052; R. Bersohn, *J. Chem. Phys.* **24**, 1066 (1956); R. Dehl and G. K. Fraenkel, *ibid.*, **39**, 1793 (1963). The value of λ in the McLachlan calculation was -1.2. The parameters h_x and k_{xy} are defined as $\alpha_x = \alpha_C + h_x \beta_{CC}$, $k_{xy} = \beta_{xy}/\beta_{CC}$. The use of an inductive parameter for the methyl group in such calculations has been suggested by D. Lazdins and M. Karplus, *J. Am. Chem. Soc.*, **87**, 920 (1965).

II. DETECTION AND IDENTIFICATION OF SEMIDIONES

Semidiones with aromatic substituents $(ArC(O\cdot){=}C(O^-)Ar)$ are colored and can be detected by their visible, ultraviolet, or infrared absorptions as well as from their magnetic properties. Apparently the first such observations of a semidione was reported by Laurent in 1836 from the action of alcoholic potassium hydroxide on benzil to yield a violet color (16). This reaction was investigated by Liebermann and Homeyer in 1879 and claimed to be general for α–diketones by Bamberger in 1885 (17,18). However, Scholl later pointed out that benzoin was also required for the formation of the violet color (19). Hantzsch in 1907 isolated a product for which he claimed the structure $C_6H_5C(OH)(COC_6H_5)$-$C_6H_4COCOC_6H_5$ (20). The violet color is produced from benzoin and is readily destroyed by excess oxygen to yield benzil or benzilic acid (21,22). This intermediate is now recognized as the benzil radical anion (7).

$$C_6H_5COCOC_6H_5 + C_6H_5C(O^-){=}C(O^-)C_6H_5 \rightleftarrows 2C_6H_5\overset{O_2}{\underset{}{\overbrace{\dot{C}(O\cdot){=}C(O^-)C_6H_5}}} \xrightarrow{O_2}$$

$$(7)$$

$$C_6H_5COCOC_6H_5 \xrightarrow{OH^-} (C_6H_5)_2C(OH)CO_2H$$

Fischer in 1882 observed that furil (8) formed a blue solution in the presence of alcoholic base (23). Such solutions are now recognized to contain the semidione (9) (24).

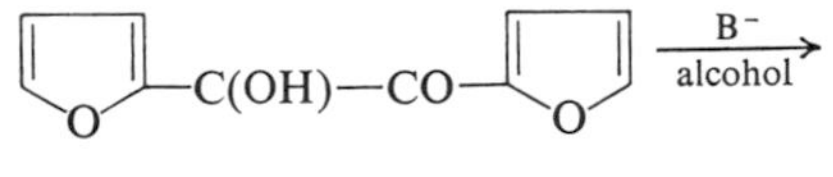

$$C(OH){-}CO \xrightarrow[\text{alcohol}]{B^-}$$

(8)

$$C(O\cdot){=}C(O^-)$$

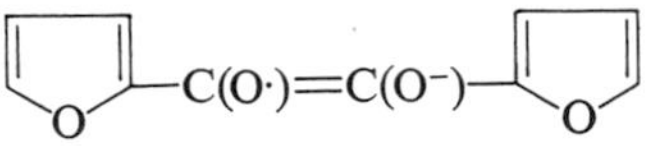

(9)

Considerable doubt existed about the structure of radical ions prior to the work of Michaelis (25), although Weitz had presented evidence for the monomeric nature of certain cation radicals at a much earlier date (26). Dimeric structures of the quinhydrone-type were advocated by Willstätter (27) and apparently accepted by many workers in the area. These structures (for example, 10) were referred to as "meriquinones" and considered to involve dynamic equilibria.

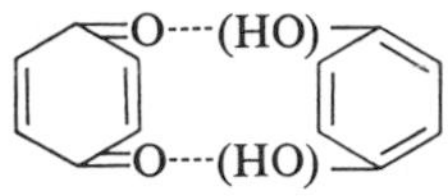

(10)

Michaelis in the early 1930's strongly supported and documented the concept of monomeric radical anions and cations with a quinoid structure. He introduced the electrochemical technique by which the presence of radical anions can be inferred by the observation of a reversible one-electron reduction. Modern developments in this area involve the dropping mercury electrode, cyclic voltammetry, and electroreduction at a mercury pool electrode directly in an ESR cavity.

That the formulation of (7) as a paramagnetic, monomeric species was indeed correct was established by Michaelis and Fletcher in 1936 (28) and confirmed by magnetic susceptibility measurements in 1956 (29). The benzil radical anion was one of the radical anions investigated in the early stages of ESR spectroscopy (30) and the spectrum has been thoroughly analyzed in terms of spin density (31).

ESR spectroscopy is particularly useful when applied to aliphatic semidiones. The number of hydrogen atoms alpha to the dicarbonyl system of a semidione can be readily ascertained from the fact that in d_6-dimethyl sulfoxide in the presence of potassium t-butoxide the α-hydrogen atoms exchange for deuterium atoms (32) (eq. 8).

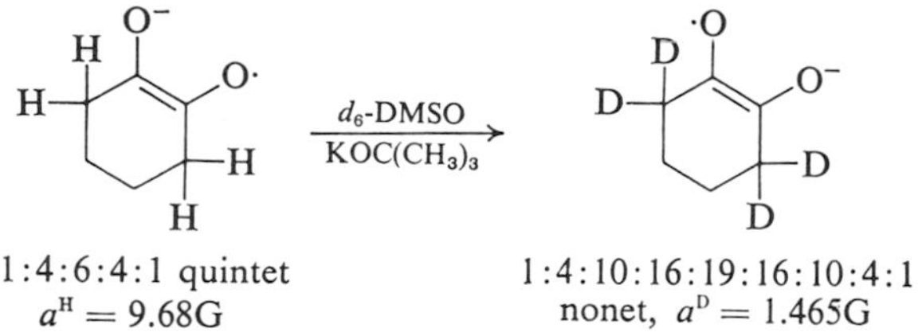

$$\begin{array}{cc} \text{1:4:6:4:1 quintet} & \text{1:4:10:16:19:16:10:4:1} \\ a^H = 9.68\text{G} & \text{nonet, } a^D = 1.465\text{G} \end{array}$$

(8)

Unfortunately, ESR spectroscopy does not always immediately distinguish between the ketyl and acylyl structure from a consideration of only the number of hyperfine interactions. It has developed that a number of radical anions, prepared from monoketones under reductive conditions and to which the ketyl structure has been assigned, are indeed the semidione radical anions formed by a carbonyl insertion reaction (33) or by oxidation of the monoketone (34–36).

III. PREPARATION OF SEMIDIONE RADICAL ANIONS

The reduction of aromatic ketones by alkali metals was investigated by Beckmann and Paul in 1891 (37). At this time the action of sodium on benzil in ether solution was recognized to give a violet substance that upon hydrolysis yielded benzil and benzoin. Beckman and Paul formulated this substance as the dimeric glycol, $C_6H_5COC(O^-)(C_6H_5)C(O^-)(C_6H_5)$-$COC_6H_5$. It is now recognized as the benzil radical anion (38) (eq. 9).

$$2C_6H_5C(O^-)=C(O\cdot)C_6H_5 + H_2O \longrightarrow$$
$$C_6H_5COCOC_6H_5 + C_6H_5COCH(OH)C_6H_5 \qquad (9)$$

Bauld has surmised that the reduction of benzil by alkali metal gives rise mainly to the *cis* radical anion in dimethoxyethane from analysis of the products of benzoylation of the final reduction product, $C_6H_5C(O^-)=C$ $(O^-)C_6H_5$ (28). Chelation of the alkali metal must play an important role since the ratio of *cis-trans* benzoylation products are solvent dependent. Pivalil, $(CH_3)_3CCOCOC(CH_3)_3$, has been reduced by alkali metals to give the semidione and it has been deduced from the lack of alkali metal splitting that this semidione exists in the *trans* form in dimethoxyethane (39).

Treatment of a variety of cycloalkanones by potassium in dimethoxyethane solution has been claimed to yield stable ketyls (34–36). However, the spectra observed are those of semidiones and the overall process is one of oxygenation (from air) followed by reduction of the diketone to the semidione.

Electrolytic reductions of many α-diketones yield the semidiones. However, chemical generation of the semidiones is often less complicated from side reactions. Although biacetyl radical anion can be readily generated by chemical methods all attempts to form the semidione by electrolytic reduction in acetonitrile have yielded 2,5-dimethyl-p-benzosemiquinone (eq. 10). Geske and Balch have used electrolytic reduction in

$$2CH_3COCOCH_3 \longrightarrow \qquad \xrightarrow{e} \qquad (10)$$

acetonitrile to form the benzocyclobutene derivative (11) (40) while acenaphthene quinone has been reduced to the semidione (12) both electrolytically (31) and by zinc in basic solutions (41). Reduction of diketones or triketones with sodium dithionite is a useful technique,

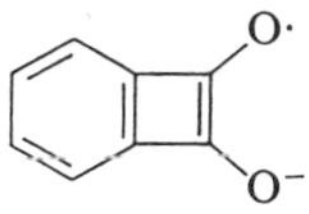

(11)

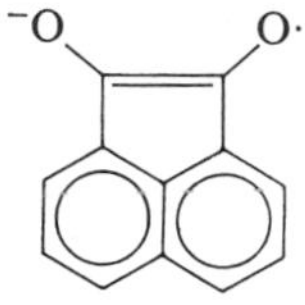

(12)

particularly in aqueous solution for polyketones wherein condensation is not a problem, e.g., alloxan (42). Zinc in aqueous or alcoholic base is a mild reducing agent capable of reducing ninhydrin to the semitrione **(13)** (41,42).

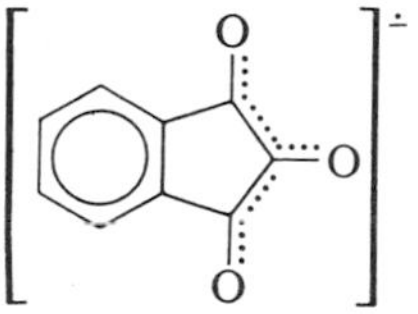

(13)

Diketones can be reduced to semidiones by a wide variety of carbanions, including the enolate anion of propiophenone or the anion of the diketone (43,44). The process occurs readily in dimethyl sulfoxide solution containing excess potassium *t*-butoxide for diketones such as cycloheptane-1,2-dione or 1-phenylpropane-1,2-dione (44).

$$C_6H_5COCOCH_3 + B^- \rightleftharpoons C_6H_5COCOCH_2^- + HB$$

$$C_6H_5COCOCH_3 + C_6H_5COCOCH_2^- \longrightarrow$$

$$C_6H_5C(O\cdot)=C(O^-)CH_3 + C_6H_5COCOCH_2\cdot$$

$$C_6H_5COCOCH_2\cdot \longrightarrow \text{dimer or other nonradical products}$$

However, the process gives rise to condensation products when applied to the simple aliphatic diketones and is very inefficient for those α-diketones that are highly enolized (diosophenols) such as 3,4-diketo-17β-hydroxyandrostane (which exists as the Δ^4-enol) (45).

The most effective method of generating a semidione appears to be an oxidative technique. α-Hydroxy ketones, or their precursors (α-bromo ketones, or α-acetoxy ketones) upon treatment with potassium *t*-butoxide in dimethyl sulfoxide solution undergo a disproportionation reaction yielding the semidione.

$$RCOCH(OH)R \rightleftharpoons \rightleftharpoons RC(O^-)=C(O^-)R$$

$$RCOCH(OH)R \overset{B^-}{\rightleftharpoons} RCOCOR + RCH(OH)CH(OH)R$$

$$RCOCOR + RC(O^-)=C(O^-)R \rightleftharpoons 2RC(O\cdot)=C(O^-)R$$

The electronic disproportionation between the diketone and the dianion is but one of many examples known that fit the following generalized equation (46).

$$\pi + \pi^{-2} \rightleftharpoons 2\pi \cdot {}^{-}$$

Yields of semidione are generally in the range of 5% based on starting α-hydroxy ketone (44). The success of this technique apparently involves the formation of an α-diketone in the presence of a large excess of its dianion whence the diketone is reduced to the semidione before side reactions can occur. Some α-hydroxy ketones may be oxidized slowly to the diketone by the preferred reaction solvent, dimethyl sulfoxide.

$$RCOCH(OH)R + DMSO \xrightarrow{B^-} RCOCOR + DMS + H_2O$$

Particularly high yields of semidiones are observed when mixtures of diketone and hydroxy ketone are treated with base. The reaction may also be facilitated by the addition of traces of oxygen since oxygen can convert some of the α-hydroxy ketone to the dione or from the semidione directly.

$$RC(O^-)=C(O^-)R + O_2 \longrightarrow RC(O\cdot)=C(O^-)R + O_2 \cdot {}^{-}$$

A very convenient method of generating semidiones is to expose a solution of a monoketone in DMSO containing potassium t-butoxide to a trace of oxygen (13). Hexamethylphosphoramide or DMSO–THF or DME mixtures can also be employed. Yields of semidione (using 10 mole % of oxygen based on ketone) are in the range of 0.01–0.1% based on ketone. However, this is a sufficient concentration of radicals to produce a satisfactory ESR signal from 3–5 mg of a ketone with a molecular weight in the range of 300. This technique undoubtedly involves the α-diketone as an intermediate.

$$RCOCH_2R + B^- + O_2 \longrightarrow RCOCH(OOH)R$$

$$RCOCH(OOH)R + B^- \longrightarrow RCOCOR + HB + OH^-$$

The method will not work for most methyl ketones (e.g., acetophenone, methyl ethyl ketone) nor with many ketones containing an alpha methine hydrogen. In the latter case apparently oxidation occurs preferentially at the methine carbon to yield products (alcohol, hydroperoxide) incapable of yielding paramagnetic products (44,45). When two alpha methylene groups are present two semidiones can be expected (eq. 11).

$$RCH_2COCH_2R' - \left[\begin{array}{l} \rightarrow RCH=C(O^-)CH_2R' \xrightarrow{O_2} RC(O\cdot)=C(O^-)CH_2R' \\ \rightarrow RCH_2C(O^-)=CHR' \xrightarrow{O_2} RCH_2C(O\cdot)=C(O^-)R' \end{array} \right. \tag{11}$$

However, this can be used as a tool to determine the preferred position of ionization for such a ketone and can be used empirically for structure determination in the alkylcycloalkanones, decalones, and steroidal ketones (44,45,47,48).

Side reactions leading to coupling or condensation products are occasionally observed in the oxidation of monoketones in basic solution. Oxidation of 2-butanone yields 2,5-dimethyl-p-benzosemiquinone while treatment of 1,3-dihydroxyacetone with base and air (49) yields a radical now recognized as 2,5-dihydroxy-p-benzosemiquinone (48) (eq. 12).

$$HOCH_2COCH_2OH \xrightarrow[O_2]{B^-} [HOCH_2COCHO] \longrightarrow \quad\quad\quad (12)$$

Oxygenation of bicyclo[2.2.2]octan-2-one gives semidione (14). The same semidione is formed from a mixture of bicyclo[2.2.2]octane-2,3-dione and

(14)

bicyclo[2.2.2]octan-2-one in DMSO solution in the absence of oxygen. Reduction of the dione by propiophenone anions or oxidation of the α-hydroxy ketone gives the expected 2,3-semidione. Although the oxidation of monoketones is not free of certain limitations it is pertinent that only a single type of radical anion, the semidione, has been observed as the paramagnetic oxidation product. Unfortunately, β-diketones do not react readily with oxygen in basic solutions (50).

The paramagnetic species reported by Lown (34–36) to be cycloalkyl ketyls are indeed the cyclic semidiones. These substances were formed by Lown by the reaction of potassium metal with the cycloalkanone in the presence of traces of air in dimethyoxyethane solution. Apparently oxidation of the enolate anion is involved since ESR signals are not detected when the reaction is performed in a helium atmosphere (44). Lown has argued (36) that the semidione structure could be eliminated because 1,1,6,6-tetradeuteriocyclohexanone gave a radical anion with four α-deuterium atoms. However, the formation of cyclohexane-1,2-semidione in the presence of a large excess of the tetradeuterioketone would be expected to yield the tetradeuteriosemidione (32) (eq. 13).

The preferred route to the semidiones is through the α-hydroxy ketone. Monoketones can be brominated and then hydrolyzed to the α-hydroxy ketones without isolation of the bromination products (48). Of course, elimination reactions may occur in preference to hydrolysis. Olefins can be converted to epoxides and the epoxides converted to hydroxy ketones by treatment with boron trifluoride in DMSO solution (51). Again the pure α-hydroxy ketone need not be isolated. α-Acetoxy ketones can be hydrolyzed directly in the DMSO–potassium t-butoxide solution without isolation of the acyloin. It should be possible to convert esters to semidiones by subjecting them to the acyloin condensation followed by oxidation disproportionation in DMSO solution.

$$RCO_2Et \xrightarrow[\text{toluene}]{Na} RC(O^-)\!\!=\!\!C(O^-)R \xrightarrow[O_2]{DMSO} RC(O\cdot)\!\!=\!\!C(O^-)R$$

A novel synthesis of a semidione occurs in the electrolytic reduction of acetophenone at high electrode potentials in dimethylformamide (33). The resulting radical anion is clearly the 1-phenylpropane-1,2-semidione, possibly formed via the reaction sequence shown in equation 14 (52).

$$C_6H_5COCH_3 \rightleftarrows \rightleftarrows [C_6H_5COCH_3]^{-2} \xrightarrow{DMF}$$

$$\tag{14}$$

Dimethyl sulfoxide in basic solutions can serve as a methylating agent (53). Reaction of phenylglyoxal with DMSO containing potassium t-butoxide slowly forms the radical anion of 1-phenylpropane-1,2-dione (48) (eq. 15).

$$\tag{15}$$

Reaction of lactic esters with DMSO containing potassium *t*-butoxide leads to biacetyl semidione. Here the ester condensation with the methylsulfinylcarbanion (54) can be followed by elimination of CH_3SO^- (eq. 16).

$$CH_3CH(OH)CO_2Et + CH_3SOCH_2^- \longrightarrow CH_3CH(OH)COCH_2SOCH_3 \rightleftharpoons$$

$$CH_3C(O^-)=C(O^-)CH_2SOCH_3 \longrightarrow \qquad (16)$$

$$CH_3COC(O^-)=CH_2 + CH_3SO^- \rightleftharpoons CH_3COCOCH_3$$

Reaction of titanous ion and hydrogen peroxide with α-hydroxy ketones at pH $\sim$ 1 produces short-lived radicals which appear to be the radical $R\dot{C}(OH)COR$ (55). The radical cations $(R\dot{C}(OH)—\overset{+}{C}(OH)R)$ can be produced from the diketones upon reduction by sodium dithionite in 60–100% sulfuric acid and have quite a different ESR spectra (1). The short lifetime of the semidiones in the presence of water may reflect destruction via reactions of the neutral radical.

$$RC(O^-)=C(O\cdot)R + H^+ \rightleftharpoons RC(OH)=C(O\cdot)R \longrightarrow \text{nonradical products}$$

The semidione radical anions are not stable to oxygen. Presumably excess oxygen converts the radical anion to the diketone, which can be isolated in certain ketone oxidations (56–59).

A few semitriones have been generated from materials of biological interest by the action of turnip peroxidase (and hydrogen peroxide) upon hydroxy diketones (3,60). Among the radical anions formed have been **1** and **15–17**.

$$HO_2C—C(O\cdot)=C(O^-)—CO_2H$$
(15)

(16)

$$[H—\overset{O}{\underset{\|}{C}} \cdots \overset{O}{\underset{\|}{C}} \cdots \overset{O}{\underset{\|}{C}} —H]^{\bar{\cdot}}$$
(17)

Semidiones can be very conveniently generated from certain glycols which will undergo a pinacol–ketyl type of dissociation in basic solution.

$$H—\pi—\pi—H \underset{\longleftarrow}{\longrightarrow} \underset{\longleftarrow}{\longrightarrow} {}^-\pi—\pi^- \underset{\longleftarrow}{\longrightarrow} 2\pi\cdot^-$$

The ninhydrin semitrione radical anion (13) has been formed in high yield from hydrindantin (18) (42). In a similar manner, alloxantin (19)

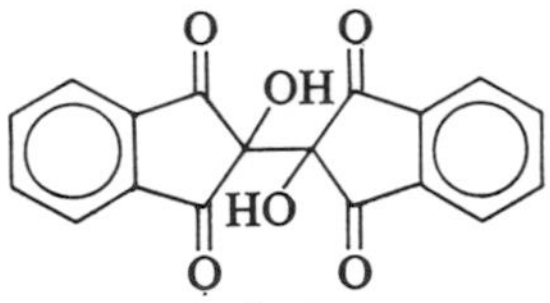

(18) 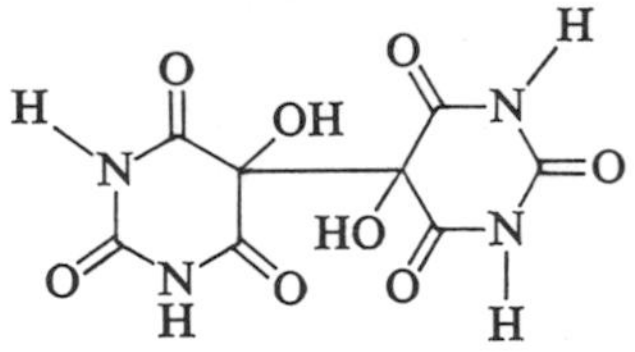　　　　　　　　　　　　(19)

$$C_6H_5COCH(OH)CH(OH)COC_6H_5$$

(20)

and glycol (20) dissociate in basic solution to form alloxan and phenyl-glyoxal radical anions (42,53).

IV. ACYCLIC SEMIDIONES

A. Semidiones Containing Hydrogen Substituents

Treatment of acetoxyethanal ($CH_3CO_2CH_2CHO$) with potassium t-butoxide in DMSO solution gives a short-lived paramagnetic intermediate (3–10 sec) at 25° that shows a 1:2:1 triplet ESR spectrum, $a^H = 7.7$ G. The spectrum is assigned to the glyoxal radical anion. Treatment of ω-hydroxyacetophenone, the glycol (20), hydroxyacetone, or 1-hydroxy-2-butanone with potassium t-butoxide in DMSO solution yields (21)

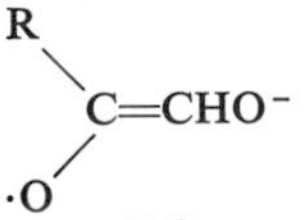

(21)

(a) $R = C_6H_5$
(b) $R = CH_3$
(c) $R = CH_3CH_2$

(48,52). The values of a_{CHO}^H for 21a, b, c are 6.88, 8.72, and 8.4 G, respectively. The spin densities at the aldehydic carbon atoms are $\rho_C = 0.31$, 0.39, and 0.37, respectively. When compared to a value of ρ_C of 0.34 for glyoxal radical anion it appears that the net effect of the aromatic ring is to reduce electron density (delocalization) while the next effect of the methyl substitutent is to increase electron density. In 21b, $a_{CH_3}^H = 7.46$ G. This corresponds to a spin density at the substituted carbonyl atom of $\rho_C = 0.34$, considerably greater than ρ_{C_π} calculated previously for the biacetyl radical anion ($\rho_{C_\pi} = 0.25$). These values of ρ_{C_π} may indicate that

21 exists in the *cis* structure (**22**) which gives rise to the high carbonyl carbon spin densities. Apparently, the potassium salt of **21a** in DMSO solution also exists mainly in the *cis* form (61). However, **21a** formed by electrolysis of benzaldehyde in DMF solutions of tetraethylammonium perchlorate is apparently the *trans* isomer (52). The *cis* and *trans* isomers of 3,4,5-trimethoxyphenylglyoxal semidione have been detected in DMSO and DMF (61).

$$\left[\begin{array}{c} R \qquad\qquad H \\ C \cdots\!\cdots C \\ O \cdots\quad\cdots O \\ K \end{array} \right]^{\overset{\bullet}{-}}$$

(22)

B. Semidiones with a Single Aryl Substituent

Table II lists the hfsc observed for a series of 1-aryl-2-alkyl semidiones in DMSO (80%)–*t*-butyl alcohol (20%) solution. The semidiones were prepared by oxygenation of the corresponding phenones ($0.05M$) in the presence of $0.1M$ potassium *t*-butoxide. The semidiones have very similar spin densities in the aromatic rings. For benzil radical anion in dimethylformamide the values of a_p^H, a_o^H, and a_m^H were found to be 1.12, 0.99, and 0.36, respectively (31). The values of a_α^H and a_β^H show considerable variations. The sharp drop between $a_{\alpha-CH_3}^H \cong a_{\alpha-CH_2}^H$ and $a_{\alpha-CH<}^H$ suggests a decided conformational preference for the isopropyl compound that places the methine hydrogen atom (on a time average) closer to the nodal plane

TABLE II
Hyperfine Splitting Constants of Semidione Radical Anions
$(C_6H_5C(O\cdot)\!=\!C(O^-)R)$ at $25 \pm 1°$

R	a_α^{H} [a]	a_β^{H} [a]	a_p^H	a_o^H	a_m^H
CH_3	3.43	—	1.84	1.59	0.53
CH_3CH_2	3.38	[b]	1.82	1.61	0.54
$CH_3CH_2CH_2$	3.12	0.11	1.85	1.62	0.55
$CH_3CH_2CH_2CH_2$	3.15	[c]	1.82	1.59	0.54
$(CH_3)_2CH$	1.45	[b]	1.84	1.60	0.53
$(CH_3)_3C$	—	0.18	1.84	1.58	0.54
$(CH_3)_2CHCH_2$	3.05	0.14	1.85	1.61	0.53

[a] Hydrogens α or β to the dicarbonyl system.
[b] Not observed.
[c] No attempt made to resolve splitting.

of the π system than in the freely rotating methyl group. A conformation such as (23) is apparently preferred. In 23 the dihedral angle between the

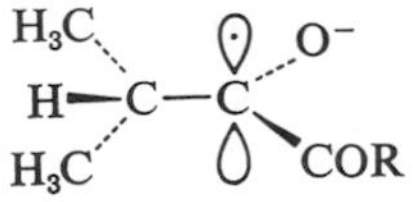

(23)

C_π—C_α—H plane and the p-orbital—C_π—C_α plane is 90° and a_α^H would be zero from the $\cos^2 \theta$ relationship.

β-Hydrogen atoms show little hfs when R is ethyl. However, when R=$CH_3CH_2CH_2$ or $(CH_3)_2CHCH_2$, the β-methylene and β-methine hydrogens interact appreciably, $a^H = 0.11, 0.14$ G, respectively.

This is consistent with a hyperconjugation mechanism for β interaction (52).

$$R—CO—\dot{C}(O^-)CH_2—R \longleftrightarrow RCO—C(O^-)=CH_2 \ R\cdot$$
(24)

Such delocalization apparently follows the stability of R· in ordinary chemical processes. Of course in 24, R· is not planar as is a free alkyl radical. The stability of R = $(CH_3)_2CH\cdot > R = CH_3CH_2\cdot > R = CH_3\cdot$ explains the trend in hfsc noted. Of course, conformational effects may also be involved. When the hfs, $a_{\beta-CH_3}^H$, is compared for R = CH_3CH_2, R = $(CH_3)_2CH$, and R = $(CH_3)_3C$, we see an increase in $a_{CH_3}^H$ from < 0.05 G for R = CH_3CH_2 and $(CH_3)_2CH$ to 0.18 G for R = $(CH_3)_3C$. This can be taken as an indication of a steric driving force for hyperconjugation. The strain in the C_α–C_β bonds of R = t-butyl causes a stronger interaction to occur with the unpaired spin.

The 1-phenylpropane-1,2-semidione is a good example for molecular orbital calculations. Because of the freely rotating methyl group empirical spin density estimates can be made for atoms 1, 2, 3, 4, 5, 9, and 12 in formula 25. Spin density on atom 11 will be assumed to be zero.

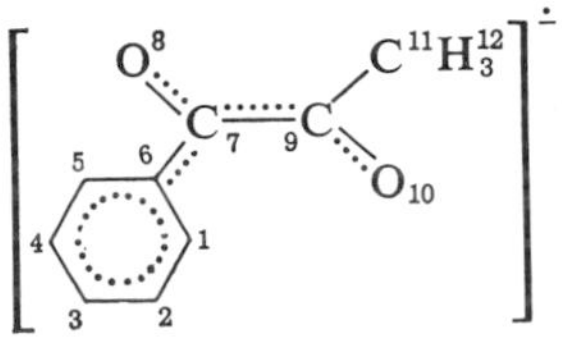

(25)

Table III lists the empirical spin densities and those calculated by treating the methyl group in an inductive manner, in a conjugation manner, and as a heteroatom. The parameters h_O and k_{CO} (defined in Table I) were

TABLE III

Theoretical and Empirical Spin Densities in 1-Phenylpropane-1,2-Semidione (per atom)[a]

Positions	1,5	2,4	3	6	7	8	9	10	11	12	k_{6-7}
Empirical	0.071	−0.024	0.082	—	—	—	0.151	—	~0	0.0068	—
Inductive Model[b]	0.071	−0.026	0.086	0.000	0.342	0.210	0.172	0.099	—	—	0.75
Conjugation Model[c]	0.072	−0.026	0.088	0.002	0.341	0.205	0.162	0.094	0.006	0.007	0.75
Heteroatom Model[d]	0.068	−0.025	0.084	0.002	0.346	0.208	0.169	0.098	0.006	—	0.725

[a] McLachlan calculations (15) with $\lambda = -1.2$.

[b] $h_9 = -0.45$ (a value of -0.5 is suggested by A. J. Streitwieser, *Molecular Orbital Theory for Organic Chemists*, Wiley, New York, 1961, Chapter 5.

[c] $h_9 = -0.50$; for other parameters see Table I.

[d] $h_9 = -0.3$, $h_{11} = 2.0$, $k_{9-11} = 0.7$.

held constant at 1.5 and 1.6. For the conjugation model the parameters for $h_{C(CH_3)}$, $h_{H(CH_3)}$, k_{CH}, and $k_{C_\pi CH_3}$ used are those given in Table I except that an inductive parameter, $h_9 = -0.50$, was employed. Values of k_{6-7} were varied to give the best fit with the data. All three models yield satisfactory results, particularly when the sums of ρ_9, ρ_{11}, and ρ_{12} are considered.

C. Symmetrical Dialkyl Semidiones

Treatment of acetoin with base gives a mixture of paramagnetic products whose ratio depends on the cation present, its concentration, the solvent, and the temperature (7). The radical anions both have a hfs pattern consistent with six equivalent hydrogens and we assign the spectra to the *cis* and *trans* radical anions, (26) and (27). The spectra observed in DMSO at

25° containing a low concentration of potassium *t*-butoxide or tetramethylammonium *t*-butoxide is given in Figure 1. The major radical anion shows ^{13}C satellites, $a^C = 4.5$ G. The ratio of major/minor radicals in Figure 1 is 20:1 at 25°. When prepared using lithium *t*-butoxide as the base, only the radical with the larger value of $a^H_{CH_3}$ (the minor radical in Fig. 1) is formed and this radical shows a well-defined $a^{Li} = 0.60$ G. We thus conclude that the minor radical in Figure 1 is the *cis* structure (27) and that it can be stabilized by chelation with Li^+. From the temperature studies at low $[K^+]$ we conclude that 27 is more stable than 26 by $\Delta H = 2$ kcal/mole. In the presence of lithium ions the only species present is 28, even in DMSO solution. Dilution of the DMSO solutions giving rise to

Figure 1 with dimethoxyethane or tetrahydrofuran also causes the *cis* structure to become the sole radical anion present. We thus have a new and sensitive technique for studying ion pairing effects in those solvents in which the semidiones can be prepared (DMSO, HMPA, THF, DME, pyridine).

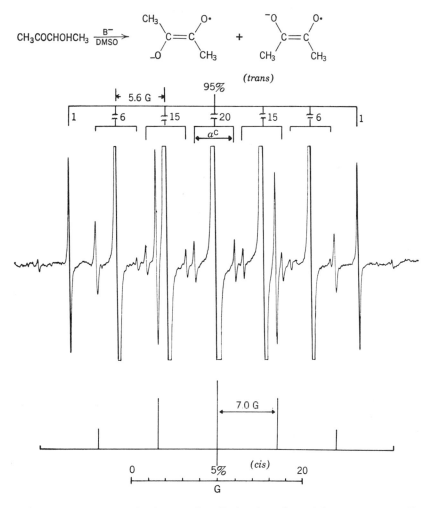

Fig. 1. ESR spectra of mixture of radical anions formed by spontaneous disproportionation of acetoin in dimethyl sulfoxide in the presence of potassium *t*-butoxide.

The diisopropyl semidione exists in only one form at 25–100° in DMSO. This form does not show any a^{Li} at concentrations of Li^+ in the range of $0.1M$ and it is believed that this semidione has the *trans* structure. A similar conclusion has been drawn in regard to the di-*t*-butyl semidione (39). Steric hindrance between two *cis*-isopropyl or *t*-butyl groups completely overcomes any stabilizations there may be in the *cis* structure from chelation or 1,4-overlap.

TABLE IV

Hyperfine Splitting Constants for Dialkyl Semidiones
$(RC(O\cdot)=C(O^-)R)$ at $25°$ in DMSO Solution

R	Cis a_α^H	Trans a_α^H	a_β^H	a^C
CH_3	6.90	5.70	—	4.44
CH_3CH_2	6.00	4.90	~ 0.02	4.4
$CH_3CH_2CH_2$	5.60	4.60	0.20	4.4
$(CH_3)_2CH$	—	2.0	0.033	
$(CH_3)_3C$	—	—	0.29	
$(CH_3)_2CHCH_2$	5.3	4.3	0.28	4.4

Hyperfine splittings for a series of dialkyl semidiones are given in Table IV.

In d_6-dimethyl sulfoxide acetoin gives a radical anion with six equivalent deuterium atoms, $a^D = 0.855$. For biacetyl radical anion the value of a^H/a^D is 6.60 in agreement with the theoretical ratio of 6.514 based on the ratio of nuclear magnetic moments (32).

The larger hfs constants for the *cis* structures relative to the *trans* structures are consistent with chelation which would increase the spin density on the carbonyl carbon atoms. Whether or not the *cis–trans* isomerization involves rotation about the partial double bond in structures **5** and **6** or involves an electron transfer mechanism cannot be stated.

$$RC(O\cdot)=C(O^-)R^* + RCOCOR \rightleftharpoons RCOCOR^* + RC(O\cdot)=C(O^-)R$$
cis   *trans*

In structure **5**, R = CH_3, there exists 43% of a double bond between the carbonyl carbons according to the valence bond treatment given earlier. For structure **6**, R = CH_3, one estimates 32% double bond character or a bond order of 1.32 between C-2 and C-3.

Table IV shows the same effect on a_α^H as was noted previously for 1-aryl semidiones—namely, a large decrease in a_α^H from α-methyl or α-ethyl to α-isopropyl. Presumably this effect is one of conformation of the isopropyl group (see **23**). When structure **5**, R = isopropyl, was examined over a temperature range of 25–100°, it was observed that there was little change in $a_{\alpha-CH}^H$. This must mean that the conformational preference is solely determined by entropy considerations. The time average conformation for the α-hydrogen in structure **5**, R = isopropyl, can be calculated by assuming that ρ_{C_π} is similar to ρ_{C_π} of the biacetyl radical anion, namely 0.25. Applying the equation $a^H = 40 \, \rho_C \cos^2 \theta$ yields $\theta = 63°$.

The data of Table IV show the same dependencies of a_β^H on structure as noted before. The value of $a_{\beta-CH_3}^H$ increases sharply from structure **5**, $R = C_2H_5$ (0.02 G), to structure **5**, $R = CH(CH_3)_2$ (0.033 G), to structure **5**, $R = C(CH_3)_3$ (0.29 G). Moreover, a_β^H increases drastically from β-methyl ($R = C_2H_5$, $a_\beta^H = 0.02$ G) to β-ethyl ($R = CH_3CH_2CH_2$, 0.20 G) to β-isopropyl ($R = CH_2CH(CH_3)_2$ (0.28 G) in agreement with the postulated hyperconjugation interaction.

D. Semidiones with Cycloalkyl Substituents

A series of dicycloalkyl semidiones (**29**) have been prepared including cycloheptenyl, cyclohexyl, cyclopentyl, and cyclobutyl. They show a predominant triplet hfs from the pair of α-hydrogen atoms with $a_\alpha^H = 2.0$,

$$(CH_2)_x \overset{O^-}{\underset{O\cdot}{C}}=C \quad (CH_2)_x$$

(29)

1.9, 1.9, and 2.2 G, respectively. Dicyclopropyl semidione does not show a predominant triplet splitting. An analysis of the complex spectra leads to $a^H = 0.57, 0.57, 0.37, 0.37, 0.37, 0.37, 0.20, 0.20, 0.20,$ and 0.20 G. Figure 2

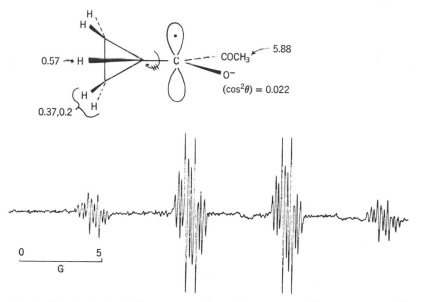

Fig. 2. First derivative ESR spectrum of semidione prepared by spontaneous disproportionation of methyl cyclopropyl acyloin in dimethyl sulfoxide solution containing potassium *t*-butoxide.

gives the ESR spectrum of methyl cyclopropyl semidiones, $CH_3C(O\cdot)=C$ $(O^-)-\triangleleft$. The spectrum shows the expected quartet splitting, $a^H_{CH_3} =$ 5.88 G. In addition the fine structure demands $a^H = 0.57, 0.37, 0.37, 0.20$, and 0.20 G. Thus, the cyclopropyl ring is unique from the other cycloalkyl ring in that there is a high conformational preference for structure **30**.

(30)   (31)

The observed value of a^H_α is consistent with a single conformation in which the methine hydrogen is only 6° from the nodal plane of the π system. The hfsc of the β-hydrogens is somewhat larger than usual (compare with 0.20 for the β-methylene group in di-*n*-propylsemidione). However, the magnitude of a^H_β does not demand extensive delocalication of carbon–carbon bonds of the cyclopropyl ring, e.g., structure **31**.

The cyclopropyl-substituted semidiones thus have similar geometry to the cyclopropylcarbinyl cation (62), cyclopropanecarboxaldehyde (63), phenylcyclopropane (64), and vinylcyclopropanes (65). However, from ESR results we are not prepared to ascribe the conformational preference to a delocalization phenomenon. Of course, the observed conformational preference may result from the same delocalization that is present in cyclopropane–carboxaldehyde and which would not place unpaired spin density on the β carbon atom.

V. MONOCYCLIC SEMIDIONES

A. Unsubstituted Rings

2-Acetoxycyclobutanone reacts with potassium *t*-butoxide in DMSO solution to produce a semidione (**32**) with hyperfine splitting by four equivalent hydrogen atoms, $a^H = 13.9$ G and $a^C = 5.4$ G. Under the same conditions α-hydroxycyclopentanone yields **33**, whose spectrum

(32)   (33)

shows four equivalent hydrogens, readily exchangeable with d_6-DMSO, and with $a^H = 13.12$ G. In d_6-DMSO, deuterium atoms are observed, $a^D = 1.99$; $a^H/a^D = 6.60$ (32). Cyclopentanone or cyclopentane-1,2-dione do not yield high concentrations of **33** in basic solution (in the presence of a trace of oxygen for the monoketone) presumably because the diketone exists in a highly enolic state.

Cyclohexanone can be oxidized in basic solution to the semidione. Both the cyclohexane-1,2-dione and α-hydroxycyclohexanone yield semidione (**34**) in appreciable yield. At 25° the semidione shows only four equivalent

(**34**)

hydrogen atoms, $a^H = 9.68$ G and one ^{13}C hfs, $a^C = 4.9$ G in DMSO. In dimethoxyethane a^H is reported to be 10.4 G (34). In d_6-DMSO a deuterium splitting of $a^D = 1.465$, $a^H/a^D = 6.60$ is observed (32).

Upon cooling, the lines of the quintet due to **34** broaden, particularly the second and fourth peaks. At $-96°$ (in dimethoxyethane) a poorly resolved seven-line pattern consistent with a^H (two equivalent) $\simeq 14.2$ and a^H (two equivalent) $\simeq 6.9$ G is observed (34). The average of these constants is 10.55 G in excellent agreement with the value of a^H observed at 25°. At $-96°$ the interconversion between half-chair structures (**34**) is sufficiently slow that the magnetic difference of quasi-axial and quasi-equatorial α-hydrogen atoms can be distinguished. At this temperature the interconversion of half-chair forms must be slow compared to the frequency of precession of the electron magnetic moment around the nuclear magnetic moments. At 25° in dimethoxyethane solution we can estimate that the frequency of half-chair interconversions is faster than $(14.2-6.9) \times 2.8 \times 10^6 = 2 \times 10^7$ cps, i.e., the lifetime of a given conformer is less than 5×10^{-8} sec. This analysis is fully borne out in the following section when frozen cyclohexane-1,2-semidiones are considered (e.g., 4-t-butyl).

It is possible to calculate dihedral angles and empirical spin densities for **34** from a knowledge of the hfsc for axial and equatorial hydrogen atoms and the assumption that the α-carbon atom is tetrahedral. This assumption leads to the relationship,

$$\theta_{\text{equatorial}-H} = 60° - \theta_{\text{axial}-H} \quad \text{(see structure 35) (13)}.$$

The two simultaneous equations,

$$a_{\text{axial}}^{\text{H}} = 40 \, \rho_{\text{C}} \cos^2 \theta_{\text{axial}}$$

$$a_{\text{equatorial}}^{\text{H}} = 40 \, \rho_{\text{C}} \cos^2 \theta_{\text{equatorial}} = 40 \, \rho_{\text{C}} \cos^2 (60° - \theta)$$

wherein θ can be negative, can be solved simultaneously to yield two possible solutions for ρ_{C} and θ_a or θ_e. Using $a_{\text{axial}}^{\text{H}} = 14.2$ and $a_{\text{equatorial}}^{\text{H}} = 6.90$ leads to the realistic solutions of $\theta_{\text{axial}} = 13°$, $\rho_{\text{C}} = 0.27$ and the unrealistic solution of $\theta_{\text{axial}} = -54°$, $\rho_{\text{C}} = 0.91$. Correction of the value of $\rho_{\text{C}_\pi - \text{CH}_2}$ for spin in the methylene group yields $\rho_{\text{C}_\pi} = 0.27 - 21.1/508 = 0.23$. The spin density of the oxygen atoms can now be assigned a value of $[1.0 - 2(0.27)]/2 = 0.23$. A McLachlan calculation with the parameters previously employed for the *trans*-acyclic semidiones ($h_{\text{O}} = 1.8$, $k_{\text{CO}} = 1.6$, $h_{\text{C(CH}_2)} = -0.1$, $h_{\text{H}} = -0.5$, $k_{\text{C}_\pi - \text{CH}_2} = 0.93$, $k_{\text{CH}} = 2.5$) yields $\rho_{\text{O}} = 0.321$, $\rho_{\text{C}_\pi} = 0.153$, $\rho_{\text{C(CH}_2)} = -0.013$, $\rho_{\text{H}} = 0.013$.

The time average dihedral angle in structure **34** must be 30°, i.e., $\frac{1}{2}(\theta_{\text{axial}} + \theta_{\text{equatorial}})$. This cannot be calculated from the value of a^{H} when rapid conformational interconversion is observed because $\frac{1}{2}\cos^2 \theta_{\text{axial}} + \frac{1}{2}\cos^2 \theta_{\text{equatorial}}$ is not equal to $\cos^2 \theta_{\text{av}}$. If it is assumed that cyclopentane-1,2-semidione has a rigid geometry with tetrahedral angles at the α-carbon atoms ($\theta = 30°$) we can calculate that $\rho_{\text{C}_\pi - \text{CH}_2} = 17.5/40 = 0.44$, and $\rho_{\text{C}_\pi} = 0.44 - 0.05 = 0.39$. Using cyclopentene as a model where θ has been found to be 27° by NMR (66) yields $\rho_{\text{C}_\pi} = 0.36$. Cyclooctane-1,2-semidione shows four equivalent α-hydrogen atoms in DMSO solution at 25°, $a^{\text{H}} = 3.33$ G (a^{H} dimethoxyethane, 3.45 G) (35). Upon cooling, additional fine structure appears at higher temperature than required for additional hfs in the cyclohexane-1,2-semidione spectrum. At $-35°$ in dimethoxyethane the spectrum appears to result from three equivalent hydrogens, $a^{\text{H}} = 4.47$ and a single hydrogen, $a^{\text{H}} = 2.35$.

At this temperature the conformations are not symmetrical. There still may be conformational interconversion occurring at $-35°$, but in the time scale of $\sim 10^{-7}$ sec the four α-hydrogen atoms do not become equivalent. At 25° in this time the conformational equilibria make all four hydrogen atoms equivalent.

Cycloheptane-1,2-semidione, cyclononane-1,2-semidione, cyclododecane-1,2-semidione, cyclododecane-1,2-semidione and cyclopentadecane-1,2-semidione all show conformational stability at 25° with conformational lifetimes $> \sim 10^{-7}$ sec (13). In the cycloheptane-1,2-semidione hfs is observed up to 86° (36) for a pair of quasi-axial hydrogen atoms $[a^{\text{H}} = 6.70$ G (DMSO)] and a pair of quasi-equatorial hydrogen atoms $[a^{\text{H}} = 1.97$ G (DMSO)]. In DME the splittings are reported to be 7.02 and 2.08 G (36). We thus observe for the medium-sized cycloalkane-1,2-

semidiones that the rate of conformational interconversion is $C_6 \gg C_8 \gg C_7$. Since these cycloalkane semidiones are derivatives of the cycloalkenes, presumably the same rate sequence persists in the cycloalkenes. Exact rate measurements on the basis of line broadening experiments are not available as yet (32).

Cyclononane-1,2-semidione is reported to possess at room temperature a pair of quasi-axial hydrogen atoms, $a^H = 4.92$ G, and a pair of quasi-equatorial hydrogen atoms, $a^H = 2.46$ G (36). Heating to 58° resulted in time averaging of the α-hydrogen atoms to give $a^H = 3.68$ G (four equivalent). Thus, the cyclononane-1,2-semidione is intermediate in conformational stability between the cycloheptane and cyclooctane derivative. Apparently the stable conformer of the cyclononane-1,2-semidione is a symmetrical one. Cyclopentadecanone-1,2-semidione also appears to exist in a "frozen" symmetrical conformation at 25° in DMSO, a^H (two equivalent) = 7.23 and 2.07 (13).

Although the conformation may be stable in regards to rotation about the CH_2—CO bond in these semidiones, other rotations about CH_2—CH_2 bonds may still be occurring. This can have the effect of making a nonsymmetrical conformation appear to be symmetrical. This appears to be the case for cyclodecyl and cyclododecyl semidiones. At $-35°$ both semidiones show two doublet splittings (cyclodecyl 10.78, 6.30 G; cyclododecyl 11.02, 7.30 G) in DME (36). Apparently we have nonsymmetrical conformations with two (quasi-equatorial) hydrogens in the nodal plane of the π system. However, the two quasi-axial hydrogens are not equivalent because of the conformation of the polymethylene chain. Note that time averaging between two or more conformations cannot make the equatorial hydrogens appear to be in the nodal plane—time averaging cannot cause θ to appear to be 0° or 90°. Only a hydrogen atom rigidly fixed in the nodal plane will have $\theta = 90°$. Upon heating the cyclodecyl semidione to 25° in DMSO or 90° in DME, the movement of the polymethylene chain becomes rapid and we observe two equivalent alpha hydrogen atoms, $a^H = 8.52$ (DME); 8.33 (DMSO) G. The equatorial hydrogen atoms remain fixed in the nodal plane even at 90°.

For cyclododecyl semidione the lines are somewhat broad and the equatorial hydrogen atoms may not be exactly in the nodal plane but may have a very small hfsc at 25° or below. At 25° in DME or DMSO the axial hydrogen atoms are now equivalent and at 83° in DME a splitting by the equatorial hydrogens can be detected, $(a^H_{axial} = 9.02, a^H_{equatorial} = 1.63$ G). In DMSO at 25° or DME at 61° the values of a^H_{axial} are reported to be 7.88, and 9.27 G, respectively (13,36).

Calculations of dihedral angles can be performed for the symmetrical conformations in the manner previously employed for cyclohexane.

Using the equation

$$a^H = 40 \, \rho_{\pi-CH_2} \cos^2 \theta$$

the following spin densities and dihedral angles (Table V) were calculated for the cycloheptyl, cyclononyl, cyclodecyl (DMSO, 25°), and cyclododecyl (DME, 83°).

The foregoing analysis is based on the assumption that the hfsc are defined by the equation $a^H = B\rho_C \cos^2 \theta$ and that B is a constant in the range of $+40$ G for radical anions. Moreover, it is assumed that these radical anions all have a *cis* configuration. There is also another dihedral angle to be considered which for a symmetrical system measures the intersection of the H—C—H plane and this *p*- orbital— C_π—C_α plane (see **35**). This is particularly important when C_α is not tetrahedral, e.g., cyclobutane-1,2-semidione, but can be expected to be reasonably constant for the other semidiones considered in Table V.

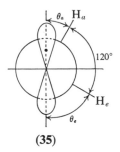

(35)

(35)

B. Alkyl-Substituted Cyclopentane-1,2-Semidiones and Cyclohexane-1,2-Semidiones

Oxidation of an unsymmetrical alkyl-substituted ketone in basic solution can give rise to two semidiones. In addition, in cyclohexane-1,2-semidione the alkyl substituent will confer extra conformational stability to one of the two possible conformers, presumably the conformer with the alkyl group situated in the equatorial position (13,44).

Oxidation of 3-methylcyclopentanone in DMSO solutions of potassium *t*-butoxide produces three parts of the Δ^3 semidione to one of the Δ^2

TABLE V

Dihedral Angles of H_α—C_α—C_π and p_z- Orbital—C_π—C_α Planes and Carbonyl Carbon Spin Densities in Cycloalkyl Semidiones.

Ring size	Solvent (temp.)	a_α^H,G	θ_{axial}	$\rho_{C_\pi - CH_2}$	ρ_{C_π}
5	DMSO (25°)	13.12 (4)	+30	0.44	0.39
			+27	0.41	0.36
6	DME (−96°)	14.2 (2)	+13	0.38	0.34
		6.9 (2)			
7	DMSO (25°)	6.70 (2)	+3 or	0.17 or	0.16 or
		1.97 (2)	−50	0.41	0.39
9	DME (25°)	4.92 (2)	+13 or	0.13 or	0.12 or
		2.46 (2)	−54	0.35	0.34
10	DMSO (25°)	8.33 (2)	−30	0.28	0.26
		0.0 (2)			
12	DME (87°)	9.02 (2)	−5	0.23	0.21
		1.63 (2)			
15	DMSO (25°)	7.23 (2)	+2	0.18	0.16
		2.07 (2)			

semidione (48) (eq. 17). Bromination of 3-methylcyclopentanone in *t*-butyl alcohol followed by hydrolysis of the crude α-bromo ketones in

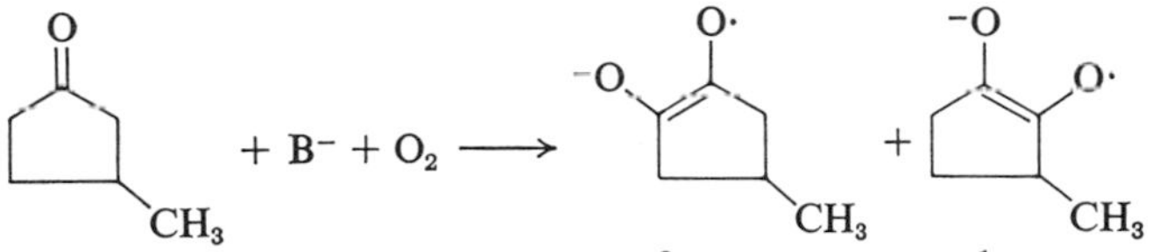

DMSO solution leads to the same ratio of semidiones. Either both processes are measuring the relative stability (rate of formation or equilibrium concentrations) of Δ^2- and Δ^3-enolate anions or both processes are measuring the equilibrium between radical anions and the two possible diketones (eq. 18). That the latter process is not involved in all cases is

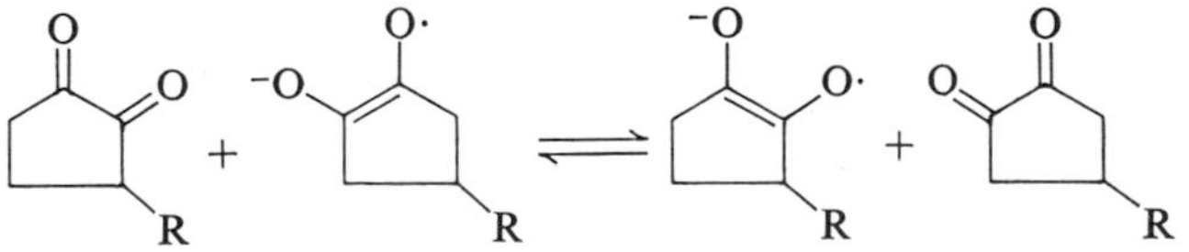

(36)
(a) R = CH₃
(b) R = (CH₃)₃C

(37)
(a) R = CH₃
(b) R = (CH₃)₃C

demonstrated by the fact that bromination of 3-*t*-butylcyclopentanone followed by treatment with base in DMSO yields >90% **36b** whereas oxygenation in basic solution produces >90% **37b** (48). The preferred oxygenation of 3-*t*-butylcyclopentanone at C-2 is in line with a preferred enolization at C-2 because of relief of eclipsing strain. Apparently oxygen traps the resulting enolate anion with little kinetic discrimination. Bromination, on the other hand, appears to give kinetic discrimination with the bromine directed as far from the *t*-butyl group as possible because of steric considerations. The ESR spectra of **37a** and **37b** contain eight lines with a^H = 14.46, 14.01, and 11.62 G for **37a** and 14.40, 13.96, and 12.38 G for **37b**. The ESR spectra of **36a** and **36b** are triplets of triplets, a^H = 14.36, 12.48, and 15.68, 11.30 G, respectively.

Oxidation of the three methylcyclohexanones gives the ESR spectra of Figure 3.

2-Methylcyclohexanone produces a single semidione in low yield. Apparently the major oxidation is at C-2 and this does not yield a paramagnetic product. 4-Methylcyclohexanone also produces a single semidione while 3-methylcyclohexanone yields a mixture of the two semidiones. The fact that a mixture of semidiones is formed can be readily ascertained by observing the spectrum as a function of time. The lines due to **38** decay more rapidly than those due to **39**. The same ratio of **38** and **39** is formed when 3-methylcyclohexanone is first brominated in basic solution and the resulting α-bromo ketones converted to hydroxy ketones and hence to semidiones in DMSO solution containing potassium *t*-butoxide.

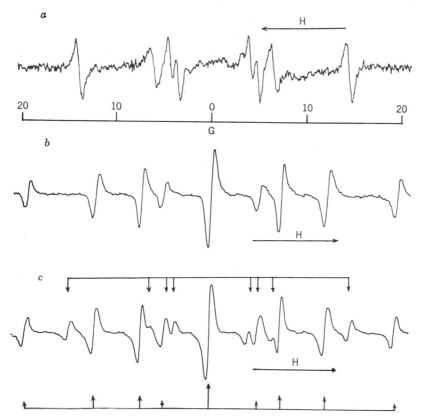

Fig. 3. First derivative ESR spectra of oxidates of 2-, 3-, and 4-methylcyclohexanone in dimethyl sulfoxide at 25°; (*a*) 2-methylcyclohexanone; (*b*) 4-methylcyclohexanone; (*c*) 3-methylcyclohexanone.

The spectrum of **38** shows three different α-hydrogen atoms while **39** is a triplet of triplets due to two pairs of α-hydrogen atoms. The α-hydrogen atoms no longer spend one-half of the time in the quasi-axial position and one-half the time in the quasi-equatorial position as in cyclohexane-1,2-semidione. The 3- or 4-methyl group causes one conformation to be more

(40)   **(41)**

highly populated than the other because of the well-known greater stability of an alkyl substituent in the equatorial position. That the rate of interconversion between conformers must still be quite fast (lifetime of a given conformer $< 10^{-7}$ sec) is shown by the fact that for 3,3-dimethyl and 4,4-dimethylcyclohexane-1,2-semidione the hydrogen atoms of the α-methylene groups are magnetically equivalent at 25° (44). 3,3,5,5-Tetramethylcyclohexane-1,2-semidione demonstrates a measurable rate of interconversion of the two half-chair conformations at 25°. Figure 4 shows the spectrum at 25° and it is apparent that the central line of the triplet is considerably broadened. At 90° this broadening has disappeared and a sharp 1:2:1 triplet results. From the line broadening a rate constant for conformation interchange of 10^8–10^9 sec^{-1} at 25° is obtained; $E_a = 2.5 \pm 0.5$ kcal/mole, $\Delta S^{\ddagger} = -8 \pm 1$ eu (32).

Line broadening of the central line results because the half-chair–half-chair interconversion switches axial and equatorial hydrogen atoms. The two states $ax^{\alpha}eq^{\beta}$ and $ax^{\alpha}eq^{\beta}$ (wherein ax and eq refer to axial and equatorial hydrogens; α and β refer to the nuclear spin states of the hydrogen atoms) are not of equal energy and when the lifetime of a conformer

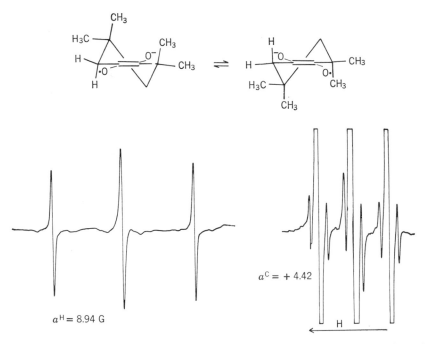

Fig. 4. First derivative ESR spectrum of semidione prepared by oxidation of 3,3,5,5-tetramethylcyclohexanone in dimethyl sulfoxide solution containing potassium *t*-butoxide.

is $> \sim 10^{-7}$ sec the energy difference between these states can be accurately measured by ESR. The interconversions, $ax^\alpha eq^\alpha \rightleftarrows eq^\alpha ax^\alpha$ and $ax^\beta eq^\beta \rightleftarrows eq^\beta ax^\beta$, do not change the energy of the molecule with which an electron of given spin is associated and the wing peaks of Figure 4 are sharp at all temperatures. Upon cooling, the center peak of Figure 4 should split into two peaks corresponding to the two energy levels possible when the two hydrogen nuclei have opposite spin. Figure 4 also shows the ^{13}C hfs of the 3,3,5,5-tetramethylcyclohexane-1,2-semidione. The ^{13}C doublet shows a sharper low field line than high field line and this is interpreted to mean that the sign of a^c is positive (67).

The monosubstituted cyclohexane-1,2-semidiones have α-hydrogen atoms that spend unequal times in quasi-axial and quasi-equatorial positions. We will refer to those hydrogens that spend most of their time in quasi-axial positions as "axial" hydrogen atoms. We find that hfsc for axial hydrogen atoms increases as the 4-alkyl group is changed from methyl to ethyl, to isopropyl, to t-butyl. However, the sum of a_{ax}^H and a_{eq}^H stays remarkably constant. The data are given in Table VI together with the values of a_{ax}^H and a_{eq}^H for the frozen semidione (42) (44).

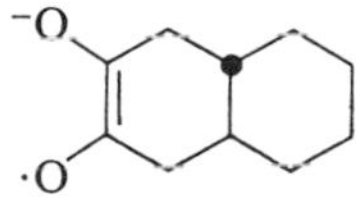

(42)

TABLE VI

Hyperfine Splitting Constants for Alkylcyclohexane-1,2-Semidiones at 25° in DMSO Solution.

4-Alkyl subst.	a_{ax}^H	a_{eq}^H	$a_{ax}^H + a_{eq}^H$
H	9.83	9.83	19.66
Methyl	12.33	7.34	19.67
Isopropyl	12.63	7.02	19.65
t-Butyl	13.02	6.64	19.66
trans-4,5-(CH$_2$)$_4$-	13.18	6.59	19.77
3,3-Dimethyl	9.74	9.74	19.48

The results of Table VI suggest that the observed hfsc (a_{ax}^H, a_{eq}^H) are correlated with the true axial and equatorial hfsc (13.18, 6.59 G) by the simple equations:

$$a_{ax}^H = 13.18(f) + 6.59(1 - f)$$
$$a_{eq}^H = 6.59(f) + 13.18(1 - f)$$

wherein f is the fraction of the molecules in the more stable conformation (equatorial alkyl substituent). Results of this calculation are given in Table VII.

TABLE VII
Conformational Preference of Substituted Cyclohexane-1,2-Semidiones in Dimethyl Sulfoxide at $25 \pm 3°$

| | Fraction of molecules in thermodynamically stable conformation (f) | | | |
Subst.	Calculated from a_{ax}^H	Calculated from a_{eq}^H	"A" value, kcal/mole[a]	A value, alkylcyclo-hexanes[b]
4-t-Butyl	0.98	0.99	> 2.3[c]	~ 5.6
4-Isopropyl	0.92	0.93	1.5	2.1
4-Methyl	0.87	0.89	1.2	1.7
3-Methyl	0.69	0.70	0.5	—

[a] Calculated from the equation, $A = RT \ln K$; S. Winstein and N. J. Holness, *J. Am. Chem. Soc.*, **77**, 5562 (1955).

[b] E. L. Eliel, N. L. Allinger, S. J. Angyal, and G. A. Morrison, *Conformational Analysis*, Wiley, New York, 1965, p. 44.

[c] Assuming f to be at least 0.98.

The "A" values of Table VII are smaller than the A values in cyclohexane derivatives, as might well be reasonably expected. The alkylcyclohexane-1,2-semidiones appear to represent an ideal model for studying the effect of temperature on conformational equilibria.

The 3-methylcyclohexane-1,2-semidione is particularly interesting. The 3-methyl group shows less conformational preference than the 4-methyl group, presumably because of eclipsing with the oxygen atom at C-2.

The hfsc for the 3-methylcyclohexane-1,2-semidione are 11.15, 10.29, and 8.56 G. The hfsc of 11.15 and 10.29 are obviously axial hydrogens at C-3 and C-6 and 8.56 the equatorial hydrogen at C-6. Since $11.15 + 8.56 = 19.71$ the hfsc of 10.29 has been assigned to the methine hydrogen at C-3. We would expect this hydrogen atom and the axial hydrogen at C-6 to have nearly identical time averaged geometries. Thus, the difference between the hfsc, $11.15 - 10.29 = 0.86$ G, may reflect an electronic effect of alkyl substitution on a hfsc and on the degree of hyperconjugation. We conclude the methine hydrogen in **38** hyperconjugates to a slightly smaller extent than the axial methylene hydrogen at C-6. Hyperconjugation represents 2.20% of the total valence bond structures for each methylene hydrogen at C-6 and 2.03% of the total valence bond structures for the methine hydrogen at C-3.

The question of the existence of boat conformations for the mono-alkylcyclohexane-1,2-semidiones seems to be completely answered by the constancy of $a_{ax}^H + a_{ex}^H$ (Table VI) and the agreement between these values in the cyclohexane semidiones and *trans*-decalin-2,3-semidione wherein a boat conformation of the unsaturated ring cannot be achieved. Moreover, for cyclohexene itself the boat conformation has been shown not to represent an energy minimum (69).

The foregoing analysis of cyclohexane-1,2-semidiones presents another method of calculating the detailed geometry and spin density of the system (13,44). Using the hfsc for pure quasi-axial and pure quasi-equatorial carbon–hydrogen bonds from Table VI one can calculate θ_{ax} for a frozen cyclohexane-1,2-semidione conformer and $\rho_{C_\pi - CH_2}$ at 25° in DMSO solution to be +13° and 0.38 ($\rho_{C_\pi} = 0.34$).

VI. SEMIDIONES DERIVED FROM DECALINS

Three semidiones obtained by oxygenation of the decalones are recognized (**43–45**). The isomeric *cis*- and *trans*-Δ^2-decalin semidiones (**43** and

45) are readily distinguished since in the *trans* structure there are two pairs of magnetically equivalent hydrogen atoms whereas the *cis*-2-decalin semidione has four magnetically nonequivalent α-hydrogen atoms. It is expected that the *trans* structure will be frozen in the diequatorial conformation. However, the *cis* semidione can exist as a pair of equally populated conformations in rapid equilibrium. Such conformational inter-conversion would cause each α-hydrogen to spend equal times in quasi-axial and quasi-equatorial positions. It is true that C-1 and C-4 are never exactly equivalent in the *cis*-octalin structures. However, one would expect

trans, H_e equivalent   *cis*, H_e not equivalent

two pairs of very nearly equivalent hydrogens if rapid interconversion occurred and four different α-hydrogens if the conformations were frozen. At 25° in DMSO solution the conformation is frozen (lifetime $\gg 10^{-7}$ sec) and four different α-hydrogen atoms are seen for structure **45**. Figures 5 and 6 give the ESR spectra of the oxidation products of *trans*-2-decalone and *cis*-2-decalone, respectively. In structure **43** α-hydrogen atoms have hfsc in the ratio of 1:2 and a seven-line 1:2:3:4:3:2:1 spectrum results (44). In structure **45**, 14 lines with two of double intensity are observed. The hfsc are 13.18, 13.18, 6.59, and 6.59 G for structure **43** and 13.83, 12.72, 7.37, and 6.55 G for structure **45**. The oxidation of *trans*-β-decalone produces a minor radical with nearly a 1:1:2:2:1:1 structure while the oxidation of *cis*-β-decalone produces the same radical as the major species. Since the same sextet spectrum, $a^H = 13.17$, 12.66, and 7.09 G, is produced by oxidation of *cis*- or *trans*-*a*-decalone, it is obvious that this semidione must have structure **44**. The *cis* isomer of structure **44** has not been detected in the oxidations of the unsubstituted decalones. Semidione **44** is less stable than **43** or **45** and will decay upon standing 10–20 hr to leave a pure spectrum of structure **43** or **45**.

Epimerization must occur in the conversion of *cis*-β-decalone to **44**. This is consistent with the intervention of a diketone in the oxygenation sequence (eq. 19). The oxidation products observed from the β-decalones correlate fairly well with the kinetic controlled rates of ionization of the hydrogen at C-1 and C-3 measured with triphenylmethyllithium in 1,2-dimethoxyethane (70) and suggest that the relative amounts of semidiones formed is a good measure of the relative rates of ionization of these hydrogen atoms. However, there is no difference in the ratio of oxidation products when the decalone is mixed with base and oxygen or when the ketone is extensively ionized by the base before exposure to oxygen. Alternatively, we may be observing the equilibria (eqs. 20 and 21) wherein the ratio of observed radical anions is determined by the relative amounts of the diketones formed by oxidation and the values of the equilibrium constants.

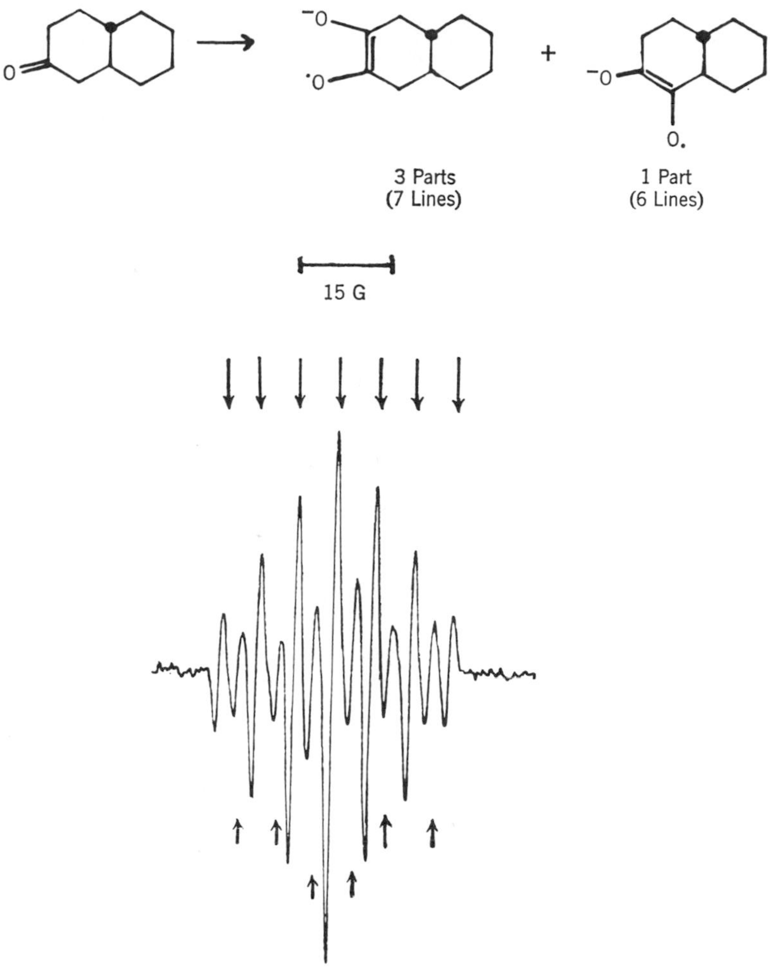

3 Parts
(7 Lines)

1 Part
(6 Lines)

15 G

Fig. 5. Semidiones produced in the oxidation of *trans*-β-decalone at 25° in dimethyl sulfoxide solution containing potassium *t*-butoxide.

The results with *cis*- and *trans*-β-decalones suggest a novel approach to structure assignment for steroidal ketones which will be developed more fully in the next section.

Oxidation of the *cis*- and *trans*-2-keto-9- and 10-methyldecalins gives rise to considerably different products. Four semidiones are recognized (**46–49**) and a fifth (**50**) is possibly present.

The *cis*- and *trans*-2-keto-9-methyldecalins give quite different products (20% and 0% attack at C-1, respectively) and can be readily distinguished.

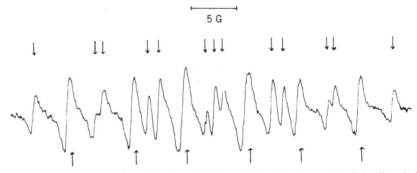

1 Part   2 Parts

(13 Lines)   (6 Lines)

5 G

Fig. 6. Semidiones produced in the oxidation of *cis*-β-decalone at 25° in dimethyl sulfoxide solution containing potassium *t*-butoxide.

(19)

(44) ← (45)

(20)

(21)

The *cis*- and *trans*-3-keto-10-methyldecalin give rather similar ratios of attack at C-1 and C-3 to yield semidiones that cannot be distinguished by elementary considerations of the splitting pattern. The *trans*-2-keto-9-methyldecalin and the *trans*-2-keto-10-methyldecalin are readily distinguished by the oxidation products as are the *cis*-2-keto-9-methyldecalin and *cis*-2-keto-10-methyldecalin. For the latter pair, minor radical **50** from the 2-keto-9-methyldecalin shows two doublet splittings, whereas minor radical **48** from *cis*-2-keto-10-methyldecalin shows three doublet splittings or at low resolution a doublet and a triplet splitting. Figure 7 gives the observed spectra and the structural assignments.

The values of the hfsc assigned to structures **43–50** are listed in Table VIII. The sums of a_{ax}^H and a_{eq}^H at a given carbon atom (from Table VIII) are relatively constant for the semidiones and in the 19.5–21 G range for all of the radical anions except **50**. With the exception of **50** an undistorted half-chair structure is indicated for the semidione ring of these three radical anions. Structure **50** can be rationalized with the hfsc only if it is a highly distorted chair or possibly a boat conformation. A boat structure will have a very large axial hfsc and a very small equatorial hfsc (see **51**).

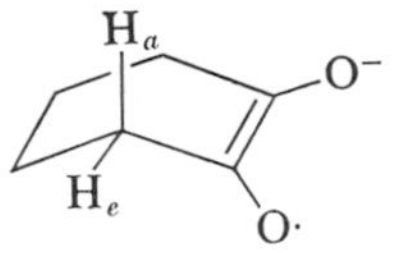

(51)

TABLE VIII

Hyperfine Splitting Constants (G) of Semidiones Formed from β-Decalones at 25° in DMSO.

Semidione	Position of Oxygen function	a_{ax}^{Ha}					a_{eq}^{Ha}			
		C-1	C-2	C-3	C-4	C-5	C-1	C-2	C-3	C-4
43	C-2,3	13.18			13.18		6.59			6.59
44	C-3,4		13.17			12.66		7.09		
45	C-2,3	13.83			12.72		7.37			6.55
46	C-2,3	12.40			13.05		7.11			5.77
47	C-2,3	12.37			13.11		6.83			6.83
48	C-3,4		13.32			12.40		8.14		
49	C-1,2			12.95					7.11	
50	C-3,4		19.75			8.21		4.33		

[a] Steroid numbering system employed, axial or equatorial relative to the A ring.

VII. SEMIDIONES DERIVED FROM STEROIDAL KETONES

A. 19-Nor-A-Ring Semidiones and 18-Nor-D-ring Semidiones

When 18-nor-D-homo and 19-nor steroids are considered it is of interest that the parent molecule possesses a point of symmetry. Thus in structure **52** the 3- and the 17-ketones are enantiomeric compounds and should

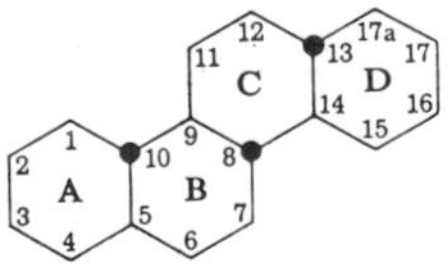

(52)

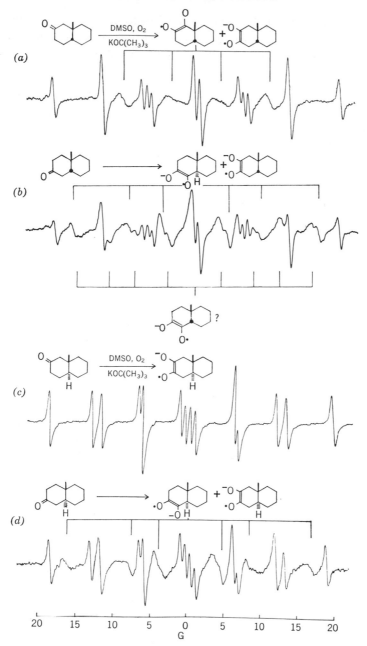

Fig. 7. ESR spectra of semidiones obtained in the oxidation of methyl-β-decalones in dimethyl sulfoxide solutions; (*a*) *cis*-9-methyl-2-decalone; (*b*) *cis*-9-methyl-3-decalone; (*c*) *trans*-9-methyl-2-decalone; and (*d*) *trans*-9-methyl-3-decalone.

yield identical ESR spectra. The 3- and 17-ketones give rise to identical mixtures of radical anions upon oxidation in basic solution as long as the partial structures shown for **53–60** are retained. The semidiones **53** and **54**

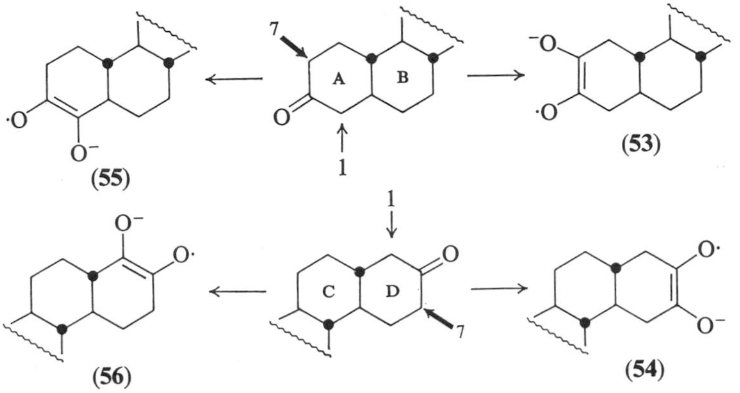

have identical hfsc, a^H = 13.44 (two) and 6.72 (two) G due to pairs of quasi-axial and quasi-equatorial hydrogen atoms in these *trans*-decalin derivatives. The semidiones **55** and **56** show hyperfine splitting by three different hydrogens, quasi-axial hydrogens at C-2 and C-5 (or C-13 and C-16), a^H = 13.70 and 12.88, and a quasi-equatorial hydrogen at C-2 or C-16, a^H = 7.12 G.

When the isomeric *cis*-A/B ($5\beta,10\beta$) or *cis*-C/D ($13\alpha,14\alpha$) ring fused ketones are considered, we find the major point of oxygenation is C-4 (or C-17a). The same difference between point of oxidation exists for the 19-nor-3-ketones and 18-nor-D-homo-17-keto steroids with *cis*- and *trans*-A/B or C/D ring junctions as for the simple *cis*- and *trans*-β-decalones.

Again, structures **57** and **58** have identical hfsc. For example, the specific structures **57a** and **58a** give the hfsc listed here.

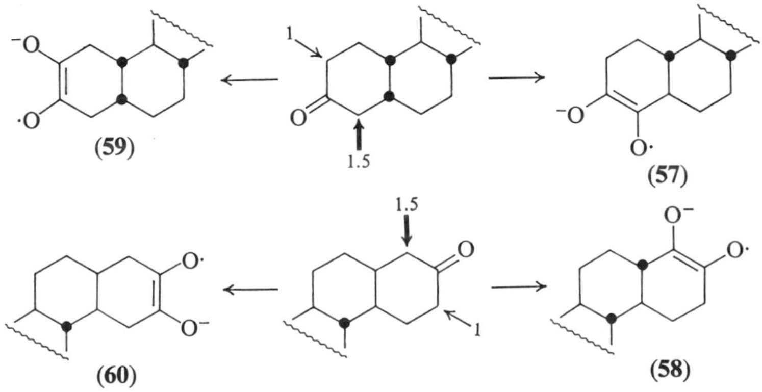

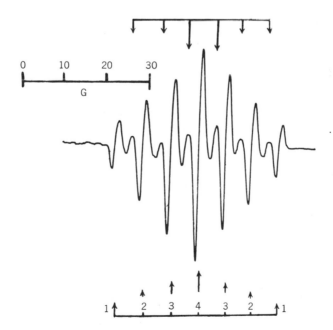

$a^H = 13.66, 12.89, 7.13G$

(57a)

$a^H = 13.75, 12.87, 7.10G$

(58a)

The hfsc of structures **59** and **60** are identical. Moreover, in this case since we are dealing with *cis*-decalin derivatives the alpha axial and equatorial hydrogen atoms are not equivalent and we see spectra due to four magnetically different hydrogen atoms, a^H = 14.34, 12.74, 8.20, and 5.20 G. Figures 8 and 9 give typical ESR spectra of the oxidation products of a 13β,14α-17-one and the isomeric 13α,14α-17-one. Comparison of the major semidiones from the *trans* ketone and the minor radical from the *cis* ketone allows the stereochemistry of the initial ring juncture to be specified without resort to empirical comparisons. Two pairs of equivalent α-hydrogens can give only a triplet of triplets, or as often observed in

Fig. 8. ESR spectrum of semidiones formed in the oxidation of 3-methoxy-D-homo-18,19-bisnorandrosta-1,3,5(10)-trien-17-one in dimethyl sulfoxide solution.

Fig. 9. ESR spectrum of semidiones formed in the oxidation of 3-methoxy-D-homo-18,19-bisnor-13α,14α-androsta-1,3,5(10)-trien-17-one in dimethyl sulfoxide solution.

cyclohexane derivatives, a 1:2:3:4:3:2:1 spectrum ($a_{ax}^H = 2a_{eq}^H$). Four magnetically nonequivalent hydrogens can give spectra containing 11–16 lines with an appropriate number of lines of double intensity (total intensity relative to wing peaks = 2^4).

Isomeric *cis*-fused 3- and 17-ketones can be distinguished in an empirical manner. The 3-keto-5β,10β-compounds give predominant attack at C-4. However, the 3-keto-5α,10α compounds give only attack at C-2. The hfsc for **61** are as expected, a^H = 13.90, 12.65, 7.75, and 6.56 G.

The effect of varying the stereochemistry at C-8 or C-9 was examined by comparing the oxidation products of **63** with appropriate 3- and 17-ketones. Epimerization at C-9 in the 5α,10α-3-ketone to give **63** has an

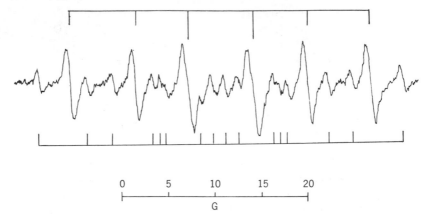

appreciable effect on the products of oxidation. Epimerization of C-9 in the 13α,14α-17-ketone to give **63** has no effect upon the oxidation products. Thus, we conclude that in these molecules the products of oxidation of a 3-ketone depends only on the stereochemistry at C-5, C-9, and C-10 and for the 17-ketones at C-8, C-13, and C-14.

The similarity of hfsc observed for 4-*t*-butylcyclohexane-1,2-semidione, the decalin semidiones **43** and **45** and the steroidal Δ²-semidiones **53**, **54**, **59**, and **60** is noteworthy. For the Δ²-semidiones in the steroid nucleus a boat conformation is impossible for the A ring because the B ring is locked in place. For the Δ²-semidione in the decalins a boat conformation is impossible for the *trans* ring fusion but may be introduced into the *cis* semidione if both rings assume the boat structure. The similarity of spectra and hfsc, and particularly the constancy of $a_{ax}^H + a_{eq}^H$ indicate that all of the semidiones have a half-chair structure and boat conformations can be eliminated. Boat conformations are possible for Δ¹-octalin derivatives and in semidione **64** there is evidence from hfsc that a boatlike conformation of the A ring is involved (44). Similarly, if the hfsc tentatively assigned to structure **50** are correct, some sort of a distorted boat structure must be involved.

(64)
$a^H = 13.08, 10.84, 5.95G$

(50)
$a^H = 19.75, 8.21, 4.33G$

We thus have a very useful technique for establishing the stereochemistry of the A/B or C/D ring junction for 2- or 3-keto-19-nor and 16- or 17-keto-D-homo steroids. Moreover, in appropriate cases the stereochemistry of the B/C ring juncture can also be specified.

The products of oxidation of steroidal 3-ketones (C-2 vs. C-4 attack) compare favorably with the products of alkylation, bromination, or enol acetate formation (44). Thus, observation of the nature of the mixture of semidiones formed is a good guide to which α-position will be reactive in ordinary chemical syntheses.

B. Steroidal A-Ring Semidiones Substituted at C-10

The steroidal ketones exist as rigid structures as far as the B/C rings are concerned. Before considering the semidiones produced upon oxidation it

is worthwhile to mention the geometry of the systems. The normal
steroid involves an all *trans* equatorial arrangement. Structure **65** shows
the geometry of the A, B, and C rings. A less common *cis* fusion of rings

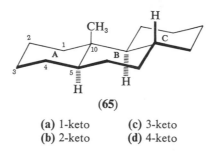

(65)

| (a) 1-keto | (c) 3-keto |
| (b) 2-keto | (d) 4-keto |

A and B is possible. The more common of these fusions involves the 5β,10β
structure, **66**. An abnormal *cis* fusion, 5α,10α is known and is shown in
structure **67**. These rigid geometries become conformations when applied

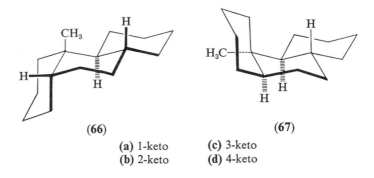

(66)   (67)

| (a) 1-keto | (c) 3-keto |
| (b) 2-keto | (d) 4-keto |

to the *cis*-9- and 10-methyl-2-decalones. For the *cis*-methyldecalones a
steroidlike conformation (like **66**) and a nonsteroid conformation (like **67**)
are possible. Structures **68–71** consider the possible conformations of
cis-9- and 10-methyl-2-decalones.

Oxidation of the 1-,2-,3-, and 4-ketones in both the *trans* series **(65)** and
in the normal *cis* series **(66)** have been examined. The 1-ketones give *cis*
and *trans*-$\Delta^{1,2}$-semidiones, but at much different rates. The *cis*-1-ketone
(5β,10β) **(66a)** immediately forms the semidione whereas the *trans*-1-
ketone (5α,10β) **(65a)** forms a semidione very slowly. The *cis*- and *trans*-4-
ketones **(65d, 66d)** both form a mixture of $\Delta^{3,4}$-semidiones containing
mainly the *trans* structure (5α), but with a minor amount (15%) of the
cis structure (5β).

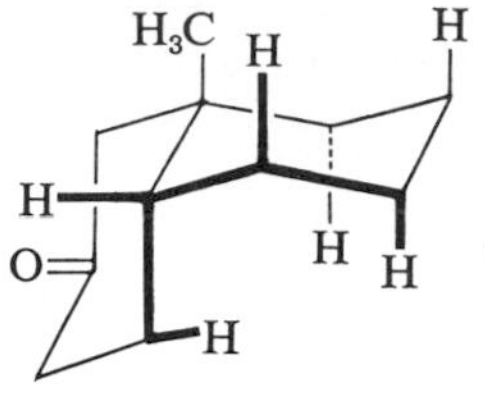

(68) (69) Steroid conformations

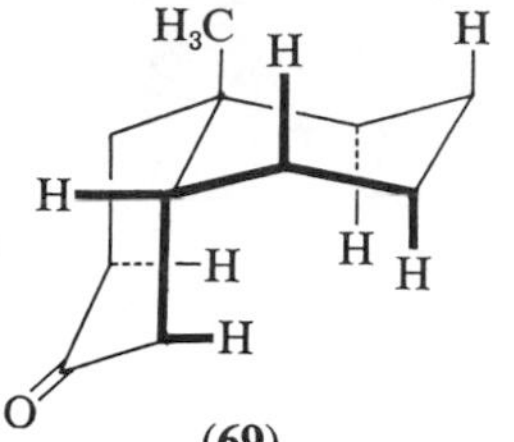

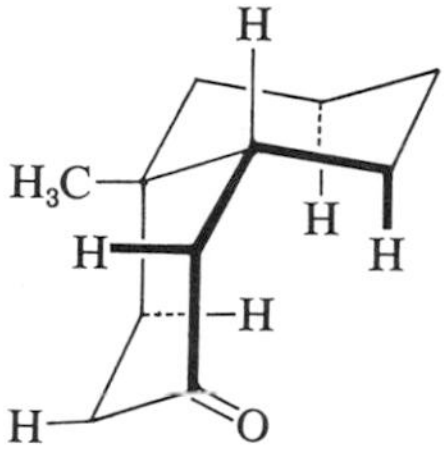

(70) (71) Nonsteroid conformations

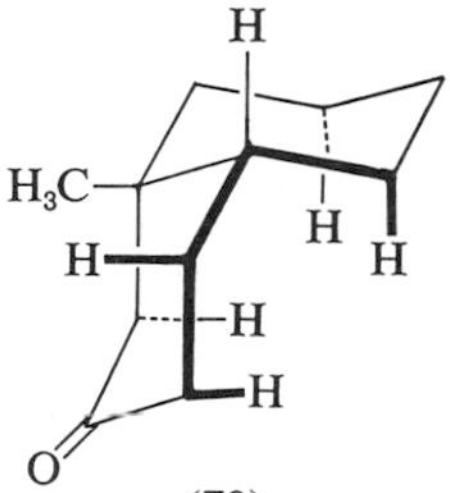

cis-9-methyl-2-decalone cis-10-methyl-2-decalone

The *cis-* and *trans-*2- and 3-ketones can be readily distinguished from the ESR spectra of the oxidation products (Fig. 10). The *trans-*2-ketone (**65b**) gives 100% oxygenation at C-3 and thus behaves like *trans-*9-methyl-2-decalone.

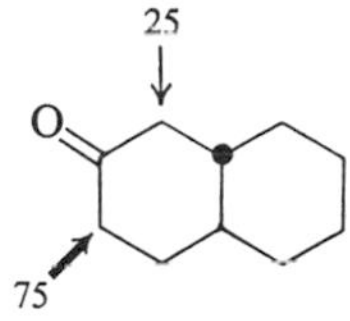

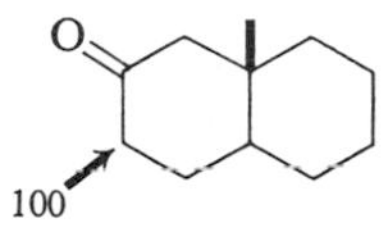

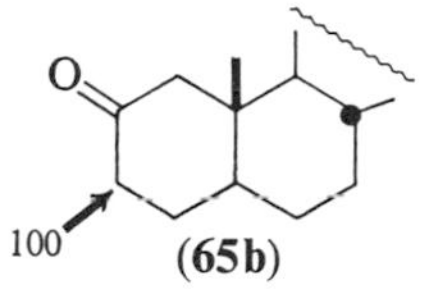

(65b)

The *cis-*2-ketone (5β,10β) (**66b**) gives > 60% oxygenation at C-1 and re-sembles *cis-*β-decalone, but not *cis-*9-methyl-2-decalone.

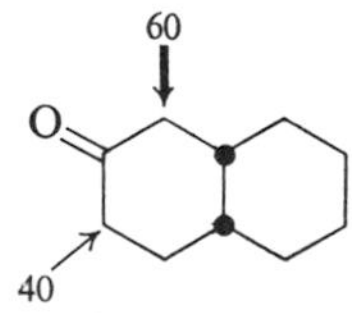

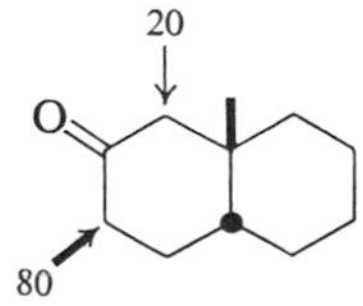

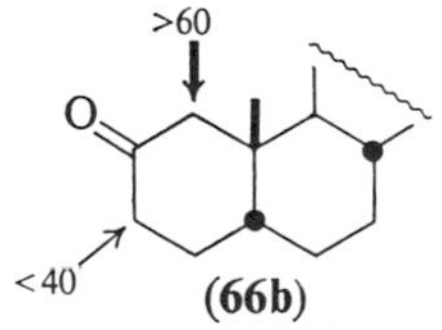

(66b)

When the abnormal 2-keto steroid (**72**) was examined it was found that the major point of oxygenation was at C-3, as in the *cis-*9-methyl-2-decalone, and that furthermore the ESR spectra of the $\Delta^{2,3}$-semidiones

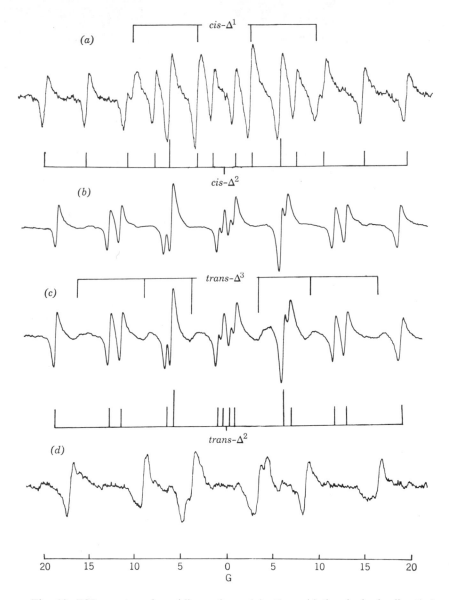

Fig. 10. ESR spectra of semidiones formed in the oxidation in basic dimethyl sulfoxide solution of 2- and 3-keto-*cis*- and *trans*-A/B ring fused steroids; (*a*) 5β-spirostan-2-one; (*b*) 5α-androstan-17β-ol-2-one; (*c*) 5α-androstan-17β-ol-3-one; and (*d*) 5β-androstan-17β-ol-3-one.

were nearly identical in hfsc. It appears that *cis*-9-methyl-2-decalone has a conformation similar to the rigid geometry of structure **72**, i.e., the

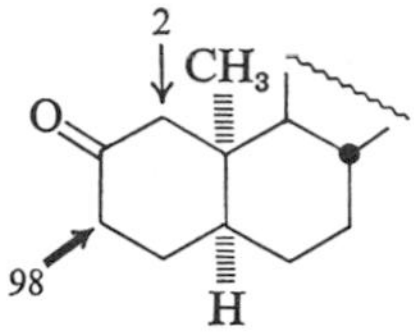

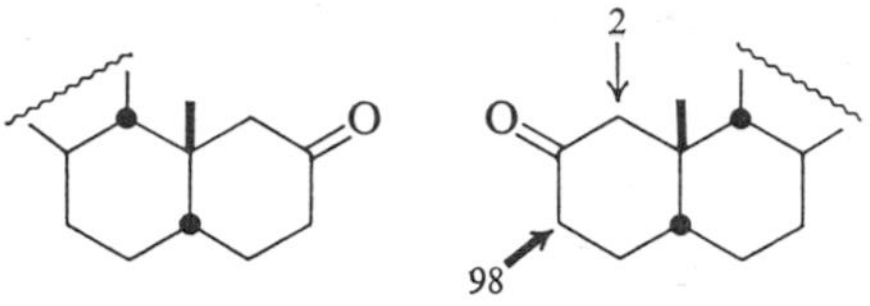

Enantiomeric structures

(72)   **(72E)**

nonsteroidal conformation (**70**). Again we note that epimerization at C-9 has a major effect on the point of oxygenation (compare **72E** with **66b**).

The *trans*-3-ketone, **65c**, gives major oxygenation (92%) at C-3 and only minor oxygenation at C-4. The *trans*-3-ketone behaves similar to β-decalone, the 19-nor-3-keto steroids, and to *trans*-10-methyl-2-decalone.

Epimerization at C-9 has a large effect on the point of oxygenation while epimerization at C-8 has little effect (compare **73E** and **74E** with **65c**). Obviously the *trans*-β-decalone and *trans*-2-keto-10-methyldecalin have conformations similar to the rigid structure **65c**.

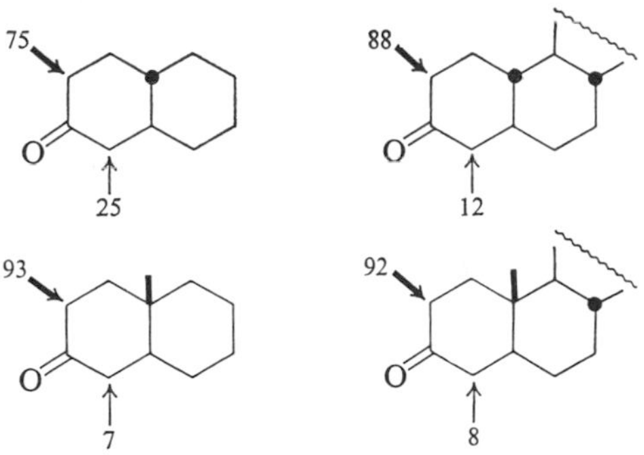

(65c)

cis-3-Keto steroids (5β,10β) **66c**, give predominant oxygenation at C-4 as does *cis*-β-decalone, and *cis*-3-keto-19-nor steroids. However, *cis*-2-keto-10-methyl decalin gives predominant oxidation at C-2, suggesting an abnormal steroid conformation (**71**).

Epimerization at C-8 has little effect upon the point of oxygenation (compare **75E** and **66c**).

The *cis*-9,10-dimethyl-2-decalone, **76**, and the 3-keto steroid (5β,10β), **77**, have been examined. Again we find a great difference in the point of attack suggesting that the decalone exists in the nonsteroid conformation (**71**).

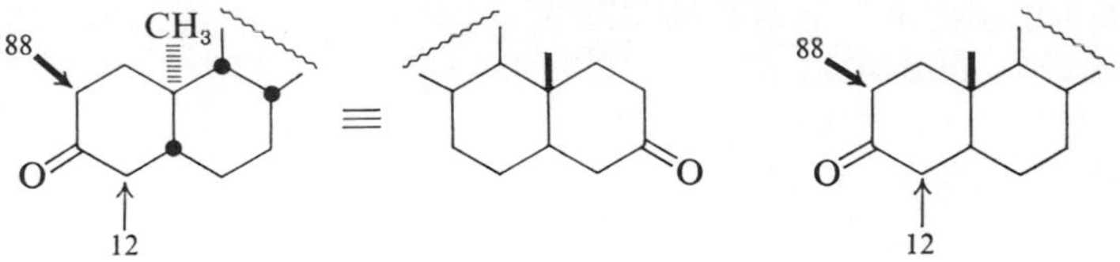

$\equiv$

(73)   (73E)

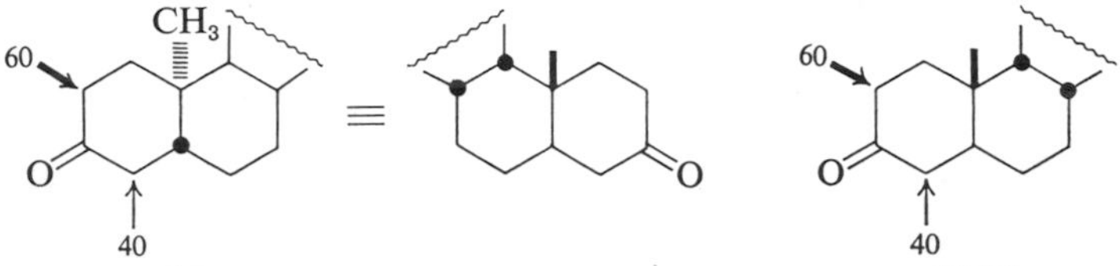

(74)   (74E)

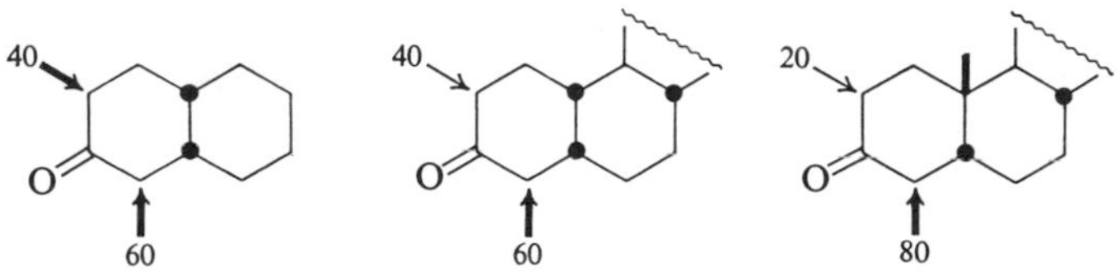

(66 c)

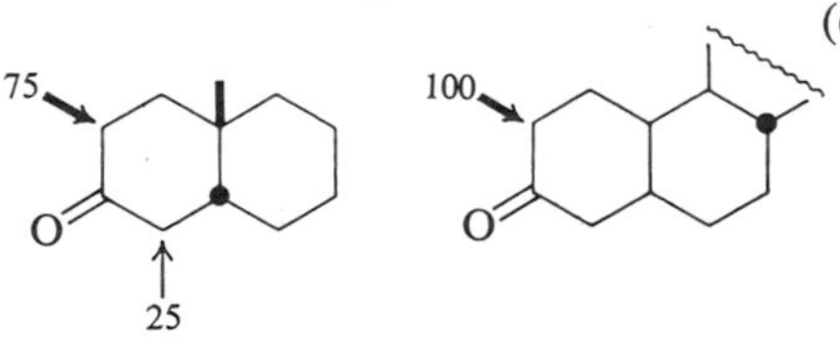

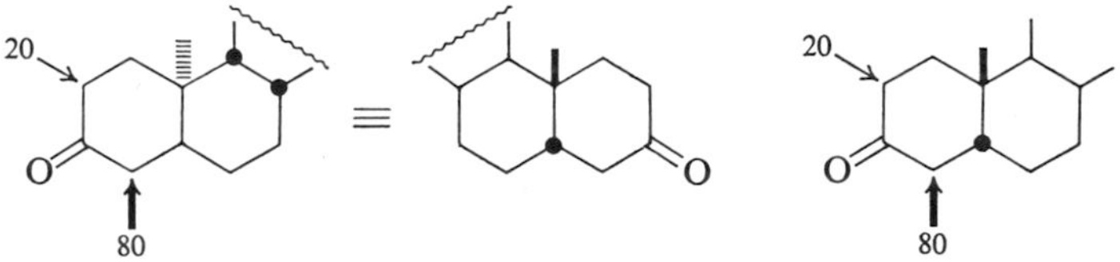

(75)   (75E)

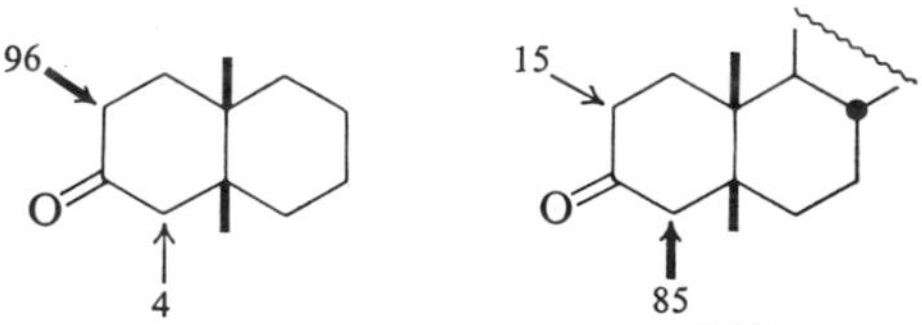

(76)   (77)

The detailed reasons for the preferred point of oxygenation have been discussed elsewhere (45).

It is obvious that ESR spectroscopy of the semidiones produced by oxygenation in basic solution of steroidal ketones cannot only provide information about the positional and geometric structure, but can also provide information about the conformations of the methyl-decalones. Moreover, the ratios of semidiones observed in oxygenation of steroidal ketones agree well with synthetic base-catalyzed alkylations, brominations, etc., and can be used as a guide to the course of a synthetic reaction of this type (45).

Table IX summarizes the hfsc of the steroidal semidiones.

C. D-Ring Steroidal Semidiones

The oxidation in basic solution of ketones **78** and **79** have been studied (71). Compounds **79a** and **79b** yield the same semidione with hyperfine

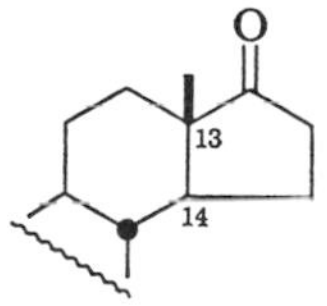

(78a) 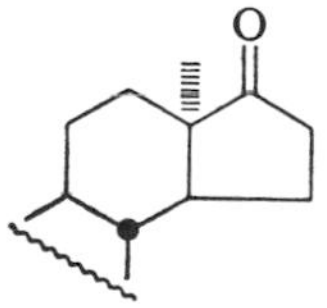   (78b) 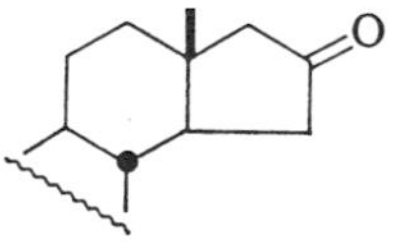   (79a) 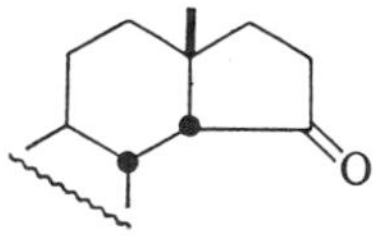   (79b)

splitting by three magnetically different hydrogen atoms to which structure **80** is assigned. For **79a** epimerization at C-14 has occurred to yield the

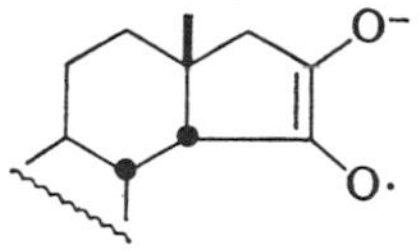

(80)

more stable *cis*-C/D ring junction. Similarly the A-nor ketones (4α or 4β) (**81**) yielded semidiones **82** from exclusive attack at C-3.

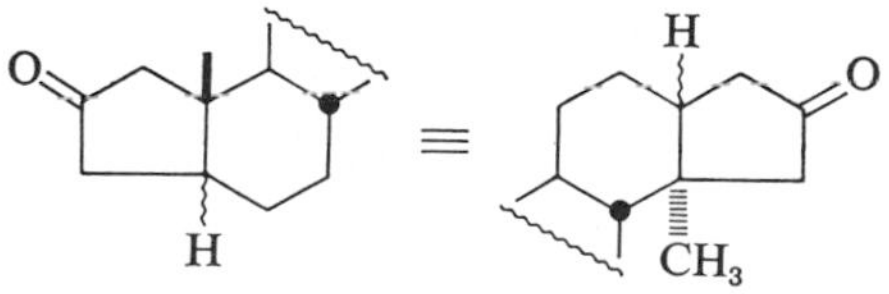

(81) 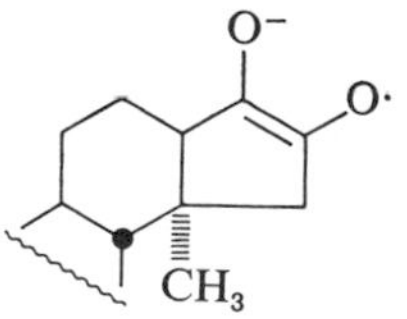   (82)

TABLE IX

Hyperfine Splitting Constants of Some Steroidal Semidiones

Parent ketone	Semidione %	a_{ax}^H (Position)	a_{eq}^H (Position)
65a	5α-$\Delta^{1,2}$ (100)	12.29 (C-3)	7.19 (C-3)
66a	5β-$\Delta^{1,2}$ (100)	13.18 (C-3)	7.54 (C-3)
65b	5α-$\Delta^{2,3}$ (100)	12.37, 13.00 (C-1,4)	7.16, 5.81 (C-1,4)
66b	5β-$\Delta^{1,2}$ (> 60)	13.18 (C-3)	7.54 (C-3)
	5β-$\Delta^{2,3}$ (< 40)	12.19, 14.00 (C-1,4)	9.08, 4.79 (C-1,4)
65c	5α-$\Delta^{2,3}$ (92)	12.37, 13.00 (C-1,4)	7.16, 5.81 (C-1,4)
	5α-$\Delta^{3,4}$ (8)	13.23, 12.43 (C-2,5)	8.44 (C-2)
66c	5β-$\Delta^{2,3}$ (19)	12.19, 14.00 (C-1,4)	9.08, 4.79 (C-1,4)
	5β-$\Delta^{3,4}$ (~ 5)	13.2, 12.0 (C-2,5)	6.6 (C-2)
	5α-$\Delta^{3,4}$ (76)	13.23, 12.43 (C-2,5)	8.07 (C-2)
65d } 66d }	5α-$\Delta^{3,4}$ (84)	13.23, 12.43 (C-2,5)	8.07 (C-2)
	5β - $\Delta^{0,1}$ (16)	13.2, 12.0 (C-2,5)	6.6 (C-2)
72	$5\alpha,10\alpha$-$\Delta^{1,2}$ (2)	12.80 (C-3)	7.58 (C-3)
	$5\alpha,10\alpha$-$\Delta^{2,3}$ (98)	12.17, 12.90 (C-1,4)	6.86, 6.86 (C-1,4)
73	$5\beta,8\beta,9\beta,$ 10α-$\Delta^{2,3}$ (88)	11.89, 12.47 (C-1,4)	6.99, 5.58 (C-1,4)
	$5\beta,8\beta,9\beta,$ 10α-$\Delta^{3,4}$ (12)	12.73, 12.73 (C-2,5)	7.68 (C-2)
74	$5\beta,8\alpha,9\alpha,$ 10α-$\Delta^{2,3}$ (60)	12.65, 12.65 (C-1,4)	5.04, 7.49 (C-1,4)
	$5\beta,8\alpha,9\alpha,$ 10α-$\Delta^{3,4}$ (40)	12.67, 12.67 (C-2,5)	7.55 (C-2)
75	$5\alpha,8\beta,9\beta,$ 10α-$\Delta^{2,3}$ (~ 20)	Spectrum not resolved.	
	$5\beta,8\beta,9\beta,$ 10α-$\Delta^{3,4}$ (~ 80)	12.73, 12.73 (C-2,5)	7.68 (C-2)
76	$\Delta^{2,3}$ (96)	12.85, 13.22 (C-1,4)	6.88, 6.88 (C-1,4)
	$\Delta^{1,2}$ (4)	12.74 (C-3)	7.22 (C-3)
77	$5\beta,10\beta$-$\Delta^{2,3}$ (15)	13.35, 12.32 (C-1,4)	7.44, 5.56 (C-1,4)
	$5\beta,10\beta$-$\Delta^{3,4}$ (85)	12.40 (C-2)	7.22 (C-2)

Surprisingly **78a** and **78b** give very different ESR spectra upon oxidation. The *trans*-17-ketone yielded a 1:2:3:4:3:2:1 pattern consistent with two pairs of α-hydrogen atoms while the *cis*-17-ketone gave two major doublet splittings consistent with structure **83**.

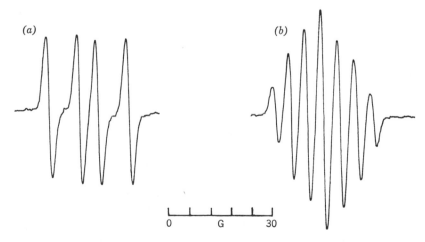

(83) **(84)**

Treatment of the 16-hydroxy derivative of **78a** with base, or reduction of the 16,17-diketone with propiophenone anion, yielded a different spectrum than oxidation of the monoketone. A four-line spectrum similar to structure **83** was observed and to which structure **84** is logically assigned. The spectrum resulting from oxidation of **78a** is also formed from a mixture of **78a** and the 16,17-diketone and must be due to the dimerization product, **85**. Treatment of **85** with excess oxygen will eventually convert

$$78a \xrightarrow[O_2]{B^-} \quad\quad\quad \xrightarrow[B^-]{78a}$$

(85)

the seven-line ESR spectrum to the four-line spectrum assigned to **84**. These observations define a new method for assigning the stereochemistry

(a) *(b)*

0		G		30	

Fig. 11. Oxidation products of 17-keto steroids in basic dimethyl sulfoxide solutions; (a) 3β-hydroxy-13α,14α-androst-5-en-17-one; (b) 5α-androstan-17-one.

at C-14 to a C-17 ketone. Figure 11 gives typical spectra of **85** and **83** obtained by oxidation of **78a** and **78b**, respectively. Table X lists the hfsc observed for these semidiones.

TABLE X

Hyperfine Splitting Constants of Semidiones Derived from
D-Ring Ketones

Semidione	hfsc, a^H, G
80	16.29, 14.25, 8.35
82	16.17, 14.29, 8.30
83	14.23, 8.80
84	12.67, 7.18, plus additional hyperfine structure
85	9.34, 9.34, 4.67, 4.67

VIII. SEMIDIONES DERIVED FROM BICYCLOHEXANES

Of the three bicyclohexanones capable of yielding a semidione upon oxidation, only the bicyclo[3.1.0]hexan-2- and 3-ones yield stable paramagnetic oxidation product. Semidione **86** shows hfsc by all six of the hydrogen atoms, $a^H = 14.9, 7.86, 4.0, 4.0, 0.79$, and 0.79 G (71). These are assigned to *exo*-C-4, *endo*-C-4, C-1, *anti*-C-6, C-5, and *syn*-C-6, respectively. This assignment was made possible by a study of the derivatives shown in Table XI.

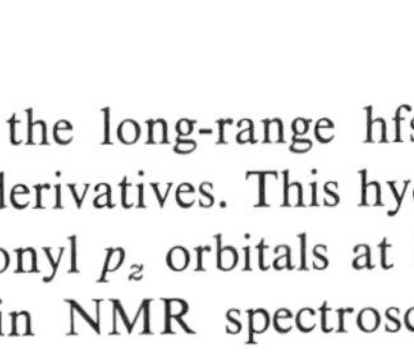

(**86**)

Of particular interest is the long-range hfs of a 4–5 G for the *anti*-hydrogen at C-6 in **86** and derivatives. This hydrogen atom is in a *W*-plan arrangement with the carbonyl p_z orbitals at C-2. Such long-range splittings are well recognized in NMR spectroscopy (10–12) and in other bicyclic semidiones (6,8).

TABLE XI
Hyperfine Splitting Constants of Substituted Bicyclo[3.1.0]-Hexan-2,3-Semidione

Substituents	a^H	Assignments
1-Isopropyl-*endo*-4-methyl	6.20, 4.80, 0.82, 0.58	*Exo*-C-4, *anti*-C-6, C-5, *syn*-C-6
1-Isopropyl-*exo*-4-methyl	13.85, 4.90, 0.70, 0.58	*Endo*-C-4, *anti*-C-6, C-5, *syn*-C-6
1-Isopropyl-4,4-dimethyl	4.83	*Anti*-C-6
6,6-Dimethyl	14.59, 7.62, 5.08, 0.90, $a^H_{CH_3} = 0.45$	*Endo*-C-4, *exo*-C-4, C-1, C-5, *anti*-C-6 methyl

IX. SEMIDIONES DERIVED FROM BICYCLOHEPTANES

Three of the six possible bicycloheptane semidiones have been examined (**87**-**89**). The cyclopentene derivative, **87**, does not apparently

show a long-range coupling since only $a^H = 16.6$, 11.0, and 11.0 G are observed. The bicyclo[3.1.1]heptene derivative (**88**) shows hfs by two hydrogens, exchangeable in d_6–DMSO and therefore assigned to position 4, $a^H = 9.46$ and 9.04 G, another doublet splitting of 3.88 G, possibly the *anti*-hydrogen (*W*-plan) at C-7 and a sextet (0.42 G) due to the *anti*-methyl group at C-6, the bridgehead hydrogen at C-1, and the *syn*-hydrogen at C-7.

Derivatives of bicyclo[2.2.1]heptane have been extensively investigated (6). The spectrum of the parent semidione, **89**, prepared by reductions of the 2,3-dione, is shown in Figure 12. The ESR spectrum requires doublet splittings of 6.47 (*anti*-C-7) and 0.41 (*syn*-C-7) G and a quintet splitting from four magnetically equivalent hydrogen atoms of 2.49 G (*exo*-C-5,6, C-1,4). These assignments were made to be consistent with the spectra of numerous derivatives of **89** listed in Table XII.

In structure **89** the three hydrogens in a *W*-plan with the carbonyl p_z orbital show a strong interaction, particularly the *anti*-hydrogen at C-7

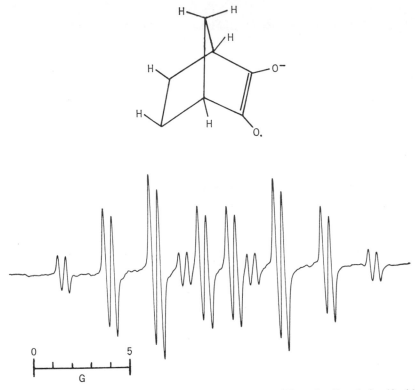

Fig. 12. ESR spectrum of bicyclo[2.2.1]heptane-2,3-semidione in dimethyl sulfoxide solution.

which is in a double *W*-arrangement with C-2 and C-3, suggesting that the long-range interactions actually involve partial bonding between the carbonyl p_z orbital and C-7, C-5, and C-6, such as structures **90** and **91**.

These interactions can be considered to be homohyperconjugation and are related to homoenolization (72). Structures similar to **90** or **91** make contributions of approximately $6.34/508 = 1\%$ (**90**) and $2(2.49)/508 = 1\%$ (**91**) (two structures).

TABLE XII
Hyperfine Splitting Constants of Bicyclo[2.2.1]heptane-2,3-Semidiones

Substituent	Assigned hyperfine splitting constants						
	C-1	C-4	C-5	C-6	anti-C-7	syn-C-7	methyl
None	2.49	2.49	2.49 (exo)	2.49 (exo)	6.47	0.41	—
exo-C5,6-dideuterio	2.49	2.49	0.40 (exo)[a]	0.40 (exo)[a]	6.48	0.40	—
1-Methyl	—	2.51	2.51 (exo)	2.51 (exo)	6.29	0.46	—
1,syn-7-Dimethyl	—	2.55	2.55 (exo)	2.55 (exo)	3.05	—	0.18, 0.18
7,7-Dimethyl	2.07	2.07	2.90 (exo) 0.26 (endo)	2.90 (exo) 0.26 (endo)	—	—	0.53 (syn-7)
7,7-Dimethoxy	1.99	1.99	2.59 (exo)	2.59 (exo)	—	—	—
1,4,7,7-Tetramethyl			3.0 (exo)	3.0 (exo)			
1,7,7-Trimethyl		2.08	3.01 (exo) 0.22 (endo)	3.01 (exo)			0.55 (syn-7) 0.15
endo, endo-5,6-Dimethyl	2.33	2.33	—	—	6.97	0.40	0.20

[a] a^D

Semidiones in the bicyclo[2.2.1] system can be prepared by oxidation of only those monoketones that have a *syn*-methyl group at C-7. This substituent greatly facilitates the synthesis of 2,3-diketones in this ring system by conventional methods, such as oxidation with selenium dioxide. For the derivatives without a *syn*-7-methyl substituent the semidione can be prepared by treatment of the 2,3-diketone with propiophenone enolate anion.

X. SEMIDIONES DERIVED FROM BICYCLOOCTANES

Of the numerous possible bicyclooctane semidiones, four have been examined, structures **92–95**.

The ESR spectrum of structure **92** appears to be quite normal. Values of the hfsc are 15.4, 13.8, and 13.8 G and are undoubtedly due to the three α-hydrogen atoms.

Bicyclo[2.2.2]octane derivatives have been more thoroughly investigated (6). The parent system (**93**) shows a quintet splitting of 2.09 G assigned to the *anti*-hydrogens at C-5, 6, 7, and 8. This assignment was made on the basis of the spectra of the substituted derivatives given in Table XIII.

The quartet splitting observed for structure **96** is in complete accord with the suggested long-range hfs via a *W*-plan interaction and suggests

TABLE XIII
Hyperfine Splitting Constants of Substituted Bicyclo[2.2.2]Octane-2,3-Semi-diones

Substituent	a^H (Assignment)
None	2.09, 2.09, 2.09, 2.09 (*anti*-C-5,6,7,8)
1-Methyl-4-methoxy	2.14, 2.14, 2.14, 2.14 (*anti*-C-5,6,7,8)
syn-5,6-Dimethyl	2.12, 2.12 (*anti*-C-7,8); 1.34, 1.34 (*anti*-C,5,6)
Atisine (**96**)	2.20, 2.20, 2.20 (*anti*-hydrogens)
97a	2.28, 2.28 (*anti*-C-3,4); 0.29, 0.29 (Aromatic hydrogens)
97b	0.15 (eight equal) (Aromatic hydrogens)

the possible use of this interaction for structural assignments in bicyclo-octane derivatives.

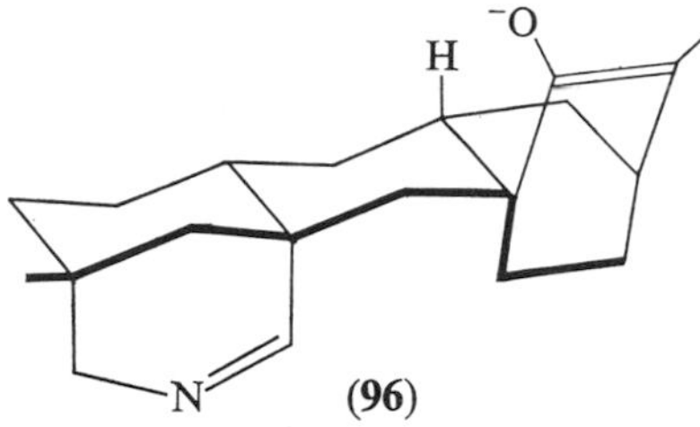

(96) 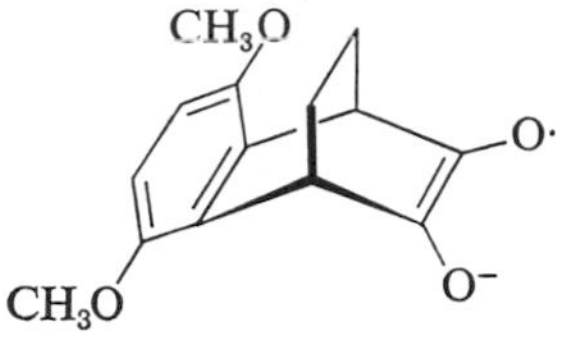   (97a)

The unsaturated derivatives of structure **93** are very interesting. The $\Delta^{5,6}$-olefin (Fig. 13) shows a very large triplet splitting of 2.62 G, undoubted-ly associated with the *anti*-hydrogens at C–7,8. The spectrum is unaltered by substitution of deuterium at C–1,4. Thus, the 0.14 G quintet splitting is due to the vinyl hydrogens and the *syn*-hydrogens at C–7,8.

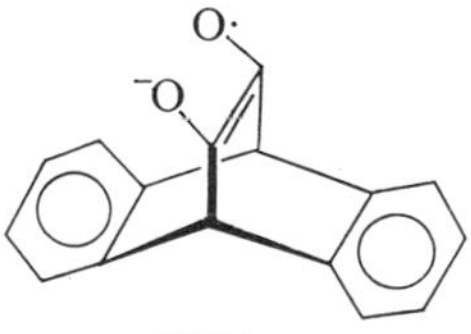

(97b)

Bicyclo[2.2.2]octane-2,3-semidione and derivatives are best prepared by reduction of the 2,3-diketones or oxidation of the α-hydroxy ketones. Oxidation of bicyclo[2.2.2]octan-2-one in DMSO solutions of potassium *t*-butoxide generally gives another radical anion presumed to be **14**. This dimeric structure shows hfs by the two types (four each) of *anti*-hydrogen atoms, $a^H = 1.50$ and 1.09 G. It appears that the spin density is about 50% greater at C-1 than at C-2 in structure **14**. The dimeric semidione can also be formed by mixing the 2-one and the 2,3-dione in basic solution. It is interesting that oxidation of the 2-one in d_6-DMSO solution yields the monomeric semidione. It appears in the oxidation of this ketone that the diketone is probably not an important intermediate prior to formation of the monomeric semidione. The effect of d_6-DMSO then can be rational-ized as follows:

$$RCOCH_2R \xrightarrow[B^-]{d_6\text{-DMSO}} RCOCD_2R \xrightarrow[O_2]{B^-} RCOCD(OOD)R$$

$$RCOCD(OOD)R \left[\begin{array}{l} \xrightarrow{B^-} RCOCOR + DB + OD^- \\ \xrightarrow[B^-]{DMSO} RCOCD(OD)R + DMSO_2 \end{array} \right.$$

$$RCOCD(OD)R \xrightarrow[O_2]{B^-} RC(O\cdot)=C(O^-)R$$

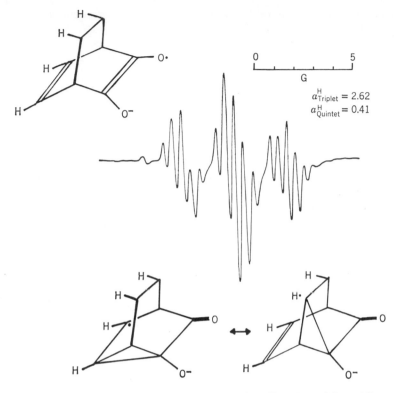

$a^H_{Triplet} = 2.62$

$a^H_{Quintet} = 0.41$

Fig. 13. First derivative ESR spectrum of bicyclo[2.2.2]oct-5-ene-2,3-semidione in dimethyl sulfoxide solution at 25°.

As illustrated, decomposition of the initial oxidation product, RCOCH(OOH)R, in DMSO can lead mainly to diketone which must condense readily with the monoketone. In d_6-DMSO the intermediate, RCOCD(OOD)R, would be much less prone to this type of decomposition; reduction to give the alcohol, and hence the semidione, is the preferred reaction course. In line with this observation is the fact that mixtures of camphor and camphorquinone give low concentrations of the semidione (3). Concentrations approximately ten times greater can be obtained by oxidation of camphor in basic solution, a process that must form the intermediate α-hydroxy ketone.

Semidiones in the bicyclo[3.2.1]octane family have been examined because of interest in long-range interactions and because a number of naturally occurring substances contain this carbocyclic ring system (e.g., kaurene, phyllocladene, stachenone, garryine, steriol, hibaene, and giberellic acid).

Semidione **94** is formed readily by oxidation of the 6-ketone. It gives an ESR spectrum showing a 5.51 G triplet splitting, a 4.03 G doublet splitting, and a 0.53 G sextet splitting. The garryine derivative, **98**, shows only two major splittings, $a^H = 5.14$ and 3.83 G. It has developed that the

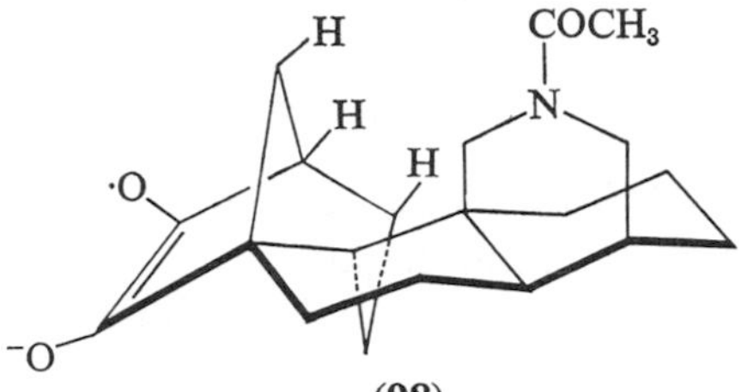

(98)

simple norketones from kaurene or phyllocladene do not oxidize to yield a semidione in basic solution and derivatives similar to **98** must apparently be prepared via α-hydroxy ketones or diketones.

It should be pointed out that at the present time it is not known if an epimer of **96**, such as **99**, would show a long-range W-plane splitting of the *exo*-methine hydrogen atom. It may be that in **99** the bonds to the bridgehead carbon and to the methine carbon prevent the long-range interaction

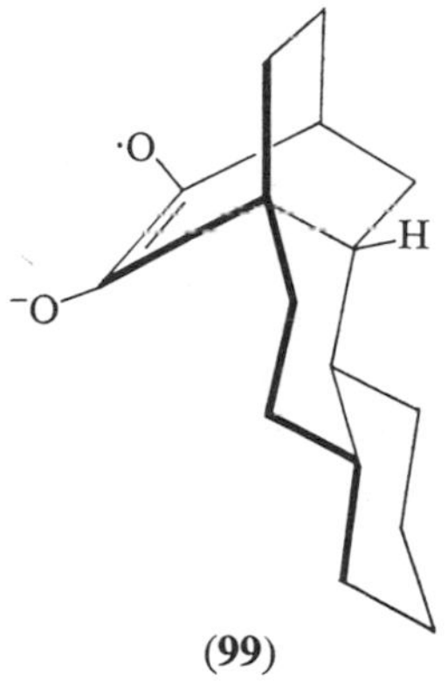

(99)

from occurring (73). If so, this could be taken as evidence in favor of a through space interaction. Unfortunately there may be significant changes in dihedral angles in going from structure **93** to **99** that present an additional complication. The *anti*-hydrogen hfs in **100, 101,** and **102** are very suggestive of an effect wherein alkyl substitution greatly decreases the ability of a carbon atom to participate in long-range interactions (73).

The semidione **95** gives a rich hyperfine spectrum with $a^H = 13.5$, 8.69, 3.45, 2.13, 1.42, 0.28, and 0.28 G. The 1,8,8-trimethyl derivative gives $a^H = 12.5$, 8.4, and 4.1 G due to the α-hydrogens at C-4 (12.5 and 8.4 G,

(100)   **(101)**   **(102)**

exchangeable in d_6-DMSO) and the *exo*-hydrogen at C-7. The 2.13 and
1.42 G splittings in **95** are assigned to the *anti*-hydrogen at C-8 and the
bridgehead hydrogen at C-1. The 0.28 G splittings are apparently due to
the *syn*-hydrogen at C-8 and the *exo*-hydrogen at C-7. The unsaturated
derivative of **95**, compound **103**, gives $a^H = 8.74$, 7.70, 2.66, 1.20, 0.71,
0.49, 0.14, and 0.14 G. Apparently considerable spin is transmitted from
C-2 to C-7 via overlap of p orbitals.

(103)

XI. SEMIDIONES DERIVED FROM BICYCLONONANES

Semidiones **104, 105**, and **106** have been prepared by oxidation of the
appropriate ketones. Semidione **104** gives $a^H = 14.6$, 9.2, and 9.2 G. The
cis-1,2,2,6-tetramethyl derivative yields $a^H = 14.1$ and 8.6 G. Apparently
in **104** the hydrogens at C-7 are not equivalent.

(104)   **(105)**   **(106)**

Semidione **105** gives a very symmetrical spectrum with $a^H = 10.5$, 10.5,
2.2, and 2.2 G. The hydrogens involved are the α-hydrogens at C-4
(exchangeable in d_6-DMSO) and the *anti*-hydrogens at C-7 and C-8.
Since there is no bridgehead hydrogen hfs and since time averaging cannot
yield a dihedral angle of 90 or 0°, the conformation of **105** must be
symmetrical.

Semidione **106** gives a complex spectrum with $a^H = 12.74, 6.93, 3.35,$ 1.96, and 0.56 G. The two larger hfs are exchangeable in d_6-DMSO and must be the hydrogens at C-4. Probably the *anti*-hydrogen at C-9 and the bridgehead hydrogen are involved. The 7β-methyl derivative of compound **106** yields $a^H = 12.78, 8.00, 3.40,$ and 1.60 G suggesting a long-range splitting by the *exo*-hydrogen at C-7. Semidione **107** was prepared from a lycopodine alkaloid. It gave $a^H = 14.14$ and 3.69 G. These hydrogens are probably those labeled H_1 and H_2.

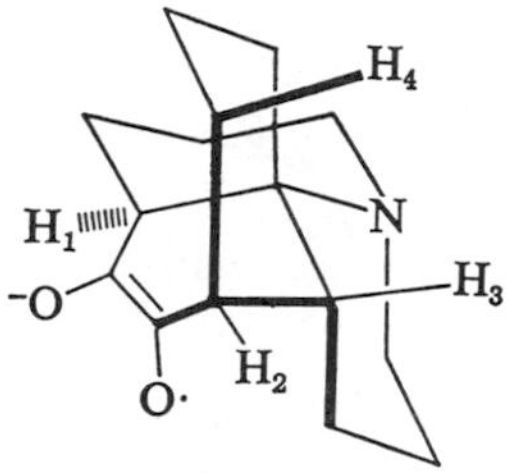

(107)

XII. SEMITRIONES AND SEMITETRAONES

By far the most stable members of these series are the radical anions formed by the base-catalyzed dissociation of hydrindantin or alloxantin. These radical anions can be prepared in aqueous solution. Semitrione **13**

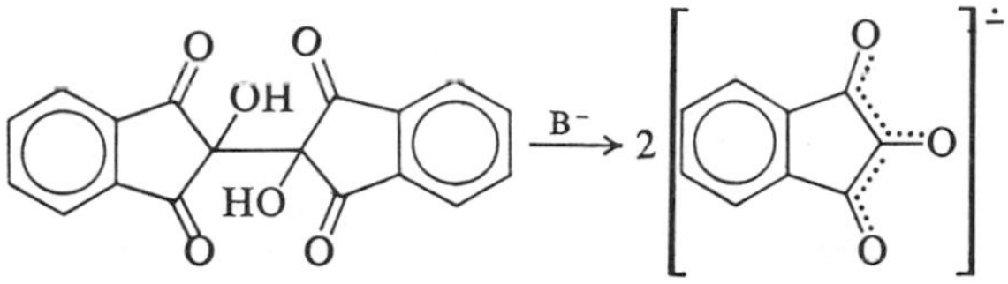

(13)

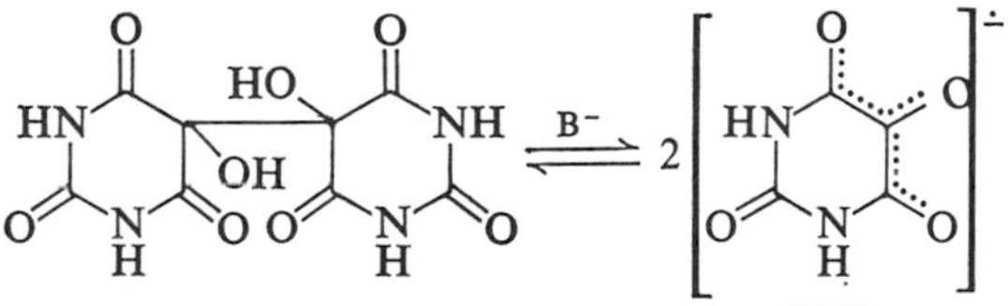

(108)

can also be prepared by the reduction of ninhydrin. In DMSO containing excess base the dissociation of hydrindantin to **13** is nearly complete. Radical anion **108** can be prepared by the oxidation of dialuric acid or by the reduction of alloxan. In DMSO the dissociation of alloxantin at $[KOC(CH_3)_3]_\infty$ is such as to yield a dissociation constant of 2–3×10^{-4} (42).

Attempts to prepare **109** from the corresponding triketone led to the production of **12**, which is also obtained by the reduction of acenaphthene quinone (41) or by disproportionation of an α-hydroxy ketone.

(109)

Reaction of benzil radical anion with diphenyltriketone in DMSO yields **110**. Hydroxy radicals generated

$$[C_6H_5COCOC_6H_5]^{\cdot -} + C_6H_5COCOCOC_6H_5 \longrightarrow$$
$$[C_6H_5COCOC_6H_5 + [C_6H_5COCOCOC_6H_5]^{\cdot -}$$
(110)

$a_o^H = a_p^H = 0.54\ G$ $\qquad\qquad\qquad a_o^H = a_p^H = 1.04\ G$

$a_m^H = 0.17\ G$ $\qquad\qquad\qquad\qquad a_m^H = 0.34\ G$

from hydrogen peroxide and peroxidase will convert reductive acid and triose reductone to radical anions **16** and **17** which have $a^H(water) = 6.3$ and 3.6 G, respectively. Similar treatment of dihydroxyfumaric acid is reported to yield **15**, $a^H = 2.4\ G$.

Although semitriones may be thermodynamically more stable than semidiones, it appears that decomposition mechanisms are available to the semitriones which makes them hard to observe except in five-membered rings (**1, 13, 10,** and **16**) wherein ring contractions to a four-membered ring would be highly unlikely.

Acknowledgment

Co-workers not completely cited in the bibliography were E. Thomas Strom, Erach R. Talaty, Kuo-Yuan Chang, Maria C. Young, Robert D. Stephens, Robert Horrocks, Graham Underwood, George Holland, Philip R. Whittle, Stephen A. Weiner, Herbert Malkus, David C. Lini, and John McDonnell.

This work was supported primarily by the National Science Foundation and by the Petroleum Research Fund, administered by the American Chemical Society in the form of an unrestricted research grant.

Much of this work would not have been possible except for the generous donation of samples of bicyclic ketones from many workers in the natural products area, and in particular from G. D. Searle and Co. and Shinogi and Co., Ltd.

References

1. G. A. Russell, E. R. Talaty, and M. C. Young, *J. Phys. Chem.*, **70**, 1321 (1966).
2. I. Yamazaki and L. H. Piette, *J. Am. Chem. Soc.*, **87**, 986 (1965).
3. I. Yamazaki, H. S. Mason, and L. Piette, *J. Biol. Chem.*, **235**, 2444 (1960).
4. C. Lagercrantz, *Acta Chim. Scand.*, **18**, 562 (1964).
5. G. A. Russell, E. T. Strom, E. R. Talaty, K.-Y. Chang, R. D. Stephens, and M. C. Young, *Record Chem. Progr.* (*Kresge-Hooker Sci. Lib.*), **27**, 3 (1966).
6. G. A. Russell and K.-Y. Chang, *J. Am. Chem. Soc.*, **87**, 4381 (1965).
7. G. A. Russell and R. D. Stephens, *J. Phys. Chem.*, **70**, 1320 (1966).
8. G. A. Russell, K.-Y. Chang, and C. W. Jefford, *J. Am. Chem. Soc.*, **87**, 4383 (1965).
9. D. Kosman and L. M. Stock, *J. Am. Chem. Soc.*, **88**, 843 (1966).
10. J. Meinwald and A. Lewis, *J. Am. Chem. Soc.*, **83**, 2769 (1961).
11. C. W. Jefford, B. Waegell, and K. Ramey, *J. Am. Chem. Soc.*, **87**, 2191 (1965).
12. M. Barfield, *J. Chem. Phys.*, **41**, 3825 (1964).
13. G. A. Russell and E. T. Strom, *J. Am. Chem. Soc.*, **86**, 744 (1964).
14. E. T. Strom and G. A. Russell, *J. Chem. Phys.*, **41**, 1514 (1964).
15. A. D. McLachlan, *Mol. Phys.*, **1**, 233 (1958).
16. A. Laurent, *Ann. Chem.*, **17**, 91 (1836).
17. C. Liebermann and J. Homeyer, *Chem. Ber.*, **12**, 1971 (1879).
18. E. Bamberger, *Chem. Ber.*, **18**, 865 (1865).
19. R. Scholl, *Chem. Ber.*, **32**, 1809 (1899).
20. A. Hantzsch and W. H. Glower, *Chem. Ber.*, **40**, 1519 (1907).
21. A. Weissberger, *Chem. Ber.*, **65**, 1815 (1932).
22. A. Weissberger, H. Mainz, and E. Strasser, *Chem. Ber.*, **62**, 1942 (1929).
23. E. Fischer, *Ann. Chem.*, **221**, 214 (1882).
24. E. T. Strom, G. A. Russell, and J. H. Schoeb, *J. Am. Chem. Soc.*, **88**, 2004 (1966).
25. L. Michaelis, *Chem. Revs.*, **16**, 243 (1935).
26. E. Weitz, *Angew. Chem.*, **66**, 658 (1954).
27. R. Willstätter and J. Piccard, *Chem. Ber.*, **41**, 1458 (1908).
28. L. Michaelis and E. S. Fletcher, *J. Am. Chem. Soc.*, **59**, 1246 (1936).
29. J. L. Ihrig and R. G. Caldwell, *J. Am. Chem. Soc.*, **78**, 2097 (1956).
30. B. Venkataraman and G. K. Fraenkel, *J. Am. Chem. Soc.*, **77**, 2707 (1955).
31. R. Dehl and G. K. Fraenkel, *J. Chem. Phys.*, **39**, 1793 (1963).
32. G. A. Russell and G. Underwood, *Angew. Chem.*, **78**, 989 (1966).
33. P. H. Rieger and G. K. Fraenkel, *J. Chem. Phys.*, **37**, 2811 (1962).
34. J. W. Lown, *Can. J. Chem.*, **43**, 2571 (1965).
35. J. W. Lown, *J. Phys. Chem.*, **70**, 591 (1966).
36. J. W. Lown, *Can. J. Chem.*, **43**, 3294 (1965).
37. E. Beckmann and T. Paul, *Ann. Chem.*, **266**, 1 (1891).
38. N. L. Bauld, *J. Am. Chem. Soc.*, **84**, 4345 (1962).
39. G. R. Luckhurst and L. E. Orgel, *Mol. Phys.*, **7**, 297 (1963).
40. D. H. Geske and A. C. Balch, *J. Phys. Chem.*, **68**, 3423 (1964).
41. M. Adams, M. S. Blois, and R. H. Sands, *J. Chem. Phys.*, **28**, 774 (1958).
42. G. A. Russell and M. C. Young, *J. Am. Chem. Soc.*, **88**, 2007, (1966).
43. G. A. Russell, E. G. Janzen, and E. T. Strom, *J. Am. Chem. Soc.*, **86**, 1807 (1964).
44. E. R. Talaty and G. A. Russell, *J. Am. Chem. Soc.*, **87**, 4867 (1965).
45. E. R. Talaty and G. A. Russell, *J. Org. Chem.*, **31**, 3455 (1966).
46. G. A. Russell, E. G. Janzen, and E. T. Strom, *J. Am. Chem. Soc.*, **84**, 4155 (1962).
47. G. A. Russell and E. R. Talaty, *Science*, **148**, 1217 (1965).

48. G. A. Russell, R. D. Stephens, and E. R. Talaty, *Tetrahedron Letters*, **1965,** 1139.
49. C. Lagercrantz, *Acta Chim. Scand.*, **18**, 1321 (1964).
50. G. A. Russell, A. J. Moye, and K. Nagpal, *J. Am. Chem. Soc.*, **84**, 4154 (1962).
51. T. Cohen and T. Tsuji, *J. Org. Chem.*, **26**, 1681 (1961).
52. G. A. Russell, E. T. Strom, E. R. Talaty, and S. A. Weiner, *J. Am. Chem. Soc.*, **88**, 1998 (1966).
53. G. A. Russell and S. A. Weiner, *J. Org. Chem.*, **31**, 248 (1966).
54. H.-D. Becker, G. J. Mikol, and G. A. Russell, *J. Am. Chem. Soc.*, **85**, 3410 (1963).
55. J. R. Steven and J. C. Ward, *Chem. Commun. (London)*, **1965**, 273.
56. R. Hanna and G. Ourisson, *Bull. Soc. Chim. France*, **1961**, 1945.
57. B. Camerino, B. Patelli, and R. Sciaky, *Tetrahedron Letters*, **1961**, 554.
58. L. J. Chinn, *J. Org. Chem.*, **29**, 3304 (1964).
59. S. Nakajima and K. Takeda, *Chem. Pharm. Bull. (Tokyo)*, **12**, 1530 (1964).
60. L. H. Piette, I. Yamazaki, and H. S. Mason, *Free Radicals in Biological Systems*, M. S. Blois, Ed., Academic Press, New York, 1961, p. 195.
61. C. Corvaja, P. L. Nordio, and G. Giacometti, *J. Am. Chem. Soc.*, **89**, 1751 (1967).
62. C. U. Pittman, Jr., and G. A. Olah, *J. Am. Chem. Soc.*, **87**, 5123 (1965).
63. L. S. Bartell, B. L. Carroll, and J. P. Guillory, *Tetrahedron Letters*, **1964**, 705.
64. G. L. Closs and H. B. Klinger, *J. Am. Chem. Soc.*, **87**, 3265 (1965).
65. H. Günther and D. Wendlisch, *Angew. Chem. Intern. Ed. Engl.*, **5**, 251 (1966).
66. G. V. Smith and H. Kriloff, *J. Am. Chem. Soc.*, **85**, 2016 (1963).
67. E. de Boer and E. L. Mackor, *J. Chem. Phys.*, **32**, 1579 (1960).
68. J. R. Bolton and G. K. Fraenkel, *J. Chem. Phys.*, **40**, 3307 (1964).
69. R. Bucourt and D. Hainaut, *Compt. Rend.*, **258**, 3305 (1964).
70. H. O. House and B. M. Trost, *J. Org. Chem.*, **30**, 1341 (1965).
71. G. A. Russell, E. R. Talaty, and R. H. Horrocks, *J. Org. Chem.*, **32**, 353 (1967).
72. A. Nickon and J. L. Lambert, *J. Am. Chem. Soc.*, **88**, 1905 (1966).
73. G. A. Russell, G. Holland, K. Y. Chang, and L. H. Zalkow, *Tetrahedron Letters*, **1967**, 1955.

CHAPTER 4

Radical Cations

GERSHON VINCOW*

*Department of Chemistry, University of Washington, Seattle,
Washington*

* Alfred P. Sloan Foundation Research Fellow.

I. INTRODUCTION

This chapter consists of a discussion of the results obtained by electron spin resonance spectroscopy on π electron radical cations in liquid solution.

The most interesting and important feature of these spectra is the hyperfine splitting, which arises from the interaction of the electron spin magnetic moment with moments of various magnetic nuclei present in the cations, such as the proton, carbon-13, and nitrogen-14. Primary emphasis in this review is given to the correlation of the nuclear hyperfine splittings with valence theory. Two aspects are treated:

(1) The general but approximate relationships between the splittings and the π electron spin density distribution are discussed. An appreciation of the approximations made in the derivation of these equations is stressed. Also emphasized are the variations in theory required to account for the characteristic differences between the splittings of cation and anion radicals.

(2) Valence theory calculations of the π spin density distribution for numerous families of free radical cations are described. The relationships mentioned above are employed to compute theoretical splittings which are compared with the experimental values. *Semiquantitative agreement is found.* This concordance of experiment with the predictions of rather approximate π electron theory is the most significant result of the electron spin resonance investigations of radical cations.

Other topics which are treated in detail in this chapter are: (*1*) the differences between *g* values of hydrocarbon cation and anion radicals, (*2*) effects of restricted rotation on hyperfine splittings and line widths, (*3*) effects of spatial near degeneracy on electron spin resonance (ESR) spectra, (*4*) radical cations of biological interest, and (*5*) preparation of radical cations.

II. HYDROCARBON CATION RADICALS

A. Proton Hyperfine Splittings of Unsubstituted Even-Alternant Hydrocarbon Ions

1. Experimental Results

The monopositive and mononegative ion radicals of the even-alternant hydrocarbons have been extensively investigated by ESR (1–21). Table I consists of a list of the radical cations which have been studied. A few examples of the measured proton hyperfine splittings are presented in Table II. It can be observed in this sample of data that the splittings of the cation and anion of the same hydrocarbon are similar in value. Further, with the general exception of the 2 position, the splittings of the cations are about 10–20% larger than those at corresponding ring positions in the anions.

TABLE I

Even-Alternant Hydrocarbon Cation Radicals Investigated
by ESR

Hydrocarbon	Ref.
Benzene	16, 18
Naphthalene (dimer)	17
Anthracene	2, 3, 5, 6, 8, 15
Naphthacene (tetracene)	3, 5, 6, 12, 14, 21
1,2-Benzanthracene	4
Pentacene	14, 20, 21
Diphenylene	7, 13
Perylene	1, 3, 5, 6, 9, 10, 14, 21
Pyrene	2, 4, 17
3,4-Benzpyrene	4
Coronene	11, 21
Dibenzo(*a*,*c*)triphenylene	17
Tetraphenylethylene	17
9,10-Diphenylanthracene	19, 21

TABLE II

Proton Hyperfine Splittings of Even-Alternant Hydrocarbon Ion Radicals

Hydrocarbon	Position	Experimental (G)[a]		Calculated			Ref.
		Cation	Anion	$-27\rho_{HMO}$[b]	$-27\rho_{UHF}$[c]	$-27\rho_M$[d]	
1. Anthracene	9	6.533	5.337	-5.21	-7.02	-6.91	15
	1	3.061	2.740	-2.59	-2.84	-3.19	
	2	1.379	1.509	-1.30	-0.76	-0.86	
2. Naphthacene	5	5.06	4.25	-3.97	-5.32	-5.10	12e, 28
	1	1.684	1.55	-1.51	-1.49	-1.76	
	2	1.020	1.15	-0.89	-0.43	-0.63	
3. Pentacene	6	5.083	4.263	-3.81	—	-5.13	20
	5	3.554	3.032	-2.86	—	-3.79	
	1	0.975f	0.915f	-0.95	—	-1.10	
	2	0.757f	0.870f	-0.68	—	-0.40	

4. Perylene

3	4.10	3.53	−2.92	−3.94	−3.91	28
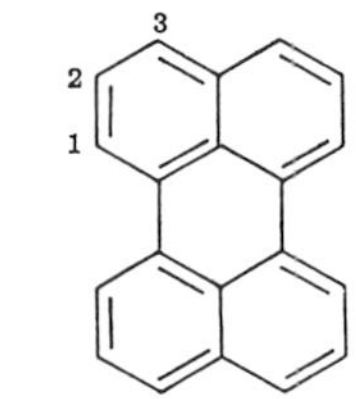 1	3.10	3.08	−2.24	−2.67	−3.10	
2	0.46	0.46	−0.35	+0.54	+0.84	

5. Dibenzo(a,c)-triphenylene

4	2.28	2.06^g	−1.81	—	—	17
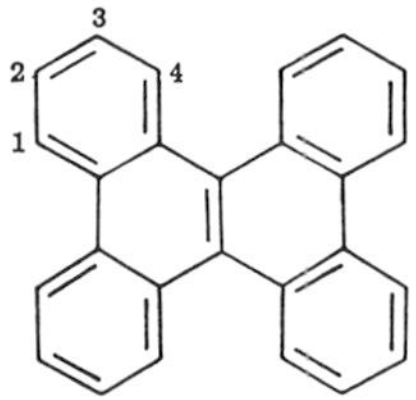 2	1.99	1.71	−1.51	—	—	
1	0.60	0.62	−0.73	—	—	
3	<0.03	<0.03	−0.054	—	—	

[a] For free radicals in solution only the *magnitudes* of the hyperfine splittings can be obtained from the spectral spacings.

[b] ρ_{HMO} designates diagonal elements of the π-spin density matrix in the Hückel MO approximation.

[c] ρ_{UHF} designates diagonal elements of the π-spin density matrix after annihilation in an unrestricted Hartree-Fock calculation incorporating the semiempirical integral scheme of Pariser and Parr (28).

[d] ρ_M designates diagonal elements of the π-spin density matrix in McLachlan's approximation to the unrestricted SCF theory [*Mol. Phys.*, **3**, 233 (1960)].

[e] Refined measurements of the cation splittings at the 1 and 2 positions were communicated privately by Dr. J. S. Hyde.

[f] Assignment of splitting to ring position is uncertain.

[g] See Lewis and Singer, *J. Chem. Phys.*, **44**, 2082 (1966).

Our goal in this section is to account for the magnitudes of the proton hyperfine splittings of these ion radicals, and in particular to explain the small differences between the spectra of cations and anions.

2. Theory

As was pointed out initially by Weissman (22) the proton hyperfine splitting exhibited by π-electron free radicals in solution is due to the Fermi contact interaction. This interaction measures the unpaired spin density at the magnetic nuclei. Since the protons are located in the nodal plane of the π electrons and yet splittings are observed, a σ–π exchange interaction has been invoked in order to account for the splittings (23).*

A general theory of the σ–π exchange interaction for hydrocarbon radicals has been formulated and solved using first-order perturbation theory (25,26). The final result relates the elements of the σ-electron spin density matrix,† ρ^σ, to those of the π-electron spin density matrix, ρ^π, as follows:

$$\rho^\sigma_{ab} = \text{Tr}(\rho^\pi G^{ab}) = \sum_{l,m} \rho^\pi_{lm} G^{ab}_{ml} \tag{1}$$

In this relationship a and b designate σ-type orbitals (s_a and s_b) which form the basis set for the σ-spin density matrix; l and m, correspondingly, denote π-type orbitals (p_l and p_m) on carbon. The elements of the G matrix are given by:

$$G^{ab}_{ml} = \sum_{j}{}' \sum_{c,d} \frac{\langle mc|dl\rangle \rho^\sigma(0 \to j)_{cd}\rho^\sigma(j \to 0)_{ab}}{\epsilon_j - \epsilon_0} \tag{2}$$

where c, d are σ-type orbitals,

$$\langle mc|dl\rangle \equiv \iint p^*_m(1)s_d(1)(e^2/r_{12})s^*_c(2)p_l(2)\,d\tau_1\,d\tau_2 \tag{3}$$

$\epsilon_j - \epsilon_0$ is the excitation energy to the jth excited configuration of the σ electrons, and $\rho^\sigma(0 \to j)_{cd}$ is the cd matrix element of the σ-electron spin density between the ground and jth excited configurations.

The hyperfine splitting, a^H, for a particular proton in a radical is directly proportional to the σ spin density evaluated at the position of that nucleus (designated 0):

$$a^H = (8\pi/3)g_N\beta_N \sum_{a,b} \rho^\sigma_{ab}a^*(0)b(0) \tag{4}$$

where g_N, β_N are the proton g factor and the nuclear magneton, respectively.

---

* A purely vibrational mechanism has been considered and rejected (see Ref. 23c).
† See Chapter 1 of this volume for the definition and examples of spin-density matrices.

One might consider then that it would be necessary to calculate for each radical the ρ^π matrix as well as the numerous G^{ab} matrices—*rather a formidable theoretical task*. This is not the case. McConnell (25) has suggested two approximations which considerably simplify the calculation of hyperfine splittings.

Consider that the proton of interest is located at the center of the $1s$–σ orbital designated c and that it is bonded to carbon atom k with π orbital p_k and σ orbital d.

Approximation I: The dominating contribution to ρ^σ is from $G_{kk}\rho_{kk}^\pi$. Contributions of the off-diagonal terms of the G matrix, such as $G_{lm}\rho_{ml}^\pi$, are negligible as are the diagonal terms $G_{mm}\rho_{mm}^\pi$ $(m \neq k)$. We have then for the splitting at proton c,

$$a_c^H = \left[(8\pi/3)g_N\beta_N \sum_{a,b} G_{kk}^{ab}a^*(0)b(0)\right]\rho_{kk}^\pi \tag{5}$$

Approximation II: McConnell further asserted that the bracketed term in equation 5 is to be considered *approximately constant for all hydrocarbon radicals*.

Thus we arrive at the familiar McConnell relationship in which the bracketed terms of equation 5 are designated Q:

$$a_c^H = Q\rho_{kk}^\pi \tag{6}$$

With a semiempirical value of Q one has an "experimental" measure of the diagonal elements of the π-spin density matrix. Or, conversely, one has a means of computing proton hyperfine splittings from the spin densities predicted by π-electron theory in its various approximate forms.

3. Comparison of Theory with Experiment

McConnell's relationship has proved to be quite successful in the semi-quantitative correlation of ESR data for hydrocarbon ions with π-electron theory. A reasonable semiemprical value of $Q = -27$ G is chosen for the comparison of theory with experiment (15,28). The splittings predicted by the Hückel molecular orbital theory, McLachlan's approximate SCF theory (29), and Snyder's and Amos' UHFPP theory (28) are presented in Table II for five representative cation–anion pairs. Note that in these various approximations the diagonal elements of the π-spin density matrix are *identical for cation and anion* as is predicted by the pairing theorem for even-alternant hydrocarbons (15,30).

Most of the calculated splittings shown in Table II are within 20% of experiment. The rather low values predicted for the 2 position by the more sophisticated orbital theories constitute a consistent exception. This anomaly has been discussed in the literature (28) and is believed to arise from an insufficiency of the π-electron theory rather than of McConnell's relationship.

The good overall agreement for the even-alternant hydrocarbon ions is generally interpreted as a *significant verification of the accuracy of the ground state wave functions predicted by π-electron theory*. Such accuracy is especially noteworthy in the case of the rather simple Hückel MO theory. Furthermore the good agreement obtained is an indication that the two approximations made by McConnell lead to a *relationship of at least semiquantitative validity*.

Inspection of Table II reveals, however, that all theories fail to predict the difference in splittings between cation and anion. Since it is generally felt that the pairing theorem does hold quite well for these radicals, we are led to conclude that $a_c^H = Q\rho_{kk}^\pi$ must be modified in order to obtain *quantitative* agreement with experiment.*

4. Extensions of the McConnell Relationship

A number of attempts to improve upon this relationship have been made (32–35). We will discuss two of these which have had the greatest measure of success.

A logical place to start our discussion of these efforts is in a reconsideration of the approximations made by McConnell and cited above. McConnell appreciated the possibility that approximation I may not always be valid. He pointed out (25), for example, that in cases of very small ρ_{kk}^π the term $G_{(k+1)k}\rho_{k(k+1)}^\pi$ may contribute significantly to the hyperfine splittings.

Giacometti, Nordio, and Pavan (GNP) (35) have extended this idea and proposed that the off-diagonal matrix elements involving nearest-neighbor π atomic orbitals, $G_{k(k\pm1)}^{ab}$ and $\rho_{k(k\pm1)}^\pi$, make a significant contribution in general. Including these off-diagonal terms, the proton hyperfine splitting is given by:

$$a_c^H = Q\rho_{kk}^\pi + (8\pi/3)g_N\beta_N \sum_{a,b} (G_{(k-1)k}^{ab}\rho_{k(k-1)}^\pi$$

$$+ G_{k(k-1)}^{ab}\rho_{(k-1)k}^\pi + G_{k(k+1)}^{ab}\rho_{(k+1)k}^\pi + G_{(k+1)k}^{ab}\rho_{k(k+1)}^\pi)a^*(0)b(0) \qquad (7)$$

Since the G^{ab} and ρ^π matrices are Hermitean and further since $G_{k(k-1)}^{ab} \approx G_{k(k+1)}^{ab}$:

$$a_c^H = Q\rho_{kk}^\pi + \left[(8\pi/3)g_N\beta_N \sum_{a,b}(2G_{(k-1)k}^{ab})a^*(0)b(0)\right](\rho_{k(k-1)}^\pi + \rho_{k(k+1)}^\pi) \qquad (8)$$

---

* Consideration of the HMO theory *with overlap* leads to a breakdown of the pairing theorem, but the prediction that ρ_{kk}^π is greater for *anions* than cations—just the reverse of the experimental effect, if $a = Q\rho$ holds.

Taking the quantity in square brackets immediately above as a second semiempirical parameter, Q', assumed constant for all hydrocarbon radicals, we obtain the GNP equation:

$$a_c^H = Q\rho_{kk}^\pi + Q'(\rho_{k(k-1)}^\pi + \rho_{k(k+1)}^\pi) \tag{9}$$

In the HMO and UHFPP approximations the off-diagonal elements of the π-spin density matrix $\rho_{k(k\pm1)}^\pi$, are equal in magnitude and opposite in sign for cation and anion; the cations have the positive values. Thus, provided Q' is negative, as is reasonable to expect, the GNP equation predicts larger splittings for the cations. Suggested values of the parameters are $Q = -27\,G$ and $Q' = -6.3\,G$ (28). Overall agreement with experiment is improved (see Table III).

In an alternative approach, Bolton (32) has chosen to reconsider the other approximation made by McConnell—namely that $G_{kk}^{\gamma b}$ is a constant for all hydrocarbon radicals. Bolton has proposed that G_{kk}^{ab} is a function of the excess charge on carbon atom k, ϵ_k^π (unity minus the total π-electron charge on k). He has treated the effect of charge on the orbital exponent of the π function in the exchange integrals $\langle kd|dk\rangle$ and $\langle kc|ck\rangle$ and concludes that this is of the correct sign and order of magnitude to explain the cation-anion effect. Bolton suggests a two-parameter equation of the form:*

$$a_c^H = (Q'' + K\epsilon_k^\pi)\rho_{kk}^\pi \tag{10}$$

and evaluates the constants from experimental data. His procedure, outlined in Chapter 1 of this volume, leads to the values $Q'' = -27\,G$ and $K = -12\,G$. Calculated values of the splittings are given in Table III for the representative case of the anthracene ions.

Examination of Table III reveals that both the GNP and Bolton equations result in a generally better correlation of experiment with π-electron theory than does $a_c^H = Q\rho_{kk}^\pi$.

Although the percentage deviations obtained using the Bolton and GNP equations are not significantly smaller than those obtained with the McConnell relationship, the *differences* in splittings between cation and anion are predicted by the two-term equations. This observation applies to the 1 and 9 positions of the anthracene ions. The 2 position is again a trouble spot since the measured anion splitting is *larger* than the cation splitting. No explanation for this anomaly has been proposed.

Snyder and Amos (28) have made a comparison of the two extensions of McConnell's relationship, as applied to polycyclic even alternants, and

---

* Excess charge effects were first considered by Colpa and Bolton (33) and an equation of the form of equation 10 proposed.

TABLE III

Experimental and Calculated Splittings for the Anthracene Cation and Anion

Position[a]	Experimental (G)	Calculated (UHFPP)[b]			Calculated (HMO)		
		$-27\rho_{UHF}$	GNP	Bolton	$-27\rho_{HMO}$	GNP	Bolton
9C[c]	6.533	-7.02 (8)[d]	-7.64 (17)	-7.74 (18)	-5.21 (-20)	-5.71 (-12)	-5.66 (-13)
9A	5.337	-7.02 (31)	-6.40 (20)	-6.32 (18)	-5.21 (-2)	-4.71 (-12)	-4.76 (-11)
1C	3.061	-2.84 (-7)	-3.03 (-1)	-2.97 (-3)	-2.59 (-15)	-2.84 (-7)	-2.70 (-12)
1A	2.741	-2.84 (4)	-2.65 (-3)	-2.72 (-1)	-2.59 (-5)	-2.34 (-15)	-2.48 (-9)
2C	1.379	-0.76 (-45)	-0.87 (-37)	-0.80 (-42)	-1.30 (-6)	-1.43 (+4)	-1.33 (-4)
2A	1.509	-0.76 (-50)	-0.65 (-57)	-0.73 (-52)	-1.30 (-14)	-1.17 (-22)	-1.27 (-16)

[a] See Table II for the numbering scheme of ring positions.
[b] See reference 28.
[c] C and A designate cation and anion, respectively.
[d] Percentage deviation of the *magnitude* of the computed splitting from the measured value.

conclude that it is impossible to say that either results in significantly better agreement with experiment than the other. Carter and Vincow (18) have prepared the benzene cation, $C_6H_6^+$, in a rigid sulfuric acid matrix and have compared the splitting (4.44 G at $t = -150°C$) with that of the benzene anion (3.82 G at $t = -130°C$) (37). Application of the GNP and Bolton equations to these radicals leads to the predicted splittings shown in Table IV. The agreement for this pair of ions is better in the case of the Bolton correlation.

TABLE IV

Experimental and Computed Splittings for the Benzene Cation and Anion

	Experimental (G)	Bolton[a,b]	GNP[c]
$C_6H_6^+$	4.44[d]	−5.00	−5.55
$C_6H_6^-$	3.82[e]	−4.00	−3.45

[a] ρ_{kk}^π and ϵ_k^π calculated from HMO theory.

[b] The application of Bolton's equation is not made with the values 1/6 for spin density and excess charge, but rather with the general linear combination of the two degenerate Hückel orbitals. The result is independent of the particular linear combination chosen and is somewhat different from that obtained using the values 1/6. (G. Vincow, to be published.)

[c] ρ_{kk}^π and $\rho_{k(k \pm 1)}^\pi$ calculated from HMO theory.

[d] $t = -150°C$.

[e] $t = -130°C$.

5. Further Improvements

The best calculated splittings available deviate, by and large, from the experimental values by amounts far in excess of the experimental error. No doubt significant improvements in the calculation of ρ^π (especially at the 2 position) can and will be made. But our approximate computations of ρ^π are not the entire cause of the discrepancy. An even more complex relationship than either the Bolton or GNP equation will be required in order to obtain quantitative agreement. To derive such a relationship it will probably be necessary to make a quantitative calculation of the various matrix elements G_{ml}^{ab} and perhaps also to solve the $\sigma–\pi$ interaction to second order in the perturbation.

A search for agreement within a few percent introduces other complexities as well. Up until this point we have been discussing the theory of an isolated rigid molecule. *Solvent effects* and the *effect of intramolecular nuclear motions* probably influence the splittings to the extent of a few percent.

For example, in the case of the anthracene anion solvent effects of 1–2% are found (15). Comparable magnitudes are reported by Lewis and Singer (17) for the hydrocarbon cations. A theory of solvent effects in electron spin resonance spectra has been proposed by Gendell, Freed, and Fraenkel (38).

The effect of intramolecular motions on the proton hyperfine splitting has only recently become an active subject of investigation, although it has long been appreciated that the Fermi contact interaction must be averaged over the rapid motions of the protons. Theoretically, what is required is a computation of the expectation value of the contact interaction in the various molecular vibrational states followed by a statistical averaging for the temperature of interest. The experimental manifestations of this effect are (*1*) a temperature dependence of the hyperfine splitting and (*2*) at very low temperature the residual contribution of zero-point motions.

Typical magnitudes of the temperature coefficient (normalized approximately to unit ρ_{kk}^{π}) are:

Radical	Temp. coefficient	Ref.
$CH_3 \cdot$	$-2 \text{ mG}/°C (10 \leq t \leq 60)$	39
$C_6H_6^-$	$-10 \text{ mG}/°C (t = -80)$	37
$C_6H_6^+$	$-5.2 \pm 3 \text{ mG}/°C (-110 \leq t \leq -190)$	18
$C_7H_7 \cdot$	$-9 \text{ mG}/°C (+80 \leq t \leq +196)$	40
$C_4N_2H_6^+$ [a]	$-4 \text{ mG}/°C (-30 \leq t \leq +25)$	41

[a] N,N'-dihydro-1,4-diazine cation (CH proton splitting).

From the data above we note that splittings may vary by 1–3% over a 100°C temperature range. Further, theoretical work of Schrader and Karplus (42) on $CH_3 \cdot$ indicates that averaging over the zero-point motions may modify splittings by a few percent.

B. Carbon-13 Splittings of Even-Alternant Hydrocarbon Ions

The theory of carbon-13 nuclear hyperfine splittings in π-electron radicals has been developed by Karplus and Fraenkel (43). Splittings are linearly related to diagonal elements of the π-spin density matrix at the center containing the magnetic nucleus and at those adjacent. The form of the Karplus-Fraenkel equation is developed in Section IV-A-2 in connection with the discussion of nitrogen-14 hyperfine splittings. Q-type parameters have been calculated which result in good agreement with experiment for hydrocarbon radicals.

Of special interest is the study made by Bolton and Fraenkel (15) in which the ^{13}C splittings of anthracene cation and anion are measured and compared. This investigation was undertaken in order to provide a quantitative test of the pairing theorem. If (a) the pairing theorem holds and if (b) the Q parameters for ^{13}C splittings are insensitive to charge effects, then the various carbon-13 splittings should be the same for cation and anion. The cation and anion splittings are $a_9^{C-13} = 8.48$ and 8.76 G, $a_{11}^{C-13} = -4.50$ and -4.59 G, and $a_2^{C-13} = \pm 0.37$ and -0.25 G, respectively. If we omit the 2-position data from consideration, since the splittings are very small and result from near cancellation of terms with opposite signs, then the splitting differences are *only* 3% (9 position) and 2% (11 position). The authors conclude that, barring an unlikely cancellation of effects due to deviations from a and b, the above results demonstrate that the pairing theorem holds to a high degree of approximation for the even-alternant hydrocarbon ions.

C. Proton Hyperfine Splittings of Nonalternant Hydrocarbon Ions

Since the pairing theorem no longer applies for nonalternant hydrocarbon ions we might expect quite dissimilar ESR spectra for the cation and anion. Further, one might expect that HMO theory would not give an adequate representation of the π-electron distribution for nonalternant systems and hence would not correlate well with the hyperfine splittings.

In their pioneering investigation of radical ions, de Boer and Weissman (5) reported that the spectra of acepleiadylene cation and anion differ and that neither is in good agreement with HMO theory. These spectra have been reinvestigated and reduced to coupling constants (44). Also studied recently are the cation and anion of acenaphth[1,2-a]acenaphthylene(AN) and of $\Delta^{9,9'}$-bifluorene (44,45). It is clear that there are large differences between cation and anion spectra. For example, the total width of the AN$^-$ spectrum is 29.44 G while that of AN$^+$ is only 12 G. The question of whether or not HMO theory gives a reasonable approximate description of the unpaired-electron distribution is still a moot one in the opinion of this author. The best one can say at present is probably not.

In order to pin down this question, *experimental* means of assigning the splittings to proton positions will have to be employed. Further, since these radicals involve five- and seven-membered rings, the variation of Q with ring size should be taken into account in the theoretical analysis.

D. g Values of Hydrocarbon Cations and Anions

1. Experimental Results

The average value of the g tensor, g_0, is measured in the solution spectra of free radicals. For hydrocarbon radicals this g value is within 0.1% of the free-electron value, $g_e = 2.002319$. Typical results for hydrocarbon cations and anions are (46):

	Cation	Anion
Anthracene	2.002565	2.002709
Naphthacene	2.002598	2.002682
Pentacene	2.002605	2.002686
Perylene	2.002578	2.002667

The experimental observation which must be explained is that each hydrocarbon cation g value is smaller than that for the corresponding anion by an amount which varies, but is of the order of 1×10^{-4} (46–48).

2. Theory

The deviation of the g value from the free-electron value is determined by the small perturbation of the combined spin-orbit and orbital Zeeman interactions to the energy of the free radical. The theory for π-electron radicals was first treated by McConnell and Robertson (49). In order to compute a nonzero g shift, excited configurations must be admixed to the principal configuration. McConnell and Robertson observed that an excitation of the form $\pi \to \sigma^*$ (antibonding σ orbital) would reduce the g value from the free-electron value by an amount proportional to $\xi/\Delta E_1$, where $\xi = 28$ cm^{-1} is the $2p$ spin-orbit coupling parameter of the carbon atom and ΔE_1 is an average energy for such an excitation. Further a σ(bonding orbital) $\to \pi$ excitation would increase the g value by an amount of the same form ($\xi/\Delta E_2$). Since experimental g values have positive deviations from g_e it is concluded that $\Delta E_1 > \Delta E_2$.

Stone (50) has proposed a more detailed theory of the g value. His work was motivated by the consideration that a discrepancy arises when McConnell and Robertson's ideas are applied to the data on the hydrocarbon ions. In the cation radicals the odd electron is in a bonding π orbital (closer to σ orbitals) and in the anions it is in an antibonding π orbital (closer to σ^*). Applying the arguments of McConnell and Robertson it is easily seen that the cation should have the larger g value—in disagreement with experiment.

Stone has applied his general theory for a spatially nondegenerate doublet molecule to the case of the hydrocarbon ions. The energy of the unpaired-electron MO enters his derivation and is approximated by the HMO value, $E = \alpha + \lambda\beta$. The major result obtained is that the deviation of the average g value from the free-electron value, Δg, is linearly related to λ:

$$\Delta g \equiv g_0 - g_e = b + c\lambda \qquad (11)$$

3. Comparison of Experiment with Theory

An excellent linear fit is indeed obtained with experimental g values of hydrocarbon radicals (46–48). For example, Segal, Kaplan, and Fraenkel (46) report:

$$\Delta g = [31.9 \pm 0.4 - (16.6 \pm 1.0)\lambda] \times 10^{-5} \qquad (12)$$

where the errors are obtained from the residual sum of squares of the fit.

For each cation–anion pair λ's are equal in magnitude and opposite in sign, the value for cations being positive. The negative value of c, which correlates with the smaller g values for cations, is explained by Stone as the result of two competing effects. One of these involves the fact that the unpaired-electron MO in the cations is closer in energy to the filled localized orbitals and, as previously mentioned, should result in a larger g value for cations. The other effect is that there is a greater tendency for the MO coefficients to be of opposite sign on adjacent atoms in the unpaired-electron orbitals of the anions since these are antibonding. This leads to a greater coupling with the filled orbitals and a higher g factor for anions. The second effect predominates.

E. Alkyl Proton Splittings in Radical Cations

1. Magnitudes of Methyl Proton Splittings: Cations vs. Anions

Hyperfine splitting, due to protons of methyl groups bonded directly to π-electron rings, is generally observed. The origin of the unpaired spin density at these methyl protons has been the subject of numerous theoretical investigations and will be discussed below. First let us consider some experimental results.

A number of methyl-substituted hydrocarbon cations have been investigated (51–60). Some examples are reported in Table V along with the results for the corresponding anions in such cases as they are available. Reasonable approximations to ρ_{kk}^{π} at the ring position adjacent to the methyl group are included for certain radicals. If we assume that there is an approximate proportionality between $a_k^{CH_3}$ and ρ_{kk}^{π} then the constant for cations is about 40 G. For the neutral radicals a value close to 30 G has been proposed (61). In the case of 9-methylanthracene anion the value seems to be about 20 G. Further, the author has examined methyl splittings for a series of methyl-substituted naphthalene anions (62) and estimates, using MO calculations of the spin-density distributions, a value of 20 ± 5 G. We now turn to the various theoretical treatments of methyl-proton splitting in search for an explanation of this *pronounced variation* among the cations, neutral radicals, and anions.

Until recently calculations have been made along two main lines: (*1*) HMO hyperconjugation model (52,54,63,64) and (*2*) valence bond model (65,66).

TABLE V
Hyperfine Splitting of Methyl-Substituted Hydrocarbon Ions

Cation structure	Position	Methyl splitting (G)	Ring splitting	ρ_{kk}^{π} [a]	Ref.
1. Hexamethylbenzene		6.53		1/6	55,59

Cation structure	Position	Methyl splitting (G)	Ring splitting	ρ_{kk}^{π} [a]	Ref.
2. Pentamethylbenzene[b]	1 or 2	10.85		1/4	58
	2 or 1	10.3		1/4	
	6	0.56			

Cation structure	Position	Methyl splitting (G)	Ring splitting	ρ_{kk}^{π} [a]	Ref.
3. Durene	1	11.0		1/4	55
	6		—[c]		

Cation structure	Position	Methyl splitting (G)	Ring splitting	ρ_{kk}^{π} [a]	Ref.
4. 9-Methylanthracene	C 9	7.79		0.2	51,52
	A 9	4.27		0.2	
	C 10		7.03		
	A 10		5.16		
	C 1		2.81		
	A 1		2.94		
	C 2		1.46		
	A 2		1.39		
	C 3		1.19		
	A 3		1.73		
	C 4		2.85		
	A 4		2.77		
5. 9,10-Dimethyl-anthracene	C 9,10	8.00			51,52
	A 9,10	3.88			

(*continued*)

TABLE V (*continued*)

Cation structure	Position	Methyl splitting (G)	Ring splitting	ρ_{kk}^{π} [a]	Ref.
6. Pyracene 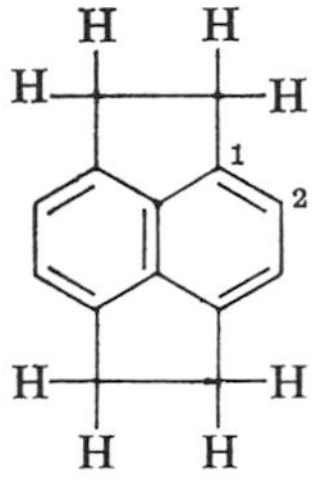	C 1	12.80			53,54
	A 1	6.58			
	C 2		2.00		
	A 2		1.58		

[a] Reasonable approximate values.

[b] According to the authors it is possible that this radical is not penta-methylbenzene cation (R = H), but rather the cation with R = CO_2H or SO_3H.

[c] Unresolved; splitting is smaller than the line width.

In the hyperconjugation approach the atomic orbitals of the methyl-group hydrogens are rehybridized to form one with π symmetry. This orbital is then considered to conjugate with the π-electron system and an HMO calculation is performed with or without overlap. The details of this method, pioneered by Mulliken (67,68), have been thoroughly reviewed elsewhere (69). With reasonable MO parameters, sufficient spin is de-localized into the methyl group to account for the order of magnitude of the proton splitting. The splitting depends both on ρ_{kk}^{π} and on the prox-imity of the energy of the unpaired electron MO to that of the methyl group "π system." This second factor leads to the correct prediction of larger spin density at the proton for the hydrocarbon cations than for the corresponding anions (52,54). The experimental ratio for 9-methyl-anthracene, 9,10-dimethylanthracene, and pyracene is about 2.

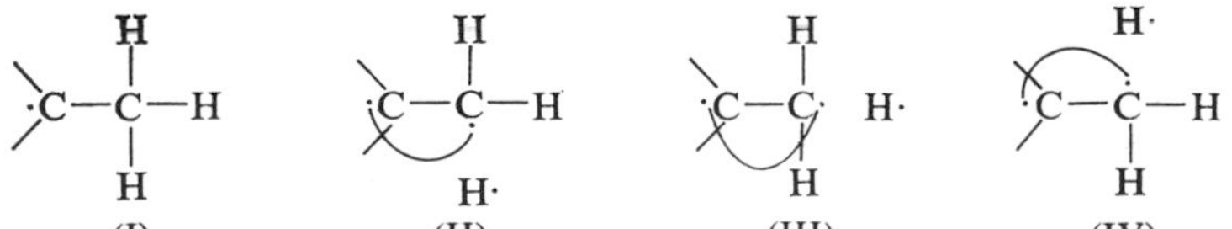

In the valence bond calculation the splitting arises through a σ–π exchange interaction ("spin polarization") mechanism similar to that dis-cussed in a previous section for ring-proton splittings. As illustrated below, configurations II, III, and IV are admixed to I. A perturbation calculation with reasonable semiempirical estimates leads to sufficient spin density at the protons to account for the methyl splitting. The splitting should be approximately proportional to ρ_{kk}^{π} and should not be very different for positive and negative ions—in contrast with experiment.

A direct comparison of the results of the MO and VB theories, in order to assess the relative importance of hyperconjugation and spin-polarization contributions, is not meaningful. Such an assessment is possible only in terms of a more complete theory which includes either every VB structure or each MO configuration.

Recently, Lazdins and Karplus (70,71) have chosen the second alternative and have made a three-electron treatment of the ethyl radical including all excited MO configurations. Some of these describe spin delocalization through electron migration (hyperconjugation) and others through spin polarization. The most important result obtained, for this prototype neutral radical, is that 60% of the splitting arises from spin polarization and 40% through electron migration. Thus, neither of the two simpler models is adequate to describe the methyl splitting.

It is to be hoped that this treatment will be extended to cation and anion radicals, and that such a theory will lead to a useful approximate dependence of the methyl splitting on such parameters as ρ_{kk}^{π}, ϵ_k^{π} and the energy of the unpaired-electron MO. A linear dependence of methyl splitting on excess charge has indeed been suggested by Hulme and Symons (55) on semiempirical grounds.

2. Magnitudes of Methylene Proton Splittings: Restricted Rotation

a. Methylene vs. Methyl Proton Splittings. It is naturally of interest to compare the magnitudes of hyperfine splittings of methyl-group protons with those of the methylene protons (β protons) for other alkyl groups bonded to the same π system. Results for methyl- and ethyl-substituted hydrocarbon cations are listed in Table VI. The designation β proton and γ proton are defined in the illustration below:

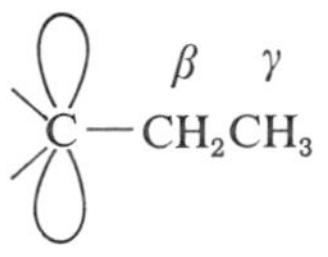

Surprisingly, the methyl and β-proton splittings are not very close in value. That this is not due to large changes in the π-spin distribution is evidenced by the fact that the ring splittings in the methyl- and ethylanthracenes are within 10% of each other. The *ratios* of methylene to methyl splitting for

TABLE VI

Hyperfine Splittings of Methyl- and Ethyl-Substituted Hydrocarbon Cations

Radical cation	β Proton (G)	γ Proton (G)	Ref.
1. Hexaethylbenzene (HEB)	2.67 (20°C)	0.37	59
2. Hexamethylbenzene (HMB)	6.53		55,59
3. 9-Ethylanthracene	3.6	0.3	72
4. 9-Methylanthracene	7.79		51,52
5. 9,10-Diethylanthracene	3.75	0.22	72
6. 9,10-Dimethylanthracene	8.00		51,52

the three cases cited in the table are quite similar and equal 0.41, 0.46, and 0.47.

Similar results have been reported for neutral and anion radicals. For example, Sevilla and Vincow have investigated the neutral xanthyl radicals (1) (73). The 9-methyl splitting is 12.2 G whereas the 9-ethyl

(1)

β-proton splitting is only 6.2 G ($t \approx 100°C$); the ratio mentioned above has the value 0.51. Carrington and Todd (74) have reported on the alkyl-substituted cyclooctatetraene anions, $C_8H_7R^-$. Values of the ethyl β-proton and methyl splittings are 2.5 G and 5.1 G, respectively (ratio 0.49).

We conclude that any theory developed for β-proton splittings must account for this ratio of about 1/2. Another experimental observation which must be rationalized is the occurrence of a large positive temperature coefficient of the β-proton hyperfine splitting. Carter and Vincow (59) report for the hexaethylbenzene cation (HEB^+):

$$|a_\beta^H| = 2.640 \pm 0.007 + (1.1 \pm 0.5) \times 10^{-3}t$$
$$+ (2.5 \pm 1.2) \times 10^{-5}t^2 \qquad (-20 \leq t \leq +60°C)$$

The temperature coefficient, $d|a_\beta^H|/dt$, is $+2$ mG/°C at 20°C. Coefficients of similar magnitude have been measured for the β protons in 9-ethyl-xanthyl and 9-benzylxanthyl (73). A much smaller temperature dependence of the order of $+0.1$ mG/°C is observed for the methyl protons of HMB$^+$ (59).

b. Restricted Rotation: Model and Theory.   The model which has been proposed to account for the above-mentioned experimental observations is that rotation of the ethyl group about the C—C bond is severely hindered whereas that of the smaller methyl group is not. Let us first consider an oversimplified picture in which the methyl rotation is free and the ethyl group is locked in the conformation of minimum energy. For the radicals mentioned above, this conformation is the one shown below:

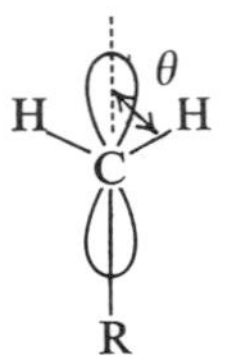

The view is end-on down the C—C bond joining the alkyl group to the π system.

An approximate relationship governing the angular dependence of the β-proton splitting has been proposed and confirmed experimentally (75):

$$a_\beta^H(\theta) = (B_0 + B_2 \cos^2 \theta)\rho_{kk}^\pi$$

where θ is the angle shown in the illustration, k designates the carbon atom bonded to the alkyl group, B_0 and B_2 are constants, and B_2 is at least an order of magnitude larger than B_0. Let us neglect B_0 for the purpose of a crude comparison. If the methyl rotation is free we average with equal weight over all θ and obtain $\langle \cos^2 \theta \rangle = \frac{1}{2}$ and $a_{CH_3}^H \approx B_2 \rho_{kk}^\pi/2$. For a locked ethyl group in the above conformation, $\theta = 60°$, $\cos^2 \theta = \frac{1}{4}$ and $a_\beta^H \approx B_2 \rho_{kk}^\pi/4$. The predicted ratio is just 1/2 in agreement with experiment.

Further confirmation for this model is obtained from the β-proton splitting of 9-isopropylxanthyl. Here the lowest-energy conformation is that with $\theta = 90°$ or $a_\beta^H \approx 0$. The measured splitting is only 0.8 G as compared with the 12.2 G methyl splitting.

Actually these alkyl groups are neither freely rotating nor completely locked. The ethyl group executes torsional oscillations about its equilibrium position. These motions are determined by the restricting potential exerted by the remainder of the molecule. An approximate theory has been proposed by Stone and Maki (76) for the case in which the internal rotation is separable and the barrier to rotation can be adequately described by a static twofold sinusoidal potential:

$$V = V_0(1 - \cos 2\alpha)/2$$

Unfortunately, the eigenfunctions of the resultant eigenvalue equation, the Mathieu equation, have not been tabulated for values of the reduced moments of inertia corresponding to radicals as large as those mentioned above. Stone and Maki approximate the eigenfunctions by using the limiting harmonic-oscillator and free-rotor solutions for eigenvalues below and above the top of the barrier, respectively. The expectation value of $(B_0 + B_2 \cos^2 \theta)\rho_{kk}^\pi$ is computed in these eigenstates, and a statistical average is taken in order to calculate the splitting at each temperature.

In qualitative agreement with the data of Table VI, the splittings in the zero point and low-lying torsional states ($V_0 > 5$ kcal/mole) are very close to $(B_0 + B_2/4)\rho_{kk}^\pi$. Further, a positive temperature coefficient of the splitting is predicted; comparison of its magnitude with experiment should lead to an estimate of the height of the barrier to rotation.

Fessenden (77) has made a rather successful application of these ideas to the calculation of the β-proton splitting temperature dependence in the case of the neutral alkyl radicals. Fortunately, for these radicals the eigenfunctions have been tabulated and approximations to the eigenfunctions are not necessary. As an example of Fessenden's results, the computed temperature dependence is in fairly good agreement with experiment for the propyl radical, and a barrier $V_0 = 400$ cal/mole is obtained.

The application of a restricted-rotation theory to the calculation of the temperature dependence for more complex radicals such as HEB$^+$, the ethylanthracene cations, and the 9-ethylxanthyl radical has not yet been reported. In these cases one would probably want to take into consideration (1) a more complex form for the restricting potential, (2) the various normal modes of torsional oscillation as in HEB$^+$, and (3) the influence of any displacement of the methylene carbon out of the aromatic plane.

As far as the methyl group is concerned, there is good evidence that for molecules such as HMB$^+$, rotation is not essentially free (78). The same is likely true for the methylanthracenes and 9-methylxanthyl. The equivalence of the splittings for the three-methyl protons in these cases indicates, however, that, with respect to the ESR time scale of $\approx 10^{-7}$ sec, the methyl protons are *rapidly interconverting*. For any angle θ', the three-methyl-proton splittings are approximately:

$$[B_0 + B_2 \cos^2 \theta']\rho_{kk}^\pi, \qquad \left[B_0 + B_2 \cos^2 \left(\theta' + \frac{2\pi}{3}\right)\right]\rho_{kk}^\pi$$

and

$$\left[B_0 + B_2 \cos^2 \left(\theta' + \frac{4\pi}{3}\right)\right]\rho_{kk}^\pi$$

The average value of these three splittings is $(B_0 + B_2/2)\rho_{kk}^\pi$, independent of θ' (and hence of temperature), in agreement with experiment.

At very low temperature the three methyl protons will no longer be equivalent. The detailed quantum-mechanical theory of the splittings and line widths for this case has been reported by Freed (79).

c. A Case of Conformational Interconversion. De Boer and Praat (80) have made an ESR study involving an interesting instance of restricted motion of methylene-group protons. The spectrum of 1,2,3,6,7,8-hexahydropyrene cation (2) in SO_2 at $-95°C$ consists of a superposition of two resonances of identical g value; these are attributed to the boat and chair conformations of the ion (2), present in equal amounts. The equatorial and axial protons have different splitting constants which are assigned in accordance with $a_\beta^H = (B_0 + B_2 \cos^2 \theta)\rho_{kk}^\pi$. As the temperature is raised,

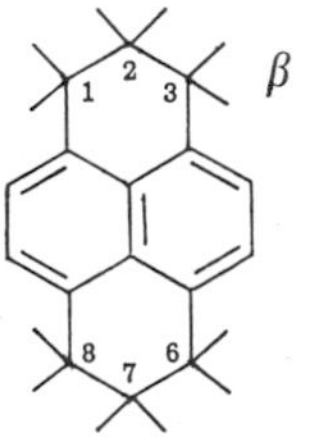

(2)

pronounced changes in the spectrum occur which are qualitatively correlated with a dynamical equilibrium between boat and chair forms. Further investigation of these spectra is expected to yield detailed information on the kinetics of the interconversion of boat and chair conformations.

This phenomenon, which leads to a pronounced alternation in line widths at the higher temperatures, will again be encountered in the following section on oxygen heteroatom radicals.

III. RADICAL CATIONS CONTAINING OXYGEN HETEROATOMS
A. Introduction

Various homologous series of π-electron free radicals containing heteroatoms were of great interest to chemists long before the advent of

ESR. Among these are the metal ketyls, the Wurster's salts, and the semi-quinones. The semiquinones, such as p-benzosemiquinone anion (3), were among the first series of π radicals to be studied systematically by ESR.

(3)

Following the publication of the spectra of the alternant hydrocarbon ions and the correlation of their hyperfine splittings with HMO theory through $a_c^H = Q\rho_{kk}^\pi$, it became of interest to consider the relationship of splittings to ρ_{kk}^π for heteroatom radicals. Vincow and Fraenkel (81,82) chose the semiquinone anions for such a study. Their approach was to calculate π-spin density distributions using HMO theory with various sets of coulomb and resonance integral parameters for oxygen. Sets of parameters were found which resulted in good agreement with splittings when used in conjunction with a Q value in the low 20's (then, the semi-empirical value of choice). This agreement pointed to an extension of the usefulness both of McConnell's relationship and of HMO theory to the case of heteroatom radicals.

Numerous investigations on a variety of heteroatom radicals have followed along these lines.

It has always been assumed that $a_c^H = Q\rho_{kk}^\pi$ holds for the proton splittings and that the same value of Q applies as for hydrocarbon radicals. This assumption has never been subjected to theoretical examination. Further, the extensions of GNP and Bolton to McConnell's relationship have not been applied to heteroatom radicals.*

It should be noted that the excess charge for heteroatom radicals is not as simply expressed as for hydrocarbon ions. The neutral hydrocarbons have very close to unit π charge on each center and the excess charge is well approximated by $\epsilon = \pm\rho_{HMO}^\pi$ for cations and anions, respectively. The influence of a heteroatom, such as oxygen or nitrogen, is to produce a markedly nonuniform charge distribution. For example in the case of p-benzosemiquinone anion, as calculated by HMO theory, the two oxygen atoms have about 1.5 π electrons each and the carbon atoms closer to unit π charge. For the optimum choice of MO parameters, ρ_{kk}^π on the carbons

---

* Recently Gilbert et al. (83) have applied these extensions to two phenothiazine radical cations.

bonded to hydrogen is 0.107 whereas the excess charge on these centers is only -0.039.

We turn now to ρ_{kk}^{π}. The problem of how to treat the heteroatom in calculating π-electron wave functions has always been a thorny one and involves some additional parametrization. There is good reason to expect that the HMO theory will be less satisfactory for heteroatom radicals than for even-alternant hydrocarbon ions. To the extent that in a particular case a heteroatom radical is not very different from its homocyclic analogue, reasonable success may be obtained. In our review of π radicals containing heteroatoms we will find that the HMO theory has been extensively employed to calculate ρ_{kk}^{π} and that, in many cases, it results in good approximate correlations with proton hyperfine splittings.

B. Diprotonated Radical Anions

1. Semiquinones

We begin our discussion of the oxygen heteroatom by considering a family of radicals which are radical cations only by virtue of their formal charge. They are the diprotonated semiquinone anions (84,85). The diprotonated p-benzosemiquinone anion (4) is generated by oxidation of hydroquinone or reduction of quinone in very strongly acidic media.

(4)

The number of π electrons for this radical is nine just as in the case of the anion (3). It is important to realize that 4 is a perturbed anion, especially when one considers the influence of excess charge on ring-proton splittings. Further, as far as the methyl-proton splitting in derivatives of 4 is concerned, the unpaired electron is likely in an antibonding MO characteristic of anion radicals and a value of Q closer to 20 G than to 40 G will probably apply.

We turn now to a comparison of the splittings for the acid- and base-stabilized parasemiquinones. The data is given in Table VII. A striking feature of the spectra for the acid-stabilized radicals is the occurrence of hyperfine splitting due to the protons bonded to oxygen. This splitting, a_{OH}, decreases with increasing size of the semiquinone. The proton splittings in the quinoid rings are seen to be the *same* for the two forms of the

TABLE VII
Proton Hyperfine Splittings of Parasemiquinones

Cation structure	Hyperfine splittings (G)			
	Cation	Ref.	Anion	Ref.
1. p-Benzosemiquinone	$\lvert a_2^H \rvert = 2.36$	84	$\lvert a_2^H \rvert = 2.368$	86
	$\lvert a_{OH}^H \rvert = 3.44$		—	
2. 1,4-Naphthosemiquinone	$\lvert a_2^H \rvert = 3.20$	84	$\lvert a_2^H \rvert = 3.23$	81
	$\lvert a_5^H \rvert = 1.80$		$\lvert a_5^H \rvert = 0.513$	
	$\lvert a_6^H \rvert = 0.86$		$\lvert a_6^H \rvert = 0.655$	
	$\lvert a_{OH}^H \rvert = 2.42$		—	
3. 9,10-Anthrasemiquinone	$\lvert a_1^H \rvert = 1.66$	84	$\lvert a_1^H \rvert = 0.550$	81
	$\lvert a_2^H \rvert = 1.07$		$\lvert a_2^H \rvert = 0.962$	
	$\lvert a_{OH}^H \rvert = 1.31$		—	

anion, but one notes an increase of splittings in the adjacent rings for the protonated species.

These results obtained by Bolton, Carrington, and Santos-Veiga (84) have been rationalized by means of an HMO calculation such as that performed by Vincow and Fraenkel for the unprotonated anions. Diagonal elements of the π-spin density matrix are computed for various values of the MO parameters and compared with a^H/Q. Quite good agreement (of the order of 20% deviations or less) is obtained for a particular choice of parameters (see Table VIII). This optimum set of parameters is different from that assigned to the unprotonated anions:

	h_O	k_{CO}	
Anions	1.2	1.56	$\alpha_O \equiv \alpha_C + h_O \beta_{CC}$
Cations	2.0	1.1	$\beta_{CO} \equiv k_{CO} \beta_{CC}$

TABLE VIII

Diprotonated Parasemiquinone Anions: Comparison of HMO Calculations
with Experiment

Cation		ρ_{11}^{π}	ρ_{22}^{π}	ρ_{55}^{π}	ρ_{66}^{π}	ρ_{00}^{π}
1. p-Benzosemiquinone	a^{H}/Q^{a}	—	0.094	—	—	—
	HMO[b,c]	0.206	0.090	—	—	0.113
	% Deviation		-4			
2. 1,4-Naphthosemiquinone	a^{H}/Q	—	0.128	0.072	0.034	—
	HMO	0.184	0.106	0.074	0.042	0.079
	% Deviation		-17	$+3$	$+26$	
3. 9.10-Anthrasemiquinone	a^{H}/Q	0.066	0.043	—	—	—
	HMO	0.055	0.042	—	—	0.065
	% Deviation	-17	-1			

where the column group header ρ_{kk}^{π} spans ρ_{11}^{π}, ρ_{22}^{π}, ρ_{55}^{π}, ρ_{66}^{π}, ρ_{00}^{π}.

[a] The value $Q = -25$ G is employed.

[b] The choice of MO parameters is $h_{O} = 2.0$, $k_{CO} = 1.1$.

[c] The assignment of a number of the splittings to ring positions is made by optimizing agreement with the HMO calculations.

Bolton, Carrington, and Santos-Veiga have drawn the interesting conclusion that "these changes are physically realistic; for, bonding a proton to the oxygen will both lower the energy of one of the oxygen nonbonding orbitals, thus lowering the coulomb integral of the oxygen, and also decrease the conjugation with the ring system, leading to a smaller resonance integral."

The MO calculations also predict a decreasing value of ρ_{00}^{π} with increasing size of semiquinone. On the basis of a $\sigma-\pi$ interaction mechanism one might expect a relationship $a_{OH}^{H} = Q'\rho_{00}^{\pi}$ for the OH group. Although the calculations follow the trend of the splittings, a direct proportionality is not obtained for the three radicals studied. Of course the theoretical values of ρ_{00}^{π} are only approximate. Other factors leading to deviation from such a proportionality are: (1) the OH group is probably especially sensitive to interactions with the polar solvent and (2) the OH group is undergoing some rotational motion and hence additional mechanisms for the hyperfine splitting must be considered (85).

Very interesting consequences of the OH group motion have been investigated by Carrington and co-workers (87,88) in their studies of the diprotonated durosemiquinone (5) and naphthazarin semiquinone (6) anions. Spectra of these radicals have been recorded at various temperatures

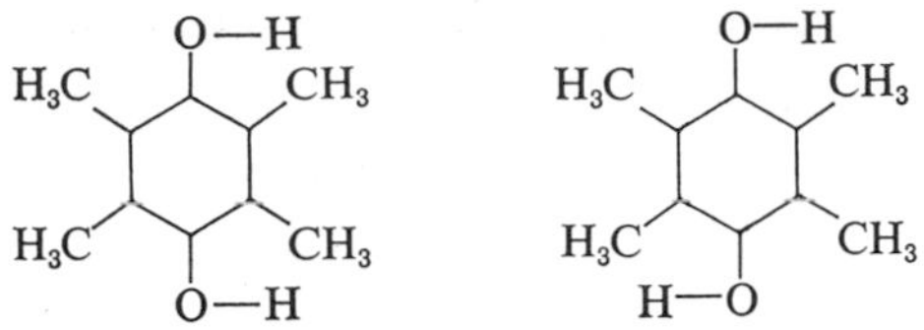

cis (5) trans

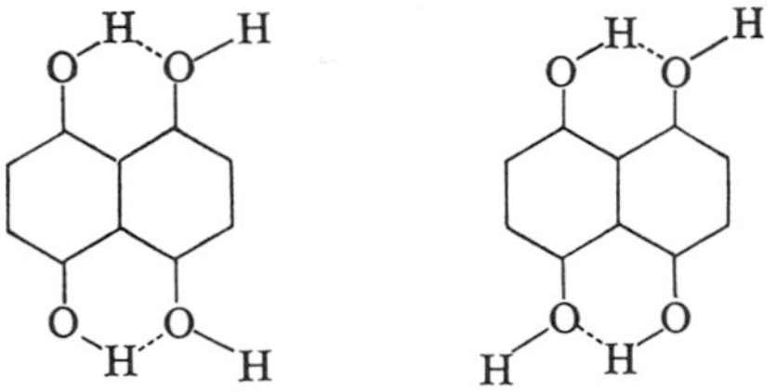

cis (6) trans

and pronounced variations in the line widths of certain components have been observed. The detailed theoretical interpretation of this effect, which has been called "line width alternation," is reviewed elsewhere (89). Here we will only outline the model and present the most important result.

This phenomenon is explained on the basis of the occurrence of restricted rotation of the OH group about the C—O bond. The existence of *cis* and *trans* isomers, as illustrated above, is postulated. At sufficiently low temperatures the rate of *cis–trans* isomerization is slow compared to the hyperfine frequency separations. A superposition of the spectra of the isomers will be observed. These spectra should be different. At very high temperature the interconversion will be very rapid and a single spectrum with averaged splittings should be recorded. In the intermediate temperature range the isomerization rate is comparable to hyperfine frequency separations and marked changes in the spectrum occur.

The shapes of the spectra for the protonated naphthazarin semiquinone (6) have been analyzed at various temperatures and a *rate of cis–trans isomerization* computed for each. These rates are fit to the Arrhenius form and an activation energy—the potential barrier to rotation—of 4 ± 1 kcal/mole is obtained. The authors (88) make the observation that this magnitude is consistent with a mechanism of isomerization which involves the breaking of an intramolecular hydrogen bond.

2. Semidiones

The semidione radical anions and their diprotonated derivatives have been extensively investigated by Russell and co-workers (90). These radicals are the subject of another chapter in this volume and will not be discussed here.

C. Radical Cations

Tomita, Ueda, and co-workers (91) have studied the radical cations produced by one-electron oxidation of dibenzo-p-dioxin (7) and a large

(7)

number of its derivatives. The spectrum of dibenzo-p-dioxin cation consists of five lines with binomial intensities and splitting 2.52 G (92). A line width of 0.17 G, reported by Tozer and Tuck (92), sets an upper limit for the splitting due to the other set of 4 protons. Assignment of the 2.52 G splitting to the 2,3,7,8 protons is made by considering the spectra of a variety of substituted dibenzo-p-dioxin cations. This use of substituents as "blocking groups" in ESR will be discussed below in the section on sulfur heteroatom radicals.

Cation radicals of various methoxybenzenes have been investigated (93–95) and will be treated in the section on radicals with near degeneracy.

IV. RADICAL CATIONS CONTAINING NITROGEN HETEROATOMS

A. Diprotonated Diazine Anions

1. Introduction

The first series of nitrogen heteroatom cations to be considered are the diprotonated diazine anions (41,84,96–105). A comparison of splittings, anions vs. protonated anions, for four unsubstituted members of this series is given in Table IX. The occurrence of hyperfine interaction with the nitrogen-14 nucleus is the important new feature in these spectra. In addition, hyperfine splitting due to the proton bonded to nitrogen is observed in the cations. Quantitatively, the data of Table IX reveal that (1) the nitrogen-14 hyperfine splitting is usually somewhat greater in the protonated anion than in the corresponding unprotonated radical, (2) the NH proton splitting is consistently 5–10% greater than the corresponding nitrogen splitting in the cations, and (3) CH proton splittings for the protonated anions are greater than the unprotonated anion splittings at the carbon position adjacent to nitrogen, smaller at the next-neighbor, etc. This alternation was not observed for the parasemiquinones, in which case the splittings in the quinoid ring were the same for cation and anion.

TABLE IX

Hyperfine Splittings of Diazine Ion Radicals

Cation structure	Hyperfine splittings (G)			
	Cation	Ref.	Anion	Ref.
1. N,N'-Dihydropyrazine	$\|a^N\| = 7.40^a$ $\|a^H_{NH}\| = 7.94$ $\|a^H_2\| = 3.13$	104	$\|a^N\| = 7.22$ — $\|a^H_2\| = 2.66$	106
2. N,N'-Dihydrophenazine	$\|a^N\| = 6.14$ $\|a^H_{NH}\| = 6.49$ $\|a^H_1\| = [0.66]^b$ $\|a^H_2\| = [1.71]$	104	$\|a^N\| = 5.14$ — $\|a^H_1\| = [1.93]$ $\|a^H_2\| = [1.61]$	106
3. N,N'-Dihydro-4,4'-dipyridyl	$\|a^N\| = 3.56$ $\|a^H_{NH}\| = 4.06$ $\|a^H_2\| = [1.61]$ $\|a^H_3\| = [1.45]$	104	$\|a^N\| = 3.64$ — $\|a^H_2\| = 0.43$ $\|a^H_3\| = 2.35$	106
4. N,N'-Dihydroquinoxaline	$\|a^N\| = 6.65$ $\|a^H_{NH}\| = [7.17]$ $\|a^H_2\| = [3.99]$ $\|a^H_5\| = [0.78]$ $\|a^H_6\| = [1.38]$	104	$\|a^N\| = 5.64$ — $\|a^H_2\| = [3.32]$ $\|a^H_5\| = [2.32]$ $\|a^H_6\| = [1.00]$	106

[a] Only the magnitudes of the various hyperfine splittings are listed. It has been well established that the nitrogen splittings are positive and the CH and NH proton splittings are negative.

[b] The splittings which could not be unambiguously assigned to positions by experimental means alone are bracketed. Assignments are based on the results of MO calculations and/or analogy with other compounds.

2. Theory of ^{14}N and NH Proton Splittings

In order to understand these results, the theoretical relationships between the π-spin distribution and the ^{14}N and NH proton splittings, a^N and a_{NH}^H, respectively, must be developed.

By analogy with the case of the ring proton of hydrocarbon radicals, one writes for the NH proton an equation with the form of McConnell's relationship,

$$a_{NH}^H = Q_{NH}^H \rho_N^\pi \tag{13}$$

and introduces a new parameter, Q_{NH}^H, to be evaluated empirically. It should be noted that a single-subscript notation has been introduced in equation 13 to represent the diagonal elements of the π-spin density matrix. This will be used throughout the remainder of the chapter since off-diagonal elements of ρ^π will not be considered. Further, the cumbersome phrase, "diagonal element of the π-spin density matrix," will be designated by the commonly used terms "spin density" or "π-spin density."

The theory of the ^{14}N splitting follows along the same lines as that for ^{13}C splitting, which was developed by Karplus and Fraenkel (43).

Consider, for example, the case of a nitrogen atom bonded as in the dihydropyrazine cation (Table IX, compound 1):

	σ Orbitals (a,b)		
	C	N	C'	H
		$1s_N$		
	h_C	h_{1N}		
		h_{2N}	$h_{C'}$	
		h_{3N}		$1s_H$

The σ orbitals are shown above, with those involved in a chemical bond on the same line; h designates a hybrid orbital, usually approximated for computational purposes as sp^2 in cases with 120° geometry. Recalling equations 1 and 4 we have for the hyperfine splitting of the ^{14}N nucleus (position designated 0):

$$a^N = \frac{8\pi}{3} g_N \beta_N \sum_{a,b} \rho_{ab}^\sigma a^*(0)b(0)$$

$$= \frac{8\pi}{3} g_N \beta_N \sum_{a,b} Tr(G^{ab}\rho^\pi)a^*(0)b(0) \tag{14}$$

A number of approximations are made, the justification of which is discussed by Karplus and Fraenkel (43).* (1) Only the diagonal elements of ρ^σ and G^{ab} (and hence ρ^π) are included. (2) Only the diagonal

* The approximations have recently been discussed for the ^{14}N case (107).

elements G_{NN}^{ab} and G_{kk}^{ab} (where k denotes the nearest-neighbor carbons, C and C') are included. (3) The contributions proportional to $h_C^*(0)h_C(0)$ $h_{C'}^*(0)h_{C'}(0)$ and $1s_H^*(0)1s_H(0)$ are neglected. (4) A few other terms, mentioned below, are neglected. The various contributions to a^N are then designated as follows:

σ Orbital	Contribution to splitting	Neglecting terms proportional to:
$1s_N$	$S^N \rho_N^\pi$	$\rho_C^\pi, \rho_{C'}^\pi$
h_{1N}	$Q_{NC}^N \rho_N^\pi + Q_{CN}^N \rho_C^\pi$	$\rho_{C'}^\pi$
h_{2N}	$Q_{NC}^N \rho_N^\pi + Q_{CN}^N \rho_{C'}^\pi$	ρ_C^π
h_{3N}	$Q_{NH}^N \rho_N^\pi$	$\rho_C^\pi, \rho_{C'}^\pi$

Thus, for the protonated diazine anions,

$$a^N = (S^N + Q_{NH}^N + 2Q_{NC}^N)\rho_N^\pi + Q_{CN}^N(\rho_C^\pi + \rho_{C'}^\pi) \tag{15}$$

$$= Q_{N(C_2 H)}^N \rho_N^\pi + Q_{CN}^N(\rho_C^\pi + \rho_{C'}^\pi) \tag{16}$$

For the azine anions, the contribution Q_{NH}^N is replaced by P^N to designate the effect of the lone pair, which may be significantly different.

For p-phenylenediamine and benzidine cations (see Table X for structural formulas),

$$a^N = (S^N + 2Q_{NH}^N + Q_{CN}^N)\rho_N^\pi + Q_{CN}^N \rho_C^\pi \tag{17}$$

For NH_3^+,

$$a^N = (S^N + 3Q_{NH}^N)\rho_N^\pi \tag{18}$$

The extension of this formalism to other nitrogen cations is obvious. It should be noted that (1) the effects of both σ-core and π-electron charge on the nitrogen atom have not been included and may be significant and (2) effects of variations in molecular geometry in the neighborhood of the nitrogen atom have not been considered. Thus, there is the possibility that the parameters in equations 15–18 may vary significantly in value among the various families of nitrogen-containing cations.

3. Evaluation of Q-Type Parameters

Our theoretical digression concluded, we return to the discussion of the diprotonated diazine anions. The most important problem in the interpretation of the hyperfine spectra of these radicals is the evaluation of the parameters which enter into equations 13 and 16, Q_{NH}^H, $Q_{N(C_2 H)}^N$, and Q_{CN}^N.

The usual procedure, which has been applied to all families of nitrogen heteroatom radicals, is to calculate ρ_k^π by means of the HMO or McLachlan theory. Optimum values of heteroatom parameters are chosen to fit the CH proton splittings through the McConnell relationship. The nitrogen

TABLE X

Radical Cations of Amino- and Methylaminohydrocarbons

Cation structure	Splittings (G)	Ref.
1. p-Phenylenediamine	$\|a^N\| = 5.29$ $\|a^H_{NH}\| = 5.88$ $\|a^H_{CH}\| = 2.13$	113
3. N,N,N',N'-Tetramethyl-*p*-phenylenediamine	$\|a^N\| = 6.99$ $\|a^H_{NMe}\| = 6.76$ $\|a^H_{CH}\| = 1.97$	118
3. Benzidine	$\|a^N\| = 3.60$ $\|a^H_{NH}\| = 3.97$ $\|a^H_2\| = 1.08$ $\|a^H_3\| = 1.62$	121
4. N,N,N',N'-Tetramethylbenzidine	$\|a^N\| = 4.86$ $\|a^H_{NMe}\| = 4.74$ $\|a^H_2\| = 0.79$ $\|a^H_3\| = 1.63$	120

and NH proton splittings and the calculated ρ^π_k are then used to estimate the *Q*-type parameters of equations 13 and 16. Values obtained for the diazine cations display quite a variation: $Q^H_{NH} = -35$ to -39 G, $Q^N_{N(C_2H)} = 32$–36 G, $Q^N_{CN} \equiv 0$ (84); $|Q^H_{NH}| = 25$ G, $Q^N_{N(C_2H)} = 22$ or 26 G, $Q^N_{CN} \equiv 0$ (101).

Barton and Fraenkel (104) have suggested that in certain instances it is possible to evaluate these parameters without recourse to valence-theory calculations and their attendant uncertainties.

a. Q^H_{NH}. These investigators consider the *N,N'*-dihydropyrazine cation (Table IX, compound *1*). It is assumed that the linear relationships $a^H_{CH} = Q^H_{CH}\rho^\pi_C$ (McConnell's relationship) and $a^H_{NH} = Q^H_{NH}\rho^\pi_N$ adequately describe the proton splittings for this radical. Further the good approximation is made that the trace of the π-spin density matrix is unity:

$$4\rho^\pi_C + 2\rho^\pi_N = 1 \tag{19}$$

For a given value of Q_{CH}^H, Q_{NH}^H can be directly computed *from the splittings,*

$$Q_{NH}^H = 2a_{NH}^H/[1 - 4a_{CH}^H/Q_{CH}^H] \tag{20}$$

Thus, for $Q_{CH}^H = -23.7$ G, $Q_{NH}^H = -33.7$ G and for $Q_{CH}^H = -30$ G, $Q_{NH}^H = -27.2$ G. The "true" value of Q_{NH}^H is probably bracketed by these extremes. It should be recalled in the selection of an empirical Q_{CH}^H that this radical is a *protonated anion.*

b. $Q_{CH_3}^H$. Barton and Fraenkel also analyze the ESR results for a series of methyl-substituted pyrazine cations in an attempt to evaluate $Q_{CH_3}^H$ in the assumed proportionality,

$$a_{CH_3}^H = Q_{CH_3}^H \rho_C^\pi \tag{21}$$

Using equations 13, 19, and 20 and McConnell's relationship, and further neglecting the delocalization of π spin onto the methyl groups, one can compute ρ_C^π at the methyl-substituted positions from the measured CH and NH proton splittings. An average value of $Q_{CH_3}^H$ is thus obtained from the methyl-proton splittings of tetramethyl-, 25,-dimethyl-2,6-di-methyl-, and 2-methylpyrazine cations. For $Q_{CH}^H = -23.7$ G, $Q_{CH_3}^H = 18.4$ G (average deviation 0.8 G) and for $Q_{CH}^H = -30$ G, $Q_{CH_3}^H = 21.9$ G (average deviation 1.0 G). This value of $Q_{CH_3}^H \approx 20$ G for the protonated pyrazine *anions* is quite reasonable in view of our previous discussion of methyl splittings for hydrocarbon cations ($Q \approx 40$ G) and anions ($Q \approx 20$ G).

c. $Q_{N(C_2H)}^N$ and Q_{CN}^N. These investigators (104) also consider the *nitrogen splittings* for pyrazine cation and its methyl derivatives. Using the various assumptions and equations mentioned above one can easily relate a^N to a^{NH} for these compounds. The relationship which applies for pyrazine, tetramethyl- and 2,5-dimethylpyrazine cations is:

$$a^N = [(Q_{N(C_2H)}^N - Q_{CN}^N)/Q_{NH}^H]a_{NH}^H + \tfrac{1}{2}Q_{CN}^N \tag{22}$$

A similar equation holds for the other methyl-substituted cations. Least squares fit of the data for the five compounds leads to:

$$[(Q_{N(C_2H)}^N - Q_{CN}^N)/Q_{NH}^H] = -0.7674 \tag{23}$$

and

$$Q_{CN}^N = +2.61 \text{ G} \tag{24}$$

This value of Q_{CN}^N, obtained independently of any valence-theory calculation, is particularly significant since many attempts had previously been made to assess its magnitude for various nitrogen radicals, with both positive and negative values in the range -1.5 G $\leq Q_{CN}^N \leq +9$ G being obtained. Barton and Fraenkel point out that "since the magnitude is small, the exact numerical value of Q_{CN}^N is probably particularly sensitive to structural features such as bond angle, bond length, and charge, and thus its value may have larger than usual variations from compound to compound." Thus, one can possibly understand a variety of suggested values, but these authors point out that a *large magnitude* is unlikely.

Since Q_{CN}^N is small, a linear relationship, $a^N \approx Q_{N(C_2H)}^N \rho_N^\pi$, will often be a useful approximation in estimating ρ_N^π.

As far as $Q_{N(C_2H)}^N$ is concerned, a limiting range is suggested by equation 23; for $Q_{CH}^H = -23.7$ G and -30 G, $Q_{N(C_2H)}^N = +28.4$ G and 23.5 G, respectively.

The corresponding parameter for the azine anions, $(S^N + P^N + 2Q_{NC}^N)$, has been variously estimated to be 20.9 G($Q_{CN}^N = 7.0$ G) (108), 30.9 ± 2 G($Q_{CN}^N = -2 \pm 2$ G) (102), 25 ± 2 G($Q_{CN}^N \equiv 0$) (84), 19.1 ± 1.7 G($Q_{CN}^N = +9.1 \pm 1.7$ G),...(107). It seems fairly sure that the value lies in the range 20–30 G and is therefore not very different from the corresponding parameter for protonated azine anions.

4. Discussion of Results: Protonated Azine Anions

We return to a consideration of the observations made in the introduction to this section regarding the data of Table IX. Barton and Fraenkel (104) have rationalized the fact that $|a_{NH}^H|$ is 5–10% larger than $|a^N|$. The equation for the nitrogen splitting, 16, can be rewritten:

$$a^N = [Q_{N(C_2H)}^N + RQ_{CN}^N]\rho_N^\pi \qquad (25)$$

where

$$R = \sum_i^{adj} (\rho_{C_i}^\pi/\rho_N^\pi) \qquad (26)$$

Further equation 13 can be employed to write:

$$a^N/a_{NH}^H = [Q_{N(C_2H)}^N + RQ_{CN}^N]/Q_{NH}^H \qquad (27)$$

Detailed consideration of the ESR splitting data for the protonated azine ions reveals that R, the ratio of spin densities on adjacent centers to spin density on nitrogen, usually falls in the small range 0.9–1.4. This, combined with the small value of Q_{CN}^N relative to $Q_{N(C_2H)}^N$, leads one to conclude, by inspection of equation 27, that a^N/a_{NH}^H *is roughly a constant.* Best fit of data leads to $a^N = 0.94a_{NH}^H$.

The magnitudes of the various splittings for the cations in Table IX can be related to valence-theory calculations of ρ^π through the Q-type parameters which are determined independently. HMO calculations using the parameter $h_N = +1.2$ are in fairly good agreement with experiment (84,104). Comparable agreement has been obtained for the azine anions with $h_N = +0.75$ (106). The change in this parameter is pictured physically as resulting from the lowering of the energy of the nitrogen non-bonding orbital due to the bonding with the proton (84).

Effects of electron correlation have recently been included in calculations of ρ^π for the dihydropyrazine cation radical. Corre and Odiot (105) have performed HMO, PPP, and PPP–CI calculations. They find that the spin densities for the first two methods are essentially the same, but that inclusion of configuration interaction causes a significant change—it raises the spin density on nitrogen by 25% and lowers that on carbon by 22%.

One final remark regarding the above discussion of nitrogen and NH proton splittings. It has been assumed throughout that $a^N > 0$, and $a^H_{NH} < 0$. Barton and Fraenkel (103) have made a study of the *line widths* in the spectrum of the dihydropyrazine cation and have been able to confirm these signs for the splittings and have also determined that $Q^H_{NH} < 0$.

B. Cations

1. 1,3,6,8-Tetraazapyrene Cation and Anion Radicals

The cation and anion radicals of 1,3,6,8-tetraazapyrene (8) have been investigated by Gerson (109). As far as we are aware, this is the only pair

(8)

of ions of the same azaaromatic which has been studied. Although the pairing theorem no longer applies, the proton and nitrogen splittings are reasonably close for the cation and anion. Further the proton splittings are close to those for the pyrene cation and anion.

No NH proton splittings are observed. The author suggests that this is due to the weak basicity of the azaaromatic compound ($pK_a = 0.3$). One might add that the positively charged radical should be even more weakly basic than the parent compound.

2. Cation Radicals of Amino- and Dimethylaminohydrocarbons (110–122)

Four radical cations which fall into this category will be discussed—two are Wurster's ions (*p*-phenylenediamine and *N,N,N',N'*-tetramethyl-*p*-phenylenediamine cations) and two are benzidine ions (benzidine and

N,N,N',N'-tetramethylbenzidine cations). The ESR results are presented in Table X.

Smejtek, Honzl, and Metalova (121) have reported the most detailed theoretical treatment of these results. These authors seek to evaluate Q_{NH}^{H}, $Q_{NCH_3}^{H}$, $(S^N + 2Q_{NH}^N + Q_{NC}^N)$ and Q_{CN}^N by comparison of splittings to π-spin densities calculated by the HMO and McLachlan theories. The heteroatom parameters are chosen to optimize the linearity of the relationship between CH proton splittings and ρ_C^π. For the HMO theory, $h_N = 1.0$ (0.65 for nitrogen bonded to methyl—an inductive effect). In the case of the McLachlan theory the optimum value is $h_N = 1.25$ (1.00 for nitrogen bonded to methyl). The values obtained for the Q-type parameters are seen in Table XI.

TABLE XI

Values of Q-Type Parameters

	HMO	McLachlan	Comment
$\|Q_{CH}^H\|$	28	30	Similar to hydrocarbon cations.
$\|Q_{NH}^H\|$	26	28	Cf. results for diazine cations, $27 \le \|Q_{NH}^H\| \le 34$ G.
$\|Q_{NCH_3}^H\|$	24	25	This value is quite close to the methyl splitting in $[N(CH_3)_3]^+$, $a_{NCH_3}^H = 26$ G$(\rho^\pi \approx 1)$. The trimethylamine cation is produced by irradiation in the solid state (123).
$S^N + 2Q_{NH}^N + Q_{NC}^N$	$+26$	$+27$	No distinction is made between the NH and NCH$_3$ bonds.
Q_{CN}^N	-2.6	-3.1	Small but opposite in sign to the value obtained for diazine cations.

A comparison of $(S^N + 2Q_{NH}^N + Q_{NC}^N) = 26$ or 27 G with the value $Q_{N(C_2H)}^N \equiv (S^N + Q_{NH}^N + 2Q_{NC}^N) = 24$ to 28 G obtained by Barton and Fraenkel indicates that $Q_{NH}^N \approx Q_{NC}^N$. From this result one might predict an approximate range of 24 to 28 G for the nitrogen splitting in the NH$_3^+$ radical $(\rho_N^\pi \approx 1$; $a^N = [S^N + 3Q_{NH}^N])$. The measured splitting is only 20 G (124) which reinforces the idea that transfer of parameters for nitrogen heteroatom radicals is at best semiquantitative.

3. The Hydrazine Cation, $N_2H_4^+$

Adams and Thomas (125) have detected a hyperfine spectrum when hydrazine is oxidized in a flow apparatus by ceric ion in dilute sulfuric acid. They ascribe this spectrum to the radical cation of hydrazine, $N_2H_4^+$ (9).

$$
\begin{bmatrix}
H & & H \\
& \ddot{N}\!\!-\!\!\dot{N} & \\
H & & H
\end{bmatrix}^+
$$
(9)

$|a^N| = 11.5$ G
$|a_{NH}^H| = 11.0$ G

A theoretical analysis of these splittings would be of great interest since this radical is isoelectronic with the ethylene anion. It should be possible to construct a reasonably good π-spin density matrix for this radical. The contribution of the off-diagonal matrix elements is expected to be unusually large (25b).

4. Triphenylamine Cation, $[(C_6H_5)_3N\cdot]^+$

Stamires and Turkevich (126) have produced a radical from triphenylamine (ϕ_3N:) in molten iodine. The spectrum is highly overlapped, but consists of a basic triplet with further hyperfine splitting. These investigators tentatively ascribed the spectrum to the cation radical of triphenylamine. They observe a different spectrum when triphenylamine and iodine are mixed in equimolar amounts in chloroform, benzene, or dioxane. The splitting pattern consists of five overlapped lines separated by about 6 G intervals. It is proposed that this radical is the bimolecular triphenylamine radical ion, $[(C_6H_5)_3N\cdot N(C_6H_5)_3]^+$, with hyperfine splitting from two equivalent nitrogens.

Allara, Gilbert, and Norman (94) have subsequently oxidized ϕ_3N: with lead tetraacetate in methylene chloride in the presence of boron trifluoride-ether complex as catalyst. The spectrum of this system consists of 45 equally spaced lines with separation 1.05 G and $g = 2.0028$ and is believed to be the same as observed by Stamires and Turkevich in molten iodine. When the *ortho* and *para* positions on the phenyl rings are deuterated, the spectrum collapses to a triplet with intensities 1:1:1 and splitting $a^N = 8.55$ G. Further study of the proton splittings of this radical should prove to be quite interesting since $(\phi_3N)^+$ is isoelectronic with the classic free radical, triphenylmethyl ($\phi_3C\cdot$).

With excess ϕ_3N, Allara, Gilbert, and Norman detect a spectrum identical to that of the N,N,N',N'-tetraphenylbenzidine cation. The largest hyperfine interaction is due to two nitrogens with splitting 4.3 G. These investigators suggest that this cation radical is produced by reaction between $(\phi_3N)^+$ and the excess (ϕ_3N).

5. Tetraphenylhydrazine Cation Radical

Free radicals have been detected in samples of tetraphenylhydrazine dissolved in various acid media (127,128). The spectra are highly overlapped but have been tentatively ascribed to the radical cation formed by oxidation of tetraphenylhydrazine ($|a^N| \approx 7$ G) and, under different conditions of acidity, to the conjugate acid of that radical (protonated form: $|a^N| \approx |a^H_{NH}| \approx 6.5$ G). Two structures for the tetraphenylhydrazinium ion radical (10) have been suggested. Further work on this spectrum under conditions of higher resolution would be of interest.

(10)

(Ref. 127)   (Ref. 128)

6. Phenothiazine Radical Cation and Related Radicals

Radical cations derived from phenothiazine (11) and related compounds have been of considerable interest because (1) the tranquilizer drug chlorpromazine is a substituted phenothiazine and (2) many dyestuffs, such as methylene blue, Lauth's violet, and Capri blue are oxidation products of substituted phenothiazines. Investigations related directly to chlorpromazine will be discussed in the section on cations of biological interest.

Phenothiazine (11) undergoes one-electron oxidation in acidic media to

(11)   (12)   (13)

form the radical cation (12). Upon treatment with triethylamine or water the conjugate base (13) is formed and has been detected. This radical is also formed by illumination of phenothiazine in ethanol (137). It should be noted that this radical is, in a sense, a *neutral radical cation.*

Many papers have been written on the ESR of the radical cation of phenothiazine and its derivatives (129–138). The best-resolved spectra have been obtained by Gilbert, Hanson, Norman, and Sutcliffe (138). Splitting constants and g values are reported (Table XII). MO calculations have been employed as an aid in the assignment of certain splittings to ring positions and these must be regarded as tentative.

TABLE XII
Radical Cation of Phenothiazine and Structurally Similar Radicals

	Radical cation (12) $g = 2.0051$	Neutral radical (13) $g = 2.0053$	Xanthyl radical (1) with R = H
$|a_{NH}^H|$	7.36 G	—	—
$|a^N|$	6.52	7.06	—
$|a_{3,7}^H|$	2.58	3.64	4.05
$|a_{1,9}^H|$	1.23	2.68	3.42
$|a_{2,8}^H|$	0.46	1.00	0.99
$|a_{4,6}^H|$	0.46	0.73	0.89

HMO calculations for these radicals, involving both nitrogen and sulfur hetcroatom parameters, have been performed. Gilbert et al. (138) report that the agreement is not very good. Part of the disagreement may be explained as follows. The neutral phenothiazine radical is structurally very similar to the xanthyl radical, 1. The splittings are also quite similar (see Table XII). There is good reason to believe that the splittings at the 2,4,6,8 positions of xanthyl are *positive* in sign ($\rho_k^\pi < 0$) (73). This means that the unpaired π spin at these carbon atoms is oppositely polarized to the unpaired spin of the molecule as a whole (such carbon atoms are commonly called positions of "negative spin density"). Since the HMO theory always predicts diagonal spin densities at all positions with the same polarization as the molecule, it will therefore not be very successful in the case of xanthyl and, arguing by analogy, the phenothiazine radicals.

Radical cations formed from a number of thiazine and oxazine dyes have been investigated by Heineken, Bruin, and Bruin (132). These cationic dyes, such as methylene blue (14), are reduced in acid and alkaline media

(14)

to form substituted phenothiazine cation radicals with structures similar to 12 and 13, respectively. In acid solution, at relatively high concentration of dye, the spectra consist of four overlapped lines ($a^N \approx a_{NH}^H$). For thiazine and oxazine dyes the splittings are 6.6 and 7.6 G, respectively. In alkaline solution the unprotonated cations are observed. At high dye concentration an overlapped triplet (a^N) is detected; splittings are 7.4 and 7.7 G for thiazines and oxazines, respectively. The greater nitrogen splitting for the neutral thiazine radicals is consistent with the results for phenothiazine. At lower concentrations of dye most spectra could be resolved further into many components.

V. RADICAL CATIONS CONTAINING SULFUR HETEROATOMS

A. Introduction

Radical cations containing sulfur atoms were generated in three early studies (139–141) in which compounds, such as thiophenol, thiocresol, and thianthrene, were dissolved in concentrated sulfuric acid. A summary of more recent results (142–153) on the sulfur-containing ions is found in Table XIII.

B. Thianthrene Cation and Related Radicals

The thianthrene cation (Table XIII, compound 3) has been the most extensively investigated of these radicals. Its spectrum consists of five components arising from four equivalent protons and separated by 1.30 ± 0.05 G. Each line has a width of 0.5 G. The assignment of the splitting to the 2,3,7,8 ring positions was made by consideration of numerous results involving substituted thianthrenes. For example, the spectrum of 2,7-dichlorothianthrene cation (Table XIII, compound 6) consists of three lines (1:2:1) with splitting 1.3 G and width 0.5 G. The splitting is the same as for thianthrene and only two protons are interacting. It is concluded that the protons in the 2,7 positions of thianthrene give rise to the 1.3 G splitting. This is a good example of the use of chlorine as a "blocking group" to aid in the assignment of splittings. The method is successful since the substitution of a chlorine atom often does not strongly influence the remaining proton splittings of a radical. Other blocking groups, such as methyl, have also been employed. There is good empirical evidence that this method will not work for monocyclic radicals (86,104). The splitting from the 1,4,6,9, protons is small and unresolved. It contributes to the unusually large (0.5 G) line width.

The splitting pattern of the oxygen analog to thianthrene cation, the dibenzo-p-dioxin cation (8), is strikingly similar. In this case $|a_{2,3,7,8}^{H}| = 2.52$ G and $|a_{1,4,6,9}^{H}| < 0.1$ G.

The g value of thianthrene cation is 2.0081; this relatively large deviation from the free-electron value is characteristic of sulfur-containing radicals and is associated with the large spin-orbit coupling parameter for that atom (49,50). Further, the principal components of the g tensor have been evaluated from the spectrum of the solid thianthrene antimony pentachloride adduct and are 2.0048, 2.0086, and 2.0142 (145,146). The

TABLE XIII
Radical Cations with Sulfur Heteroatoms

Cation structure	Splittings (G)	Ref.
1. 1,4-Dithiin		
	$\|a_2^H\| = 2.80 \pm 0.05$	146
2. 1,4-Benzodithiin		
	$\|a_2^H\| = 3.20 \pm 0.05$ $\|a_5^H\| < 0.5$ $\|a_6^H\| = 1.05 \pm 0.05$	146
3. Thianthrene		
	$\|a_1^H\| < 0.5$ $\|a_2^H\| = 1.30 \pm 0.05$	139–146
4. 6-Methyl-1,4-benzodithiin		
	$\|a_2^H\| \approx \|a_3^H\| \approx 1.5$ $\|a_7^H\| \approx \|a_{Me}^H\| \approx 3.0$ $\|a_5^H\|, \|a_8^H\| < 0.5$	146
5. 2,7-Dimethylthianthrene		
	$\|a_1^H\|, \|a_4^H\| < 0.5$ $\|a_3^H\| \approx \|a_{Me}^H\| \approx 1.4$	146–149
6. 2,7-Dichlorothianthrene		
	$\|a_1^H\|, \|a_4^H\| < 0.5$ $\|a_3^H\| = 1.3$	146,147,149

(continued)

TABLE XIII (*continued*)

Cation structure	Splittings (G)	Ref.
7. Other substituted thianthrenes		
(*A*) 2,7-Dimethoxy-, 2,7-di-*t*-butyl-, 1,6-di-*t*-butyl-, 1,3,6,8-tetra-*t*-butyl-, 2,3,7,8-tetrabromothianthrene.		148
(*B*) 1-NH$_2$, 2-NH$_2$, 1-Br, 2-Br, 1-Cl, 2-Cl, 1-OH, 2-OH, 1-COOH, 2-COOH, 2,7-Me$_2$, 2,7-(OH)$_2$, 2,7-Cl$_2$, 2,7-Br$_2$, 2,7-(*t*-Bu)$_2$-thianthrene.		149
8. Phenoxanthiine	Incompletely resolved; 31 equally spaced lines separated by ≈ 0.3 G.	150
9. Aromatic thioether R=H, R=OCH$_3$	Single component; $\Delta H_{ms} \approx 6$ G.	151
10. 1,4-Dimethylthiobenzene	$\|a^H_{SCH_3}\| = 4.56$ (CH$_3$CN) $\|a^H_{SCH_3}\| = 5.33$ (H$_2$SO4) $\|a^H_2\| =$ (Unresolved)	152
11. 1,2,4,5-Tetramethylthiobenzene	$\|a^H_3\| = 0.71$ $\|a^H_{SCH_3}\| = 2.57$	153

anisotropy of the g-tensor components is considerably greater than that expected for hydrocarbon radicals. This is of interest since a major contribution to the magnitude of line widths in solution spectra is directly related to the magnitude of the g-tensor anisotropy (89). Thus, the unusual line widths in thianthrene cation may be explained.

A correlation of the proton hyperfine splittings with theoretical spin-density distributions has been made for the homologous series 1,4-dithiin, 1,4-benzodithiin, and thianthrene cation (146). Hückel MO and McLachlan SCF calculations are performed allowing for variation of the sulfur heteroatom parameters. Two models are tested: one involving only p orbitals and the other expansion of the sulfur valence shell to include $3d$ orbitals. Sets of MO parameters are found for which both models are in fairly good agreement with experiment; the $3d$ model gives somewhat better results.

It is quite interesting to note that the ^{33}S hyperfine splitting of thianthrene cation appears to have been observed in the early study of Fava, Sogo, and Calvin (141). These authors detected two additional groups of five lines each, symmetrically displaced on either side of the principal resonance by 16 ± 1 G with intensity about 1/500 the height of the principal resonance. This observation can be most readily interpreted as the central two multiplets of the quartet in the spectrum of thianthrene cation with one ^{33}S nucleus (natural abundance 0.74%; $I = \frac{3}{2}$). The ^{33}S splitting is 32 ± 2 G. Further, the peak intensity of the low-field resonance is reported to be about twice that of the high-field multiplet. It is likely that this is a line-width variation; such variations have been employed in other cases to determine the sign of the hyperfine splitting (89).

C. Other Sulfur Radical Cations

The 1,4-dimethyl- and 1,2,4,5-tetramethylthiobenzene cations have been investigated (152,153) and will be discussed in the section on radicals with near degeneracy.

VI. RADICAL CATIONS WITH NEAR DEGENERACY

A. Introduction

In addition to the twofold spin degeneracy a twofold *spatial* degeneracy is theoretically predicted for certain very highly symmetrical radicals. Examples are: $C_3H_3\cdot$, $C_5H_5\cdot$, $C_7H_7\cdot$, $C_6H_6^{\pm}$, $C_8H_8^{\pm}$, coronene$^{\pm}$, triphenylene$^{\pm}$, HMB$^{\pm}$, and hexamethoxybenzene$^{\pm}$. The prediction of spatial degeneracy is illustrated by the HMO theory orbital-energy diagram for $C_6H_6^{+}$ (configurations I and II). Configurations I and II for the π electrons are degenerate.

It is expected that for such radicals consideration of the *vibronic* wave function (154,155) (dynamical Jahn-Teller theory) as well as of the solvent perturbation will lead to a lifting of the degeneracy of the order of 10–1000 cm^{-1}. Thus, these radicals are termed nearly degenerate.

Our goal in this section is to present the *experimental evidence*, which demonstrates that these radicals are indeed nearly degenerate.

(I)   (II)

B. ESR of the Highly Symmetrical Free Radicals

The ESR of these highly symmetrical species in solution has been found to display certain characteristic differences from the spectra of the less symmetrical radicals, such as the perylene, anthracene, and naphthacene cations:

1. The minimum line widths obtained for the symmetrical molecules such as coronene[+] (11), HMB[+] (55,59), hexamethoxybenzene cation (93), and certain neutral radicals and anions (37,40,156,157), are about 0.2–0.25 G, whereas component widths of 0.04 G are observed for the less symmetrical radicals, such as anthracene cation (15). A theory relating the enhanced magnitude of the line width to the near degeneracy has been proposed (155c,158).

2. Spin-lattice relaxation of the highly symmetrical radicals is more efficient. This has been studied experimentally in the cases of $C_6H_6^+$ (18), coronene[+] (11), HMB[+] (55,59), and anion radicals (157,159) and has also been treated theoretically assuming spatial near degeneracy (160).

3. Small, but statistically significant, deviations of the average *g* value from the value predicted by the semiempirical equation of Stone have been noted in several instances of the highly symmetrical hydrocarbon radicals (18,46). It should be recalled that Stone's theory is derived for the case of a *nondegenerate* hydrocarbon radical.

C. Substituted Benzene Cations

Further evidence for the near degeneracy has been obtained from the interpretation of the magnitudes of the splittings in the ESR spectra of derivatives of these symmetrical radicals. Examples are the alkylbenzene (161) and alkylcyclooctatetraene (74) anions, alkylcycloheptatrienyl radicals (162), and a number of substituted benzene cations, which are treated in detail below.

Hyperfine spectra have been reported for the cations of 1,4-dimethoxybenzene, 1,4-dimethylthiobenzene, 1,2,4,5-tetramethylbenzene (durene), 1,2,4,5-tetramethoxybenzene, 1,2,4,5-tetramethylthiobenzene, pentamethylbenzene, and pentamethoxybenzene (55,58,59,93–95,152,153).

A very simple model for these cations is discussed first. Effects of vibronic coupling and of the polar solvent are neglected. The HMO theory, which predicts a twofold spatial degeneracy for the unsubstituted cation, is applied. The substituent groups are included in the calculation through a variation of the coulomb integral at the carbon positions to which they are bonded (163). For the substituents CH_3, OCH_3, and SCH_3, which have common "electron-releasing" character with respect to electrophilic substitution reactions, we choose a perturbation which makes the attached carbon somewhat *less* electronegative ($\alpha' = \alpha_C - p\beta_{CC}$; $1 > p > 0$). This perturbation lifts the degeneracy of the HMO π-electron configurations, but affects the π-electron wave function only slightly.* As a reasonable first approximation the effect on the wave function is neglected. The proper zeroth-order linear combinations of the degenerate molecular orbitals for $C_6H_6^+$ are therefore employed to predict approximate π-spin density distributions in the substituted radicals.

For the various substituted cations cited above, the appropriate linear combinations of the degenerate Hückel molecular orbitals, ω_{+1} and ω_{-1} are:

$$\psi_S = (\omega_{+1} + \omega_{-1})/\sqrt{2}$$

$$= \frac{2}{\sqrt{12}} \sum_{k=1}^{6} \cos\frac{2\pi k}{6} \varphi_k$$

$$= \frac{1}{\sqrt{12}} (\varphi_1 - \varphi_2 - 2\varphi_3 - \varphi_4 + \varphi_5 + 2\varphi_6)$$

and

$$\psi_A = (-i/\sqrt{2})(\omega_{+1} - \omega_{-1})$$

$$= \frac{2}{\sqrt{12}} \sum_{k=1}^{6} \sin\frac{2\pi k}{6} \varphi_k$$

$$= \frac{1}{2} (\varphi_1 + \varphi_2 - \varphi_4 - \varphi_5)$$

where $\omega_{\pm 1} = (1/\sqrt{6}) \sum_{k=1}^{6} \exp(\pm 2\pi i k l/6)\varphi_k$ and φ_k designates a $2p$-π atomic orbital on carbon.

---

* The spin densities corresponding to the molecular orbital ψ_A, which will be introduced below, are not affected at all, and the spin densities corresponding to ψ_S are modified at most by 0.01 for the reasonable choice of parameter, $\alpha' = \alpha_C - 0.1\beta_{CC}$.

The result of an HMO calculation for the disubstituted cations is to put ψ_A below ψ_S; the unpaired electron is therefore in ψ_S as is illustrated below (energy splittings are exaggerated):

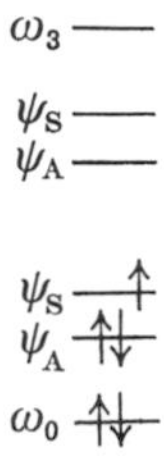

$$
\begin{array}{ll}
\omega_3 & \text{——} \\[4pt]
\psi_S & \text{——} \\
\psi_A & \text{——} \\[10pt]
\psi_S & \uparrow \\
\psi_A & \uparrow\!\downarrow \\
\omega_0 & \uparrow\!\downarrow
\end{array}
$$

For the 1,2,4,5-tetra- and pentasubstituted radicals the ordering is *reversed* and the unpaired electron is predicted to be in ψ_A.

The data required for a comparison of the predicted spin densities with hyperfine splittings is presented in Table XIV. In the first column of this table the predicted spin densities for the various substituted cations are listed.

We consider first the methyl-substituted benzene cations. It is assumed that the methyl (also OCH_3 and SCH_3) proton splitting is directly proportional to the spin density at the adjacent carbon atom and further that the proportionality factor is the same within a series of compounds. The values of the spin densities at the 1,2,4, and 5 positions of durene and pentamethylbenzene cations are predicted to be $\frac{1}{4}$. Corresponding methyl-proton splittings should then be $\frac{6}{4}$ the magnitude of the splitting in HMB^+ ($\rho_k^\pi = \frac{1}{6}$), or about 10 G. Agreement with the experimental values, 11.0, 10.85, and 10.3 G, is quite good. At the 3,6 positions there is a node in the calculated wave function and indeed the splittings are very small—less than the line width for durene cation and less than 0.6 G in the case of pentamethylbenzene cation.

The second group of cations are those derived from methoxybenzenes. At the 1,2,4,5 positions of the tetra- and pentamethoxybenzene cations a splitting of $(\frac{6}{4})(1.4) = 2.1$ G is predicted. Experimental values are 2.21, 2.28, and 1.98 G, in excellent correspondence. At the nodal (3,6) positions splittings are not resolved (< 0.5 G) in the case of pentamethoxybenzene, but for the tetramethoxybenzene cation, $|a_{3,6}^H| = 0.89$ G. Using $|Q_{CH}^H| = 27$ G for these ring protons we compute $|\rho_3^\pi| = |\rho_6^\pi| = 0.03$, which is quite small and hence in good agreement with theory.

For the dimethoxybenzene cation the calculated 3,6 position methoxy-proton splitting ($\rho_{3,6}^\pi = \frac{1}{3}$) is $2(1.4) = 2.8$ G, which deviates by only 15% from the experimental value, 3.30 G. The magnitude of the predicted

1,2,4,5 ring-proton splitting is $(27)(\frac{1}{12}) = 2.2$ G, in fair agreement with the measured 1.56 G splitting.

A similar analysis cannot be made for the alkylthiobenzene cations since the hexamethylthiobenzene cation has not been reported. Two observations can be made however. (*1*) The 3,6 splitting of the tetra-substituted ion is predicted to be zero and actually corresponds to a very small spin density of magnitude 0.03. (*2*) One can predict that the 3,6 splitting of the dimethylthiobenzene ion $(\rho_{3,6}^{\pi} = \frac{1}{3})$ should be $\frac{4}{3}$ the 1,2,4,5 splitting of the tetramethylthiobenzene cation. The experimental ratio is 1.8 and the agreement is only fair.

We have gone through the above rather detailed analysis of the spectra for the substituted benzene cations in order to demonstrate that *a very simple theory, which involves near spatial degeneracy, leads to good agreement with experiment.**

There are a number of refinements to our model which should be considered in any attempt at achieving quantitative accuracy. These are:

1. Delocalization of the π spin into the substituent group through oxygen and sulfur atom conjugation and methyl group hyperconjugation (93,153).

2. Vibronic coupling (155f).

3. Introduction of configuration interaction in the π-electron wave function.

4. Influence of restricted rotation on $a_{OCH_3}^H$ and $a_{SCH_3}^H$ (93,152).

5. Perturbation of the polar solvent.

6. The effect of low-lying excited states.

The last item in the above list is of special interest. It has been found, for certain alkylbenzene anions (161d) and alkylcycloheptatrienyl radicals (162) that the proton hyperfine splittings are *markedly temperature dependent*. This effect has been successfully interpreted in terms of the hypothesis that the energy difference between the ground and lowest-lying excited π configurations is of the order of kT (200 cm^{-1}). Measured splittings are then *statistical averages* of the values in the ground and thermally populated excited states and should be very dependent on temperature. This thermal effect is perhaps the most satisfying evidence of the occurrence of spatial near degeneracy.

A preliminary report (95) of a temperature dependence of the methoxy-proton splitting in the dimethoxydurene cation spectrum may be the first observation of this phenomenon for a substituted benzene cation.

---

* Good agreement has also been obtained using the valence bond method in the case of the alkylbenzene anions (165).

TABLE XIV

Substituted Benzene Cations: Experimental Splittings and Calculated Spin Densities

Predicted spin density distributions		Hyperfine splittings (G)	
		$|a^H_{CH_3}| = 6.53$	$|a^H_{OCH_3}| = 1.3^a$ $= 1.4^b$
		$|a^H_{1,5}| = 10.85$ or 10.3 $|a^H_{2,4}| = 10.3$ or 10.85 $|a^H_3| = 0.56$ $|a^H_6| = $ (Unresolved)	$|a^H_{1,5}| = 2.28$ or 1.98 $|a^H_{2,4}| = 1.98$ or 2.28 $|a^H_3| < 0.5$ (Unresolved) $|a^H_6| < 0.5$ (Unresolved)

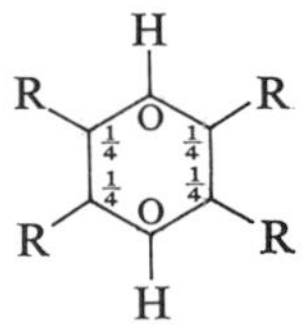

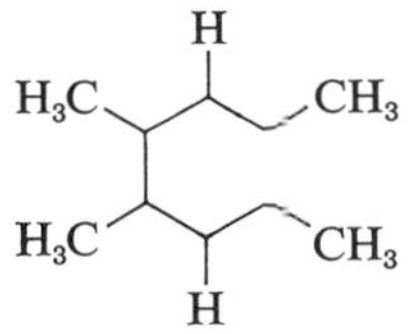

$|a_{CH_3}^H| = 1.0$

$|a_{3,6}^H| = $ (Unresolved)

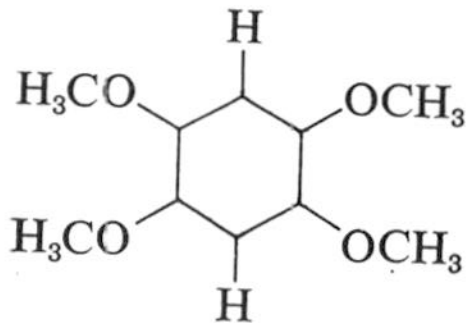

$|a_{OCH_3}^H| = 2.21$

$|a_{3,6}^H| = 0.89$

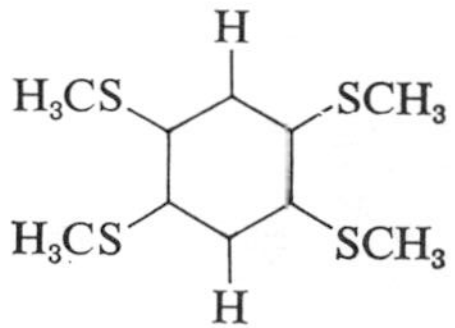

$|a_{SCH_3}^H| = 2.57$

$|a_{3,6}^H| = 0.71$

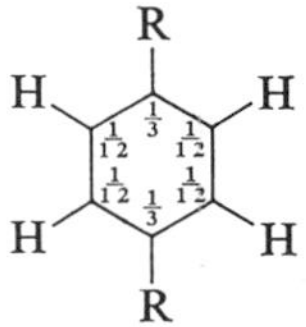

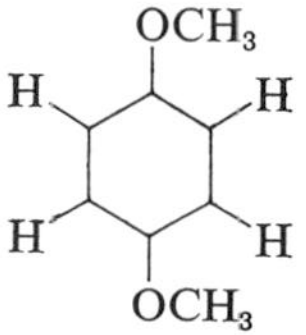

$|a_{OCH_3}^H| = 3.30$

$|a_{1,2,4,5}^H| = 1.56$

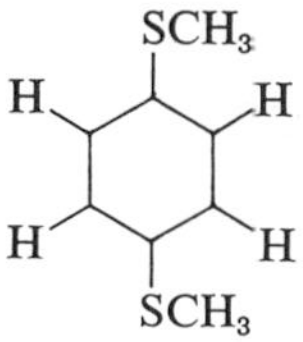

$|a_{SCH_3}^H| = 4.56^a, 5.33^b$

$|a_{1,2,4,5}^H| = $ (Incompletely resolved)

a. Measured in CH_3CN.

b. Measured in 96% sulfuric acid.

D. Other Cations with Near Degeneracy

Other cations possessing spatial near degeneracy have been investigated. These are (*1*) an alkyl-substituted $C_{14}H_{14}^{+}$, *trans*-15,16-dimethyldihydropyrene cation (57) and (*2*) the pentaphenylcyclopentadienyl cation which has a singlet ground state and a low-lying triplet state (166).

VII. RADICAL CATIONS OF BIOLOGICAL INTEREST

A. Protonated Semiquinones of Riboflavin and Related Radicals

The protonated semiquinone anions formed by reduction of riboflavin (**15**) and related molecules in acid medium have been the subject of numer-

$$R = CH_2(CHOH)_3CH_2OH$$

(**15**)

ous investigations (167–179). These free radicals are of interest because of the possible role of flavin semiquinones as intermediates in some enzymic reactions. Electron spin resonance and optical studies of radicals formed by flavoproteins at intermediate oxidation stages are indeed indicative of the occurrence of flavin semiquinones (167–176).

Protonated flavin radicals derived from the model compounds riboflavin, FMN (riboflavin-5′-phosphate), and FAD (flavin adenine dinucleotide) have been investigated, but the spectra have been only partially resolved. In order to obtain further information regarding the magnitudes of splittings arising from the isoalloxazine nucleus and the assignment of splittings to positions, the ESR of a series of alkyl-, halo-, and isotopically substituted isoalloxazine and alloxazine semiquinone cations has been studied (177–179). Unfortunately, an unequivocal interpretation of these spectra is still not available (180).

B. Cations of Phenothiazine Drug Derivatives

Phenothiazine drug derivatives, such as chlorpromazine, trifluoropromazine, trifluoroperazine, and promazine, have been treated with a variety of oxidizing agents to form the radical cations (114,117,181–183). The ESR spectra have not been completely resolved, but are characterized by a nitrogen splitting of about 6 G. This is in good agreement with the 6.5 G nitrogen splitting reported for the phenothiazine cation (138).

Ohnishi and McConnell (184) have reported an interesting study of the interaction of the chlorpromazine cation (CPZ$^+$) with DNA. This ion radical has a similar structure to certain mutagenic acridine dyes which are known to intercalate in DNA.

These investigators have added CPZ$^+$ to solutions of calf thymus DNA (one radical per five base pairs) and have found that CPZ$^+$ is *markedly stabilized*. They have studied the ESR of such samples. By flowing the solution through the resonant cavity in directions perpendicular and parallel to the external field, they line up the helix axes correspondingly and observe gross changes in the CPZ$^+$ spectrum. An analysis of the "perpendicular-flow," "parallel-flow," and "no-flow" spectra in terms of the theory of anisotropic hyperfine interactions, leads to the conclusion that the aromatic plane of CPZ$^+$ is *perpendicular* to the helix axis—that is to say, CPZ$^+$ has intercalated in DNA.

Referring to a suggestion by Piette, Bulow, and Yamazaki (183) that CPZ$^+$ may be responsible for the psychotropic activity of the tranquilizer chlorpromazine, Ohnishi and McConnell state that "a direct causal relationship between intercalation in DNA (or RNA) and the psychotropic activity of CPZ$^+$ is . . . an interesting possibility" (184).

C. Cation Radicals Derived from Hormones

Borg (185,186) has investigated the initial redox reactions of a number of hormones and their analogs *in vitro* and has detected free radicals, most of which are short-lived. The oxidation-reduction potentials of the reactions studied are within the range of oxidative metabolism and the author states that "presumably the free-radical forms are relevant to some of the physiological chemistry of the same hormones *in vivo*."

Radicals are generated by ceric-ion oxidation of epinephrine, norepinephrine, dopa (dihydroxyphenylalanine), and phenylephrine in acid, and their hyperfine spectra are partially resolved; these species are presumably protonated orthosemiquinones. A high-velocity continuous-flow apparatus is employed because of the short lifetimes of these radicals ("reducing the dead time for flow from the locus of reaction to the midsection of the detection volume from about 12 to 5 msec increased the EPR signal amplitude of epinephrine oxidized by cerium by roughly 45 percent").

The corresponding semiquinones in alkaline media have also been generated and in general have longer lifetimes (≈ 0.1 sec), different hyperfine patterns, and a smaller total extent of spectrum than the acid-stabilized species.

Further, a free radical has been produced by TiCl$_3$ reduction of adenochrome in acid.

Radical cations from the oxidation of tryptamine, indole hormones (indole acetic and butyric acids), estrogens (17-β-estradiol, estriol, and estrone; hexestrol and diethylstilbestrol), and the protein hormone insulin have also been investigated. Spectra from tryptamine, indole acetic and indole butyric acid are similar; likewise for estradiol, estriol, and estrone. The resolved hyperfine structure observed for the insulin radical in solution is evidence for at least partial motional averaging of the anisotropic hyperfine interaction in macromolecules bearing free-radical moieties.*

D. The Chlorophyll Radical Cation

The chlorophyll radical cation has been invoked as a participant in the photosynthetic process and is therefore of considerable interest. As far as we are aware no ESR study of this radical has appeared in print. Further the ESR signals detected in photosynthetic systems have not been ascribable to this species.

Tollin and Green (188) have investigated the light-induced single-electron transfer reactions between chlorophyll *a* and quinones in solution. In these model systems only the spectra of the semiquinones, produced by electron transfer, are detected.

VIII. PREPARATION OF RADICAL CATIONS

A. Reagents

A great variety of reagents have been employed in the oxidation of π-electron molecules to form radical cations. A *sample* of these, with representative literature references for each, follows: concentrated sulfuric acid (6,12), concentrated sulfuric plus organic solvents (19), concentrated sulfuric plus trace H_2O_2, $FeCl_3$, $KMnO_4$,...(91), methane sulfonic acid in nitrobenzene (21), fuming sulfuric acid (58,59), ceric ion in dilute sulfuric acid (125), iodine (121), molten iodine (9,126), silver perchlorate (121), $SbCl_5$ in CH_2Cl_2 (17), $SbCl_5$ in C_6H_6–CH_3NO_2 (146), $AlCl_3$ in CH_3NO_2 (95,189), SO_2–BF_3 (54), lead tetraacetate and BF_3 (94), *hv* (photoionization in liquid solution) (55), *hv* (photoionization in solid solution) (18,190), and e^- (electrolytic oxidation) (21,93,113,117,121,149).

B. Mechanism

The mechanism of the formation of radical cations has been discussed in numerous studies (6,10,93,117,137,143,191–194). On the basis of the results of these investigations one can state the requirements for the

---

* McConnell and co-workers have recently made several studies of the mobility of nitroxide radicals bonded to selected sites in a variety of macromolecules of biological interest (187).

formation of an appreciable concentration of radical cation in systems involving chemical oxidation. The *oxidation potential* of the π-electron molecule should be relatively small, the *electron affinity* of the oxidizing agent relatively large and the solvent should be of *maximum polarity* in order to stabilize the ionic reaction products.

A few applications of these requirements to specific cases are discussed.

1. The higher oxidation potentials of benzene, alkyl-substituted benzenes, naphthalene, and alkyl-substituted naphthalenes relative to the values for compounds, such as anthracene and naphthacene, explains the fact that cations of the first group of hydrocarbons have not been prepared in solution whereas the anthracene and naphthacene cations have been made.

2. A recent report illustrates the role of the oxidizing agent and solvent in promoting cation formation (95). For the compounds 1,4-dimethoxybenzene and 1,4-diethoxybenzene, the radical concentration obtained using $AlCl_3$ in CH_3NO_2 is approximately 100% whereas considerably less than 1% of the aromatic is converted to the cation in the traditional reagent, concentrated sulfuric acid.*

3. The role of solvent polarity in promoting electron transfer has been demonstrated in studies of the oxidation of *N,N,N',N'*-tetramethyl-*p*-phenylenediamine (TMPD) by tetrachloro-*p*-benzoquinone (chloranil) (193). In nonpolar solvents, such as benzene, dioxane, chloroform, and ethylene dichloride, a charge-transfer complex is formed but no spin resonance signal is detected. If an equimolar solution of TMPD and chloranil is prepared in *polar* solvents, such as acetonitrile or ethanol, ESR spectra of both the TMPD cation and chloranil anion are observed. In mixed ethanol–chloroform solvents the signal strength is found to increase with increasing polarity of the medium. Charge-transfer absorption of the TMPD–chloranil complex is initially observed in the polar solvents, but its intensity decreases as the electron transfer proceeds to completion:

$$D + A \rightleftharpoons DA \rightleftharpoons D^+ + A^- \qquad (28)$$

where D = electron donor and A − electron acceptor. The polar solvent enhances the formation of the radical cation through stabilization of D^+ and A^- and perhaps also through enhancement of the polar ("dative") contribution to the ground state of the intermediate complex DA.

C. Cations in Friedel-Crafts Reaction Mixtures

An interesting instance of radical cation formation has been investigated in connection with the Friedel-Crafts alkylation reaction (195–197).

* The formation of proton adducts in concentrated sulfuric acid is a competing process which will in general lower the yield of radical cations in that medium.

Although this reaction is known to have an ionic mechanism, free radicals have been observed in the following reaction mixtures: $AlCl_3$ in benzene plus (*1*) dichloromethane, (*2*) benzyl chloride, (*3*) 1,2-dichloroethane, or (*4*) 1-chlorobutane. As the temperature of these chilled mixtures is allowed to approach room temperature, the reaction produces a separate, highly colored phase in the bottom of the tube. Bubbles of HCl are released from the interface of the two solution phases. An ESR signal is observed only when the interface and the highly colored phase are in the resonant cavity.

A single narrow line ($\Delta H_{ms} < 1$ G) is observed, which grows in intensity with time. Then a spectrum with 19 hyperfine components, centered at $g = 2.0025$, appears. This hyperfine spectrum has been found to be identical with that of the anthracene cation, generated by adding anthracene to $AlCl_3$–$CHCl_3$. Thus, it is concluded that the free radical observed in Friedel-Crafts reaction mixtures is not an intermediate of that reaction but is the result of Lewis-acid oxidation of the side product anthracene.

Acknowledgments

Support from the U.S. Army Research Office, Durham, North Carolina, and from the Petroleum Research Fund, administered by the American Chemical Society, is gratefully acknowledged. I would also like to thank Mrs. Donna Jones for her expert typing of the manuscript.

References

1. Y. Yokozawa and I. Miyashita, *J. Chem. Phys.*, **25**, 796 (1956).
2. C. MacLean and J. H. Van der Waals, *J. Chem. Phys.*, **27**, 827 (1957).
3. S. I. Weissman, E. de Boer, and J. J. Conradi, *J. Chem. Phys.*, **26**, 963 (1957).
4. H. Kon and M. S. Blois, Jr., *J. Chem. Phys.*, **28**, 743 (1958).
5. E. de Boer and S. I. Weissman, *J. Am. Chem. Soc.*, **80**, 4549 (1958).
6. A. Carrington, F. Dravnieks, and M. C. R. Symons, *J. Chem. Soc.*, **1959**, 947.
7. C. A. McDowell and J. R. Rowlands, *Can. J. Chem.*, **38**, 503 (1960).
8. H. M. Buck, W. Bloemhoff, and L. J. Oosterhoff, *Tetrahedron Letters*, **1960**, 5.
9. J. Kommandeur, *Mol. Phys.*, **4**, 509 (1961).
10. W. I. Aalbersberg, J. Gaaf, and E. L. Mackor, *J. Chem. Soc.*, **1961**, 905.
11. J. R. Bolton and A. Carrington, *Mol. Phys.*, **4**, 271 (1961).
12. J. S. Hyde and H. W. Brown, *J. Chem. Phys.*, **37**, 368 (1962).
13. A. Carrington and J. Dos Santos-Veiga, *Mol. Phys.*, **5**, 285 (1962).
14. E. C. Baughan, T. P. Jones, and L. G. Stoodley, *Proc. Chem. Soc.*, **1963**, 274.
15. J. R. Bolton and G. K. Fraenkel, *J. Chem. Phys.*, **40**, 3307 (1964).
16. F. Hughes, R. D. Kirk, and F. W. Patten, *J. Chem. Phys.*, **40**, 872 (1964).
17. I. C. Lewis and L. S. Singer, *J. Chem. Phys.*, **43**, 2712 (1965).
18. M. K. Carter and G. Vincow, *Bull. Am. Phys. Soc.*, **10**, 374 (1965); M. K. Carter and G. Vincow, *J. Chem. Phys.*, **47**, 292 (1967).
19. L. O. Wheeler, K. S. V. Santhanam, and A. J. Bard, *J. Phys. Chem.*, **70**, 404 (1966).
20. K. W. Bowers and F. J. Weigert, *J. Chem. Phys.*, **44**, 416 (1966); J. R. Bolton (to be published).

21. P. A. Malachesky, L. S. Marcoux, and R. N. Adams, *J. Chem. Phys.*, **70**, 2064 (1966).

22. S. I. Weissman, *J. Chem. Phys.*, **22**, 1378 (1954).

23. (a) H. M. McConnell, *J. Chem. Phys.*, **24**, 632, 764 (1956); (b) H. M. McConnell. *Proc. Natl. Acad. Sci. U.S.*, **43**, 721 (1957); (c) B. Venkataraman and G. K. Fraenkel, *J. Chem. Phys.*, **24**, 737 (1956); (d) R. Bersohn, *ibid.*, **24**, 1066 (1956); (e) S. I. Weissman, *ibid.*, **25**, 890 (1956).

25. (a) H. M. McConnell and D. B. Chesnut, *J. Chem. Phys.*, **28**, 107 (1958); (b) H. M. McConnell, *ibid*, **28**, 1188 (1958).

26. A. D. McLachlan, H. H. Dearman, and R. Lefebvre, *J. Chem. Phys.*, **33**, 65 (1960).

28. L. C. Snyder and T. Amos, *J. Chem. Phys.*, **42**, 3670 (1965).

29. A. D. McLachlan, *Mol. Phys.*, **3**, 233 (1960).

30. A. D. McLachlan, *Mol. Phys.*, **2**, 271 (1959).

32. J. R. Bolton, *J. Chem. Phys.*, **43**, 309 (1965).

33. J. P. Colpa and J. R. Bolton, *Mol. Phys.*, **6**, 273 (1963).

34. J. Higuchi, *J. Chem. Phys.*, **39**, 3455 (1963).

35. G. Giacometti, P. L. Nordio, and M. V. Pavan, *Theoret. Chim. Acta (Berlin)*, **1**, 404 (1963).

37. R. W. Fessenden and S. Ogawa, *J. Am. Chem. Soc.*, **86**, 3591 (1964).

38. J. Gendell, J. H. Freed, and G. K. Fraenkel, *J. Chem. Phys.*, **37**, 2832 (1962).

39. I. A. Zlochower, W. R. Miller, Jr., and G. K. Fraenkel, *J. Chem. Phys.*, **42**, 3339 (1965).

40. G. Vincow, M. L. Morrell, W. V. Volland, H. J. Dauben, Jr., and F. R. Hunter, *J. Am. Chem. Soc.*, **87**, 3527 (1965).

41. M. R. Das and G. K. Fraenkel, *J. Chem. Phys.*, **42**, 792 (1965).

42. D. M. Schrader and M. Karplus, *J. Chem. Phys.*, **40**, 1593 (1964).

43. M. Karplus and G. K. Fraenkel, *J. Chem. Phys.*, **35**, 1312 (1961).

44. F. Gerson and J. Heinzer, *Chem. Commun.*, **1965**, 488.

45. I. C. Lewis and L. S. Singer, *J. Chem. Phys.*, **44**, 2082 (1966).

46. B. G. Segal, M. Kaplan, and G. K. Fraenkel, *J. Chem. Phys.*, **43**, 4191 (1965).

47. M. S. Blois, H. W. Brown, and J. E. Maling, *Arch. Sci. (Geneva)*, **13** No. FASC. SPEC., 243 (1960).

48. K. Mobius, Talk delivered at XIV Colloque Ampere, Ljubljana, Yugoslavia, 1966.

49. H. M. McConnell and R. E. Robertson, *J. Phys. Chem.*, **61**, 1018 (1957).

50. A. J. Stone, *Mol. Phys.*, **6**, 509 (1963); **7**, 311 (1964).

51. J. A. Brivati, R. Hulme, and M. C. R. Symons, *Proc. Chem. Soc.*, **1961**, 384.

52. J. R. Bolton, A. Carrington, and A. D. McLachlan, *Mol. Phys.*, **5**, 31 (1962).

53. E. de Boer and E. L. Mackor, *Mol. Phys.*, **5**, 493 (1962).

54. J. P. Colpa and E. de Boer, *Mol. Phys.*, **7**, 333 (1963–64).

55. R. Hulme and M. C. R. Symons, *Proc. Chem. Soc.*, **1963**, 241; *J. Chem. Soc.*, **1965**, 1120.

56. J. Dos Santos-Veiga, *Rev. Port. Quim.*, **6**, 1 (1964).

57. F. Gerson, E. Heilbronner, and V. Boekelheide, *Helv. Chim. Acta*, **47**, 1123 (1964).

58. R. Hulme and M. C. R. Symons, *Nature*, **206**, 293 (1965).

59. M. K. Carter and G. Vincow, *Bull. Am. Phys. Soc.*, **10**, 374 (1965); M. K. Carter and G. Vincow *J. Chem Phys.*, **47**, 302 (1967).

60. L. S. Singer and I. C. Lewis, *J. Am. Chem. Soc.*, **87**, 4695 (1965).

61. R. W. Fessenden and R. H. Schuler, *J. Chem. Phys.*, **39**, 2147 (1963).
62. C. de Waard and J. C. M. Henning, *Phys. Letters*, **4**, 31 (1963).
63. R. Bersohn, *J. Chem. Phys.*, **24**, 1066 (1956).
64. D. B. Chesnut, *J. Chem. Phys.*, **29**, 43 (1958); S. Aono and J. Higuchi, *Progr. Theoret. Phys.* (*Kyoto*), **28**, 589 (1962).
65. A. D. McLachlan, *Mol. Phys.*, **1**, 233 (1958).
66. P. G. Lykos, *J. Chem. Phys.*, **32**, 625 (1960).
67. R. S. Mulliken, C. A. Rieke, and W. G. Brown, *J. Am. Chem. Soc.*, **63**, 41 (1941).
68. C. A. Coulson and V. A. Crawford, *J. Chem. Soc.*, **1953**, 2052.
69. A. Streitwieser, Jr., *Molecular Orbital Theory for Organic Chemists*, Wiley, New York, 1961, p. 131 ff and references cited therein.
70. D. Lazdins and M. Karplus, *J. Chem. Phys.*, **44**, 1600 (1966).
71. P. Nordio, M. V. Pavan, and G. Giacometti, *Theoret. Chim. Acta* (*Berlin*), **1**, 302 (1963).
72. D. Bachmann, *Z. Physik. Chem.* (Frankfurt), **43**, 198 (1964).
73. M. D. Sevilla and G. Vincow, *Abstr. Am. Chem. Soc.* (*Atlantic City*) *150th Meeting*, p. 39V (1965); M. D. Sevilla and G. Vincow (to be published).
74. A. Carrington and P. F. Todd, *Mol. Phys.*, **7**, 533 (1963–64); **8**, 299 (1964).
75. C. Heller and H. M. McConnell, *J. Chem. Phys.*, **32**, 1535, (1960); D. Pooley and D. H. Whiffen, *Mol. Phys.*, **4**, 81 (1961); J. R. Morton and A. Horsfield, *ibid.*, **4**, 219 (1961); A. Horsfield, J. R. Morton, and D. H. Whiffen, *Mol. Phys.*, **4**, 425 (1961); I. Miyagawa and K. Itoh, *J. Chem. Phys.*, **36**, 2157 (1962); J. R. Morton, *ibid.*, **41**, 2956 (1964).
76. E. W. Stone and A. H. Maki, *J. Chem. Phys.*, **37**, 1326 (1962).
77. R. W. Fessenden, *J. Chim. Phys.*, **61**, 1570 (1964).
78. J. J. Rush and T. I. Taylor, *J. Phys. Chem.*, **68**, 2534 (1964).
79. J. H. Freed, *J. Chem. Phys.*, **43**, 1710 (1965).
80. E. de Boer and A. P. Praat, *Mol. Phys.*, **8**, 291 (1964).
81. G. Vincow and G. K. Fraenkel, *J. Chem. Phys.*, **34**, 1333 (1961).
82. R. W. Brandon and E. A. C. Lucken, *J. Chem. Soc.*, **1961**, 4273; Y. Matsunaga, *Bull. Chem. Soc. Japan*, **33**, 1436 (1960).
83. B. C. Gilbert et al., *Chem. Commun.*, **1966**, 161.
84. (a) J. R. Bolton, A. Carrington, and J. Dos Santos-Veiga, *Mol. Phys.*, **5**, 465 (1962); (b) J. R. Bolton and A. Carrington, *Proc. Chem. Soc.*, **1961**, 174; (c) **1961**, 385.
85. S. Goodman, Dissertation, Columbia University, 1962; *Abstr. Papers Am. Chem. Soc.*, 46R (1959).
86. B. Venkataraman, B. G. Segal, and G. K. Fraenkel, *J. Chem. Phys.*, **30**, 1006 (1959).
87. J. R. Bolton and A. Carrington, *Mol. Phys.*, **5**, 161 (1962).
88. J. R. Bolton, A. Carrington, and P. F. Todd, *ibid.*, **6**, 169 (1963).
89. G. K. Fraenkel, *J. Phys. Chem.*, **71**, 139 (1967).
90. (a) G. A. Russell, E. R. Talaty, and M. C. Young, *J. Phys. Chem.*, **70**, 1321 (1966); (b) G. A. Russell, E. T. Strom, E. R. Talaty, and S. A. Weiner, *J. Am. Chem. Soc.*, **88**, 1998 (1966); (c) G. A. Russell and M. C. Young, *ibid.*, **88**, 2007 (1966).
91. (a) M. Tomita, S. Ueda, Y. Nakai, Y. Deguchi, and H. Takaki, *Tetrahedron Letters*, **1963**, 1189, 1920; (b) M. Tomita and S. Ueda, *Chem. and Pharm. Bull.* (*Japan*), **12**, 33, 40 (1964).
92. T. N. Tozer and L. D. Tuck, *J. Chem. Phys.*, **38**, 3035 (1963).

93. A. Zweig, W. G. Hodgson, and W. H. Jura, *J. Am. Chem. Soc.*, **86**, 4124 (1964).
94. D. L. Allara, B. C. Gilbert, and R. O. C. Norman, *Chem. Commun.*, **1965**, 319.
95. W. F. Forbes and P. D. Sullivan, *J. Am. Chem. Soc.*, **88**, 2862 (1966).
96. Y. Fellion and J. Uebersfeld, *Arch. Sci. (Geneva)*, **10**, 95 (1957).
97. Y. Matsunaga and C. A. McDowell, *Proc. Chem. Soc.*, **1960**, 175.
98. K. H. Hausser, A. Häbich, and V. Franzen, *Z. Naturforsch.*, **16a**, 836 (1961).
99. D. W. Schieser and P. Zvirblis, *J. Chem. Phys.*, **36**, 2237 (1962).
100. F. Bruin, F. W. Heineken, M. Bruin, and A. Zahlan, *J. Chem. Phys.*, **36**, 2783 (1962).
101. (a) C. S. Johnson, Jr., R. E. Visco, H. S. Gutowsky, and A. M. Hartley, *J. Chem. Phys.*, **37**, 1580 (1962); (b) C. S. Johnson, Jr. and H. S. Gutowsky, *ibid.*, **39**, 58 (1963).
102. E. W. Stone and A. H. Maki, *J. Chem. Phys.*, **39**, 1635 (1963).
103. B. L. Barton and G. K. Fraenkel, *J. Chem. Phys.*, **41**, 695 (1964).
104. B. L. Barton and G. K. Fraenkel, *J. Chem. Phys.*, **41**, 1455 (1964).
105. F. Corre and S. Odiot, *J. Chim. Phys.*, **62**, 1202 (1965).
106. A. Carrington and J. Dos Santos-Veiga, *Mol. Phys.*, **5**, 21 (1962).
107. J. C. M. Henning, *J. Chem. Phys.*, **44**, 2139 (1966).
108. R. L. Ward, *J. Am. Chem. Soc.*, **84**, 332 (1962).
109. F. Gerson, *Helv. Chim. Acta*, **47**, 1484 (1964).
110. S. I. Weissman, J. Townsend, D. E. Paul, and G. E. Pake, *J. Chem. Phys.*, **21**, 2227 (1953); S. I. Weissman, *J. Chem. Phys.*, **22**, 1135 (1954).
111. T. R. Tuttle, Jr., *J. Chem. Phys.*, **30**, 331 (1959).
112. K. H. Hausser, *Naturwissenschaften*, **47**, 251 (1960).
113. M. T. Melchior and A. H. Maki, *J. Chem. Phys.*, **34**, 471 (1961).
114. L. H. Piette, P. Ludwig, and R. N. Adams, *J. Am. Chem. Soc.*, **83**, 3909 (1961).
115. D. H. Anderson, R. M. Elofson, H. S. Gutowsky, S. Levine, and R. B. Sandin, *J. Am. Chem. Soc.*, **83**, 3157 (1961).
116. Z. Galus and R. N. Adams, *J. Chem. Phys.*, **36**, 2814 (1962).
117. L. II. Piette, P. Ludwig, and R. N. Adams, *Anal. Chem.*, **34**, 916 (1962).
118. J. R. Bolton, A. Carrington, and J. Dos Santos-Veiga, *Mol. Phys.*, **5**, 615 (1962).
119. K. H. Hausser, *Mol. Phys.*, **7**, 195 (1963–64).
120. J. M. Fritsch and R. N. Adams, *J. Chem. Phys.*, **43**, 1887 (1965).
121. P. Smejtek, J. Honzl, and V. Metalova, *Collection Czech. Chem. Commun.*, **30**, 3875 (1965).
122. F. Tonnard, *Compt. Rend.*, **260**, 2793 (1965).
123. (a) R. Drews, D. Cadena, Jr., and J. Rowlands, *Can. J. Chem.*, **43**, 2439 (1965); (b) A. J. Tench, *J. Chem. Phys.*, **38**, 593 (1963).
124. T. Cole, *J. Chem. Phys.*, **35**, 1169 (1961); J. S. Hyde and E. S. Freeman, *J. Phys. Chem.*, **65**, 1636 (1961); M. Fujimoto and J. R. Morton, *Can. J. Chem.*, **43**, 1012 (1965).
125. J. Q. Adams and J. R. Thomas, *J. Chem. Phys.*, **39**, 1904 (1963).
126. D. N. Stamires and J. Turkevich, *J. Am. Chem. Soc.*, **85**, 2557 (1963).
127. M. R. Das, A. V. Patankar, and B. Venkataraman, *Proc. Indian Acad. Sci.*, **53**, 273 (1961).
128. G. A. Razuvaev, G. A. Abakumov, and V. A. Pestunovich, *Zh. Strukt. Khim.*, **5**, 307 (1964).
129. J. P. Billon, G. Cauquis, J. Combrisson, and A. M. Li, *Bull. Soc. Chim. France*, **1960**, 2062.
130. C. Lagercrantz, *Acta Chem. Scand.*, **15**, 1545 (1961).

131. J. P. Billon, G. Cauquis, and J. Combrisson, *Compt. Rend.*, **253**, 1593 (1961).

132. F. W. Heineken, M. Bruin, and F. Bruin, *J. Chem. Phys.*, **37**, 1479 (1962).

133. D. Gagnaire, H. Lemaire, A. Rassat, and P. Servoz-Gavin, *Compt. Rend.*, **255**, 1441 (1962).

134. C. Bodea and I. Silberg, *Nature*, **198**, 883 (1963).

135. J. P. Billon, G. Cauquis, and J. Combrisson, *J. Chim. Phys.*, **61**, 374 (1964).

136. S. Odiot and F. Tonnard, *J. Chim. Phys.*, **61**, 382 (1964).

137. H. J. Shine and E. E. Mach, *J. Org. Chem.*, **30**, 2130 (1965).

138. B. C. Gilbert, P. Hanson, R. O. C. Norman, and B. T. Sutcliffe, *Chem. Commun.*, **1966**, 161.

139. J. M. Hirshon, D. M. Gardner, and G. K. Fraenkel, *J. Am. Chem. Soc.*, **75**, 4115 (1953).

140. J. E. Wertz and J. L. Vivo, *J. Chem. Phys.*, **23**, 2193 (1955).

141. A. Fava, P. B. Sogo, and M. Calvin, *J. Am. Chem. Soc.*, **79**, 1078 (1957).

142. E. A. C. Lucken, *J. Chem. Soc.*, **1962**, 4963.

143. H. J. Shine and L. Piette, *J. Am. Chem. Soc.*, **84**, 4798 (1962).

144. M. Kinoshita and H. Akamatu, *Bull. Chem. Soc. Japan*, **35**, 1040 (1962).

145. M. Kinoshita, *Bull. Chem. Soc. Japan*, **35**, 1137 (1962).

146. E. A. C. Lucken, *Theoret. Chim. Acta (Berlin)*, **1**, 397 (1963).

147. H. J. Shine, C. F. Dais, and R. J. Small, *J. Chem. Phys.*, **38**, 569 (1963).

148. W. Rundel and K. Scheffler, *Tetrahedron Letters*, **1963**, 993.

149. H. J. Shine, C. F. Dais, and R. J. Small, *J. Org. Chem.*, **29**, 21 (1964).

150. B. Lamotte, A. Rassat, and P. Servoz-Gavin, *Compt. Rend.*, **255**, 1508 (1962).

151. U. Schmidt, K. Kabitzke, and K. Markau, *Angew. Chem.*, **72**, 708 (1960).

152. A. Zweig, W. G. Hodgson, W. H. Jura, and D. L. Maricle, *Tetrahedron Letters*, **1963**, 1821.

153. A. Zweig and W. G. Hodgson, *Proc. Chem. Soc.*, **1964**, 417.

154. (a) A. D. Liehr, *Z. Physik. Chem. (Frankfurt)*, **9**, 338 (1956); (b) J. P. Colpa, *Proc. Inter. Meeting Mol. Spectr., 4th, Bologna*, **1**, 210 (1959), published 1962; (c) L. C. Snyder, *J. Chem. Phys.*, **33**, 619 (1960); (d) A. D. Liehr, *Z. Naturforsch.*, **16a**, 641 (1961); (e) L. C. Snyder, *J. Phys. Chem.*, **66**, 2299 (1962); (f) C. A. Coulson and A. Golebiewski, *Mol. Phys.*, **5**, 71 (1962).

155. (a) W. D. Hobey and A. D. McLachlan, *J. Chem. Phys.*, **33**, 1695 (1960); (b) A. D. McLachlan, *Mol. Phys.*, **4**, 417 (1961); (c) H. M. McConnell and A. D. McLachlan, *J. Chem. Phys.*, **34**, 1 (1961); (d) A. D. McLachlan and L. C. Snyder, *ibid.*, **36**, 1159 (1962); (e) A. D. Liehr, *Ann. Rev. Phys. Chem.*, **13**, 41 (1962); (f) W. D. Hobey, *J. Chem. Phys.*, **43**, 2187 (1965).

156. (a) T. J. Katz and H. L. Strauss, *J. Chem. Phys.*, **32**, 1873 (1960); (b) H. L. Strauss, T. J. Katz, and G. K. Fraenkel, *J. Am. Chem. Soc.*, **85**, 2360 (1963).

157. M. G. Townsend and S. I. Weissman, *J. Chem. Phys.*, **32**, 309 (1960).

158. J. H. Freed, *J. Chem. Phys.*, **43**, 1427 (1965).

159. M. T. Jones, *J. Chem. Phys.*, **42**, 4054 (1965).

160. H. M. McConnell, *J. Chem. Phys.*, **34**, 13 (1961).

161. (a) T. R. Tuttle, Jr. and S. I. Weissman *J. Am. Chem. Soc.*, **80**, 5342 (1958); (b) V. V. Voevodskii, S. P. Solodovnikov, and V. N. Chibrikin, *Dokl. Akad. Nauk SSSR*, **129**, 1082 (1959); (c) J. R. Bolton and A. Carrington, *Mol. Phys.*, **4**, 497 (1961); (d) T. R. Tuttle, Jr., *J. Am. Chem. Soc.*, **84**, 1492, 2839 (1962); (e) J. R. Bolton, A. Carrington, A. Forman, and L. E. Orgel, *Mol. Phys.*, **5**, 43 (1962); (f) J. R. Bolton, *J. Chem. Phys.*, **41**, 2455 (1964).

162. G. Vincow, L. M. Morrell, F. R. Hunter, and H. J. Dauben, Jr., *J. Chem. Phys.* (to be published).

163. (a) D. Lazdins and M. Karplus, *J. Am. Chem. Soc.*, **87**, 920 (1965); (b) C. de Waard and J. C. M. Henning, *Phys. Letters*, **4**, 31 (1963); (c) R. L. Flurry, Jr. and P. G. Lykos, *Mol. Phys.*, **6**, 283 (1963).

165. T. H. Brown, M. Karplus, and J. C. Schug, *J. Chem. Phys.*, **38**, 1749 (1963); T. H. Brown and M. Karplus, *ibid.*, **39**, 1115 (1963).

166. R. Breslow, H. W. Chang, and W. A. Yager, *J. Am. Chem. Soc.*, **85**, 2033 (1963).

167. A. Ehrenberg, *Acta Chem. Scand.*, **11**, 205 (1957).

168. A. Ehrenberg and G. D. Ludwig, *Science*, **127**, 1177 (1958).

169. B. Commoner, B. B. Lippincott, and J. V. Passonneau, *Proc. Natl. Acad. Sci. U.S.*, **44**, 1099 (1958).

170. B. Commoner and B. B. Lippincott, *Proc. Natl. Acad. Sci. U.S.*, **44**, 1110 (1958).

171. A. Ehrenberg, *Acta Chem. Scand.*, **14**, 766 (1960).

172. I. Isenberg, A. Szent-Györgyi, and S. L. Baird, Jr., *Proc. Natl. Acad. Sci. U.S.*, **46**, 1307 (1960).

173. H. Beinert and R. H. Sands in *Free Radicals in Biological Systems*, M. S. Blois, Jr., et al., Eds., Academic Press, New York, London, 1961, Chapter 2.

174. A. Ehrenberg in *Free Radicals in Biological Systems*, M. S. Blois, Jr. et al., Eds., Academic Press, New York, London, 1961, Chapter 27.

175. H. Beinert, W. Heinen, and G. Palmer, *Brookhaven Symp. Biol.*, **15**, 229 (1962).

176. P. Hemmerich, D. V. Dervartanian, C. Veeger, and J. D. W. van Voorst, *Biochim. Biophys. Acta*, **77**, 504 (1963).

177. A. V. Guzzo and G. Tollin, *Arch. Biochem. Biophys.*, **103**, 231, 244 (1963).

178. A. V. Guzzo and G. Tollin, *Arch. Biochem. Biophys.*, **105**, 380 (1964).

179. A. Ehrenberg and L. E. G. Eriksson, *Arch. Biochem. Biophys.*, **105**, 453 (1964).

180. G. Tollin (private communication).

181. L. H. Piette and I. S. Forrest, *Biochim. Biophys. Acta*, **57**, 419 (1962).

182. D. C. Borg and G. C. Cotzias, *Proc. Natl. Acad. Sci. U.S.*, **48**, 617, 623, 643 (1962).

183. L. H. Piette, G. Bulow, and I. Yamazaki, *Biochim. Biophys. Acta*, **88**, 120 (1964).

184. S. Ohnishi and H. M. McConnell, *J. Am. Chem. Soc.*, **87**, 2293 (1965).

185. D. C. Borg, *Proc. Natl. Acad. Sci. U.S.*, **53**, 633 (1965).

186. D. C. Borg, *Proc. Natl. Acad. Sci. U.S.*, **53**, 829 (1965).

187. O. H. Griffith and H. M. McConnell, *Proc. Natl. Acad. Sci. U.S.*, **55**, 8 (1966) and references cited therein.

188. G. Tollin and G. Green, *Biochim. Biophys. Acta*, **60**, 524 (1962); **66**, 308 (1963).

189. H. M. Buck, W. Bloemhoff, and L. J. Oosterhoff, *Tetrahedron Letters*, **1960**, 5.

190. G. Vincow and P. M. Johnson, *J. Chem. Phys.*, **39**, 1143 (1963).

191. W. I. Aalbersberg, G. J. Hoijtink, E. L. Mackor, and W. P. Weijland, *J. Chem. Soc.*, **1959**, 3049, 3055.

192. T. Takamura and K. Takamura, *Z. Physik. Chem.*, **35**, 146 (1962).

193. J. W. Eastman, G. Engelsma, and M. Calvin, *J. Am. Chem. Soc.*, **84**, 1339 (1962); I. Isenberg and S. L. Baird, Jr., *J. Am. Chem. Soc.*, **84**, 3803 (1962).

194. D. F. Ilten and M. Calvin, *J. Chem. Phys.*, **42**, 3760 (1965).

195. J. Q. Adams and S. W. Nicksic, *J. Am. Chem. Soc.*, **84**, 4355 (1962).

196. R. E. Banks, L. F. Farnell, R. N. Haszeldine, P. N. Preston, and L. H. Sutcliffe, *Proc. Chem. Soc.*, **1964**, 396.

197. M. K. Carter, Ph.D. Thesis, University of Washington, 1966.

CHAPTER 5

Orbital Degeneracy in Benzene and Substituent Effects*

KERRY W. BOWERS

Department of Chemistry and Research Laboratory of Electronics, Massachusetts Institute of Technology, Cambridge, Massachusetts

I. THE ELECTRONIC STRUCTURE OF BENZENE

For the purpose of our discussion, benzene may be viewed from a purely pi-ological approach. By naively considering that benzene consists solely of six carbon $2p$ orbitals located at the corners of and oriented normal to the plane of a regular hexagon, one obtains the energy levels and wave functions indicated diagrammatically as in Scheme I. The levels

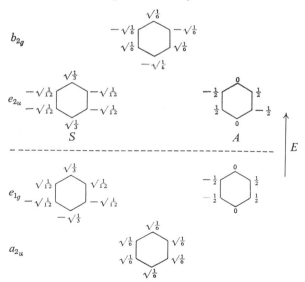

Scheme I

*This chapter will not be concerned with a detailed treatment of Jahn-Teller effects but rather with some of the chemical aspects of orbital degeneracy. We will be concerned with substituted benzenes.

211

labelled S (for symmetric) and A (for antisymmetric) are the ones of interest. The ground state of benzene may be represented as having the lower three levels occupied by six electrons:

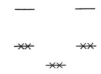

producing a singlet state. If an additional electron is added to produce the radical anion, two possibilities are available:

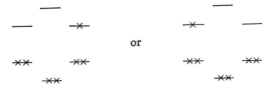

Since the A and S levels are degenerate there is no preference of one over the other in the case of the unsubstituted molecule and a linear combination makes up the ground state. Upon substitution, the situation is slightly different. In most cases the molecule behaves much like benzene and may be treated in a quasi-ligand field theoretic approach.

The spin density distributions for the odd electron in the benzene anion for the symmetric and antisymmetric levels are:

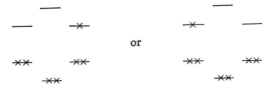

Assuming that the addition of a substituent is only a small perturbation on the parent molecule and that the benzene nucleus is only slightly changed, the addition of a substituent will remove the degeneracy and will raise or lower the energy of one level with respect to the other. An electron-donating substituent would prefer (i.e., the energy would be lower) the antisymmetric level since a node (position of zero unpaired electron density) can be occupied as:

thereby minimizing electron repulsion interactions. In the case of an electron-withdrawing group, the symmetric level would be preferred as it could be located at a position of high electron density:

Withdrawing group

To illustrate these arguments, the coupling constants (in gauss) are given for cyano (withdrawing) and methoxy (donating). These illustrate qualitative agreement but rather poor quantitative agreement. From the

Cyano   Methoxy
Coupling constants

McConnell (1) relation $a_i^H = Q\rho_i$, and from the theoretical spin distribution given above one would expect the *ortho* and *meta* coupling constants to be the same and small for benzonitrile; the same and large for anisole. The *para* coupling constant should be large for benzonitrile and zero for anisole. Although the experimental results indicate that our model leaves something to be desired quantitatively, it may still be quite useful for qualitative purposes. Obviously, substituent groups are not vanishingly small perturbations on a benzene molecule.

The major discrepancy here is the existence of a nonzero coupling constant in the *para* position of anisole radical ion or any donating group substituted benzene anion. Bolton, Carrington, Forman, and Orgel (2) have considered this problem in some detail and suggest that the deviation of the proton coupling constants from the values predicted by simple theory is due either to vibration-electronic interaction or to a mixing of electronic states through thermal agitation.

Lawler, Bolton, Fraenkel, and Brown (27) have discovered that even so insignificant a substituent as deuterium will split the degeneracy. An explanation has been given by Karplus, Lawler, and Fraenkel (28).

II. MONOSUBSTITUTED BENZENES

Monosubstituted benzenes offer the opportunity of studying the electronic effects of *closely* related substituent groups. If one assumes (2) that the two relevant electronic wave functions occur with probability P_S and P_A where $P_A + P_S = 1$ (the subscripts S and A refer to the symmetric and antisymmetric levels, respectively) then the hyperfine coupling constants for the two types of protons should be:

$$a_{o,m} = \left[\frac{1}{4} P_A + \frac{1}{12} P_S\right] Q$$

$$a_p = \frac{1}{3} P_S Q$$

(1)

where Q is McConnell's proportionality constant. It is evident that if equation 1 holds, one may determine the admixture of the wave functions and the energy separating the formerly degenerate levels if one so desired. It is also evident that the *para* proton coupling constant should depend only (in this simple approach) on the extent of symmetric level "participation" and therefore should be an indication of the electron-withdrawing power of a substituent group. Table I gives the *para* proton hyperfine coupling constant in gauss for a variety of monosubstituent groups.

It is immediately obvious to the most casual observer that Table I does

TABLE I (3)

Groups	Coupling Constant
Trimethylsilyl	8.73
Cyano	8.4
Trimethylgermyl	7.61
Acetyl	6.6
Formyl	6.47
Triphenylacetyl	5.78
Nitro	3.9
α-Methylcyclopropyl	1.86
t-Butyl	1.74
Ethyl	0.82
Propyl	0.82
Methoxy	0.64
iso-Propyl	0.61
Methyl	0.59

not indicate the usual Hammett sigma ordering. Thus, equation 1 does not strictly apply. The most blatant exception here is the nitro group. The anomaly of the nitro group is, however, readily explainable: the nitro group simply overpowers the rest of the molecule as most of the unpaired electron density resides there. It would perhaps be better to describe the phenyl group as the substituent rather than the reverse. However, within a *closely* related series, such as the alkyl groups the correlation is probably of some value. It should be noted that substituents which have π orbitals available for bonding with benzene change the nature of the basic problem and the Hückel functions for these systems give rise to large *ortho* and *para* splitting constants and small *meta* splitting constants.

III. DISUBSTITUTED BENZENES

Disubstituted benzenes, with particular emphasis on methoxy, cyano, and nitro groups, have been extensively studied in our laboratory (4,5). One might hope that coupling constants obtained from monosubstituted benzenes might be related via some linear combination to the coupling constants in disubstituted benzenes. If one assumes that substitutents are a small perturbation on the basic benzene structure this is a reasonable premise. Rarely, however, is this true. The only cases seem to be when the substituents are alkoxy and/or alkyl. Usually, one group overpowers the other. Figures 1–6 indicate this effect for methyl vs. nitro and methyl vs. cyano. These "contour plots" of the odd electron density are drawn

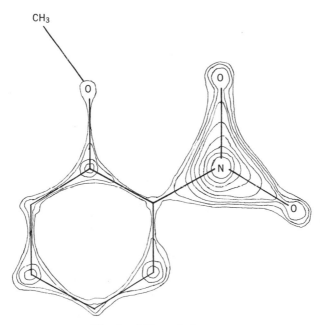

Fig. 1. *o*-Nitroanisole.

schematically on the basis of ESR coupling constants and the Hückel calculations that fit them. The enormous electron withdrawing effect of the nitro group is immediately apparent.

Since substitutent effects from monosubstituted radical anions are not related very meaningfully in a quantitative way to the usual substitutent constants of physical organic chemistry, perhaps a more relevant approach might be found if one looks at substitutent effects where one level (the symmetric one) is more or less in the ascendency. The nitro group may be chosen as "indicator" since its anion has a large *para* coupling constant (vestigial symmetric level effect) and the spectra are generally easy to analyze for the nitrogen splitting, e.g., Figures 7–14.

One of the oldest and most familiar of the quantitative relationships relating structure and reactivity is the Hammett equation (6). Classically, the equation relates structure to both equilibrium constants and rate

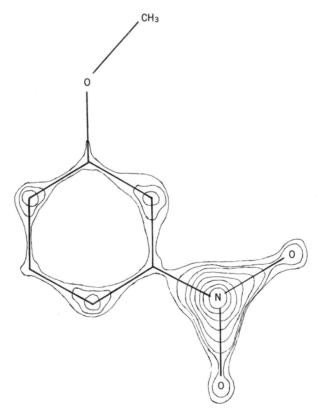

Fig. 2. *m*-Nitroanisole.

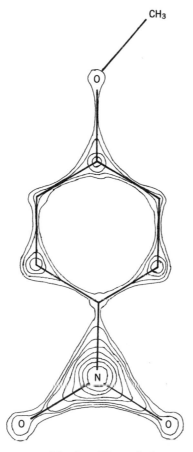

Fig. 3. *p*-Nitroanisole.

constants for the reactions of *meta*- and *para*-substituted benzene derivatives. It stipulates that the rate or equilibrium constant associated with the
reaction of any one of these derivatives is dependent on a parameter of
the corresponding unsubstituted compound and two other parameters. The
first parameter, σ, is dependent on the substituent and represents its ability
to attract or repel electrons. The second parameter, ρ, is dependent on the
particular reaction series being considered. Thus, the Hammett equation
is written:

$$\log {}_{10}(k/k_o)(\text{or } K/K_o) = \rho\sigma$$

where k (or K) is a constant of the unsubstituted or "parent" compound.

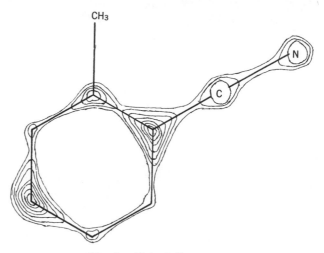

Fig. 4. *o*-Tolunitrile.

Originally, σ for any substituent, X, was defined as:

$$\sigma = \log_{10}\left(K_{\mathrm{XC_6H_4COOH}}/K_{\mathrm{C_6H_6COOH}}\right)$$

where the K's are the ionization constants for the corresponding benzoic acids (thus, ρ has been chosen equal to unity for this system). A positive

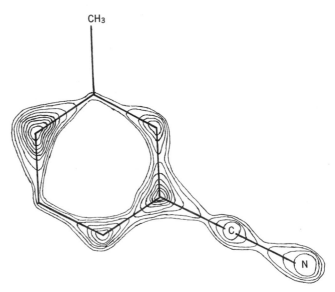

Fig. 5. *m*-Tolunitrile.

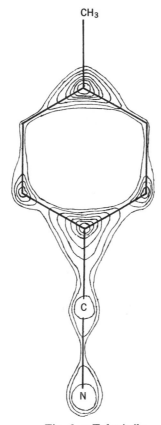

Fig. 6. *p*-Tolunitrile.

σ indicates that the substituent is a stronger electron attractor than hydrogen, while a negative σ indicates the opposite. Reactions with positive ρ's are aided by electron withdrawal, while those with negative ρ's are aided by electron donation with respect to the ionization of benzoic acids.

The rationale for the Hammett equation is thermodynamic. The log of the equilibrium constant is proportional to the standard free energy change, ΔF^0, and the log of the rate constant is proportional to the free energy of activation, $\Delta F_0^{\ddagger}$ (according to transition-state theory). Thus, the Hammett equation may be rewritten as:

$$-\Delta F(\text{or } -\Delta F^+) = (RT\rho)\sigma - \Delta F^0(\text{or } -\Delta F_0^+)$$

For a given reaction series at a given temperature, T, ΔF, and ρ are constants. Thus, the free energy changes associated with the reactions of a series are linearly related to the σ values. This is considered to be some justification of why the equation may perhaps hold.

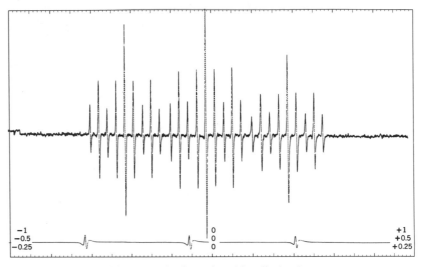

Fig. 7. *p*-Nitrobenzoic acid radical anion.

The equation may be modified to accommodate ESR data. This is done by equating the log of the ratio of coupling constants to $\rho\sigma$, instead of using the log of the ratio of rate or equilibrium constants. In particular, the value of the nitrogen coupling constants in unsubstituted nitrobenzene is used as the "parent" value, while the value in the numerator (of the ratio) is the

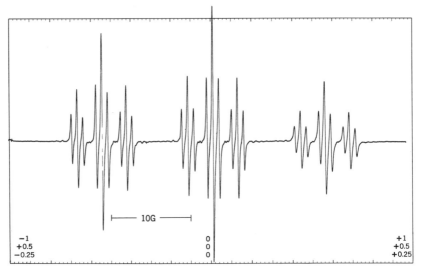

Fig. 8. *p*-Nitrophenol radical anion.

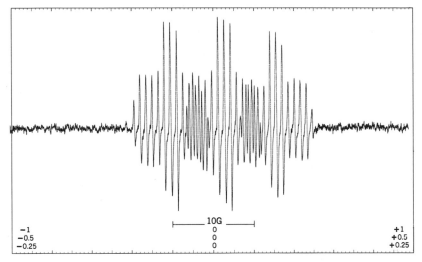

Fig. 9. *p*-Nitrobenzonitrile radical anion.

nitrogen coupling constant for a substituent other than hydrogen in the *para* position. σ, again, is dependent on the particular substituent, while ρ is no longer dependent on the reaction series (since there is in reality only one series, the *p*-nitrobenzenes), but rather on the solvent in which the ESR spectrum is being measured. The final equation thus becomes:

$$\log_{10}(a_N^X/a_N^H) = \rho\sigma$$

for a series of compounds such as:

$$X-\!\!\left\langle\!\!\bigcirc\!\!\right\rangle\!\!-NO_2$$

This equation is only postulatory; in the following pages data are presented to test it.

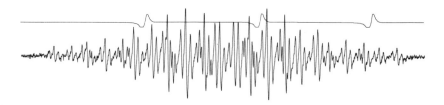

Fig. 10. *p*-Tolunitrile radical anion.

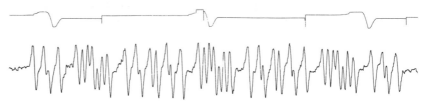

Fig. 11. *o*-Nitroanisole radical anion.

Much effort is made in the literature to fit seemingly anomalous cases into the general Hammett equation by making suitable "corrections." For example, one explains the fact that a *para* nitro group enhances the acidity of phenol by a factor of ca. 600 (as opposed to 36 predicted by the conventional Hammett σ constant), while enhancing the acidity of benzoic acid by a factor of only 6 by saying that the phenol is directly conjugated to the nitro group, while it is partially inductively linked in the case of the acid. One goes on to define a new set of σ's, σ_p^c's, which are to be used in the case of anilines, phenols, and their derivatives. Such patch-up work does yield correct answers, but it is unfortunate. As a second example, one may go to great lengths to separate polar, steric, and resonance effects. One defines more new σ's (σ*'s, σ^+'s, σ^-'s, etc.) each describing a separate effect. It seems dubious that such a rigorous separation of effects can be truly physically significant.

The advantage of investigating the Hammett equation through ESR data is to eliminate this arbitrary separation of effects. Rather, the σ's now represent the total electronic effect of the substituent. This is a more general parameter and is likely to be constant over a greater range of applicability. In addition, ESR coupling constants can be measured with considerable precision. Finally, if the ρ of a solvent is known and the σ of a particular substituent has been determined, it is possible to predict the nitrogen coupling of a substituted nitrobenzene (and perhaps other systems, if relevant, with reasonable accuracy).

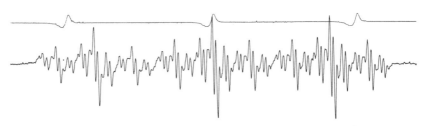

Fig. 12. *p*-Nitroanisole radical anion.

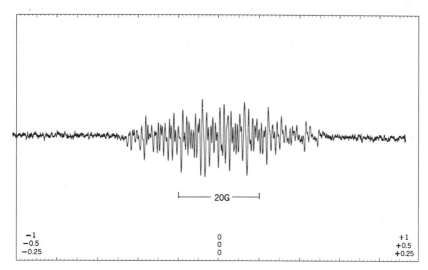

Fig. 13. Spectrum from *p*-nitrobenzenearsonic acid in DMSO.

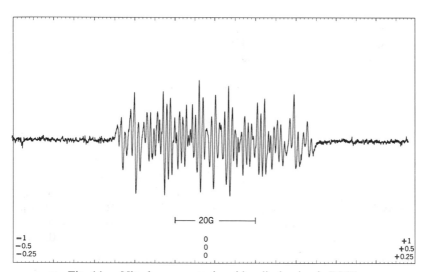

Fig. 14. *p*-Nitrobenzenearsonic acid radical anion in DMF.

The nitrogen coupling constants of 13 substituted benzenes (in addition to the "parent" compound, nitrobenzene) were used in the Hammett equation plots. The coupling constants were measured in three solvents: *N,N*-dimethylformamide (DMF), dimethylsulfoxide (DMSO), and acetonitrile (AcCN). When possible, the values used were taken from the literature. This was possible for most of the compounds run in DMF and AcCN. For values in DMSO, most had to be determined in our laboratory. Table II lists the compounds used and their nitrogen coupling constant (of the nitro group) in each of the solvents.

TABLE II
Nitrogen Coupling Constants

Substituent	DMF	DMSO	AcCN
H	9.75[a]	9.87[a]	10.32[a]
CN	6.24[a]	6.50[b]	7.15[a]
CHO	5.11[a]	5.38[a]	5.83[a]
Br	9.04[a]	9.10[b]	9.70[a]
COOH	9.57[b]	9.69[b]	10.04[b]
$COCH_3$	5.86[a]	6.24[b]	7.02[a]
OCH_3	10.60[b]	10.93[b]	11.57[a]
CH_3	10.14[b]	10.19[b]	10.79[a]
OH	13.90[b]	13.59[b]	13.88[a]
Cl	9.16[a]	9.18[b]	9.83[a]
NO_2	1.48[a]	1.53[b]	1.74[a]
NH_2	11.35[b]	—	12.18[a]
C_6H_5	8.59[b]	8.88[b]	9.24[b]
$C_6H_4NO_2$	2.69[a]	2.96[a]	3.45[a]

[a] Reference 3.
[b] Reference 5.

Most spectra were obtained routinely, but three compounds, *p*-nitroaniline, *p*-iodonitrobenzene, and *p*-nitrobenzenearsonic acid, showed anomalous behavior. A word must be said about them. *p*-Nitroaniline gave no signal in DMSO despite the fact that it gives the expected signal in DMF and AcCN. *p*-Iodonitrobenzene, in both DMF and AcCN, lost iodine to give the nitrobenzene radical anion. However, by far the most curious behavior was shown by *p*-nitrobenzenearsonic acid. In both DMF and AcCN, it showed an interpretable signal, although the interpretation is given as tentative, because some lines seem to be extraneous. Meanwhile, in DMSO, a complex, uninterpretable signal was obtained. The explanation for this is as yet unknown.

The values in Table II make up the left side of the Hammett equation in the form of $\log_{10} (a_N^X/a_N^H)$ and are thus fixed quantities. This term is plotted on the ordinate. On the abscissa is plotted the σ value of the corresponding substituent. The slope of the resulting straight line is then the ρ value of the solvent.

Choosing the final σ values was not a trivial process. The best straight line through the points was determined by the least squares procedure with the actual mechanics of the process facilitated by use of a 7094 computer. The inputs to the program are the ordinate and abscissa values. The outputs are the best straight line, given as $y = mx + b$, the calculated σ values, and the difference between the calculated σ values and the input σ values. Thus, by examining this difference value, it is easy to determine which σ's are already close to the correct value and which are far from the value given by the best line. In addition, it is now possible to use self-consistency as a criterion for finalizing the σ value. When an input sigma is unchanged through a least squares fit (its difference value is sufficiently close to zero), it is judged to be finalized.

Through the least squares fitting for each solvent, it was attempted to use σ values which were close to the literature values. Thus, for the initial σ's, the literature values were chosen when possible. However, in several cases, it became obvious that a choice of the literature value for an initial σ would be so far removed from the line (its difference value would be huge) as to unbalance the entire line. In particular, the literature values of p-nitro, p-formyl, p-amino, and p-carboxy were in this category. To make the line physically more significant, it was first calculated omitting these errant points. Then calculating backwards, reasonable initial σ values for these four substituents were determined (the initial σ value for p-phenyl-nitro was also determined in this fashion, but only because no literature value was available). Finally with all the points now included, the fitting process was iterated until the above mentioned self-consistency was attained. Two iterations proved sufficient.

The line for each solvent was first determined separately, giving rise to slightly different σ values (of a given substituent) for each solvent. These values were then averaged to obtain a final constant σ for all solvents. Table III shows literature σ values, final σ values for each solvent, and the average σ value which was then used in the calculation of the solvent σ's.

Table IV shows the data for the calculation of the solvent ρ's. One point requires special explanation. The point for the p-hydroxy substituent in DMF was not included in the calculation because it was clearly an anomalous point. Why this should be so is not known. The values for the ρ's of the three solvents are: DMF, $\rho = -0.319$; DMSO, $\rho = -0.312$; AcCN, $\rho = -0.295$. A smaller negative ρ indicates that the nitrogen coupling

TABLE III
Sigma Constants

Substituent	DMF	DMSO	AcCN	Final	Literature value (7)
CN	0.57	0.57	0.54	0.56	0.66
Br	0.07	0.10	0.10	0.09	0.23
$COCH_3$	0.66	0.63	0.57	0.62	0.50
OCH_3	−0.16	−0.16	−0.16	−0.16	−0.27
CH_3	−0.09	−0.06	−0.06	−0.08	−0.17
Cl	0.05	0.09	0.08	0.07	0.23
C_6H_5	0.17	0.16	0.17	0.17	−0.01
OH	−0.51	−0.46	−0.42	−0.44	−0.37
NH_2	−0.25	—	−0.23	−0.24	−0.66
NO_2	2.55	2.59	2.60	2.58	0.78
CHO	0.85	0.83	0.84	0.84	0.22
COOH	−0.01	0.02	0.05	0.02	0.27
$C_6H_4NO_2$	1.72	1.68	1.63	1.68	—

constant will be larger, i.e., the nitrogen coupling will be largest in AcCN, smaller in DMSO, and smallest in DMF. Figures 15–17 show the plots of the Hammett equation for the calculation of ρ's.

Calculation of the solvent ρ's was also carried out using σ values taken entirely from the literature (p-nitrophenyl was, of course, omitted). Table IV gives the data for these calculations, and Figures 18–20 show the resulting plots. The lines are of little significance, as it can be seen the points do not form an obvious straight line. The difference values, on the order of 0.01–0.06 for the previous plots, are here as large as 0.575. Thus, the classical σ values generally do not correlate ESR data well, and in several cases, the noncorrelation is horrendous.

A logical extension is now to consider the physical interpretation of the data. As mentioned above, four substituents, p-nitro, p-formyl, p-amino, and p-carboxy, show final ESR σ's which are grossly different from their classical values. It is tempting to explain this fact by noting the p-nitro, p-formyl, and p-carboxy probably have strong and direct resonance interaction with the benzene ring. However, this still leaves the effect of the p-amino substituent to be explained and if p-formyl has a grossly different σ value, why should p-acetyl not show this effect, also? Thus, no further explanation is attempted; the above four substituents are merely grouped together as showing some common (or perhaps individual?) effect which other substituents do not show.

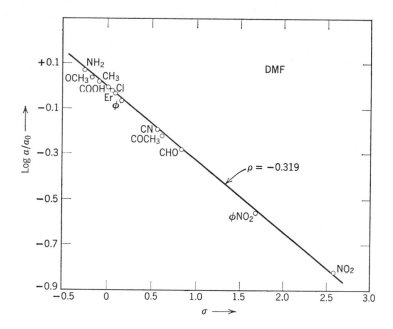

Fig. 15. Rho-sigma plot for dimethylformamide.

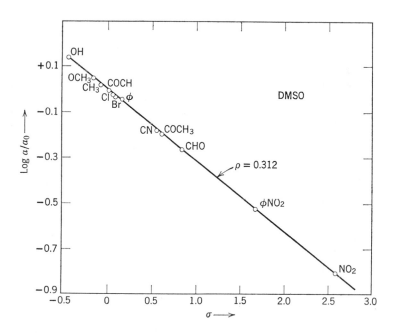

Fig. 16. Rho-sigma plot for dimethylsulfoxide.

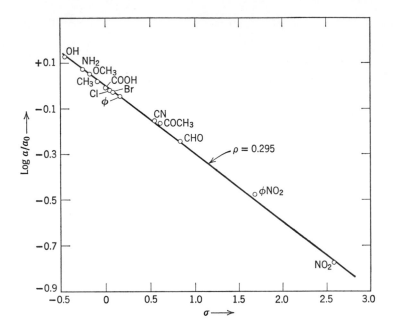

Fig. 17. Rho-sigma plot for acetonitrile.

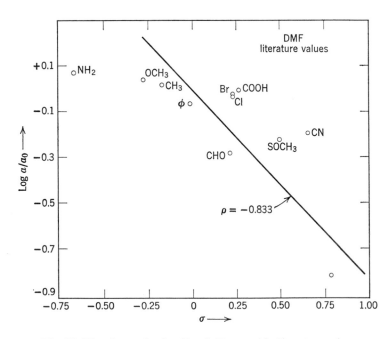

Fig. 18. Rho-sigma plot for dimethylformamide, literature values.

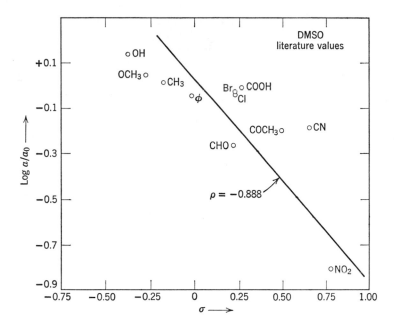

Fig. 19. Rho-sigma plot for dimethylsulfoxide, literature values.

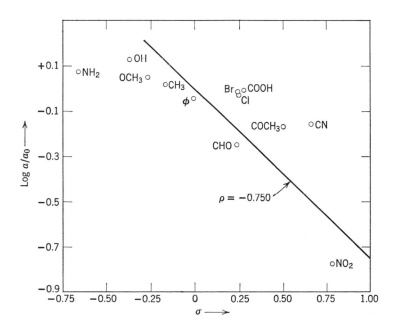

Fig. 20. Rho-sigma plot for acetonitrile, literature values.

TABLE IV
Calculation of Solvent ρ's

Substituent	Sigma	$\text{Log}_{10}(a_N^X/a_N^H)$	Calculated sigma	Difference
DMSO—Final sigma values			$\rho = -0.312$	
CN	0.56	−0.182	0.572	−0.012
Br	0.09	−0.035	0.100	−0.010
$COCH_3$	0.62	−0.199	0.627	−0.007
OCH_3	−0.16	+0.045	−0.156	−0.004
CH_3	−0.08	+0.014	−0.057	−0.023
Cl	0.07	−0.031	0.088	−0.018
C_6H_5	0.17	−0.046	0.136	+0.034
OH	−0.44	+0.139	−0.458	+0.018
NO_2	2.58	−0.809	2.585	−0.005
CHO	0.84	−0.263	0.832	+0.008
COOH	0.02	−0.008	0.014	+0.006
$C_6H_4NO_2$	1.68	−0.523	1.667	+0.013
AcCN—Final sigma values			$\rho = -0.295$	
CN	0.56	−0.158	0.540	+0.020
Br	0.09	−0.027	0.096	−0.006
$COCH_3$	0.62	−0.168	0.574	+0.046
OCH_3	−0.16	+0.050	−0.164	+0.004
CH_3	−0.08	+0.019	−0.059	−0.021
Cl	0.07	−0.021	0.076	−0.006
C_6H_5	0.17	−0.049	0.171	−0.001
OH	−0.44	+0.128	−0.429	−0.011
NH_2	−0.24	+0.072	−0.239	−0.001
NO_2	2.58	−0.774	2.628	−0.048
CHO	0.84	−0.248	0.845	−0.005
COOH	0.02	−0.012	0.046	−0.026
$C_6H_4NO_2$	1.68	−0.478	1.625	+0.055
DMF—Final sigma values			$\rho = -0.319$	
CN	0.56	−0.194	0.575	−0.015
Br	0.09	−0.033	0.070	+0.020
$COCH_3$	0.62	−0.221	0.660	−0.040
OCH_3	−0.16	+0.037	−0.150	−0.010
CH_3	−0.08	+0.017	−0.087	+0.007
Cl	0.07	−0.027	0.051	+0.019
C_6H_5	0.17	−0.067	0.176	−0.006
NH_2	−0.24	+0.066	−0.241	+0.001
NO_2	2.58	−0.819	2.537	+0.043
CHO	0.84	−0.281	0.848	−0.008
COOH	0.02	−0.008	−0.009	+0.029
$C_6H_4NO_2$	1.68	−0.559	1.721	−0.041

(continued)

TABLE IV (*continued*)

Substituent	Sigma	$\text{Log}_{10}(a_N^X/a_N^H)$	Calculated sigma	Difference
DMSO—Literature sigma values			$\rho = -0.888$	
CN	0.66	−0.182	0.252	+0.408
Br	0.23	−0.035	0.087	+0.143
COCH$_3$	0.50	−0.199	0.272	+0.228
OCH$_3$	−0.27	+0.045	−0.003	−0.267
CH$_3$	−0.17	+0.014	0.032	−0.202
Cl	0.23	−0.031	0.082	+0.148
C$_6$H$_5$	−0.01	−0.046	0.099	−0.109
OH	−0.37	+0.139	−0.109	−0.261
NO$_2$	0.78	−0.809	0.959	−0.179
CHO	0.22	−0.263	0.344	−0.124
COOH	0.27	−0.008	0.056	+0.214
AcCN—Literature sigma values			$\rho = -0.750$	
CN	0.66	−0.158	0.196	+0.464
Br	0.23	−0.027	0.022	+0.209
COCH$_3$	0.50	−0.168	0.210	+0.291
OCH$_3$	−0.27	+0.050	−0.081	−0.189
CH$_3$	−0.17	+0.091	−0.040	−0.130
Cl	0.23	−0.021	0.014	+0.217
C$_6$H$_5$	−0.01	−0.049	0.051	−0.061
OH	−0.37	+0.128	−0.185	−0.185
NH$_2$	−0.66	+0.072	−0.110	−0.550
NO$_2$	0.78	−0.774	1.017	−0.237
CHO	0.22	−0.248	0.316	−0.096
COOH	0.27	−0.012	0.002	+0.269
DMF—Literature sigma values			$\rho = -0.833$	
CN	0.66	−0.194	0.228	+0.432
Br	0.23	−0.033	0.034	+0.196
COCH$_3$	0.50	−0.221	0.260	+0.240
OCH$_3$	−0.27	+0.037	−0.050	−0.220
CH$_3$	−0.17	+0.017	−0.026	−0.144
Cl	0.23	−0.027	0.027	+0.203
C$_6$H$_5$	−0.01	−0.067	0.075	−0.085
NH$_2$	−0.66	+0.066	−0.084	−0.576
NO$_2$	0.78	−0.819	0.978	−0.198
CHO	0.22	−0.281	0.332	−0.112
COOH	0.27	−0.008	0.004	+0.266

Physically, the ρ value of the solvent is a measure of the effect of that solvent on the electronic properties of the substituent. The fact that different solvents have different ρ values may be significant.

IV. THE STRANGE BEHAVIOR OF THE ANISOLES (4.5)

Relatively few ESR studies of alkoxy-substituted aromatics have appeared in the literature. Spectra of the radical anions of o-methoxynitrobenzene (11,12) and p-methoxynitrobenzene (11–13), p-ethoxynitrobenzene (13), p-(n-butoxy)nitrobenzene (13), and 2,5-diethoxybenzosemiquinone (14) have been reported. The oxidation of methoxybenzenes (15) has been studied in some detail by both ESR and polarographic techniques. In the present work, a series of substituted anisoles and related alkoxy-substituted naphthalenes and biphenyls have been studied employing both the alkali metal and electrolytic methods of radical ion generation.

Such studies are of interest in connection with the known metalation and cleavage reactions of aryl ethers and related compounds in the presence of alkali metals. They also relate to the few studies of the chemistry of alkali metal-aromatic compound adducts. Further, the substituted anisoles offer a convenient series in which the benzene molecular orbital model may be examined with regard to substituent effects.

Anisole radical anion can be generated in convenient concentrations for ESR study with sodium–potassium alloy (Na/K) in THF–DME at $-110°$C. The spectrum of the radical anion appears in Figure 21. Upon warming to ca. $-40°$C, the anisole spectrum becomes very weak and the biphenyl radical anion spectrum begins to appear. The latter increases in intensity as the temperature is warmed to ca. $+10°$C. Cooling the sample to $-110°$C again produces the spectrum of anisole radical anion. This behavior is reversible through many temperature cycles.

Sodium–potassium alloy in pure THF yields with anisole the anisole spectrum at $-95°$C and biphenyl at $+10°$C. Potassium in THF–DME gives with anisole the anisole spectrum at $-110°$C and no signal upon warming and recooling. Anisole treated with sodium–potassium alloy in pure DME gives only the biphenyl radical anion spectrum at temperatures down to $-45°$C (just above the freezing point of the solvent). With sodium in THF–DME, with anisole, only the anisole radical anion can be seen in the temperature range -110 to $+20°$C. Thus, the active role of potassium in the cleavage coupling of anisole to biphenyl under these conditions is identified.

Eargle (16) reported similar cleavage coupling of anisole and some other aryl ethers under slightly different conditions. He found that anisole was inert to sodium in THF, but cleaved readily with potassium in DME.

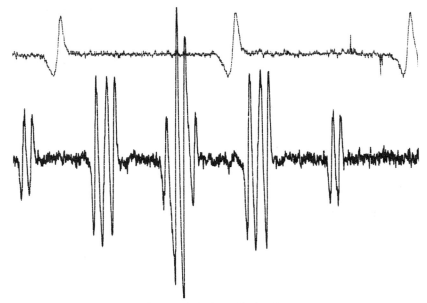

Fig. 21. Anisole radical anion.

Other workers have employed the reaction of anisole with potassium in heptane as a convenient preparative method for phenylpotassium, reporting no coupling products.* Their result points to the importance of the ether solvents in facilitating the coupling process.

Similarly, studies of the metalation of anisole by alkyl- or arylpotassium compounds (18,19) and with lithium compounds (20) report the clean o-metalation of the anisole with no coupling side reactions. Birch-type reductions of anisole also fail to give coupling products (21–23).

Phenetole behaves in identical fashion to anisole under similar conditions, giving phenetole and biphenyl spectra.

Attempts to generate the anisole radical anion electrolytically failed to give any detectable ESR signal.

The methyl- and the methoxyanisoles provide an interesting study in the relative effect on radical anion stability of the substitution of two electron-repelling groups into the benzene nucleus in various positions. Both o-methyl- and o-methoxyanisole lose one methoxy group in the presence of Na/K alloy in THF–DME, giving spectra of the radical anions of toluene (Fig. 11) and anisole, respectively. The latter then gives biphenyl on

---

* Based on our inability to detect biphenyl from the coupling of anisole by vapor phase chromatographic or mass spectral techniques, the possibility of trace amounts of coupling products in these and other studies cannot be absolutely excluded.

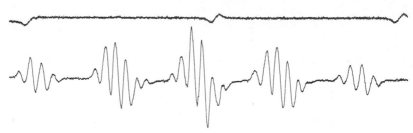

Fig. 22. *p*-Methylanisole radical anion.

warming. *o*-Methoxyanisole is cleaved even by the milder sodium mirror distillation.

m-Methylanisole gives toluene by loss of a methoxy group on a Na/K alloy mirror, but remains intact in the THF–DME solution containing Na/K alloy. *m*-Methoxyanisole is not cleaved by the Na/K mirror but loses one methoxy group to give anisole radical anion in solution at low temperatures and biphenyl radical anion on warming.

p-Methylanisole gave in solution a clean spectrum (Fig. 22), consistent with its structure, at low temperatures which disappeared on warming but reappeared on cooling. *p*-Methoxyanisole gave at low temperatures a clean spectrum consistent with its structure (Fig. 23) which was unchanged but reduced in intensity on warming.

The results can be understood in terms of the electron distribution in the benzene molecular orbitals. It is seen that in the case of *p*-disubstitution by

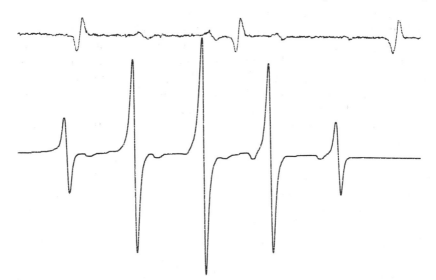

Fig. 23. *p*-Methoxyanisole radical anion.

electron-repelling groups, the extra electron in the radical anion may occupy the antisymmetric orbital, thereby avoiding the substituents. In the *o*- and *m*-disubstituted cases, appreciable electron density on at least one of the substituted ring carbon atoms is unavoidable. This might be expected to give rise to some instability in the radical anion due to electronic repulsion effects. The experimental results substantiate this point. Molecular orbital calculations that have been performed on anisole and phenol are not inconsistent with this interpretation.

Attempts to generate the radical anions of 3,5-dimethylanisole and 2,6-dimethylanisole with Na/K alloy in THF–DME failed to give any detectable concentrations of paramagnetic species. This is in agreement with earlier reports (24) that it was not possible to prepare radical anions of trimethylbenzenes whereas the xylenes form them readily.

p-Anisaldehyde gives a clean ESR spectrum under the alloy sample conditions, but *p*-methoxyacetophenone gives no signal (apparently due to metalation of the methyl group).

In order to examine the coupling reaction of anisole to biphenyl, the three monodeuteroanisoles, the three monomethoxybiphenyls, and 4,4′-dideuterobiphenyl were prepared.

The *o*- and *p*-methoxybiphenyls cleave in the presence of Na/K alloy in THF–DME to give spectra of biphenyl radical anion. They do not appear to cleave on electroreduction. Experiments with *m*-methoxybiphenyl yielded the same poorly resolved spectra under alloy and electrolytic conditions. The envelope structure (no fine structure could be completely resolved) of this spectrum resembled that of biphenyl. However, since one would expect only very small effects on the overall spectrum appearance by substitution in the *meta* position of biphenyl this result is inconclusive.

Nevertheless, these data do show that the intermediacy of the monomethoxybiphenyls in the cleavage coupling of anisole to biphenyl under the conditions mentioned cannot be excluded.

o-, *m*-, and *p*-Deuteroanisole all give spectra at $-110°C$ under the usual alloy conditions consistent with their structures and identical to theoretically calculated* spectra for the given percentages of deuteration and very close to the theoretical spectra for 100% monodeuteration. On warming

---

* Theoretical spectra are calculated and plotted by means of an ESR plotting computer program, WESRP, developed by F. J. Weigert and K. W. Bowers. Theoretical deuterium coupling constants were determined from the ratio of magnetic moments using the formula $a_D = 0.1552a_H$ where a_D is the theoretical deuterium coupling constant in the position where a_H is the observed proton coupling constant. This relationship works well in most cases. Exceptions include deuterobenzene, the deuteronaphthalenes, and 4,4′-dideuterobiphenyl. In the latter case it was found that the best fit of the experimental and calculated spectra is obtained when the *p*-deuterium splitting constant is 0.40 G instead of the expected 0.85 G $[a_D = (0.1552)(5.46)]$.

to $+10°C$, complex spectra are obtained in the same reversible fashion that biphenyl is obtained from anisole. By comparison to the theoretically calculated spectra for the various mono- and dideuterobiphenyls, one concludes that the experimental spectra are in fact the superposition of several spectra of the coupling products of the deuteroanisoles resulting from several mechanistic pathways. Simple coupling at the alkoxyl positions is not occurring as the sole or major mechanistic pathway.

Possible pathways include benzyne intermediates, direct coupling at various positions, involvement of radical and/or radical anion intermediates, involvement of neutral molecules, involvement of phenylsodium and/or phenylpotassium, cleavage of and reaction with solvent, involvement of ring-metalated anisoles, and deuterium exchange and/or rearrangement in the anisoles of biphenyls. The literature review presented earlier establishes the plausibility of these mechanistic complications in the highly reactive sample medium.

Several determinations of the concentration of anisole radical anion derived from anisole are summarized in Table V. The per cent conversion of anisole to its radical anion varies with the starting concentration of anisole, higher conversions being observed at lower starting anisole concentrations. Biphenyl radical anion concentrations measured upon warming the anisole samples were approximately an order of magnitude smaller than the measured anisole spin concentration. Deviations in the experimental results are attributed to experimental error stemming from two major sources: (*a*) problems inherent in working with ca. 0.5 mg samples of anisole on the high vacuum line and (*b*) problems of reproducibility of the exact amount and surface of the Na/K alloy used.

Several experiments were carried out in an attempt to isolate and identify the biphenyl produced by the coupling of anisole. In none of these could the presence of biphenyl be detected on vapor phase chromatographic analysis of the reaction mixture. Failure to detect the biphenyl is attributed to the metalation–decomposition and metalation–polymerization reactions of biphenyl in the presence of Na/K alloy in the THF–DME.

At least in the cases of electron-donating substituents in the anisole series the predictions as regards stability seem to hold well and the behavior of the antisymmetric level established. The behavior of the symmetric level is not nearly as well substantiated. A typical electron-withdrawing group is the nitro group. The unpaired electron is expected to occupy primarily the symmetric level in the radical anion of nitrobenzene. Although a large *para* proton coupling is observed as expected, the *ortho* and *meta* couplings are not nearly equivalent as would be expected for the symmetric level distribution. Agreement with theory is not much better with other withdrawing groups, also. Furthermore, there was no evidence

TABLE V
Studies of Anisole Radical Anion Concentrations

Corrections	Results
Na/K alloy THF–DME $-110°C$ initial anisole $\quad = 9.4 \times 10^{-2}M$ (anisole distilled from Na/K mirror on vacuum line)	At $-110°C$ a spectrum was observed consisting of a mixture of anisole and benzene, the latter having been introduced as a vacuum line impurity. After calculation of the total measured spin concentration ($9.5 \times 10^{-4}M$) a correction was made, estimating the portion of the total due to anisole at ca. 40–60%. Thus the concentration of anisole radical anion was ca. 4×10^{-4}–$5 \times 10^{-4}M$ corresponding to a 0.4–0.5% conversion of anisole to its radical anion.
Na/K alloy THF–DME -110 to $+10°C$ initial anisole $\quad = 2 \times 10^{-1}M$ (anisole distilled from Na/K mirror on vacuum line)	At $-110°C$ a strong anisole spectrum was observed containing a trace of benzene impurity. The measured spin concentration $= 1.13 \times 10^{-3}M$, corresponding to a 0.6% conversion of the anisole to its radical anion. The sample was then warmed to $+10°C$ where a spectrum of biphenyl radical anion was observed. The measured spin concentration was ca. $10^{-4}M$ (poor lineshape prevented measuring the concentration with greater accuracy).
Na/K alloy THF–DME -110 to $+10°C$ initial anisole $\quad = 2 \times 10^{-1}M$ (anisole distilled from Na/K alloy mirror on vacuum line)	At $-110°C$ an anisole spectrum was obobserved. It remained unchanged in intensity over a 1 hr period. The sample was then warmed to $+10°C$ for 10 min where a clear biphenyl spectrum was observed. Cooling again to $-110°C$ reproduced the original intensity anisole spectrum. The measured spin concentration at $-100°C = 3.73 \times 10^{-4}M$, corresponding to a 0.187% conversion of anisole to its radical anion. At $+10°C$, the biphenyl anion concentration $= 5.12 \times 10^{-4}M$.
Na/K alloy THF–DME $-110°C$ initial anisole $\quad = 2.77 \times 10^{-2}M$	At $-110°C$ the spectrum of anisole radical anion was observed. The measured spin concentration $= 3.64 \times 10^{-3}M$, corresponding to 13% conversion of anisole to its radical anion.

(continued)

TABLE V (*continued*)

Corrections	Results
(anisole distilled from Na/K alloy mirror on vacuum line)	
Na/K alloy THF–DME −110°C initial anisole $= 1.1 \times 10^{-2}M$ (anisole distilled from Na/K alloy mirror on vacuum line)	The anisole spectrum was observed at −110°C. The measured spin concentration = 1.1 × $10^{-3}M$, corresponding to a 10% conversion to its radical anion.
Na/K alloy THF–DME −110 to +10°C initial anisole $= 1.24 \times 10^{-2}M$ (anisole distilled from Na/K alloy mirror on vacuum line)	At −110°C an anisole spectrum was observed having a trace benzene impurity. The measured spin concentration = 2.2 × $10^{-3}M$ corresponding to a 17.7% conversion of anisole to its radical anion. The sample was then warmed to +10°C and allowed to remain at that temperature for ½ hr. Upon cooling again to −110°C, a spin concentration was measured $= 6.45 \times 10^{-4}M$.
Na/K alloy THF–DME −110 to +10°C initial anisole $= 9.34 \times 10^{-2}M$ (anisole distilled from Na/K mirror on vacuum line)	At −110°C the anisole spectrum was detected. The measured spin concentration = 4.85 × $10^{-3}M$ corresponding to a 5.19% conversion of anisole to its radical anion. The sample was then warmed to +10°C for ca. 1 hr. Upon cooling again to −110°C, a spin concentration was measured $= 5.18 \times 10^{-4}M$.

of instability of disubstituted benzene caused by the symmetric level analogous to that of the methoxybenzenes in the antisymmetric case.

We attempted to study the behavior of the symmetric level by studying the ESR spectra of several series of di- and polysubstituted benzenes containing at least one electron-withdrawing group. It was hoped that an unstable radical anion arising from the symmetric level would be found.

We attempted to obtain the ESR spectra of the following compounds: *o*-, *m*-, and *p*-nitroanisole; *o*-, *m*-, and *p*-tolunitrile; *o*-*m*-, and *p*-fluoro-anisole; pentafluoroanisole; *p*-methoxybenzaldehyde; 2,4-dinitroanisole;

p-methoxybenzonitrile; 2,4,6-trinitrotoluene; *p,p'*-azoanisole; *p,p'*-dicyano-biphenyl; and 2,6-dinitro-4-*t*-butyl-3-methoxytoluene.

Of the compounds run, no signal was obtained from *m*-fluoroanisole, pentafluoroanisole, and *p*-methoxybenzaldehyde. The remaining compounds gave signals and are tabulated in Table VI.

2,4,6-Trinitrotoluene, *p,p'*-azoanisole, and 2,4-dinitroanisole all gave signals, but none were sufficiently resolved to permit interpretation of the spectra. The only item of note is the asymmetry of the spectrum of 2,4-dinitroanisole (Fig. 24) about its center. In the absence of unusual relaxation effects, an ESR spectrum of a single radical species is symmetrical about its center. This indicates that the spectrum may be a superposition of two, or perhaps more, radical species or a manifestation of an unusual relaxation mechanism. As the compound was not investigated further, no guess can be made as to the identity of the radical species present.

The nitroanisoles and the tolunitriles were thoroughly investigated. All six compounds eventually gave interpretable spectra and all coupling constants were checked by reproducing the spectra using WESRP.

The coupling constants are assigned to specific protons on the basis of tenuous molecular orbital calculations. When a question mark appears next to an assignment, it indicates that the molecular orbital calculations were not precise enough to differentiate between two or among three or more different assignments. Although predictable instabilities were found for the antisymmetric level, no such analog was found for the symmetric level among the six compounds considered. It is expected that an electron-donating group *para* or *ortho* with respect to an electron withdrawing group would produce a compound whose corresponding radical anion would be unstable with respect to the loss of a substituent group (more so with the *para* compounds than with the *ortho*). The *meta* compounds should produce a relatively stable radical anion. The *para* compounds were investigated over a wide range of temperatures, but the anions proved to be stable under all conditions.

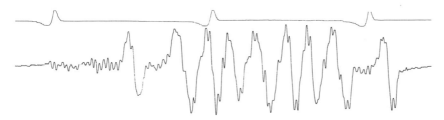

Fig. 24. 2,4-Dinitroanisole radical anion.

TABLE VI
Coupling Constants

Compound	a_N	a_1	a_2	a_3	a_4	Solvent

| o-Nitroanisole | 10.18 | 1.14 | 4.02 | 0.89 | 3.56 | DMF |

| m-Nitroanisole | 9.49 | 3.29 | 1.01 | 3.29 | 3.85 | DMF |

| p-Nitroanisole | 10.60 | 3.43 | 1.10 | 0.37 | | DMF |

| o-Tolunitrile | 2.12 | 3.17 | 0.66? | 8.36 | 4.18? | DMF |

| m-Tolunitrile | 2.16 | 0.43 | 8.56 | 3.85? | 3.77? | DMF |

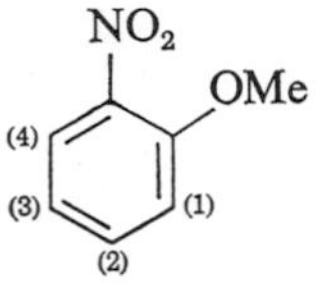

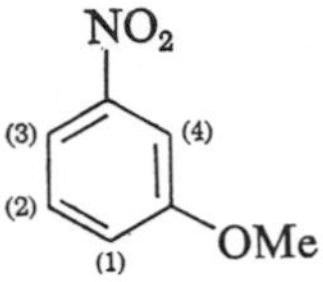

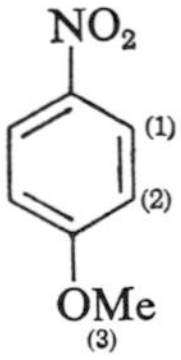

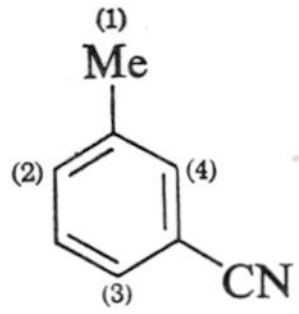

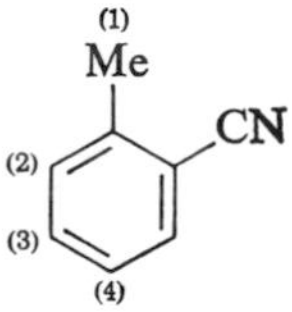

(continued)

TABLE VI (*continued*)

Compound	a_N	a_1	a_2	a_3	a_4	Solvent

Compound	a_N	a_1	a_2	a_3	a_4	Solvent
p-Tolunitrile	2.07	9.23	0.57	3.84		DMF
2,4-Dinitroanisole			Uninterpretable			DMF
p,p'-Azoanisole			Uninterpretable			DMF
p-Methoxybenzo-nitrile			Uninterpretable			DME

Compound	a_N	a_1	a_2	a_3	a_4	Solvent
2,6-Dinitro-4-*t*-butyl-3-methoxytoluene	0.76	9.02	3.06	3.41		DMF
o-Fluoroanisole			Anisole uninterpretable			THF–DME THF–DME
p-Fluoroanisole			Biphenyl			THF–DME
p,p'-Dicyano-biphenyl			Uninterpretable			THF–DME
2,4,6-Trinitro-toluene			Uninterpretable			DMF

All coupling constants are in gauss.

In all figures the scale is either indicated or it can be found by noting that the distances between peaks of the reference signal is 13.00 G.

This result is surprising. It would be expected that placing a donating group at a ring position of high unpaired electron density would render that compound's radical anion unstable, regardless of whether or not the compound possessed benzenelike molecular orbitals. Other cases must be considered before any conclusions are reached.

The radical anion of *p*-methoxybenzonitrile showed evidence of instability. When treated with potassium in DME at $-90°C$, it gave a clean symmetric spectrum (Fig. 25), which was uninterpretable due to its complexity. It was, however, possible to conclude positively that the spectrum was not due to the radical anion of *p*-methoxybenzonitrile. (Its spectrum would include only four different splittings and would be easily recognizable.) The spectrum has perhaps (?) the general appearance of a substituted biphenyl. Such an assignment must, at best, be taken to be highly tentative, however, since a radical anion of *p,p'*-dicyanobiphenyl (a possible coupling product) was found to give a totally different spectrum (Fig. 14).

Another example of anion radical instability was found with the fluoroanisoles. As mentioned earlier, the *meta* compound gave no signal, but the *ortho* and *para* compounds both lost fluorine when treated with sodium–potassium alloy in 2:1 THF–DME at $-100°C$ and showed the spectrum of the anisole radical anion. As has been reported, upon warming to 0°C, the anisole radical anion is expected to lose methoxyl and subsequently couple to give the biphenyl radical anion. This was indeed found to be the case for the anisole formed from the *para* fluoro compound. Curiously, however, the anisole formed from the *ortho* compound gave a different species. The spectrum still has the gross features of the biphenyl spectrum, but there are distinct differences. The resolution is too poor to permit interpretation, but it was interesting to note the similarities in general features and especially in line shapes between this spectrum and the spectrum obtained from *p*-methoxybenzonitrile. Since it is reasonable to assume that the anisole from *o*-fluoroanisole will couple (upon warming) to form some type of biphenyl, this strengthens the supposition that *p*-methoxybenzonitrile lost methoxyl and coupled to give a biphenyl. However, the evidence is not conclusive.

Fig. 25. Spectrum from *p*-methoxybenzonitrile.

It thus seems that the instability of radical anions of benzene compounds depends to some extent on whether or not the compound possesses benzenelike molecular orbitals. Of the compounds considered, the fluoro compounds undoubtably have molecular orbitals which are most closely like those of benzene and they both are unstable. The cyano compounds, which are further removed from benzene, show stability in one case and instability in another. And finally, the nitro compounds, very likely completely different systems, are all stable. The rationale for this result is not obvious and further research will be needed before it perhaps becomes so.

References

1. H. M. McConnell, *J. Chem. Phys.*, **24**, 764 (1965).
2. J. R. Bolton, A. Carrington, A. Forman, and L. E. Orgel, *Mol. Phys.*, **5**, 43 (1962).
3. Unless otherwise mentioned, data were obtained from the tables in K. W. Bowers, *Advances in Magnetic Resonance*, Vol. 1, Academic Press, New York, 1965, p. 317.
4. George J. Nolfi, Jr., Ph.D. Thesis, Massachusetts Institute of Technology, 1966
5. Peter A. Lehman, B.S. Thesis, Massachusetts Institute of Technology, 1966.
6. L. P. Hammett, *Physical Organic Chemistry*, McGraw-Hill, New York, 1940, pp. 184–199.
7. J. E. Leffler and E. Grunwald, *Rates and Equilibria of Organic Reactions*, Wiley, New York, 1963.
8. R. Parsons, *Handbook of Electrochemical Constants*, Academic Press, New York, 1959.
9. J. J. Lindberg and J. Kenttämea, *Suomen Kemistilehti*, **33B**, 104–107 (1960).
10. H. Lenormant and P. L. Clement, *Bull. Soc. Chim. France*, **1946**, 559.
11. A. H. Maki and D. H. Geske, *J. Am. Chem. Soc.*, **83**, 1852 (1961).
12. D. H. Geske and J. L. Rogle, *J. Am. Chem. Soc.*, **83**, 3532 (1961).
13. (a) L. H. Piette, P. L. Ludwig, and R. N. Adams, *J. Am. Chem. Soc.*, **84**, 4212 (1962); (b) P. B. Ayscough, F. P. Sargent, and R. Wilson, *J. Chem. Soc.*, **1963**,. 5418; (c) P. L. Kolker and W. A. Waters, *Proc. Chem. Soc.*, **1963**, 55; (d) P. L. Kolker and W. A. Waters, *J. Chem. Soc.*, **1964**, 1136.
14. (a) Y. Matsunaga and C. A. McDowell, *Can. J. Chem.*, **38**, 1158 (1960). (b) D. C. Reitz, J. R. Hallohan, F. Dravnieks, and J. E. Wertz, *J. Chem. Phys.*, **34**, 1457 (1961).
15. A. Zweig, W. G. Hodgson, and W. H. Jura, *J. Am. Chem. Soc.*, **86**, 4124 (1964).
16. D. H. Eargle, Jr., *J. Org. Chem.*, **28**, 1703 (1963).
17. A. A. Morton and E. J. Lanpher, *J. Org. Chem.*, **23**, 1636 (1958).
18. A. A. Morton and E. J. Lanpher, *J. Org. Chem.*, **23**, 1639 (1958).
19. R. A. Benkesser, D. J. Foster, and D. M. Suave, *Chem. Rev.*, **57**, 867 (1957).
20. H. Gilman, in *Organic Reactions*, Vol 8, R. Adams, A. H. Blatt, A. C. Cope, D. Y. Curtis, F. C. McGrew, and C. Niemann, Eds., Wiley, New York, 1954, p. 258.
21. G. Rubottom, Private communication.
22. C. Djerassi, Ed., *Steroid Reactions*, Holden-Day, San Francisco, 1963, pp. 267–325.
23. A. J. Birch, *Quart. Rev.*, **4**, 69 (1950).

24. J. R. Bolton and A. Carrington, *Mol. Phys.*, **4**, 497 (1961).
25. A. Carrington and P. F. Todd, *Mol. Phys.*, **7**, 533 (1964).
26. H. L. Strauss, T. J. Katz, and G. K. Fraenkel, *J. Am. Chem. Soc.*, **85**, 2360 (1963).
27. R. G. Lawler, J. R. Bolton, G. K. Fraenkel, and T. H. Brown, *J. Am. Chem. Soc.*, **86**, 520 (1964).
28. M. Karplus, R. G. Lawler, and G. K. Fraenkel, *J. Am. Chem. Soc.*, **87**, 5260 (1965).

CHAPTER 6

Recent Advances in the Chemistry of Aromatic Anion Radicals*

M. Thomas Jones

Department of Chemistry, St. Louis University, St. Louis, Missouri

I. INTRODUCTION

Organic anion radicals in liquid solution were among the first paramagnetic systems to be studied by electron spin resonance (ESR) (1). During the period of time since the first studies were reported the emphasis has been gradually changing from a concern with the technique of ESR *per se* to its use as a tool in elucidation of biological, chemical, and

---

* The following abbreviations have been used in this chapter: ESR (electron spin resonance); hfs (hyperfine splitting); ENDOR (electron nuclear double resonance); NMR (nuclear magnetic resonance); T_1 (spin-lattice relaxation time); MO (molecular orbital); HF (Hartree-Fock); SCF (self-consistent field); CI (configuration interaction); DPPH (α,α'-diphenyl-β-picrylhydrazyl); and TCNE (tetracyanoethylene).

physical problems. The rate at which this metamorphosis is taking place has been increasing in the last few years. As a recognition of this situation the emphasis of this chapter will tend toward the applications and use of ESR for the study of organic anion radicals in liquid solution.

The restriction of limiting the discussion to anion radicals is necessary in order to keep the size of the chapter within bounds. This review primarily covers the time period from 1963 to March, 1967. In spite of these limitations, the amount of literature to be reviewed was still considerable. Rather than prune too severely the quantity of material which fell into our area of interest and perhaps limit the usefulness of the chapter, it was decided to attempt to include or cite as much of the material as was reasonably possible. This was probably accomplished at some sacrifice in the readability. If however as a result the chapter proves to be of greater utility then the decision will have been justified.

II. ELECTRONIC STRUCTURE OF ANION RADICALS

A. Hyperfine Splittings

The hyperfine splittings one observes in a magnetic resonance experiment are related to the electronic structure of the radical from which they arise. The exact relationship between hyperfine splitting and electronic structure depends upon the particular nucleus giving rise to the observed splitting and its function in the molecule. One of the major activities of magnetic resonance spectroscopists has been in the area of theoretical and empirical evaluation of the relationships which form the bridge between the electronic structure of a radical and the experimentally observed hyperfine splitting. The reader is referred to Chapter 1 ("Electron Spin Densities") for a detailed discussion of these relationships.

Until recently there was only one technique by which hyperfine splittings could be measured, i.e., ESR. Now several new techniques are available, namely electron nuclear double resonance (ENDOR) (2–4) and NMR contact shifts (5–19).

ENDOR can be visualized as an NMR experiment in which an ESR spectrometer is used as a detector. Hyde (2) has given a very detailed description of the experiment, the instrumentation, and established that ENDOR can be used to study organic free radicals in solution. The advantages of ENDOR relative to ESR include improved resolution, simplification of spectra, and more accurate measurements of hyperfine splittings.

There are three different experimental conditions, any one of which, if satisfied, will lead to the observation of contact shifts in the NMR of paramagnetic species. These conditions are as follows:

1. That the inverse of the electronic spin-lattice relaxation time (T_1) must be greater than the hyperfine splittings expressed in units of frequency (i.e., $T_1^{-1} \gg A_i$). The electronic spin-lattice relaxation times of ordinary organic free radicals are too long to satisfy this condition. However, it is satisfied by organic complexes or chelates of transition metal ions which have extremely short relaxation times. Studies of this type have been well reviewed by Eaton and Phillips (5).

2. That the electron spin–spin exchange frequency (T_{ex}^{-1}) be greater than the hyperfine splittings expressed in units of frequency (i.e., $T_{ex}^{-1} \gg A_i$). From 1958 to 1963 there were several reports of the observations of NMR contact shifts in organic radical solids at low temperatures (6–11). However, the identical effects were not observed in solutions until very recently (12,13).

3. That the electron transfer frequency (T_{et}^{-1}) between paramagnetic and diamagnetic species, related to each other by the absence or presence of a single electron, be greater than the hyperfine splitting in units of frequency (i.e., $T_{et}^{-1} \gg A_i$). This technique offers much more general applicability than the other two. The technique and its application has been well described by several authors (14–20).

The direction and magnitude of the contact shift can be related, respectively, to the sign and value of the appropriate hyperfine splitting. As in the ENDOR experiment the resolution is improved. In many cases the assignment of hyperfine splittings is not only simplified but rendered unambiguous.

B. Hydrocarbon Anion Radicals

A number of interesting anion radicals involving large ring compounds have been recently reported, for example, cyclononatriene (21,22), *sym*-dibenzocyclooctatetraene (23), triphenyl- and tritolylbenzenes (24), tribenzocyclododecahexene (25), tribenzocyclododecatrienetriyne (25), 1,8-bisdehydro-14-annulene (26), and 1,3,5-cycloheptatriene (27). The latter was prepared in liquid ammonia by electrolytic reduction. Satisfactory agreement between calculated and observed hyperfine splittings is obtained only if two assumptions are made: *(1)* that the radical is in the nonplanar boat form, and *(2)* that the methylene hyperfine splitting arises primarily from spin polarization by unpaired spin density at the adjacent carbon atoms. A value of $Q_{C'CH}^{H} = 4.33$ or -3.09 Oe is suggested. Other anion radicals produced in liquid ammonia include 1,3-butadiene (28), 2,3-dimethyl-1,3-butadiene (29), 1,3-cyclohexadiene (29), and isoprene (29).

Studies of the bridged systems 1,6-methanocyclodecapentacene, 1,6-epoxycyclodecapentacene, and some of their deuteroderivatives, show that the observed spin densities are essentially in agreement with simple

Hückel MO calculations, if one accounts for the electron repelling effect of the bridging groups (30). Anion radicals of several radialenes have been reported (31,32). The observed hyperfine splittings are in good agreement with calculated values.

A variety of substituted acetylene anion radicals have been reported (33–35). Hückel and McLachlan (36) MO calculations are reported to give agreement with experiment for the anion radicals of diphenylacetylene (33,35), p,p'-dimethyldiphenylacetylene (35), and p-nitrophenylacetylene (35). Hückel MO parameters are suggested for the acetylenic bond (35).

The reports of the preparation of the anion radicals of cyclopropane (37), adamantane (38), and hexamethylenetetramine (38) have been seriously called into question (39–41). In the case of the reported adamantane anion radical, it appears certain that benzene anion radical was the source of the observed spectrum (39). The sources of the spectra reported for the other two compounds have not been established. However, the evidence indicates that the reported spectra did not arise from the anion radicals of cyclopropane and hexamethylenetetramine (40). Recent attempts by the authors of these reports (37,38) to repeat their work have been unsuccessful (41). It is perhaps interesting to note, at this point, that extended Hückel calculations (42) which gave reasonable fits to the experimentally observed hyperfine splittings for aliphatic radicals (43) did not yield values in agreement with those reported (37,38) for adamantane and cyclopropane anion radicals.

The mono- and dianions of bis(2,2'-biphenylene) methane are both paramagnetic (44). The latter exists as a ground state triplet. In contrast, only the monoanion of bis(2,2'-biphenylene) silane is paramagnetic (45). Presumably this difference reflects the availability of the d orbitals on the silicon atom. Other examples of mono- and dianion pairs, both of which are paramagnetic, include triphenylbenzene (24,46), decacylene (46), and coronene (47). However, in coronene dianion the paramagnetism arises from an excited triplet state which lies about 0.1 eV above a singlet ground state. The other two dianions are ground state triplets.

A series of doublet state dianion radicals have been reported which include those prepared from cycloheptatriene (48), tetraphenylallyl (49), Koelsch's radical (50), 4,5-methylenephenanthrene (50,51), pentaphenylcyclopentadienyl (50), 9-phenylfluorene (50,51), fluorene (51,52), benzofluorene (51), carbazole (51,52), and 4,5-iminophenanthrene (51). The g values are about 0.00025 larger than they are for monoanions of similar structures. Reasonable agreement was found between experiment and McLachlan MO calculations of the spin densities.

Other reports of hydrocarbon anion radicals include alkyl-substituted cyclooctatetraenes (53,54), phenylcyclooctatetraene (55), tetraphenylene

(56), 1,2:5,6-dibenzocyclooctatetraene (56,57), biphenyl (58), substituted biphenyls (59), hexa-*m*-phenylene (60), *o*-, *m*-, *p*-terphenyl (61), 9,10-diethyl-, 9-ethyl-anthracenes (62), 9,10-diphenyl-anthracene (63), and a series of dimethylnaphthalenes (64).

Hindered rotation in the stilbene anion radical has been observed (65,66). It leads to asymmetry in the spin density distribution which has been analyzed in terms of simple modifications to the conventional MO theory (66,67).

C. Anion Radicals Containing Heteroatoms

1. Group IV Elements

In spite of its rather low natural abundance of 1.1%, ^{13}C hfs is frequently observed in ESR spectra. Because few studies are deliberately concerned with ^{13}C splittings, those cited here probably represent only a fraction of the total number of observations of ^{13}C hfs. In general, the application of the Karplus-Fraenkel (68) theory of ^{13}C hfs has been successful. An exception to this rule appears to have occurred in some cyanocarbon radicals (69–71). This may just be the result of poor choices for the sigma–pi parameters.

A redetermination of the sign of the methyl ^{13}C hfs in triphenylmethyl (72) shows it to be positive in agreement with theory (68). The solvent theory of Gendell, Freed, and Fraenkel (73) was confirmed by a study of the dependence of ^{13}C hfs in benzosemiquinone-1-^{13}C upon the solvent composition (74).

Reports of other ^{13}C hfs include 2-*t*-butyl-^{13}C semiquinone (75), cyclohexane-1,2-dione (76), benzene (77), anthracene (78), dibenzo-*p*-dioxin (79), perinaphthenyl (80), hexakis (trifluoromethyl) benzene (81,82), methyl (83), fluoromethyls (84), 1,4-benzosemiquinone (85) and 2,5-dihydroxy-1,4-benzosemiquinone (85).

A method has been reported which will allow the assignment of nuclear positions and signs of the ^{13}C and ^{14}N hfs (86,87). The technique depends upon line width effects.

Radicals containing Si and other heavier Group IV atoms display phenomena which appear to be the result of *d*-orbital participation (45,88–90). A rather extensive study was made of the anion radicals of 4-$(CH_3)_3MC_6H_4C_6H_5$ and 4,4'-$(CH_3)_3MC_6H_4C_6H_4M(CH_3)_3$, where M = Si, Ge, and Sn (89). The results are interpreted as indicating that these elements participate in π-bonding with the aromatic rings. The observation of the anion radical of dodecamethylcyclohexasilane (90) strongly suggests that the odd electron is in a π- or δ-type molecular orbital made up of silicon 3*d* atomic orbitals.

2. Group V Elements

The line widths of the anion radicals of nitrobenzene and p-nitrobenzoic acid have been measured and analyzed (91) in terms of the Freed-Fraenkel theory (92–96). The analysis suggests that the radical tumbling in solution is anisotropic. Rather large line width variations have been observed in the o-, m-, and p-fluoronitrobenzene anion radicals (97). A detailed analysis shows that it is possible to estimate the principal g tensor components for the p-fluoronitrobenzene anion radical.

Estimates of the ^{14}N hyperfine tensors of alkyl-substituted nitrobenzenes and their conjugate acids indicate that the ratio of the anisotropic to isotropic ^{14}N interaction decreases with increasing spin density in the nitro group (98). This is interpreted as a pyramidal distortion of the nitro group. New values for the sigma–pi parameters for N—O bonds which are deduced from the ^{14}N hyperfine coupling constants of various small radicals are offered in support of this postulate (99).

A series of alkyl-substituted nitrobenzene anion radicals (100), display a linear relationship between A_N, the frequency of the IR symmetric NO stretch, and $\cos^2 \theta$, where θ is the twist angle of the NO_2 deduced from the UV spectrum (101). Geske et al. (102) have reported a rather extensive study of the steric effects in o-substituted nitrobenzenes and nitroanilines. Their results show that as the nitro group is twisted out of the plane of the aromatic ring by large substituents the nitrogen hyperfine splitting increases while the proton hyperfine splitting decreases.

Rieger and Fraenkel (103) have reported the results of Hückel and McLachlan MO calculations on a large series of nitro-substituted aromatic anion radicals. Other nitro group containing anion radicals have been prepared from nitrophenol (104), nitrobiphenyl (105), nitrochlorobenzene (106), bis-p-nitrophenyls (107), nitrobenzophenones (108), tetraisopropylnitrobenzene (109), nitro-p-terphenyl (110), nitronaphthalene (111), and nitromesitylene (111).

The observation of line width alternation in dioxane–water mixtures containing p-dinitrobenzene anion radical (112) has led to a new interpretation of Ward's (113) observation of apparent hfs by a single nitrogen nucleus. Ward's results can be explained by postulating that a small difference exists between the coupling constants associated with each nitro group together with a fluctuation between the two at a frequency of the order of the difference in the coupling constants. This leads to a broadening of two of the five expected nitrogen hfs (93,114). Hence only three lines of equal intensity separated by $(A_1 + A_2)$ rather than five lines separated by $(A_1 + A_2)/2$ of relative intensity 1:2:3:2:1 are observed. A similar line width alternation is observed for m-dinitrobenzene in DMF–ethanol solutions (115).

A number of other studies have demonstrated that the nitrobenzene anion radical hyperfine splittings are strongly influenced by their environment (116–122). These effects will be discussed in Section III-D.

The reports of anion radicals prepared from polynitro compounds (123–134) include polysubstituted naphthalenes (125–127), 1,3,5-trinitrobenzene (128), polynitromesitylene (129), polynitrodurene (129), mono- and dinitro derivatives of phenol and benzoic acid (130), and trinitromethyl (131–133). The latter has been analyzed in terms of a modulation of the ^{14}N isotropic hfs (134). It has been concluded that the observed effects are probably caused by steric hindrance and consequent noncoplanarity of the nitro groups.

Lown (135) reports a configurational effect in the 1-acetoxyl-1-nitroso-4-t-butylcyclohexane. The nitrosobenzene anion radical also has received considerable attention (136,137). The spectra indicate that the protons *ortho* and *meta* to the N—O group are not equivalent. This suggests that the C—N—O group is not linear and that the rotation frequency is low. Modifications to MO theory to account for this nonlinearity are suggested (137).

The application of the Karplus-Fraenkel theory for ^{13}C hfs (68) to 41 ^{14}N containing radicals yields three different sets of sigma–pi parameters for ^{14}N, each set of which is able to reproduce the experimental coupling constants within 5–10% (138). However, before we conclude that this implies that unique values do not exist for ^{14}N sigma–pi parameters, we should consider whether or not unique values do exist for specific classes of radical systems (i.e., taking into consideration the specific chemical function of the nitrogen, the type of solvent in which it is studied, the electronic charge of the radical, etc.). This observation serves to emphasize and perhaps to point the way toward resolving the sometimes conflicting reports of values for ^{14}N sigma–pi parameters.

One of the earlier considerations of cyano aromatic anions in terms of Hückel and McLachlan MO calculation and empirical evaluation of the sigma–pi parameters was reported by Rieger and Fraenkel (139). The preparation of many of the radicals they studied was reported elsewhere (140). In more recent studies of the anion radicals of azodicarbonitrile (141), tetracyanopyridine, and pentacyanopyridine (142) it has been found necessary to modify the sigma–pi parameters suggested by Rieger and Fraenkel (139).

Reports of other cyano-containing anion radicals include phthalonitrile (143,144), benzonitrile (144), terphthalonitrile (144), p-tolunitrile (144), p-dicyanotetrazine (145), tetracyanoquinodimethan (69,70), and tetracyanoethylene (70,140,146). The latter serves as a convenient g value and scan rate standard because of its stability in ether type solvents in the absence of oxygen (70).

Stone and Maki (147) have reported sigma–pi parameters for hetero-cyclic nitrogen derived from *sym*-tetrazine, pyridazine, phthalazine, and phenazine anion radicals. The spin densities were calculated using the McLachlan MO method. These parameters have been used with a moderate amount of success to calculate ^{14}N hfs for anion radicals of azodicarbon-itrile (141), tetracyanopyridine (142), pentacyanopyridine (142), 3-nitropyridine (148), 3,5-dinitropyridine (148), 2-chloro-5-nitropyridine (148), 5-nitropyrimidine (148), 3-acetylpyridine (148), 9,10-diazaphenan-threne (149), 2,2′-bipyrimidine (149), Δ2,2′-biisobenzimidazolylidene (149), benzo(*c*)cinnoline (150), *trans*-azobenzene (150) and 1,4-dimethyl-tetrazine (150).

Strom, Russell, and Konaka (150) believe that they obtain a better fit to experiment if they use a value for $Q_{CN}^{N} = +13.8$ Oe. On the other hand, Cottrell and Rieger (148) find from the analysis of the ESR spectra of the above series of substituted pyridines and pyrimidines that the value probably lies in the range from 0 to -2.5 Oe. This is in good agreement with Stone and Maki's value of -2 Oe.

Ali and Hinchliffe (151) using a refined MO method for calculation of spin densities in the 9,10-diazaphenanthrene, 2,2′-bipyrimidine, and Δ2,2′-biisobenzimidazolylidene anion radicals suggest that an earlier report (149) of the assignment in the latter may be incorrect.

Two other reports of sigma–pi interaction parameters for nitrogen have recently appeared (152,153). The latter were derived using only simple Hückel MO calculation for the charge densities.

Calculations of the expected ^{14}N hfs for tricyano-*sym*-triazine using parameters that gave good agreement with experiment for tetra- and pentacyanopyridine anion radicals have been reported (142). They suggest that an explanation of the hfs observed upon the reduction of tricyano-*sym*-triazine based upon a permanent Jahn-Teller distortion (154) is incorrect. A structural rearrangement is suggested.

The following are some of the other heterocyclic nitrogen compounds studied; 3-nitropyridine (155), a series of substituted pyridinyl systems (156,157), methyl-substituted pyrazines and pyridines (158,159), pheno-thiazine and some of its derivatives (160), 1,3,6,8-tetraazapyrene (161), and cyclo(3.2.2)azine (162).

ESR studies of a series of semiquinone (163) and nitro aromatic (164) phosphate anion radicals show that the phosphorus splittings are very sensitive to steric interaction. For example, large *ortho* substituents lead to large phosphorus splittings. It also appears that the phosphorus splittings are influenced by inductive as well as hyperconjugative effects.

Britt and Kaiser (165) have shown that the reaction of triphenylphos-phine with alkali metal leads to a radical derived from diphenylphosphine.

They have also found that reaction of phenylbiphenylenephosphine with alkali metals leads to the formation of anion radicals of a metal biphenylenephosphine and diphosphine (166).

Alkali metal reduction of a series of phosphines and phosphine oxides leads to different anion radical species depending upon the solvent and alkali metal (167). For example, the sodium reduction of $(C_6H_5)_3PO$ in 1,2-dimethoxyethane and tetrahydrofuran gives only the anion radical of biphenyl. On the other hand, reduction with potassium yields the radical $(C_6H_5)_2POK^-$ and $(C_6H_5)_3POK^-$. The anion radical of $(CH_3)_2PC_6H_4—C_6H_4P(CH_3)_2$ was also reported (167).

The reaction of triphenylphosphine and triethylphosphine with chloranil gives radicals containing phosphorus (168). Other phosphorus-containing radicals that have recently been reported include 2,4,6-triphenylphosphobenzene (169) and phosphonitrile (170).

3. Group VI Elements

A comparison of the ring proton hfs constant of the benzocyclobutadienoquinone anion radical has led to qualitative indications of the electrophilic nature of the *ortho* substituents (171). Russell and Young (172) recently questioned the original hfs assignments of this radical.

The ESR spectra of pyrogallol semiquinone radical in aqueous solutions of varying pH show several distinct species possessing zero, one, and two hydroxyl protons (173). From these spectra values for the first and second acid dissociation constants of the radical have been estimated. Upper limits have been placed upon the rate of the hydroxyl proton exchange. A similar situation has been observed when hydroquinone is oxidized in acid solution (174). At pH's greater than 4 the dissociated form is observed. The undissociated form is observed at pH's less than 4.

A recent report of the preparation of dicyclopropyl ketyl (175) has been challenged by Russell and Malkus (176). They believe it may be a poorly resolved spectrum of the biphenyl anion radical.

Long range coupling constants have been observed in the spectra of several bicyclic semiquinones and semidiones (177–180). They have been useful aids in establishing the structures of the parent compounds (179, 180). Russell and co-workers (181–188) have performed extensive ESR studies on the anion radicals prepared from semiquinones and semidiones. Here too ESR has been useful in establishing the structures of the radical and the parent compounds.

Stock and Suzuki (75) have discussed the ESR results obtained from the anions of 2-*t*-butyl, 2-*t*-butyl-^{13}C, 2-trifluoromethyl-semiquinone, and the semiquinones prepared from 1-methyl-2,5-dihydroxy- and 2,5-dihydroxytriptycene. Their results are discussed with reference to the conclusions derived from the reaction chemistry of these compounds concerning the relative importance of C—H, C—C, and C—F hyperconjugation.

The spin–density distributions in the 1,4-benzosemiquinone and 2,5-dihydroxy-1,4-benzosemiquinone (85) ions have been estimated by measuring the proton and ^{13}C hfs and using reasonable choices for the values of the sigma–pi parameters which relate these splittings to the spin densities. It was necessary to determine the signs as well as the magnitudes of the ^{13}C hfs to obtain the spin densities.

The conformational equilibria of a number of alicyclic ketyls with ring size varying from six to twelve carbon atoms have been studied (189,190). Several ortho-substituted benzhydryl and diaryl ketone anion radicals have been studied (191,192). The aryl rings appear to be rotating freely.

Anion radicals of terephthalaldehyde-2,5-d_2, phthalaldehyde, phthalaldehyde-4-d, o-nitrobenzaldehyde, and p-nitrobenzaldehyde have been reported (193). The trans rotamer of terephthalaldehyde is more stable than the cis and has a larger ratio of ring proton hfs constants. Corvaja et al. (194) report they have been able to distinguish between the anion radicals of cis- and trans-3,4,5-trimethoxyphenylglyoxal semidione. The ESR spectra of a series of methyl-9,10-anthrasemiquinones indicate that methyl groups in the α position are not free to rotate (195).

Some of the other anion radicals prepared from ketones and aldehydes include fluorenone (196), 2,7-difluorenone (196), 4,5-phenanthrylene ketone (196), o-phenanthrenequinone (196), acenaphthenequinone (196), benzil (196,197), 2,2,5,5-tetramethylhexane-3,4-dione (197), diquinone (198), acetophenone (199), benzaldehyde (199), and 4-fluoroacetophenone (199).

An ESR study of an extensive number of 1,4-naphthoquinones and naphthazarines has been reported (200). A crude correlation was found between hfs constants and quinoidal character of the ring hydrogens. A large number of hydroxy and methoxy derivatives were involved. In a related study (201), it was deduced from the ESR spectra of a rather large number of methoxy-substituted parasemiquinones and MO calculations that the methoxy proton hfs must arise, in part, from spin density on the oxygen. From the use of model compounds it was also concluded that only one conformational isomer can give rise to methoxy proton hfs. A value of 5.6 Oe is suggested for $Q^H_{OCH_3}$. The authors have also tabulated all the previous reports of transmission of spin density across ether and acyl bonds.

Other methoxy- and phenoxy-type radicals which have been reported include anisole (202), phenol (203), p-chlorophenol (203), 2,6-dichlorophenol (203) and 2,4-dichlorophenol (203), 1,2,3,6,7,8-hexahydropyrene (204,205), 4,5,9,10-tetrahydropyrene (205), and sym-tri-t-butylphenoxyl (206).

The anion radicals of several cyclic imide and anhydride derivatives of phthalic and naphthalic acids have been prepared electrolytically (207). Hückel and McLachlan spin density calculations give reasonable agreement with experiment. The authors also note a correlation of the half wave reduction potential and the calculated energy of the first antibonding MO. This latter correlation has been observed by many investigators on a rather large variety of systems (102,103,208–211). However, strictly speaking it should only be true for aromatic hydrocarbons (208).

A number of recent reports of radicals containing isotopically enriched [17]O are of interest since they permit the direct observation of oxygen hfs and hopefully will ultimately lead to direct measurement of the spin density at the oxygen atom. The systems which have been studied to date and the conclusions derived from them are summarized below.

Studies of the nitrobenzene anion radical by Gulich and Geske (212) show that as the solvent polarity is increased both the ^{14}N and [17]O hfs increase. These results are in agreement with MO calculations.

The p-benzosemiquinone [17]O enriched anion radical has been prepared (213,214). The exchange rate of the oxygen with water was found to be greater for the semiquinone than for the quinone (214). The hfs constant for [17]O in peroxylamine disulfonate was found to be negative (215). Finally, the [17]O hfs has been observed in 2,4,6-triphenylphenoxyl (216,217).

Sulfur-containing anion radicals have proved to be of strong interest. the questions for which answers are being sought are: (1) Is there d orbital participation or interaction with the pi bonds of aromatic derivatives? (2) What effects do the higher oxidation states of sulfur have upon the ESR spectra? (3) How do the ESR spectra of a homologous series of compounds prepared from Group VI elements compare?

Vincow's (218) assignment of the hfs constants in thioxanthone-5,5-dioxide which has served as the basis for assignments of many similar anion radicals has been recently confirmed by chemical substitution (219). The assignment had been questioned (220) on the basis of MO calculations.

Strom and Russell (221) concluded from their study of the anion radicals of 2,1,3-benzoxadiazole, -benzothiodiazole, and -benzoselenadiazole that sulfur and selenium atoms could accept the unpaired electron more readily than oxygen. They found good agreement between experiment and simple Hückel calculations. They found that a p-orbital model for sulfur gave results just as satisfactory as those obtained from a d-orbital model.

Gerdil and Lucken (222) obtained somewhat more definitive results from their study of the anion radicals of dibenzothiophene and its oxygen and selenium homologs. Their calculations of the spin density distribution assuming p-orbital participation gave good agreement with experiment whereas those for d-orbital participation were in poor agreement.

Reports of other sulfur-containing radicals include aryl sulfonyls (223) which show a significant amount of sigma character, phenylthio-1,4-semiquinones (224), benzylthio-1,4-semiquinones (224), thianthrene oxides (225), dibenzothiophenes (226,227) *cis-* and *trans-*thianthrene-5,10-dioxide (227,228), diphenyl sulfone (227), thioxanthone (229), thioxanthone sulfone (229), dibenzothiophene (229), dibenzothiophene sulfone (229), and some nitrothiophenes (230).

4. Group VII Elements

A rapidly increasing number of studies have been reported which involve fluorine-substituted radicals. As a general rule the fluorine-containing radicals are stable and the fluorine hfs constants are larger than those of hydrogen at equivalent positions.

Carrington et al. (231) studied five different fluoronitrobenzene anion radicals. They found evidence for steric hindrance of the nitro group when it has two *ortho* fluorine neighbors. Studies of the *o-*, *m-*, and *p-*fluoronitrobenzene anion radicals have already been cited (97).

The perfluorotriphenylmethyl radical has been prepared (232). A comparison of its hfs constants with those of triphenylmethyl shows that the ratio A_F/A_H is not a constant for the three different molecular positions, thus adding to the already substantial amount of evidence indicating that fluorine hfs cannot be described by a simple relationship between spin density and hfs similar to the one proposed by McConnell for hydrogen.

The synthesis as well as several ESR studies of bis(trifluoromethyl) nitroxide have been reported (233–236). Its ESR spectrum in several solvents has been investigated (235) as well as the temperature dependence of the fluorine and nitrogen hfs (236). In the latter study the fluorine hfs increases with decreasing temperature. This has been interpreted as being due to enhanced conjugation of the fluorine p orbital with the nitrogen π orbitals at the lower temperatures. A similar effect has been observed in the anion radical of hexakis(trifluoromethyl)benzene (82).

Several chlorophenols (205) have already been cited. A series of halogenated phenol-indophenols have been produced by electrolytic reduction (237). Analysis of the ESR spectra gave qualitative agreement with the calculated valence bond structures of the corresponding radicals.

D. Orbitally Degenerate and Near-Orbitally Degenerate Radicals

A number of phenomena are either enhanced in or appear to be peculiar to orbitally degenerate radicals. The resonance line widths are larger (238), the spin-lattice relaxation times are shorter (81,238), the temperature dependence of the hyperfine splittings is greater (39,82,239–243) and anomalous hfs arise in deuterium-substituted systems (244–246).

Several models and theories have been proposed to explain the larger line widths and enhanced spin-lattice relaxation (247–250). One of the first models (248) proposed that solvent-induced spin switching was the source of the large line width and enhanced spin-lattice relaxation. An application (249) of the recently developed line width theories of Freed and Fraenkel (93,251) to the spin switching model suggested that it would lead to alternating line width phenomena which have not been observed in such systems. However, if the switching frequency were greater than 10^9–10^{10} Hz, the alternating line width phenomena would not be expected to occur.

Kivelson considered various possible contributions to the spin-lattice relaxation in the benzene anion radical (250). He concluded that the most important contribution may arise from Orbach relaxation processes which are effective because of low-lying excited electronic states.

The experimental evidence indicates that the spin-lattice relaxation times in orbitally degenerate free radicals are shorter than in nondegenerate systems. This is borne out by spin-lattice relaxation measurements on the hexakis(trifluoromethyl)benzene (81) and coronene (252) anion radicals in which the spin-lattice relaxation times are short.

The benzene (39,239) and hexakis(trifluoromethyl)benzene (82) anion radical hfs constants show a strong inverse dependence upon temperature. A similar dependence is observed in cycloheptatrienyl (240,241) and methyl (242) radicals. Calculations involving incomplete sigma orbital following (253) and vibronic (254) effects have been performed for the methyl radical. Both treatments appear to give agreement with experiment. The latter treatment when applied to the benzene anion radical did not give agreement with experiment.

When one isotope of an element replaces another, it is assumed that the ratio of the hfs constants for each pair of the isotopes will be given by the ratio of their magnetogyric ratios. Several orbitally degenerate systems and one nonorbitally degenerate system violate this rule. The observed ratios of hydrogen to deterium hfs constants obtained from monodeuterobenzene anion radical (245), perdeuterobenzene anion radical (246), perdeutero-cycloheptatrienyl radical (246), and monodeuterocyclooctatetraene anion radical (244) are smaller than the value of 6.514 calculated from the ratio of the hydrogen to deuterium magnetogyric ratios. It appears that the observed ratio of hydrogen to deuterium hfs increases toward 6.514 as the ring size increases. A similar effect in the nonorbitally degenerate N,N'-disubstituted-1,4-diazine cation and other related radicals has been observed (255). Observation of the hydrogen to deuterium hfs ratio in 1,4-dideuteronaphthalene anion radical, the only other accurately measured nonorbitally degenerate system reported, gives a value very near the expected value of 6.514 (246).

Substitution of deuterium for hydrogen also alters the spin density distribution in some systems (245,246,255). The deuterium appears to act as if it were slightly electropositive relative to hydrogen. This effect does not occur in monodeuterooctatetraene anion radical (244). Carrington et al. (244) interpret the difference between monodeuterobenzene and monodeuterocyclooctatetraene anion radicals in terms of a Jahn-Teller effect. Karplus, Lawler, and Fraenkel (256) have offered a more general explanation of the isotope effect based on the vibrational perturbation of the Hückel resonance–integral parameter β.

Nearly-orbitally degenerate systems have also been the object of considerable attention both experimentally (17,20,257–260) and theoretically (261–267). They display temperature dependent hyperfine splittings and variations in the signs of the spin densities which have been analyzed in terms of configuration interaction, vibronic coupling, and thermal equilibrium between the two lowest antibonding orbitals.

E. g Values

With the availability of better equipment and techniques it is now possible to measure g values quite accurately. In fact, measurements are accurate enough to detect some structural dependences of the g value. Two detailed discussions of the techniques and their limitations have been given (268,269). The latter study finds good agreement between experiment and the theory of g values proposed by Stone (270–272). One report indicates that g values of simple aliphatic radicals may be useful in diagnosis of the radical structure (273).

F. Recent Theoretical Developments

The type of theoretical developments which will be of most concern in this section are either related to calculation of spin densities or the determination of sigma–pi interaction parameters.

A restricted HF perturbation method employing semiempirical SCF-MO closed-shell MO's has been described and used to calculate spin densities and charge densities of 16 hydrocarbon ions (274). It was concluded that the empirical relationship between charge density, spin density, and hfs was no better for the Colpa-Bolton equation (275) or the Giacometti, Nordio, and Pavan equation (276) than for the simple McConnell equation. On the other hand, Snyder and Amos (277) using unrestricted HF wave functions for a number of conjugated hydrocarbon radicals find that of the above three equations, McConnell's gave the poorest agreement with experiment. Good agreement with experiment has been reported for open-shell SCF-LCAO-MO calculations on polyazine anion radicals (278).

Amos and Davison have performed unrestricted HF calculations for several nonalternant radicals including some linear polyenes (279). Spin density calculations on nitro-substituted conjugated anions using SCF-CI, unrestricted HF, and unrestricted HF with annihilation of the quartet spin function have also been reported (280). A simple method of calculating π-spin densities has been reported in which the positive and negative spin densities are obtained separately (281). The effects of spin projection on spin densities have been discussed by Harris (282).

Two studies indicate that the effect of the toluene anion radical methyl group is better described by an inductive model than by hyperconjugation (265,283). Dixon (284) has extended the MO theory of hyperconjugation to account for the hfs constants observed in such simple free radicals as cyclopentyl and vinyl. Similar results were obtained by using the extended Hückel theory (43). Levy (285) has used a hyperconjugation theory which includes a small spin polarization term to calculate the methyl and methylene proton hfs in aromatic radicals. He finds agreement with experiment.

Lazdins and Karplus (286) have performed an analysis of the π electron spin delocalization into the methyl group hydrogen pseudo-pi orbital in the ethyl radical. They conclude that neither an exchange polarization nor a simple electron transfer gives by itself a completely satisfactory description of spin delocalization in these systems.

Wave functions for nitroxide radicals have been calculated using a method derived from SCF theory (287). The method yields both σ and π molecular orbitals and gives reasonable agreement with experiment. Kaplan et al. (288) have proposed a method for the determination of spin densities in aromatic radicals which is independent of calculations of $\sigma-\pi$ interactions. It employs line width studies of solution spectra and is based on broadening arising from electron–nuclear anisotropic intramolecular magnetic dipole interactions. The technique was applied to the anion radical of 3,5-difluoronitrobenzene anion radical.

The vast majority of the calculations of the spin density distributions in radical systems have been done within the MO framework. Only a relatively few calculations have involved the use of VB methods (289–293). In general both the MO and VB theories have given satisfactory agreement with each other and with the available experimental evidence. However, recently Brown and Karplus (294) have reported results of VB spin-density calculations for several positive and negative aromatic anion radicals.They find that the spin densities at a given molecular position are not equivalent for a negative and positive ion pair. This contrasts with the situation which occurs in the MO theory in which they are equivalent. Also noted was that for a number of ion radicals, mostly positive ions, the symmetries of the ground states as predicted by MO and VB theories are not the same.

III. EXTRA MOLECULAR INTERACTIONS

A. Spin–Spin Exchange

Spin–spin exchange frequencies as a function of radical concentration have been measured for several free radicals in solution (295–298). The studies show that the exchange frequencies are proportional to the radical concentration and are diffusion controlled. Therefore, the second-order rates, at which the spin–spin exchange occurs for various systems show small variations, i.e., they appear to be little affected by such factors as solvation, ion pairing, substituents, etc. Until recently all such studies reported were in the slow exchange region. One has now been reported for the fast exchange region (297).

Viscosity changes produced by hydrostatic pressure and changes in temperature (299,300) yield interesting effects upon the resonance line width and apparent hfs. Kivelson's (301) theory gives good agreement with experiment.

Two new and more general theories (302,303) of spin–spin exchange interactions have been proposed. They are applicable over all ranges of the exchange frequency which was true only for one (304) of the two earlier treatments (301,304).

B. Electron Transfer

In contrast to the spin–spin exchange rates the measured electron transfer rates for a wide variety of systems have been shown to be strongly dependent upon solvent, ion-pairing, substituents, optical configuration, etc. (298,305–312). Chang and Johnson (309) have studied the naphthalene–naphthenlide system in the fast transfer region and find they can obtain rate constants for electron transfer between ion pairs and free ions. A correlation between alkali metal hfs in the xanthone and benzophenone systems and electron transfer rate was observed by Hirota and Weissman (310). They found rates in the range 10^7–10^9 liters mole^{-1}sec^{-1}. Layloff et al. (311) studied a variety of systems at room temperature using dimethylformamide as the solvent. Most of the rates they observed fell into the 10^7–10^9 liters mole^{-1}sec^{-1} range except for the nitrobenzene–nitrobenzenide system in dimethylformamide containing 10% water in which the rate decreased to approximately 10^5 liters mole^{-1}sec^{-1}.

Bruning and Weissman (312) studied electron transfer between optical isomers of 1-(α-naphthyl)-1-phenylethane and its anion radical. They found that the d–l electron transfer rate was about twice that of the d–d electron-transfer rate in 1,2-dimethoxyethane whereas the rates were equal in tetrahydrofuran. These results indicate a small but real deviation from the Marcus relation (313,314) for the rate of reaction of $A^- + B \rightleftarrows A + B^-$.

C. Spin-Lattice Relaxation

The number of experimental studies of spin-lattice relaxation of organic radicals in liquid solution have been relatively few (81,252,315–320). Such studies under the proper circumstances are capable of yielding considerable information about the interaction of the radical with its environment, i.e., radical–radical, radical–solvent, and radical–counterion interactions.

The various mechanisms for electron spin-lattice relaxation of radicals in solution which have been considered are modulation of anisotropic g tensors (93,321) and of hyperfine interaction (322,323) by molecular rotation or tumbling, and electric field fluctuations (301,324). In the latter treatment, the conditions are discussed for which contributions from Van Vleck, Van Vleck-Raman, and Orbach mechanisms become important.

D. Solvation Effects

Quite a variety of solvent effects upon the hfs of radicals in solution have been observed. Studies of such effects present considerable potential for obtaining detailed information about the interaction of radical systems with their environments.

Chambers and Adams (116) have found a correlation between solvent shifts in the optical spectra of the nitrobenzene anion radical and changes in the nitrogen hfs as water is added to dimethylformamide solutions. They propose that the effects they observe are due to hydrogen bonding of the water to the oxygen of the nitro group. A similar argument has been presented for hydrogen bonding with the anion radical of fluorenone (325). Levy and Meyers (117) suggested that the results of their study of nitrogen hfs in the nitrobenzene anion radical in liquid ammonia are consistent with some sort of hydrogen bonding.

Studies of other systems which have also led to suggestions of possible hydrogen bonding include nitrobenzene anion radical in aqueous alcohol solutions prepared by chemical and photochemical reduction (122), substituted nitric oxides (326,327), and the hydroxyl radical (328).

A detailed study of the effect of various protic solvents upon the nitrogen hfs of a number of aromatic and aliphatic nitro anion radicals has been reported (121). Other studies of the effect of solvent upon the ESR spectra of radical systems include nitrobenzene and its derivative (118–120), substituted nitric oxides (329–331), p-aminophenoxyls (332), and semi-quinones (333,334).

Zandstra (335) found that the g value is also solvent dependent in the p-benzosemiquinone radical ion. Apparently, changes in spin-orbit coupling in going from one solvent to another are reflected in g value changes.

Scheffler and Stegmann (336) were able to measure relative rate constants for the formation of radical–solvent adducts for 4-amino-2,6-di-*tert*-butylphenoxyl with various solvents. They measured an upper limit on the lifetimes of the complexes at room temperature of approximately 2×10^{-8} sec. Finally a recent report of the formation of an "ion pair" between nitroaromatics and organic electron donor molecules has appeared (337).

E. Liquid Crystals as Solvents

Nematogenic molecules can be oriented in magnetic fields of 1000 Oe or larger when they are in the liquid crystal range. Radical systems which are dissolved in liquid crystals are no longer able to average out the anisotropic contributions to the g factor and hfs constants. For example the nitrogen hfs in DPPH and TCNE$^-$, when dissolved in p-azoxyanisole in its isotropic range ($T > 136°$C) gave the normal solution spectrum values of 9.2 and 1.58 Oe, respectively (338), whereas, the nitrogen hfs for the same solution at 119°C (i.e., the nematic range) are 7.8 and 0.62 Oe, respectively. Longuet-Higgins and Luckhurst (339) deduced on the basis of these results that the mole fraction of clusters in the nematic phase is greater than 0.9 at temperatures just above the solid → nematic phase (116°C) and greater than 0.6 at temperature just below the nematic → isotropic transition (136°C).

Two reports of liquid crystal studies of perinaphthenyl radical have appeared (340,341). Glarum and Marshall (341) studied the g tensor, hfs tensors for the two protons and three of the four ^{13}C hyperfine splittings. In most cases they found agreement with theory. A general expression for the effective spin Hamiltonian of a radical in a liquid crystal solution was derived.

An increase in the hfs of ring and bridge protons of Coppinger's radical was observed in the nematic phase of p-azoxyanisole (342). Extra transitions were observed in the spectra of nitroxide biradicals dissolved the nematic phase of p-azoxyanisole (343). It is suggested that they arise from incomplete averaging of the zero-field splitting.

F. Kinetics of Formation, Reaction, etc.

Gerson (80) has observed a temperature dependence of the ESR signal intensity of the perinaphthenyl radical which is interpreted as arising from a monomer–diamagnetic dimer equilibrium. The reaction of triphenylmethyl and molecular oxygen has been found to be reversible (344,345). The measured enthalpy of reaction was given as -9 kcal.

The heat of dissociation of hexaphenylethane, long ago measured by optical methods, has been measured by ESR (346). Wurster's blue perchlorate which in the solid state shows triplet exciton behavior has been found to dimerize in solution by ESR studies (347). The disproportionation equilibrium of N-diphenylmethyleneaniline anion radical as a function of temperature has been measured by ESR (348). It was observed that irradiation of the dianion with light of wavelength 3660 Å converts it to the radical anion.

Thermodynamic values have been obtained by optical methods and ESR for the cleavage of the anion radical of dibenzofuran and the counterions Li^+, Na^+, K^+, and Cs^+. The cleavage rate increases 25-fold from Cs^+ to Li^+ (349). The disproportionation of the benzil anion radical in THF has been studied by ESR (350). The equilibrium constant increases from Li^+ through Cs^+.

G. Ion Pairing

The phenomenon of ion pairing occurs quite generally with anion radicals. The reader is referred to Chapter 2 ("Metal Ketyls and Related Radical Ions").

IV. INTRAMOLECULAR INTERACTIONS

A. Conformational Effects

A very important application of ESR has been found in the study of conformational effects. This area has been thoroughly reviewed very recently by Geske (351).

B. Intramolecular Electron Transfer

Surprisingly, few examples of intramolecular electron transfer have been observed (71,352–355). By this name we shall mean electron transfer between aromatic rings or conjugated groups joined together by saturated linkages. Weissman found the rate of electron transfer decreased as the chain length increased in the paracyclophane anion radicals (352). Recent ESR and optical studies of benzene and 2,2-paracyclophane anion radicals combined with MO calculations have led to the conclusion that an electron resonance interaction exists between the π–electron systems of the two rings (353). The interaction energy is estimated to be of the order of 0.82 eV. McConnell (354) assumed that all direct Hamiltonian matrix elements between the aromatic rings were negligible and used d orbitals centered on the carbon atoms bonded to the bridging group and on each of the carbon atoms in the bridging group to construct virtual excited states.

Voevodskii et al. (355) found that the intramolecular electron transfer decreased as the chain length was increased for α,ω-diphenylalkane anion radicals. Harriman and Maki (107) found similar results for anion radicals of the type $(p\text{-}NO_2C_6H_4)_2X$ [X = CH_2, CH_2CH_2, O, and S]. Finally, Jones et al. found fast electron transfer in bis(dicyanomethylene)-2,2,4,4-tetramethylcyclobutane (71). They concluded that the predominant mechanisms for electron transfer were 1,3-π interaction across the cyclobutane ring and hyperconjugation.

V. TECHNIQUES OF PREPARATION

The two most commonly used techniques for the preparation of anion radicals (i.e., alkali metal and electrochemical reduction) have been so thoroughly discussed throughout the literature cited in this review it seems pointless to discuss them here. However, some of the new and lesser known techniques will be cited.

A recent review of the use of electrochemical reduction techniques has been given by Adams (356). Alkaline and rare-earth metals have been used for reduction in ether-type solvents (357). The use of alkali and alkaline earth metals in liquid ammonia has been described by Maximadshy and Dörr (358). Levy and Meyers (27–29) have made considerable use of the electrolytic technique in which liquid ammonia is used as the solvent.

The number of studies involving the use of fast flow techniques to produce anion radicals has been increasing rapidly. One of the more recent examples of the use of the fast flow technique has been reported by Griffiths et al. (337). Good descriptions of the technique have been given by Borg (359) and Dixon and Norman (360). The possibilities for various combinations of oxidation–reduction couples would seem to be enormous. Reports of various reducing agents include hydroxymethylene (361), alkoxides (362), dithionate (363,364), and a variety of others used by Russell and co-workers (172,365–367).

Other techniques of preparation have involved photolytic generation in the presence of potential reductants, for example, phenyllithium (368), alkoxide-containing solutions of the radical parent (369,370) and ether-type solvents (371). Livingston and Zeldes (372–374) have combined photolysis and fast flow techniques. They report quite a variety of short-lived radicals.

VI. MISCELLANEOUS

A pulsed X-band spectrometer has been described (375). The application of electron–spin echo methods has also been described and illustrated with experimental examples (376). The equipment is also described. Kenworthy et al. (377) have discussed the use of low field ESR. Silsbee (378) has suggested that poorly resolved ESR spectra might better be interpreted by studies of the Fourier transformation of experimental and model spectra. The use of the slow wave spiral-type cavity in ESR has been discussed by Lebedev et al. (379).

Fraenkel (380,381) has given two very detailed accounts of the factors which affect the positions and line widths of free radicals in dilute solutions.

Freed (382,383) has presented a detailed analysis of saturation and double resonance effects in ESR spectra. The effects of internal rotation (i.e., methyl group rotation) upon hfs and line widths of ESR spectra have been analyzed in terms of a quantum mechanical description of the motion (384).

Acknowledgments

The author expresses his thanks and appreciation to Miss Mary C. Altgilbers and Rachael Goodman for their patience and expert typing of the manuscript and to Professor A. H. Maki for sending a preprint of his chapter on "Electron Spin Resonance" (385). The help and support of the Department of Chemistry is gratefully acknowledged as is the partial support of the National Science Foundation through grant number GP-7011.

References

1. S. I. Weissman, J. Townsend, D. E. Paul, and G. E. Pake, *J. Chem. Phys.*, **21**, 227 (1953).
2. J. S. Hyde, *J. Chem. Phys.*, **43**, 1806 (1965).
3. J. S. Hyde, *J. Phys. Chem.*, **71**, 68 (1967).
4. J. S. Hyde and A. H. Maki, *J. Chem. Phys.*, **40**, 3117 (1964).
5. D. R. Eaton and W. D. Phillips, in *Advances in Magnetic Resonance*, Vol. 1, J. S. Waugh, Ed., Academic Press, New York, 1965, p. 103.
6. G. Berthet and R. Rieman, *Compt. Rend.*, **246**, 1830 (1958).
7. H. S. Gutowsky, H. Kusumoto, T. H. Brown, and D. H. Anderson, *J. Chem. Phys.*, **30**, 860 (1959).
8. T. H. Brown, D. H. Anderson, and H. S. Gutowsky, *J. Chem. Phys.*, **33**, 720 (1960).
9. M. E. Anderson, G. E. Pake, and T. R. Tuttle, *J. Chem. Phys.*, **33**, 1581 (1960).
10. M. E. Anderson, P. J. Zandstra, and T. R. Tuttle, *J. Chem. Phys.*, **33**, 1591 (1960).
11. M. E. Anderson, R. S. Rhodes, and G. E. Pake, *J. Chem. Phys.*, **35**, 1527 (1961).
12. K. H. Hausser, H. Brunner, and J. C. Jochims, *Mol. Phys.*, **10**, 253 (1966).
13. R. W. Kreilick, *J. Chem. Phys.*, **45**, 1922 (1966).
14. C. S. Johnson, Jr., in *Advances in Magnetic Resonance*, Vol. 1, J. S. Waugh, Ed., Academic Press, New York, 1965, p. 33.
15. C. S. Johnson, Jr., *J. Chem. Phys.*, **39**, 2111 (1963).
16. E. de Boer and C. MacLean, *Mol. Phys.*, **9**, 191 (1965).
17. E. de Boer and C. MacLean, *J. Chem. Phys.*, **44**, 1334 (1966).
18. G. T. Jones and J. N. Murrell, *Chem. Commun.*, **1965**, 28.
19. C. S. Johnson, Jr., and R. Chang, *J. Chem. Phys.*, **43**, 3183 (1965).
20. E. de Boer and J. P. Colpa, *J. Phys. Chem.*, **71**, 21 (1967).
21. R. Rieke, M. Ogliainso, R. McClung, and S. Winstein, *J. Am. Chem. Soc.*, **88**, 4729 (1966).

22. T. J. Katz and C. Talcott, *J. Am. Chem. Soc.*, **88**, 4732 (1966).
23. T. J. Katz, M. Yoshida, and L. C. Siew, *J. Am. Chem. Soc.*, **87**, 4516 (1965).
24. C. L. Pan, T. J. Chu, K. H. Fu, Y. C. Hu, and H. Y. Sheng, *Sci. Sinica (Peking)*, **14**, 477 (1965).
25. H. Brunner, K. H. Hausser, M. Rawtischer, and H. A. Staab, *Tetrahedron Letters*, **1966**, 2775.
26. N. M. Atherton, R. Mason, and R. J. Wratten, *Mol. Phys.*, **6**, 525 (1966).
27. D. H. Levy and R. J. Meyers, *J. Chem. Phys.*, **43**, 3063 (1965).
28. D. H. Levy and R. J. Meyers, *J. Chem. Phys.*, **41**, 1062 (1964).
29. D. H. Levy and R. J. Meyers, *J. Chem. Phys.*, **44**, 4177 (1966).
30. F. Gerson, E. Heilbronner, W. A. Böll, and E. Vogel, *Helv. Chim. Acta*, **48**, 1494 (1965).
31. F. Gerson, *Helv. Chim. Acta*, **47**, 1941 (1964).
32. F. Gerson, E. Heilbronner, and G. Köbrich, *Helv. Chim. Acta*, **48**, 1525 (1965).
33. T. S. Zhuravleva, E. S. Petrov, and D. N. Shigorin, *J. Struct. Chem. (USSR) (English Transl.)*, **5**, 723 (1964).
34. J. G. Broadhurst and E. Warhurst, *J. Chem. Soc.*, **1966A**, 351.
35. R. E. Sioda, D. O. Cowan, and W. S. Koski, *J. Am. Chem. Soc.*, **89**, 230 (1967).
36. A. D. McLachlan, *Mol. Phys.*, **3**, 233 (1960).
37. K. D. Bowers and F. D. Greene, *J. Am. Chem. Soc.*, **85**, 2331 (1963).
38. K. D. Bowers, G. J. Nolfi, Jr., and F. D. Greene, *J. Am. Chem. Soc.*, **85**, 3707 (1963).
39. M. T. Jones, *J. Am. Chem. Soc.*, **88**, 174 (1966).
40. F. Gerson, E. Heilbronner, and J. Heinzer, *Tetrahedron Letters*, **1966**, 2095.
41. K. D. Bowers, G. J. Nolfi, Jr., T. H. Lowry, and F. D. Greene, *Tetrahedron Letters*, 1966, 4063.
42. R. Hoffmann and W. N. Lipscomb, *J. Chem. Phys.*, **36**, 2179, 3489 (1962); R. Hoffmann, *ibid.*, **39**, 1397 (1963).
43. G. A. Petersson and A. D. McLachlan, *J. Chem. Phys.*, **45**, 628 (1966).
44. R. D. Cowell, G. Urry, and S. I. Weissman, *J. Chem. Phys.*, **38**, 2028 (1963).
45. R. D. Cowell, G. Urry, and S. I. Weissman, *J. Am. Chem. Soc.*, **85**, 822 (1963).
46. R. E. Jesse, P. Biloen, R. Prins, J. D. W. van Voorst, and G. J. Hoijtink, *Mol. Phys.*, **6**, 633 (1963).
47. M. Glasbeek, J. D. W. van Voorst, and G. J. Hoijtink, *J. Chem. Phys.*, **45**, 1852 (1966).
48. N. L. Bauld and M. S. Brown, *J. Am. Chem. Soc.*, **87**, 4390 (1965).
49. P. Dowd, *J. Am. Chem. Soc.*, **87**, 4968 (1965).
50. E. G. Janzen, and J. G. Pacifici, *J. Am. Chem. Soc.*, **87**, 5504 (1965).
51. E. G. Janzen, J. G. Pacifici, and J. L. Gerloch, *J. Phys. Chem.*, **70**, 3021 (1966).
52. N. L. Bauld and J. H. Zoeller, Jr., *Tetrahedron Letters*, **1967**, 885.
53. A. Carrington and P. F. Todd, *Mol. Phys.*, **7**, 533 (1963–64).
54. H. L. Strauss, T. J. Katz, and G. K. Fraenkel, *J. Am. Chem. Soc.*, **85**, 2360 (1963).
55. A. Carrington, R. E. Moss, and P. F. Todd, *Mol. Phys.*, **12**, 95 (1967).
56. A. Carrington, H. C. Longuet-Higgins, and P. F. Todd, *Mol. Phys.*, **8**, 45 (1964).
57. J. F. Garst, *Mol. Phys.*, **10**, 207 (1966).
58. T. W. Lapp, J. G. Burr, and R. B. Ingalls, *J. Chem. Phys.*, **43**, 4183 (1965).
59. K. Ishizu, *Bull. Chem. Soc. Japan*, **37**, 1093 (1964).
60. P. H. H. Fischer, and K. H. Hausser, *Z. Naturforsch.*, **19a**, 816 (1964).
61. K. H. Hausser, L. Mongini, and R. van Steenwinkel, *Z. Naturforsch.*, **19a**, 777 (1964).

62. D. Bachmann, *Z. Physik. Chem. (Frankfurt)*, **43**, 198 (1964).
63. L. O. Wheeler, K. S. V. Santhanam, and A. J. Bard, *J. Phys. Chem.*, **70**, 404 (1966).
64. F. Gerson, B. Weidmann, and E. Heilbronner, *Helv. Chim. Acta*, **47**, 1951 (1964).
65. R. Chang and C. S. Johnson, Jr., *J. Chem. Phys.*, **41**, 3272 (1964).
66. C. S. Johnson, Jr., and R. Chang, *J. Chem. Phys.*, **43**, 3183 (1965).
67. N. M. Atherton, F. Gerson, and J. N. Ockwell, *J. Chem. Soc.*, **1966A**, 109.
68. M. Karplus and G. K. Fraenkel, *J. Chem. Phys.*, **35**, 1312 (1961).
69. P. H. H. Fischer and C. A. McDowell, *J. Am. Chem. Soc.*, **85**, 2694 (1963).
70. M. T. Jones and W. R. Hertler, *J. Am. Chem. Soc.*, **86**, 1881 (1964).
71. M. T. Jones, E. A. LaLancette, and R. E. Benson, *J. Chem. Phys.*, **41**, 401 (1964).
72. H. van Willigen and S. I. Weissman, *J. Chem. Phys.*, **44**, 420 (1966).
73. J. Gendell, J. H. Freed, and G. K. Fraenkel, *J. Chem. Phys.*, **37**, 2832 (1962).
74. E. W. Stone and A. H. Maki, *J. Am. Chem. Soc.*, **87**, 454 (1965).
75. L. M. Stock and J. Suzuki, *J. Am. Chem. Soc.*, **87**, 3909 (1965).
76. E. T. Strom and G. A. Russell, *J. Chem. Phys.*, **41**, 1514 (1964).
77. J. R. Bolton, *Mol. Phys.*, **6**, 219 (1963).
78. J. R. Bolton and G. K. Fraenkel, *J. Chem. Phys.*, **40**, 3307 (1964).
79. T. N. Tozer and L. D. Tuck, *J. Chem. Phys.*, **38**, 3035 (1963).
80. F. Gerson, *Helv. Chim. Acta*, **49**, 1463 (1966).
81. M. T. Jones, *J. Chem. Phys.*, **42**, 4054 (1965).
82. J. C. Danner and A. H. Maki, *J. Am. Chem. Soc.*, **88**, 4297 (1966).
83. R. W. Fessenden, *J. Phys. Chem.*, **71**, 74 (1967).
84. R. W. Fessenden and R. H. Schuler, *J. Chem. Phys.*, **43**, 2704 (1965).
85. M. R. Das and G. K. Fraenkel, *J. Chem. Phys.*, **42**, 1350 (1965).
86. E. de Boer and E. L. Mackor, *J. Chem. Phys.*, **38**, 1450 (1963).
87. J. R. Bolton and G. K. Fraenkel, *J. Chem. Phys.*, **41**, 944 (1964).
88. M. L. Khidekel', B. R. Shub, G. A. Razuvaev, N. A. Zadorozhnyi, and V. A. Ponomarenko, *Bull. Acad. Sci. (USSR) Div. Chem. Sci. (English Transl.)*, **1964**, 729.
89. M. D. Curtis and A. L. Allred, *J. Am. Chem. Soc.*, **87**, 2554 (1965).
90. G. R. Husk and R. West, *J. Am. Chem. Soc.*, **87**, 3993 (1965).
91. F. Milliett and J. E. Harriman, *J. Chem. Phys.*, **44**, 1945 (1966).
92. J. H. Freed and G. K. Fraenkel, *J. Chem. Phys.*, **40**, 1815 (1964).
93. J. H. Freed and G. K. Fraenkel, *J. Chem. Phys.*, **39**, 326 (1963).
94. J. H. Freed and G. K. Fraenkel, *J. Chem. Phys.*, **41**, 699 (1964).
95. J. H. Freed, *J. Chem. Phys.*, **41**, 2077 (1964).
96. J. H. Freed and G. K. Fraenkel, *J. Am. Chem. Soc.*, **86**, 3477 (1964).
97. A. Carrington, A. Hudson, and G. R. Luckhurst, *Proc. Roy. Soc. (London)*, **A284**, 582 (1965).
98. W. M. Fox, J. M. Gross, and M. C. R. Symons, *J. Chem. Soc.*, **1966A**, 448.
99. J. M. Gross and M. C. R. Symons, *J. Chem. Soc.*, **1966A**, 451.
100. Y. Nakai, *Bull. Chem. Soc. Japan*, **39**, 1372 (1966).
101. E. A. Brande and F. Sondheimer, *J. Chem. Soc.*, **1955**, 3754.
102. D. H. Geske, J. L. Ragle, M. A. Bembenek, and A. L. Balch, *J. Am. Chem. Soc.*, **86**, 987 (1964).
103. P. H. Rieger and G. K. Fraenkel, *J. Chem. Phys.*, **39**, 609 (1963).
104. K. Umemoto, Y. Deguchi, and T. Fujinaga, *Bull. Chem. Soc. Japan*, **36**, 1539 (1963).
105. Y. Nakai, K. Kawamura, K. Ishiza, Y. Deguchi, and J. Takaki, *Bull. Chem. Soc. Japan*, **39**, 847 (1966).

106. N. N. Vylegzhanina, A. V. Il'yason, and Yu. P. Kitaev, *J. Struct. Chem.* (*USSR*) (*English Transl.*), **6**, 135 (1965).
107. J. E. Harriman and A. H. Maki, *J. Chem. Phys.*, **39**, 778 (1963).
108. K. Maruyama and R. Goto, *Rev. Phys. Chem. Japan*, **34**, 30 (1964).
109. T. M. McKinney and D. H. Geske, *J. Chem. Phys.*, **44**, 2277 (1966).
110. R. L. Hansen, R. H. Young, and P. E. Toren, *J. Phys. Chem.*, **70**, 1657 (1966).
111. W. Kemula and R. Sioda, *J. Electroanal. Chem.*, **7**, 233 (1964).
112. J. M. Gross and M. C. R. Symons, *Mol. Phys.*, **9**, 287 (1965).
113. R. L. Ward, *J. Am. Chem. Soc.*, **83**, 1296 (1961).
114. J. H. Freed and G. K. Fraenkel, *J. Chem. Phys.*, **41**, 3623 (1964).
115. C. J. W. Gutch and W. A. Waters, *Chem. Commun.*, **1966**, 39.
116. J. Q. Chambers and R. N. Adams, *Mol. Phys.*, **9**, 413 (1965).
117. D. H. Levy and R. J. Meyers, *J. Chem. Phys.*, **42**, 3731 (1965).
118. J. Q. Chambers, III, T. Layloff, and R. N. Adams, *J. Phys. Chem.*, **68**, 661 (1964).
119. J. Pannell, *Mol. Phys.*, **7**, 599 (1964).
120. C. Corvaja and G. Giacometti, *J. Am. Chem. Soc.*, **86**, 2736 (1964).
121. P. Ludwig, T. Layloff, and R. N. Adams, *J. Am. Chem. Soc.*, **86**, 4568 (1964).
122. P. B. Ayscough, F. P. Sargent, and R. Wilson, *J. Chem. Soc.*, **1963**, 5418.
123. I. Bernal and G. K. Fraenkel, *J. Am. Chem. Soc.*, **86**, 1671 (1964).
124. J. H. Freed and G. K. Fraenkel, *J. Chem. Phys.*, **40**, 1815 (1964).
125. F. Gerson and R. N. Adams, *Helv. Chim. Acta*, **48**, 1539 (1965).
126. P. H. H. Fischer and C. A. McDowell, *Can. J. Chem.*, **43**, 3400 (1965).
127. E. Brunner, R. Mücke, and F. Dörr, *Z. Physik Chem.* (*Frankfurt*), **50**, 30 (1966).
128. P. H. H. Fischer and C. A. McDowell, *Mol. Phys.*, **8**, 357 (1964).
129. R. D. Allendoerfer and P. H. Rieger, *J. Am. Chem. Soc.*, **88**, 3711 (1966).
130. P. L. Nordio, M. V. Pavan, and C. Corvaja, *Trans. Faraday Soc.*, **60**, 1985 (1964).
131. C. Lagercrantz, *Acta. Chem. Scand.*, **18**, 582 (1964).
132. C. Lagercrantz, *Acta. Chem. Scand.*, **18**, 1384 (1964).
133. C. Lagercrantz, K. Torssell, and S. Wold, *Arkiv. Kemi*, **25**, 567 (1966).
134. A. Hudson, C. Lagercrantz, and G. R. Luckhurst, *Mol. Phys.*, **11**, 321 (1966).
135. J. W. Lown, *J. Chem. Soc.*, **1966B**, 441.
136. E. J. Geels, R. Konaka, and G. A. Russell, *Chem. Commun.*, **1965**, 13.
137. D. H. Levy and R. J. Meyers, *J. Chem. Phys.*, **42**, 3731 (1965).
138. J. Q. Adams, S. W. Nicksic, and J. R. Thomas, *J. Chem. Phys.*, **45**, 654 (1966).
139. P. H. Rieger and G. K. Fraenkel, *J. Chem. Phys.*, **37**, 2795 (1962).
140. P. H. Rieger, I. Bernal, W. H. Reinmuth, and G. K. Fraenkel, *J. Am. Chem. Soc.*, **83**, 683 (1963).
141. M. T. Jones, *J. Am. Chem. Soc.*, **88**, 227 (1966).
142. M. T. Jones, *J. Am. Chem. Soc.*, **88**, 5060 (1966).
143. K. Nakamura and Y. Deguchi, *Bull. Chem. Soc. Japan*, **36**, 359 (1963).
144. A. Carrington and P. F. Todd, *Mol. Phys.*, **6**, 161 (1963).
145. A. Carrington, P. Todd, and J. dos Santos-Veiga, *Mol. Phys.*, **6**, 101 (1963).
146. J. Gendell, J. H. Freed, and G. K. Fraenkel, *J. Chem. Phys.*, **41**, 949 (1964).
147. E. W. Stone and A. H. Maki, *J. Chem. Phys.*, **39**, 1635 (1963).
148. P. T. Cottrell and P. H. Rieger, *Mol. Phys.*, **12**, 149 (1967).
149. D. H. Geske and G. R. Padmanabhan, *J. Am. Chem. Soc.*, **87**, 1651 (1965).
150. E. T. Strom, G. A. Russell, and R. Konaka, *J. Chem. Phys.*, **42**, 2033 (1965).

151. M. A. Ali and A. Hinchliffe, *Trans. Faraday Soc.*, **62**, 3273 (1966).
152. P. Smejtek, *Collection Czech. Chem. Commun.*, **31**, 2601 (1966).
153. J. C. M. Henning, *J. Chem. Phys.*, **44**, 2139 (1966).
154. A. Carrington, H. C. Longuet-Higgins, and P. F. Todd, *Mol. Phys.*, **9**, 211 (1965).
155. M. Itoh and S. Nagakura, *Bull. Chem. Soc. Japan*, **38**, 825 (1965).
156. M. Itoh and S. Nagakura, *Bull. Chem. Soc. Japan*, **39**, 369 (1966).
157. M. Itoh and S. Nagakura, *Tetrahedron Letters*, **1965**, 417.
158. C. A. McDowell and K. F. G. Paulus, *Can. J. Chem.*, **43**, 224 (1965).
159. C. A. McDowell and K. F. G. Paulus, *Mol. Phys.*, **7**, 541 (1963–64).
160. M. Bruin, F. Bruin, and F. W. Heineken, *J. Org. Chem.*, **29**, 507 (1964).
161. F. Gerson, *Helv. Chim. Acta*, **47**, 1484 (1964).
162. N. M. Atherton, F. Gerson, and J. N. Murrell, *Mol. Phys.*, **6**, 265 (1963).
163. B. T. Allen and A. Bond, *J. Phys. Chem.*, **68**, 2439 (1964).
164. W. M. Gulick, Jr., and D. H. Geske, *J. Am. Chem. Soc.*, **88**, 2928 (1966).
165. A. D. Britt and E. T. Kaiser, *J. Phys. Chem.*, **69**, 2775 (1965).
166. A. D. Britt and E. T. Kaiser, *J. Org. Chem.*, **31**, 112 (1966).
167. A. H. Cowley and M. H. Hnoosh, *J. Am. Chem. Soc.*, **88**, 2595 (1966).
168. E. A. C. Lucken, F. Ramirez, V. P. Catto, D. Rhum, and S. Dershowitz, *Tetrahedron*, **22**, 637 (1966).
169. K. Dimroth, N. Greif, H. Perst, and F. W. Steuber, *Angew. Chem., Intern. Ed.*, **6**, 85 (1967).
170. D. Chapman, S. H. Glarum, and A. G. Massey, *J. Chem. Soc.*, **1963**, 3140.
171. D. H. Geske and A. L. Balch, *J. Phys. Chem.*, **68**, 3423 (1964).
172. G. A. Russell and M. C. Young, *J. Am. Chem. Soc.*, **88**, 2007 (1966).
173. A. Carrington and I. C. P. Smith, *Mol. Phys.*, **8**, 101 (1964).
174. I. Yamazaki and L. H. Piette, *J. Am. Chem. Soc.*, **87**, 986 (1965).
175. N. K. Raiz, R. K. Gupta, and P. T. Narasimhan, *Mol. Phys.*, **10**, 601 (1966).
176. G. A. Russell and H. Malkus, *J. Am. Chem. Soc.*, **89**, 160 (1967).
177. D. Kosman and L. M. Stock, *J. Am. Chem. Soc.*, **88**, 843 (1966).
178. 3. F. Nelsen and B. M. Trost, *Tetrahedron Letters*, **1966**, 3737.
179. G. A. Russell and K. Y. Chang, *J. Am. Chem. Soc.*, **87**, 4381 (1965).
180. G. A. Russell, K. Y. Chang, and C. W. Jefford, *J. Am. Chem. Soc.*, **87**, 4383 (1965).
181. G. A. Russell and E. T. Strom, *J. Am. Chem. Soc.*, **86**, 744 (1964).
182. G. A. Russell and E. R. Talaty, *J. Am. Chem. Soc.*, **86**, 5345 (1964).
183. G. A. Russell and E. R. Talaty, *Science*, **148**, 1217 (1965).
184. E. T. Strom, G. A. Russell, and R. D. Stephens, *J. Phys. Chem.*, **69**, 213 (1965).
185. E. R. Talaty and G. A. Russell, *J. Am. Chem. Soc.*, **87**, 4867 (1965).
186. E. T. Strom, G. A. Russell, and J. H. Schoeb, *J. Am. Chem. Soc.*, **88**, 2004 (1966).
187. E. T. Strom, *J. Am. Chem. Soc.*, **88**, 2065 (1966).
188. G. A. Russell and R. D. Stephens, *J. Phys. Chem.*, **70**, 1320 (1966).
189. J. W. Lown, *J. Phys. Chem.*, **70**, 591 (1966).
190. J. W. Lown, *Can. J. Chem.*, **43**, 3294 (1965).
191. H. R. Falle and F. C. Adam, *Can. J. Chem.*, **44**, 1387 (1966).
192. F. C. Adam and H. R. Falle, *Can. J. Chem.*, **44**, 1396 (1966).
193. E. W. Stone and A. H. Maki, *J. Chem. Phys.*, **38**, 1999 (1963).
194. C. Corvaja, P. L. Nordio, and G. Giacometti, *J. Am. Chem. Soc.*, **89**, 1751 (1967).
195. R. M. Elofson, K. F. Schulz, B. E. Galbraith, and R. Newton, *Can. J. Chem.*, **43**, 1553 (1965).
196. R. Dehl and G. K. Fraenkel, *J. Chem. Phys.*, **39**, 1793 (1963).

197. G. R. Luckhurst and L. E. Orgel, *Mol. Phys.*, **7**, 297 (1963–64).
198. E. W. Stone and A. H. Maki, *J. Chem. Phys.*, **41**, 284 (1964).
199. N. Steinberger and G. K. Fraenkel, *J. Chem. Phys.*, **40**, 723 (1964).
200. L. H. Piette, M. Okamura, G. P. Rabold, R. T. Ogata, R. E. Moore, and P. J. Scheuer, *J. Phys. Chem.*, **71**, 29 (1967).
201. G. P. Rabold, R. T. Ogata, M. Okamura, L. H. Piette, R. E. Moore, and P. J. Scheuer, *J. Chem. Phys.*, **46**, 1161 (1967).
202. J. K. Brown, D. R. Burnham, and N. A. J. Rogers, *Tetrahedron Letters*, **1966**, 2621.
203. B. T. Allen and W. Vanneste, *Nature*, **204**, 991 (1964).
204. E. de Boer and A. P. Praat, *Mol. Phys.*, **8**, 291 (1964).
205. M. Iwaizumi and T. Isobe, *Bull. Chem. Soc. Japan*, **38**, 1547 (1965).
206. N. M. Atherton, E. J. Land, and G. Porter, *Trans Faraday Soc.*, **59**, 818 (1963).
207. R. E. Sioda and W. S. Koski, *J. Am. Chem. Soc.*, **89**, 475 (1967).
208. A. Maccoll, *Nature*, **163**, 178 (1949).
209. A. Pullman, B. Pullman, and G. Berher, *Bull. Soc. Chim. France*, **17**, 591 (1950).
210. P. Balk, S. de Bruijn, and G. J. Hoijtink, *Rec. Trav. Chim.*, **76**, 860 (1957).
211. T. J. Katz, W. H. Reinmuth, and D. E. Smith, *J. Am. Chem. Soc.*, **84**, 802 (1962).
212. W. M. Gulich, Jr., and D. H. Geske, *J. Am. Chem. Soc.*, **87**, 4049 (1965).
213. W. M. Gulich, Jr., and D. H. Geske, *J. Am. Chem. Soc.*, **88**, 4119 (1966).
214. B. L. Silver, Z. Luz, and C. Eden, *J. Chem. Phys.*, **44**, 4258 (1966).
215. Z. Luz, B. L. Silver, and C. Eden, *J. Chem. Phys.*, **44**, 4421 (1966).
216. K. Dimroth, F. Bär, and A. Berndt, *Angew. Chem. Intern. Ed.*, **4**, 240 (1965).
217. K. Dimroth, A. Berndt, F. Bär, A. Schweig, and R. Volland, *Angew Chem.*, *Intern. Ed.*, **6**, 34 (1967).
218. G. Vincow, *J. Chem. Phys.*, **37**, 2484 (1962).
219. J. P. Keller and R. G. Hayes, *J. Chem. Phys.*, **46**, 816 (1967).
220. R. Gerdil and E. A. C. Lucken, *Mol. Phys.*, **9**, 529 (1965).
221. E. T. Strom and G. A. Russell, *J. Am. Chem. Soc.*, **87**, 3326 (1965).
222. R. Gerdil and E. A. C. Lucken, *J. Am. Chem. Soc.*, **87**, 213 (1965).
223. M. McMillan and W. A. Waters, *J. Chem. Soc.*, **1966B**, 422.
224. E. A. C. Lucken, *J. Chem. Soc.*, **1964**, 4240.
225. E. T. Kaiser and D. H. Eargle, Jr., *J. Phys. Chem.*, **69**, 2108 (1965).
226. D. H. Eargle, Jr., and E. T. Kaiser, *Proc. Chem. Soc.*, **1964**, 22.
227. R. Gerdil and E. A. C. Lucken, *Proc. Chem. Soc.*, **1963**, 144.
228. E. T. Kaiser and D. H. Eargle, Jr., *J. Chem. Phys.*, **39**, 1353 (1963).
229. E. T. Kaiser, M. M. Urberg, and D. H. Eargle, Jr., *J. Am. Chem. Soc.*, **88**, 1037 (1966).
230. E. A. C. Lucken, *J. Chem. Soc.*, **1966A**, 991.
231. A. Carrington, A. Hudson, and H. C. Longuet-Higgins, *Mol. Phys.*, **9**, 377 (1965).
232. C. Trapp, C. W. Wang, and R. Filler, *J. Chem. Phys.*, **45**, 3472 (1966).
233. W. D. Blackley and R. R. Reinhard, *J. Am. Chem. Soc.*, **87**, 802 (1965).
234. W. D. Blackley, *J. Am. Chem. Soc.*, **88**, 480 (1966).
235. I. V. Miroshnichenko, G. M. Larin, S. P. Makarov, and A. F. Videnko, *J. Struct. Chem. (USSR) (English Transl.)*, **6**, 737 (1965).
236. P. J. Scheidler and J. R. Bolton, *J. Am. Chem. Soc.*, **88**, 371 (1966).
237. P. L. Kolker and W. A. Waters, *Chem. Ind. (London)*, **1963**, 1205.
238. M. G. Townsend and S. I. Weissman, *J. Chem. Phys.*, **32**, 309 (1960).
239. R. W. Fessenden and S. Ogawa, *J. Am. Chem. Soc.*, **86**, 3591 (1964).

240. H. J. Silverstone, D. E. Wood, and H. M. McConnell, *Chem. Phys.*, **41**, 2311 (1964).
241. G. Vincow, M. L. Morrell, W. V. Volland, H. J. Dauben, Jr., and F. R. Hunter, *J. Am. Chem. Soc.*, **87**, 3527 (1965).
242. I. A. Zlochower, W. R. Miller, Jr., and G. K. Fraenkel, *J. Chem. Phys.*, **42**, 3339 (1965).
243. G. R. Liebling and H. M. McConnell, *J. Chem. Phys.*, **42**, 3931 (1965).
244. A. Carrington, H. C. Longuet-Higgins, R. E. Moss, and P. F. Todd, *Mol. Phys.*, **9**, 187 (1965).
245. R. G. Lawler, J. R. Bolton, G. K. Fraenkel, and T. H. Brown, *J. Am. Chem. Soc.*, **86**, 520 (1964).
246. M. T. Jones, A. Cairncross, and D. W. Wiley, *J. Chem. Phys.*, **43**, 3403 (1965).
247. H. M. McConnell and A. D. McLachlan, *J. Chem. Phys.*, **34**, 1 (1961).
248. H. M. McConnell, *J. Chem. Phys.*, **34**, 13 (1961).
249. J. H. Freed, *J. Chem. Phys.*, **43**, 1427 (1965).
250. D. Kivelson, *J. Chem. Phys.*, **45**, 751 (1966).
251. J. H. Freed and G. K. Fraenkel, *J. Chem. Phys.*, **41**, 3623 (1964).
252. G. Bignol and W. Müller-Warmuth, *Phys. Letters*, **11**, 292 (1964).
253. D. M. Schrader and M. Karplus, *J. Chem. Phys.*, **40**, 1593 (1964).
254. R. E. Moss, *Mol. Phys.*, **10**, 339 (1966).
255. M. R. Das and G. K. Fraenkel, *J. Chem. Phys.*, **42**, 792 (1965).
256. M. Karplus, R. G. Lawler, and G. K. Fraenkel, *J. Am. Chem. Soc.*, **87**, 5260 (1965).
257. J. R. Bolton and A. Carrington, *Mol. Phys.*, **4**, 497 (1961).
258. T. R. Tuttle, *J. Am. Chem. Soc.*, **84**, 2839 (1962).
259. T. R. Tuttle, *J. Am. Chem. Soc.*, **84**, 1492 (1962).
260. J. R. Bolton, A. Carrington, A. Forman, and L. E. Orgel, *Mol. Phys.*, **5**, 43 (1962).
261. W. D. Hobey, *Mol. Phys.*, **7**, 325 (1963/64).
262. W. D. Hobey, *J. Chem. Phys.*, **45**, 2718 (1966).
263. R. E. Moss, *Mol. Phys.*, **10**, 501 (1966).
264. J. P. Malrieu, A. Pullman, and M. Rossi, *Theoret. Chim. Acta*, **3**, 261 (1965).
265. D. Lazdins and M. Karplus, *J. Am. Chem. Soc.*, **87**, 920 (1965).
266. W. D. Hobey, *J. Chem. Phys.*, **43**, 2187 (1965).
267. T. H. Brown and M. Karplus, *J. Chem. Phys.*, **39**, 1115 (1963).
268. M. S. Blois, H. W. Brown, and J. E. Maling, in *Free Radicals in Biological Systems*, M. S. Blois, Jr., H. W. Browne, R. M. Lemmon, R. O. Lindblom, and M. Weissbluth, Eds., Academic Press, New York, 1961.
269. B. G. Segal, M. Kaplan, and G. K. Fraenkel, *J. Chem. Phys.*, **43**, 4191 (1965).
270. A. J. Stone, *Proc. Roy. Soc. (London)*, **A271**, 424 (1963).
271. A. J. Stone, *Mol. Phys.*, **6**, 509 (1963).
272. A. J. Stone, *Mol. Phys.*, **7**, 311 (1963/64).
273. R. O. C. Norman and R. J. Pritchett, *Chem. Ind. (London)*, **1965**, 2040.
274. J. E. Bloor, B. R. Gilson, and P. N. Daykin, *J. Phys. Chem.*, **70**, 1457 (1966).
275. J. P. Colpa and J. R. Bolton, *Mol. Phys.*, **6**, 273 (1963).
276. G. Giacometti, P. L. Nordio, and M. V. Pavan, *Theoret. Chim. Acta*, **1**, 404 (1963).
277. L. C. Snyder and T. Amos, *J. Chem. Phys.*, **42**, 3670 (1965).
278. J. F. Mucci, M. K. Orloff, and D. D. Fitts, *J. Chem. Phys.*, **42**, 1841 (1965).
279. A. T. Amos and S. G. Davison, *Mol. Phys.*, **10**, 261 (1966).

280. A. Hinchliffe, *Theoret. Chim. Acta.* (*Berlin*), **5**, 451 (1966).

281. F. C. Adam and W. G. Laidlaw, *Australian J. Chem.*, **19**, 897 (1966).

282. F. E. Harris, *Mol. Phys.*, **11**, 243 (1966).

283. J. P. Malrieu, A. Pullman, and M. Rossi, *Theoret. Chim. Acta*, **3**, 261 (1965).

284. W. T. Dixon, *Mol. Phys.*, **9**, 201 (1965).

285. D. H. Levy, *Mol. Phys.*, **10**, 233 (1966).

286. D. Lazdins and M. Karplus, *J. Chem. Phys.*, **44**, 1600 (1966).

287. G. Berthier, H. Lemaire, A. Rassat, and A. Veillard, *Theoret. Chim. Acta*, **3**, 213 (1965).

288. M. Kaplan, J. R. Bolton, and G. K. Fraenkel, *J. Chem. Phys.*, **42**, 955 (1965).

289. J. C. Schug, T. H. Brown, and M. Karplus, *J. Chem. Phys.*, **35**, 1873 (1961).

290. J. C. Schug, T. H. Brown, and M. Karplus, *J. Chem. Phys.*, **37**, 330 (1962).

291. T. H. Brown, *J. Chem. Phys.*, **39**, 1115 (1963).

292. T. H. Brown, M. Karplus, and J. C. Schug, *J. Chem. Phys.*, **38**, 1749 (1963).

293. T. H. Brown, *J. Chem. Phys.*, **41**, 2223 (1964).

294. T. H. Brown and M. Karplus, *J. Chem. Phys.*, **46**, 870 (1967).

295. M. T. Jones, *J. Chem. Phys.*, **38**, 2892 (1963).

296. J. Danner and T. R. Tuttle, Jr., *J. Am. Chem. Soc.*, **85**, 4052 (1963).

297. T. A. Miller, R. N. Adams, and P. M. Richards, *J. Chem. Phys.*, **44**, 4022 (1966).

298. T. A. Miller and R. N. Adams, *J. Am. Chem. Soc.*, **88**, 5713 (1966).

299. N. Edelstein, A. Kwok, and A. H. Maki, *J. Chem. Phys.*, **41**, 3473 (1964).

300. N. Edelstein, A. Kwok, and A. H. Maki, *J. Chem. Phys.*, **41**, 179 (1964).

301. D. Kivelson, *J. Chem. Phys.*, **33**, 1094 (1960).

302. J. H. Freed, *J. Chem. Phys.*, **45**, 3442 (1966).

303. C. S. Johnson, Jr., *Mol. Phys.*, **12**, 25 (1967).

304. J. D. Currin, *Phys. Rev.*, **126**, 1995 (1962).

305. J. M. Fritsch, T. P. Layloff, and R. N. Adams, *J. Am. Chem. Soc.*, **87**, 1724 (1965).

306. A. Ishitani and S. Nagakura, *Bull. Chem. Soc.*, *Japan*, **38**, 367 (1965).

307. J. W. Lown, *Proc. Chem. Soc.*, **1963**, 283.

308. W. L. Reynolds, *J. Phys. Chem.*, **67**, 2866 (1963).

309. R. Chang and C. S. Johnson, Jr., *J. Am. Chem. Soc.*, **88**, 2338 (1966).

310. N. Hirota and S. I. Weissman, *J. Am. Chem. Soc.*, **86**, 2537 (1964).

311. T. Layloff, T. Miller, R. N. Adams, H. Fah, A. Horsfield, and W. Proctor, *Nature*, **205**, 382 (1965).

312. W. Bruning and S. I. Weissman, *J. Am. Chem. Soc.*, **88**, 373 (1966).

313. R. A. Marcus, *Ann. Rev. Phys. Chem.*, **15**, 155 (1964).

314. R. A. Marcus, *J. Phys. Chem.*, **67**, 853 (1963).

315. J. W. H. Schreurs and G. K. Fraenkel, *J. Chem. Phys.*, **34**, 756 (1961).

316. J. S. Hyde and H. W. Brown, *J. Chem. Phys.*, **37**, 368 (1962).

317. W. Müller-Warmuth, *Z. Naturforsch.*, **18a**, 1001 (1963).

318. J. Haupt and W. Müller-Warmuth, *Z. Naturforsch*, **17a**, 1011 (1962).

319. W. Müller-Warmuth, *Z. Naturforsch*, **15a**, 927 (1960).

320. K. D. Kramer, W. Müller-Warmuth, and J. Schindler, *J. Chem. Phys.*, **43**, 31 (1965).

321. H. M. McConnell, *J. Chem. Phys.*, **25**, 709 (1956).

322. R. Wilson and D. Kivelson, *J. Chem. Phys.*, **44**, 154 (1966).

323. P. Atkins and D. Kivelson, *J. Chem. Phys.*, **44**, 169 (1966).

324. D. Kivelson, *J. Chem. Phys.*, **45**, 1324 (1966).

325. G. R. Luckhurst and L. E. Orgel, *Mol. Phys.*, **8**, 117 (1964).

326. T. Kawamura, S. Matsunami, T. Yonezawa, and K. Fukui, *Bull. Chem. Soc. Japan*, **38**, 1935 (1965).
327. A. L. Buchachenko and O. P. Sukhanova, *J. Struct. Chem. (USSR) (English Transl.)*, **6**, 24 (1965).
328. H. Yoshida and B. Ranby, *Acta. Chem. Scand.*, **19**, 1495 (1965).
329. A. L. Buchachenko, *Dokl. Phys. Chem. Sect. (English Transl.)*, **158**, 913 (1964).
330. P. B. Ayscough and F. P. Sargent, *J. Chem. Soc.*, **1966B**, 907.
331. J. Pannell, *Mol. Phys.*, **7**, 317 (1963/64).
332. K. Scheffler and H. B. Stegmann, *Tetrahedron Letters*, **1964**, 3035.
333. T. E. Gough, *Trans. Faraday Soc.*, **62**, 2321 (1966).
334. T. A. Claxton, T. E. Gough, and M. C. R. Symons, *Trans. Faraday Soc.*, **62**, 279 (1966).
335. P. J. Zandstra, *J. Chem. Phys.*, **41**, 3655 (1964).
336. K. Scheffler and H. B. Stegmann, *Z. Physik. Chem. (Frankfurt)*, **44**, 353 (1965).
337. W. E. Griffiths, G. F. Longster, J. Myatt, and P. F. Todd, *J. Chem. Soc.*, **1966B**, 1130.
338. A. Carrington and G. R. Luckhurst, *Mol. Phys.*, **8**, 401 (1964).
339. H. C. Longuet-Higgins and G. R. Luckhurst, *Mol. Phys.*, **8**, 613 (1964).
340. H. R. Falle and G. R. Luckhurst, *Mol. Phys.*, **11**, 299 (1966).
341. S. H. Glarum and J. H. Marshall, *J. Chem. Phys.*, **44**, 2884 (1966).
342. G. R. Luckhurst, *Mol. Phys.*, **11**, 205 (1966).
343. H. R. Falle, G. R. Luckhurst, H. Lemaire, Y. Marechal, A. Rassat, and P. Rey, *Mol. Phys.*, **11**, 49 (1966).
344. C. L. Ayers, E. G. Janzen, and F. J. Johnston, *J. Am. Chem. Soc.*, **88**, 2610 (1966).
345. E. G. Janzen, F. J. Johnston, and C. L. Ayers, *J. Am. Chem. Soc.*, **89**, 1176 (1967).
346. K. H. Fleurke, J. De Jong, and W. Th. Nauta, *Rec. Trav. Chim.*, **82**, 713 (1963).
347. A. Kawamari, A. Honda, N. Joo, K. Suzuki, and Y. Ooshika, *J. Chem. Phys.*, **44**, 4363 (1966).
348. A. G. Evans and J. C. Evans, *J. Chem. Soc.*, **1966B**, 271.
349. A. G. Evans, P. B. Roberts, and B. J. Tabner, *J. Chem. Soc.*, **1966B**, 269.
350. A. G. Evans, J. C. Evans, and E. H. Godden, *Trans. Faraday Soc.*, **63**, 136 (1967).
351. D. H. Geske, in *Progress in Physical Organic Chemistry*, Vol. 4, S. J. Cohen, A. Streitwieser, and R. W. Taft, Eds., Interscience, New York, 1967, p. 125.
352. S. I. Weissman, *J. Am. Chem. Soc.*, **80**, 6422 (1958).
353. A. Ishitani and S. Nagakura, *Mol. Phys.*, **12**, 1 (1967).
354. H. M. McConnell, *J. Chem. Phys.*, **35**, 508 (1961).
355. V. V. Voevodskii, S. P. Solodovnikov, and V. M. Chibrikin, *Dokl. Akad. Nauk. SSSR*, **129**, 1082 (1959).
356. R. N. Adams, *J. Electroanal. Chem.*, **8**, 151 (1964).
357. N. Hirota and S. I. Weissman, *J. Am. Chem. Soc.*, **86**, 2538 (1964).
358. A. Maximadshy and F. Dörr, *Z. Naturforsch.*, **19b**, 359 (1964).
359. D. C. Borg, *Nature*, **201**, 1087 (1964).
360. W. T. Dixon and R. O. C. Norman, *J. Chem. Soc.*, **1963**, 3119.
361. A. L. Buley and R. O. C. Norman, *Proc. Chem. Soc.*, **1964**, 225.
362. P. B. Ayscough, F. P. Sargent, and R. Wilson, *J. Chem. Soc.*, **1964**, 5418.
363. P. L. Kolker and W. A. Waters, *J. Chem. Soc.*, **1964**, 1136.
364. C. J. W. Gutch and W. A. Waters, *Chem. Commun.*, **1966**, 39.

365. G. A. Russell, E. T. Strom, E. R. Talaty, and S. A. Weiner, *J. Am. Chem. Soc.*, **88**, 1998 (1966).
366. E. T. Strom, G. A. Russell, and J. H. Schoeb, *J. Am. Chem. Soc.*, **88**, 2004 (1966).
367. G. A. Russell and R. D. Stephens, *J. Phys. Chem.*, **70**, 1320 (1966).
368. H. J. S. Winkler, H. Winkler, and R. Bollinger, *Chem. Commun.*, **1966**, 70.
369. P. B. Ayscough and R. Wilson, *J. Chem. Soc.*, **1963**, 5412.
370. R. Wilson, *Can. J. Chem.*, **44**, 551 (1966).
371. R. L. Ward, *J. Chem. Phys.*, **38**, 2588 (1963).
372. R. Livingston and H. Zeldes, *J. Chem. Phys.*, **44**, 1245 (1966).
373. H. Zeldes and R. Livingston, *J. Chem. Phys.*, **45**, 1946 (1966).
374. R. Livingston and H. Zeldes, *J. Am. Chem. Soc.*, **88**, 4333 (1966).
375. D. E. Kaplan, M. E. Browne, and J. A. Cowen, *Rev. Sci. Instr.*, **32**, 1182 (1961).
376. W. B. Mims, *Rev. Sci. Instr.*, **36**, 1472 (1965).
377. J. G. Kenworthy, G. F. Longster, and R. E. Richards, *Trans. Faraday Soc.*, **62**, 534 (1966).
378. R. H. Silsbee, *J. Chem. Phys.*, **45**, 1710 (1966).
379. Y. S. Lebedev and O. M. Taranukha, *Theoret. Exptl. Chem.* (*USSR*) (*English Transl.*), **1**, 171 (1965).
380. G. K. Fraenkel, *J. Phys. Chem.*, **71**, 139 (1967).
381. G. K. Fraenkel, *J. Chem. Phys.*, **42**, 4275 (1965).
382. J. H. Freed, *J. Chem. Phys.*, **71**, 38 (1967).
383. J. H. Freed, *J. Chem. Phys.*, **43**, 2312 (1965).
384. J. H. Freed, *J. Chem. Phys.*, **43**, 1710 (1965).
385. A. H. Maki, *Ann. Rev. Phys. Chem.*, **18** (1967).

CHAPTER 7

Some Organometallic Radicals and Ion Radicals of the Group IV Elements

GRANT URRY

Department of Chemistry, Purdue University, Lafayette, Indiana

I. INTRODUCTION

The elegant regularity of organic chemistry and the simple systematic approach possible in the chemistry of carbon compounds has provided chemists with great incentive for the extension of the knowledge of the chemical reactions and the systematics of organic chemistry to the chemistries of other elements. One might naturally expect the congeners of carbon to be the most amenable elements for these analogous extensions. The success of such analogy is evident in the development of the field of organosilicon chemistry beginning with the preparation by Friedel and Crafts (1) of tetraethylsilane and proceeding through the monumental work of Kipping to the present time. Such attempts generally have met with less than this success and have raised interesting questions as to the reasons for the irregular congenital differences in the chemical behaviors of carbon, silicon, germanium, tin, and lead. With an improvement in our descriptions of atomic structure and with the consequent development of a reasonable theory of covalent bonding, it has been natural for chemists to attribute the chemical differences to the principal difference in the atomic structures of the Group IV elements participating in covalently bonded compounds, namely, the presence of the vacant *d* subshell in tetracovalent compounds of silicon, germanium, tin, and lead.

There are many examples of differences in chemical behavior which are most easily rationalized by an assignment of an important bonding role for the orbitals of this vacant subshell.

The octahedral structure of the SiF_6^{2-} ion, formed by the treatment of silicon tetrafluoride with fluoride ion (2), is most satisfactorily rationalized by assuming the participation of the $3d$ orbitals of the central silicon atom in an sp^3d^2 hybridized set.

The reaction between silicon tetrachloride and β-diketones to form compounds containing an octahedral complex cation of silicon (3,4) has no analogy in carbon chemistry. This class of compounds also can be used to illustrate in a convincing fashion differences in the chemistry of carbon and the Group IV-B elements probably arising from this difference in electronic configuration of the higher congeners.

There are chemical differences among the Group IV elements which have been the subject of much speculation where multiple interpretations have been offered, each with plausible arguments supporting them. A comparison of the properties of trimethylamine with those of trisilylamine provides an example of just such a difference. From *a priori* consideration of simple electronegativity trends in the periodic system one can argue that since carbon is more electronegative than silicon the methyl group will exert a greater attractive effect upon the nonbonding pair in trimethylamine than the silyl group will exert upon the nonbonding pair in trisilylamine. Such being the case one might predict that trimethylamine would be the weaker donor in forming donor–acceptor complexes with Lewis acids. On the other hand, one can apply the sort of thinking that has been quite successful in accounting for the trends in Lewis acidity observed for the boron halides (5), namely, the possible interactions between nonbonding electron pairs and vacant orbitals in covalently bonded molecules. Such interactions have been termed "partial double-bond character" and were used by Pauling to account for anomalously short silicon halogen distances in the silicon halides (6). One can visualize the nonbonding pair on nitrogen interacting with the vacant $3d$ orbitals on silicon in trisilylamine in such a fashion where in trimethylamine this interaction is not energetically favorable. One would predict from consideration of interactions of this sort that trisilylamine should be a weaker donor than trimethylamine. This appears to be the case (7,8). Such "partial double-bond character" also would be expected to make the trisilylamine molecule planar through contributions of resonance forms such as structure 1. Where the trimethylamine is apparently pyramidal (9), trisilylamine is likely a planar molecule (10). Thus, there appear to be good sound reasons for accepting the postulate of an interaction between the nonbonding pair and the vacant $3d$ orbitals in the case of trisilylamine.

On the other hand, one might equally well, out of some laudable scientific perversity, describe the situation in terms of simple electronegativity arguments as follows: Since silicon is less electronegative than

$$
\begin{array}{c}
\text{H} \quad \text{H} \\
\diagdown \mid \\
\text{Si} \qquad\qquad \text{H} \\
\diagup \quad \diagdown \quad \delta^+ \; \delta^- \diagup \\
\text{H} \qquad \text{N} = \text{Si} - \text{H} \\
\qquad \diagup \qquad\qquad \diagdown \\
\text{H} \qquad\qquad\qquad \text{H} \\
\diagdown \\
\text{H} - \text{Si} \\
\diagup \\
\text{H}
\end{array}
$$

(1)

carbon, more positive charge resides on each silyl group in the trisilylamine molecule than resides on each methyl group in the trimethylamine molecule. This positive charge should tend to make trisilylamine a planar molecular to minimize repulsions between silyl groups. The silylamine would be expected to be a weaker donor than trimethylamine *because* it is planar while trimethylamine is not.

There has been a definite lack, until recently, of an experimental method capable of reducing such ambiguity in discussions relative to the electronic distribution in molecules. The role of the *d* orbitals in the bonding of tetracovalent compounds of the Group IV-B elements, because of this lack, has remained obscure or controversial.

With the development of electron spin resonance a more direct experimental method of deducing electronic distributions has become available. There are several published discussions of this method applied to such problems, including some in this present volume. Several review articles, valuable for novices such as this writer, have appeared during the past several years. Notable among these are the articles by Carrington (11), McClelland (12), McDowell (13), Robertson (14), Symons (15), and Weissman (16).

The electron spin resonance method, being applicable only to molecules with unpaired electrons, suffers some disadvantage from the chemist's point of view since the large majority of the molecules in which the bonding is of interest are diamagnetic. Sound deductions concerning the electronic distribution in such molecules are possible, however, if ion radicals sufficiently stable to be examined by the electron spin resonance method can be formed by oxidation or reduction.

Among the tetracovalent organometallic compounds of the Group IV-B elements, silicon, germanium, tin, and lead, such ion radicals have yielded meaningful and persuasive results in studies of silicon and germanium compounds. In the case of organotin and organolead compounds the ion radicals generally do not appear to be sufficiently stable to allow definitive studies, although some success has been achieved in working with the ion radicals of especially stable aryl tin derivatives (17) or with a triaryl tin substituent on a stable neutral aromatic free radical (18). Similar ESR studies of lead compounds so far have proved impossible.

II. ANION RADICALS OF ORGANOSILANES

A. Trialkylsilylbenzene Anion Radicals

One of the earliest reported attempts using electron spin resonance to shed light upon the bonding in tetracovalent silicon compounds was Townsend's examination of the ESR spectra of various anion radicals derived from tetraarylsilanes (19). The fact that the anion radical produced by the potassium metal reduction of tetraphenylsilane displayed a hyperfine spectrum with an odd number of lines was used to support arguments in favor of a rapid exchange of the odd electron between phenyl groups. Barring accidental coincidences, interaction of the electron spin with the five protons in a single phenyl group would be expected to yield an even number of hyperfine lines with the probable maximum number being 18 lines. Furthermore, the total breadth of the spectrum of the anion radical of tetraphenylsilane was observed to be no greater than 17.4 G. The expected breadth of the spectrum of deuterobenzene anion radical is 18.3 G. If the difference between these two spectral widths is attributed to spin residence upon the silicon (a reasonable assumption since one would predict that the total breadth of resonance for a system of rapidly exchanging phenyl groups would be virtually identical to that of monodeuterobenzene), then one can suggest that such residence utilizes the vacant $3d$ orbitals. Townsend was unable to observe splittings from the ^{29}Si present in the natural abundance of 4.7%. Attempts to prepare the anion radical of tetraphenylmethane for comparison with its silicon analog were not successful. Similarly unsuccessful was the study of anion radicals of 4-biphenyltriphenylsilane and bis-4-biphenyldiphenylsilane since, in these cases, the hyperfine spectra indicated a localization of the electron spin in the biphenyl group without measurable exchange with the phenyl groups. This effect Townsend interpreted as resulting in the large difference in electron affinity of biphenyl and phenyl groups.

This early report leaves one with the same vague dissatisfaction intrinsic in previous attempts at experimental elucidation of the role of the $3d$ orbitals in organosilicon compounds. The results, while suggestive, are not persuasive.

More cogent arguments are offered by Solodovnikov and Chernyshev (17,20) and by Carrington and co-workers (11,21). During the examination of the anion radicals of various trialkylsilylbenzenes, Solodovnikov and Chernysehv (20) found that they are considerably more stable than the analogous anion radicals of the carbon compounds. For example, the anion radical of trimethylsilylbenzene is stable for long periods at room temperature while the anion radical of t-butylbenzene is not. The anion radical of trimethylsilylmethylbenzene is less stable than trimethylsilylbenzene but more stable than t-butylbenzene. Among the anion radicals in the series $(CH_3)_3Si(CH_2)_nC_6H_5$ the stability decreases with increasing n.

In this work the electron spin resonance spectra offered more convincing evidence of interactions between the odd electron and the $3d$ orbitals of the silicon atom. In addition to demonstrating the effect of a silicon atom in narrowing the spectrum, similar to the evidence presented by Townsend, Solodovnikov and Chernyshev observed weak satellite hyperfine components with a splitting of 14 G and intensities similar to that expected from the natural abundance of ^{29}Si. The spectrum of the anion radical of 1,4-bis-trimethylsilylbenzene displays additional hyperfine components attributed to splittings by the methyl protons. These splittings resulted in an even number of hyperfine components which led to the conclusion that they are produced by the nine protons in one trimethylsilyl group since the 18 protons in two trimethylsilyl groups would be expected to produce an odd number of lines. From this these workers deduced an exchange frequency of the odd electron between the two silicon atoms in 1,4-bis-trimethylsilylbenzene anion radical which is small compared with the hyperfine frequency (10^6 sec^{-1}). In this light it would be very interesting to examine the methyl proton splittings, if observable, for the anion radical of 1,3-bis-trimethylsilylbenzene. If there is rapid spin exchange in this latter case, it would furnish additional support for a resonance interaction involving silicon in such species.

Solodovnikov and Chernyshev reported no splittings by the aliphatic protons in either trimethylsilylbenzene or triethylsilylbenzene anion radicals. Carrington and co-workers, however, did observe hyperfine splittings by the methyl protons in trimethylsilylbenzene anion radical. The deductions derived from these splittings will be discussed in a later portion of this chapter.

The total breadth of the resonance of the anion of 1,4-bistrimethylsilylbenzene is only two-thirds that of the anion radical of trimethylsilylbenzene, indicating a correspondingly lower spin density in the aromatic ring. Solodovnikov and Chernyshev compared the sums of the spin densities at the *ortho* and *meta* positions calculated from the hyperfine coupling constants in both the anion radicals of trimethylsilylbenzene and 1,4-bistrimethylsilylbenzene. These total 0.4 in the case of the trimethylsilylbenzene and 0.33 in the case of 1,4-bistrimethylsilylbenzene. This difference best can be interpreted by invoking the electron withdrawing effect of the second silicon in the latter case. No measurable differences were found between the ESR spectra of the anion radicals of trimethyl-silylbenzene and triethylsilylbenzene.

Carrington and co-workers, in a more general study, observed the anion radicals of *t*-butylbenzene, trimethylsilylbenzene, and trimethylgermyl-benzene. From the hyperfine spectra of these anion radicals a comparison was made between the proton coupling constants for the *para* proton and the *meta* and *ortho* protons to demonstrate that in the anion radical of *t*-butylbenzene the odd electron occupied the antisymmetric orbital while in the cases of trimethylsilylbenzene and trimethylgermylbenzene the odd electron occupies the symmetric orbital.

In the benzene molecule these orbitals are degenerate and antibonding. The antisymmetric orbital possesses a node which intersects the 1 and 4 positions in the benzene ring with equal density at the other four positions. The symmetric orbital has electron density at all six positions in the ben-zene ring with highest density at the 1 and 4 positions. Bolton and Carring-ton (22) have shown that electron-repelling substituents on the benzene ring lift this degeneracy by lowering the energy of the antisymmetric orbital and raising that of the symmetric orbital. Thus, the anion radicals of substituted benzenes where the substituent is electron repelling would display ESR spectra in which the *para*-proton splittings are smaller than the *ortho* and *meta* splittings. In most cases the *ortho* and *meta* splittings should be roughly equal. In the anion radicals of substituted benzenes where the substituent group is electron attracting the opposite case would prevail and the odd electron occupation of the symmetric orbital is energetically favored. In this case the *para*-proton splittings should be larger than the *ortho* and *meta* splittings.

On the basis of arguments of this kind both the trimethylsilyl and the trimethylgermyl substituents are electron attracting while the *t*-butyl substituent is electron repelling.

A comparison of the *ortho*- and *meta*-proton splittings for the anion radicals of trimethylsilylbenzene and trimethylgermylbenzene allowed Carrington and co-workers to compare the electron withdrawing ability of the trimethylsilyl and the trimethylgermyl substituents. In cases where the substituent on a benzene ring is strongly electron attracting and con-sequently the odd electron is in the symmetric orbital one might expect greater splitting from the *ortho* protons than the *meta* protons as well as observing the greatest splittings from the *para* protons. This arises from the difference in polarity of the substituted benzene. In the symmetric orbital of unsubstituted benzene the electron density is equal at the *ortho* and *meta* positions and highest at the *para* position. To the extent which an electron withdrawing substituent increases the polarity of the substi-tuted benzene the electron density at the *meta* and *para* will decrease and that at the *ortho* position will increase. Using this principle a comparison of the various proton splittings in the hyperfine spectra of anions of substituted benzenes can be used to estimate the relative magnitude of the electron attracting ability of different substituents. Using these differences Carrington shows that the trimethylsilyl group is more electron attracting than the trimethylgermyl group. It is a real temptation to ascribe this difference to the more effective interaction of the $3d$ orbitals of silicon with the π system of the benzene ring compared with the lesser overlap of the $4d$ orbitals of germanium. The reported splittings of the electron spin by the methyl protons in trimethylsilylbenzene anion radical were observed to be 0.40 G. The same splittings in the germanium analog are 0.10 G. This difference also supports such a point of view. However, it is also possible to account for this difference in electron attracting power by the differences in electronegativity of germanium and silicon.

No such ambiguity exists when one compares the data from *t*-butylbenzene and trimethylsilylbenzene. Electronegativity arguments would lead to results just the opposite of those obtained, the *t*-butyl group should be more electron attracting and it is not. The most logical explanation of the differences in the hyperfine spectra of *t*-butylbenzene and trimethylsilylbenzene anion radicals would require the involvement of the $3d$ orbitals on silicon in the latter molecule in a resonance interaction with the π system of the benzene ring.

B. Anions of 2,2'-Biphenylenesilanes and Related Molecules

A similar resonance effect is observed among the negative ions of bis-2,2'-biphenylenesilane, **2**, (23). A solution of this compound in 2-

(2)

methyltetrahydrofuran is rapidly reduced at $-79°$ by potassium metal to form a deep wine-red solution of the uninegative anion radical. Further treatment of this solution with potassium metal produces a deep purple-colored solution of a diamagnetic species, the dinegative ion of bis-2,2'-biphenylenesilane. The electron spin resonance spectrum obtained on a solution of the uninegative ion at $-60°$ is shown in Figure 1. It consists of nine components separated by 1.3 G with a total breadth of some 10.5 G. Of particular interest is the considerable narrowing of the spectrum. The

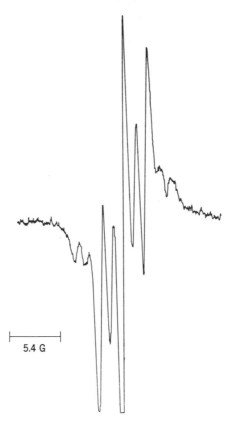

5.4 G

Fig. 1. Electron spin resonance spectrum of bis-2,2'-biphenylenesilanide.

hyperfine structure of the spectrum is consistent with delocalization of spin over the entire molecule and other evidence discussed later supports this point of view. The total breadth of resonance expected for such a system, ruling out any effect of the silicon $3d$ orbitals, should be about equal to that of 2,2'-dideuterobiphenyl or some 19 G. A comparison of the observed width with this value indicates a spin density on the silicon of approximately 0.45. In spite of the high value for this estimate the natural abundance of [29]Si did not give satellite lines that were observable in this experiment.

The role of silicon in these very stable ions can best be demonstrated by comparing them with their carbon analogs (24).

The uninegative ion of bis-2,2'-biphenylenemethane, produced by the usual potassium metal reduction, displays an electron spin resonance spectrum shown in Figure 2. While the assignments of coupling constants

Fig. 2. Electron spin resonance spectrum for the anion radical of
bis-2,2′-biphenylenemethane.

which produce the well-resolved 55 line spectrum have not been made, the
intensity pattern clearly cannot arise from interactions between the four
pairs of equivalent protons and the natural abundance of ^{13}C in a single
biphenylene system. The spin must be delocalized over both biphenylene
systems with an exchange frequency greater than or equal to the hyperfine
frequency. Assuming, as a limiting case, that the breadth of the individual
lines results solely from an incomplete averaging of the spin over the two-
ring systems, a lower limit of 10^8 sec^{-1} is obtained for the exchange frequency When a solution of the uninegative ion is treated further with
potassium the pink solution of the uninegative ion becomes a more intense
color. This color change can be shown to result from the formation of the
dinegative ion. The electron spin resonance spectrum of this species dissolved in a rigid glass matrix is shown in Figure 3. The center line in the

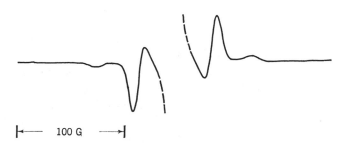

Fig. 3. Electron spin resonance spectrum for the dianion of
bis-2,2′-biphenylenemethane.

spectrum is due to the uninegative ion radical also present in the solution. Ignoring this central line, we see that the spectrum shows unusually small splitting for spin–spin interactions for a two-electron system. From this splitting an average value of the interaction distance of 7 Å can be calculated. The wing components of the triplet resonance are two in number and furnish proof that the dinegative ion possesses the same D_{2d} symmetry of the neutral molecule since any deviation from this symmetry (other than square planar) would produce at least two additional components. It is highly probable that the dinegative ion of bis-2,2′-biphenylenemethane is a ground state triplet. In any event, it is no greater than $1.5 \times 10^{12} \sec^{-1}$ in energy above the singlet state.

The magnetic behavior of the uninegative and dinegative ions of bis-2,2′-biphenylenemethane best can be rationalized by assuming an interaction between the unoccupied orbitals of lowest energy in each of the biphenylene π systems. The magnitude of this interaction can be estimated reasonably as being approximately equal to the exchange frequency $(10^8 \sec^{-1})$. The triplet state of the dinegative ion is readily understood since the magnitude of this interaction is much smaller than the mutual electrostatic repulsion between electrons in a bonding orbital. The dinegative ion triplet, then, is best described by a single occupancy of the lowest unoccupied orbital in each of the individual biphenylene π systems. In the uninegative ion there is single occupancy of an orbital which is a combination of the lowest vacant orbitals of both biphenylene π systems

An alternate explanation of the spin exchange process in the uninegative ion radical might invoke hyperconjugation of the *spiro* atom. If such a hyperconjugative mechanism is operative in this radical, the atomic orbitals of the *spiro* atom probably would be involved. An experiment has been performed which eliminates this possibility in a fairly conclusive fashion (25). A sample of the uninegative ion radical with 65% ^{13}C substituted in the *spiro* position was examined. The amount of line broadening in the hyperfine spectrum of the radical was unmeasurable. This observation lends strong support to the π-orbital description previously advanced.

Although the behavior of organic anion radicals is beyond the scope of the present discussion it is difficult to proceed without commenting upon the nature of this unusual and unexpected interaction. While it is a very weak interaction, it has properties which suggest that this geometry of aromatic systems, i.e., mutually perpendicular, might be extremely important in some organic reaction mechanisms. Essentially, the aromatic systems interact in such a fashion to allow passage of a single electron but not an electron pair. In such case it functions as a one-electron gate. It also is possible to visualize this as a model for the simplest metallic conduction band reduced to a single level which, half filled, is a good electronic conductor, but completely filled becomes a resistor to electronic conduction. There is a considerable variety of electronic configurations possible if tetrahedral atoms other than carbon are placed in the *spiro* position in such D_{2d} group molecules.

The effect of silicon in the *spiro* position in large part destroys such interesting properties as evidenced by the fact that the dinegative ion of bis-2,2'-biphenylenesilane is diamagnetic. The best explanation of this diamagnetic character does, however, furnish persuasive evidence of $3d$ orbitals participation in bonding for this species. In order to visualize the weak interaction between mutually perpendicular aromatic systems the simplest approach is to consider the symmetry properties of the π orbitals involved in the interaction. To consider these symmetry properties in a planar representation it is expedient to use the atomic $2p$ orbitals of the carbons in the 2,2' positions of each biphenylene system. This is not too violent a mistreatment of the molecular orbital description since the symmetry properties of the atomic $2p$ orbitals which participate in the π orbitals are identical to those of the π orbitals themselves.

If we visualize the bis-2,2'-biphenylenemethane molecule in such an aspect that we look in a line of sight along the intersection of the planes of both the biphenylene ring systems which passes through the center of the *spiro* atom, the projection will be that presented in Figure 4.

The orbitals shown are the $2p$ orbitals of the carbons in the 2,2' positions in both biphenylene systems. These four orbitals interact in this symmetry

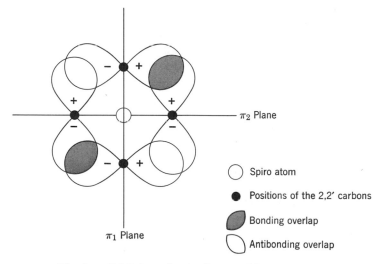

Fig. 4. π Orbital overlap in D_{2d} symmetry.

with a diagonal overlap as shown. While the two biphenylene systems are separated from one another by the *spiro* atom, it should be remembered that the diagram does not show the shape of the orbitals along the line of sight. The orbitals are antibonding relative to the biphenylene systems and have a higher density outside the ring systems. They are, therefore, directed along the line of sight in Figure 4 as follows: If the vertical plane represents the biphenyl system first in our line of sight, the interacting orbital is outside this biphenyl ring system away from the viewer. The horizontal plane then is that of the rear biphenyl system and the π orbitals represented perpendicular to that plane are directed toward the viewer. This orientation of the interacting orbtials in part overcomes the spacing impressed upon the interacting orbitals by the size of the *spiro* atom. One intuitively accepts the proposition that as the size of the *spiro* atom increases the magnitude of this π–π interaction should decrease. Thus, with silicon as the *spiro* atom the interaction should be less than when carbon is the *spiro* atom and we should expect the dinegative ion of bis-2,2'-biphenylenesilane, even more readily than the analogous methane ion, to be a triplet. The fact that it is a singlet ground state molecule is good evidence that a stabilizing factor is operative in enhancing this very weak bonding interaction. Such enhancement in the case of silicon undoubtedly arises from an interaction of the $3d$ orbitals on silicon with this combination orbital of the two biphenylene π systems. In D_{2d} symmetry the d_{xy}, d_{zy}, and d_{xz} orbitals are suitably oriented to interact well with the diagonal bonding orbital represented in Figure 4.

It is difficult to make a sensible prediction concerning the manner in which germanium as a *spiro* atom would serve to stabilize the singlet state in this geometry. It has not been possible so far to prepare the dinegative ion of bis-2,2'-biphenylenegermane.

Recently, Hellwinkel (26) reported the reduction of bis-2,2'-biphenylene-phosphonium iodide to the neutral bis-2,2'-biphenylenephosphonium radical and reported a phosphorus coupling constant of 18 G. This radical reduced further to an apparently diamagnetic anion. The neutral radical of bis-2,2'-biphenylenephosphine is isostructural and isoelectronic with the anion radical of bis-2,2'-biphenylenesilane and the phosphorus splitting of the electron spin should be similar to the effect of substituting ^{29}Si in the *spiro* position of the silane which we have not yet done.

Obviously, the diamagnetic anion, bis-2,2'-biphenylenephosphite, would be another example of stabilization of the weak diagonal overlap of perpendicular π systems.

The 2,2'-biphenylene aromatic system also stabilized other silane ion radicals to allow a study of the effect of aliphatic protons on the electron spin in anion radicals of D_{2d} symmetry.

In 2,2'-biphenylenecyclotetramethylene silole (3) the α protons in the aliphatic ring occupy positions with symmetry properties identical with those of the interacting biphenylene π orbitals in bis-2,2'-biphenylenesilane.

(3)

A consequence of this is the unusually large splittings, for aliphatic protons, observed in the electron spin resonance spectrum of the anion radical of the cyclotetramethylenesilole (27). In Figure 5 the observed electron spin resonance spectrum is compared with a line spectrum constructed using the following coupling constants:

$$A^*_{H5,5'} \text{ (aromatic)} = 4.10 \text{ G}$$
$$A_{H\alpha} \text{ (aliphatic)} = 1.04 \text{ G}$$
$$A_{H4,4'} \text{ (aromatic)} = 0.55 \text{ G}$$

The total breadth of resonance is 13.5 G. The observed α splittings probably represent considerably greater spin densities at each α proton in the present case than in the case of the methyl protons in trimethylsilyl-benzene anion. A rough approximation gives a total spin density of 0.20 at *all* nine of the methyl positions in the latter example where in the cyclotetramethylenesilole anion radical a similar approximation gives a total spin density of 0.23 at the four α positions in 2,2'-biphenylene-cyclotetramethylenesilole.

This large spin density at the aliphatic proton positions can be rationalized by assuming a high spin density in the $3d_{xy}$, $3d_{zy}$, and $3d_{xz}$ orbitals which are directed in space towards the α protons in this molecule.

---

* In order to assign conclusively the proton splittings to specific aromatic pairs it will be necessary to deuterate the biphenylene group in specific positions. We have made the assignments above solely on the basis of the fact that the *para*-proton splittings in biphenyl anion radical are smaller than those observed for trimethysilyl-benzene anion radical (21). This is not a particularly sound criterion since the total spin density in *para* positions in biphenyl anion radical is greater than the total density at the *para* position in the trimethylsilylbenzene anion radical. The constructed spectrum in Figure 4 shows good agreement with the observed spectrum independent of which pair of aromatic protons interacts most strongly with the electron spin.

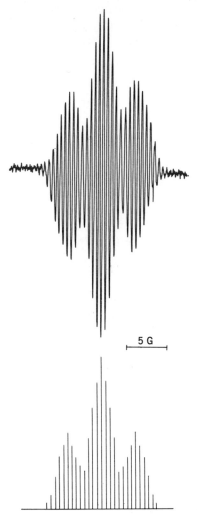

Fig. 5. Electron spin resonance spectrum of 2,2′-biphenylenecyclotetramethylene-silole anion radical.

C. Anion Radicals of Organosilyl Olefins

The treatment of various vinyltriarylsilanes and vinyltrialkylsilanes with lithium metal results in a metal adduct which upon hydrolysis forms 1,4-disilylbutanes. The overall effect of this reaction then is the reductive coupling of the vinylsilane (28). The similarity between this reaction and the reduction dimerization of many aryl-substituted olefins led Eisch and

Beuhler to suggest that an important intermediate in this reaction is a radical anion. They suggested further that this anion radical was stabilized by $d\pi$–$p\pi$ interactions. A similar kind of anion radical was invoked by Seyferth, Suzuki, and Vaughan to account for the lithium-induced isomerization of certain propenylsilanes (29).

Recently, Husk and West have confirmed the existence of such ion radicals (30). They have been shown to exist in solutions prepared by the alkali metal reduction of various silyl-substituted olefins dissolved in a dimethoxyethane–tetrahydrofuran mixture at $-100°$. Husk and West used sodium–potassium alloy to effect these reductions. Many of these anion radicals are sufficiently stable to allow for their examination by electron spin resonance techniques. It appears that the 1,2-disubstituted olefins result in anion radicals of greater stability than those of the monosubstituted olefins.

Husk and West reported that the anion radical of 1,2-bistrimethylsilyl-ethylene exhibits very interesting behavior insofar as the electron spin resonance spectrum is concerned. At approximately $-60°$ the spectrum consists of a 1:2:1 triplet with a splitting, presumably due to the ethylenic protons, of 7.3 G. This triplet is split further into a multiplet with a splitting of 0.32 G and intensity ratios consistent with the assignment of this coupling constant to the methyl protons. When the solution is cooled to $-100°$ the spectrum is seen to consist of a pair of overlapping triplets, each similar in splittings and intensities to the single triplet obtained from the same solution at $-60°$, but with different g values. These g values were determined by Husk and West to be 2.0031 and 2.0041, respectively. They attribute this spectral behavior to an anion radical which at temperatures of $-60°$ and above has free rotation about the carbon–carbon bond. At temperatures lower than $-60°$ the rotation becomes restricted and at $-100°$ it is essentially frozen out. The overlapping triplets observed at $-100°$ are attributed to the *cis* and *trans* isomers that are possible when there is restricted rotation about the carbon–carbon bond.

The observed difference in g values attributed to the *cis* and *trans* isomers probably arises as a result of a greater contribution of the orbital magnetic moment to the total magnetic moment for the molecule in one isomer than in the other. In this case the *trans* isomer is likely to be the isomer exhibiting the highest g value.

This work by Husk and West lends considerable support to the suggestions of Eisch and Beuhler (28) and of Seyferth, Suzuki, and Vaughan (29). Anion radicals virtually identical with the intermediates postulated to account for the reductive dimerization of the vinylsilanes and the *cis–trans* isomerization of propenylsilanes have been shown capable of independent existence. Also, the lower stability of the anion radicals of the monosubstituted olefins described by Husk and West could be the result of the dimerization reaction as postulated by Eisch et al.

D. Anion Radicals of Molecules Containing the Silicon–Silicon Bond

Perhaps more interesting than the question of the importance of the $3d$ orbitals on silicon in bonding of that atom to carbon is the question whether the silicon homonuclear bond is best described as having some $3d$ character. If the $3d$ orbitals on silicon are utilized in molecules such as disilane, Si_2H_6, and its derivatives, then these compounds might be expected to behave chemically less like their saturated carbon analogs than as unsaturated molecules. It is difficult to decide whether the silicon–silicon bond in hexachlorodisilane is chemically like the carbon–carbon bond in hexachloroethane or like the carbon–carbon bond in tetrachloroethylene. Certainly the silicon–silicon bond in hexaphenyldisilane is different chemically and physically from the carbon–carbon bond in hexaphenylethane. Any appreciable interaction of the $3d$ orbitals of the two silicon atoms in disilane would produce π-bonding character in such molecules. Where higher polysilanes are considered such, $3d$ orbital involvement should result in delocalized π bonds. In cyclic polysilanes these delocalized π bonds might be of sufficient importance to class this group of compounds as aromatic compounds. Since at least two (and possibly three) $3d$ orbitals on each silicon in a tetracovalent compound are available for such π interactions, silicon functions as a conjugative atom. In the dianion of bis-2,2′-biphenylenesilane already discussed the silicon atom serves such a function (23). Because of this conjugative property of the silicon atom, the effectiveness of this $d\pi$ overlap in stabilizing ring structures should not seriously depend upon ring size. Odd-membered and even-membered rings should enjoy similar stabilization. Another aspect of this property of $d\pi$ overlap bears on the various attempts to prepare mixed silicon–carbon aromatic systems (31,32). The $3d$ orbitals on silicon in such sila-aromatic molecules should operate in a conjugative role making the five-membered ring, sila-cyclopentadiene, and the seven-membered ring, sila-cycloheptatriene, similar in bonding to the alternant hydrocarbons, cyclobutadiene and benzene.

In cyclic polysilanes, such as dodecamethylcyclohexasilane, such $d\pi$-aromatic character is probably of little importance in the bonding. The anion radicals of such molecules, though, could have considerable $3d$ character in the orbital occupied by the odd electron. If the $3d$ orbitals do interact to produce delocalized $d\pi$-aromatic-type orbitals in the cyclo-polysilanes, it should prove possible to produce more highly charged anions than the simple anion radicals. Reaction between alkali metals and perphenylcyclopolysilanes (33–35) would seem to indicate that the dinegative ions of four-, five-, and six-membered rings of silicon atoms are unstable with respect to ring opening.

Some electron spin resonance spectra have been obtained for anion radicals containing silicon–silicon bonds. Solodovnikov and Chernysehv studied anions of pentamethyldisilylbenzene, 1,4'-bispentamethyldisilylbenzene, benzylpentamethyldisilane, and pentaethyldisilylbenzene (17). Recently, Husk and West have reported a stable anion radical of dodecamethylcyclohexasilane (36). At low gain a 19 line spectrum is obtained with a splitting of 0.53 G and intensity ratios which led to the assignment of these splittings to 36 equivalent protons. This suggests that the six-membered ring of silicon atoms is either rapidly equilibrating or is planar. It is also possible that the coupling to the methyl protons is not largely different for axial and equatorial methyl groups in a rigid chair form. Satellite doublets of the original spectrum could be resolved from this spectrum under high resolution conditions. One doublet having a splitting of 15.8 G consisted of a multiplet replica of the central proton spectrum. This doublet band had intensities compatible with it being assigned to natural abundance ^{13}C. A similar satellite doublet with a splitting of 5.2 G was attributed to natural ^{29}Si in the Si_6 ring since the doublet band had the appropriate intensity for this to be the case. It is somewhat unexpected to observe larger ^{13}C splittings than ^{29}Si splittings in this case; especially since Solodovnikov reported ^{29}Si splittings in 1,4-bistrimethylsilylbenzenide ion of 14 G (20). Some unusual effect seems to be operating in the case of the cyclohexasilane anion radical.

Husk and West also have prepared stable anion radicals of tetradecamethylcycloheptasilane and linear decamethyltetrasilane but have yet to publish the spectra for these most interesting anion radicals (30).

III. COMPARISONS OF BONDING IN ORGANOMETALLIC ANION RADICALS OF SILICON, GERMANIUM, AND TIN

Perhaps one of the most elegant applications of the electron spin resonance method in estimating bonding parameters among the Group IV-B elements is described in the recent work of Curtis and Allred (37). These investigators prepared stable anion radicals of 4-trimethylsilylbiphenyl, 4-trimethylgermylbiphenyl, 4,4'-bistrimethylsilylbiphenyl and 4,4'-bistrimethylgermylbiphenyl. The analogous tin compounds, 4-trimethylstannylbiphenyl and 4,4'-bistrimethylstannylbiphenyl, were easily reduced but neither gave stable anion radicals.

An anion radical of limited stability can be formed by brief treatment of a solution of 4,4'-bistrimethylstannylbiphenyl in tetrahydrofuran at $-50°$ with sodium–potassium alloy. In examining this solution Curtis and

Allred obtained a five-line spectrum with spacing of 2.36 ± 0.04 G and an overall breadth of some 10 G. The simplicity of this spectrum precluded any but the most general conclusions in comparing it with the analogous silicon and germanium anion radicals. The room temperature electron spin resonance spectrum of 4,4'-bistrimethylsilylbiphenylide and the − 10° spectrum of 4,4'-bistrimethylgermylbiphenylide also consist of five lines with intensity ratios of 1:4:6:4:1 similar to the spectrum obtained from the 4,4'-bistrimethylstannylbiphenylide. The splittings for these main components are 2.24 G for the silicon compound and 2.41 G for the germanium compound. On the basis of these facts, 4,4'-bis-trimethyl-stannylbiphenyl would appear to have an electronic distribution more closely similar to that of 4,4'-bistrimethylgermylbiphenyl than to that of 4,4'-bistrimethylsilylbiphenyl. A comparison of the polarographic half-wave potentials for 4-trimethylsilylbiphenyl, 4-trimethylgermylbiphenyl, and 4-trimethylstannylbiphenyl also illustrates a closer similarity between the effects of tin and germanium than between tin and silicon.

While the results obtained from anion radicals of tin compounds were not particularly informative, the treatment of the data obtained from the electron spin resonance spectra of the silicon and germanium anion radicals produced results that were impressive and convincing. To begin with, the choice of the 4,4'-disubstituted biphenyls greatly simplified the problems in the assignment of coupling constants. These anion radicals both gave spectra consisting of five bands and the coupling constants for the four protons *meta* to the 4,4' substituents (the 2,2', 6,6' protons) were consequently easily determined. The unscrambling of the methyl proton splittings from the aromatic ring 3,3', 5,5' protons from the expected intensity values allowed good assignments to be made in these cases without the tedium of deuterium substitution in specific sites. The assignments of proton splittings in the case of the 4-monosubstituted biphenyl-ides was possibly made easier by this choice as well.

From the observed proton coupling constants Curtis and Allred calculated so-called "experimental" spin densities and compared these with spin densities calculated by the Hückel method corrected first for configuration interaction effects and then for the resonance and inductive effects of the organometallic substituent in the 4-monosubstituted biphenylides. The magnitudes of the inductive and resonance effects were estimated by plotting the calculated spin densities at selected positions versus the proportionality constant for the resonance effect assuming various values of the proportionality constant for the inductive effect and then by plotting ratios of spin densities at various selected pairs of positions versus the proportionality constant for the resonance effect assuming various values for the inductive, or coulombic, proportionality constant.

The pair of values for these constants which gave the best fit for the "experimental" spin densities were assumed to be the correct operative constants. Spin densities at all positions calculated using the constants thus obtained show remarkably close agreement with the "experimental" values as shown in Table I. Similarly good agreement was obtained for all of the anions studied in this work.

TABLE I

Coupling Constants and Spin Densities for Various Group IV-B Anion Radicals [a]

Anion	Atom	A_{Hi} (G)	ρ_i (Expt'l)	ρ_i(Calc)
4-Trimethylsilylbiphenylide	2,6	2.08	0.074	0.077
	3,5	0.16	0.006	−0.002
	2′,6′	2.72	0.097	0.096
	3′,5′	0.48	0.017	−0.026
	4′	4.96	0.177	0.174
	CH$_3$	0.16	0.006	—
4-Trimethylgermylbiphenylide	2,6	2.38	0.085	0.086
	3,5	0.00	0.00	−0.013
	2′,6′	2.70	0.096	0.096
	3′,5′	0.52	0.019	−0.025
	4′	5.08	0.181	0.183
	CH$_3$	0.00	0.00	—
Trimethylsilylbenzenide	ortho	2.66	0.095	0.075
	meta	1.06	0.038	−0.004
	para	8.13	0.290	0.279
	CH$_3$	0.40	0.014	—
Trimethylgermylbenzenide	ortho	2.33	0.083	0.057
	meta	1.46	0.052	−0.003
	para	7.61	0.272	0.222
	CH$_3$	<0.10	<0.004	—

[a] Calculated using McConnell's expression $A_i = Q\rho_i$ (38); a Q of 28 was used for these calculations.

Since the estimated inductive and resonance effects of the organo-metallic substituent gave such close agreement with directly measurable parameters in the anion radicals, Curtis and Allred, with some confidence, calculated bond orders and charge densities in the neutral molecule. From these calculations they obtained a π-bond order of 0.18 for the silicon–carbon (aromatic) bond in 4-trimethylsilylbiphenyl and a π-bond order of 0.12 for the germanium–carbon (aromatic) bond in 4-trimethylgermyl-biphenyl.

A further experimental check was applied to test the validity of the chosen inductive and resonance parameters of the heteroatom in these compounds. From these parameters a value for the energy of the lowest unoccupied orbital could be calculated for each compound investigated. This in turn could be compared with reduction potentials obtained by polarographic reductions of these compounds. Such comparison gave good agreement and instills great confidence in the accuracy with which Curtis and Allred estimated the resonance and inductive effects.

One additional conclusion was drawn in this work based upon the difference in the inductive effects of the trimethylsilyl group and the trimethylgermyl group, namely, that silicon is more electropositive than germanium. Nuclear magnetic resonance data was obtained but did not add measurably to the already high level of confidence one has in the validity of the conclusions drawn by these investigators.

The work of Carrington and colleagues on the trimethylsilylbenzene and trimethylgermylbenzene anion radicals already has been discussed (21). Some of the spin densities calculated from their electron spin resonance spectra also are listed in Table I.

IV. SOME NEUTRAL FREE RADICALS OF GROUP IV-B ELEMENTS

Some workers have reported that various distannanes (39) and diplumbanes (40–42) are dissociated, to a greater or lesser extent, into $R_3M\cdot$ radicals. Magnetic measurements have not given evidence of such dissociations (43,44). Hexamesityldiplumbane probably represents the most favorable example where homolytic dissociation might occur. This compound, earlier reported as partially dissociated in solution, does not dissociate sufficiently to be detected by electron spin resonance.

Both cryoscopic (46,47) and magnetic susceptibility measurements (48) give no evidence of dissociation of digermanes and disilanes into radicals. Thus, the triarylmethyl radicals which have been useful in electron spin resonance studies (49) have no analogs stable enough to study in solution among the Group IV-B elements.

Electron spin resonance has been useful in studying neutral radicals containing Group IV-B elements but such studies so far have been limited to stable aromatic radicals upon which a Group IV-B substituent can be placed or to radicals which can be formed in rigid matrices and possess finite lifetimes because of limited diffusion rates in the solid state.

An example of a tin containing radical of the first kind is the [4-oxyl-3,5-di-*tert*-butyl-phenyl] triphenylstannane (**4**) reported by Stegmann and

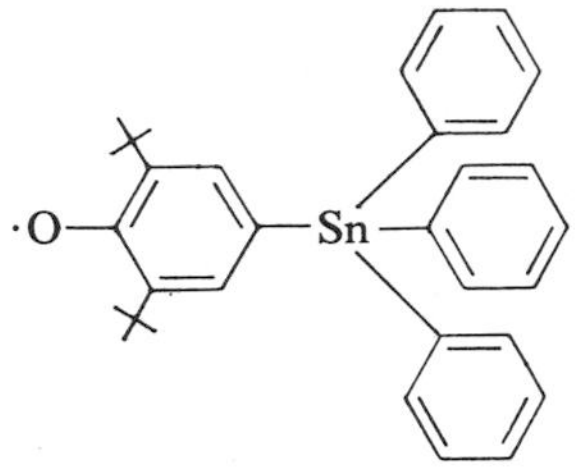

(**4**)

Scheffler (18). The electron spin resonance spectrum of this radical furnished evidence for resonance contributions from the 5*d* orbitals of the tin atom. Coupling constants of 58.13 G for [117]Sn and 61.00 G for [119]Sn were used to construct a spectrum which matched the observed spectrum. The arguments in favor of these assignments are somewhat involved and not particularly convincing. The effect of the 5*d* orbitals on the tin atom in this compound is certainly tremendously greater than that estimated by Curtis and Allred (37) for the anion of 4,4′-bistrimethylstannylbiphenyl, if Stegmann's interpretation of the spectrum is correct.

An interesting tetraradical (**5**) was prepared by Rozantsev and Golubev

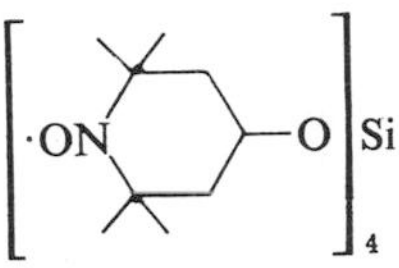

(**5**)

(50). The hyperfine structure of the electron spin resonance spectrum of this tetraradical apparently arises from spin interactions with the four nitrogen atoms. Although these investigators report no evidence for an effect of silicon upon the electron spin distribution, a comparison between the analogous tetraradicals of silicon, germanium, tin, and lead might be worthwhile. This could be a series in which all four derivatives are sufficiently stable for electron spin resonance studies. The effect, upon the coupling constant of the nitrogen, of varying the Group IV-B element might give a measure of relative inductive effects among this series of elements.

The study of free radicals generated in the irradiation of polysiloxane resins also has yielded electron spin resonance results which show that silicon free radicals are involved (51–53). Most such work has been directed toward an understanding of radiation-induced polymer degradation. This method of study is possible because the radicals formed are trapped in the matrix of the polymer lattice and hence are relatively long-lived even at room temperature. It is possible to examine such systems at lower temperatures and detect transient species which may also be important in the degradation mechanism.

The simplest possible radicals in the Group IV-B, the silyl ($\dot{S}iH_3$), germyl ($\dot{G}eH_3$), and stannyl ($\dot{S}nH_3$) radicals, have been studied in a rigid matrix by Morehouse, Christiansen, and Gordy (54). These are formed by the γ irradiation of solid solutions of the parent hydride in an argon matrix. Spectra are obtained in all three cases but only the $\dot{S}iH_3$ spectrum has sufficiently well resolved hyperfine components upon which to base deductions concerning the bonding in the radical. In the spectrum for the silyl radical a ^{29}Si s-orbital coupling of 266 G and an anisotropic p-orbital coupling of 24 G are observable. The proton couplings in this radical are unusually small (8.1 $\pm$ 0.5 G). In a comparison of the proton coupling constants of methyl (23 G), silyl (8.1 $\pm$ 0.5 G), germyl (15 $\pm$ 2 G), and stannyl (26 $\pm$ 4 G) radicals, Gordy comments on the probable negative spin densities in the methyl radical, as found by McConnell and Chestnut (55), and the silyl radical. He suggests that the observed proton coupling constants in the Group IV series would be converted to a regular decreasing order if one assumes positive spin densities on the protons in germyl and stannyl radicals. This desire for regular order does not fit the currently accepted irregular order in the electronegativities of these four elements. Silicon currently is believed to be the most electropositive of the group. The order of the presently accepted values for the electronegativities of the Group IV elements could account for the observed order in proton coupling constants without the necessity of invoking a change in the sign of the spin density.

From the ^{29}Si coupling constants Gordy calculated 22% s character and 78% p character for the unshared orbital in the silyl radical. This corresponds to 26% s character and 74% p character for the Si—H bonding orbitals. The bond angle of 110.6°, calculated from this hybridization, is further supported by an interpretation of the g-value anisotropy which is well accounted for by a pyramidal model with rotation about an axis perpendicular to the symmetry axis.

Gordy rules out the contributions of the 3d orbitals on silicon to account for the pyramidal structure of silyl radical as opposed to the planar structure of the methyl radical. He attributes this difference in structure to differences in electronegativity of carbon and silicon relative to hydrogen. Perhaps the role of the $3d$ orbitals is dismissed in too cavalier a fashion in this discussion. Certainly the assertion that germyl radical is probably pyramidal because the electronegativity of germanium is lower than hydrogen should be questioned. The electronegativity of germanium currently is believed to be almost identical with that of hydrogen.

Gordy proposes to examine isotopically enriched germyl and stannyl radicals in an effort to obtain information descriptive of bonding in these radicals as detailed as the information he obtained for silyl radical. We await these results with great interest to see if his present predictions are justified.

V. SUMMARY

The total experimental effort expended in attempts to arrive at satisfactory bonding descriptions, consistent with known chemistry, for compounds of the Group IV elements has been prodigious. For the past 15 or 20 years the most controversial aspect of such bonding descriptions has been the assessment of the role of the vacant d orbitals. As a consequence of this controversy an overwhelming volume of work has been published. Against the mountainous background of this mass of work the efforts described in this chapter are miniscule. In the opinion of this writer, however, the most satisfactory and unambiguous evidence for such d-orbital participation so far obtained for the Group IV-B elements is contained in these pages. Clearly, electron spin resonance is a tool capable of arriving at highly sophisticated bonding descriptions in a satisfying direct experimental manner. For the chemist this method is a "Greek gift" since it demands more from the chemist than most other spectroscopic methods. For most spectroscopic methods the chemist's role is essentially that of a technician in the preparation of pure compounds. That this role can be an important one is a fact to which many spectroscopic blunders will attest. In order to obtain satisfactory electron spin resonance results the chemists must synthesize stable compounds among a class of compounds formidable in their generally high reactivity, the odd-electron radicals and ion radicals. As in most kinds of spectroscopy, the operation of the spectrometer is by far the smallest part of the labor in obtaining useful electron spin resonance spectra. Much of the progress in this field of spectroscopy probably will come from chemists interested in the syntheses of unusually bonded odd-electron molecules or ions. Among this class of compounds the anion radicals promise to be the most prolific of convincing results. The easily obtained examples have been examined mostly in the recent past.

References

1. C. Friedel and J. M. Crafts, *Ann. Chem.*, **127**, 28 (1863).
2. J. A. A. Ketelaar, *Z. Krist.*, **92**, 155 (1935).
3. W. Dilthey, *Chem. Ber.*, **36**, 923 (1903); *Ann. Chem.*, **344**, 300 (1906).
4. S. K. Dhar, V. Doron, and S. Kirschner, *J. Am. Chem. Soc.*, **81**, 6372 (1959).
5. H. C. Brown and R. R. Holmes, *J. Am. Chem. Soc.*, **78**, 2173 (1956).
6. L. Pauling, in *The Nature of the Chemical Bond* 3rd ed., Cornell University Press, Ithaca, New York, 1960, p. 310.
7. S. Sujishi and S. Witz, *J. Am. Chem. Soc.*, **76**, 4631 (1954).
8. H. M. Manasevit, *U.S. Dept. Comm., Off. Tech. Serv., P.B. Rept.*, 143, 572, 1–92 (1959).
9. D. R. Lide and D. E. Mann, *J. Chem. Phys.*, **28**, 572 (1958).
10. K. Hedberg, *J. Am. Chem. Soc.*, **77**, 6491 (1955).
11. A. Carrington, *Quart. Rev.*, **17**, 67 (1963).
12. B. J. McClelland, *Chem. Rev.*, **64**, 301 (1964).
13. C. A. McDowell, *Rev. Mod. Phys.*, **35**, 528 (1963).
14. R. E. Robertson, *The Determination of Organic Structure by Physical Methods*, Vol. 2, F. C. Nachod and W. D. Phillips, Eds., Academic Press, New York, 1962, p. 617.
15. M. C. R. Symons, in *Advances in Physical Organic Chemistry*, Vol. 1, V. Gold, Ed., Academic Press, New York, 1963, p. 283.
16. S. I. Weissman, *Ann. Rev. Phys. Chem.*, **12**, p. 151 (1961).
17. S. P. Solodovnikov and E. A. Chernyshev, *Tr. Soveshch po Fiz. Metodam Issled. Organ. Soedin. i Khim. Protsessov, Akad, Nauk Kirg. SSR, Inst. Organ. Khim., Frunze*, **1962**, 196–212 (1964).
18. H. B. Stegmann and K. Scheffler, *Tetrahedron Letters*, **1964**, 3387–3392.
19. M. G. Townsend, *J. Chem. Soc.*, **1962**, 51.
20. S. P. Solodovnikov and E. A. Chernyshev, *J. Struct. Chem. (USSR) (Eng. Trans.)*, 3, 642 (1962).
21. J. A. Bedford, J. R. Bolton, A. Carrington, and R. H. Prince, *Trans. Faraday. Soc.*, **59**, 53 (1963).
22. J. R. Bolton and A. Carrington, *Mol. Phys.*, **4**, 497 (1961).
23. R. D. Cowell, G. Urry, and S. I. Weissman, *J. Am. Chem. Soc.*, **85**, 822 (1963).
24. R. D. Cowell, G. Urry, and S. I. Weissman, *J. Chem. Phys.*, **38**, 2028 (1963).
25. G. Urry, R. D. Cowell, and S. I. Weissman, unpublished results.
26. D. Hellwinkel, *Angew. Chem.*, **78**, 985 (1966); *Intern. Ed (in English)*, **75**, 968 (1966).
27. R. D. Cowell, Ph.D. dissertation, Purdue University, August 1965.
28. J. J. Eisch and R. J. Beuhler, *J. Org. Chem.*, **28**, 2876 (1963).
29. D. Seyferth, R. Suzuki, and L. G. Vaughan, *J. Am. Chem. Soc.*, **88**, 286 (1966).
30. G. R. Husk and R. West, private communication of unpublished results.
31. R. A. Benkeser and G. M. Stanton, *J. Am. Chem. Soc.*, **85**, 834 (1963).
32. R. A. Benkeser, Y. Nagai, J. L. Noe, R. F. Cunico, and P. H. Gund, *J. Am. Chem. Soc.*, **86**, 2446 (1964).
33. F. S. Kipping and J. E. Sands, *J. Chem. Soc.*, **119**, 830 (1921).
34. F. S. Kipping, *J. Chem. Soc.*, **123**, 2590 (1923); **125**, 2291 (1924); **1927**, 2719.
35. H. Gilman, D. J. Peterson, A. W. Jarvie, and H. J. S. Winkler, *J. Am. Chem. Soc.*, **82**, 2076 (1960), **83**, 1921 (1961); **83**, 4089 (1961).
36. G. R. Husk and R. West, *J. Am. Chem. Soc.*, **87**, 3993 (1965).
37. M. D. Curtis and A. L. Allred, *J. Am. Chem. Soc.*, **87**, 2554 (1965).
38. H. M. McConnell, *J. Chem. Phys.*, **24**, 632, 764 (1956).

39. C. A. Kraus and W. V. Sessions, *J. Am. Chem. Soc.*, **47**, 2361 (1925).
40. E. Krause and G. G. Reissaus, *Chem. Ber.*, **55**, 888 (1922).
41. T. Midgley, Jr., C. H. Hockwalt, and G. Calingaert, *J. Am. Chem. Soc.*, **45**, 1821 (1923).
42. M. Lesbre, J. Satge, and D. Voigt, *Compt. Rend.*, **246**, 594 (1958).
43. H. Morris, W. Byerly, and P. W. Selwood, *J. Am. Chem. Soc.*, **64**, 1727 (1942).
44. R. Preckel and P. W. Selwood, *J. Am. Chem. Soc.*, **62**, 2765 (1940).
45. E. Muller, F. Günter, K. Scheffler, and H. Fettel, *Chem. Ber.*, **91**, 2888 (1958).
46. G. T. Morgan and H. D. K. Drew, *J. Chem. Soc.*, **127**, 1760 (1925).
47. H. Gilman and G. E. Dunn, *J. Am. Chem. Soc.*, **73**, 5977 (1951).
48. P. W. Selwood, *J. Am. Chem. Soc.*, **61**, 3168 (1939).
49. H. S. Jarrett and G. J. Sloan, *J. Chem. Phys.*, **22**, 1783 (1954).
50. E. G. Rozantsev and V. A. Golubev, *Izv. Akad. Nauk. SSSR, Sev. Khim.*, **1965** (4) 718; *Bull. Acad. Sci. USSR, Chem.*, **1965**, 695.
51. M. G. Ormerod and A. Charlesby, *Polymer*, **4**, 459 (1963).
52. E. L. Zhuzhgov, N. N. Bubnov, and V. V. Voevodskii, *Kinetika i Kataliz*, **6**, 56 (1965).
53. A. S. Kuz'minskii, T. S. Fedoseyeva, Ya. S. Lebedev, A. L. Buchachenko, and Ye. V. Zhuravskaya, *Polymer Sci. USSR*, **6**, 1445 (1964).
54. R. L. Morehouse, J. J. Christiansen, and W. Gordy, *J. Chem. Phys.*, **45**, 1751 (1966).
55. H. M. McConnell and D. B. Chesnut, *J. Chem. Phys.*, **28**, 107 (1958).

CHAPTER 8

Radical Anions of Sulfur-Containing Aromatic Compounds

M. M. URBERG* AND E. T. KAISER

Department of Chemistry, University of Chicago, Chicago, Illinois

I. INTRODUCTION

In this chapter we shall divide radical anions of sulfur-containing aromatic compounds into two general categories. The first, which we shall call the perturbation case, consists of paramagnetic species in which the presence of sulfur-containing groups causes only small perturbations to the parent aromatic system. These species include radicals formed from aryl- and alkylthio-substituted aromatic systems which show little dependence on the substituents for their basic characteristics. The other category will be called the direct conjugation case and comprises those species in which the sulfur-containing groups are integral components of the conjugated system.

The chapter will begin with a review primarily of experimental results which have been obtained for the two categories of radical anions and then will proceed with a theoretical discussion.

II. EXPERIMENTAL RESULTS

A. The Perturbation Case

By their very nature, radicals in the perturbation category will not give as much useful information for theoretical discussions about sulfur-containing groups as will radicals which fall into the direct conjugation

---

* Predoctoral Fellow of the National Science Foundation.

category. Nevertheless, several interesting studies on the former group of radicals have been reported.

A large number of arylthiosemiquinone radicals have been prepared by Lucken by air oxidation or by reduction in basic alcoholic solutions of hydroquinones or quinones of the general formulas **1** and **2** (1).* Some of his EPR results are summarized in Table I. Splittings which were not due to protons associated with the quinoid part of the molecule were only observed in the case of benzylthiosemiquinone.

(1)   (2)

TABLE I

Proton Hyperfine Splitting Constants for Arylthio-1,4-Benzosemiquinones

X substituent	Coupling constants (in gauss)		
	a_3	a_5	a_6
H	1.52	2.72	2.12
CH$_3$	1.44	2.75	2.07
F	1.53	2.78	2.15
Cl	1.67	2.68	2.14
CH$_3$CO	2.24 $\pm$ 0.1	2.33	2.24 $\pm$ 0.1
NO$_2$	2.23 $\pm$ 0.1	2.59	2.23 $\pm$ 0.1
				Alkyl
Benzylthiosemiquinone	1.28	2.77	2.10	0.61

Lucken plotted the three splitting constants a_3, a_5, and a_6 against the pK_a values of the corresponding thiophenols for the radicals studied and found approximately linear curves for the three sets of points. He also did simple Hückel calculations on the radicals making the assumption that the arylthio group is a weak inductive electron donor. This model gave reasonable results as shown in Table II.

* For an early reference to EPR studies on semiquinone radicals prepared in basic alcoholic solutions see reference 2.

TABLE II

Comparison of Theoretical and Experimental Results on 1,4-Benzosemiquinones

1,4-Benzosemiquinone		Theory	Expt.
Phenylthio-[a]	a_3	1.50	1.52
	a_5	2.89	2.72
	a_6	2.50	2.12
2,5-Diphenylthio-[a]	a_3, a_6	1.58	1.25
2,6-Diphenylthio-[a]	a_3, a_5	1.99	1.91
Benzylthio-[b]	a_3	1.27	1.28
	a_5	3.05	2.77
	a_6	2.56	2.10
2,5-Dibenzythio-[b]	a_3, a_6	1.33	0.91
2,6-Dibenzythio-[b]	a_3, a_5	1.77	1.77

[a] $\Delta\alpha = -0.3\beta$ for substituted carbon atom, value of Q not reported.

[b] $\Delta\alpha = -0.4\beta$ for substituted carbon atom.

The assignment of coupling constants was made by Lucken on the basis of a comparison of the EPR spectra of the diarylthiosemiquinones and the monoaryl species. The large variations in the coupling constants as shown in the tables above, and the known ability of sulfide sulfur to participate in conjugation lead the present authors to feel that diarylthio substitution is too drastic a change from the parent molecules to give completely reliable results based on analogy. This is especially true for the 5 and 6 positions. The fact that splittings by the alkyl protons are seen in benzyl-thiosemiquinone suggests that the sulfur can act as more than an inductive electron donor. The great electronegativity of the semiquinone residue seems to mask the conjugating ability of the sulfur in these systems.

We have made some of these radicals by potassium metal reduction in 1,2-dimethoxyethane (DME) solutions (3), and we found spectra similar to those of Lucken. Phenylsulfonyl-1,4-benzosemiquinone has been prepared by Eargle and Kaiser(4). The coupling constants measured are 4.1, 2.2, and 1.3 G. Assignments of these constants have not been made as yet.

Bis(*p*-nitrophenyl)sulfide has been reduced electrolytically (5) and with alkali metals (3). When the electrolytic reduction was done in dimethyl-sulfoxide (DMSO) solvent, the EPR spectrum showed that the rate of electron transfer between the two aromatic rings was of the order of the hyperfine coupling energies. In acetonitrile (ACN) the electron transfer rate was slower than in DMSO at 25° and too slow to measure at −40°. These results are summarized in Table III. It has been suggested (5) that localization of the spin in one ring is due to a solvent cage effect.

TABLE III
Electron Transfer Rates in the Bis(p-Nitro-phenyl)Sulfide Radical (5)

DMSO	25°	9×10^6/sec
ACN	25°	2×10^6/sec
ACN	$-40°$	$< 10^6$/sec

We have reduced bis(p-nitrophenyl)sulfide, -sulfoxide, and -sulfone with alkali metals in DME solutions (3). In all cases the EPR spectra show the odd electron to be localized in one ring. For the sulfoxide radical, the nitrogen splitting depends on the metal used (sodium does not appear to reduce the sulfone under our conditions). Thus, we feel that the metal coordinates in some way with the nitro group on one ring causing spin localization. We have not rigorously determined the assignment of coupling constants, but we note that they are similar to those found for *para*-substituted nitrobenzene anion radicals by Maki and Geske (6). The coupling constants for these radicals are given in Table IV. Since sodium metal did not reduce our sulfone sample but did reduce the sulfoxide, the identity of the EPR spectra of the radicals obtained from these two com-

TABLE IV
Coupling Constants for the Radicals from Bis(p-Nitrophenyl) -Sulfide, -Sulfoxide, and -Sulfone

Radical	Source	Splittings (gauss)[d]		
		a_N	a_o	a_m
Bis(p-nitrophenyl)sulfide	ACN[a]	8.80	3.22	0.99
	DMSO[a]	8.07	3.19	0.90
	K metal in DME[b]	8.60	3.34	0.90
Bis(p-nitrophenyl)sulfoxide	K metal in DME[b]	6.55	2.94	0.57
	Na metal in DME[b]	6.90	3.03	0.64
Bis(p-nitrophenyl)sulfone	K metal in DME[b]	6.55	2.94	0.57
Methyl p-nitrobenzene-sulfonate	ACN[c]	6.90	3.03	0.64

[a] Electrolytic reduction, $0.1M$ tetrapropyl ammonium perchlorate supporting electrolyte (5).

[b] Metallic reduction *in vacuo*. Spectra observed at $-40°$ (3).

[c] Reference 6.

[d] a_o and a_m are the splitting constants for the positions *ortho* and *meta* to the nitro group, respectively.

pounds on reduction with potassium metal is felt to be real and not due to contamination. Thus, it would appear that the spin density distribution in the radical species is essentially unaffected here by the difference in the oxidation state of the sulfur in the sulfoxide and sulfone.

B. The Direct Conjugation Case

The nature of π bonding to a sulfur atom depends strongly on the geometry of the aromatic system relative to that of the sulfur-containing group. For this reason we have chosen to divide this section into three parts, considering planar molecules, diphenyl sulfone, and intermediate cases separately. Unfortunately, complete studies have been made on all of the possible oxidation states of the sulfur atom for only one system, and there are numerous gaps in the information available.

1. Planar Systems

The EPR spectra of the radical anions of 2,1,3-benzoxadiazole, -benzothiadiazole, and -benzoselenadiazole (3) were reported by Strom and Russell (7). The radicals were formed by electron exchange from various other anion species, and the assignments of splitting constants and results of theoretical calculations are given in Table V.

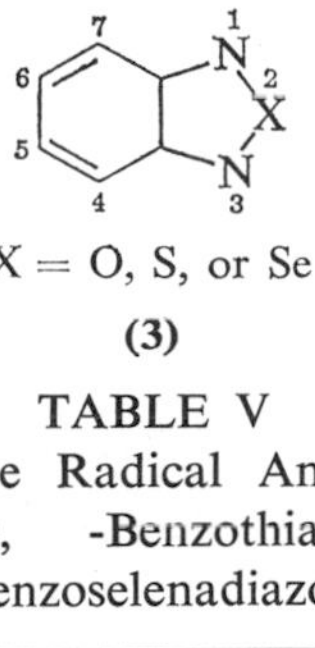

X = O, S, or Se

(3)

TABLE V

Results for the Radical Anions of 2,1,3-Benzoxadiazole, -Benzothiadiazole, and -Benzoselenadiazole

X	Splitting constants (G)		
	a_N	$a_{4,7}$	$a_{5,6}$
O	5.24	3.33	2.02
O (calc.)		3.41	2.01[a]
S	5.26	2.63	1.53
S (calc.)		2.64	1.52[b]
Se	5.97	1.99	1.99

[a] $Q = 24.2$ G (8).

[b] $Q = 24.2$ G. The same results were reported for "p" orbital and "d" orbital models.

The data recorded in Table V indicate that sulfur and selenium are better able to attract spin density from the aromatic rings than is oxygen. Strom and Russell used two models to theoretically calculate the spin density for the 2,1,3-benzothiadiazole radical, a "p" model and a "d" model (see "Theoretical Section"). Both models give identical results for the spin distribution which agree well with experiment.

Gerdil and Lucken (9) and Eargle and Kaiser (11) have reported the EPR spectrum of the dibenzothiophene radical anion (4), X = S. The measured coupling constants are shown in Table VI. The small spin densities *ortho* and *para* to the sulfur atom indicate that the conjugation through the sulfur is weaker than through the direct ring–ring bond—not a surprising conclusion.

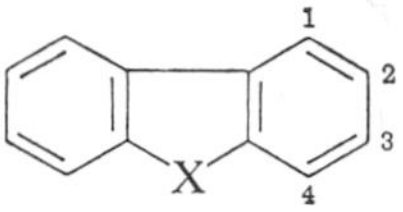

X = S, SO, and SO_2

(4)

TABLE VI
EPR Results for the Radical Anion of Dibenzothiophene

	Splitting constants (G)			
	a_1	a_2	a_3	a_4
Gerdil and Lucken (9)	4.48	0.86	5.16	1.46[a]
Eargle and Kaiser (11)	4.60	1.05	5.04	1.45[b]
Calculated[c]	3.99	−1.23	5.03	0.75

[a] A very approximate early calculation by Gerdil and Lucken which appeared in reference 9 implied a different assignment than that shown in Table VI.

[b] Assignment of results made here according to reference 10.

[c] Calculated by "p" orbital model using McLachlan's method (8).

Dibenzothiophene-S-oxide (11) and -S,S-dioxide (11,12) have been reduced and the principal features of the EPR spectra of the radical anions are listed in Table VII.

From the data in Tables VI and VII there appears to be greater conjugation through the sulfoxide and sulfone groups than through the sulfide group in the dibenzothiophene ring system. This is shown by the observation that the spin densities *para* to the more strongly conjugating groups are large while those at the *meta* position are smaller. The experimental evidence used in reference 12 to assign splitting constants is not com-

TABLE VII

EPR Results for the Radical Anions of Dibenzothiophene-S-oxide and
-S,S-dioxide

Radical anion	Splitting constants (G)			
	a_1	a_2	a_3	a_4
Sulfoxide (11)[a] (S-oxide)	?	> 2.4	< 2.4	0.20
Sulfone (12) (S,S-dioxide)	< 0.2	2.50	2.16	< 0.4
Sulfone (11)[b]	0.12	2.36	1.84	0.24
Sulfone, calc. (12)[c]	0.015	1.65	2.11	0.15

[a] As indicated in reference 11, assignments of splitting constants made
in that paper were very tentative and in the light of later data, they have
been revised here.

[b] Assignments made to correspond to reference 12.

[c] "d orbital" sulfone model, $Q = 25$ G.

pletely unambiguous in our opinion, and it is possible that a_2 and a_3 could
be reversed. This would lead to better agreement with theory. The assignment of coupling constants for the sulfone radical is completely different
from the sulfide case. We might expect that the sulfoxide radical anion
should have a spin distribution intermediate between these two species.
In Table VII the assignment for the sulfoxide radical anion has been made
to correspond to the results obtained in reference 12 for the sulfone
species. However, in the absence of any further information this assignment must be regarded as indefinite.

In general, the spectra reported for the radical anions formed from
dibenzothiophene and its oxides have been poorly resolved, and the
agreement between the data found by the two groups of workers, Gerdil
and Lucken, and Kaiser and Eargle, is not good. Because the observed
spectra were poorly resolved the values of the coupling constants are somewhat uncertain. In addition, labeling experiments to determine the assignments of the coupling constants for the sulfone radical anion (in particular,
to positions 2 and 3) give results which, in our opinion, are not completely
unambiguous. This is unfortunate for theoretical reasons because the
spectrum calculated by Gerdil and Lucken (12) predicts the reverse order
of coupling constants from that found experimentally for positions 2 and 3.
We have repeated their calculation (3) and find that if we raise the carbon-
sulfur "d" orbital overlap integral above the value which they used, the
relative magnitudes of the spin densities at positions 2 and 3 become equal
and finally are reversed.

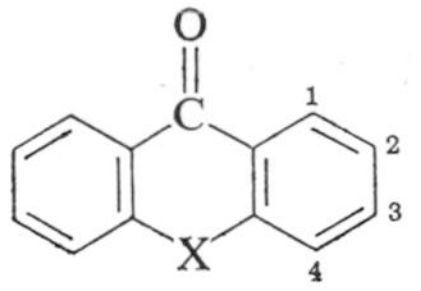

$X = S, SO_2$

(5)

The thioxanthone ring system (5) is similar in geometry to dibenzothiophene. The radical anion of thioxanthone has been observed by Kaiser and Eargle (13) and Urberg and Kaiser (14). The splitting constants measured are summarized in Table VIII (14). As can be seen from the

TABLE VIII

Splitting Constants in Gauss for the Thioxanthone Radical
Anion in DME[a]

	Sodium ketyl	Potassium ketyl[b]
a_1	3.35	3.380
a_2	0.90	0.95
a_3	3.80	3.75
a_4	0.45 ± 0.1	0.345
Metal	0.45	0.11

[a] The coupling constants were assigned by studying the radicals produced from various methyl-substituted thioxanthones.

[b] In the case of the potassium ketyl the values of the coupling constants given here were used by Dr. M. Sakamoto of the Computer Division of JEOLCO, Medford, Mass., to calculate a theoretical EPR spectrum which was in excellent agreement with that observed experimentally.

data shown there, considerable metal splittings are found for the sodium and potassium ketyls. Metal ketyls in ether solutions are known to have large metal–oxygen interactions (15).

Thioxanthone-S,S-dioxide radical anion (14,16) prepared in alkaline alcoholic solution has the following proton hyperfine coupling constants, 3.10, 2.35, 0.84, and 0.52 G. Vincow (16) assigned positions for these couplings as 3, 1, 4, and 2, respectively, on the basis of analogy to the benzophenone ketyl. That is, he assumed that there is only a small perturbation by the sulfone linkage. He was able to do a calculation which fitted his assignments using a "d" orbital model. However, the sulfone model of Gerdil and Lucken (12) (see reference 16, page 2486, $\delta\alpha_S = -2\beta_{CC}$ and $\beta_{CS}/\beta_{CC} = 0.7$) gives quite different results which do not approximate the experimental findings for any possible assignment of coupling constants. Experimental results and those calculated are given in Table IX.

TABLE IX

Thioxanthone-S,S-dioxide Radical Anion[a] in Alkaline Alcoholic Solution

| | Spin densities, ρ_i | | | |
	1	2	3	4
Vincow experimental	0.102	0.023	0.135	0.036
Vincow calculated	0.105	−0.025	0.139	−0.037
Gerdil and Lucken model	0.0668	0.0049	0.109	−0.0324

[a] $Q = 23$ G in this table. $a_i = Q|\rho_i|$.

We must note that Gerdil and Lucken (12) based their calculations on $Q = 25$ G instead of 23 G. With the larger value of Q smaller values for the experimental spin density are obtained. The model of Gerdil and Lucken predicts the order and sign of the coupling constants to be the same as that calculated by Vincow, but their values for the spin densities are uniformly smaller.

The present authors (14) have confirmed Vincow's assignment of the coupling constants by examining the EPR spectra of several methyl-substituted thioxanthone-S,S-dioxide anion radicals. We have also prepared the thioxanthone-S,S-dioxide radical in DME using potassium metal reduction of the parent compound, and we have found the coupling constants listed in Table X.

TABLE X

Splitting Constants in Gauss
for the Thioxanthone-S,S-
dioxide Radical Anion in DME

	Potassium ketyl
a_1	2.04
a_2	0.36
a_3	3.07
a_4	0.78
Metal	0.11

The order of the coupling constants and their magnitudes are similar to the values measured for the radical in alcohol. The close association of the metal to the oxygen of the carbonyl group in the ether solution seems to withdraw some of the spin density from the aromatic rings in comparison to the situation in alcohol.

2. Diphenyl Sulfone

Since the phenyl rings of diphenyl sulfone approach being perpendicular to the $C\alpha$–S–$C\alpha$ plane, the sulfone orbitals available to conjugate with the π system in this case are orthogonal to the π molecular orbitals in the previously discussed planar molecules. Thus, we expect different results for this system. The radical anion of diphenyl sulfone has been prepared by metallic reduction, and the EPR spectrum which was observed by the present authors (17) and by Gerdil and Lucken (9,12) is rather similar to that of the biphenyl anion. This suggests that there is a strong conjugative interaction through the sulfone group between the two aromatic rings of the radical. Another possible explanation is that due to the nonplanar geometry of diphenyl sulfone, the direct interaction between the rings is large enough to cause the observed conjugation. However, the present authors (17) have shown that such interaction would probably be too small to be the only source of conjugation. A "d orbital" model for conjugation through the sulfone group was independently employed both by us as well as by Gerdil and Lucken (12) and it gave good agreement with experiments as illustrated in Table XI.

TABLE XI
EPR Results for the Diphenyl Sulfone Radical Anion

Radical	Splittings in gauss			Calculated "d" model		
	a_o	a_m	a_p	a_o	a_m	a_p
Diphenyl sulfone (12)	2.41	0.65	4.64	2.18	-0.56	4.46
Diphenyl sulfone (17)	2.37	0.70	4.74	2.37	-0.61	4.71
Biphenyl (8)	2.75	0.45	5.50			

3. The Intermediate Cases

Thianthrene is a compound whose geometry places the sulfur atoms in an environment which is intermediate between the previous cases. The planes of the phenyl rings are intermediate between being in the $C\alpha$–S–$C\alpha$ plane as in dibenzothiophene and being perpendicular to the $C\alpha$–S–$C\alpha$ plane as in diphenyl sulfone.

With the exception of thianthrene itself, all of the possible sulfur oxides derived from the ring system have been reduced to give radical anions (9,12,13,19).

X = S, SO, or SO_2
Thianthrene system

(6)

Gerdil and Lucken (9) have reported an EPR spectrum for the monosulfoxide radical anion which has coupling constants $a_H = 2.06$ and 0.13 G. The number of equivalent protons in this species was not reported. Kaiser and Eargle* have found a complex spectrum which is 17 G wide for the monosulfoxide radical and one which is 15.4 G wide for the *trans-S,S'*-dioxide radical anion (19). The *cis-S,S'*-dioxide radical anion has a spectrum which consists of five major groups of lines ($a_H = 2.1$ G) split into five hyperfine lines per group. The radicals from the sulfone–sulfide, the sulfone–sulfoxide, and the disulfone all have simple five line EPR spectra ($a_H = 2.11$ G). From a study using a methyl-substituted disulfone it was shown that the five-line spectrum of the radical anion of the parent disulfone is attributable to splittings by the four protons in the β-positions of the aromatic rings (13). Assignments of the splittings observed for the radicals of the other oxides have not as yet been firmly established by labeling experiments. The identity of the EPR spectra of the radicals obtained from several oxides makes the problem of elucidating the mechanism of the interaction between the rings a particularly intriguing one. Until assignments have been made of all of the coupling constants for the radicals produced from the oxides we feel that any theoretical explanation of the spectra is only preliminary.

Nevertheless, two explanations are available for the disulfone radical anion at present. The first was offered by Gerdil and Lucken (12), who applied their diphenyl sulfone model directly to thianthrene tetroxide. They found that if they used their previous sulfone parameters directly, the theoretical fit to the observed EPR spectrum was not good. They were able to get much better agreement if they lowered the sulfur–carbon overlap integral from $0.8 \beta_{cc}$ to $0.6 \beta_{cc}$ for the tetroxide system. An alternative explanation merely invokes direct ring-ring overlap to a very small extent (20) and will be discussed in Section III of this chapter.

---

* Note the printing error in Table I of reference 18. Entries 3 and 4 should be -SO-,-SO-(*trans* (V) and -SO-,-SO-(*cis*) (VI), respectively, and entry 7 should read, total width 8.6 G instead of 6.8.

III. THEORETICAL SECTION

A. Sulfur Bonding Orbitals

We will review the LCAO description for sulfur in order to develop a consistent nomenclature with which to describe the theoretical models which have been proposed to explain the EPR spectra of sulfur-containing aromatic radical anions. The language of group theory is used for convenience.

Let us choose a coordinate system with which to describe all sulfur compounds under consideration. The sulfur–carbon σ bonds are chosen to lie in the X–Z plane with the positive Z axis bisecting the C–S–C angle and pointing away from the carbons. The Y axis is chosen so as to form a right-handed system. The coordinates are shown below:

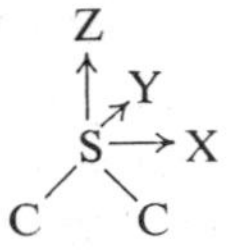

In sulfone molecules the two sulfur–oxygen bonds are in the Y–Z plane. Local C_{2v} symmetry is assumed. The well known C_{2v} character table (21) is given below along with the transformation symmetries of the coordinate axes (Table XII).

TABLE XII
Character Table for C_{2v} (21)

	E	C_2	$\sigma_v{}^a$	$\sigma_{v'}{}^b$	Coordinate
A_1	1	1	1	1	Z, X^2, Y^2, Z^2
A_2	1	1	-1	-1	XY
B_1	1	-1	1	-1	X, XZ
B_2	1	-1	-1	1	Y, YZ

[a] σ_v is a reflection through the X–Z plane.
[b] $\sigma_{v'}$ is a reflection through the Y–Z plane.

The third shell sulfur orbitals then can be catalogued according to symmetry as follows:

$$A_1: 3s, 3p_z, 3d_{(3z^2-r^2)}, 3d_{(x^2-y^2)}$$
$$A_2: 3d_{xy}$$
$$B_1: 3p_x, 3d_{xz}$$
$$B_2: 3p_y, 3d_{yz}$$

The σ bonding orbitals of the carbon ligands can be combined in the following way to give symmetrized orbitals (Fig. 1).

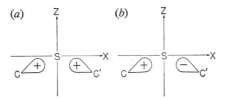

Fig. 1. Carbon σ bonding orbitals. (a) $R_{\sigma A1} = \dfrac{(R_\sigma + R_{\sigma'})}{\sqrt{2}}$ (b) $R_{\sigma B1} = \dfrac{(R_\sigma - R_{\sigma'})}{\sqrt{2}}$

If the molecule under consideration is planar, e.g., dibenzothiophene, the π system has a node in the X–Z plane, so only A_2 and B_2 ring π orbitals exist. These are shown schematically below (Scheme I):

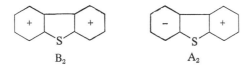

$$B_2 \qquad\qquad A_2$$

In diphenyl sulfone, A_1 and B_1 π orbitals can be chosen as shown (Fig. 2): The A_2 and B_2 ring π orbitals have a node in the 1 and 4 ring positions and do not overlap the sulfur orbitals.

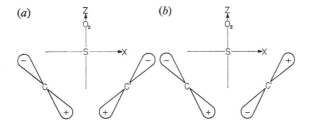

Fig. 2. Carbon π bonding orbitals in diphenyl sulfone. (a) $R_{\pi A1} = \dfrac{(\pi_c + \pi_c')}{\sqrt{2}}$

(b) $R_{\pi B1} = \dfrac{(\pi_c - \pi_c')}{\sqrt{2}}$

σ Bonding oxygen orbitals in sulfones can be described as A_1 and B_2 as shown below (Fig. 3).

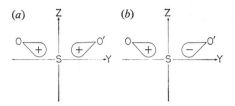

Fig. 3. σ-bonding oxygen orbitals in sulfones. (a) $O\sigma_{A1} = \dfrac{(\sigma_0 + \sigma_0')}{\sqrt{2}}$

(b) $O\sigma_{B2} = \dfrac{(\sigma_0 - \sigma_0')}{\sqrt{2}}$

There are two p orbitals on each oxygen and combinations of these can be made to form symmetrized orbitals as indicated (Figs. 4 and 5).

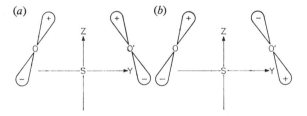

Fig. 4. π bonding oxygen orbitals in sulfones. (a) $O\pi_{A1} = \dfrac{(\pi_{0y} + \pi_{0y}')}{\sqrt{2}}$

(b) $O\pi_{B2} = \dfrac{(\pi_{0y} - \pi_{0y}')}{\sqrt{2}}$

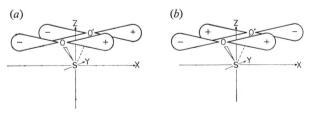

Fig. 5. π bonding oxygen orbitals in sulfones. (a) $O\pi_{B1} = \dfrac{(\pi_{0x} - \pi_{0x}')}{\sqrt{2}}$

(b) $O\pi_{A2} = \dfrac{(\pi_{0x} - \pi_{0x}')}{\sqrt{2}}$

It can be proved with group theory that only orbitals of the same symmetry can combine to give molecular orbitals of that symmetry. Thus, we can separate the discussion of the bonding structure into a consideration of each symmetry separately.

B. Planar Molecules

We now have enough information to proceed with a qualitative discussion of the π bonding of sulfur to aromatic systems. For planar sulfide molecules all σ bonds are A_1 and B_1 while all π orbitals are A_2 and B_2, so we do not expect any complications from the σ framework. The $3d_{xy}$ orbital can combine with the A_2 ring orbitals, and the $3p_y$ and $3d_{yz}$ orbitals on sulfur combine with the B_2 orbitals. In the sulfone case, the σ bonding to the oxygen involves the B_2 sulfur p orbital, making it less available for overlap with the ring π system, but overlap with the filled σ bonding structure is still possible, i.e., the σ and π bonds compete for this orbital.

C. Diphenyl Sulfone

In the diphenyl sulfone case, the σ bonding orbitals to the carbons have the same symmetry as the available π orbitals. In this case it is not valid to discuss the σ framework and the π structure separately. An additional complication arises due to the possibility of direct carbon π overlap between the 1,1' positions. The odd electron goes into an A_1 orbital in the radical anion, so it is necessary to consider one p and two d sulfur orbitals in the bonding structure.

It should be obvious that a qualitative description of the π system of sulfur compounds is fairly easy to construct, but a quantiative description of the system is expected to be rather difficult.

D. Models and Calculations

The first attempt at a theoretical calculation of planar sulfur systems was done by the valence bond technique on thiophene (22). The following resonance structures for the molecule were drawn and weights were assigned to each in such a way as to reproduce the observed dipole

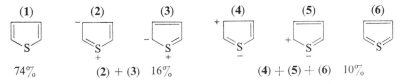

moment. The procedure is actually a correlation of observed data and not a calculation. Prediction of spin densities and properties of larger molecules on this basis is impossible.

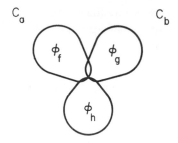

Fig. 6. Sulfide–sulfur π bonding orbitals according to Longuet-Higgins (23).

The molecular orbital theory is more suited to our present needs. Longuet-Higgins (23) was the first to construct a molecular orbital model for sulfur, again for thiophene. He was interested in explaining the similarity of thiophene and benzene. Orbitals were constructed as follows (Fig. 6):

$$\varphi_c = 3p_y$$

$$\varphi_d = 3d_{yz}$$

$$\varphi_e = 3d_{xz}$$

$$\frac{\varphi_f}{\varphi_g} = \frac{S_{ac}S_{ae}\varphi_c + S_{ad}S_{ae}\varphi_d \pm (S_{ac}^2 + S_{ad}^2)\varphi_e}{[(S_{ac}^2 + S_{ad}^2)(S_{ac}^2 + S_{ad}^2 + S_{ae}^2)]^{1/2}}$$

$$\varphi_h = \frac{S_{ad}\varphi_c - S_{ac}\varphi_d}{(S_{ac}^2 + S_{ad}^2)^{1/2}}$$

φ_h is constructed in such a way that it becomes a noninteracting empty orbital which is expected to be mainly the $3d_{xz}$ orbital. φ_f overlaps carbon a and φ_g overlaps carbon b. Overlap between the two sulfur bonding orbitals f and g is expected to be large. In this model H_2S has the same structure as ethylene. The ionization energy of H_2S (10.47 eV) is almost the same as that of ethylene (10.50 eV), so Longuet-Higgins equated the energy of the low energy H_2S orbital ($\alpha_f + \beta_{fg}$) with the lowest energy ethylene Hückel orbital ($\alpha_c + \beta_{cc}$). He then made the assumption that $\beta_{fg} = \beta_{cc}$. The primary justification for this assumption appears to be that satisfactory results could be obtained in this way. Longuet-Higgins showed that if β_{fa}, the resonance integral between a sulfur orbital and a carbon π orbital, is postulated to be equal to 0.8 β_{cc}, the "resonance energy" of approximately 30 kcal/mole which has been measured for thiophene can be reproduced (24). This is the "d orbital" model for a sulfide mentioned earlier and used by Gerdil and Lucken (12) and Strom and Russell (7).

If we assume that the $3d_{yz}$ orbital is not important in π bonding, i.e., that the p_z orbital is much more important, and further that Longuet-Higgins' argument about ionization potentials is valid, we can see that:

$$\frac{\varphi_f}{\varphi_g} \simeq \frac{1}{\sqrt{2}} (3p_y \pm 3d_{xy})$$

but $\varphi_f - \varphi_g = 3d_{xy}$. Taking Longuet-Higgins' parameters, we find:

$$\alpha_{3dxy} = \alpha_c - \beta_{cc}$$

That is, the d orbital has an energy only slightly higher than a carbon p orbital. We know, however, that atomic sulfur has an ionization potential of about 13 eV, and there is a configuration of the type $3s^2$, $3p^3$, $3d$ which is only about 2 eV below ionization (27), indicating that the sulfur d orbitals are of very high energy. Also Bendazzoli and Zauli (28) showed by an SCF calculation that divalent sulfur has a very high d orbital energy. Because of this, the Longuet-Higgins model overemphasizes the effect of the A_2 d orbital on the π structure. Gerdil and Lucken (12) found that this effect lowered the energy of the A_2 orbital below the energy of the B_2 orbital, while the spin distribution of the B_2 orbital agreed with experimental results.

In a C_{2v} molecule, it is not necessary to hybridize the orbitals in this way, and the $3d_{xy}$ orbital can be considered separately from the p orbital. If we do this and neglect the d orbital altogether, we arrive at the "p orbital" model. This is not as drastic an assumption as it appears, as in all molecules studied thus far the symmetry of the first unfilled orbital is such that it does not combine with the sulfur $3d_{xy}$.

The parameters used by Gerdil and Lucken (12) and Stromm and Russell (7) for the "p" model are derived from the Longuet-Higgins model and are $\alpha_s = \alpha_c + \beta_{cc}$ and $\beta_{cs} = 0.522 \, \beta_{cc}$.

The increase in the oxidation state of sulfur to the sulfone stage adds the complication that σ and π bonding orbitals have the same symmetry. In addition, the sulfur becomes highly positively charged (about $\frac{1}{2}$ electron according to Koch and Moffitt) (25). This lowers the energy of both the p and d orbitals on sulfur and contracts the d orbitals to the dimensions more suitable for bonding (28). Thus, d orbital interactions become much more important.

Moffitt (26) and Koch and Moffitt (25) have tackled this problem and their treatment afforded great simplification, although at the loss of some rigor. They formed sulfur σ and π bonding orbitals of A_1 and B_2 symmetry in the following way:

$$3t_{al} = (\sin x)(3s) + (\cos x)(3p_z)$$
$$3r_{al} = (\cos x)(3s) - (\sin x)(3p_z)$$

These form σ bonding orbitals to oxygen and carbon, respectively.

$3t_{bz} = 3p_y$ is σ bonding to oxygen. $3d_{yz}$ σ bonding to oxygen is neglected. $3d_{(3z^2 - r^2)}$, $3d_{(x^2 - y^2)}$, and $3d_{yz}$ are not used in σ bonding and are the only orbitals available for π bonding.

In this model the $3s$ and $3p$ sulfur orbitals are completely used up in σ bonding. Thus only d orbitals are left to conjugate with ring π orbitals, i.e., instead of the σ and π systems competing for p and d orbitals, the σ system gets the p orbitals and the π system gets the d orbitals. It seems to the present authors that the large density of the $3d_{yz}$ orbital in the region of the sulfur oxygen σ bonds, and the availability of the $3p_y$ orbital for ring conjugation which was demonstrated in dibenzothiophene, and similar conditions in the A_1 symmetry case makes the simplification of questionable interpretive value. It is just these symmetries with which we will be concerned.

A test of the usefulness of this model would be to see if the EPR spectra of planar molecules and of diphenyl sulfone could be reproduced by a calculation invoking only empty "d orbitals" on sulfur. This has in fact been done for diphenyl sulfone, dibenzothiophene sulfone, and thioxanthone sulfone, but the parameters necessary are different in each case. For diphenyl sulfone, Gerdil and Lucken found the parameters $\alpha_d = \alpha_c - 2\beta_{cc}$ and $\beta_{cd} = 0.8\,\beta_{cc}$ gave fairly good results. Kaiser, Urberg, and Eargle (17) found that the slightly larger parameters $\alpha_d = \alpha_c - 2.6\beta_{cc}$ and $\beta_{cd} = 0.99\,\beta_{cc}$ reproduced the observed spectrum within experimental error. No provision was made to account for 1–1' carbon overlap in either case. Gerdil and Lucken tried to use their same parameters for dibenzothiophene sulfone, but the order of coupling constants was not predicted correctly. The present authors (17) have repeated this calculation and we find that a larger value of β gives better results. As was pointed out before, we feel that the assigment of the coupling constants is not completely certain, and if the assignments to positions 2 and 3 were in fact reversed, experimental and theoretical results would compare more favorably.

Vincow (16) had to use significantly smaller values of β to fit the spectrum of the thioxanthone sulfone radical anion. It should be noted, however, that there is a larger C–S–C bond angle in thioxanthone sulfone than in dibenzothiophene sulfone, so the d orbital would be expected to interact less strongly with the neighboring p orbitals. A further point is in order. If one examines the calculation results in references 12 and 17 one finds that the predicted spectra vary rapidly with small changes in the parameters, especially β. In this situation we expect a small change in the environment of the sulfone group from molecule to molecule to have a large effect on the interaction of the sulfone residue with the π system. This must be reflected in variations in the Hückel parameters necessary to describe the EPR spectra of different systems.

In the thianthrene tetroxide system because of the high symmetry of the molecule several models predict essentially the same EPR spectrum for the radical. Since no completely general model for the sulfone group has been shown to be valid, it is permissible to examine each case separately. As was mentioned earlier, Gerdil and Lucken (12) applied their diphenyl sulfone parameters directly to thianthrene tetroxide and found it necessary to reduce the value of β to get good results. We wish to propose another explanation for the observed spectrum based only on direct ring-ring overlap and similar in procedure to that by Carrington, Longuet-Higgins, and Todd (20) for dibenzocyclooctatetraene.

We require maximum in phase overlap of the two phenyl ring π orbitals. The required orbital with Hückel coefficients is shown below:

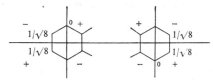

Assuming that $Q = 22.5$ G as in benzene, we find that the coupling constant at the 1 position is zero and at the 2 position is 2.8 G, compared with zero and 2.11 G experimentally determined. This is good agreement for such a simple model and it shows that the effect of the sulfone groups in this molecule need not be large.

E. Conclusions

Sulfide interactions with aromatic systems seem to be fairly well understood. Experimental and theoretical evidence shows that sulfur does not depart much from the behavior of oxygen in these systems and suggests that the small differences which exist can be explained on the basis of the different electronegativities of the elements and small d orbital interactions of the sulfur atom.

Few results are available for the radical anions of sulfoxides and little can be said about these species from a theoretical point of view. The EPR results for the radicals formed from sulfones have only been explained qualitatively and the available calculation procedures do not allow us to go much further. Furthermore, in many cases experimental data are either lacking or inconclusive. It is well established, however, that sulfone interactions with aromatic systems are large in many cases, and the effect of d orbitals seems to be at least a contributing factor, if not the main contribution to these interactions. With the presently available theoretical approaches and the experimental results on sulfones which are at hand it is not possible to unequivocally separate p and d orbital effects, and it seems to us that arguments in the current literature which attempt such separations must be considered with a reasonable measure of skepticism.

We should point out that there has been no attempt to evaluate the effect of the sulfone dipole on the π structure of sulfone-containing aromatic systems. This dipole could make the carbon to which the sulfone group is attached much more electronegative than the other carbons in the system and could affect the π structure in a manner similar to that which would be observed for conjugation through the sulfone residue.

In our review on radical anions of sulfur-containing aromatic compounds we have tried to present a criticial analysis of the work which has been done and the conclusions drawn from these investigations. We can only hope that we have succeeded at least in part in our effort.

Acknowledgment

Acknowledgment is made to the donors of the Petroleum Research Fund, administered by the American Chemical Society, for partial support of this research.

References

1. E. A. C. Lucken, *J. Chem. Soc.*, **1964** 4240.
2. B. Venkataraman and G. K. Fraenkel, *J. Am. Chem. Soc.*, **77**, 2707 (1955).
3. M. M. Urberg and E. T. Kaiser, unpublished results.
4. D. H. Eargle, Jr. and E. T. Kaiser, presented in part at the *148th Natl. Meeting Am. Chem. Soc., Chicago*, Sept., 1964.
5. J. E. Harriman and A. H. Maki, *J. Chem. Phys.*, **39**, 778 (1963).
6. A. H. Maki and D. H. Geske, *J. Am. Chem. Soc.*, **83**, 1852 (1961).
7. E. T. Strom and G. A. Russell, *J. Am. Chem. Soc.*, **87**, 3326 (1965).
8. A. D. McLachlan, *Mol. Phys.*, **3**, 233 (1960).
9. R. Gerdil and E. A. C. Lucken, *Proc. Chem. Soc.*, **1963**, 144.
10. R. Gerdil and E. A. C. Lucken, *J. Am. Chem. Soc.*, **87**, 213 (1965).
11. D. H. Eargle, Jr. and E. T. Kaiser, *Proc. Chem. Soc.*, **1964**, 22.
12. R. Gerdil and E. A. C. Lucken, *Mol. Phys.*, **9**, 529 (1965).
13. E. T. Kaiser and D. H. Eargle, Jr., *J. Am. Chem. Soc.*, **85**, 1821 (1963).
14. M. M. Urberg and E. T. Kaiser, *J. Am. Chem. Soc.*, **89**, 1937 (1967).
15. N. Hirota, "Electron Spin Resonance Study of Metal Ketyls," Ph.D. Thesis, Washington University (St. Louis) (1963). See also Chapter 2 in this book.
16. G. Vincow, *J. Chem. Phys.*, **37**, 2484 (1962).
17. E. T. Kaiser, M. M. Urberg, and D. H. Eargle, Jr., *J. Am. Chem. Soc.*, **88**, 1037 (1966).
18. E. T. Kaiser and D. H. Eargle, Jr., *J. Phys. Chem.*, **69**, 2108 (1965).
19. E. T. Kaiser and D. H. Eargle, Jr., *J. Chem. Phys.*, **39**, 1353 (1963).
20. A. Carrington, H. C. Longuet-Higgins, and P. F. Todd, *Mol. Phys.*, **8**, 45 (1964).
21. H. Eyring, J. Walter, and G. E. Kimball, *Quantum Chemistry*, Wiley, New York, 1944, p. 384.
22. V. Schomacher and L. Pauling, *J. Am. Chem. Soc.*, **61**, 1769 (1939).
23. H. C. Longuet-Higgins, *Trans. Faraday Soc.*, **45**, 173 (1949).
24. G. W. Wheland, *Resonance in Organic Chemistry*, Wiley, New York, 1955.
25. H. P. Koch and W. E. Moffitt, *Trans. Faraday Soc.*, **47**, 7 (1951).
26. W. E. Moffitt, *Proc. Roy. Soc. (London)*, Ser. A, **200**, 409 (1950).
27. "Atomic Energy Levels as Derived from the Analysis of Optical Spectra," Vol. 1, *Nat. Bur. Std.* **467**, 181 (1949).
28. G. L. Bendazzoli and C. Zauli, *J. Chem. Soc.*, **1965**, 6827.

CHAPTER 9

Ionic Processes in γ-Irradiated
Organic Solids at −196°

WILLIAM H. HAMILL*

*Department of Chemistry and the Radiation Laboratory,†
University of Notre Dame, Notre Dame, Indiana*

* In collaboration with P. S. Rao, J. R. Nash, J. P. Guarino, M. R. Ronayne, M. Kondo, J. B. Gallivan, D. W. Skelly, E. P. Bertin, and T. Shida, in approximate chronological order.

† The Radiation Laboratory of the University of Notre Dame is operated under contract with the U.S. Atomic Energy Commission. This is AEC document COO-38-481.

I. INTRODUCTION

A commonly observed effect of high energy radiation is the coloration of solids, including ionic crystals and organic glassy solids. The former have been intensively studied, and with considerable success, by both optical and EPR spectroscopy. Systems of the latter type were formerly examined principally by EPR and many neutral radicals have been identified, but there has been little systematic development. In particular, radical ions were observed only rarely and rather accidentally.

The possibility of systematically developing an experimental investigation of ionic color centers in organic solids following exposure to high energy irradiation was suggested by the studies of Lewis and associates (1,2) on photoionization. As an example, a dilute solution of N,N,N',N'-tetramethyl-p-phenylene diamine (TMPD) in ether–isopentane–alcohol glass at $-183°$ was exposed to the light of a mercury arc. The absorption spectrum of the sample then agreed with that of TMPD$^+$, Wurster's Blue, prepared by chemical oxidation. The solvent-trapped electron spectrum was first observed by Linschitz et al. (3) by photoionization of organic molecules in an appropriate glass and was established by comparison with a glassed solution of lithium in the same solvent mixture, both at $-195°$. These authors also identified delayed luminescence, which is induced by warming glassy solutions of aromatic amines or other easily oxidized solutes, with phosphorescence from an excited state produced by ion–electron recombination.

These techniques were deficient in one critical respect since they did not provide a test reagent for the "free" electron. An electron trap which generates an identifiable color center would provide a test. Fortunately, a number of appropriate reagents are well known, such as biphenyl and other aromatic hydrocarbons. They have distinctive spectra and large extinction coefficients and their anions are easily prepared in ether solution by reduction with alkali metals.

It is to be expected that the variety of phenomena relating to ions and secondary electrons in organic solids exposed to high energy radiation, and therefore to electron impact, will exceed those accessible to UV excitation. The possibilities are indicated appropriately, but only in part, by electron impact phenomena in the mass spectrometer: simple and dissociative ionization, electronic excitation of ions, simple and dissociative electron attachment, charge transfer, and proton transfer. An important difference in the two modes of excitation depends upon the localization of positive charge by near-ultraviolet excitation of an isolated molecule with low lying states of the radical ion. Thus, TMPD$^+$ cannot extract an electron from MTHF and the positive charge (hole) is bound. By contrast, high energy deposition is practically random and involves the matrix primarily, with the possibility that the positively charged hole may migrate and be transferred to a minor component of somewhat lower ionization potential (trapped hole).

Reagents producing authentic cations with low ionization potentials, distinctive spectra, and known extinction coefficients are required to test for the occurrence of this phenomenon and for related effects. Several aromatic amines have been thoroughly studied and meet these requirements (1–4). Some of these amines, TMPD in particular, allow comparison of the behavior of photoelectrons to electrons released by high energy radiation.

II. EXPERIMENTAL PROCEDURES

In all instances to be considered, only ^{60}Co γ rays were used for high energy irradiation. Except studies with CCl_4 or *sec-* and *n*-C_4H_9Cl matrices, all samples were prepared under vacuum since O_2, even at rather small concentrations, traps electrons effectively. This precaution is unimportant when only cations are to be examined.

Conventional 1 cm $\times$ 1 cm cells commonly used for spectrophotometry are too fragile to survive formation of an organic glass. High purity silica cells made from 1 cm $\times$ 1 cm drawn tubing with rounded corners, provided with a graded seal to Pyrex, are satisfactory. When examination below ~ 310 mμ is not required, standard square cross section drawn Pyrex tubing is adequate. Filled cells were sealed, plunged into liquid nitrogen, γ-irradiated, then transferred to a custom-made, fused silica dewar provided with windows and filled with liquid nitrogen filtered through a common towel. Most color centers are light-sensitive and the quantum yield for optical bleaching may approach unity. Consequently, γ-irradiated samples must be protected from light (including near-infrared).

The spectrophotometer light beam must be monochromatized before entering the sample and, even so, measurable bleaching occurs during prolonged exposure. The Cary Model 14R spectrophotometer meets this requirement, but the model 14 does not. Except the earliest work at the University of Notre Dame, all spectrophotometric measurements have been made using the Model 14R instrument, to which related experimental procedures refer. The Beckman Model DK-2 instrument has also been used (5). Since measurements are relative to air, the spectrum of the sample was always scanned prior to irradiation and differences are reported.

Unless the cell compartment can be flushed with dry gas, the dewar flask must be provided with a windowed container to prevent condensation of atmospheric moisture on the outer dewar windows. If the container is closed and vented (to exclude H_2O and CO_2) the nitrogen will not become turbid and deposition of frost on the cell and dewar walls is avoided. Dissolving of O_2 is also avoided, improving constancy of temperature. Nitrogen bubbles in the light path are troublesome. They are most easily prevented by inserting a small copper tube, pinched nearly closed, to the bottom of the liquid nitrogen and pumping. After several minutes the pumping may be stopped since the bubble nucleation sites lose their effectiveness. Simple, useful equipment appears in Figure 1.

Mixed solvents which form crack-free "glasses" (arbitrarily so called) were used for the early work at low temperature, but single-component matrices (excepting solutes) are often preferred, particularly when hole migration is being studied. Cracked organic glasses can be tolerated and

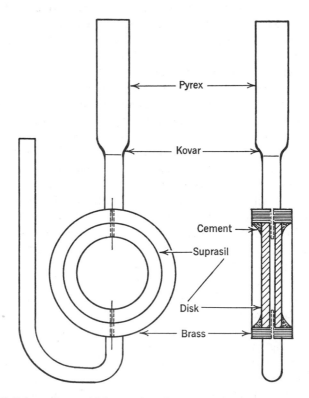

Fig. 1. Cell for ~1 mm thick samples; the annular body and filling tube may be constructed of stainless steel. The upper tubulation should be of Kovar if connection to Pyrex is required. Polished Suprasil flat windows can be secured with Dow-Corning Silastic 731 cement.

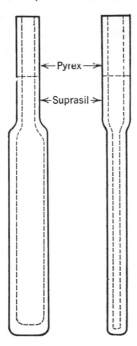

Fig. 2. Thin, flat Suprasil cells with graded seal to Pyrex are suitable for poly-crystalline samples, which must be maintained under vacuum.

thus greatly extend the choice of one-component matrices. This is highly desirable since solubility in a solid matrix at low temperature is often limited. Suitable glassy matrices at −196° are provided by tetrahydro-2-methylfuran (MTHF), triethylamine (TEA), 3-methylpentane (3MP), 2-methyl-1-pentene (2MP-1), and n-butyl chloride (BuCl). (These abbreviations are collected for convenient reference, see p. 414.)   The choice of matrix depends critically upon the phenomenon to be examined. Thus, holes migrate in 3MP, but not in MTHF, and electrons migrate in 3MP and in MTHF, but not in BuCl. Other potentially useful glassing solvents can sometimes be inferred from handbooks when melting points of compounds are unlisted. Frequently solvents will glass in 1 mm thick cells which crystallize in 1 cm × 1 cm cells. Solvent mixtures are chosen particularly with reference to trapping electrons, holes or H atoms. Thus, 2% 2MP-1 in 3MP forms a desirable glass which conducts electrons, but traps holes and H atoms. Even when neutral radical species are not of primary interest they may generate color centers which interfere by spectral overlap or simply confuse by resisting identification. The purification of solvents evidently depends upon similar considerations and the identification of solute anions at 10^{-5} mole fraction of solute and a dose of $\sim 10^{18}$ eV g^{-1} demonstrates the sensitivity of γ-irradiated glasses to additives, whether intentional or unintentional. The freeze–pump–thaw cycle is altogether inappropriate for glassing liquids and removal of air

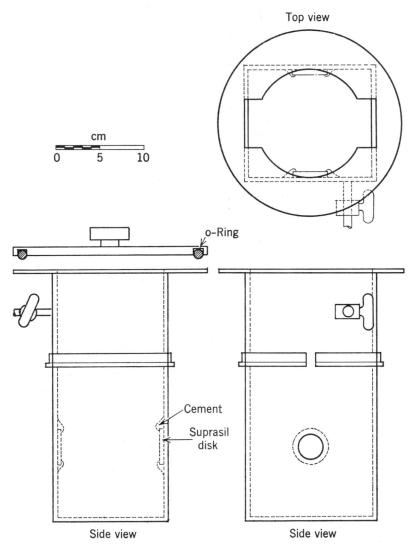

Fig. 3. Housing for an optical dewar flask used in the Cary Model 14R spectrophotometer, which can be partially evacuated to maintain temperatures somewhat below $-196°$.

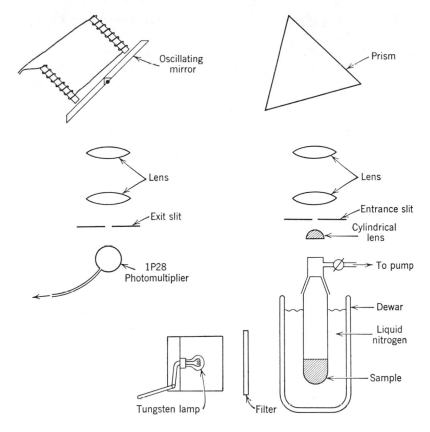

Fig. 4. Simple, rapid scanning spectrophotometer.

(especially CO_2) or recovery of gaseous radiation products, is accomplished much more efficiently by simple refluxing under vacuum.

Polycrystalline matrices are not excluded from consideration and carbon tetrachloride has proved to be quite useful and interesting. Such matrices should be finely crystalline and cell thickness decreased to ~ 1 mm. Since light is strongly scattered, a stronger lamp is very desirable and the effective length of the light path through the matrix must be established with an appropriate colored solute. "Concentrations" are meaningless unless the additives dissolve and solubility can be inferred from changes in optical density (OD) of an appropriate radiation-produced color center with concentration of additive. Suitable cells are shown in Figure 2.

When cations are to be observed and exclusion of air is unnecessary, simple thin cells with polished, high purity silica windows cemented (e.g., with Dow-Corning Silastic 731) to a metal frame are convenient. Examples are shown in Figure 3.

Optical excitation of color centers in γ-irradiated glasses may induce migration of electrons and holes leading to their transfer between sites of the same or different types and to charge recombination. The mono-chromatized beam of the spectrophotometer, with the high intensity lamp, was used for measuring quantum yields of bleaching and also for inducing recombination luminescence. Otherwise, optical excitation of color centers was provided by the 100-W tungsten ("IR-2") lamp of the spectro-photometer, about 25 cm from the cell. Appropriate Corning filters were interposed by removing the lid of the lamp-detector compartment. This practice cannot be recommended, however, and it is much better to provide a sliding carrier for the filter affixed to the dewar housing.

Recombination luminescence spectra were presented on an oscilloscope by using the arrangement shown in Figure 4. When total luminescence was

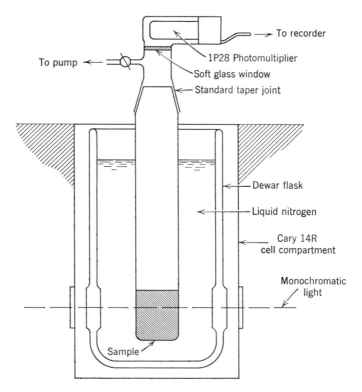

To recorder

To pump

1P28 Photomultiplier

Soft glass window

Standard taper joint

Dewar flask

Liquid nitrogen

Cary 14R
cell compartment

Monochromatic
light

Sample

Fig. 5. Arrangement for measuring luminescence induced by near-infrared
excitation.

to be measured, the cap was removed from the evacuated, irradiated sample and replaced by a head fitted with a 1P28 photomultiplier and again evacuated while the sample was kept at $-196°$, as in Figure 5.

The ^{60}Co-irradiation dose rates were $\sim 10^{17}$ eV g^{-1} min^{-1} for early stages of the work. Subsequently larger sources were used at 2.7×10^{18} or 1.5×10^{18} eV g^{-1} min^{-1}. The differences may be significant only when the rate of spontaneous decay of the color center is appreciable, as for the solvent-trapped electron in 3MP.

III. ELECTRONS AND ANIONS

The first studies of γ-irradiated organic glasses emphasized solute anions and (e^{-}), the solvent-trapped electron (6–8). Both naphthalene and biphenyl, ϕ_2, were reduced by Na-K in MTHF and the anion spectra were measured in glassy solutions at $-196°$. They were similar to spectra of the same samples at $\sim 20°$, but sharper. For $C_{10}H_8^-$, $\epsilon(325 \text{ m}\mu) = 3.0 \times 10^4$ and for ϕ_2^-, $\epsilon(410 \text{ m}\mu) = 3.7 \times 10^4$ liter mole^{-1} cm^{-1}, both at $-196°$. Substantially identical spectra were observed following γ-irradiation of MTHF glassy solutions of these test aromatic hydrocarbons which contained no alkali metal. The results are summarized in Table I. Because simple molecular orbital theory predicts identical spectra for alternant hydrocarbon radical anions and cations, these results were partly inconclusive. Either or both ionic species could explain the results for the irradiated samples. Parallel experiments with tetracyanoethylene clearly demonstrated anion formation, and therefore electron trapping by solute, in the irradiated glassy solution (Table I). Since the irradiated solutions contain no alkali metal, they are necessarily thermodynamically unstable and the ions disappear upon warming. This applies equally to all such experiments, except for very special cases to be described later.

Solutions of biphenyl or naphthalene in hydrocarbon solvents, or of biphenyl in ethanol, also exhibited spectra following irradiation at $-196°$ which matched those in MTHF (7). The test reagents are therefore apparently useful in any matrix without the necessity of using chemically prepared reference samples for each matrix, which is often impossible.

The yield of solute anion is proportional to absorbed energy (dose) over the useful working range. The yield per unit absorbed energy (represented by G for 100 eV) increases with increasing solute concentration and reaches a well-defined plateau, shown for naphthalene in MTHF in Figure 6 where the limiting $G(C_{10}H_8^-)$ was ~ 2.5 (ions per 100 eV). It must be remembered that this evaluation depends upon the assumption that $\epsilon(C_{10}H_8^-)$ is the same for chemically prepared $Na^+C_{10}H_8^-$, which is ion-paired, and for $C_{10}H_8^-$ in the γ-irradiated sample, where a greater average

TABLE I

Absorption Spectra (λ_{max}, Å) at $-196°$ of Naphthalene, Biphenyl, and Tetracyanoethylene in Methyl Tetrahydrofuran, Ethanol, and Hydrocarbon Solutions Following Chemical Reduction or Gamma Radiation (7)

Methyl tetrahydro-furan, Na-K	Methyl tetrahydro-furan, γ	Hydro-carbon, γ	Ethanol, γ
Naphthalene			
3250	3250	3250	
3700	3700	3700	
4350	4350	4350	
4550	4550	4550	
4650	4650	4650	
7400	7800	7600	
8400	8650		
Biphenyl			
3800	3800	3800	3790
3950	3950	3950	3950
4100	4100	4100	4090
6500	6600	6600	6500
Tetracyanoethylene			
3995	4000		
4100	4100		
4190	4195		
4290	4295		
4395	4395		
4495	4495		
4615	4625		
4720	4730		

charge separation prevails. The marked similarity of the spectra supports the assumption. A parallel series of measurements with ϕ_2 gave the limiting yield $G(\phi_2^-) \simeq 3.1$, also in MTHF.

The matrix serves not only to isolate and stabilize reactive intermediates, but in γ-irradiated systems it is also the principal target and the source of migrating electrons and holes. The reactivity of additive and electron depends, among other things, upon electron mobility and therefore on the matrix. Moreover, the matrix either provides a conducting medium for holes and favors solute cation formation and charge recombination, or it traps holes and thereby protects anions and solvent-trapped electrons

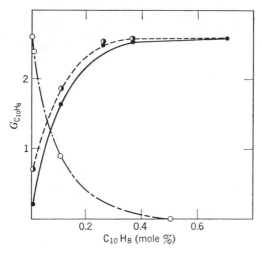

Fig. 6. ●, G(naphthalene anions) vs. mole % naphthalene in tetrahydro-2-methyl-furan; ○, G(naphthalene anions) vs. mole % naphthalene in tetrahydro-2-methyl-furan after bleaching solvated electrons; ◐, G(solvated electrons) vs. mole % naphthalene in tetrahydro-2-methylfuran, all at $-196°$. Dose was $\sim 10^{18}$ eV g^{-1} (7).

[denoted by (e^-)]. Consequently, the observed G(anions) is equal to or less than the primary yield of electrons from the matrix and should be compared with G(ion pairs) of 3–4 for gases.

In the pure γ-irradiated MTHF matrix at $-196°$ there is a very broad nearly structureless absorption band, with $\lambda_{max} \cong 1300$ mμ, which can be photobleached. The intensity of this band decreases with addition of $C_{10}H_8$ or ϕ_2 and there is an approximately complementary increase in $C_{10}H_8^-$ or ϕ_2^- (see Fig. 6). When the residual 1300 mμ band is bleached, the solute anion bands are enhanced, strongly suggesting that the responsible color centers are solvent-trapped electrons. To support this assignment, MTHF with 20% dimethoxyethane (which proved to be necessary) and Na-K was examined at $-196°$ for comparison. An absorption band at $\lambda_{max} = 600$ mμ (half-width ~ 100 mμ) could be photobleached and was replaced by structureless absorption resembling that of the γ-irradiated sample. Just this behavior had been observed by Linschitz et al. (3) in an amine glass. These authors suggested that electrons in chemically prepared glasses are completely solvated, but photodetached electrons are more shallowly trapped in a rigid environment which cannot entirely relax.

Color centers in other γ-irradiated matrices have been assigned to solvent-trapped electrons by this technique, using principally $C_{10}H_8$ or ϕ_2 as test reagents. These matrices include alcohols, amines, alkanes, and alkenes, as well as their binary and ternary mixtures with each other and with ethers (7–9). In each instance the spectrum is changed little, or not at all, by partial polychromatic photobleaching or by spontaneous thermal decay. Similarly, monochromatic light (or tungsten light with a narrow band pass filter) bleaches no window in the (e^-) band which is therefore optically homogeneous, or nearly so.

The band attributed to (e^-) in ethanol is wide, with $\lambda_{max} = 540$ mμ, and can be photobleached. It is diminished by ϕ_2, with an approximately complementary increase in ϕ_2^-. It does not appear when CCl_4 is added. Optical excitation of the 540 mμ band in ethanol glass containing $\sim 0.1\%$ ϕ_2 removes this band, but does not lead to enhanced ϕ_2^- absorption. Evidently, the electron is not released from the trap by optical excitation although the color center is destroyed, suggesting dissociative attachment to form $C_2H_5O^- + H$ (7).

The problem of distinguishing between radical cations and anions of alternant hydrocarbons was resolved within the empirical framework of these techniques. Assuming that organic halides will trap electrons efficiently in these matrices, it follows that the yield of ϕ_2^- or $C_{10}H_8^-$ will be decreased by addition of the halide. In fact, less than 1% CCl_4 completely suppresses the characteristic spectra of these hydrocarbon ions in MTHF or ethanol (7). They are, therefore, necessarily anions. Since no absorption appeared which could possibly be attributed to ϕ_2^+ or $C_{10}H_8^+$, it can be concluded that there is little or no hole migration in these matrices.

IV. POSITIVE HOLES AND CATIONS

Before undertaking the study of the positive hole in γ-irradiated systems (10), it was desirable to reexamine the photochemistry using N,N-dimethyl-p-phenylenediamine (DMPD). In MTHF, DMPD produced DMPD$^+$ and (e^-) at concentrations 2.2 and $0.3 \times 10^{-4} M$. Bleaching (e^-) completely only decreased the cation band by about 10%. (It was shown later that the aromatic amines trap electrons and these entities will be arbitrarily designated DMPD$^-$, etc.) All color disappeared when the sample thawed. When 2% CCl_4 or i-C_3H_7Cl was also present in the glass the yield of DMPD$^+$ doubled and no (e^-) absorption appeared. A green precipitate formed in the thawed sample which dissolved in water to give the spectrum of DMPD$^+$. The precipitate is presumed to be DMPD$^+Cl^-$. In a parallel experiment with 2 mole % benzyl chloride (BzCl) the spectrum of DMPD$^+$ appeared in the glass once more together with that of Bz· ($\lambda_{max} = 320$ mμ), and the green precipitate of DMPD$^+Cl^-$ appeared on warming. The result demonstrates dissociative electron attachment: BzCl + $e^- \rightarrow$ Bz· + Cl$^-$. With 0.1 mole % ϕ_2 the yields of DMPD$^+$ and ϕ_2^- were 4.6 and $2.0 \times 10^{-5} M$.

DMPD is not photoionized in 3MP or in 2MP-1 alone or mixed, but DMPD$^+$ forms when electron acceptors are present. TMPD has been shown to photoionize in 3MP (11) and the yield is enhanced by electron acceptors (10).

In γ-irradiated MTHF (6.5×10^{18} eV g^{-1}) containing 1 mole % DMPD, $G(\text{DMPD}^+) = 0.27$ while $G(e^-) = 2.6$. With 5% CCl$_4$ also present, $G(\text{DMPD}^+) = 0.88$ and a precipitate of DMPD$^+$Cl$^-$ formed upon warming. There is therefore some hole migration, but the range appears to be less than that of the electron in this medium. Due to the very limited solubility of DMPD in 3MP, the latter could not be examined.

It was convenient to use the more soluble triphenylamine (TPA) to examine hole migration in hydrocarbons although no extinction coefficient is available and $G(\text{cation})$ cannot be measured. In parallel γ irradiations with 0.1 mole % TPA and 1 mole % CCl$_4$, OD(TPA$^+$) = 0.16 in MTHF, 0.8 in 3MP and 0.7 in 2MP-1. Correspondingly, OD(TPA$^+$) was greater in mixed methylcyclohexane–isopentane than in ether–pentane–alcohol or in ether–pentane–triethylamine glasses. Methyldiphenylamine and TMPD showed the same effect: for otherwise comparable conditions, the yield of aromatic amine cation is much greater in nonpolar than in polar media using γ irradiation. This contrasts with photoionization, where the contrary is observed. The difference can be attributed to the indirect nature of the former process, viz. hole migration, and the direct electron ejection of the latter. If so, alkanes and alkenes conduct holes while alcohols, ethers, etc. trap them. Mass spectrometry provides a clue: alcohols, ethers, ketones, amines, nitriles, etc., commonly exhibit very efficient proton transfer, being favored by high potential energy of the proton donor cation and high proton affinity of the neutral acceptor (12). Excepting the well-known proton transfer process CH$_4^+$ + CH$_4$ → CH$_5^+$ + CH$_3$, which is driven by the very high ionization potential of CH$_4$, alkanes do not undergo reactions of this type efficiently.

It is to be expected that additives of relatively low ionization potential, such as olefins and aromatics, will act as hole traps in the 3MP matrix. If the radical cation has an optical transition in an accessible spectral range, it can be tentatively identified if addition of an electron acceptor promotes the intensity of the band. Some examples appear in Table II.

Increasing the concentration of CCl$_4$ from 0.12 to 2.5 mole % increased the OD of the 2MP-1 cation band at 680 mμ from 0.25 to only 0.33, indicating the electron trapping efficiency of CCl$_4$, and a new band appeared at 480 mμ. The same band appeared with CCl$_4$ in 3MP without 2MP-1 and is therefore attributable to CCl$_4$, as shown in Table III. Addition of 2MP-1 depressed the 480 mμ band (see Table IV), suggesting competition for the positive hole. Other solutes which have been tentatively

TABLE II
Effect of Carbon Tetrachloride on Cation Absorption Bands in 3MP[a]

Solute	λ_{max}, $m\mu$	OD 0% CCl_4	OD 0.12% CCl_4
1% Cyclohexene	710	0.12	0.38
20% 2MP-1	680	0.05	0.25
1% Cyclopentene	700	0.15	0.50
8% Toluene	1075, 425	0.10, 0.07	0.60, 0.30
2% Benzene	930, 450	0.12, 0.04	0.52, 0.19
2% Isobutylene	400	0.15	0.19

[a] Dose = 6.5×10^{18} eV/g.

TABLE III
480 $m\mu$ Band from Carbon Tetra-chloride in 3MP[a] (9)

Mole % CCl_4	OD 480 $m\mu$
0.00	0.00
0.12	0.29
2.58	0.67
5.16	0.90
11.70	0.98

[a] Dose = 6.5×10^{18} eV/g.

TABLE IV
Effect of 2MP-1 on the 480 $m\mu$ Band from Carbon Tetrachloride in 3MP[a] (9)

Mole % 2MP-1	OD 480 $m\mu$	OD 680 $m\mu$
0[b]	0.67	0.00
4[b]	0.46	0.04
20[b]	0.17	0.43
100[b]	0.00	0.60
0[c]	0.29	0.00
2[c]	0.19	0.08
20[c]	0.00	0.25

[a] Dose = 6.5×10^{18} eV/g.
[b] 2.6 mole % CCl_4.
[c] 0.12 mole % CCl_4.

identified as cation formers also depress the 480 mμ band (Table V), and additives which are expected to trap the hole by proton transfer are even more efficient (Table IV). The 480 mμ band of CCl_4 is quite unrelated to the reaction with electrons since the (e^-) band of 3MP was entirely suppressed in these glasses.

The salient phenomena which are associated with the production of γ-irradiated organic glassy solids have been outlined and working hypotheses proposed. They must be examined now in greater detail.

TABLE V

Effect of Various Additives on the 480 mμ Band of Carbon Tetrachloride[a] in 3MP[b] (9)

%	Additive	OD 480 mμ	%	Additive	OD 480 mμ
	None	0.29	1	Triethylamine	0.05
1	Cyclohexene	0.27	1	MTHF	0.07
2	Isobutylene	0.16	4	MTHF	0.00
8	Toluene	0.00	4	1-Propanol	0.08
2	Benzene	0.00			

[a] 0.12 mole % CCl_4.
[b] Dose $= 6.5 \times 10^{18}$eV/g.

V. ELECTRONS IN 3-METHYLPENTANE

The broad, near-infrared absorption band in γ-irradiated, pure 3MP appears in Figure 7. Because 1–2% cyclopentene, cyclohexene, isobutene, hexene-1, or 2MP-1 considerably enhanced the band it appeared quite possible at first that electrons were trapped by olefins and that impurity in 3MP or olefinic products of γ-irradiation were responsible (9). Since $OD(e^-)$ is quite reproducible for given conditions of irradiation and constant dose and for different batches of 3MP (13), adventitious impurity is not responsible. Radiation debris was eliminated as the source of trapping sites by using photoelectrons from TMPD (13), the two spectra shown in Figure 7 being practically indistinguishable. The spectrum of (e^-) in 3MP is not distinctive since the corresponding color centers in γ-irradiated TEA or 2MP-1 are fairly similar. They are corresponding centers in the sense that when a small concentration of anion-forming solute is present, e.g., ϕ_2, optical excitation of the IR band removes it while OD (ϕ_2^-) increases. Moreover, (e^-) are regenerated by photobleaching ϕ_2^-. As mentioned previously, the (e^-) centers are homogeneous with respect to spectral invariance upon partial bleaching either with tungsten or monochromatic light.

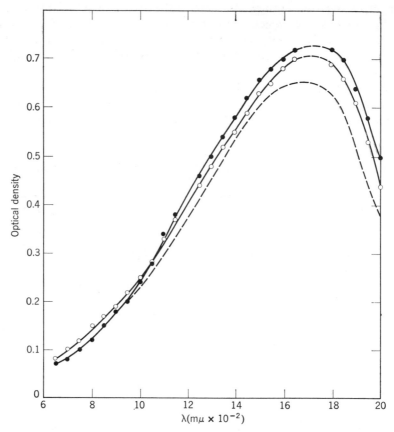

Fig. 7. Spectrum of electrons trapped in 3-methylpentane (3MP) after γ irradiation at 2.3×10^{18} eV ml^{-1}, $\bigcirc$; the normalized optical density after photoionization of $2 \times 10^{-3}\%$ N,N,N',N'-tetramethyl-p-phenylene diamine, $\bullet$; 45 min after γ irradiation of 3MP (4.6×10^{18} eV ml^{-1}), broken curve (13).

The (e^-) center in 3MP gives no resolvable EPR spectrum in the γ-irradiated sample (14), in disagreement with other work (15). It had appeared that photoelectrons from TMPD yielded an EPR spectrum (16), but it has now been established that CO_2^- was responsible (17).*

A. Quantum Yields for Bleaching (18)

When γ-irradiated 3MP (2.7×10^{18} eV ml^{-1}) was bleached at 950 mμ the quantum yield, $\Phi(e^-)$, was initially almost unity. The efficiency

---

*The EPR spectrum of (e^-) in 3MP has been observed by K. Tsuji, H. Yoshida, and K. Hayashi, *J. Chem. Phys.*, **46**, 810 (1967).

diminished steadily as bleaching progressed until it approached zero with
∼ 10% of the initial (e^-) remaining, as shown in Figure 8.

The initial $OD(e^-)$ at 950 mμ was 0.3, which represents a compromise
between uniformity of light absorption along a 1-cm path and reliability
for decrements of $OD(e^-)$ when a large fraction of (e^-) has been bleached.
Since the extinction coefficient $\epsilon(e^-)$ is three times as great as 1600 mμ as
at 950 mμ, the longer wavelength was used for analysis. The initial value
of $\Phi(e^-)$ was independent of dose from 0.7 to 2.7 × 10^{18} eV ml^{-1}.

At 1300 and 1600 mμ, $\Phi(e^-)$ was appreciably smaller, approximating
0.4 initially. At $\lambda > 1700$ mμ, using a glowbar light source and $\frac{1}{16}$ in
germanium filter and taking the effective $\lambda = 1900$ mμ, $\Phi(e^-) \cong 0.01$
which cannot be distinguished from zero.

The diminishing $\Phi(e^-)$ with progressive bleaching is not reminiscent
of photochemistry, but there is still a classical photochemical question
to be put: What is the efficiency of the primary act? Are electrons not
being efficiently detached after prolonged bleaching, perhaps because
there is a distribution of trap depths? Or are they being more efficiently
retrapped? The photochemical analog suggests using an efficient scavenger
for the reactive intermediate, in this instance the "free" electron. When
0.02 or 0.05 mole % ϕ_2 was added, $\Phi(e^-)$ approached unity and remained

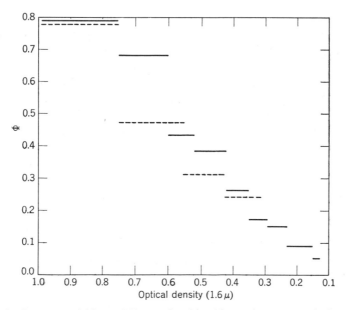

Fig. 8. Quantum yields at 950 mμ for bleaching solvent-trapped electrons in
γ-irradiated 3MP at −196° vs. the extent of bleaching for two series of measurements
(2.7 × 10^{18} eV ml^{-1}) (18).

high throughout, as shown in Table VI. It must be concluded that $\Phi(e^-) \simeq 1$ for the primary act.

TABLE VI

Relative Quantum Yield of Bleaching Solvent-
Trapped Electrons at 1550 mμ in γ-Irradiated 3MP
with Added Biphenyl at $-196°$ (18)

Mole % biphenyl	Φ_{rel}	Range OD(e^-) 1550 mμ
0.02[a]	1.0	0.29–0.15
0.02	1.1	0.15–0.08
0.02	0.91	0.08–0.04
0.02	0.76	0.04–0.01
0.05[b]	1.0	0.16–0.06
0.05	0.81	0.06–0.03
0.05	0.87	0.03–0.01

[a] 2.7×10^{18} eV/ml.
[b] 5.3×10^{18} eV/ml.

The result just described made it possible to reexamine with much greater sensitivity the quantum yield of bleaching at $\lambda > 1700$ mμ, since the point is of some importance. Using the same experimental conditions which had been employed previously with pure 3MP, but adding 0.02 mole % ϕ_2 in order to measure the primary quantum yield, the value $\Phi(e^-) \simeq 0.014$ was again indistinguishable from zero. This result appears to establish the minimum trap depth of (e^-) in 3MP as 0.7 eV.

Either electrons are retrapped more efficiently as bleaching progresses, or they combine with holes less efficiently. The latter interpretation appears to be self-evident within the framework of conventional kinetics but is contrary to the Samuel-Magee theory (19). The theory, though devised for water, must apply equally in its essentials to an amorphous, solid, paraffinic hydrocarbon. Low energy electrons in gases are known to undergo slightly inelastic collisions with large cross sections. The electrons of interest necessarily reach energies below the lowest electronic state of any major component of the system almost immediately after leaving the parent ion (20). To achieve even 20 Å separation by a random walk, and against the coulombic field, the electron experiences hundreds of scattering collisions, each removing several percent of the kinetic energy. If the critical coulombic escape radius is determined by kT, the preceding considerations indicate not only that the electron never escapes, but that it reaches a turning point at ~ 20 Å (19).

Quite apart from any details of the theory, or the values of scattering cross section, and the energy loss parameter to be adopted, and bearing in mind the main features of the experimental situation—particularly the separation of charge in a dense, low-dielectric medium—it is evident that the fundamental physical situation is complex. The theory, if logically extended, does, however, require the electron to recombine with its parent ion. Such an associated ion pair would recombine with a comparatively high quantum yield, and the large initial $\Phi(e^-)$ observed may be due to a population of such ion pairs. If associated ion pairs alone were involved, then since the quantum yield for the primary process was shown to be near unity, the quantum yield for recombination should not diminish with progressive bleaching, according to this model. The observed decrease suggests instead a randomness of holes and electrons, with trapping by solvent in competition with recombination. As the number of holes per unit volume decreases, recombination becomes less efficient, trapping by the matrix becomes more probable and $\Phi(e^-)$ diminishes. The data suggest that there are two populations of (e^-), some with small charge separation and large values of $\Phi(e^-)$, others with much larger charge separation and small $\Phi(e^-)$. The first group would account for the large initial value of $\Phi(e^-)$ which was independent of dose.

In pure 3MP the photoejected electron either combines with the hole, h, or is trapped by the solvent in an interstitial cavity or vacancy, v. The simplest possible assumption is that the probability of either event depends only upon the numbers of sites per unit volume, N, and the cross sections, σ. Then:

$$\Phi = \sigma_h N_h / (\sigma_h N_h + \sigma_v N_v) \tag{1a}$$

Since the concentrations of h and (e^-) are equal and Φ is proportional to $\Delta OD(e^-)$, equation 1a is not applicable to the data of Figure 8 where $\Phi(e^-)$ is proportional to $OD(e^-)$. The preceding description is also clearly deficient in failing to provide any possibility of accounting for the dependence of $\Phi(e^-)$ on the wavelength. In a merely qualitative way it will be tentatively assumed that the photoejected electron is not retrapped principally by preexisting defects in the matrix, but that it can be trapped at ordinary sites whenever it reaches a suitable energy. Then N_v has no meaning and the length of track l depends only upon the initial energy of the electron. Clearly, the probability of recombination, viz. $\Phi(e^-)$, depends on the length of track and therefore on λ (18). Also, the probability that an ejected electron encounters a hole becomes simply:

$$\Phi = \sigma_h l N_h \tag{1b}$$

as observed.

B. Spontaneous Decay of Solvent-Trapped Electrons

The (e^-) band in 3MP gradually decays even when γ-irradiated samples are carefully shielded from light. The effect was overlooked when weak ^{60}Co sources were used and irradiation times were long.

Since $G(e^-)$ is time-dependent, it is of interest to measure the yield shortly after γ irradiation and this necessitates somewhat different experimental arrangements (see Section II) (18). The time dependence of $OD(e^-)$ during the first few minutes after irradiation appears in Figure 9. It does not conform either to simple first- or second-order rate laws. Taking $\epsilon(e^-) = 3.0 \times 10^4$ liter mole^{-1} cm^{-1} at 1600 mμ (see Section VII), $G(e^-) = 0.77$ at 18 sec. The matrix does not trap electrons efficiently since the expected yield of ion pairs per 100 eV is expected to be three or more. This result cannot be interpreted with confidence on this basis alone because it must depend also upon the efficiency of trapping holes (see Section IX).

Three samples of pure 3MP were γ-irradiated (2.7×10^{18} eV ml^{-1}) to an initial $OD(e^-) \simeq 0.87$. Two of these were photobleached until OD's reached 0.52 and 0.42, while the third was not exposed. The results in Figure 10 show that all three samples have the same rate of spontaneous decay of (e^-) when the zero time of the partially bleached samples is arbitrarily adjusted by fitting the first point (18). It can be assumed that whatever distribution of (e^-) develops spontaneously, either with respect to trap depth or charge separation, photodetachment of all electrons of the freshly γ-irradiated sample can lead to the same distribution. The

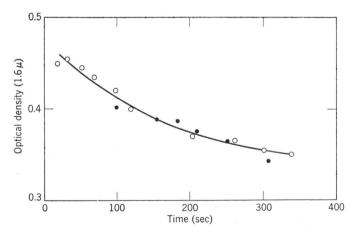

Fig. 9. Decay of trapped electron absorption in 3MP at $-196°$: ●, calibrating measurements with ^{60}Co irradiation, using Cary spectrophotometer; ○, bremsstrahlung irradiation and abridged spectrophotometer (13).

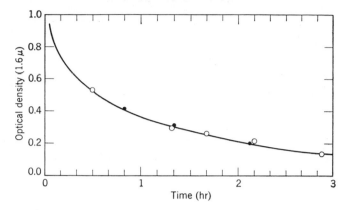

Fig. 10. Solvent-trapped electron decay in γ-irradiated 3MP at −196° (2.7 × 10¹⁸ eV ml⁻¹): curve, continuous dark decay; initial photobleaching to OD = 0.52 (○) and 0.42 (●) followed by dark decay. Zero time for bleached samples is arbitrary (18).

evidence does not support the notion that there is a considerable variation in trap depth, since this would necessarily lead to steadily increasing average trap depth by spontaneous decay and continually increasing half-lives for decay. A partially photobleached sample would then contain mostly (e^-) in shallow traps. The simplest assumption is that solvent-trapped electrons differ from each other only by their local electric fields and either aging or optical excitation rather selectively removes electrons in high fields (18).

The rate of spontaneous decay of (e^-) in 3MP was measured for samples differing 20-fold in γ-irradiation dose (from 10^{18} to 2×10^{19} eV ml⁻¹) during 1–10 hr. To test for the effect of radiolytic products, two samples were irradiated to 2.3×10^{19} eV ml⁻¹, photobleached without warming, and reirradiated to 2.3×10^{18} eV ml⁻¹. The OD(e^-) for one sample after 1 hr decay and for the other after 5 hr decay was practically unaffected by the preliminary treatment when compared with other samples which received a single irradiation to 2.3×10^{18} eV ml⁻¹. It was also demonstrated that the measured rate of decay was not significantly affected by brief exposure of samples to the monochromatic analytical light beam of the spectrophotometer (13).

The normalized (e^-) decay curves for times not exceeding 1 hr, shown in Figure 11, are substantially the same at all doses. The subsequent decay is evidently dose-dependent.

The initial decay $(t < 1$ hr) is not exponential, but it is first-order in the sense that the probability of recombination of an ion pair in unit time is independent of the density of ion pairs. These electrons combine only with

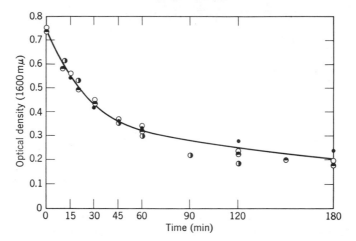

Fig. 11. Spontaneous dark decay of trapped electrons in γ-irradiated 3 methyl-pentane at $-196°$. The data have been normalized by dividing the observed optical densities (OD) by the irradiation time in minutes (2.3×10^{18} eV ml^{-1} min^{-1}) ●, 0.5 min; ○, 1 min; ◐, 2 min; ◑, 10 min. The OD's for the 10-min irradiation were measured at 800 mμ and converted to 1600 mμ by multiplying by $\epsilon_{1600}/\epsilon_{800}$ (13). Normalization at zero time required dividing by 5.95 rather than by 10 and this factor was employed for all other points at that dose.

parent positive ions (associated ion pairs) and include roughly one-half of the (e^-) present at ~ 3 min after irradiation at all doses, or ~ 0.3 per 100 eV.

The remaining one-half of (e^-) which have dose-dependent lifetimes must conform to a higher order rate law. Quite empirically the data are presented in terms of simple second-order decay in Figure 12. In terms of concentrations of electrons and holes, N_e and N_h, this would be:

$$\frac{dN_e}{dt} = k_2 N_e N_h = k_2 N_e^2 \tag{2}$$

The purely formal agreement of the data with this description is confined to linearity since the slopes for plots of $1/\mathrm{OD}(e^-)$ vs. t in Figure 12 decrease to about one-third with a 20-fold increase in dose. In terms of a diffusion-controlled recombination of ions in a low dielectric medium, the expected rate law is second-order, but the rate constant depends exponentially on the coulombic energy (21). It is quite impossible to assess the effect of ionic strength (or dose) and the linearity of $1/\mathrm{OD}(e^-)$ vs. t alone does not establish the random distribution of holes and electrons in the matrix. At $t = 1$ hr the calculated average ion-pair separation, assuming uniform distribution, is 170–350 Å while the coulombic escape radius is

$\sim 10^3$ Å for a dielectric constant of 2.5. To be randomized, therefore, ion pair separation need not exceed 10^3 Å, but only 170–350 Å. Even this value cannot now be reconciled with the Samuel-Magee theory. The results for spontaneous and photoinduced decay of (e^-), described by equations 1a and 2, are entirely compatible. For both conditions the probability that one electron disappears is proportional to N_h and therefore to N_e.

The preceding considerations have implicitly assigned the significant role exclusively to the migrating electron while ignoring the hole. Phenomena relating to the latter will be considered in detail later (see Section IX) but it will be assumed now without proof that small additions of 2MP-1 to 3MP exert only one effect—to trap the hole. Empirically, the optimum effect occurs at 2% 2MP-1 on the basis of a maximized $OD(e^-)$. The decay of such a sample, shown in Figure 13, is linear in $1/OD(e^-)$ vs. t from 3 min to 2 hr (the last observation). Unlike the results for pure 3MP in Figure 11, there is no preliminary, rapid, first-order decay. Also, the initial yield for trapped electrons which undergo second-order decay is now 0.91, which exceeds the combined yields of all (e^-) in pure 3MP. In

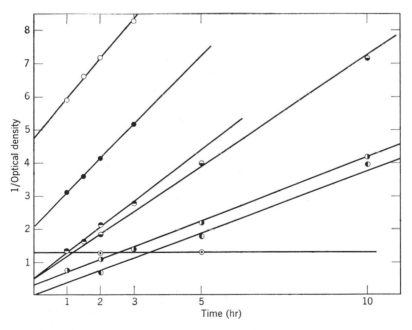

Fig. 12. Empirical second-order spontaneous decay of trapped electrons in γ-irradiated 3MP at −196° at doses $= n \times 2.3 \times 10^{18}$ eV ml^{-1} where n is 0.5, 1, 2, 2.5, 5, and 10 from top to bottom. One sample (⊙) irradiated to 5.8×10^{18} eV ml^{-1}, held 1 hr at −196°, then held at −210° (13).

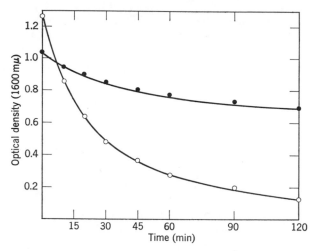

Fig. 13. Spontaneous decay of trapped electrons in γ-irradiated 3-methylpentane containing $\bigcirc$, 0.01% $N,N,N'N'$-tetramethyl-p-phenylene diamine at 6.9×10^{18} eV ml^{-1}; $\bullet$, 2% 2-methylpentene-1 at 2.3×10^{18} eV ml^{-1} (13).

pure 3MP the holes must migrate before some are trapped by the matrix and others recombine with (e^-). Those (e^-) which exhibited first-order decay must have been generated from some of those ion pairs which proved to be second-order type when extensive hole migration was prevented. It appears that only electrons and holes which are initially randomized can be trapped and that over two-thirds of the ion pairs formed do not survive. Both holes and electrons migrate, and the associated ion pair is the metastable intermediate between randomization and recombination.

This interpretation suggests an improved kinetic description. Introducing N_p and N_n for concentrations of associated pairs and neutral products of recombination, and rate constants k_1 and k_2 for the processes,

$$e^- + h \longrightarrow p; k_2$$
$$p \longrightarrow n; k_1$$

we have

$$\frac{dN_n}{dt} = -\frac{dN_e}{dt} = k_1 N_p \tag{3}$$

for ion-pair recombination. If N_e represents all trapped electrons, then $\mathcal{N}_e = N_e - N_p$ is the concentration of randomized electrons and

$$\frac{d\mathcal{N}_e}{dt} = k_2 N_e^2 \tag{4}$$

$$\mathcal{N}_e^{-1} = (N_e - N_p)^{-1} = k_2 t + \text{const} \tag{5}$$

The value of N_p can be obtained, in principle, from equation 3, requiring only OD(e^-) and k_1. The data of Figure 11 provide a guide for trial values of k_1, and equation 5 can be fitted to the decay of (e^-) about as well as equation 2. There is no basis for choosing between these descriptions simply on the basis of rate law plots.

To speculate about the mechanism of charge separation is not going to generate any understanding of what does occur, but it may help define the problem. For reasons already given, let it be assumed that the appreciable charge separation required for randomization of ion pairs cannot be achieved in a single, energetic, primary act. Then the only alternative assumption is that electrons migrate slowly, conserving energy. The initial kinetic energy of the electron would suffice to allow it to occupy a small preexisting interstitial cavity, and trapping would have to occur before inelastic collisions had dissipated much of the initial energy. Since the electron can escape from any trap which it can penetrate unless kinetic energy is removed, excitation of lattice vibrations through transient negative-ion formation is postulated. The primitive (e^-) would be unstable both with respect to charge recombination and to "digging its own hole." If the latter occurs to any appreciable degree the electron will be unable to tunnel to new cavities or vacancies, since they will be smaller. If (e^-) diffuses, accumulating free volume, its kinetic energy could be used to overcome the coulombic force of the parent positive hole. There is no evident reason why diffusion would increase charge separation even when it is allowed by the available energy.

The difficulties which follow from the assumption that electron scattering is somewhat inelastic, with large cross sections, are so serious that its validity must be doubted. If the matrix does not behave simply as a dense gas with respect to electron scattering, and if cross sections and inelastic losses are both considerably smaller for the matrix than for the gas, then the difficulty vanishes and large charge separation becomes normal. This opinion has been advanced by Platzman (20).

VI. THE TRAPPED ELECTRON IN METHYLTETRAHYDROFURAN

A. The Optical Absorption and EPR Spectra of (e^-)

Electrons are trapped more efficiently in MTHF than in 3MP and are less susceptible to photobleaching and to spontaneous decay. The optical absorption, shown in Figure 14, extends from ~ 2000 mμ into the near-ultraviolet. Since there is a nearly complementary dependence between the OD's of (e^-) and solute anion, it can be tentatively assumed that $G(e^-)$ is equal to the limiting yield of an authentic solute anion (e.g., naphthalene, shown in Fig. 6) and thus establish approximate values of

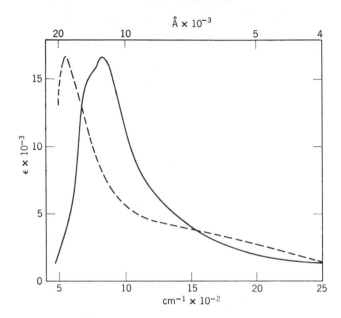

Fig. 14. Extinction coefficient vs. wave number for the solvent-trapped electron band in MTHF (————) and in 2MP-1 (— — —) (9).

$\epsilon(e^-)$. In fact, since OD(anion) increased somewhat after OD(e^-) fell to zero, the estimate of $G(e^-)$ is high and $\epsilon(e^-)$ low. On this basis, using the relation $f = 4.3 \times 10^9 \times \int \epsilon(\bar{v}) \, d\bar{v}$ and Figure 13, the oscillator strength $f(e^-) \cong 0.8$ which suggests from the approximation for $G(e^-)$ that $f(e^-)$ has a value near unity, as expected.

In γ-irradiated MTHF there is an EPR singlet, reported by Salmon (22), which bleaches together with the (e^-) color center. Smith and Pieroni (23) have carefully examined this singlet (which is only 4.5 G wide) and have assigned it to the trapped electron. They concluded that the spin density of the trapped electron at any proton is less than that for an unpaired electron in a free radical and that its distance is greater. Since the trapped electron is comparatively independent of molecular orbitals it can be regarded as an independent entity—the physically trapped electron. It was also concluded that electrons were trapped in environments which had local concentrations of electrons and free radicals which were 11 ± 5 times greater than the overall average. They estimated that (e^-) was 40–50 Å from its parent ion.

The EPR singlet of (e^-) in 3MP could not be detected (14), but considering also the general similarity of other phenomena in both matrices the total evidence strongly suggests that a physically trapped electron is also involved in 3MP.

Smith and Pieroni (24) have extended their EPR studies to establish $G(e^-)$ in MTHF at about 2.6. With increasing concentrations of biphenyl the EPR spectrum of ϕ_2^- appears and increases relative to that for (e^-), the combined yields remaining constant with an average $G(e^- + \phi_2^-) =$ 2.5. Only ϕ_2^- was detected at 0.2 and 0.39 mole % ϕ_2, in complete agreement with measurements based on optical spectra. Since $G(e^-) = G(\phi_2^-)_{max} = 3.0$ from optical spectra was known to be high, it appears better to adopt the lower value which gives $f \cong 0.9$.

B. The Decay and Photobleaching of (e^-)

The chemically prepared, solvated electron cannot be removed in a rigid medium by photobleaching because it is thermodynamically stable with respect to recombination. In the same matrix, (e^-) produced by ionizing radiation may be solvated to the same degree and is probably in a much lower electric field, but cannot form a stable associated ion pair. Since the oscillator strength of (e^-) will probably approach unity, γ-irradiated organic solids can be expected to exhibit color centers (provided easily reducible halides, etc. are absent) and to be susceptible to efficient photobleaching. The large number of color centers observed by Alger, Anderson, and Webb (25) for alcohols, ethers, esters, and ketones subjected to high energy irradiation at $-196°$ were very probably mostly trapped electrons although they were not identified.

In earlier work (7) the (e^-) band in MTHF appeared to bleach without spectral change. Dyne and Miller (5) have reported a somewhat more rapid decay of the short-wavelength branch which may be related to Salmon's observation (22) that the absorption for $\lambda < 400$ mμ correlates with a seven-line EPR spectrum. The kinetics of (e^-) decay are neither first- nor second-order. For different concentrations of electrons the rate curves are superimposable and about half of the electrons decay much more slowly than the others (23). Since the hole migrates very little in MTHF it might have been expected, by analogy with 3MP containing 2% 2MP-1, that the entire decay would be second-order.

Dyne and Miller (5) found that $\Phi(e^-)$ in γ-irradiated MTHF at $-196°$ decreased progressively with the extent of bleaching until, at $\sim 50\%$ bleaching, the efficiency was ~ 0.05 as great as initially shown in Figure 15. Those (e^-) which bleached easily were identified with the high energy branch of the optical band and the authors concluded that this simple distribution accounts for the linear decrease of $\Phi(e^-)$ with the fraction of (e^-) bleached.

This appears to provide a rather approximate description of Figure 15,

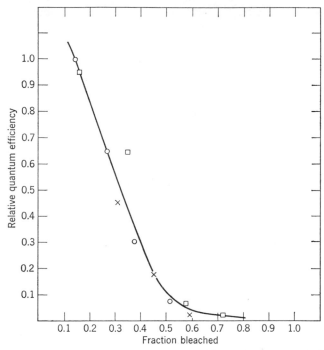

Fig. 15. Relative quantum efficiency for bleaching solvent-trapped electrons in MTHF at $-196°$; dose rate 3.7×10^{17} eV min^{-1} ml^{-1}. Irradiation times (○) 4, (×) 2, and (□) 1 min (5).

but can be amplified. Let the two populations of (e^-), N_1 and N_2 have quantum yields Φ_1 and Φ_2. Then the apparent yield Φ_a is:

$$\Phi_a = (N_1\Phi_1 + N_2\Phi_2)/(N_1 + N_2)$$

Since $\Phi_1 \gg \Phi_2$, the model requires Φ_a to be proportional to the fraction of electrons remaining which belong to the population N_1. Since Φ_a increases with decreasing λ (Fig. 16), it may be assumed again that the path of the photoejected electron is dependent upon the energy. Ignoring the term in Φ_2 and applying equation 16 again gives $\Phi_a = \sigma_h l/N_h = \sigma_h l/(N_1 + N_2)$, which agrees with Figure 15.

Initial values of $\Phi(e^-)$ depend upon the wavelength, shown in Figure 16, and this also seems to correlate with the (e^-) spectrum. The band with $\lambda_{max} = 1200$ mμ was interpreted as a bound state of excited (e^-) at ~ 1 eV, and the blue band as the continuum. On this basis, the ionization potential of (e^-) is ~ 1.4 eV. For comparison, Jortner has calculated for electrons in ammonia ~ 0.8 eV for the excited state and ~ 2.0 eV for the continuum (26).

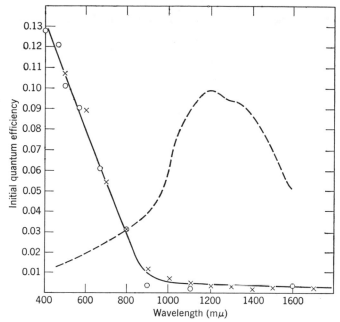

Fig. 16. Quantum efficiency for bleaching solvent-trapped electrons in MTHF at −196° as a function of the wavelength of the bleaching light. The trapped-electron absorption band is shown for comparison; ○ absolute and × relative measurements (5).

Fueki (27) has applied Jortner's model to (e^-) in MTHF with the results shown in Table VII where r_0 is cavity radius; W_{1s} is the energy of the electron in the ground state without electronic polarization; S_{1s} is the contribution to the energy of the ground state of the electronic polarization; $E_{1s} = W_{1s} + S_{1s}$; $\bar{r}_{1s}$ is the mean radius of the ground state; the W_i, S_i, E_i, and $\bar{r}_i$ refer to excited states. The $3p$ and $4p$ states are insensitive to r_0. Transition energies $h\nu(1s \rightarrow 2p)$, etc. can be read from the table, e.g., 1.04 eV for $1s \rightarrow 2p$ at $r_0 = 1.5$ Å and 0.87 eV at $r_0 = 2.0$ Å compare with the experimental value $h\nu_{\max} = 0.95$ eV.

In the polaron model of the trapped electron the depth of the trap is given by $(e/4\pi r^2)(1/\epsilon_{\mathrm{op}} - 1/\epsilon_s)$ where $\epsilon_{\mathrm{op}} = 2.0$ and $\epsilon_s = 4.6$ are the optical and static dielectric constants, referring to MTHF. For 3MP this contribution is negligible, although the optical spectra do not differ greatly ($\lambda_{\max} = 1.3$ and 1.6 μ). Until the theoretical description improves, the crude particle-in-a-box model will serve for low dielectrics.

C. The Effect of Biphenyl

The inefficiency of bleaching, even in the 400–800 mμ range, implies either an inefficient primary process or efficient trapping by solvent. At

TABLE VII

Calculated Energy Levels in eV of the Solvent-Trapped Electron in MTHF (27)

$r_0(\text{Å})$	W_{1s}	S_{1s}	E_{1s}	$\bar{r}_{1s}$
1.5	-0.803	-0.891	-1.694	4.05
2.0	-0.720	-0.794	-1.514	4.53
2.5	-0.651	-0.718	-1.369	5.01
3.0	-0.596	-0.658	-1.254	5.46
	W_{2p}	S_{2p}	E_{2p}	F_{2p}
1.5	-0.271	-0.382	-0.653	9.44
2.0	-0.270	-0.377	-0.647	9.54
2.5	-0.267	-0.364	-0.636	9.76
3.0	-0.263	-0.360	-0.623	10.00
	W_{3p}	S_{3p}	E_{3p}	$\bar{r}_{3p}$
	-0.121	-0.154	-0.275	23.4
	W_{4p}	S_{4p}	E_{4p}	$\bar{r}_{4p}$
	-0.068	-0.084	-0.152	43.0

800 mμ $\Phi(e^-)$ was increased linearly from ~ 0.03 to 0.16 by adding up to 0.08 mole % ϕ_2. From the dependence of $G(\phi_2^-)$ vs. % ϕ_2 (similar to Fig. 6) it was assumed that the relative cross sections for an electron to be trapped by solvent (σ_v) or biphenyl (σ_{ϕ_2}) could be deduced from the observed equality of yields $G(e^-) = G(\phi_2^-)$ at 0.04 mole % ϕ_2, or $N_{\phi_2} = 2.9 \times 10^{18}$ molecules cm^{-3}. Letting N_v be the concentration of solvent trapping sites, $N_v\sigma_v = N_{\phi_2}\sigma_{\phi_2}$. Combined with the measured decrease in $G(e^-)$ with dose, amounting to 10% at 2×10^{17} trapped electrons cm^{-3} (24) and attributing the dose dependence to competition between solvent traps and holes for electrons, it would follow that $\sigma_h \cong 3\sigma_{\phi_2}$. This is a remarkably small ratio, considering the strong coulombic effects involved in ion recombination. Finally, if the quantum yield for bleaching solvent-trapped electrons in pure MTHF is approximately proportional to the ratio $N_h\sigma_h/N_v\sigma_v$, then for a dose corresponding to $N_h \cong 2 \times 10^{16}$ cm^{-3}

$$\Phi(e^-) \cong (3 \times 2 \times 10^{16}/2.9 \times 10^{18}) \cong 0.02\Phi°$$

where $\Phi°$ is the quantum yield for the primary act. Assuming that $\Phi° = 1$, the expected $\Phi(e^-) \cong 0.02$, which is less than the observed $\Phi(e^-) \geq 0.03$ for $\lambda < 80$ mμ during the early stages of bleaching. Since the preceding development implies a homogeneous distribution, it was concluded that these electrons correspond to small charge separation. The residual half of the trapped electrons were identified with homogeneously distributed electrons since $\Phi(e^-) \gtrless 0.005$ and the dependence on wavelength attributed to Φ^0.

It would be expected from the preceding conclusions that spontaneous decay of (e^-) in pure MTHF would exhibit an initial rate per unit dose which was independent of dose. The last $\sim 50\%$ of trapped electrons should then disappear at rates which increase with dose, but which are not necessarily second-order. Although the measurements of Smith and Pieroni (23) do not cover as great a range of dose or time as would be desired, they do appear to be independent of dose for $\sim 65\%$ decay.

VII. ELECTRON ATTACHMENT BY BIPHENYL

A. Concentration Dependence in 3-Methylpentane

In γ-irradiated solutions of ϕ_2 in 3MP at $-196°$ the OD(ϕ_2^-) is linear in concentration of ϕ_2 to at least 0.015 mole $\%$ ϕ_2 at 3×10^{18} eV cm^{-3}. The approximate slope, $G(\phi_2^-)/(\text{mole fraction } \phi_2) \cong 2.8 \times 10^3$ per 100 eV. If the yield of ion pairs produced is taken to be 2.6, then the electrons concerned appear to encounter $\sim 10^3$ molecules prior to trapping by solvent or recombination (13). When all solvent-trapped electrons in such glasses have been bleached, $G(\phi_2^-)$ is still larger at low concentrations of biphenyl, as shown in Figure 17. For an initial population of electrons n_i^0 of various

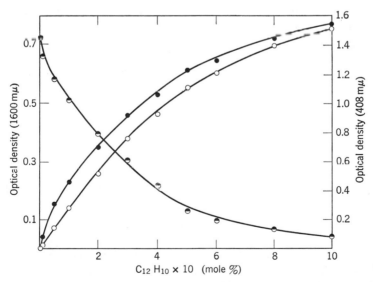

Fig. 17. Yields of solvent-trapped electrons ◖ and biphenyl anions ○ after γ irradiation of biphenyl in 3-methylpentane (dose $= 2.3 \times 10^{18}$ eV ml^{-1}), and yield of biphenyl anions ● after photodetachment of all solvent-trapped electrons (13).

track lengths l_i which can react with solute at concentration N and cross section σ [when all (e^-) have been bleached] it would be expected that the number surviving to recombine would be:

$$n = \sum n_i = \sum n_i^0 \exp\left(-\sigma l_i N\right) \tag{6}$$

At small N,

$$\sum n_i = \sum n_i^0 - \sigma N \sum n_i^0 l_i \tag{7}$$

The probability of attachment would be:

$$\frac{\sum n_i^0 - \sum n_i}{\sum n_i^0} \cong \sigma \bar{l} N \tag{8}$$

where $\bar{l}$ is the mean free path for recombination. Since the upper curve in Figure 17, to which equation 8 applies, shows a steadily decreasing efficiency to form ϕ_2^-, it appears that $\sigma \bar{l}$ is too large for the approximation, at least for some electrons. Thus, at $10^{-2}\%$ ϕ_2, about one-third of electrons bleached from solvent traps produce ϕ_2^- and $\sigma \bar{l} \cong 4 \times 10^{-19} \text{ cm}^{-3}$; if $\sigma = 3 \times 10^{-15} \text{ cm}^2$, $\bar{l} \cong 10^{-4} \text{ cm}$.

The linearity of $G(\phi_2^-)$ with N_{ϕ_2} for unbleached samples can be attributed to shorter l_i imposed by solvent trapping. Electrons having small l_i will form little ϕ_2^- at small concentrations of ϕ_2 and can be ignored. Assume that electrons with large l_i are trapped by solvent fairly efficiently as soon as the kinetic energy reaches a critical value E_1 (cf. Section V-B) and that attachment to form ϕ_2^- is also limited to energy below E_2, with $E_2 > E_1$. (This is supported by optical bleaching of ϕ_2^-.) Then l tends to be small and uniform within the range E_1 to E_2 for all such electrons and equation 8 applies for small N. For this condition, and using the data cited, $\sigma \bar{l} \cong 1.6 \times 10^{-19} \text{ cm}^{-3}$.

If there is simple competition for electrons between ϕ_2 and cavities or vacancies, ignoring holes, then:

$$N_{\phi_2^-}/N_{v^-} = \sigma_{\phi_2} N_{\phi_2}/\sigma_v N_v \tag{9}$$

The data of Figure 17, before bleaching, do not conform to equation 9. Consider, then, the yields of ϕ_2^- after bleaching, when competition would involve only solute and holes with any effect of vacancies eliminated and for N^0 available electrons,

$$N_{\phi_2^-} = \frac{N^0 \sigma_{\phi_2} N_{\phi_2}}{\sigma_{\phi_2} N_{\phi_2} + \sigma_h N_h} \tag{10}$$

In terms of optical densities D and mole fractions X, this gives after rearrangement:

$$\frac{l}{D_{\phi_2^-}} = \frac{l}{D_{\phi_2^-}^0} + \frac{\sigma_h X_h}{D_{\phi_2^-}^0 \sigma_{\phi_2}} \frac{l}{X_{\phi_2}} \tag{11}$$

where X_h can be replaced by $X_{\phi_2^-} + X_{v^-}$. An appropriate plot (not shown) is linear from 4×10^{-2} to 10×10^{-2} mole % ϕ_2. The ratio of electron capture cross sections, $\sigma_h/\sigma_{\phi_2} = 110$, is much greater than that reported for MTHF, which was 3. The intercept $D_{\phi_2^-}^0 = 2.27$ corresponds to $G^0(\phi_2^-) = 1.6$ and refers only to electrons which can be trapped efficiently by small concentrations of ϕ_2. It may be significant that a previous attempt to employ the concept of N_v, equation 1a, was also unsuccessful.

B. Transfer of Electrons from Solvent to Biphenyl

Glasses of 3MP containing 5×10^{-3} to 4×10^{-2} mole % ϕ_2 were irradiated to 2.3×10^{18} eV cm^{-3} and the dependence of (e^-) absorption (1600 mμ) and ϕ_2^- absorption (408 mμ) were measured for the spontaneous transfer (Fig. 18). To facilitate comparison, the changes in OD are presented in Figure 19. The efficiency of transfer, given by $-\Delta OD(\phi_2^-)/\Delta OD(e^-)$, is greater at higher concentrations of ϕ_2 and increases with time. Some of the (e^-) are in high electric fields and travel short distances before recombining with their parent ions. They react inefficiently with ϕ_2. The other (e^-) would decay by second-order kinetics in pure 3MP. When ϕ_2 is present they decay much more rapidly (cf. Fig. 18) and by a pseudo first-order process at sufficiently high concentrations of ϕ_2, shown in Figure 20. It is qualitatively apparent that holes and ϕ_2 compete for electrons.

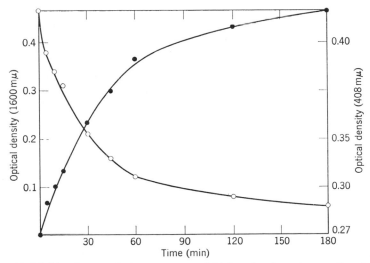

Fig. 18. Yields of trapped electrons ○ and biphenyl anions ● as a function of time after γ irradiation of 0.01% biphenyl in 3-methylpentane. Dose = 2.3×10^{18} eV ml^{-1} (13).

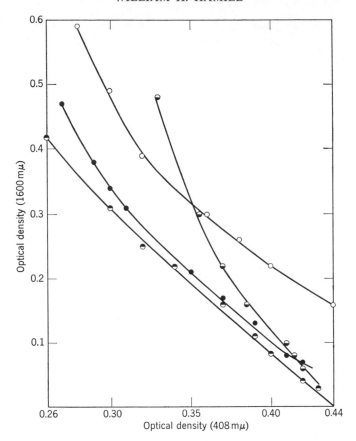

Fig. 19. Spontaneous conversion of solvent-trapped electrons (1600 mμ) to biphenyl anions (408 mμ) following γ irradiation to 2.3×10^{18} eV ml^{-1}. Measurements have been multiplied by scaling factors F_x, F_y for graphing; ○, $5 \times 10^{-3}\%$ ϕ, $F_y = 1$, $F_x = 2$; ●, 0.01% ϕ, $F_y = 1$, $F_x = 1$; ◐, 0.02% ϕ, $F_y = 1$, $F_x = 1$ and 0.26 subtracted from each OD at 408 mμ; ◓, 0.04% ϕ, $F_y = 2$, $F_x = 0.5$ after subtracting 0.26 from each OD at 408 mμ (13).

To the extent that simple competition can describe the results, let:

$$\frac{dN_{\phi_2^-}}{dt} = \nu N^0 \sigma_{\phi_2} N_{\phi_2} \, \Sigma^{-1} \tag{12}$$

$$\frac{-dN_{v^-}}{dt} = \nu N^0 (\sigma_h N_h + \sigma_{\phi_2} N_{\phi_2}) \, \Sigma^{-1} \tag{13}$$

where ν is the frequency of releasing "free" electrons from (e^-) and $\Sigma = \sigma_{\phi_2} N_{\phi_2} + \sigma_h N_h + \sigma_v N_v$. Dividing these equations and letting

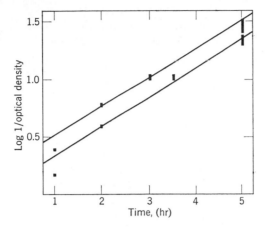

Fig. 20. Decay of solvent-trapped electrons in 3MP with 0.01 and 0.02% biphenyl at 2.4×10^{19} eV ml^{-1} (13).

$dN_{v-}/dN_{\phi_2^-} \simeq \Delta N_{v-}/N_{\phi_2^-}$ for the latter part of decay, when N_h is nearly constant, and introducing optical densities D and extinction coefficients, gives:

$$-\frac{\Delta D_{v-}}{\Delta D_{\phi_2^-}} = \frac{\epsilon_{v-}}{\epsilon_{\phi_2^-}} + \frac{\sigma_h \epsilon_{v-}}{\sigma_{\phi_2} \epsilon_{\phi_2^-}} \frac{X_{v-} + X_{\phi_2^-}}{X_{\phi_2}} \tag{14}$$

after minor rearrangement. For $> 50\%$ decay, it is sufficient to use the mean value of $X_h = X_{v-} + X_{\phi_2^-}$ of the nearly linear segment together with $\epsilon(\phi_2^-) = 3.7 \times 10^4 \, M^{-1} \, cm^{-1}$ and $\epsilon(e^-) = 3.0 \times 10^4 \, M^{-1} \, cm^{-1}$. The ratios σ_h/σ_{ϕ_2} so found are 125, 113, and 120 at 0.005, 0.01, and 0.02 % ϕ_2. The values of σ_h/σ_{ϕ_2} agree adequately with another measurement (already described in Section VII-A) for the combined yield of ϕ_2^- directly from γ irradiation together with the additional electrons released by photobleaching, and using % ϕ_2 as the independent variable.

As the concentration of ϕ_2 increases, the efficiency of transferring an electron by photoexcitation from a solvent trap to ϕ_2 increases, but changes little from 0.02 to 0.04% ϕ_2. As shown in Table VIII, after repeated transfer $-\Delta OD(e^-)/\Delta OD(\phi_2^-)$ attains a reproducible value of about 0.80. Since $\epsilon(\phi_2^-)$ was found to be 3.7×10^4 liters mole^{-1} cm^{-1}, then $\epsilon(e^-) \gtrsim 3.0 \times 10^4$ mole^{-1} cm^{-1}. Initial transfers are inefficient because some (e^-) are in high electric fields and these are quickly lost by ion recombination. Transfers from ϕ_2^- to solvent traps are rather less efficient because of the limited total cross section, $\sigma_v N_v$ and $-\Delta OD(e^-)/\Delta OD(\phi_2^-)$ approximates 0.6 leading to $\epsilon(e^-) \gtrsim 2.2 \times 10^4$ liters mole^{-1} cm^{-1}. The higher value is preferred.

TABLE VIII

Reversible Transfer of Electrons Between Solvent and Biphenyl in γ-Irradiated
3-Methylpentane at $-196°$ by Optical Excitation (13)

0.02% Φ_2				0.04% Φ_2			
$\Delta OD(e^-)$ 1600 mμ		$\Delta OD(\phi^-)$ 408 mμ		$\Delta OD(e^-)$ 1600 mμ		$\Delta OD(\phi^-)$ 408 mμ	
Initial	Final	Initial	Final	Initial	Final	Initial	Final
0.13	0.72	~2.5	0.30	0.05	0.36	~3.0	0.28
0.72	0.00	0.30	0.90	0.36	0.00	0.28	0.72
0.00	0.42	0.90	0.17	0.00	0.23	0.72	0.25
0.42	0.00	0.17	0.65	0.23	0.00	0.25	0.55
0.00	0.33	0.65	0.15	0.00	0.20	0.55	0.21
0.33	0.00	0.15	0.53	0.20	0.00	0.21	0.46
0.00	0.27	0.53	0.12	0.00	0.16	0.46	0.19
0.27	0.00	0.12	0.45	0.16	0.00	0.19	0.39

With the preceding information it is now possible to estimate the oscillator strength, $f = 4.3 \times 10^{-9} c \int \epsilon(\bar{v}) \, d\bar{v}$, where the correction for internal field is taken to be $c = 0.66$. On the basis of the (e^-) spectrum in 3MP of Figure 7, $f \cong 0.46$. The possibility of some additional contribution at $\lambda > 2000$ mμ, which cannot easily be examined, as well as weak absorption in the continuum at $\lambda < 400$ mμ, cannot be excluded. The evidence suggests, however, that one-electron transitions are responsible and are compatible with a particle-in-box model.

C. Concentration Dependence in Methyltetrahydrofuran

Using either naphthalene or biphenyl in γ-irradiated MTHF at $-196°$, G(anion) attains limiting yields of ~2.6 and 3.0, respectively. The difference probably depends upon uncertainties in ϵ(anion). In each system, G(anion) attains a limiting value at ~0.2 mole % solute which remains constant to 3% solute (7). Either these limiting yields correspond to the yields of ion pairs produced or, if others form, they cannot be stabilized because of insufficient charge separation. In fact, the usual definition of ionization as applied to gases fails for these solids when charge separation amounts to only 100–200 Å and the "free" electron is still bound. Yield of ion pairs, in the present context, has significance appropriate to the techniques being used.

Dyne and Miller used neutron scattering theory to estimate the radial mean square track length r of the thermalized electron prior to trapping by MTHF (5). The solvent-trapping cross section was equated to that for ϕ_2 at 0.04 mole % ϕ_2 when $G(\phi_2) = G(e^-)$. Taking both the microscopic cross sections for scattering by MTHF and for capture to be $\sim 10^{-15}$ cm^2 they obtained $r = 10^{-5}$ cm. Since the average concentration of ion pairs was $\sim 5 \times 10^{16}$ cm^{-3}, these authors conclude that the electrons appear to have been randomized.

The higher dielectric constant of MTHF ($\epsilon_s \simeq 4.6$) may be responsible for the greater initial yield of solvent-trapped electrons, slower decay, and smaller quantum yield for bleaching. On the other hand, very efficient hole trapping by protonation in MTHF increases charge separation and must be assigned an important part of the difference. In one critical respect the relative behaviors appear to be inverted, since (e^-) in MTHF was found to decay with a dose-independent lifetime although in this matrix both dielectric constant and hole trapping are favorable. It cannot be proposed that efficient electron trapping can occur at small charge separation because that would be contrary to efficient ϕ_2^- formation. In 3MP, however, both types of behavior with respect to dose could be observed, and the dose-independent behavior could be suppressed by providing hole traps.

VIII. DISSOCIATIVE ELECTRON ATTACHMENT

Reactions of the type $RX + e^- \rightarrow R + X^-$ have frequently been observed by mass spectrometry. The appearance potential (AP), bond dissociation energy (D) and electron affinity (A) are related by $AP(X^-) = D(R - X) - A(X) + KE$, where KE is the kinetic energy of the fragments. Since KE usually exceeds zero even at onset, the potential energy surface of RX^- must be repulsive and it should be difficult to stabilize such anions in organic matrices.

Dissociative attachment is resonant in the low pressure gas, but this restriction may be somewhat less important in condensed states. Still, the cross section may be very small for electron energies much above $AP(X^-)$ and zero below this energy. When $AP(X^-) > 0$ in γ-irradiated organic solids, $G(X^-)$ will be small if RX is a minor component of the system. As the energy of the nascent electron diminishes it makes few encounters while traversing the narrow energy range within which resonant attachment occurs. When $AP(X^-) \simeq 0$, however, the probability of reaction is much greater since once the electron reaches the turning point its kinetic energy is presumably small and the reaction cross section remains favorable throughout this part of the track (28).

For this phenomenon, as well as all others observed by mass spectrometry, an extrapolation of $\sim 10^{12}$ in density entails uncertainties. For

example, will the cage effect of the matrix prevent separation of R—X⁻,
leading to a very inefficient process? Is the zero point kinetic energy of the
electron in the matrix so high that processes with AP's $\cong 0$ *in vacuo*
cannot occur? In this instance, as well as in others which raise the question
of the relevance of processes in the dilute gas to those in condensed phases,
mass spectrometry provides a suggestion but the experiment must be
performed with the systems of interest.

In a preliminary survey a number of solutes were tested for their effectiveness in depressing the yield of ϕ_2^- in a mixture of 3MP–2MP-1 or of
naphthalenide anion in MTHF (8). Organic chlorides, bromides, and
iodides were efficient, but the mechanism could not be inferred. The
kinetic description of competition was assumed to be (in terms of biphenyl)

$$N_{X^-}/N_{\phi_2^-} = \sigma_{RX}N_{RX}/\sigma_{\phi_2}N_{\phi_2} \tag{15}$$

provided $N_{X^-} + N_{\phi_2^-} = $ constant. It follows that

$$\frac{1}{G_{\phi_2^-}} = \frac{1}{G_{\phi_2^-}^0} + \frac{\sigma_X N_X}{\sigma_{\phi_2}N_{\phi_2}} \tag{16}$$

Some results appear in Figure 21. The adequacy of this description was
tested further with ϕ_2 in 75% 3MP–25% 2MP-1. Relative capture cross
sections were found to be $\sigma_{CHCl_3}/\sigma_{CH_2Cl_2}/\sigma_{CH_3Cl} = 5.0/3.1/1$ (29).

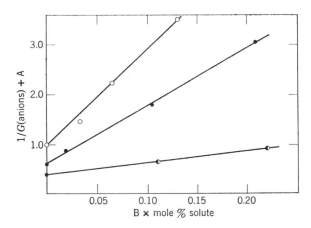

Fig. 21. $\bigcirc$, $1/G(C_{12}H_{10})$ vs. mole % CCl$_4$ (A = 0.4, B = 1) in 25 vol % 2-methyl-
pentene-1 and 75 vol % 3-methylpentane, 0.11 mole % biphenyl: $\bullet$, $1/G(C_{10}H_8-)$
vs. mole % CCl$_4$ (A = 0, B = 1) in tetrahydro-2-methylfuran, 0.11 mole % naphthalene: $\mathbf{\mathbb{O}}$, $1/G(C_{12}H_{10}-)$ vs. mole % naphthalene (A = −0.2, B = 2) in 25 vol %
2-methylpentene-1 and 75 vol % 3-methylpentane 0.11 mole % biphenyl, all at
−196°C (8).

To demonstrate dissociative attachment of RX by electrons it must be shown that RX removes electrons and that both X^- and R are products. Benzyl acetate serves this purpose since it competes for electrons with ϕ_2 in a hydrocarbon glass and with naphthalene in MTHF rather efficiently (8). In each matrix there appears a well-defined absorption at $\lambda_{max} = 320$ mμ which resembles that for $C_6H_5CH_2$. (It had already been shown by Porter and Strachan (30) that photolyses in a rigid medium of series of compounds of the types $C_6H_5CH_3$, $C_6H_5CH_2X$, $C_6H_5CHX_2$, and $C_6H_5CX_3$ gave radical spectra with a sharp maximum at ~ 320 mμ.) The responsible species must be benzyl (Bz$\cdot$) and benzyl-type radicals. Finally, in an ethanol matrix, acetic acid was recovered after thawing and $G(C_6H_5CH_2\cdot) = G(CH_3COOH)$. Acetic acid must have the acetate ion, and not the acetoxy radical, as precursor (31).

Because of possible ambiguities in the spectral identification of $C_6H_5CH_2\cdot$ (viz., solvent shifts in λ_{max} of ~ 25 Å) which were pointed out by Brocklehurst, Porter, and Savadatti (32), and because this aspect of the chemical reactivity of the "free" electron is fundamentally important, the investigation was continued (33).

γ Irradiation (1.8×10^{19} eV cm^{-3}) of ~ 0.03 mole % solutions of compounds of the type BzX(X = Cl, Br, I) in 3MP at $-196°$ produced the three indistinguishable spectra of Figure 22 and all three must be assigned to Bz$\cdot$ with $\lambda_{max} = 3200 \pm 1$ Å. The original uncertainty in identification arose from the fact that with toluene as solute the radical band in 3MP appears at 3175 Å. Since there is a solvent shift* in the radical band from photolyzed toluene (32), it is not only possible that the electric field of juxtaposed X^- would also cause a spectral shift, but quite possibly the same shift for the three halide anions. Therefore, λ_{max} is a useful guide to radical identity, but auxiliary criteria must still be used. Moreover, even supposing the spectra of Figure 22 to be authentically those of Bz$\cdot$, there are imaginable mechanisms other than dissociative electron attachment and confirmation is desirable.

If this mechanism is responsible for the effect observed, then photoionization of TMPD provides a source of low energy electrons at a wavelength greater than that required to photolyze BzCl and an induced decomposition yielding Bz$\cdot$ and Cl$^-$ is to be expected. Just this effect was observed, as shown in Figure 23. With 0.06 mole % BzCl alone, no Bz$\cdot$ absorption appeared, while 2×10^{-3} mole % TMPD alone gave OD = 0.00 at 320 mμ and OD = 0.39 for TMPD$^+$ at 632 mμ. With both solutes present OD(Bz$\cdot$) = 0.38 and OD(TMPD$^+$) = 1.02 showing enhanced cation formation due to an electron acceptor.

* This effect has been confirmed by B. Brocklehurst and M. I. Savadatti, *Nature*, **212**, 1231 (1966).

To determine whether there is a correlation between the sign of $D(Bz - X) - A(X)$ and the yield of $Bz\cdot$, a series of toluene homologs was tested in γ-irradiated 3MP with the results summarized in Table IX.

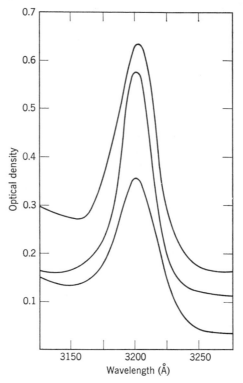

Fig. 22. Absorption spectra of the principal radical band (top to bottom) from 0.03 mole % BzBr, BzI, BzCl in 3 MP after radiolysis; dose = 5×10^{18} eV ml^{-1}. Spectra have been translated 0.13, 0.08, and -0.05 units vertically for convenience (33).

When $D < A$ an appreciable yield of $Bz\cdot$ was observed and when $D > A$ no $Bz\cdot$ appeared. Also, photoionization of TMPD formed $Bz\cdot$ from BzCl, but illumination of BzCl alone formed no $Bz\cdot$. Values of $G(Bz\cdot)$ can be estimated from $\epsilon(Bz\cdot) \cong 1.5 \times 10^4$ liters mole^{-1} cm^{-1}. Thus, $G(Bz\cdot)$ for 3% toluene is only 0.05 and may be a consequence of direct energy absorption. The benzyl halides, for example, are ~ 400 times more efficient.

This pattern of reactivity of the electron was examined for some alkyl halides, at ~ 0.1 mole %, in the γ-irradiated 3MP matrix. The results, summarized in Table X, show once more that the formation of $R\cdot$ correlates with $D(R - X) - A(X)$, although methyl acetate is a borderline case. In 0.4 mole % CH_3I, $G(CH_3)$ was 1.2. Photoionization of 0.015% TMPD in 3MP containing 0.4 mole % CH_3I also yielded methyl radicals.

Quite apart from the major features of dissociative electron attachment, which are fairly clear, one interesting detail could not be resolved. For a slightly endothermic reaction (*in vacuo*), can the zero point kinetic energy of the electron contribute to the heat of reaction? In a nonpolar matrix, such as 3MP, the polarization energies of the reacting electron and the product X^- should cancel. The data are too limited and uncertain for a decision, but they do not appear to support such a possibility.

The chemical consequences of dissociative electron attachment can usually be imagined, although in γ-irradiated systems these products may

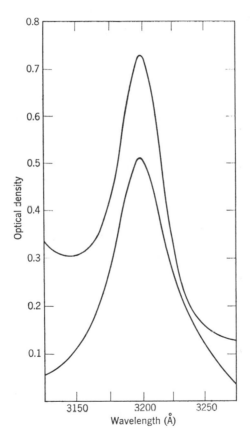

Fig. 23. Absorption of principal radical band (top) from radiolysis of 0.03 mole % BzCl in 3MP; dose $= 10^{19}$ eV ml^{-1} and (bottom) from photolysis of 0.06 mole % BzCl and 2×10^{-3} mole % TMPD in 3MP (33).

TABLE IX

Free Radicals from Radiolysis of ~ 0.03 mole % Toluene Derivatives in 3-Methylpentane at $77°K$; Dose $= 10^{19}$ eV ml^{-1} (33)

Solute (RX)	X = leaving group	$D(R—X)$ kcal/mole	$A(X)$ kcal/mole	λ_{max} Å	ODγ	OD bleach
BzH	H	77[d]	17[e]	—	0.00	0.00
BzH[a]	H	77	17	3175	0.25	0.25
BzCl	Cl	66[e]	88[e]	3200	0.48	0.60
BzBr	Br	51[e]	81[e]	3200	0.76	1.02
BzI	I	38[e]	74[e]	3200	0.70	0.84
BzOAc	OAc	~ 60[b]	76[g]	3206	0.22	0.31
BzOC$_2$H$_5$	OC$_2$H$_5$	~ 60[b]	~ 60[c]	3215	0.07	0.11
BzOH	OH	77[f]	41[g]	—	0.00	0.00
BzCN	CN	< 103[d]	64[h]	—	0.00	0.00
BzNH$_2$	NH$_2$	59[d]	28[h]	—	0.00	0.00
ϕCHCl$_2$	Cl	$\simeq 66$	88	3248	0.41	0.43
ϕCCl$_3$	Cl	$\simeq 66$	88	3236	0.90	0.94
ϕCHClCH$_3$	Cl	$\simeq 66$	88	3230	0.25	0.33
ϕCH$_2$CH$_2$Cl	Cl	> 66	88	—	0.00	0.00

[a] 3% Toluene; dose $= 1.8 \times 10^{19}$ eV ml^{-1}.

[b] Estimated.

[c] Taken equal to $A(CH_3O) = 60$ kcal.[d]

[d] Cottrell, *The Strengths of Chemical Bonds*, Academic Press, New York, 1954.

[e] Field and Franklin, *Electron Impact Phenomena*, Academic Press, New York, 1957, p. 149.

[f] Benson, *The Foundations of Chemical Kinetics*, McGraw-Hill, New York, 1960, p. 670.

[g] Tsuda and Hamill, *Advances in Mass Spectrometry III*, The Institute of Petroleum, London, 1966, p. 249.

[h] Page, *Advances in Chemistry Series*, No. 36, Amer. Chem. Soc., Washington, D.C., 1962, p. 68.

not be distinguishable from those arising by quite different mechanisms. For example, in solvent RH:

$$RH \longrightarrow RH^+ + e^-$$
$$R'X + e^- \longrightarrow R'\cdot + X^-$$
$$RH^+ + X^- \longrightarrow RH + X$$
$$RH + X \longrightarrow R\cdot + HX$$

would give products similar to

$$RH \longrightarrow RH^+ + e^-$$
$$RH^+ + e^- \longrightarrow R\cdot + H$$
$$R'X + H \longrightarrow R' + HX$$

TABLE X

Appearance Potentials for Resonance Electron Attachment[a] (14)

Process	Radical by EPR	Appearance potential of X⁻ observed (eV ± 0.1)	ΔH(eV)[b] calculated	$D_{(R-X)}$ (eV)	Electron affinity of X (eV)
$CH_3F + e^- \rightarrow CH_3\cdot + F^-$	No	—[c]	+0.4	4.3	3.6
$CH_3Cl + e^- \rightarrow CH_3\cdot + Cl^-$	Yes	—[c]	-0.3	3.5	3.8
$CH_3I + e^- \rightarrow CH_3\cdot + I^-$	Yes	0.0	-0.8	2.4	3.2
$C_2H_5I + e^- \rightarrow C_2H_5\cdot + I^-$	Yes	0.03	-0.9	2.3	3.2
$CH_3CHICH_3 + e^- \rightarrow CH_3\dot{C}HCH_3 + I^-$	Yes	0.0	-1.0	2.2	3.2
$(CH_3)_3CBr + e^- \rightarrow (CH_3)_3C\cdot + Br^-$	Yes	0.0	-0.8	2.7	3.5
$C_6H_5CHClCH_3 + e^- \rightarrow C_6H_5CHCH_3 + Cl^-$	Yes	0.0	-0.8	2.9[d]	3.8
$CH_3C(=O)OCH_3 + e^- \rightarrow CH_3\cdot + CH_3C(=O)O^-$	No	—[c]	+0.1	3.3	3.2
$(CH_3)_3CCH_2Cl + e^- \rightarrow (CH_3)_3CCH_2 + Cl^-$	Yes	0.05	-1.1	2.3[d]	3.8

[a] The appearance potentials of I⁻ from the iodides were determined using SF_6 as a standard. All other X⁻ were compared to CH_3I as a standard.

[b] $\Delta H_{calc.}$ = (electron affinity of X) − (bond dissociation energy). Data taken from S. W. Benson, *The Foundations of Chemical Kinetics*, McGraw-Hill, New York, 1960, p. 670; G. M. Barrow, *Physical Chemistry*, McGraw-Hill, New York, 1962, p. 134; S. Tsuda and W. H. Hamill, *Advan. Mass Spectrometry*, *Proc. Conf. Univ. London*, 3, 249 (1966); R. R. Bernecker and F. A. Long, *J. Phys. Chem.*, 65, 1565 (1961).

[c] CH_3F gave no detectable F⁻ signal in the region of zero energy; the negative-ion signals from methyl acetate and methyl chloride were too weak to measure onset.

[d] Estimated.

Benzene as solvent is relatively free of these complications since $G(H\cdot)$ is apparently small and besides H atoms would react preferentially with benzene. In the γ-irradiated solutions at $\sim 20°$, small concentrations of alkyl halides give appreciable yields of alkanes, alkenes, and HX which conform to the expected products of electron attachment (34). The results for solutions of C_6H_6–CCl_4 in Figure 24 for 0–15% CCl_4 demonstrate this effect. The marked decrease in $G(HCl)$ caused by 0–15% C_6H_6 is attributed to charge transfer: $CCl_4^+ + C_6H_6 \rightarrow CCl_4 + C_6H_6^+$.

The results for benzyl acetate in ethanol, shown in Figure 25, compare $G(Bz\cdot)$ in the glass with $G(CH_3COOH)$ in the thawed samples. Using $\epsilon(Bz\cdot) = 1.8 \times 10^4$ liters mole^{-1} cm^{-1}, they are the same for each sample (31). Altogether parallel results were obtained in MTHF. Moreover, these yields attained limiting values which are quite plausible for $G(e^-)$. The reactions immediately involved are considered to be:

$$C_2H_5OH^+ + C_2H_5OH \longrightarrow C_2H_5OH_2^+ + C_2H_4OH$$

$$C_6H_5CH_2CO_2CH_3 + e^- \longrightarrow C_6H_5CH_2 + CH_3CO_2^-$$

$$C_2H_5OH_2^+ + CH_3CO_2^- \longrightarrow C_2H_5OH + CH_3CO_2H$$

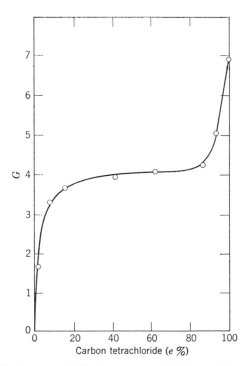

Fig. 24. Radiolysis of CCl_4 in benzene, $G(HCl)$ vs. % benzene (34).

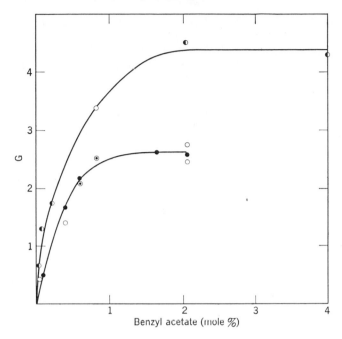

Fig. 25. γ Radiolysis of benzyl acetate in ethanol: ●, $G(C_6H_5CH_2)$ at $-196°$; ○, G(acid) for samples irradiated at $-196°$ and thawed; ◐, G(acid) for samples irradiated at $20°$ (52).

IX. POSITIVE HOLE TRAPPING IN 3-METHYLPENTANE SYSTEMS

Since pure 3MP traps electrons ($G \cong 0.7$) it must also trap a corresponding number of holes, but it has not yet been established whether these are present as carbonium ions or as relaxed molecular ions. Neither is it clear whether $G(e^-)$ is limited by the ability of the matrix to trap electrons, or by its ability to trap holes, or possibly both. The limiting yield of solvent-trapped holes cannot be equated to the limiting yield of solute anions, e.g., ϕ_2^- in Figure 17, because ϕ_2 is also an efficient hole trap.

A. Mixed Solvent Glasses (13)

To determine the extent to which hole migration depresses $G(e^-)$ in 3MP requires an additive which traps holes but does not form an anion or greatly modify the matrix. Since pure 2MP-1 forms an excellent glass and traps electrons which exhibit the same spectrum as (e^-) in 3MP and because the ionization potentials differ by ~ 1 eV, it appears to be an acceptable additive. The olefin does not trap electrons molecularly since a matrix consisting of 2% 2MP-1 in 3MP gives the same yield of (e^-) from photoionization of TMPD as a matrix of 3MP alone. To the extent that 2MP-1 traps holes, it should promote equally the yields of (e^-) and of any solute anion. Samples, therefore, contained 5×10^{-3} mole % ϕ_2 as well as various concentrations of 2MP-1 and 3MP and were all irradiated to 3.0×10^{18} eV cm^{-3} (35). The results in Figure 26 show $\sim 20\%$ increase in OD(e^-) at only 0.2% 2MP-1, with a near-limiting yield at $\sim 1\%$. The effect of 2MP-1 on OD(ϕ_2^-) is strictly parallel and it is qualitatively clear that some holes migrate many molecular diameters. The mechanism is assumed to resemble resonance charge exchange in the gas.

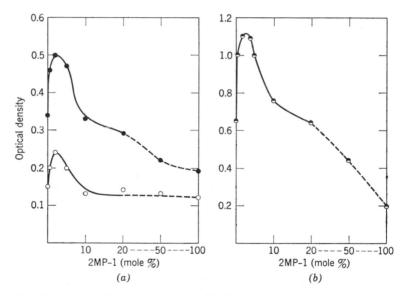

Fig. 26. (a) OD of ϕ_2^- from $5 \times 10^{-3}\%$ biphenyl (ϕ_2) in mixtures of 3-methyl-pentane (3MP) and 2-methyl-1-pentene (2MP-1) at $-196°$. ○, after γ irradiation (2.1×10^{18} eV ml); ●, after bleaching solvent-trapped electrons; (b) ◖, OD of solvated electrons (e^-) from the same samples after γ irradiation (35).

The decrease in yields of (e^-) and ϕ_2^- beyond $\sim 2\%$ 2MP-1 cannot be attributed to a deterioration of the matrix. At high concentrations of olefin it would be expected that fortuitous, continuous sequences (or chains) of olefin molecules provide hole-conducting paths by resonance charge exchange. The probability of such an arrangement must be very small for a long chain at low concentrations. If hole conduction can proceed along an interrupted chain of olefin molecules, bridging gaps of two to three paraffin molecules by electron tunneling, the effect can be accounted for and applies equally to ϕ_2^- and (e^-), as observed.

Pure TEA also forms a clear glass, has a low ionization potential

(~ 7.5 eV), and the trapped electron spectrum resembles that in 3MP. A series of samples containing 5×10^{-3} % ϕ_2 and various amounts of TEA in 3MP were irradiated to 3.0×10^{18} eV cm^{-3}. The results, shown in Figure 27, are completely similar to those of Figure 26 and the same interpretation applies.

An interesting variation can be introduced by combining 3MP with MTHF. The latter undergoes proton transfer, rather than resonance

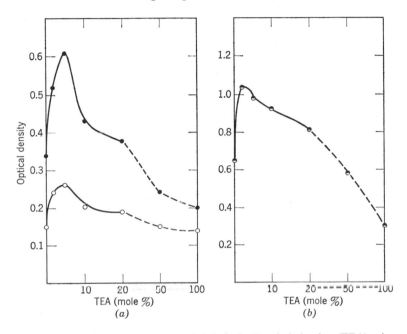

Fig. 27. (a) OD of ϕ_2^- from 5×10^{-3}% ϕ_2 in 3MP, triethylamine (TEA) mixtures at −196°. ○, after γ irradiation (2.1×10^{18} eV ml); ●, after bleaching (e^-). (b) ◐, OD of (e^-) from the same samples after γ irradiation (35).

charge transfer, both on the basis of mass spectrometric and chemical evidence, but perhaps not completely (31). Since proton transfer in a rigid medium would be expected to trap the hole irreversibly, yields of negative species would be promoted at small concentrations of MTHF as before, but conducting chains should not depress the yields at high concentrations of MTHF as efficiently as in 3MP. Solute cations are produced in γ-irradiated MTHF, but very inefficiently. Just this expected effect is observed for OD(e^-) in Figure 28. The curve is qualitatively correct but not quantitatively because λ_{max} for (e^-) is ~ 1600 mμ in 3MP and ~ 1200 mμ in MTHF. As composition changes, therefore, $\epsilon(e^-)$ is not constant at any given λ. Nevertheless, it is apparent that there is no decrease in $G(e^-)$

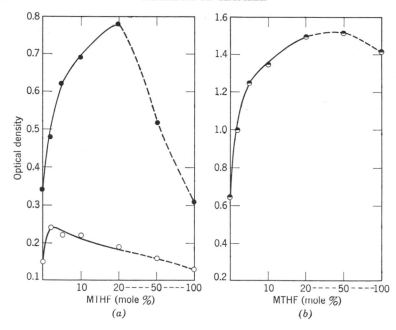

Fig. 28. (a) OD (ϕ_2^-) for $5 \times 10^{-3}\%$ ϕ_2 in mixtures of 3MP–MTHF at $-196°$, ○ before and ● after bleach. (b) OD (e^-) in the same samples (35).

below $\sim 20\%$ MTHF. The decrease in OD(ϕ_2^-) at high concentrations of MTHF is real, because the spectrum of ϕ_2^- is the same in the two pure matrices, but cannot be attributed to hole conduction. The decay of (e^-) in pure MTHF was found to be independent of dose and therefore corresponds to smaller charge separation (but see Section VII-C) than in 3MP where the rate was dose-dependent and quasi second-order. Since the concentration of ϕ_2 was small, less ϕ_2^- would be formed in MTHF, but more would survive because there is little hole conduction. Only 5% MTHF in 3MP doubles OD(ϕ_2^-) because the matrix provides high mobility for the electron and low mobility for the hole.

At 2% of each of three different additives in 3MP for Figures 26–28, OD(e^-) was increased from 0.65 to 1.10, 1.04, and 1.00 while OD(ϕ_2^-) was increased from 0.34 to 0.50, 0.52, and 0.49, respectively. This regularity suggests molecular processes with equal cross sections. Other additives (2%) which enhanced OD(e^-) are summarized in Table XI.

If the decrease in OD(e^-) and OD(ϕ_2^-) above ~ 2 mole % 2MP-1 in 3MP is due to hole conduction, then OD(Bz·) at 320 mμ arising from dissociative electron attachment may not show the corresponding effect. The reaction may be irreversible, for example, if the very unstable acetoxy radical decomposes when acetate ion is neutralized. The results were (35):

% 2MP-1	0	2.0	10	20	40	60	100
OD(Bz·)	0.21	0.36	0.42	0.52	0.49	0.44	0.31

The pattern clearly differs from that of Figure 26 and indirectly supports the assumption of hole conduction by chains of 2MP-1.

TABLE XI

Yields of Solvent Trapped Electrons in γ-Irradiated 3-Methylpentane with ~2 Mole % Additive at −196° (2×10^{18} eV ml^{-1})

Additive	OD(e^-) 1.6 μ	Additive	OD(e^-) 1.6 μ
None	0.62	TEA	1.04
C_2H_4	0.46	MTHF	1.00
C_3H_6	1.61	n-PrOH	0.79
1-Butene	0.80	n-PrCN	0.65
2-Butene	0.89	n-BuCN	0.70
2MP-1	1.10	Methylcyclohexane	0.58

B. Solute Cations

Direct observation of the effects of glass composition on yields of solute cations is necessary to support inferences drawn from studies of anionic species. There is no hole-trapping additive with known ε(cation) which is sufficiently soluble in glasses to permit an adequate measure of the concentration dependence. In the interval 10^{-3} to 10^{-2} mole % TMPD, $G(TMPD^+)$ is approximately the same as $G(\phi_2^-)$ at corresponding concentrations of solute in 3MP. For example, $G(TMPD^+) = 0.27$ at 0.013 mole % TMPD (35). Let $G^0 \sigma l N = G$, where $G^0 \cong 3$ is the yield of holes formed and G the yield of TMPD$^+$ for N molecules of TMPD cm^{-3} while σl is the volume swept out by the migrating hole, about 10^{-19} cm^3 for these data if $\sigma \cong 10^{-15}$ cm^2, $l \cong 10^{-4}$ cm. $G(TMPD^+)$ increases when electron acceptors are present, and this behavior provides a test for identifying other cationic species. Addition of either 2MP-1 or benzene to 3MP decreases $G(TMPD^+)$, as shown in Table XII, presumably by hole trapping by charge exchange. MTHF as additive also depresses $G(TMPD^+)$, probably by proton transfer from 3MP$^+$ (10).

The ambiguity of alternant hydrocarbon cation and anion spectra can now be resolved. The spectrum of γ-irradiated 0.01 mole % ϕ_2 in 3MP containing 1% i-PrCl should be that of ϕ_2^+, while 0.01% ϕ_2 in 80%

TABLE XII
The Effects of Additives on Solute Cation Yields in 3-Methylpentane at $-196°$ $(1.0 \times 10^{19}$ eV ml$^{-1})$

	3MP		3MP + Additive	
Mole % solute	λ_{max} (mμ) cation	OD λ_{max}	Mole % additive	OD λ_{max} cation
0.1% CCl$_4$	470	0.33	2% 2MP-1	0.14
1.0% CCl$_4$	470	0.64	2% 2MP-1	0.40
2.0% ϕCH$_3$	1050	0.37	2% 2MP-1	0.05
0.25% DMA	465	0.44	10% 2MP-1	0.28
0.05% TPA	645	0.61	4% 2MP-1	0.49
0.01% TMPD	632	0.96	4% 2MP-1	0.77
1% ϕH	950	0.40	10% 2MP-1	0.00
1% CCl$_4$	470	0.64	2% MTHF	0.08
0.01% TMPD	632	0.96	4% MTHF	0.32
1% ϕH	950	0.40	4% MTHF	0.02
0.05% TPA	645	0.61	4% MTHF	0.09
0.25% DMA	465	0.55	4% MTHF	0.26
0.05% TPA	645	0.61	4% TEA	0.37
1.0% ϕH	950	0.40	4% TEA	0.05
0.01% TMPD	632	0.96	1% ϕH	0.22
0.05% TPA	645	0.61	4% i-PrOH	0.18

3MP–20% 2MP-1 should give the spectrum of ϕ_2^-. The spectra, shown in Figure 29, are distinguishable. In 3MP alone the spectrum is the envelope of the separate spectra of both charge species. The cationic component was originally attributed to a neutral radical arising from H atom addition since it was suppressed by addition of 2MP-1, and the residual spectrum agreed with that of ϕ_2^- in MTHF (7). It is known now that the electron, but not the hole, migrates in MTHF and in mixtures of 3MP and 2MP-1.

The effects of several additives in 3MP which trap holes by charge exchange (2MP-1, ϕH) and by proton transfer (MTHF, i-PrOH) on yields of a number of cations are summarized in Table XII. The additive TEA could trap holes by either mechanism.

A band at ~ 1100 mμ arising from toluene in 3MP glasses is promoted by addition of organic halides and is presumed to be cationic. This species will be represented by T$^+$. The dependence of OD(T$^+$) on concentration of toluene at 0, 0.3, and 1 mole % n-PrCl, shown in Figure 30, suggests complications for hole migration and transfer not found for electrons (36).

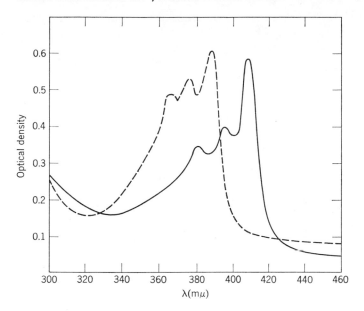

Fig. 29. Principal bands of $\phi_2^{\pm}$ and ϕ_2^{-}: (———) after γ irradiation in 20% 2MP-1, 80% 3MP glass with 0.01% ϕ_2 at 4.6 × 10^18 eV ml^-1; (— — —) 3MP with 1% i-PrCl and 0.01% ϕ_2 after bleaching all ϕ_2^{-}, at 9.2 × 10^18 eV ml^-1 (35).

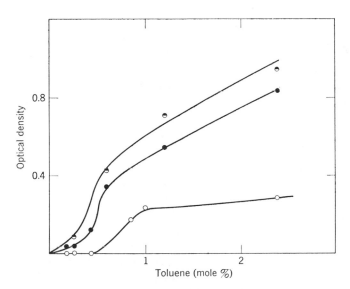

Fig. 30. Yield of toluene cation vs. mole % toluene in 3MP with (○) 0%; (●) 0.3%; (◑) 1% n-PrCl (36).

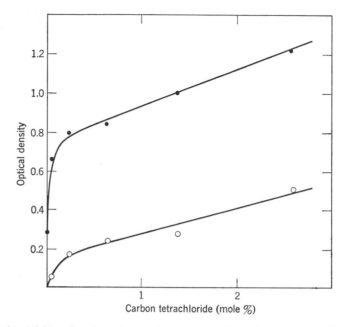

Fig. 31. Yields of cations from toluene (●) and carbon tetrachloride (○) vs. mole % carbon tetrachloride in 3MP with 2.4 mole % toluene, irradiated to 5.8×10^{18} eV g^{-1} (36).

When CCl$_4$ is added to 3MP an associated cationic species, designated C$^+$, absorbs at $\lambda_{max} \cong 480$ mμ (9). Adding CCl$_4$ to 2.4 mole % toluene in 3MP promotes OD(T$^+$), and also forms C$^+$, shown in Figure 31 (36). Since CCl$_4$ traps both electrons and holes, competition to form cations is not evident. When the concentration of toluene is varied at 2.6 mole % CCl$_4$, as shown in Figure 32, there is clear evidence that the two cations do not arise from a common precursor.

This instance might be disposed of as an erroneous assignment, but further examination indicates that the anomaly of Figure 32 may simply be one example of the complex dynamics of holes.

Glasses containing 2MP-1 in 3MP exhibit a weak band at $\lambda_{max} \cong 700$ mμ which is strongly enhanced by addition of organic halides (29) as shown in Figure 33. This species will be arbitrarily designated 2MP-1$^+$.

Keeping the concentration of CCl$_4$ at either 0.1 or 1.0 mole %, consider once more the effect of increasing concentrations of 2MP-1 shown in Figure 34 (35). It should be observed that there is little or no correlation between OD(C$^+$) and OD(2MP-1$^+$) and that the concentration dependence for the latter has positive curvature. For comparison, the results in

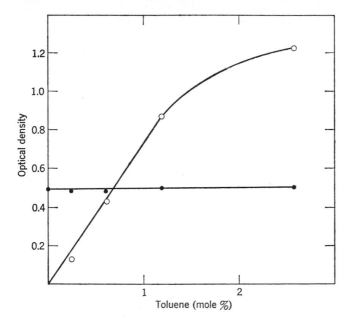

Fig. 32. Yields of cations from toluene (○) and carbon tetrachloride (●) vs. mole % toluene in 3MP with 2.6 mole % carbon tetrachloride, irradiated to 5.8×10^{18} eV g^{-1} (36).

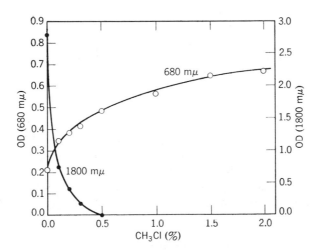

Fig. 33. The dependence of the 680 mμ cation band from 2MP-1 and the 1800 mμ electron band on the concentration of electron acceptor (29).

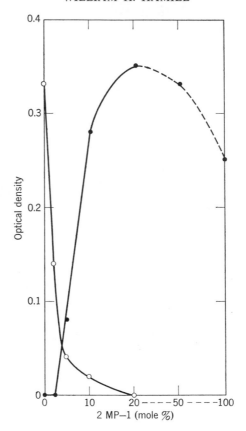

Fig. 34. Yields of cations after γ irradiation of CCl_4 in 3MP, 2MP-1 mixtures at $-196°$ (9.2×10^{18} eV ml^{-1}). $\bigcirc$, 470 mμ band of CCl_4^+ (0.1% CCl_4); $\bullet$, 700 mμ band of 2MP-1$^+$ (0.1% CCl_4) (35).

Figure 35 for 3 mole % toluene in 3MP–2MP-1 mixtures suggest a simple, plausible pattern of competition between two additives for holes. The results for 0.25 mole % dimethylaniline in similar matrices, shown in Figure 36, follow a still different pattern.

If simple competition exists between additives S and T for N^0 migrating positive holes then, in the absence of complications, it might be expected that:

$$N_{T^+} = N^0 \frac{\sigma_T N_T}{\sigma_T N_T + \sigma_S N_S} \qquad (17)$$

where σ's and N's are cross sections and number per unit volume. In terms of optical densities D and mole fractions X, after minor rearrangement:

$$\frac{l}{D_{T^+}} = \frac{l}{D^0} + \frac{\sigma_S X_S}{D\sigma_T X_T} \tag{18}$$

The data of Figures 34 and 35 fit this description, provided S corresponds to 2MP-1, as shown by Figures 37 and 38.

Hole trapping by additives in 3MP does not correlate strictly with ionization potentials. To be effective, a hole trap T in a matrix of molecules S must not only provide a potential well, but it must also reach an energy-matching vibronic state by a vertical transition in competition

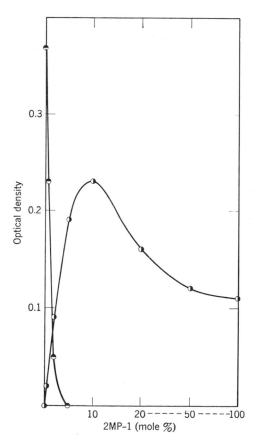

Fig. 35. Yield of cations after γ irradiation of 2.0% $C_6H_5CH_3$ in 3MP, 2MP-1 mixtures at $-196°$ (9.2×10^{18} eV ml^{-1}). ◖, OD of 1050 mμ band of cation from $C_6H_5CH_3$; ◑, OD of 700 mμ band of cation from 2MP-1 (35).

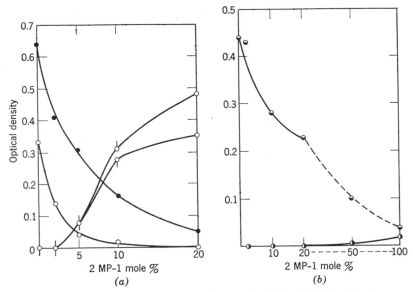

Fig. 36. (a) Yields of cations after γ irradiation of CCl₄ in 3MP, 2MP-1 mixtures at −196° (9.2 × 10¹⁸ eV ml⁻¹). ○, 470 mμ band of CCl₄⁺ (0.1% CCl₄); ○, 700 mμ band of 2MP-1⁺ (0.1% CCl₄); ●, 470 mμ band of CCl₄⁺ (1% CCl₄); ⊙, 700 mμ band of 2MP-1⁺ (1% CCl₄). (b) Yields of cations after γ irradiation of 0.25% dimethylaniline (DMA) in 3MP, 2MP-1 mixtures at −196° (9.2 × 10¹⁸ eV ml⁻¹). ◓, OD of 465 mμ band of DMA⁺. ◑, Upper limit of OD of 700 mμ band of 2MP-1⁺ (35).

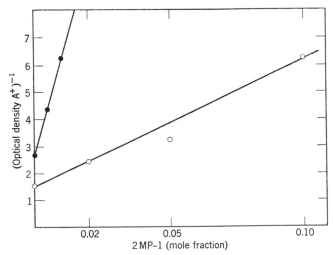

Fig. 37. Competition for positive holes between additive A and 2MP-1, based on equation 18: ○, 1/OD of 470 mμ band of CCl₄ (1% CCl₄) vs. mole fraction of 2MP-1. ●, 1/OD of 1080 mμ band of C₆H₅CH₃ (2% C₆H₅CH₃) vs. mole fraction of 2MP-1 (35).

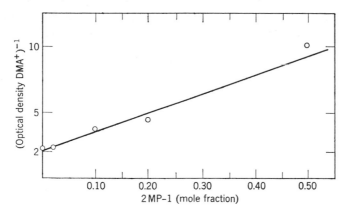

Fig. 38. Competition for positive holes between DMA and 2MP-1 based on equation 18: ○, 1/OD of 465 mμ band of DMA (0.25% DMA) vs. mole fraction of 2MP-1 (35).

with resonant transfer from S^+ to several neighboring molecules S. Transfer of charge to the trapping molecule T only becomes irreversible when T^+ relaxes or transfers at least one vibrational quantum to the matrix. (Evidence will be presented that CCl_4 both traps and conducts, although CCl_4^+ cannot be detected by mass spectrometry.)

C. Excitation and Relaxation

If inter- and intramolecular relaxation of vibrational energy are faster for larger vibrational quantum numbers, then greater differences of ionization potential between T and S would favor formation of T^+, which is observed. Also, relatively large molecules provide more vibronic states and faster intramolecular relaxation. Aromatic compounds would be expected to be particularly effective hole traps because the higher electronically excited states of the molecules are known to undergo very rapid internal conversions and the ions may do the same.

Hole trapping in pure 3MP may depend upon carbonium ion formation, but quite possibly intra- and intermolecular relaxation of the radical ion would suffice. The static and optical dielectric constants are substantially equal but electrostriction would stabilize the hole, although the possibility of slow migration (which has not yet been observed) still exists. The hole may be self-trapped in the ground electronic state if paraffins cannot ionize by 0–0 vertical transitions, which seems to be the case for photoionization (37). The combination of nonvertical transition and electrostriction would rather effectively trap the hole; migration would occur only for excited holes and self-trapping would follow electronic relaxation.

On the other hand alkenes appear to ionize adiabatically (37) and this is consistent with the evidence for hole migration by electron tunneling along interrupted chains of 2MP-1 in 3MP.

Ion–molecule reactions of the type $RH^+ + RH \rightarrow RH_2^+ + R$ have often been proposed to account for some of the facts of radiation chemistry of hydrocarbons (38,39). Hole migration in 3MP does not exclude this possibility, but since MTHF depresses hole mobility by protonation, it appears that protonation does not occur, or is rather inefficient, in pure 3MP.

The results of Figure 32 can be attributed to two species of hole, at least one being excited. Almost certainly ions in the matrix are produced in several electronic states, as they are by mass spectrometry (27,37). Since CCl_4^+ cannot be detected by mass spectrometry its ionization potential cannot be measured but it is probably greater than that for CH_3Cl (11.3 eV) and therefore lies well above the ground state of 3MP. At any rate, the lowest appearance potential for the formation of any ion by a

TABLE XIII
Ionization Potentials[a] and Electron Affinities[b]

	A, eV		A, eV
H	0.7	OH	1.8
F	3.6	NH_2	1.2
Cl	3.8	CH_3O	2.6
Br	3.5	CH_3CO_2	3.3
I	3.2		
	I, eV		I, eV
Acetone	9.69	Methanol	10.85
Benzene	9.25	3-Methylpentane	10.08
Biphenyl	8.27	2-Methyl-1-pentene	9.1 (Est)
1-Butene	9.58	2-Methylpropene	9.23
2-Butene	9.13	Methyltetrahydrofuran	<9.5 (Est)
n-Butyl chloride	10.67	Propylene	9.73
Carbon tetrachloride	11.47	Styrene	8.47
Ethanol	10.48	Toluene	8.82
Ethylene	10.52	Triethylamine	7.50

[a] K. Watanabe, T. Nakayama and J. Mottl, *J. Quant. Spectr. Radiative Transfer*, **2**, 369 (1962).

[b] Values for halogens from R. S. Berry and W. Reimann, *J. Chem. Phys.*, **38**, 1540 (1963); $A(OH)$ and $A(NH_2)$ from F. M. Page, *Advan. Chem. Ser.*, **36**, 68 (1962); $A(CH_3O)$ and $A(CH_3CO_2)$ from S. Tsuda and W. H. Hamill, *Advan. Mass Spectrometry, Proc. Conf., Univ. London*, **3**, p. 249 (1966).

vertical transition is ~ 11.5 eV (Table XIII). It follows that the C^+ band at 480 mμ requires an excited, conducting state of $3MP^+$ and that CCl_4 would not exchange with the ground (or other low-lying) state of $3MP^+$. The latter would, however, be able to transfer to toluene, and growth of $OD(T^+)$ does not require a decrease of $OD(C^+)$. There is one additional, necessary assumption: toluene does not trap or degrade the excited hole.

Addition of toluene to 3MP depressed $OD(e^-)$ and therefore it traps electrons. In Figure 30 the dependence of $OD(T^+)$ on concentration of toluene may be due to the dual role of toluene, giving an initial quadratic dependence since two molecules are required—one for the hole and one for the electron. As the concentration of PrCl increases, electrons are trapped more efficiently, more T^+ ions survive and the dependence upon concentration of toluene approaches linearity. Even if correct, this mechanism cannot apply to the behavior of 2MP-1 in Figure 34.

A somewhat similar dependence of $OD(C^+)$ on concentration of 2MP-1 also suggests the involvement of two molecules of olefin for each $2MP-1^+$ formed, but a quite different relation holds for suppression of C^+. Let it be assumed that only one molecule of olefin is required to degrade the excited hole in competition with trapping by CCl_4. Then:

$$N_{C^+} = \frac{N^0 \sigma_{CCl_4} N_{CCl_4}}{\sigma_{CCl_4} N_{CCl_4} + \sigma_{2MP-1} N_{2MP-1}} \tag{19}$$

and analogously for systems containing toluene or DMA.

The results of Figures 34–36 have been tested in this way, after rearranging equation 19 to the form of equation 18. The corresponding plots of Figures 37 and 38 are consistent with the assumptions. It should be noted that since 2MP-1 depressed $OD(T^+)$ as well as $OD(C^+)$, it must trap (or degrade) holes both in their upper and lower energy states.

Pursuing this lead, let it be further assumed that hole degradation is a result of proton transfer from paraffin to olefin, which occurs efficiently in the mass spectrometer,

$$C_6H_{14}^+ + C_6H_{12} \longrightarrow C_6H_{13} + C_6H_{13}^+$$

followed by dimerization of the juxtaposed radical and carbonium ion,

$$C_6H_{13} + C_6H_{13}^+ \longrightarrow C_{12}H_{26}^+$$

It may be doubted that the hole can migrate further and that no absorption of $2MP-1^+$ follows hole trapping initiated by olefin. As the concentration of 2MP-1 gradually increases, electron tunneling from olefin to the paraffin dimer cation would be expected by a prior assumption to become measurable somewhat above 2% 2MP-1 according to:

$$C_{12}H_{26}^+ + C_6H_{12} \longrightarrow C_{12}H_{26} + C_6H_{12}^+$$

The olefin cation thus formed would be in its ground state and is known to be unreactive. The onset of OD(2MP-1$^+$) does behave in this way (Fig. 34).

The negligible yield of 2MP-1$^+$ in systems containing 0.25% DMA (Fig. 36) can also be attributed to hole conduction along olefin chains. Although OD(DMA$^+$) in the olefin matrix is small, it must be assumed that DMA can transfer an electron to 2MP-1$^+$. By hypothesis, the onset of 2MP-1$^+$ formation coincides with the onset of hole conduction along olefin chains. Since these samples contain 0.25% DMA, even fairly short chains would suffice for charge transfer to DMA by tunneling. The cross section for charge transfer may be rather large because the hole can range repeatedly over a chain segment providing many opportunities for tunneling. The result is that very few 2MP-1$^+$ can survive.

The corresponding experiments with samples containing 2% toluene in mixtures of 3MP–2MP-1 (Fig. 35) cannot now be accounted for plausibly.

The dependence of OD(e^-) and OD(ϕ_2^-) in mixtures of 3MP with >2% TEA has been attributed to hole conduction along interrupted chains of discrete TEA molecules. Since TEA is an excellent proton acceptor, it is necessary to explain why these mixtures (Fig. 27) resemble 3MP–2MP-1 rather than 3MP–MTHF. That is, proton transfer and not electron transfer is to be expected by the reaction:

$$C_6H_{14}^+ + (C_2H_5)_3N \longrightarrow C_6H_{13}\cdot + (C_2H_5)_3NH^+$$

If the proton affinity of TEA is the same as that of NH$_3$ ($\sim$9.6 eV) and taking I(TEA) = 7.5 eV and D(C$_6$H$_{13}$ − H) $\cong$ 4.2 eV, it follows that the reaction (between nearest neighbors):

$$C_6H_{13}\cdot + (C_2H_5)_3NH^+ \longrightarrow C_6H_{14} + (C_2H_5)_3N^+$$

is exothermic by ~ -0.7 eV. The same net reaction could obviously occur exothermically in one step by electron transfer. Hole migration along chains of TEA molecules can therefore occur because TEA$^+$ is unreactive toward 3MP.

Proton transfer from 3MP to MTHF is irreversible because no two-step reaction analogous to those just considered is permitted since I(MTHF) > I(3MP).

Many solute cations in 3MP can be photobleached, e.g., C$_6$H$_6^+$ and 2MP-1$^+$, while some cannot, e.g., TMPD$^+$. The phenomenon has not been studied systematically and there is no generalization which covers the available facts. In one instance, however, a possible explanation appears. A sample containing 0.01% TMPD, 1% ϕH, and 1% i-PrCl was γ-irradiated until OD(ϕH$^+$) $\cong$ 1.48 at 950 mμ and OD(TMPD$^+$) $\cong$ 1.35 at 632 mμ. Photobleaching reduced OD(ϕH$^+$) to 0.19 and increased

OD(TMPD$^+$) to 1.69. Similar results were found using ϕCH_3 instead of ϕH, but not with 2MP-1 or ϕ_2 (13). The facts suggest formation of electronically excited benzene cation at 950 mμ (~ 1.3 eV) which combines with the ionization potential 9.25 eV to give an energy level at ~ 10.6 eV. The excited benzene ion can extract an electron from 3MP ($I = 10.1$ eV) and the hole then migrates until it is retrapped by TMPD or otherwise. For ϕ_2 ($I = 8.3$ eV) illumination in the red band at $\lambda_{max} = 680$ mμ (1.8 eV) gives an excited ionic state at ~ 10.1 eV which may be unable to transfer charge. For 2MP-1, however, the excited ionic state lies at $\sim 9.1 + 1.7$. Since 2MP-1$^+$ bleaches, but charge migration does not follow, an alternative reaction must occur.

D. Recombination Luminescence (14)

Delayed luminescence of certain UV-excited solutes in rigid media at low temperature had been known for several years before the effect was attributed by Linschitz et al. (3) to emission from electronically excited states arising from the recombination of a photoelectron with a cation. It is of interest that for N-lithium carbazole only the phosphorescence was observed. Both fluorescence and phosphorescence have been observed for $10^{-2} M$ naphthalene in γ-irradiated isopentane–methylcyclohexane as thermoluminescence (40). Apart from its intrinsic interest and evident relevance to practical applications of so-called organic scintillators it provides an additional—and very powerful—tool for investigating ionic processes.

When glassy solutions of several selected solutes in 3MP were γ-irradiated and subsequently illuminated at 77°K with 800–2000 mμ light, or removed from liquid nitrogen and warmed in air, they luminesced brightly, the color depending upon the solute. Measurement demonstrated that the emission spectrum always corresponded, in the accessible 390–700 mμ region, with the reported phosphorescence spectrum. Any fluorescence which may have occurred could not have been detected, but this is quite immaterial to our purpose for which any identifiable luminescence suffices. The spectra of Table XIV agree with reported results. All samples which luminesced under IR excitation also luminesced during warming.

The phosphorescent spectrum of TPA, for both UV and γ excitation, appears in Figure 39. The apparatus used appears in Figure 5. When IR excitation was applied briefly (~ 0.02 sec) the luminescence was prompt and decayed exponentially with $t_{1/2} \cong 0.12$ sec, the same as for UV excitation.

The phenomenon of recombination luminescence from TPA is complicated by the fact that addition of small concentrations of TPA to 3MP

TABLE XIV

Emission Spectra, 4000–7000 Å, for Various Solutes in γ-Irradiated Glassy Systems (41)

Solute	Solvent	λ_{max} observed (Å)	Phosphorescence[a] λ_{max}	Stimulus[b]
Benzophenone	3MP, 1(TEA) + 3(3MP)	5700, 5200, 4750, 4425	5128, 4739, 4403	W
Benzil	3MP	5675	5617	W
Triphenylamine	3MP, 1(TEA) + 3(3MP)	4250, 4075	4255, 4082	W, B
Biphenyl	3MP	4375, 4683, 5000	4396, 4683, 5000	W, B
Naphthalene	3MP, 1(TEA) + 3(3MP)	5500, 5125, 4692	5420, 5160, 4695	W, B
TMPD[c]	3MP	4660, 4730	~4700	B
Diphenylamine	1(TEA) + 3(3MP)	<4000		W, B
Dimethylaniline	3MP	<4000		W, B

[a] G. N. Lewis and M. Kasha, *J. Am. Chem. Soc.*, **66**, 2100 (1944); A. H. Kalantar and A. C. Albrecht, *J. Phys. Chem.*, **66**, 2279 (1962); H. L. Backstrom and K. Sandros, *Acta Chem. Scand.*, **14**, 48 (1960).

[b] W = warming sample, B = bleaching by illumination with infrared light.

[c] *N N N′N′*-tetramethylparaphenylenediamine.

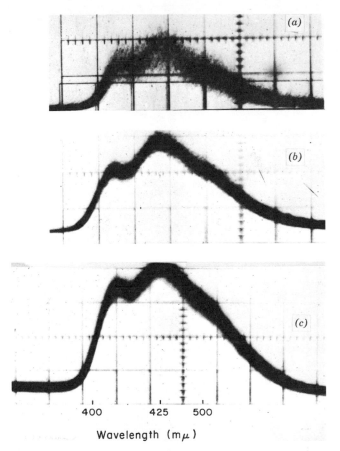

Wavelength (mμ)

Fig. 39. Emission spectra of TPA induced by: (a) bleaching e^- (1–2 μ light), (b) bleaching TPA$^-$ (0.8–1.0 μ light), (c) UV excitation. The blurred appearance of a and b are the result of high sensitivity in the detector which was necessitated by the low intensities involved (41).

decreased the yield of solvent-trapped electrons about as efficiently as the same concentrations of biphenyl, suggesting formation of TPA$^-$. A narrow band at $\lambda_{max} = 310$ mμ and a wide band which overlaps that of (e^-) are assigned to the anion (Fig. 40). While the (e^-) band bleaches easily and completely under IR illumination, the IR band of glasses containing TPA in 3MP following γ irradiation bleaches quickly under 1000–2000 mμ illumination to an unchanging residual absorption with little change in spectral quality. Further illumination at 800–1000 mμ bleaches the residual infrared band while the 310 mμ absorption simultaneously decreases.

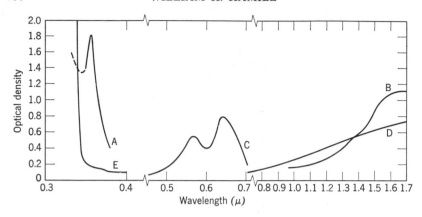

Fig. 40. Absorption spectra of: TPA⁻ (*A* and *B*), 2 × TPA⁺ (*C*), e^- (*D*), and TPA (*E*) in a solution containing 0.06 mole % TPA in 3MP at 77°K. Irradiation dose: 5.76 × 10¹⁸ eV/g. Wavelength measured in microns (41).

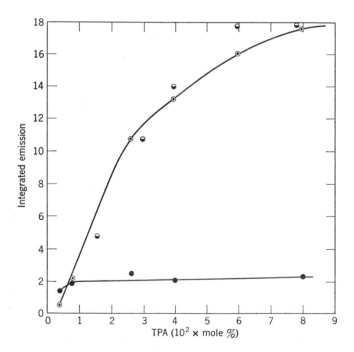

Fig. 41. Integrated emission by detachment of electrons from TPA⁻ (◉) and e^- (●) vs. mole % TPA, in 3MP glass at 77°K. Irradiation dose: 1.50 × 10¹⁸ eV/g. ◐ yields of TPA⁺ which bleached with 0.8–1.0 μ light normalized (41).

The cationic color center arising from TPA, which is designated TPA^+, has been observed previously with maxima at 570 and 656 mμ (1). Although no spectrum was published, that in Figure 40 does exhibit maxima at 565 and 642 mμ.

There is a weak luminescence from γ-irradiated solutions of TPA in 3MP and it presumably corresponds to spontaneous decay of (e^-). The enhanced intensity under 1–2 μ excitation decreases IR absorption, as expected, as well as TPA^+ absorption, but there is considerable residual absorption due to TPA^- (and TPA^+) which only bleaches at $\lambda < 1$ μ. Luminescence intensity is relatively weak for IR excitation at $\lambda > 1$ μ because most (e^-) are converted to TPA^-. The intensity is strong for excitation at $\lambda < 1$ μ because all TPA^- is removed, together with TPA^+, as shown in Figures 41 and 42. These facts demonstrate that TPA^+ decreases as electrons are photodetached from TPA^- and that these changes correlate with the integrated light intensity which presumably arises from recombination luminescence. The nearly constant luminescence intensity with increasing TPA can be understood by assuming that the probability P of electron attachment to yield TPA^- is the same for γ

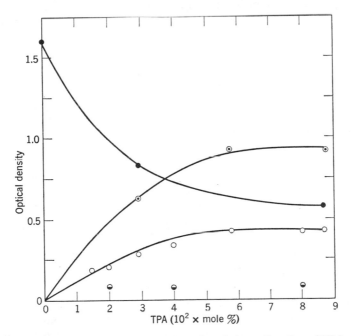

Fig. 42. Yields of TPA^+ (○), TPA^- (◉), and e^- (●) as a function of TPA concentration. Irradiation dose: 5.76×10^{18} eV/g. ◒ indicates optical density of TPA^+ after bleaching (41).

irradiation and for infrared detachment and that it is obtained from the optical densities D of Figure 42 by $1 - P = D_{e^-}/D_{e^-}^0$. Assume also that the probability of detached e^- combining with TPA$^+$ is proportional to the number of these cations and that the phosphorescence intensity I is proportional to the number of such recombinations. Then:

$$I = \text{const. } (1 - P)D(e^-)D(\text{TPA}^+)$$

Taking all D's from Figure 42, the calculated relative intensity is constant within 20% which agrees with the lower curve of Figure 41.

The strongly rising I with increasing % TPA of Figure 41 from bleaching TPA$^-$ might be expected to be proportional to the decrease of $D(\text{TPA}^+)$. These differences, shown in Figure 42, have been normalized to the intensities of Figure 41 with which they correspond by letting:

$$I_{\text{calc}} = \text{const. } \times \Delta D(\text{TPA}^+)$$

Addition of 1 or 2% ethanol to TPA in 3MP inhibited both $D(\text{TPA}^+)$ and the luminescence yield when (e^-) and TPA$^-$ were bleached to comparable degrees. The effect is attributable to hole trapping by proton transfer. Addition of alkyl halides inhibited yields of (e^-) and TPA$^-$ and also strongly diminished the integrated luminescence. Apparently, the large amount of energy dissipated by halide ion formation so diminishes the energy of ion recombination that excitation of TPA is impossible. Estimated data are:

$$\text{TPA(vac)} \longrightarrow \text{TPA}^+\text{(vac)} + e^-\text{(vac)} \qquad 7.5 \text{ eV}$$
$$e^-\text{(vac)} + \text{Cl(vac)} \longrightarrow \text{Cl}^-\text{(vac)} \qquad -3.8 \text{ eV}$$
$$\text{TPA}^+\text{(vac)} + \text{Cl}^-\text{(vac)} \longrightarrow \text{TPA}^+\text{(3MP)} + \text{Cl}^-\text{(3MP)} \quad \sim -2 \text{ eV}$$
$$\text{TPA}^+\text{(3MP)} + \text{Cl}^-\text{(3MP)} \longrightarrow \text{TPA(3MP)} + \text{Cl(3MP)} \quad \sim -1.7 \text{ eV}$$

These effects presumably correlate with the facts that C_2H_5OH and CCl_4 are very poor solvents for scintillators, although this is not the case for UV excitation, while alkanes are fairly good solvents (42).

The results of Figures 39–42 can be accounted for in terms of the regularities previously described for ionic processes, together with one additional postulate: a molecular species M which is luminescent under UV excitation will tend to exhibit a similar emission spectrum following γ excitation by ion recombination, $M^+ + e^- \rightarrow M + h\nu$. In solvent S with attractive excited states, ion recombination would contribute to formation of S*, followed by conventional transfer of electronic excitation to M. Addition of several percent TEA, for example, would quench this component by charge exchange. Any residual luminescence would be a measure of the maximum yield of primary excitation of S, although small charge separation cannot easily be differentiated.

X. CATIONS IN POLYCRYSTALLINE CCl₄ (43)

Cations can be studied with fewer complications in matrices which trap electrons very efficiently. Because it is also very desirable to include crystalline matrices in a general investigation, solutions in CCl_4 were γ-irradiated and examined at − 196°. Finely polycrystalline samples scatter light strongly and two minor modifications in experimental procedure were necessary; thin cells (see Figs. 3 and 4) and an intense light source were used. Because of repeated light scattering the effective length of light path exceeds the window-to-window separation (0.78 and 0.16 cm for one cell), but is corrigible using a colored test solute. The only test of homogeneous dispersion of solute in the matrix is the smooth variation of OD(ions) with solute concentration.

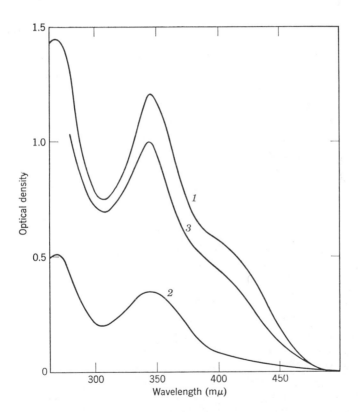

Fig. 43. Optical density of 0.16 cm thick samples of γ-irradiated polycrystalline CCl_4 at 77°K: (*1*) irradiated to 1.8 × 10¹⁸ eV ml⁻¹; (*2*) same as *1*, after warming to 143°K and returning to 77°K; (*3*) another sample, same as *1*, then photobleached (43).

A typical absorption spectrum of γ-irradiated pure CCl_4 solid appears in Figure 43. Due to the 400 mμ band the irradiated solid was bright yellow and this color disappeared rapidly when the sample was warmed from $-196°$ to $-130°$(*sec*-BuCl mush). The other two absorption bands persisted, showing that the responsible species differed from that producing the 400 mμ band. On the other hand, photobleaching with tungsten light reduced all bands slowly. The variation of OD with dose is shown in Figure 44. Due to incomplete separation of the 400 and 345 mμ bands, the curve for the former is only approximate.

Addition of TMPD to CCl_4 diminished OD(400 mμ) and the solid became blue. The new spectrum coincided with that of TMPD$^+$. Illumination with tungsten light diminished OD(400 mμ) further and enhanced OD(TMPD$^+$) (curve *2* in Fig. 45). Illumination did not reduce the absorption of TMPD$^+$. Further enhancement of OD(TMPD$^+$) occurred when the sample was warmed slightly and returned to $-196°$ (curve *3* of Fig. 45). The effect of warming and the relation between the 400 mμ and the amine cation bands are shown in Figure 46 for TPA.

Similar results were obtained with DMPD, N,N,N',N'-tetramethylbenzidine, diphenylamine, N-methyldiphenylamine, aniline, N-methylaniline, N,N-dimethylaniline, and N,N-diethylaniline, as well as triphenylphosphine. The absorption spectra appear in Figures 47 and 48.

The data points of Figure 49 represent OD(TPA$^+$) vs. concentration of TPA at different doses. The curves were calculated. The results for solutions of TMPD in Figure 50 resemble those for TPA in Figures 46 and 49.

The spectra in Figures 45, 47, and 48 agree with those of authentic amine radical cations, when they are known, and all spectra are therefore assigned to the radical cations. The results for TPA and TMPD (Figs. 46, 49, 50) show that the solute ion is produced abundantly at small concentrations of amine. Since most of the absorbed energy is deposited in the matrix, the solute positive ion must be produced by an indirect effect of radiation.

The direct effects of radiation on CCl_4 would include formation of Cl and CCl_3, directly or indirectly. Since CCl_4^+ has not been detected by mass spectrometry, the consequences of ionization must be considered.

Mechanisms which may be proposed to explain the indirect effect of γ irradiation include: (*1*) Cl atoms migrate to solute and form the positive ion; (*2*) energy absorbed by CCl_4 transfers to solute which ionizes; (*3*) primary CCl_4^+ initiates resonance charge transfer with CCl_4 and the hole is trapped by additive. The experimental results can best be accounted for by the third mechanism. Diphenyl amine and DMPD cations have been reported (1,10). Aniline was studied by Porter et al. (44) by flash photolysis

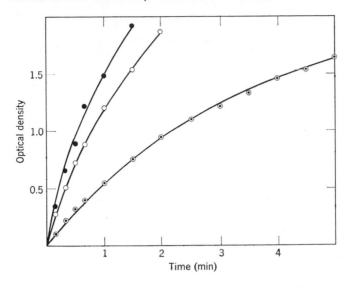

Fig. 44. Optical density of γ-irradiated CCl_4 vs. time of γ irradiation at 1.8×10^{18} eV ml^{-1}·min^{-1}, measured at 270 (●), 345 (○), and 400 mμ (◉) and 77°K (43).

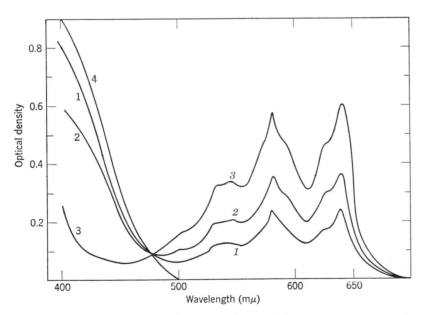

Fig. 45. Absorption spectra of γ-irradiated TMPD (7 mM ml^{-1}) in CCl_4 at 77°K: (1) irradiated to 3.6×10^{18} eV ml^{-1}; (2) same as 1, then photobleached; (3) same as 1, after warming to $\sim 140°$K and returning to 77°K; (4) pure CCl_4, same dose (43).

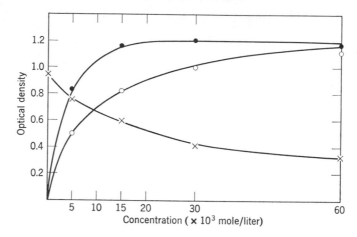

Fig. 46. Optical densities of ϕ_3N^+ at 640 mμ (○) and of CCl_4^+ at 400 mμ (×) vs. concentration of ϕ_3N after γ irradiation to 3.6×10^{18} eV ml^{-1} and at 640 mμ (●) after warming samples to 142°K, then returning to 77°K (43).

and it gave an absorption band at 423 mμ in acidified, aqueous aniline solutions. From the spectral change with pH, they ascribed the band to the end product of the reactions:

$$\phi NH_2 + h\nu \longrightarrow \phi\dot{N}H + H$$
$$\phi\dot{N}H + H^+ \longrightarrow \phi\dot{N}H_2^+$$

This assignment is supported by the present work. Other work indicates that all spectra in Figures 47 and 48 are characteristic of the solute amine radical ions since the same absorption spectra were observed in irradiated butyl chloride glass (to be described).

The limiting yield of cations at high concentrations of TPA in Figure 46 was also attained by warming irradiated samples at lower concentrations. This indicates a common intermediate which migrates during irradiation, becomes trapped, absorbs light at 400 mμ, and can be released by optical or thermal activation. The Cl atom has no transition at 400 mμ and energy transfer is clearly incapable of fitting the facts.

Enhanced yields of amine cation from optical excitation of γ-irradiated samples is not due to photoionization (curve 2 of Fig. 45). For the same illumination, unirradiated samples of TMPD gave no TMPD$^+$ and other amines are even less easily photoionized. Moreover, enhancement of amine cation yield by light is coupled with decreased absorption at 400 mμ and heating to $-130°$ produces the same effects (Figs. 45, 46, and 49).

In order to explain an efficient chain of positive charge transfer involving hundreds of steps, for a hole capable of being self-trapped, it appears to be necessary to invoke an entire series of fast, conservative, vertical transitions.

Since CCl_4^+ has not been observed, either the potential energy surface of CCl_4^+ is repulsive or it has only shallow minima at configurations rather

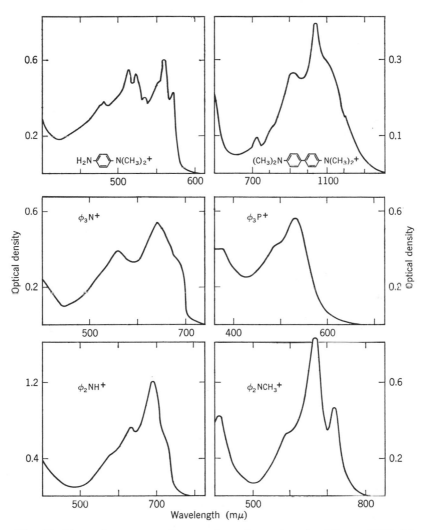

Fig. 47. Absorption spectra of aromatic amine cations in CCl_4 at 77°K (43). Doses, left to right and top to bottom, in units of 10^{18} eV ml^{-1} and parenthetic concentrations in mM, were 22 (1.6), 22 (10), 1.8 (20), 3.6 (20), 5.4 (20) and 3.6 (50).

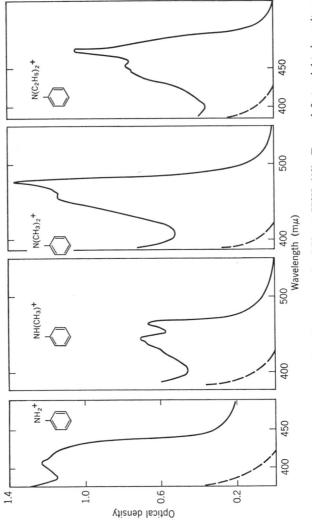

Fig. 48. Absorption spectra of aniline cations in CCl₄ at 77°K (43). Doses, left to right, in units of 10^{19} eV ml^{-1} and parenthetic concentrations in M were 1.1 (0.2), 4.0 (0.3), 4.3 (0.5), 5.4 (0.5).

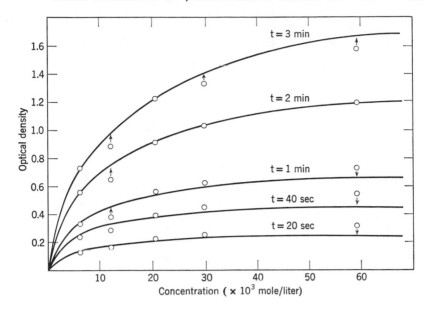

Fig. 49. Optical density of ϕ_3N^+ at 640 mμ in CCl_4 at 77°K vs. time of irradiation at 1.8×10^{18} eV ml^{-1}·min^{-1} and various ϕ_3N concentrations. The curves were calculated after equation 25 (43).

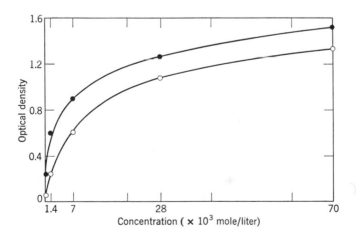

Fig. 50. Optical density of $TMPD^+$ at 640 mμ vs. initial concentration of TMPD after irradiation to 3.6×10^{18} eV ml^{-1} at 77°K ($\bigcirc$) and after warming the same samples to 143°K and returning to 77°K($\bullet$) (43).

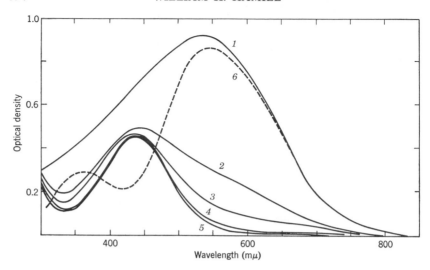

Fig. 51. (*1*) Absorption spectrum of γ-irradiated *n*-BuCl glass at −196°, 6.3 × 10^{19} cV ml^{-1}. (*2–5*) Same, after bleaching with tungsten light. (*6*) Difference spectrum for bleached band (46).

different from those for CCl_4. In a molecular crystal lattice, however, resonance charge transfer appears to be possible by electron tunneling from CCl_4 to CCl_4^+ at distances of ∼1 Å in times of the order 10^{-14} sec (45). The trapped hole may correspond to increased internuclear separation of CCl_3–Cl^+, but the separation would be limited by the cage effect of the matrix. As the lattic relaxes the cation will be stabilized further by electrostriction from the interaction between the charge and induced dipoles.

Thermal activation restores the hole to a conducting configuration. Optical excitation of the relaxed cation lowers the barrier for electron tunneling from a nearby molecule, again forming the conducting state of the ion. Optical excitation of solute cations is unlikely to generate CCl_4^+ by a vertical transition. If the ionization potential of CCl_4 is taken as ∼11.5 eV and that of aromatic amines as 7–7.5 eV, then the excitation of the amine cation must exceed 4 eV to permit charge transfer. No such transitions are optically accessible. The migrating positive hole is assumed to interact with additive by simple electron transfer if the ionization potential of the additive is somewhat lower than that of CCl_4.

In addition to the band at $\lambda_{max} \cong 400$ mμ, other bands appear at 270 and 345 mμ (Fig. 43). The assignment of these bands is not straightforward because easily imagined species such as CCl_3, Cl, and Cl^- do not explain them. Fortunately, the species responsible for these two bands are relatively inert and seem to be irrelevant to this discussion.

The data of Figure 49 show that $G(TPA^+)$ decreases markedly with increasing dose at all concentration of TPA and most strongly at low concentrations, showing competition between solutes and Cl^- for migrating positive holes. This requires that a positive hole from one electron track react with Cl^- of another track. This, in turn, requires some degree of randomization of positive holes. As a working assumption, a description in terms of homogeneous distribution of positive holes will be used. This gives rise to the following expressions, where T is solvent hole trap, S is solute, and X^- is the chloride ion:

$$\frac{dN_{T^+}}{dt} = GI\sigma_T N_T/\Sigma \tag{20}$$

$$\frac{dN_{S^+}}{dt} = GI\sigma_S N_S/\Sigma \tag{21}$$

$$\frac{dN_{X^-}}{dt} = GI - GI\sigma_X N_{X^-}/\Sigma \tag{22}$$

Here Σ stands for $\sigma_T N_T + \sigma_S N_S + \sigma_{X^-} N_{X^-}$. dN is the number of specified ions in unit volume (cm^3) produced by unit dose, $I\,dt(100$ eV$)$, I being dose rate. The σ's and N's are cross sections and numbers per ml of the respective trapping centers. N_S and N_T are effectively constant during irradiation. N_T has been introduced for the sake of consistency in the descriptions although it has purely formal significance.

Equations 20–22 provide the integrated yields at dose It of solvent-trapped positive holes and solute cations as follows:

$$N_{T^+} = \frac{\sigma_T N_T}{\sigma_{X^-}}\left[\left(1 + \frac{2\sigma_{X^-} GIt}{\sigma_T N_T + \sigma_S N_S}\right)^{1/2} - 1\right] \tag{23}$$

$$N_{S^+} = \frac{\sigma_S N_S}{\sigma_{X^-}}\left[\left(1 + \frac{2\sigma_{X^-} GIt}{\sigma_T N_T + \sigma_S N_S}\right)^{1/2} - 1\right] \tag{24}$$

Equation 24 can be expressed in terms of measurable quantities: optical density of solute cation (D), solute concentration $(C$ in mole $cm^{-3})$ and irradiation time $(t$ in min$)$.

$$\frac{D}{10^3\,\epsilon l} = k_1 C\left[\left(1 + \frac{2k_2 t}{k_3 + C}\right)^{1/2} - 1\right] \tag{25}$$

ϵ and l are the extinction coefficient and the length of light path through the sample. The k's are related to other quantities by:

$$k_1 = \sigma_S/\sigma_{X^-}$$
$$k_2 = (GI/N_0)\sigma_{X^-}/\sigma_S \quad \text{(in mole } cm^{-3} \text{ min}^{-1})$$
$$k_3 = (N_T/N_0)\sigma_T/\sigma_S \quad \text{(in mole } cm^{-3})$$

Here, N_0 is the Avogadro number.

The data points of Figure 49 represent OD(TPA$^+$) vs. solute concentration at different irradiation times. For these points a family of curves can be drawn by fitting the k's in equation 25. The values adopted are:

$$\epsilon l k_1 = 41.6 \text{ cm}^3 \text{ mole}^{-1}$$

$$k_2 = 18.36 \times 10^{-6} \text{ mole cm}^{-3} \text{ min}^{-1}$$

$$k_3 = 2.04 \times 10^{-6} \text{ mole cm}^{-3}$$

The adequacy of the description given by equation 25 and shown in Figure 49 supports the validity of the reaction mechanism described.

At large solute concentrations equation 25 approaches linearity,

$$D/10^3 \; \epsilon l = k_1 k_2 t = (GI/N_0)t \tag{26}$$

Therefore, a value for ϵl would give G, the total number of positive holes per unit dose. A single curve similar to those in Figure 49 was obtained for solutions of TMPD in CCl$_4$ from which the limiting OD at large solute concentrations was estimated roughly as 1.7 (Fig. 50). Taking ϵ of TMPD$^+$ as 19,300 (11) and the effective length of light path as 0.78 cm, gives the 100 eV yield of conducting positive holes as 1.9. Since $\epsilon l k_1 = 41.6 \text{ cm}^3 \text{ mole}^{-1}$, $\sigma_{\text{X}^-}/\sigma_{\text{S}} = 360$. This large ratio is quite plausible.

XI. CATIONS IN GLASSY BUTYL CHLORIDE (46)

Many of the advantages of CCl$_4$, and fewer disadvantages, are provided by butyl chloride (BuCl), either normal or secondary. Most important, it is a much better solvent, possibly because at $-196°$ it is glassy though badly cracked. These optical imperfections are inconvenient but tolerable when a thin cell is used. Since only solute cations were to be examined in the γ-irradiated BuCl matrix, all samples were prepared in air.

Upon γ irradiation pure n- and sec-BuCl glasses became purple and brown, respectively. The absorption spectra and the growth of optical density at λ_{max} vs. irradiation dose appear in Figures 51–53. Upon illumination of irradiated BuCl with tungsten light the optical density gradually decreased and λ_{max} shifted as Figures 49 and 50 show. The differences of optical density before and after illumination, given by the broken lines, describe the spectrum of the bleached component which has band maxima at ~ 460 and ~ 540 mμ. For the surviving, unbleached component, λ_{max} is ~ 440 mμ.

When samples contained aromatic hydrocarbons or amines, both solvent bands decreased or disappeared and new absorption bands appeared which were characteristic of the solutes. The absorption bands of irradiated pure BuCl or of solute aromatic hydrocarbon cations were decreased by the addition of small amounts of alcohols, ethers, and amines. The addition of 0.02 ml of ethanol to 5 ml BuCl, for example, made an

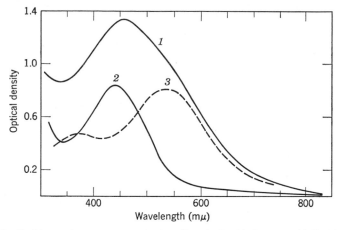

Fig. 52. (*1*) Absorption spectrum of γ-irradiated *s*-BuCl glass at −196°, 1.3×10^{19} eV ml^{-1}. (*2*) Same, after bleaching with tungsten light. (*3*) Difference spectrum for bleached band (46).

irradiated sample completely colorless which otherwise would have been deep brown.

Aromatic amines gave the same absorption spectra as those obtained in CCl$_4$. Figure 54 shows the optical densities of TMPD$^+$ at 640 mμ at various doses plotted against the initial concentration of amine in *sec*-BuCl glass.

Several aromatic hydrocarbons which had been used in the CCl$_4$ matrix to generate the corresponding cations (46), for which the spectra

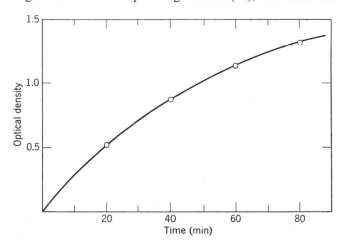

Fig. 53. OD at 455 mμ of γ-irradiated *sec*-BuCl glass as a function of irradiation time at −196°, 1.6×10^{18} eV ml$^{-1} \cdot$min^{-1} (46).

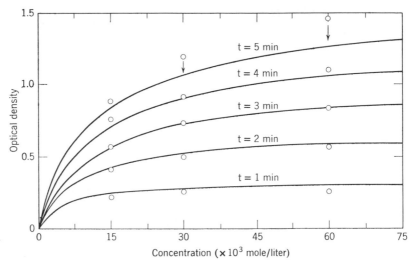

Fig. 54. OD at 642 mμ of TMPD⁺ vs. amine concentration as a function of dose at −196°, 1.58 × 10¹⁸ eV ml⁻¹·min⁻¹. Curves constructed from equation 28 (46).

appear as Figures 55 and 57 were reexamined in glassy BuCl (46). The spectra were the same. In addition, 22 other hydrocarbons which are insoluble in polycrystalline CCL_4, but are soluble in BuCl glass, were examined and their absorption spectra are shown in Figures 58–65. Those of perylene, pyrene, and triphenylene agree quite well with the spectra assigned to the molecular positive ions of these hydrocarbons (47–49) using other preparative methods. The other spectra were first observed in this work.

For comparison, and to assist in the identification of cationic species, all aromatic hydrocarbons examined in BuCl were also examined in MTHF in which solute anion formation is strongly favored. These absorption bands, except those already reported, are shown by broken lines in Figures 58–63.

Although the solute anion bands in MTHF resemble bands obtained in BuCl there are marked differences in the color centers themselves which have already been attributed to cation or anion behavior. In BuCl the solute absorption bands bleached very slowly with tungsten light (cation) whereas those in MTHF faded rapidly under illumination (anion). In BuCl small amounts of alcohol, known to be a proton acceptor, suppressed the absorption bands due to irradiated hydrocarbons (cation). On the other hand, in MTHF addition of i-PrCl, which is an efficient electron scavenger, prevented the appearance of absorption bands associated with solute hydrocarbon (anion).

The similarity in spectra for each aromatic hydrocarbon in BuCl and in MTHF γ-irradiated matrices, as well as the agreement in several instances with molecular cation and anion spectral assignments by others, together with the entire self-consistent methodology of this work, all support the assignments of these bands to the monopositive and mononegative radical aromatic hydrocarbon ionic species.

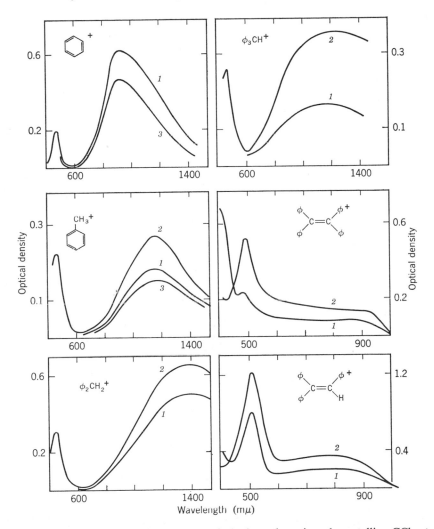

Fig. 55. Absorption spectra of aromatic hydrocarbons in polycrystalline CCl₄ at −196° (43). In each instance, curve *1* after γ irradiation, and curve *2* same sample after heating to ∼ −130°; curve *3* same as curves *1* or *2* after photobleaching. See also Figures 56 and 57.

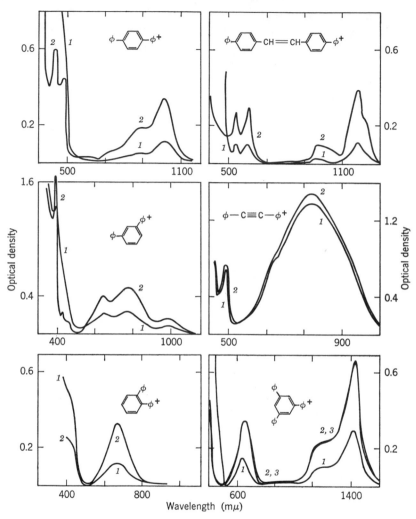

Fig. 56. See caption for Figure 55 (p. 399).

Different stabilities toward light of the bands in BuCl and in MTHF glasses are also consistent with the assignment that the bands in MTHF and in BuCl are due to ArH$^-$ and ArH$^+$, respectively. Electrons are easily photodetached from the former. Cations cannot be photobleached unless the electronically excited state produced lies above the ionization potential of molecules of the matrix. If the higher excited states of ArH$^+$ internally convert as extremely rapidly as the neutral molecules, then photoconduction of the hole can only be induced when the energy of the first excited state of ArH$^+$ exceeds the ionization potential of the matrix.

The result in Figure 63 indicates that photoexcitation of *cis*-stilbene anion in MTHF induces isomerization to *trans*-stilbene anion, as observed in the cation of *cis*-stilbene in CCl$_4$ or BuCl matrix.

The simplest solute, benzene, behaved exceptionally (Fig. 65). The spectra of benzene in BuCl and in MTHF are not at all similar. In BuCl glass, absorption bands appeared at about 470 mμ and 910 mμ. Because the two bands were also observed in CCl$_4$ matrix, it is probable that they are associated with benzene cation. Das and Basu reported that chemical

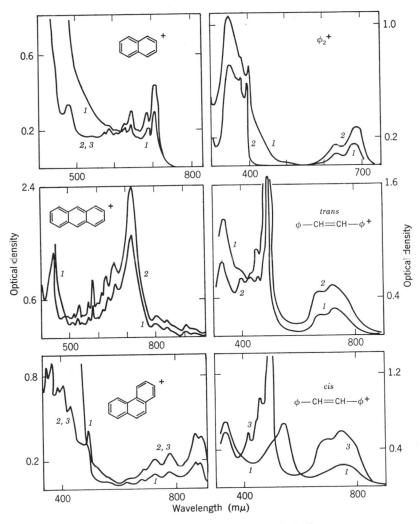

Fig. 57. See caption for Figure 55 (p. 399).

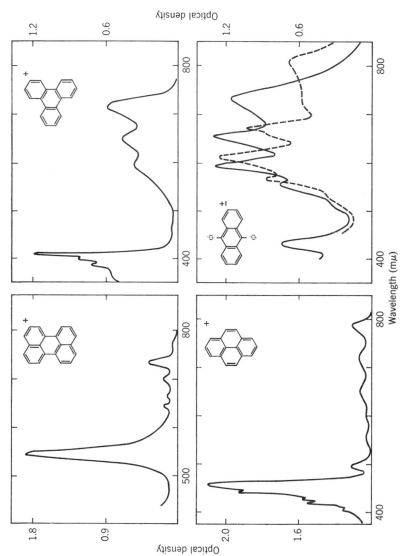

Fig. 58. Absorption spectra of aromatic hydrocarbon cations in *sec*-BuCl (solid curve) and of anions in MTHF (dashed curve) (46): perylene, near saturation, 2.8×10^{19} eV/ml; pyrene, 0.1 mole/1, 1.9×10^{19} eV/ml; triphenylene, 0.08 mole/1, 1.9×10^{19} eV ml; 9,10-diphenylanthracene, 0.05 mole/1 in *sec*-BuCl, 3.8×10^{19} eV/ml and 0.01 mole/1 in MTHF, 4×10^{19} eV/ml.

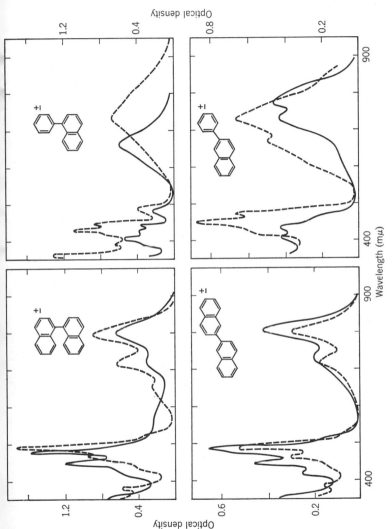

Fig. 59. Absorption spectra of aromatic hydrocarbon cations in sec-BuCl (solid curve) and of anions in MTHF (dashed curve) (46): 1,1′-binaphthyl, 0.002 mole/1 in sec-BuCl, 2.4 × 10¹⁹ eV/ml and 0.01 mole/1 in MTHF 9.0 × 10¹⁸ eV/ml; 2,2′- binaphthyl, 0.002 mole/1 in sec-BuCl, 9.5 × 10¹⁹ eV/ml and 0.1 mole/1 in MTHF, 1.2 × 10¹⁹ eV/ml; 1-phenylnaphthalene, 0.07 mole/1 in sec-BuCl, 1.9 × 10¹⁹ eV/ml and 0.03 mole/1 in MTHF, 9 × 10¹⁸ eV/ml; 2-phenylnaphthalene, 0.02 mole/1 in sec-BuCl, 1.9 × 10¹⁹ eV/ml and 0.02 mole/1 in MTHF, 9 × 10¹⁸ eV/ml.

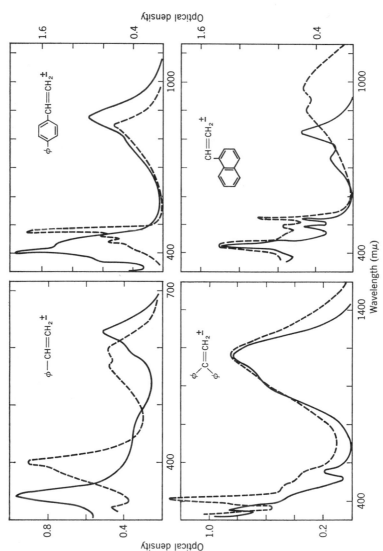

Fig. 60. Absorption spectra of aromatic hydrocarbon cations in *sec*-BuCl (solid curve) and of anions in MTHF (dashed curve) (46): styrene, 0.3 mole/l in *sec*-BuCl. 2.8×10^{19} eV/ml and 0.1 mole/l in MTHF, 9×10^{18} eV/ml; 1,1'-diphenylethylene, 0.1 mole/l in *sec*-BuCl, 2.8×10^{19} eV/ml and 0.05 mole/l in MTHF, 9×10^{18} eV/ml; 4-vinylbiphenyl, 0.2 mole/l in *sec*-BuCl, 4.0×10^{19} eV/ml and 0.2 mole/l in MTHF, 6.0×10^{18} eV/ml; 1-vinylnaphthalene, 0.3 mole/l in *sec*-BuCl, 3.8×10^{19} eV/ml and 0.3 mole/l in MTHF, 6.0×10^{18} eV/ml.

oxidation of benzene with antimony pentachloride produced benzene cation which absorbed at 445 mμ (50). As for the 910 mμ band, it might correspond to a transition of benzene cation discovered by Terenin and Vilessov (51). On the other hand, in MTHF glass benzene produces a

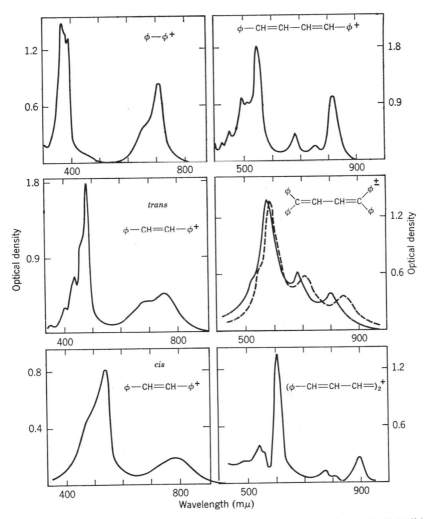

Fig. 61. Absorption spectra of aromatic hydrocarbon cations in *sec*-BuCl (solid curve) and of anions in MTHF (dashed curve) (46): biphenyl, 0.1 mole/1, 1.9 × 10¹⁹ eV/ml; *trans*-stilbene, 0.1 mole/1, 9.5 × 10¹⁸ eV/ml; *cis*-stilbene, 0.1 mole/1, 9.5 × 10¹⁸ eV/ml; 1,4-diphenylbutadiene, 0.1 mole/1, 4.8 × 10¹⁸ eV/ml; 1,1,4,4-tetraphenylbutadiene, 0.1 mole/1 in *sec*-BuCl, 9.5 × 10¹⁸ eV/ml and 0.02 mole/1 in MTHF, 9.5 × 10¹⁸ eV/ml; 1,6-diphenylhexatriene, 0.1 mole/1, 9.5 × 10¹⁸ eV/ml.

broad band starting at 800 mμ which cannot easily be ascribed to $C_6H_6^-$ because of dissimilarity with the cation bands.

The general similarity between the results obtained with BuCl and CCl_4 implies similar mechanisms. The dependences of solute cation yields on

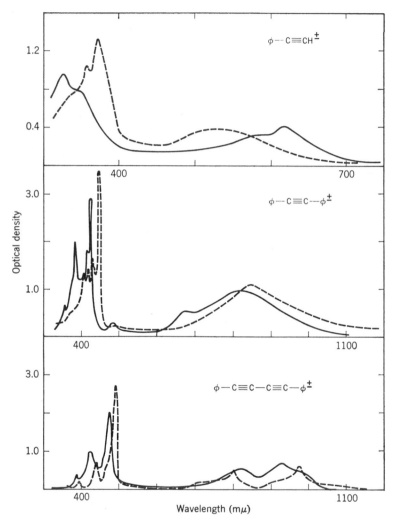

Fig. 62. Absorption spectra of aromatic hydrocarbon cations in sec-BuCl (solid curve) and of anions in MTHF (dashed curve) (46): phenylacetylene, 0.3 mole/1 in sec-BuCl, 2.9×10^{19} eV/ml and 0.2 mole/1 in MTHF, 9.0×10^{18} eV/ml; diphenyl-acetylene, 0.02 mole/1 in sec-BuCl, 1.5×10^{19} eV/ml and 0.02 mole/1 in MTHF, 3.0×10^{18} eV/ml; diphenyldiacetylene, 0.02 mole/1 in sec-BuCl, 4.7×10^{18} eV/ml and 0.02 mole/1 in MTHF, 4.7×10^{18} eV/ml.

dose and concentration are therefore expected to be entirely analogous. Assuming uniform distribution of charged species, it was found for CCl_4 that:

$$N_{S^+} = \frac{\sigma_S N_S}{\sigma_{X^-}}\left[\left(1 + \frac{2\sigma_{X^-} GIt}{\sigma_T N_T + \sigma_S N_S}\right)^{1/2} - 1\right] \tag{27}$$

N's and σ's refer to concentrations and cross sections; T and S are solvent and solute traps; G, I, and t are as before, 100 eV yield of holes formed, dose rate, and time. The same description applies to the data of Figure 52 in terms of optical density D of solute cation and solute concentration C in mole cm^{-3} and t in min.

$$D = 0.0366C\left[\left(1 + \frac{18.4t}{2.32 + C}\right)^{1/2} - 1\right] \tag{28}$$

At sufficiently large N_S equation 27 becomes

$$\frac{D}{10^3 \,\epsilon l} = \frac{GI}{6 \times 10^{23}} t \tag{29}$$

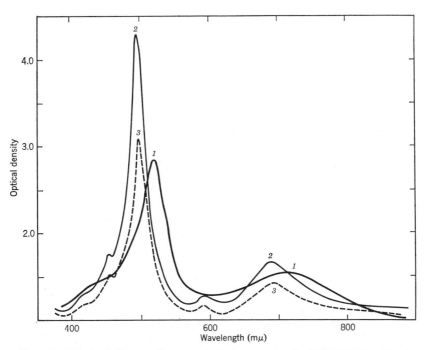

Fig. 63. Effect of illumination on *cis*-stilbene anion in MTHF (46): (*1*) after irradiation of *cis*-stilbene solution (0.01 mole/1) to 6.0×10^{18} eV/ml; (*2*) same as preceding after exposure to tungsten light; (*3*) after irradiation of *trans*-stilbene solution (0.02 mole/1) to 4.0×10^{18} eV/ml.

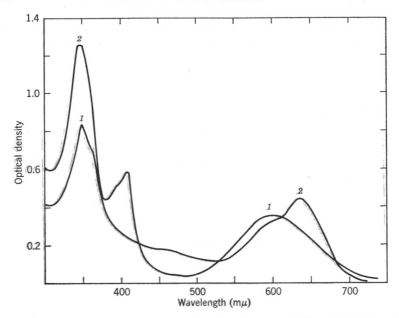

Fig. 64. (*1*) Absorption spectrum of γ-irradiated styrene, 0.02 mole/l (9.0 × 10¹⁸
eV/ml); there was no absorption between 750–2000 mμ. (*2*) Same as preceding but
with 0.02 mole/l i-PrCl (46).

Since the extinction coefficient $\epsilon(\text{TMPD}^+)$ is 1.93×10^4 liters mole^{-1}
cm^{-1} at 640 mμ and cell thickness is known, the appropriate plot gives
the 100 eV yield of available (conducting) holes, $G \cong 3$. It may be concluded that nearly all holes produced are conducting. It should be noted
that although the highest concentration of solute was $\sim 6 \times 10^{-3}$ mole
fraction, the OD of TMPD$^+$ was linear in dose, indicating substantially
no recombination of the migrating hole with Cl$^-$.

XII. CHEMICAL EFFECTS

A. Dissociative Electron Attachment

This effect has been demonstrated repeatedly and can be predicted
reliably: the process $RX + e^- \rightarrow R + X^-$ occurs efficiently whenever
$A(X) > D(RX)$, both in the mass spectrometer (12) and in condensed
phases. This implies that the electrons involved have little kinetic energy.
Indirect chemical evidence for this effect is provided by the observation
that ultimate products to be expected from the dissociative attachment
process are actually produced in γ-irradiated systems containing even a
few percent of appropriate reactive solutes. Thus, alkyl halides give large

yields of alkanes and hydrogen halides (34). Benzyl acetate gives CO_2 + CH_4 in benzene (34), but CH_3COOH in alcohol (52). The neutral radical has been identified by its optical absorption spectrum using triphenyl-methyl chloride (31) or benzyl derivatives (31,33) and by EPR using alkyl

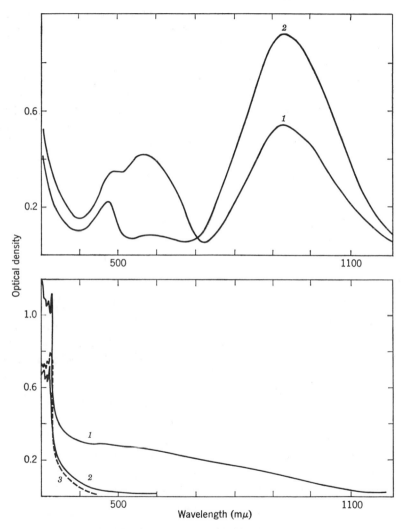

Fig. 65. Absorption spectra of benzene solutions (46): top (*1*) benzene 1.0 mole/1 in *sec*-BuCl, 2×10^{19} eV/ml; (*2*) after photobleaching with tungsten light; bottom (*1*) benzene 1.0 mole/1 in MTHF, 8×10^{18} eV/ml; (*2*) benzene 1.0 mole/1 + i-PrCl 0.3 mole/1 in MTHF, 8×10^{18} eV/ml. (*3*) after photobleaching (*1*) with tungsten light.

halides (14). Photoionization of TMPD induces the same effect as γ irradiation.

When there is no electron attachment, the energy stored in the system per ion pair at large separations is the ionization potential less the combined polarization energy of the ions. For 3MP these are 10 and ~ 2 eV, respectively. If the electron returns slowly it converts some of the coulombic energy to heat, and rather less than 8 eV is available for the final stage of charge recombination. When electron attachment has intervened, e.g., to give Cl^-, then the initial energy at large separation is $\sim (10 - 2 - 3.8)$ eV and again the ultimate charge recombination is moderated by prior degradation of coulombic energy. Since this can scarcely be less than 1 or 2 eV, the terminal reaction cannot break a C—H or C—C bond. The net effect is to transfer the chemical consequences of ionization from solvent to solute. Thus, addition of CH_3I to cyclohexane diminishes the yield of H_2 and forms instead $CH_4 + HI$ (53).

In mass spectrometry, when $D(R—X) > A(X)$, the process occurs at an electron energy given by $D - A$. To what extent the comparable process occurs in γ-irradiated organic solids is not known, but since there appear to be solvent-trapped electron bands in alcohol glasses (25) the probability of the initially energetic electron undergoing such a reaction as, e.g.,

$$CH_3OH + e^- \longrightarrow CH_3O^- + H$$

must be small for one encounter. This reaction would require:

$$D(CH_3O—H) - A(CH_3O) = 4.34 - 2.6 \text{ eV} \cong 1.7 \text{ eV}$$

(see Table XIII). The (e^-) band at $\lambda_{max} = 520$ mμ in methanol provides an opportunity to supply ~ 2.4 eV by optical excitation. In many matrices (e.g., 3MP, MTHF, and TEA) optical bleaching of (e^-) has been shown to release "free" electrons. When dilute solutions of ϕ_2 in methanol or ethanol are γ irradiated, both ϕ_2^- and (e^-) appear, but bleaching at $\lambda_{max} \cong 520$ mμ removes (e^-) without increasing $OD(\phi_2^-)$. When isobutene is present in methanol, γ irradiation forms $t\text{-}C_4H_9$ and bleaching at $\lambda > 500$ mμ enhances the yield of $t\text{-}C_4H_9$. Photoionization of TMPD in methanol containing isobutene, with concurrent bleaching of (e^-), also forms $t\text{-}C_4H_9$. H atoms are produced in both experiments, and activated dissociative electron attachment is the only plausible mechanism (54).

B. Proton Transfer

It is generally assumed that proton transfer of the type:

$$AH^+ + B \longrightarrow A + BH^+$$

occurs under mass spectrometric conditions whenever it is allowed energetically, i.e., $I(H) + D(A - H) - I(AH) - P(B) < 0$, where I's are ionization potentials, D is bond dissociation energy, and P is proton affinity. The "acidity" of HA^+ clearly parallels the value of $I(HA)$ and allows proton transfer to very weak bases, such as CH_4 from CH_4^+, when I is sufficiently large.

Protonation tends to degrade the energy of the ion pair, and the result of recombination may be simply:

$$BH^+ + e^- \longrightarrow B + H$$

since the heat of reaction *in vacuo*, $P - I(H)$, is further diminished by $\gtrsim 4\,eV$ in condensed phase due to polarization and coulombic energy effects. When electron attachment intervenes to form X^-, an additional lowering of recombination energy amounting to $A(X)$ occurs if field emission from X^- to BH^+ occurs in a low dielectric. The reaction to be expected is:

$$BH^+ + X^- \longrightarrow B + H + X$$

A possible example is acetate ion (from benzyl acetate) in benzene (34), since the ultimate products $CO_2 + CH_4$ correspond to the acetoxy radical as precursor. In a high dielectric medium, such as ethanol, the reaction tends to be:

$$BH^+ + X^- \longrightarrow B + HX$$

and acetate ion, e.g., produces acetic acid. It is a well-known fact that acetate ion gives acetic acid in acidulated alcoholic solution, not CO_2 and CH_4.

The proton affinity of acetate ion, $P(OAc^-) = I(H) + D(H-OAc) - A(OAc) \cong 15\,eV$, is far greater than necessary to abstract a proton from an alkane radical cation *in vacuo* ($\sim 8\,eV$). Allowing $\sim 4\,eV$ for combined polarization and coulombic energy dissipation in the dielectric, one estimates $\Delta H \cong -3\,eV$ for:

$$C_6H_{14}^+ + OAc^- \longrightarrow C_6H_{13} + HOAc$$

It is improbable that CO_2 would result from such a reaction. Rather, it appears that charge recombination proceeds via field emission:

$$C_6H_{14}^+ + OAc^- \longrightarrow C_6H_{14} + OAc$$

followed by prompt decomposition of the acetoxy radical. In ethanol, e.g., the reaction:

$$C_2H_5OH_2^+ + OAc^- \longrightarrow C_2H_5OH + H + OAc$$

is certainly very endothermic and both large proton affinity and large dielectric constant contribute to this effect. In all solvents of large proton affinity, radiolysis of benzyl acetate yields acetic acid. That protonation rather than dielectric constant is reponsible appears from the effect of

TABLE XV

Radiolysis of Benzyl Acetate 20° (52)

	% Benzyl acetate	G(acid)	$G(CO_2)$	$G(CH_4)$
Cyclohexane	2.1	0.0	1.6	1.2
Benzene	6	0.0	1.0	0.6
Ethanol	2	4.3	0.05	0.15
MTHF	3	3.0	0.45	0.18
Acetone	2.5	1.5	0.7	1.2
Acetonitrile	1.8	2.3	—	—
2MP-1 97%				
EtOH 3%	2	3.5	—	—

adding only 3% of ethanol to 2MP-1 (cf. Table XV). When the solvent is not particularly basic, fragment cations are unlikely to transfer protons because both I and P are unfavorable. Thus, both CH_2CN^+ and CH_3CNH^+ in acetonitrile may be produced and survive until charge recombination. When acetate ion is involved, the former would be expected to give acetoxy radical, the latter acetic acid. The production of both types of product in some solvents can be understood in terms of this assumption.

Until quite recently no proton transfer of the type:

$$B^- + HA \longrightarrow HB + A^-$$

had been observed in irradiated organic solids. A number of aliphatic and aromatic ketones trap electrons and appear to form molecular anions in 3MP or MTHF (54). In the methanol matrix however the (e^-) band at $\lambda_{max} = 520$ mμ is suppressed by acetone, but the ketyl anion band does not appear. The seven-line EPR spectrum corresponds closely with that of γ-irradiated isopropanol suggesting that the reaction is:

$$CH_3COCH_3^- + CH_3OH \longrightarrow CH_3\dot{C}(OH)CH_3 + CH_3O^-$$

Benzene and other aromatic hydrocarbons yield molecular anions with characteristic optical spectra in γ-irradiated 3MP or MTHF matrices (46). In a γ-irradiated alcohol matrix a number of these hydrocarbons give quite different spectra. That for benzene is identifiable as the cyclohexadienyl radical and resembles the spectra for toluene, the xylenes, and biphenyl. All are characterized by a sharp onset at ~ 320 mμ of a structured band system. Of the aromatic hydrocarbons examined only ϕ_2 gave the anion band, together with the band at 320 mμ. Upon standing the former slowly decreased and the latter increased. The results are consistent with the assumption (49) that reaction occurs via:

$$C_{12}H_{10}^- + ROH \longrightarrow C_{12}H_{11} + RO^-$$

and analogously for the others. In the case of stilbene the proton is transferred to β position to give $C_6H_5\dot{C}HCH_3$ which had been observed previously by dissociative electron attachment from $C_6H_5CHClCH_3$ (33). The reaction between ϕ_2^- and C_2H_5OH had been observed by pulse radiolysis (50).

C. Ion–Electron Recombination

Somewhat limited experimental evidence supports plausible inferences about the chemical consequences of charge recombination only when most of the initially deposited energy has been dissipated. For the return of a "free" electron to a polyatomic ion, even *in vacuo*, substantially nothing is known. The application of matrix isolation techniques to this problem has provided promising but limited information (53,56). For both cyclo-C_6H_{12} and cyclo-C_5H_{10} the cycloalkenes are major products of γ irradiation (~ 2.7 molecules per 100 eV), as is H_2. Both alkenes and H_2 are strongly suppressed by CH_3I (see Section XII-A). It is suggested without proof that:

$$C_nH_{2n}^+ + e^- \longrightarrow C_nH_{2n-2} + 2H$$

Support for this mechanism is provided by the fact (57) that $\sim 5\%$ C_6D_{12} and 95% C_6H_{12} gives $G(HD) \gg G(D_2)$. The polycrystalline systems have not proven suitable for optical spectroscopy and the ionic mechanism has not been substantiated.

The two cyclic olefins, C_6H_{10} and C_5H_8, can be examined readily in a 3MP matrix. Following γ irradiation at $-196°$ both olefin cation (~ 700 mμ) and (e^-) absorption (~ 1600 mμ) were observed, as well as a band at ~ 250 mμ which is characteristic of conjugated dienes. When the 1600 mμ band was bleached, 700 mμ absorption simultaneously decreased while the 250 mμ band increased. Also, 1% C_6D_{10} in C_6H_{12} gave $G(HD/G(D_2) \cong 26$. The results support the mechanism:

$$C_6H_{10}^+ + e^- \longrightarrow C_6H_8 + 2H$$

and analogously for cyclo-C_5H_8 (53).

When 1,4-cyclohexadiene was γ-irradiated at $20°$ in C_6H_{12}, G(benzene) $=$ 1.2 and $G(1,3\text{-cyclo-}C_6H_8) = 0.64$. The same yields were obtained in 3MP at $-196°$, but the very small extinction coefficient of benzene makes it impossible to demonstrate that C_6H_6 results from ion recombination. Sharp band maxima at 309 and 316 mμ were observed for runs at $-196°$

with 0.5% 1,4-cyclohexadiene in 3MP and are attributable to the cyclo-hexadienyl radical. There was also a band at 770 mμ which disappeared when the (e^-) band was bleached. In C_6D_{12} as solvent at 20°, $G(HD)/G(H_2) = 2.5$. By analogy with the results for cyclo-C_6H_{10} it is assumed that ion recombination produces unsaturation by:

$$C_6H_8^+ + e^- \longrightarrow C_6H_6 + 2H$$

The formation of C_6H_7 is attributable to:

$$C_6H_8^+ + e^- \longrightarrow C_6H_7 + H$$

and 1,3-cyclohexadiene to the subsequent reaction with solvent:

$$C_6H_{14} + C_6H_7 \longrightarrow C_6H_{13} + C_6H_8$$

Acknowledgment

For permission to reproduce tables and figures, the author is indebted to the copyright owners: Academic Press, Inc. for *Radiation Research*; the American Chemical Society for the *Journal of the American Chemical Society*; the American Institute of Physics for *The Journal of Chemical Physics*; The Faraday Society for the *Transactions of the Faraday Society*; the National Research Council of Canada for the *Canadian Journal of Chemistry*.

ABBREVIATIONS AND SYMBOLS

BuCl	Either *n*- or *sec*-butyl chloride
Bz	Benzyl
DMA	Dimethylaniline
DMPD	*N*,*N*-Dimethyl-*p*-phenylenediamine
(e^-)	Solvent-trapped electron
eV	Electron volt
h	Electron vacancy, hole
3MP	3-Methylpentane
2MP-1	2-Methyl-1-pentene
MTHF	Methyltetrahydrofuran
OD	Optical density
TEA	Triethylamine
TMPD	*N*,*N*,*N'*,*N'*-Tetramethyl-*p*-phenylenediamine
TPA	Triphenylamine
v	Molecular vacancy, cavity, in matrix
A	Electron affinity
AP	Appearance potential
D	Optical density
D	Bond dissociation energy
e	Electron charge
E	Energy
f	Oscillator strength
G	Yield per 100 eV absorbed energy
I	Ionization potential

I	Dose rate
l	Light intensity distance
N_0	Avogadro's constant
n, N	Number of particles/unit vol.
	Number of randomized electrons/unit vol.
t	Time
X	Mole fraction
ϵ	Extinction coefficient, 1/mole cm
ϵ	Dielectric constant
λ	Wavelength
$\bar{\nu}$	Wave number
σ	Cross section
$\Phi(e^-)$	Quantum yield for bleaching solvent-trapped electrons

References

1. G. N. Lewis and D. Lipkin, *J. Am. Chem. Soc.*, **64**, 2801 (1942).
2. G. N. Lewis and J. Bigeleisen, *J. Am. Chem. Soc.*, **65**, 2419 (1943).
3. H. Linschitz, M. G. Berry, and D. Schweitzer, *J. Am. Chem. Soc.*, **76**, 5833 (1954).
4. L. Michaelis, M. P. Schubert, and S. Granick, *J. Am. Chem. Soc.*, **61**, 198 (1939).
5. P. J. Dyne and O. A. Miller, *Can. J. Chem.*, **43**, 2696 (1965).
6. P. S. Rao, J. R. Nash, J. P. Guarino, M. R. Ronaync, and W. H. Hamill, *J. Am. Chem. Soc.*, **84**, 500 (1962).
7. M. R. Ronayne, J. P. Guarino, and W. H. Hamill, *J. Am. Chem. Soc.*, **84**, 4230 (1962).
8. J. P. Guarino, M. R. Ronayne, and W. H. Hamill, *Radiation Res.*, **17**, 379 (1962).
9. J. P. Guarino and W. H. Hamill, *J. Am. Chem. Soc.*, **86**, 777 (1964).
10. M. Kondo, M. R. Ronayne, J. P. Guarino, and W. H. Hamill, *J. Am. Chem. Soc.*, **86**, 1297 (1964).
11. W. C. Meyer and A. C. Albrecht, *J. Phys. Chem.*, **66**, 1168 (1962).
12. T. F. Moran and W. H. Hamill, *J. Chem. Phys.*, **39**, 1413 (1963).
13. J. B. Gallivan and W. H. Hamill, *J. Chem. Phys.*, **44**, 1279 (1966).
14. D. W. Skelly, R. G. Hayes, and W. H. Hamill, *J. Chem. Phys.*, **43**, 2795 (1965).
15. R. F. C. Claridge and J. E. Willard, *J. Am. Chem. Soc.*, **87**, 4992 (1965).
16. E. Dolan, *J. Chem. Phys.*, **37**, 2508 (1962).
17. P. M. Johnson and A. C. Albrecht, *J. Chem. Phys.*, **44**, 1845 (1966).
18. D. W. Skelly and W. H. Hamill, *J. Chem. Phys.*, **44**, 2893 (1966).
19. A. H. Samuel and J. L. Magee, *J. Chem. Phys.*, **21**, 1080 (1953).
20. R. L. Platzman, *Natl. Res. Council Pub.*, **305**, 22 (1953).
21. P. Debye, *Trans. Electrochem. Soc.*, **82**, 265 (1942).
22. G. A. Salmon, *Discussions Faraday Soc.*, **36**, 284 (1963).
23. D. R. Smith and J. J. Pieroni, *Can. J. Chem.*, **43**, 876 (1965).
24. D. R. Smith and J. J. Pieroni, *Can. J. Chem.*, **43**, 2141 (1965).
25. R. S. Alger, T. H. Anderson, and L. A. Wcbb, *J. Chem. Phys.*, **30**, 695 (1959).
26. J. Jortner, *J. Chem. Phys.*, **30**, 839 (1959).
27. K. Fueki, *J. Chem. Phys.*, **44**, 3140 (1966).
28. J. L. Magee and M. Burton, *J. Am. Chem. Soc.*, **73**, 523 (1951).
29. E. P. Bertin and W. H. Hamill, *J. Am. Chem. Soc.*, **86**, 1301 (1964)
30. G. Porter and E. Strachan, *Trans. Faraday Soc.*, **54**, 1595 (1958).

31. W. H. Hamill, J. P. Guarino, M. R. Ronayne, and J. A. Ward, *Discussions Faraday Soc.*, **36**, 169 (1963).
32. B. Brocklehurst, G. Porter, and M. I. Savadatti, *Trans. Faraday Soc.*, **60**, 2017 (1964).
33. J. B. Gallivan and W. H. Hamill, *Trans. Faraday Soc.*, **61**, 1960 (1965).
34. W. van Dusen and W. H. Hamill, *J. Am. Chem. Soc.*, **84**, 3648 (1962).
35. J. B. Gallivan and W. H. Hamill, *J. Chem. Phys.*, **44**, 2378 (1966).
36. D. W. Skelly and W. H. Hamill, *J. Phys. Chem.*, **70**, 1636 (1966).
37. B. Steiner, C. F. Giese, and M. G. Ingraham, *J. Chem. Phys.*, **34**, 189 (1961).
38. L. Kevan and W. F. Libby, *J. Chem. Phys.*, **39**, 1288 (1963).
39. T. F. Williams, *Trans. Faraday Soc.*, **51**, 755 (1961).
40. B. Brocklehurst, G. Porter, and J. M. Yates, *J. Phys. Chem.*, **68**, 203 (1964).
41. D. W. Skelly and W. H. Hamill, *J. Chem. Phys.*, **43**, 3497 (1965).
42. H. Kallman and M. Furst, *J. Chem. Phys.*, **23**, 607 (1955).
43. T. Shida and W. H. Hamill, *J. Chem. Phys.*, **44**, 2375 (1966).
44. E. J. Land and G. Porter, *Trans. Faraday Soc.*, **59**, 2027 (1963).
45. W. L. McCubbin, *Trans. Faraday Soc.*, **59**, 769 (1963).
46. T. Shida and W. H. Hamill, *J. Chem. Phys.*, **44**, 2375 (1966).
47. G. J. Hoijtink and W. P. Weijland, *Rec. Trav. Chim.*, **76**, 836 (1957).
48. W. Ij. Aalbersberg, G. J. Hoijtink, E. L. Mackor, and W. P. Weijland, *J. Chem. Soc.*, **1959**, 3049.
49. P. Bennema, G. J. Hoijtink, J. H. Lupinski, L. J. Oosterhoof, P. Selier, and J. D. W. Van Voorst, *Mol. Phys.*, **2**, 431 (1959).
50. M. Das and S. Basu, *Spectrochim. Acta*, **17**, 897 (1961).
51. A. Terenin and F. Vilessov, *Advances in Photochemistry*, Vol. 2, W. A. Noyes, Jr., G. S. Hammond, and J. N. Pitts, Jr., Eds. Interscience, New York, 1964, p. 406.
52. J. A. Ward and W. H. Hamill, *J. Am. Chem. Soc.*, **87**, 1853 (1965).
53. S. Z. Toma and W. H. Hamill, *J. Am. Chem. Soc.*, **86**, 1478 (1964).
54. T. Shida and W. H. Hamill, *J. Am. Chem. Soc.*, **87**, 3689 (1966).
55. I. A. Taub, M. Sauer, and L. M. Dorfman, *Discussions Faraday Soc.*, **36**, 206 (1963).
56. S. Z. Toma and W. H. Hamill, *J. Am. Chem. Soc.*, **86**, 4761 (1964).
57. J. Denhartog and P. Dyne, *Can. J. Chem.*, **40**, 1616 (1962).

CHAPTER 10

The Structure of Inorganic Radicals

HILARY J. BOWER, M. C. R. SYMONS, AND D. J. A. TINLING

Department of Chemistry, The University, Leicester, England

I. INTRODUCTION

In this chapter we are concerned entirely with the interpretation of the electron spin resonance (ESR) spectra of inorganic doublet- and triplet-state radicals and the ways in which the data derived from the spectra can be used both as an aid in identification and as a probe of electronic structure. Our aim is not so much to guide the reader through the intricacies of interpreting spectral detail, but rather to present some generalizations about identification and structure which we hope will be useful. The former has been treated in depth elsewhere (1). Since this source (1) covers, fairly completely, ESR studies of inorganic radicals up to the end of 1964, we have deliberately avoided repetition by confining these details to tables and figures and by elaborating on results which were not included in reference 1. (The oxyradicals of nitrogen are discussed in depth in the chapter by Cunningham (see Chapter 11) and hence are not discussed here.) In particular, we include a review of paramagnetic centers in various inorganic polymeric materials. This area, as far as we are aware, has not been reviewed before.

Among the first applications of magnetic resonance spectroscopy were gas-phase studies of stable species such as NO and NO_2 (2,3), and it is curious that until quite recently little further work had been done on radicals in the gas phase. Because of a recent upsurge of interest in this sector, we have specifically included a section which attempts to summarize the present situation.

Exposure of various materials to high-energy radiation has been found in the last decade to be a most convenient method for preparing radicals. For many years the ESR spectra of radiation damage remained largely uninterpreted because it was not appreciated that the paramagnetic centers were likely to be relatively simple molecular species having properties determined essentially by their electronic structure rather than by their environment. A link was forged when spectra obtained from NO_2 and ClO_2 in rigid glasses were found to be very similar to those from certain irradiated nitrates and perchlorates (4–6). Once this fact was established and it was realized that, in many instances, the role of the environment was relatively unimportant, progress was rapid and within a few years many previously unknown radicals were prepared, identified, and studied in detail (1). Some of these radicals are listed in Table I, together with relevant properties. It is indeed remarkable that more is now known about the electronic structure of these new radicals than about their related diamagnetic molecules or ions.

TABLE I

Hyperfine Coupling Constants for the Central Atom in Some σ and π Radicals

Type	Radical	Nucleus	Anisotropic			Isotropic, A_{iso}	a_s^2	a_p^2	p/s ratio	Bond angle	Ref.
			A_1	A_2	A_3						
π	ClO_2	^{35}Cl	57	−31	−27	15.4	0.009	0.59	65	—	4
π	SO_2^-	^{33}S				14.2	0.015	0.50		—	13
π	NO_2^{2-}	^{14}N	16.6	−9.3	−7.3	14.3	0.026	0.50	19	—	14
σ	NO_2	^{14}N	13.2	−5.3	−8.0	54.7	0.10	0.42	4.2	133°	15
σ	CO_2^-	^{13}C	27.9	−11.4	−16.4	167.2	0.15	0.50	3.3	128°	9
σ	ClO_3	^{35}Cl	29	−15	−15	122	0.073	0.29	4.0	112°	4
σ	SO_3^-	^{33}S	25	−12	−12	128	0.13	0.45	3.5	111°	16
σ	SeO_3^-	^{77}Se	126	−63	−63	490	0.10	0.47	4.7	112°	17
σ	PO_3^{2-}	^{31}P	106	−53	−53	593	0.16	0.52	3.2	110°	1
σ	AsO_3^{2-}	^{75}As	107	−53.5	−53.5	617	0.18	0.60	3.3	110°	18
σ	NO_3^{2-}	^{14}N	20.7	−10.3	−10.3	40.8	0.074	0.64	8.5	116°	14
π	NF_2	^{14}N	32.6	−16.3	−16.3	16.3	0.03	0.95	32	—	19
π	NH_2	^{14}N				10.3	0.02			—	
π		^1H				23.9	0.05			—	20

A. The Role of the Environment

Since the role of the environment is an important consideration in most of these studies, it may be worth summarizing the situation as we understand it. For trapped electrons, such as in F centers, the environment is clearly all-important. For atoms or monatomic ions it may have a significant part to play, as is suggested for the species described as F^{2-} and discussed in Section III-B. However, in the case of diatomic radicals the only major effect of the environment is to quench, to a greater or lesser extent, any rotational or orbital motion that would otherwise be present. Indeed, for π radicals, unless there is a strong interaction with the environment, spectra are unlikely to be obtained at all. For example, no spectra were found for NO or OH in rare-gas matrices. In contrast, OH radicals in ice gave a well-resolved spectrum at $77°K$ (7). Resonance from O_2^- in KCl can only be detected at very low temperatures, but from I_2^+ no signal appeared even at $4°K$.

When bent triatomic or more intricate radicals are considered, the results strongly suggest that it is the electronic configuration of the radical that determines its properties. Thus, despite the existence of a large hyperfine interaction with one sodium nucleus, the radical CO_2^- in γ-irradiated sodium formate has all the properties expected of such a radical in the absence of any perturbing cation. In this case there is a transfer of about 6% of the spin into the $3s$ orbital of Na^+, but this is an extreme example, the sodium ion being ideally placed for coupling (8,9).

B. Identification and Classification

Since most of the radicals listed in Table I were formed by irradiation, we shall confine our attention to the problem of identification in such cases. The approach is generally an admixture of chemical expectation and theoretical prediction. Coupled with this may be the application of other techniques, especially ultraviolet spectroscopy because of its relatively high sensitivity.

As with most spectroscopic techniques, ESR gives essentially four separate pieces of information. These are: (1) the intensity, which is a measure of the concentration of radicals; (2) the line position, which is usually expressed as a g tensor and gives information about the symmetry of the radical and the proximity of magnetically coupled excited states; (3) the number of lines—for doublet-state radicals these will be hyperfine lines stemming from a magnetic coupling between the electron spin and any nuclear spins in the radical; and (4) the line shape and width, which may give useful kinetic information.

Of these it is the hyperfine tensors which are of special interest to us. Perhaps the most useful factor is that there is a rather direct link between the isotropic part of the hyperfine tensor and the s character of the atomic orbital associated with the nucleus concerned. On the other hand, the anisotropic part of the tensor leads directly to the p orbital contribution (unless there is appreciable participation by d orbitals, which is unusual for the radicals under consideration). This ability to differentiate between s and p character, and to assign approximate spin densities at magnetically coupled nuclei, is the major accomplishment of the technique.

It is convenient to distinguish between radicals having the unpaired electron in a molecular orbital for which no nuclei contribute appreciable s character and those in which one (or possibly more than one) nucleus does make a contribution. We have described these as π and σ radicals, respectively (10). Unfortunately, the distinction is not immediately clear since even in pure π radicals there is a residual isotropic hyperfine coupling to most of the magnetic nuclei. This apparent paradox becomes clear when it is realized that there is always a contribution from excited states, some of which will put slight spin density into the σ framework of a π radical. This "spin polarization" can give valuable structural information and is in fact the major source of information for π radicals in solution. The factors involved are discussed in some detail in Section II. One can usually ignore this second-order effect if there is a direct admixture, and an approximate rule is that a p/s ratio, estimated from the hyperfine tensor, of less than ten almost certainly indicates direct hybridization (1).

The difference between σ and π radicals can be understood by considering the addition of an extra electron to a linear triatomic molecule such as NO_2^+. This would go into the doubly degenerate π^* level and hence a π radical would result were it not for the fact that by bending, despite the resistance of the bonding system, the molecule can lower the energy of the added electron and reduce its antibonding character. The greater the bending, the greater the $2s$ character of the orbital on nitrogen and hence the greater the localization of spin on nitrogen. Such a radical can be contrasted with the π radical that results when two more electrons are added to the system. One will pair with the electron already present with a consequent increase in bending and the other will go into the π^*-level, which is not greatly modified on bending. Hence, NO_2^{2-} should be a π radical. In fact the spin-resonance results for NO_2 and NO_2^{2-} are in good accord with these expectations (Table I).

Thus, given a knowledge of suitable hyperfine tensors, it is usually possible to select with some certainty from a relatively small range of chemically reasonable radicals. As an example, the choice of CO_2^- in irradiated formates rests upon the following observations: (1) There was no trace of any proton hyperfine coupling. (2) Only one ^{13}C nucleus was detected. (3) The p/s ratio of about 3.4 corresponds to a bond angle of 128°, which is close to that expected for CO_2^-.

Obviously, not all problems are solved so readily; for other examples see reference 1 and some of the cases discussed in Section I-C.

C. Isoelectronic Families

One aspect of the results summarized in Table I is the trend in spin densities and p/s ratios as the electronegativity of the central atom is varied within an isoelectronic family of radicals. For example, in the group PO_3^{2-}, SO_3^-, and ClO_3 the spin density at the central atom falls steadily as the electronegativity rises. This is because the unpaired electron is in an antibonding orbital and its distribution is affected by that of the bonding electrons. This is illustrated for a diatomic C—N fragment in Figure 9 in Section V-A on paramagnetic centers in diamond. These electronegativity trends are plotted in Figures 1 and 2. As expected an increase in spin density on the central atom results in an increase in bending and hence a decrease in the p/s ratio.

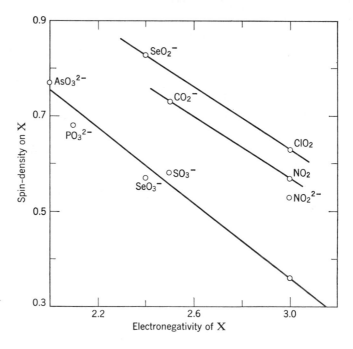

Fig. 1. Spin density on the central atom X in XO_2 and XO_3 radicals as a function of the electronegativity of X.

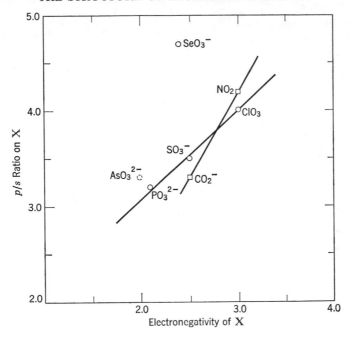

Fig. 2. Trends in the p/s ratio for the unpaired electron on X in XO_2 and XO_3 radicals as a function of the electronegativity of X.

II. Q VALUES FOR INORGANIC RADICALS

Although considerable use is made of the isotropic hyperfine coupling constants of organic π radicals, those for inorganic radicals have been largely ignored. As has already been stressed, the source of this coupling is generally ascribed to a spin polarization of the valence electrons and core electrons. We shall now consider the isotropic coupling in greater detail and show how it may be exploited to extract structural information.

A. The Adjacent-Atom Contribution

For α protons, as in the methyl radical or the benzene anion, the situation is particularly simple since there is no direct spin density on the protons and it is only spin density on the atom to which the proton is bonded that will have an appreciable influence. Then it must be the σ-bond electrons that are responsible, the effect of the unpaired electron being to induce a slight unpairing, as depicted in Figure 3. One can imagine that when one σ electron is close to the nucleus A, it will prefer to be parallel to the unpaired electron. If the σ orbital contains s character from A, then this will give a positive contribution to the net isotropic coupling for A

TABLE II

Atomic Hyperfine Coupling Data for the Interpretation of ESR Spectra[a]

n	Isotope	Abundance (%)	Spin (I)	$\lvert\psi_{ns}(0)\rvert^2$ (au)	$\langle r^{-3}\rangle_{np}$ (au)	Isotropic coupling (A_{iso}) (G)	Anisotropic coupling (2β) (G)	λ (cm^{-1})
1	^{1}H	99.9844	1/2			508		
	^{2}H	0.0156	1			78		
2	^{6}Li	7.43	1			39		
	^{7}Li	92.57	3/2	0.1673		105		0.2
	^{9}Be	100	3/2	0.5704		130		1
	^{10}B	18.83	3			242		
	^{11}B	81.17	3/2	1.408	0.775	725	38	11
	^{13}C	1.108	1/2	2.767	1.692	1,130	66	29
	^{14}N	99.635	1	4.770	3.101	552	34	76
	^{15}N	0.365	1/2			775	48	
	^{17}O	0.037	5/2	7.638	4.974	1,660	104	151
	^{19}F	100	1/2	11.966	7.546	17,200	1.084	270
3	^{23}Na	100	3/2			317		11
	^{25}Mg	10.05	5/2					20
	^{27}Al	100	5/2	2.358	1.055	985	42	75
	^{29}Si	4.70	1/2	3.8069	2.0407	1,220	62	149
	^{31}P	100	1/2	5.6251	3.3187	3,640	206	299
	^{33}S	0.74	3/3	7.9187	4.8140	975	56	382
	^{35}Cl	75.4	3/2	10.6435	6.7095	1,680	100	586
	^{37}Cl	24.6	3/2			1,395	84	

4							
^{39}K	93.08	3/2			83		38
^{41}K	6.91	3/2			45		105
^{43}Ca	0.13	7/2					386
^{67}Zn	4.12	5/2	4.5222		376	106	551
^{69}Ga	60.2	3/2	6.9493	2.8665	2,675	134	
^{71}Ga	39.8	3/2			3,400		
^{73}Ge	7.61	9/2	9.5721	4.7848	535	26	940
^{75}As	100	3/2	12.5606	6.9871	3,430	183	1,550
^{77}Se	7.50	1/2	15.7791	9.2284	4,840	270	1,688
^{79}Br	50.57	3/2	19.4127	11.8758	7,800	456	2,460
^{81}Br	49.43	3/2			8,400	564	

[a] From J. R. Morton, J. R. Rowlands, and D. H. Whiffen, *Natl. Phys. Lab., Gr. Brit.*, Circ. No. **BPR 1.3**

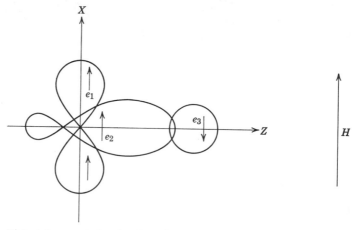

Fig. 3. Pictorial presentation for the spin polarization of the σ electrons (e_2 and e_3) in an A—H bond by a π electron (e_1) on atom A.

At the same time the other bonding electron will tend to be close to the proton and will have opposite spin. Consequently, the proton hyperfine coupling is negative. (This sign does not affect the solution spectrum directly but can be established from solid-state studies or by nuclear magnetic resonance experiments.)

The isotropic hyperfine coupling constants that might be obtained for a bent π radical, for example, AB_2, can be expressed in terms of the separate contributions from the spin on each nucleus (ρ_A or ρ_B), together with the adjacent-atom contribution considered above for protons. Thus, the isotropic coupling to A (a_A) is given by:

$$a_A = \rho_A Q^A + 2\rho_B Q_{BA}^A \tag{1}$$

and that to B by:

$$a_B = \rho_B Q^B + \rho_B Q_{AB}^B \tag{2}$$

Hence, Q^A and Q^B represent the net effect of polarization of all possible electrons, while Q_{BA}^A and Q_{AB}^B are the adjacent-atom terms which are specifically concerned with the A—B σ-bonding electrons.

B. Analysis of Q^X Terms

In principle, one should now break down Q^X into terms for the σ-bonding electrons, for any nonbonding electrons having s character, and for all core s electrons. This has been done, for example, by Karplus and Fraenkel (11) for ^{13}C hyperfine coupling constants, but we have found that a good representation of the experimental data for a very wide range of radicals can be achieved simply by using the overall term Q^X (12).

If one could analyze the results for enough radicals for which good values of the spin density ρ_X were known, it ought to be possible to decide to what extent the Q^X terms are constants and, if they proved to be so, to obtain some measure of ρ_X in unknown cases. We have attempted this task for a wide range of organic and inorganic radicals (12), and conclude that within fairly broad limits the Q^X terms are constant for a given nucleus. Some of our results are given in Table III.

C. Conversion to U Values

In order to compare results for different nuclei, we have divided all the hyperfine coupling constants by the atomic values given for the appropriate s orbital in Table II. The resulting values, expressed as percentages, are defined as the U values for the system. Similarly the adjacent-atom terms (e.g., Q_{BA}^A) can be converted into corresponding U terms (e.g., $U_{BA}^A = Q_{BA}^A/A^A$).

D. Dependence of U_{BA}^A Terms on s Character in σ Bonds

The adjacent-atom terms must be a function of the s contribution to the σ bond by atom A. For protons this is effectively unity and in some cases it

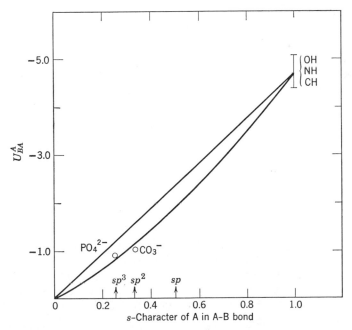

Fig. 4. Variation of the adjacent-atom term U_{BA}^A with s character on atom A for the A–B σ electrons.

TABLE III
Values of U^A and U_{BA}^A for Selected Atoms and Radicals[a]

Species	Nucleus A (ρ_A)	U_{BA}^A [b]	U^A
Atoms[c]			
N	^{14}N (1)		0.22
O	^{17}O (1)		0.20
F	^{19}F (1)		0.21
P	^{31}P (1)		0.18
Average			0.20 ± 0.02
Diatomic radicals			
NO	^{14}N (0.8)	−2 (0.5)	2.2
N_2^-	^{14}N (0.5)	−2 (0.5)	2.5
Average			2.35
Triatomic radicals			
NH_2	^{14}N (1)		2.3
	^{1}H (0)	−4.7 (1)	
$NH(SO_3)^-$	^{14}N (1)		2.4
$N(SO_3)_2^{2-}$	^{14}N (1)		2.4
NF_2	^{14}N (0.8)	−1.0 (0.33)	3.7
	^{19}F (0.1)	−0.4 (0.1)	4.9
NO_2^{2-}	^{14}N (0.6)	−1.0 (0.33)	3.7
Average (central atom)			2.9
Tetratomic radicals			
CH_3	^{13}C (1)		3.4
	^{1}H (0)	−4.5 (1)	
NH_3^+	^{14}N (1)		3.6
	^{1}H (0)	−4.9 (1)	
$(SO_3)_2NO$	^{14}N (0.6)	−1 (0.33)	4.8
	^{17}O (0.4)	−0.7 (0.2)	4.1
CO_3^-	^{13}C (0)	−1.0 (0.33)	
NO_3	^{14}N (0)	−1.0 (0.33)	
Average (central atom)			3.9
Pentatomic radicals			
PO_4^{2-}	^{31}P(0)	≈ −0.9 (0.25)	

[a] There is considerable uncertainty in several of these values but they constitute a guide to expected signs and magnitudes of hyperfine coupling constants in π radicals.

[b] The number in parenthesis gives the fractional s character used for obtaining U_{BA}^A from Figure 4.

[c] For atoms the hyperfine splitting has been divided by the number of unpaired electrons.

can be derived from the symmetry of the radical (e.g., for planar, AB_3 radicals the bonding at A will be sp^2 and hence the s orbital effect will be one-third of the total polarization). Some approximate values for U_{BA}^A are shown in Figure 4 as a function of s character. The curve is based on four points—zero, the proton value for radicals such as CH_3, NH_3^+ or OH, the ^{13}C value for CO_3^- and the ^{31}P value for PO_4^{2-} and related species. In these cases, the adjacent-atom term is the only one contributing to the hyperfine coupling, the effective spin density is unity and the hybridization is known. The straight line gives the values to be expected if spin polarization in all σ bonds in π radicals were approximately constant. In fact, it lies close to the upper limit found experimentally, but errors are sufficiently large that fairly good agreement can be achieved if this simple correlation is used for all π radicals (12).

E. Values for U^A Terms

First, some justification must be given for the use of U^A as a single parameter. Perhaps the most striking fact is that all the results for the large number of radicals covered are greater than those for the corresponding atoms by a factor of about 20. Indeed, the results for atoms are remarkably constant at about $0.20 \pm 0.02\%$ per unpaired electron (Table III) so that the far greater value of about 4% found for the π radicals must stem directly or indirectly from the σ-bonding electrons. One possible reason for this can be gauged by reference to Figure 3 and depends upon the great attenuation of the electrons within the bond. The second justification is that, for those few radicals for which the spin density is near unity on the atom concerned, so that adjacent atom terms can be neglected, U^A values usually lie close to this value.

F. Role of Lone-Pair Electrons

The results for U^A in a range of radicals do not give any clear indication of a dependence upon the number of σ bonds. Thus, for AB_3 radicals, values between 3.5 and 4.5 seem to be normal, while for AB_2 radicals results range from 2.0 to 4.0. Surprisingly, AB radicals give results in the same overall range. Closer inspection leads us to the very tentative suggestion that the value of U^A is dependent on the number of σ bonds together with the number of lone pairs of electrons in the outer shell (these being treated formally as localized s–p hybrids not symmetrically centered on the nucleus concerned). Then the low values for NO and N_2^-, for example, arise because there is only one lone pair on each nucleus. The same is true for alkyl cyanides, but not for nitroxides R_2NO, NO_2^{2-}, NF_2, etc. The radical NH_2 is exceptional because of the very small bond angle of 103°, and the consequent high $2s$ character in the lone pair, and very low $2s$ character in the bonding orbitals.

Other possible trends exist, the most marked being the increase of about 0.5 in U^A on going from AH_3 to AX_3 when X is any atom or group other than hydrogen. However, there is also a number of exceptions and, as we have stressed, errors in estimating spin densities and the ESR parameters themselves are so great that no weight can yet be placed on minor trends. The utility of these findings will become apparent, however, in our discussion of results for some of the π radicals considered in Section IV-A.

III. ATOMS, MONATOMIC IONS, AND DIATOMIC RADICALS

In Sections III to V we shall be concerned with condensed phases and then in Section VI we shall consider radicals in the gas phase.

Hydrogen atoms and alkali metal atoms have been studied extensively in rare-gas matrices and the results, which reveal very minor perturbations from those for atoms in the gas phase, have been reviewed in reference 1. Some results for silver atoms show several new features which we now discuss.

A. Silver Atoms and Ag_2^+

Recent results for trapped silver atoms are of some interest to the chemist and, indeed, suggest a possibly important approach to probing environmental interactions. If gaseous silver atoms are deposited onto a cold finger with a large excess of a solvent such as water or an alcohol, the trapped atoms have magnetic properties very close indeed to those observed for gas-phase atoms (21). If, on the other hand, solutions of silver ions, Ag^+, in these solvents are frozen and then exposed to γ radiation, then silver "atoms" are formed but with strongly modified properties. The hyperfine coupling is reduced, generally by about 10%, and there is a markedly negative g shift. We interpret this difference in terms of the following model. When silver atoms are trapped from the gas phase they simply occupy holes in the solvent lattice and are relatively free. However, silver ions coordinate solvent molecules strongly and if these are held rigidly in place in the solid phase, addition of an electron cannot displace them to any appreciable extent. Hence, the unpaired electron acts as a probe of the environment of the parent cation. Some results for trapped silver atoms formed by these two techniques, including silver atoms in alkali halide crystals (22), are given in Table IV.

We think that there is a real link between these results and those for alkali metals in fluid amine solvents (23). Well-resolved hyperfine patterns arising from a single alkali metal nucleus are observed for these solutions and the size of the splitting increases very rapidly on heating, the maximum so far detected being nearly 60% of the gas-phase atomic value. This increase appears to extrapolate at higher temperatures to a value which

TABLE IV

Hyperfine Coupling Constants for $^{109}Ag^0$ and $^{109}Ag_2^+$

Medium	$A_{\parallel}$	$A_{\perp}$	A_{iso}	% Atom character	Ref.
Species Ag^0					
MeOH			622	88	21
EtOH			620	87.6	21
$H_2O + H_2SO_4$			671	100	21
KCl			649	91	22
Species Ag_2^+					
MeOH	313	298	303	42.8	21
EtOH	311	297	301	42.6	
$H_2O + H_2SO_4$	333	317	322	45.6	21

cannot be far removed from that for the atom concerned, but for the heavier nuclei there is a parallel shift in the g value away from that for the atom. This can be rationalized if there is a rapid equilibrium between two species, one giving rise to a very small hyperfine coupling and a free-spin g value and the other, like the solvated silver atoms, to a somewhat reduced atomic hyperfine coupling and a negatively shifted g value. If the equilibrium is sufficiently rapid, only an averaged set of lines will be observed, although one might expect a nearly symmetrical broadening of the outer lines. Just such a broadening is in fact observed at low temperatures (23).

When solids containing silver atoms and an excess of silver ions are slowly warmed, the spectrum changes to that shown in Figure 5 (21). In

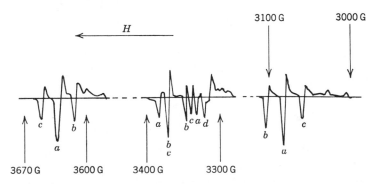

Fig. 5. ESR spectra assigned to Ag_2^+ trapped in $4M$ aqueous KF. Features a are attributed to $(^{107}Ag-^{109}Ag)^+$, b to $(^{107}Ag)_2^+$ and c to $(^{109}Ag)_2^+$, d is due to an unidentified species.

particular, the outer high-field and low-field doublets change into $1:2:1$ triplets with shoulders, suggesting a species having axial symmetry. These lines are due to coupling to ^{107}Ag and ^{109}Ag which have slightly different magnetic moments. The atoms simply give a pair of doublets, but if the new species were Ag_2^+, as seems reasonable on chemical grounds, then one would expect outer doublets from $(^{107}Ag)_2^+$, $(^{109}Ag)_2^+$, and $(^{107}Ag-^{109}Ag)^+$ lines from the mixed ion coming midway between the others and having twice the intensity. This is just what is found and leads to a complete interpretation of the complex of central lines, provided second-order corrections are incorporated (21).

B. The Ion F^{2-}

Sroubek et al. have detected an apparently isotropic doublet in irradiated beryllium oxide powder (24). The hyperfine splitting has the very large value of 760 G and so they attribute the resonance to a fluorine center which they write as F^{2-}, the extra electron being thought to be the outer $3s$ level (Table IX). This assignment is certainly possible for F^- in an oxide site and the splitting is very approximately in accord with expectation for such an electron. The major difficulty presented by this theory is that apparently only three beryllium atoms contribute to the superhyperfine coupling also detected. This result is strikingly reminiscent of a boron center also found in beryllium oxide (25) and could stem from an axial distortion characteristic of the host lattice. This, however, should not greatly alter the interaction between the beryllium atoms and an electron in the fluorine $3s$ orbital, so that it may well be that an alternative description, based on principles outlined in Section V, would be better. For this reason we defer further discussion until that section.

C. Diatomic Fluorides with σ^* Electrons

Following the realization that halogen atoms in alkali halide crystals react with neighboring halide ions to form hal_2^- σ^* radicals (26) and that such ions have considerable stability, a range of similar diatomic radicals having an unpaired electron in the σ^* orbital have been prepared and studied. Some results are given in Table V. The trends in the calculated spin density on fluorine in a range of AF radicals of this type are shown in Figure 6 as a function of the ionization potential of A and A^+ (where A represents the closed-shell atom ns^2, np^6). While neither representation is completely satisfactory, these plots nevertheless illustrate rather well the trend to higher spin density on fluorine as the ionization potential of A increases. This trend is to be expected and, in the limit of very high ionization potential for A, means that fluorine atoms would fail to form an appreciable σ bond. This same model has been proposed to explain the

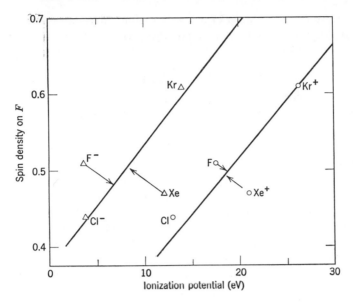

Fig. 6. Trends in the spin density of fluorine in various σ^*-diatomic radicals AF as a function of the ionization potential of A and A^+.

TABLE V
^{19}F Hyperfine Coupling Constant for AF σ^* Radicals

Radical	Nucleus	Anisotropic			Iso-tropic			p/s ratio	Ref.
		A_1	A_2	A_3	A_{iso}	a_s^2	a_p^2		
F_2^-	^{19}F	552	-276	-276	335	0.02	0.51	25	28
FCl^-	^{19}F	483	-242	-242	323	0.019	0.44	21	29
	^{35}Cl	70	-35	-35	56	0.033	0.70	21	
KrF	^{19}F	660	-330	-330	600	0.035	0.61	18	30
XeF	^{19}F	505	-252	-252	440	0.026	0.47	18	31

ability of various molecules to act as trapping sites for hydrogen atoms in such a manner that the atom character, as evidenced by the hyperfine coupling, is not greatly modified (27).

IV. TRI-, TETRA-, AND PENTATOMIC RADICALS—LIGAND HYPERFINE INTERACTIONS

Our major subdivision is now σ and π radicals, because of the very different factors contributing to their ESR spectra. In both groups, however, we focus attention onto the hyperfine interactions found for the outer or "ligand" atoms, since interaction with the "central" atoms has been covered fully elsewhere (1).

A. π Radicals

The two radicals that we highlight in this section are the isoelectronic 19-electron π radicals NF_2 and FOO. These are compared with the better known members of this family, NO_2^{2-}, O_3^-, SO_2^-, and ClO_2 (Table I) and FOO is also compared with organic peroxy radicals ROO.

The radical NF_2 exists in equilibrium with its dimer, N_2F_4, at room temperature and thus fits into the reactivity pattern set by the stable radicals NO_2^{2-}, O_3^-, ClO_2, and SO_2^-, the last forming reversibly from $S_2O_4^{2-}$ in solution. In the gas phase only a very broad structureless spectrum was obtained from NF_2 (32) but, very interestingly, well-resolved solution-type spectra were obtained when the radicals were trapped in certain molecular sieves. This effect, which has also been observed for NO_2, may stem in part from a slowing down of the dimerization process, but is most probably due to a loss of spin-rotational coupling which can lead to marked line broadening even in solution. This theory was invoked to explain the great difference between SO_2^-, which gives narrow lines in solution and ClO_2, which invariably gives very broad lines (13). Broadening by this mechanism is much reduced for SO_2^- because of the strong interaction with the medium and presumably the same applies to NF_2 in a sieve cavity.

The isotropic hyperfine parameters thus obtained are shown in Table VI and are quite normal for a π radical having an unpaired electron in a b_1 orbital. Early attempts to obtain a solid-state spectrum were not very successful (33), but recently Kasai and co-workers (19) have published a well-resolved envelope spectrum from NF_2 radicals trapped in solid neon. The resulting parameters yield isotropic hyperfine constants to ^{14}N and ^{19}F which are close to the "solution" values, but the averaged g value of 2.0044 is disturbingly far from the solution and gas-phase value of 2.009 and, hence, the interpretation must be treated with some reserve. Another puzzling feature is the total spin density of about 1.27, which is a surprisingly large deviation from unity when compared with the sort of accuracy normally obtained.

However, if the results are accepted, certain interesting comparisons can be made. Perhaps the most striking is the very high spin density on nitrogen. This is close to unity and, presumably, reflects the large difference in electronegativity between nitrogen and fluorine, which must operate so as to concentrate the four inner π electrons on the two fluorine atoms, leaving the outer electron largely on nitrogen. In fact, the situation is

TABLE VI

"Ligand" and Central Atom Hyperfine Coupling Constants for Some π Radicals

Radical	Nucleus	Anisotropic			Isotropic			p/s	Ref.
		A_1	A_2	A_3	A_{iso}	a_s^2	a_p^2	ratio	
H_2CN	^{14}N	24.8	−12.4	−12.4	9.5	0.017	0.73	36	46
	^1H				91.4	0.36			
H_2CF	^{19}F				64.3	0.004			38
	^{13}C				54.8	0.05			38
	^1H				21.1	0.04			38
NF_2	^{14}N	32.6	−16.3	−16.3	16.3	0.03	0.95	32	19
	^{19}F(i)	130	−65	−65	82	0.005	0.12	24	19
	(ii)	153	−76	−76	59	0.004	0.14	35	19
	^{19}F (In molecular sieve)				60	0.004			33
FO^1O^2	^{19}F	83	−41	−41	12.83	0.001	0.077	77	36
	$^{17}O^1$				14.50	0.009			34
	$^{17}O^2$				22.17	0.013			34
RO^1O^2 [a]	$^{17}O^1$				18.0	0.011			35
	$^{17}O^2$				23.0	0.014			35
H_2NO	^1H				11.9	0.023			40
	^{14}N				11.9	0.022			40
R_2NO	^{14}N	20.8	−10.4	−10.4	15.4	0.028	0.62	22	41
CH_2OH	^1H				17.2	0.034			39

[a] Formed from 2,2,4-trimethylpentane.

comparable to that found in CO_2^-, but the bias seems to be more marked for NF_2.

If we apply the principles outlined in Section II for the isotropic coupling constants, then U^N is found to be about 3.7 (using $U^N_{FN} = -1.2$) and U^F is very approximately equal to 4.9 (using $U^F_{NF} = -0.4$). These results fit in well with those given in Section II and help to support the concepts outlined there.

That the radical FOO is readily formed is at first sight surprising, since by reference to chlorine chemistry one might have expected to find OFO rather than FOO. However, since fluorine has a greater electronegativity than oxygen the latter structure is in fact a more satisfactory state of affairs. The radical has been studied in the liquid phase by Fessenden and Schuler (34) who used their elegant technique of *in situ* electron irradiation, using CF_4 as a medium and source of fluorine atoms and adding traces of oxygen to give FOO. This radical was relatively stable and they were able to measure the isotropic hyperfine coupling to ^{17}O in natural abundance, although the results were confirmed using enriched samples. The observation of two distinctly different oxygen coupling constants nicely confirmed the proposed structure. They also reported results for the peroxide obtained from 2,2,4-trimethylpentane and these are given in Table VI for comparison with those of FOO (35).

The solid-state spectrum reported by Kasai and Kirschenbaum (36) is again difficult to interpret, but the use of Q-band wavelengths as well as X-band wavelengths lends strong support to their analysis, the results of which are also given in Table VI. Their spectra were obtained from solid F_2O_2 and from F_2O_2 in solid $CClF_3$ and are complicated by the presence of some other radical, which was also detected by Neumayr and Vanderkooi (37), who obtained FOO as a decomposition product from FSO_2OOF and related compounds. It is more difficult to speculate about the spin distribution in this radical because of its asymmetry. The very small hyperfine coupling to fluorine shows that it is even more successful in retaining control over the inner π electrons than in NF_2.

It is interesting to examine the ^{17}O coupling constants with respect to the U values of Table III, in the hope that a reasonable estimate of the spin densities might be obtained. We start with ROO, since in this case we can consider that the unpaired electron is confined entirely to the two oxygen atoms. Using the parameters given in Section II for the outer oxygen (O^2), we obtain a spin density of about 0.5 on each oxygen and this result can be used to give a U value for the central oxygen (O^1) of about 4, which is reasonably close to expectation.

Fessenden and Schuler (34) were not able to assign the two isotropic hyperfine coupling constants to particular oxygen atoms. We have chosen the assignment given in Table VI because the reverse gives a computed spin-density distribution which favors O^1 over O^2 and this seems improbable. Even the equal distribution now deduced goes against our expectations, which would be to find most of the spin on the outer oxygen. We conclude either that our U values are unsatisfactory or that the spin distribution is only very weakly affected by the alkyl group. If the latter is in fact the case, it is a result of some significance.

Turning now to FOO, we might expect a rather similar distribution in view of the low spin density on fluorine. First, the corrected anisotropic fluorine coupling corresponds to a spin density of about 0.07. This, together with equation 1 of Section II-A and the isotropic fluorine coupling, leads to a calculated spin density on O^1 of 0.5. By difference this gives 0.43 on O^2. These results accord remarkably well with the ^{17}O isotropic results reported by Fessenden and Schuler if the smaller value is assigned to the central oxygen (O^1) (Table VI).

Unfortunately, no hyperfine parameters for ^{17}O have yet been reported for the relatively stable isoelectronic radical O_3^-. However, using the correlation of Figure 1 we obtain an approximate value of 0.5 for the spin density on the central oxygen. This leaves 0.25 on each of the outer atoms. So the effect of replacing oxygen by fluorine has been to swing spin density from fluorine to the corresponding outer oxygen atom, leaving the central atom relatively unaffected.

The radical H_2CF, obtained by Fessenden and Schuler (38), together with HCF_2 and CF_3 (which are discussed in Section IV-C), by *in situ* electron bombardment of various fluorocarbons in rare-gas matrices, is probably planar, or very nearly so and, hence, is discussed in this section. It is of particular interest just because of this question of planarity, and ought to be considered with other isoelectronic radicals such as H_2CO^- (R_2CO^-) and H_2NO (R_2NO). Unfortunately, only the isotropic hyperfine parameters are known (Table VI). The proton splitting of 21.1 G suggests a planar radical having slight delocalization onto fluorine, and the fluorine coupling of 64.3 G is certainly in reasonable accord with this. If we set $\rho_C \approx 0.9$ and $\rho_F \approx 0.1$, we get $U^F \approx 5.5$. This result is a little high, which could be the result of slight bending, but it is so sensitive to the chosen spin densities that no weight can be placed on this inference. The ^{13}C splitting does, however, lend some support to the possibility that a small degree of bending has occurred. The calculated U^C value is about 5.6 which is certainly well above the values we have obtained for planar radicals. Similar calculations for the ^{13}C isotropic hyperfine coupling in CH_2OH radicals (39) leads to a U value of 6.2, while for H_2NO (40) we get a value of about 5.4 for U^N. In all these cases, therefore, there may well be slight bending. However, for organic nitroxides R_2NO, in general, U values are reduced and, in all probability, when R is bulky the radical is essentially planar. Indeed, it should be stressed that in no instance can the bending be greater than a few degrees (41).

B. σ Radicals

Here we wish to consider some new results for the radicals HCO, HCN^-, FCO, and $S_2O_2^-$. The first two are of special interest because of their very large proton hyperfine coupling, which corresponds to about 27% hydrogen atom character. The radical FCO is isoelectronic with the radicals CO_2^- and NO_2, discussed earlier and in detail elsewhere (1), and is interesting both because of the change from oxygen to fluorine and also because of the very marked difference between hydrogen in HCO (42) and fluorine in FCO (43). The ^{13}C hyperfine tensor for HCO (44) is approximately in accord with expectation for a bond angle of 120°, but there is an unusually marked deviation from axial symmetry (Table VII), which makes the proper value for the anisotropic part of the tensor somewhat

TABLE VII

"Ligand" and Central Atom Hyperfine Coupling Constants for Some σ Radicals

Radical	Nucleus	Anisotropic			Isotropic			p/s	
		A_1	A_2	A_3	A_{iso}	a_s^2	a_p^2	ratio	Ref.
HCO	^{1}H	5	−4.2	−0.8	137	0.27			42
	^{13}C	18	−13.8	−4.2	135	0.12	0.27	2.2	44
							or 0.32	or 2.7	
HCN$^-$	^{1}H				137.5	0.27			45
	^{14}N				6.5	0.012			
	^{13}C				74.3	0.066			
FCO	^{19}F	178	−82	−98	334	0.021	0.18	8.5	43
	^{13}C				286	0.25			44
S′S″O$_2^-$	^{33}S″	26	−13	−13	158	0.16	0.45	2.8	47
	^{33}S′	16	−3.3	−13.0	24.3	0.025	0.29	11.5	
HPO$_2^-$	^{31}P	112	−56	−56	495	0.15	0.54	3.6	51
	^{1}H				82.5	0.16			
O$_2$P′—P″OH^{2-}	^{31}P′	104	−55	−47	284	0.08	0.51	6.4	51
	^{31}P″	40	−19	−20	185	0.05	0.19	3.9	
	^{1}H				32	0.06			
CF$_3$	^{19}F				143	0.008			38
	^{13}C				272	0.24			
HCF$_2$	^{19}F				84	0.005			38
	^{13}C				149	0.13			
	^{1}H				22	0.044			
SiH$_3$	^{29}Si	46–52			200–300	0.2	0.8	4	50
	^{1}H				8.1	0.016			
GeH$_3$	^{1}H				15	0.030			50

ambiguous. One could assume that it is composed of two axially symmetric tensors, as was done for CO_2^- and NO_2, and hence obtain:

$$\begin{vmatrix} -4.2 & & \\ & -18.0 & \\ & & -13.8 \end{vmatrix} = \begin{vmatrix} -10.6 & & \\ & +21.2 & \\ & & -10.6 \end{vmatrix} + \begin{vmatrix} 6.4 & & \\ & -3.2 & \\ & & -3.2 \end{vmatrix}$$

The main tensor, which presumably lies close to the bisector of the HCO angle, corresponds to 32% p character and the subsidiary tensor along x to about 10%, which was assigned to strong spin polarization in the σ orbital. This effect is surprisingly large, however, and one wonders to what extent the difficulties in arriving at a correct tensor from the envelope spectrum may have contributed to the recorded values. If we take 18 as the parallel value, then $a_p^2 = 0.27$ and the p/s ratio is about 2.2. If we take 21.2 G, then $a_p^2 = 0.32$ and the p/s ratio is about 2.7. The former is closer to that expected for a bond angle of 120°.

Unfortunately, our results (Table VII) for HCN$^-$ (45) are incomplete. This radical was prepared by γ radiolysis of sodium cyanide crystals, presumably containing traces of water or HCN, and even at 77°K the spectrum was purely isotropic, indicating that the radical was rotating rapidly in the crystal lattice. If we assume that this radical has the same bond angle as HCO (120°), then the spin density on carbon has fallen from about 0.4 to about 0.23, in accord with the expected trend for an antibonding electron (1). However, the proton coupling, which might have been expected to have followed the spin density on carbon, has hardly changed. One reason for this has been discussed in terms of a compensating effect (45). As the spin density moves onto nitrogen, so the mechanism for coupling can be thought of as changing from that outlined for HCO (45) to the hyperconjugation of H_2CN (46). Since this is very large (91 G) then one would expect only a small decrease on going from HCO to HCN$^-$ and presumably minor factors are sufficient to offset this. This seems to us to be a very awkward description, and we ought in principle to unify the two mechanisms of coupling into a single approach.

As already stressed, FCO is better compared with CO_2^- than with HCO. One difficulty is that the bond angle is not known. It is probably slightly less than that for CO_2^- (130°), since replacing oxygen by fluorine seems to produce an increased bending. We do not agree with Adrian et al. (43) that the bond angle is expected to be less than the 120° for HCO. In fact, replacing hydrogen by oxygen or fluorine in AB_2 π radicals is expected to result in an increase in the bond angle in contrast with the behavior of AB_3 π radicals.

The results for fluorine suggest that there is about 18.5% delocalization onto fluorine and that the p/s ratio is in the region of 8.5 (Table VII). This is a larger coupling than is found for π radicals and is presumably a manifestation of the σ nature of the radical. This factor is discussed further in Section IV-C.

The ^{13}C hyperfine coupling seems on inspection of the envelope spectrum to be almost isotropic (Table VII). Of the various alternatives considered to explain this result, which can hardly be accepted as it stands, we favor the suggestion that the values obtained are not the principal values of the tensor, but simply the values which relate to the axes of the fluorine hyperfine tensor, since this large coupling dominates the spectrum. Since the angle between the F—C bond and the axis of the orbital on carbon is probably about 60°, this would in fact be close to the isotropic hyperfine coupling, provided that the parallel fluorine coupling lies along this bond. The perpendicular coupling should then be composed of two terms approximately equal to $(A_{iso} + B)$ and $(A_{iso} - B)$ and again, these could well merge to give an average value of A_{iso}. (If these considerations are correct, they serve to underline one of the hazards involved in the interpretation of powder spectra.) In the absence of an anisotropic coupling, little can be said about the spin-density distribution. Our guess that the bond angle should lie between 120 and 130° would fix a_C^2 at between 0.75 and 1.0, but Adrian et al. favor a_C^2 0.53 and hence $\theta \approx 110°$.

Finally we turn to the radical $S_2O_2^-$, which was prepared by exposing sodium thiosulfate crystals to γ radiation (47). The radical was identified as a σ radical similar to SO_3^- by the hyperfine tensor to the single strongly interacting sulfur nucleus and the form of the weaker coupling to a second sulfur nucleus together with chemical expectation. The spin is distributed primarily between the two sulfur atoms with a net residual density of about 0.1 on the oxygens. The way in which it is delocalized onto the ligand sulfur is discussed in Section IV-C.

C. Hyperfine Interactions with "Ligand" Nuclei in σ Radicals

The results for hydrogen, nitrogen, fluorine, sulfur, and phosphorus hyperfine coupling in various σ radicals are summarized in Table VII. We wish to examine these results with a view to discovering more about the basic mechanism whereby "ligands" acquire spin density. There seem to be two distinct possibilities. The first is the pseudo π mechanism which is discussed, for example, by Walsh (48) and which can be depicted in terms of atomic orbitals as in Figure 7. This orbital stems from the degenerate

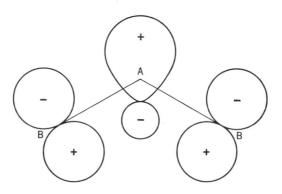

Fig. 7. The atomic orbitals which contribute to the molecular orbital of the unpaired electron in 17-electron AB_2 radicals.

π^* level of the linear molecule and tends toward an orbital localized entirely on A as the bending increases. This is because the atomic s character on A increases and also because the effective overlap with the orbitals on B decreases as the radical bends. The second mode of interaction giving rise to a hyperfine coupling with B is via the σ-bonding electrons. The principal axis of the tensor is now along the bond direction instead of being perpendicular to the molecular plane. The other major difference is that spin in the σ bond will have a relatively large s-orbital component on B. In nonplanar radicals, this coupling mechanism is more direct than in π radicals and confers positive spin density on B.

We have envisaged two extreme situations, distinguishable in principle by the different principal directions of the tensors and the differing degrees of s orbital involvement. However, both mechanisms are expected to operate in varying degrees. This will result in a net hyperfine tensor which lacks axial symmetry and which has principal directions bearing no clear relation to the molecular axes.

We now turn to the examples in Table VII. The large proton hyperfine couplings for HCO and HCN$^-$ illustrate the σ delocalization mechanism very well under conditions where π delocalization is impossible.

The proton hyperfine coupling constants for HCF_2 and for SiH_3 and GeH_3 are less clear-cut. Some time ago it was suggested that the small magnitude of the proton coupling in SiH_3 (± 8 G) was indicative of a deviation from planarity (49), since planar SiH_3 is expected to be quite similar to CH_3 (-23 G). Thus on bending, the magnitude of the isotropic coupling is expected to decrease from about 23 G, pass through zero, and then increase.

The ^{13}C isotropic coupling clearly indicates a pyramidal structure for HCF_2 and this has led to the suggestion that the proton coupling of 22 G is positive (38). Similarly, the ^{29}Si hyperfine interaction suggests that SiH_3 is indeed pyramidal (50), although, in our view, the published spectra are not well enough resolved to warrant detailed analysis.

Another example of pure σ interaction is the radical O_2P—PO_2H^{2-} studied by Morton (51). Here again π delocalization onto the PO_2H "ligand" is not likely to be important, and, indeed, the symmetry axis of the secondary phosphrous hyperfine tensor is along the direction of the P—P bond. Furthermore, the small p/s ratio of about 3.9 is clearly indicative of σ interaction.

At the other extreme, the hyperfine interaction with nitrogen in HCN$^-$ (45) strongly suggests π delocalization. It seems likely that the spin density on nitrogen is as high as 50%, which is far too large to be a σ-bond effect and it corresponds to a high p/s ratio of 30. This is probably the case also for oxygen in HCO. However, for fluorine in FCO, CF_3 and,

HCF_2, we think that σ delocalization is more important for several reasons. First, for FCO there is the high spin density of 0.185 and low p/s ratio of about 8.5. Both values are impossible for π delocalization onto fluorine. Similarly for the family H_2CF, HCF_2, and CF_3 (38), as the deviation from planarity increases, so the (positive) isotropic fluorine coupling rises steeply (Fig. 8). If our conclusion that π delocalization should decrease on bending is correct, then this must represent a more rapid onset of σ delocalization. If in the radical CF_3 we assume a p/s ratio of about 8.5 (as in FCO), then the total spin density on fluorine will be about 20%, leaving 80% on carbon. Since the ^{13}C isotropic hyperfine coupling corresponds to a spin density of nearly 25%, neglecting any extra effect from the σ electrons, we find a p/s ratio of 2.2 corresponding to a bond angle of 107°.

The situation for $S_2O_2^-$ is perhaps less clear (47). We should expect both mechanisms to play a part, so that the direction of the secondary ^{33}S hyperfine coupling might give a clue as to their relative significance. Unfortunately, there are two alternative directions and these have not been distinguished experimentally.

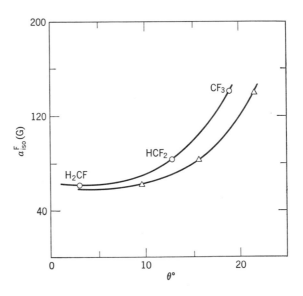

Fig. 8. Fluorine isotropic hyperfine coupling in the radicals H_2CF, HCF_2, and CF_3 as a function of the estimated deviation from planarity (θ). The △ values were calculated as outlined in the text and the ○ values were calculated by Fessenden and Schuler (38).

D. The Radicals PF_4, SF_4^+, and $As(OH)_4$

These radicals are of particular interest because the unpaired electron is in an antibonding orbital, the parent ions, PF_4^+, SF_4^{2+}, and AsO_4^{3-}, having closed-shell structures.

The molecule PF_4 can be made by exposing various hexafluorophosphates to high-energy radiation. At room temperature it is tumbling sufficiently freely to give a purely isotropic spectrum in which all four fluorine atoms are magnetically equivalent (52,53). On cooling, the spectrum broadens markedly before giving a very complex set of lines characteristic of a powder. This broadening was interpreted, in part, in terms of an inversion process of an unsymmetrical PF_4 unit such that two equivalent pairs of fluorine atoms are interconverted. This conjecture is supported by the observation that PF_4 in solid SF_6 at low temperatures gives an isotropic spectrum characterized by two pairs of nonequivalent fluorine atoms (54). The sum of the two isotropic coupling constants is approximately equal to twice that for the "symmetrical" molecule in the fluorophosphate lattice. This means that the inversion mechanism cannot be the only one responsible for the total line broadening at intermediate temperatures (52) since this would leave the outermost and central lines narrow. The results, given in Table VIII have been analyzed in terms of an

TABLE VIII

Hyperfine Coupling Constants for Some 33-Electron Pentatomic
Radicals

Radical	Nucleus	Isotropic coupling	a_s^2	Ref.
PF_4	^{31}P	1330	0.37	52,53
	^{19}F (4 Nuclei)	196	0.011	
	$^{19}F^1$ (2 Nuclei)	282	0.016	54
	$^{19}F^2$ (2 Nuclei)	59	0.0035	54
AsO_4^{4-}	^{75}As	1080	0.32	55
SF_4^+	^{33}S	310	0.32	54
	^{19}F (4 Nuclei)	143	0.008	

orbital consisting of a $p-s$ hybrid on phosphorus having some σ-antibonding character between phosphorus and fluorine (52).

In contrast, the isoelectronic radical SF_4^+ in solid SF_6 has four magnetically equivalent fluorine atoms even at $-175°$ (54). This difference between PF_4 and SF_4^+ has not been explained.

The AsO_4^{4-} or $As(OH)_4$ radical is thought to be responsible for a spectrum characterized by a very large hyperfine coupling to arsenic detected in irradiated KH_2AsO_4 at 77°K (55). This species is isoelectronic with PF_4 and certainly the hyperfine interaction to arsenic is quite comparable with that to phosphorus. Further support for the identification comes from the detection of hyperfine coupling to four equivalent protons for certain orientations of the radicals.

V. RADICALS IN INORGANIC POLYMERS

In the last few years, electron spin resonance has shown the presence of paramagnetic centers in a number of polymeric materials, the majority resulting from radiation damage.

Many of these centers seem to be associated with impurity atoms in the material, which readily become paramagnetic on irradiation by trapping a mobile electron or hole. Other centers have been postulated as involving an initial displacement of an atom to an interstitial site followed by loss or gain of an electron.

The rigidity of the three-dimensional lattice inhibits fragmentation so that the structure of a paramagnetic center is no longer almost entirely dictated by its electronic structure, as is the case with the small molecules discussed previously, but it will also depend on the amount of distortion that can take place in the lattice.

A. Nitrogen Center in Diamond

A center present in many unirradiated natural diamonds has been attributed to nitrogen atoms substituted for carbon at a diamond lattice site (56,57). Analysis of the electron spin resonance spectrum (58), which shows hyperfine interaction with ^{14}N and 1.1% abundant ^{13}C, has led to the conclusion that the unpaired electron is confined in a σ^*-antibonding orbital almost entirely localized on the nitrogen atom and one of its nearest-neighbor carbon atoms. One might expect a migration of the electron between the four equivalent bonds, but results show that at room temperature the electron must remain in any one bond for much longer than 10^{-6} sec, in order not to conflict with the observed line width. The trapping is due to an increase in bond length and since the hyperfine parameters, given in Table IX, show that the unpaired electron is more closely associated with the carbon atom, this atom will relax to a greater extent. The situation is depicted in the energy level scheme for a C—N fragment shown in Figure 9. The magnitude of the p/s ratio indicates a change in bond angle at the carbon atom of about 8°. The much higher p/s ratio for carbon than for nitrogen follows from this, since in the limiting case of complete separation the unpaired electron would be in a pure p orbital on a planar carbon atom with the bonding electrons as a lone

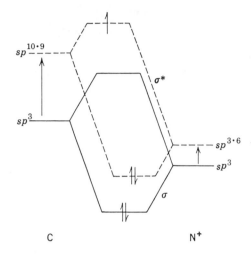

Fig. 9. Energy-level diagram from the pseudomolecule CN^+. The full lines represent the undistorted center and the dashed lines show the effect of distortion on the energy levels.

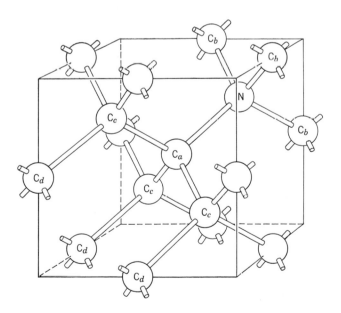

Fig. 10. Part of the diamond lattice showing the nitrogen impurity and the carbon atoms C_a, C_b, C_c, and C_d referred to in the text.

TABLE IX

Hyperfine Coupling Constants for Some Radicals in Polymeric Materials

Material	Nucleus		Hyperfine tensor			a_s^2	a_p^2	p/s ratio	Ref.
		A_1	A_2	A_3	A_{iso}				
Diamond:									
nitrogen	(1) ^{14}N	40.8	29.2	29.2	33.1	0.060	0.23	3.6	56,57
center	^{13}C	121.4	50.7	50.7	74.3	0.067	0.73	10.9	
	(2) ^{13}C	15.1	11.4	11.4	12.6	0.011	0.038	3.3	
Baldwin's									
center	(1) ^{13}C	50.5	29.2	29.2	36.3	0.033	0.22	6.7	59
	(2) ^{13}C	4.7	3.3	3.3	3.8	0.004	0.015	4	
Silicon:									
unirradiated	^{31}P				41.9	0.012			63
irradiated	B1 ^{29}Si	163.7	137.8	137.8	146.4	0.12	0.28	2.3	64,65
	G1 ^{29}Si	47.0	31.9	31.9	36.9	0.03	0.17	5.7	
	G2 ^{29}Si	142.6	119.5	119.5	127.2	0.11	0.25	2.3	
	G9 ^{29}Si	39.6	31.1	31.1	33.9	0.03	0.09	3.0	
	^{27}Al	15.15	15.58	15.56	16.5	1.7	0.7	0.4	
	G8 ^{29}Si	160.5	105.4	105.4	123.8	0.10	0.59	5.9	
	^{31}P	11.4	9.2	9.2	9.9	0.003	0.007	2.6	
	G16 ^{29}Si	139.1	76.0	76.0	97.0	0.08	0.76	8.5	
BeO	^{11}B	122	76.5	76.5	91.7	0.13	0.80	6.3	25
	^{19}F				760	0.044(2s)			24
	^{9}Be				12				
ZnS	^{19}F				465	0.026(2s)			67
	^{67}Zn				60				

pair on the nitrogen, which would therefore be expected to remain approximately tetrahedral.

Small hyperfine couplings with other ^{13}C nuclei suggest that the unpaired electron is not completely localized on the nitrogen and carbon atoms C_a in Figure 10. The largest of these secondary interactions is thought to result from unpaired-electron density on the three carbon atoms C_d, since in this way, the axial symmetry of the hyperfine tensor about a C_a—N bond direction can be explained (Fig. 10).

B. Other Centers in Diamond

Radiation damage of natural or artificial diamonds usually leads to a variety of complex paramagnetic centers.

A more simple center, formed after exposure to 0.75 MeV electrons has been investigated by Baldwin (59), who detected a large hyperfine interaction with four equivalent ^{13}C nuclei and smaller interactions with other ^{13}C nuclei, but none with any other magnetic nucleus. Therefore, it was postulated that the center was a carbon vacancy which had trapped an electron or hole during irradiation (59,60). It is also possible that an impurity atom with a nonmagnetic nucleus is involved. Here oxygen might be a likely impurity. On irradiation, an oxygen atom might lose an electron to give a system similar to the nitrogen center. The greater electron affinity of oxygen would force the unpaired electron almost entirely onto the carbon atom. A rapid reorientation of the distortion would explain the four equivalent ^{13}C nuclei detected and the hyperfine interaction, while retaining its anisotropy, would be reduced by a factor of 4, so that the spin density on any one carbon atom should be close to 25%, as is found experimentally. The p/s ratio is again high, indicating a considerable relaxation of the carbon atoms.

At lower temperatures it might be possible to detect a broadening of the hyperfine lines if migration of the electron between the four σ bonds is sufficiently slow or even a spectrum of sharp lines in which the electron is confined to one σ bond. The latter is the situation for the nitrogen center spectrum at room temperature. However, if by any chance this center is associated with a substitutional oxygen impurity atom, it is not clear why the relaxation time is so much shorter than that for the nitrogen center.

Higher energy electron or neutron irradiation forms paramagnetic centers (61,62) which are generally described in terms of an initial displacement of a carbon atom from its lattice site. This is then followed by trapping an electron or hole at the interstitial atom or the vacancy. It is, however, quite conceivable that some paramagnetism may be due to ionization of impurities.

Several of these centers exhibit fine structure, indicating that they may be triplet states. Calculations have suggested that some types of ionized vacancies or interstitial carbon atoms may have either a triplet ground state or low-lying excited state (60). It is also possible that some fine structure may be due to pairwise trapping in which there is a dipolar interaction between two localized components, e.g., a vacancy–interstitial pair. As yet, none of these centers has been positively identified.

C. Centers in Silicon

Just as nitrogen may enter substitutionally into the diamond lattice so phosphorus atoms can be introduced into silicon. However, the electron spin resonance results are not the same. At room temperature thermal energy is sufficient for the electron from the phosphorus to be excited into the conduction band, but at 1.25°K ENDOR studies (63) have shown that the electron is definitely associated with the phosphorus. The hyperfine interaction with ^{31}P is purely isotropic, and very small, the unpaired spin density on phosphorus being only 1% (Table IX). Interaction with a very large number of neighboring ^{29}Si nuclei is also observed, indicating that the electron is widely delocalized through the silicon lattice in contrast to the almost complete localization involved in the case of nitrogen in diamond. Thus in two apparently similar systems, the extra electron is accommodated in very different ways, the difference probably being associated with the presence of relatively low energy $3d$ orbitals on phosphorus and silicon.

There have been extensive studies of radiation damage in silicon, especially damage resulting from electron irradiation, and at least 20 paramagnetic centers have been observed between 4°K and 20°K. Parameters for a few of these are given in Table IX. In many cases, hyperfine interactions indicate that the unpaired electron is associated with an impurity as well as with ^{29}Si nuclei, e.g., G8, G9 (Table IX). By studying the rate of production and annealing of defects, by using ENDOR and by monitoring the changes in the ESR spectrum on application of a uniaxial stress, which leads to reorientation of anisotropic defects in the stressed crystal, these centers have been tentatively identified as isolated ionized vacancies and vacancies associated with substitutional or interstitial impurity atoms (64,65). For this to be correct, vacancies must be sufficiently mobile even at 20°K for migration through the crystal to occur, since the concentrations of defects involving impurity atoms is far too high for them to result entirely from the primary radiation process.

It is possible that one or more of the centers may be similar to the nitrogen center in diamond, especially if a first-row element impurity, with a nonmagnetic nucleus, is involved. The importance of impurities in determining the paramagnetic centers formed by radiation damage of silicon suggests the possibility of a similar involvement of impurities in irradiated diamond.

D. Boron in Beryllium Oxide

Reinberg (25) has investigated a center formed in synthetic beryllium oxide crystals irradiated with 6 MeV electrons. The observed hyperfine coupling is consistent with a boron impurity substituted for a beryllium atom at a normal lattice site. The absence of paramagnetism before irradiation suggests that the boron is originally present as B^{3+}, which is capable of trapping an electron because of its excess positive charge with respect to the normal lattice sites. As in the nitrogen center in diamond, the extra electron is thought to be almost entirely localized in a B—O σ^*-antibonding orbital. Six equivalent directions of the major hyperfine interaction are seen, which correspond to the directions of the nonaxial nearest-neighbor oxygen atoms, so that in contrast to the nitrogen center where all four possible N—C directions are observed, the unpaired electron is located in one of the *three* nonaxial B—O bonds and the fourth bond appears to be avoided. This must surely be a consequence of the fact that even the normal beryllium site does not have perfect tetrahedral symmetry. In crystalline beryllium oxide, a compression along the hexagonal axis coupled with a shift of the hexagonal close-packed lattice of oxygen with respect to that of beryllium causes the axial Be—O bond to be longer than the three equivalent basal bonds (66). In contrast with the experimental results, the electron might have been expected to favor the long axial bond in which it would cause least distortion, but the greater 2s character of the boron orbitals in the basal bonds must serve to reduce the energy of the antibonding levels sufficiently for them to be preferred.

The hyperfine parameters given in Table IX indicate a high spin density on boron and a p/s ratio of 6.3. The latter might be expected to be higher than the ratio for the nitrogen center (10.9), because of the greater spin density on boron than on carbon. However, the system differs in that even before distortion the boron orbitals have greater s character because of the inherent axial compression in the crystal and any ionic character will lead to additional s character at the boron nucleus.

Thus even in the relatively ionic beryllium oxide, bonding to neighboring atoms is a major factor in determining the manner in which the electron is trapped.

E. Fluorine Centers in Beryllium Oxide and Zinc Sulfide

Centers in isostructural zinc sulfide and beryllium oxide have both been attributed to a substitutional fluorine ion at an anion site. Such a system would be expected to act as an electron trap.

The center observed by Sroubek et al. (24) in x-irradiated beryllium oxide and assigned to F^{2-} in which the extra electron is mainly in the 3s orbital has already been described in Section III-B. It is the fact that hyperfine interaction is seen with only three of the four boron atoms surrounding the anion site which is surprising. This might arise from the same distortion of the beryllium oxide lattice as described in the previous section. Thus the system might be better described in terms of an electron in a σ^*-antibonding level between fluorine and a beryllium atom with a rapid migration between three Be—F bonds. The electron would be expected to be almost wholly confined to the beryllium atom and the low 2s character on fluorine (4%) is consistent with this. It is possible that the 12 G splitting given for ^9Be includes a small anisotropic term, so that the 2s character is somewhat less than 9% on each beryllium. A p/s ratio as low as 3 would account for all of the electron. This might not be un-reasonable if the s character is high because of the relatively ionic nature of the bonding. However, the difficulty with this model is that migration only occurs between three bonds, so that a residual anisotropy in the ^{19}F hyperfine interaction would be expected and apparently none is detected.

Kasai has found a similar center after UV photolysis of both single crystal and powdered zinc sulfide doped with fluorine (67). A doublet with a separation of 465 G indicates hyperfine coupling with one ^{19}F nucleus and there is also coupling with two different ^{67}Zn nuclei (4.1% abundant). Interaction with only one ^{67}Zn nucleus of each type is a result of its low natural abundance, but line intensities suggest that there are four strongly interacting and 12 more weakly interacting zinc atoms. The center can be simply described as before with a rapid migration between four Zn—F bonds accounting for the purely isotropic fluorine coupling.

F. Radicals in Borates

In the magnetic centers already described in this section, the three-dimensional bonding within the lattice constrains the electrons into σ or σ^* levels and there is no possibility of any π bonding. However, it seems reasonable to expect that where π levels exist electrons will be lost or added to these in preference to the σ levels, since generally π levels will be of a higher energy than σ levels, but lower than σ^*. This is thought to be the case for a magnetic center found in alkali borate and borosilicate glasses after γ or neutron irradiation (68).

An alkali borate glass is believed to be a random network of tetra-hedral BO_4 and planar BO_3 units, joined together by sharing oxygen atoms. The extra oxygen provided by the alkali oxide can either form one or two bonds with 3-coordinated boron atoms, leading to a change in coordination from 3 to 4, or leave two oxygen atoms with only one bond to boron by destroying a B—O—B linkage, but with no change in the boron coordination number (69). Irradiation is likely to lead to loss of an electron from these positions, since there will be an excess negative charge with respect to the rest of the network, although this charge will be partially offset by the alkali metal ions present. Parameters recorded by Bray (68) for such a center are given in Table X. The anisotropic g tensor, with one principal value of 2.012 and the other two close to free spin, suggests that the unpaired spin is a "hole" rather than an electron. Hyperfine interaction with one ^{11}B nucleus is detected but the total spin density on it is very low (less than 7%). This value seems very low for it to be associated with a "hole" in a B—O σ bond. However, on the basis of the above considerations it is suggested that irradiation leads to loss of an electron from one of the filled oxygen $2p\pi$ levels not involved in σ bonding.

TABLE X
Hyperfine Coupling Constants for Some Radicals in Polymeric Materials

| Material | Nucleus | Hyperfine tensor | | | | a_s^2 | a_p^2 | p/s ratio | Ref. |
		A_1	A_2	A_3	A_{iso}				
Alkali borate glass	^{11}B	17.0	14.0	14.0	15.0	0.021	0.053	2.5	68
Fused silica	^{11}B	15.0	13.4	13.4	13.9	0.019	0.028	1.5	71
Quartz	^{27}Al				6.0	0.006			61
Phosphate glass	^{31}P	41.1	30.8	30.8	34.2	0.001	0.028	2.8	75

Such a system would have a g tensor of the type found, and since the unpaired spin is confined to an orbital which has no direct interaction with any boron orbital, only a small interaction with the boron nucleus, resulting mainly from spin polarization of the σ bonding electrons, would be expected. The anisotropy of the hyperfine coupling will be due not only to negative spin density in the boron p orbital involved in σ bonding, but also to a direct dipolar interaction with the unpaired spin on oxygen. This latter effect will be of opposite sign, and calculation indicates that it leads to a major interaction, along the B—O bond direction, of about 3 G. Thus the observed anisotropy results mainly from two opposing effects which are of similar magnitudes, so it is not surprising that the calculated p/s ratio leads to no conclusion concerning the coordination number of the boron atoms. Since there is interaction with only *one* ^{11}B nucleus, the hole is probably located on a single-bonded oxygen atom, although it is possible that an oxygen atom bridging two boron atoms having different coordination numbers is involved.

It is interesting to compare the isotropic hyperfine coupling with the value of U_{OB}^B that might be expected for such a π radical. Reference to Figure 4 and Section II, suggests that for three-coordinated boron, an isotropic coupling of about 11 G is probable. The actual value of 15 G is not much greater than this and this agreement provides some support for the postulated structure.

A similar center was found in γ-irradiated wet alkali borate glasses by Nakai (70), who observed an additional doublet splitting of 504 G when measurements were made at 77°K. On replacement of the water in the glass by deuterium oxide, the doublet was largely replaced by a triplet characteristic of deuterium atoms, so it is concluded that the species is a hydrogen atom removed from an hydroxyl group by γ irradiation and trapped in the glass. The same phenomenon has been observed in other γ-irradiated compounds, such as phosphates (27).

G. Radicals in Silicates

Muha (71) has recently γ irradiated fused silica, which was prepared in such a way that it had a high surface area. The ESR spectrum has been analyzed mainly in terms of a hyperfine interaction with a single boron nucleus, lines from both the 80% abundant ^{11}B and the 20% abundant ^{10}B nuclei being observed. A number of other lines are thought to be associated with different paramagnetic centers. There is a noticeable similarity between the hyperfine parameters and g tensor for this boron center (Table X) and those observed in irradiated alkali borates. The slightly lower value of the isotropic hyperfine splitting for boron can be explained if the boron atom has a higher coordination number in this case. The measured anisotropy does not exclude such an interpretation, since although it *appears* to indicate a decrease in p character on boron, no direct conclusions can be drawn because of the comparatively large dipolar effect at the boron nucleus, due to unpaired spin in the oxygen π level. Thus, as before, the center may be interpreted as a hole located mainly on an oxygen atom which is singly bonded to a boron atom, or bridging between a boron and a silicon atom. This could result from loss of hydrogen from an hydroxyl group.

It is possible that a broad line also detected is a similar center involving silicon. If this is correct there ought to be satellite lines from ^{29}Si (4.7% abundance), but it is not possible to detect any in the published spectra.

Radiation damage in both natural and synthetic quartz has been studied fairly extensively. In the quartz crystal, each silicon atom is surrounded by an approximate tetrahedron of oxygen atoms, and each oxygen atom is bonded to two silicon atoms, although it is not located directly between the silicon atoms. Weeks (72) has examined many of these paramagnetic centers, especially those formed by neutron irradiation. Hyperfine splittings due to ^{29}Si were observed in many cases, and the separation and relative intensities of these satellites appear to be consistent with his postulate that some of these centers involved vacancies at silicon and oxygen lattice sites (72).

Other centers observed are almost certainly due to the presence of impurities. Thus a center formed in many x-irradiated quartz crystals is thought to result from an aluminum impurity. The spectra obtained for this center are complex, since there appear to be six different magnetic sites in the unit cell, and in addition to the six-line structure from hyperfine interaction with a ^{27}Al nucleus ($I = \frac{5}{2}$), lines due to the "forbidden" $\Delta M_I = \pm 1$ transitions are seen because aluminum has a relatively large quadrupole moment. As in the case of the center in borates already described, the unpaired spin is thought to be a "hole" primarily localized in an oxygen $2p\pi$ orbital. The principal values and the axes of the g tensor, which are not coincidental with those of the hyperfine tensor, are in agreement with such a model and indicate that the defect is associated with only one Al—O bond. Thus there can be no rapid migration of an electron to the other three oxygen atoms surrounding the impurity.

The hyperfine interaction with ^{27}Al is very small and it has proved difficult to measure its anisotropy. O'Brien (73) suggests the hole interacts with the ^{27}Al nucleus by a π mechanism via an s–p hybrid orbital. However, the isotropic hyperfine splitting of 6 G is of the right order for interaction resulting from spin polarization of the σ electrons in the Al—O bond (Fig. 4).

It is possible that a center formed in germanium-doped x-irradiated quartz (74) is similar, but no hyperfine interaction is observed since the ^{73}Ge magnetic isotope has only a low natural abundance.

H. Radicals in Polyphosphates

Gamma irradiation of phosphate glasses, containing alkali or alkaline earth oxides as modifier, usually leads to a spectrum with a two-line structure of separation 41 G (75). One would like to postulate a magnetic center analogous to those described in Sections V-F and V-G, in which there is a hole in an oxygen π level and a small interaction with the neighboring ^{31}P ($I = \frac{1}{2}$). Nakai has analyzed the essentially two-line structure in terms of axially symmetric hyperfine and g tensors (Table X), suggesting that the parallel features are almost lost in the line width of the perpendicular features. This analysis is by no means certain, although it is possible that measurement at a different microwave frequency might resolve the structure. However, if it is correct, the hyperfine tensor indicates that the apparent spin density on phosphorus is about 4% and the isotropic coupling is close to the value of U_{0P}^{P} (Fig. 4) that would be expected for a tetrahedrally coordinated phosphorus atom. As before, no direct measure of the p/s ratio can be obtained from the anisotropy, because of the dipolar effect at the phosphorus nucleus from spin on oxygen, although it is of the order expected. It is significant that the results can be well accommodated by invoking very little, if any, π bonding via phosphorus d orbitals.

VI. RADICALS IN THE GAS PHASE

Compared with the electron spin resonance study of radicals in condensed phases, the gas-phase counterpart is still in its infancy. At the present time gas-phase spectra have been reported for only nine monatomic (H, N, P, O, S, F, Cl, Br, I); eleven diatomic (OH, SH, SeH, TeH, NO, NS, O_2, SO, SeO, ClO, BrO); and two triatomic radicals (NO_2, NF_2) and not all of these have been fully analyzed. Consequently, we shall be able to make few structural comparisons between related species and shall concentrate for the most part on general principles, leaving the reader to search the original papers for many of the details.

Because of its subject matter electron magnetic resonance spectroscopy in the gas phase has much in common with other methods of studying gaseous radicals, such as atomic and molecular beam magnetic resonance and optical and microwave spectroscopy. In some instances the transitions observed by these other methods are the zero or low field equivalents of the electron magnetic resonance transitions.

Unlike radicals in the liquid and solid states, gaseous radicals are not subject to the environmental forces which quench orbital and rotational motions. Thus, there is the possibility for the electronic orbital and rotational angular momenta, L and N, to be constant and quantized, except, of course, that monatomic radicals may not possess rotational angular momentum. Whether or not this possibility for the electronic orbital motion is realized depends upon the symmetry of the electric field provided by the nuclei. In monatomic species, this field is spherically symmetric and the orbital angular momentum may itself be a constant of the motion, whereas in the cylindrically symmetric field of diatomic or linear polyatomic species only the component (Λ) of orbital angular momentum along the internuclear axis (A) may be constant, and in the asymmetric field of nonlinear species all components are quenched. We must qualify these statements to the extent that the interaction or coupling between the orbital motion and the electron spin (S) or the molecular rotation is not negligible in comparison with its coupling to the electric field. In the case of monatomic radicals this would be represented by a departure from Russell-Saunders coupling and for linear radicals from Hund's coupling cases a and b, which we shall now describe.

A. Hund's Coupling Schemes for Linear Radicals

The five ideal coupling schemes for linear radicals known as Hund's coupling cases a–e correspond to extreme situations regarding the relative strengths of the interactions between the orbital motion, the electron spin, and the end-over-end rotation of the nuclei and of the interaction between the axial field of the nuclei and the orbital motion (76,77). These ideal cases provide the basis for a description of any actual coupling scheme but for our present purposes we need consider only the first two cases.

In Hund's case a coupling the interaction of the orbital motion with the axial field is much stronger than its interaction with the electron spin, and this in turn is much stronger than its interaction with the rotational motion —a circumstance that we may write as $LA \gg LS \gg LN$. The orbital angular momentum is then said to be strongly coupled to the internuclear axis, about which it precesses with constant axial component Λ. The electron spin also interacts weakly with the nuclear rotation and is accordingly coupled to the internuclear axis ($SA \gg SN$) with axial component Σ, but this coupling with the axial field is an indirect one via spin-orbit coupling ($LS \gg SN$). The total electronic angular momentum along the axis is thus $\Omega = \Lambda + \Sigma$ and this couples with the rotational angular momentum (N) to produce a total angular momentum (excluding nuclear spin) $J = \Omega + N$, as shown in Figure 11a. In Hund's case b coupling the orbital motion is again strongly coupled to the internuclear axis, but the spin is less strongly coupled to the axis than to K, the total orbital angular momentum including rotation ($LA \gg LN \gg LS, SN$). Thus, $K = \Lambda + N$ and the resultant $J = K + S$, as in Figure 11b.

The electronic states of Hund's case a radicals are designated by symbols such as $^2\Pi_{3/2}$ and $^2\Pi_{1/2}$ in which the main part specifies the value of $|\Lambda|$ ($\Lambda = 0, \pm 1, \pm 2 \ldots$ for $\Sigma, \Pi, \Delta \ldots$ states), the superscript is ($2S + 1$) and the subscript $|\Omega|$. States which differ only in the value of $|\Omega|$ are nondegenerate because of differences in spin-orbit coupling and each is split by the rotational energy into levels labeled by the quantum number J. For Hund's case b Ω has no meaning and the subscript is omitted. In this case the rotational levels are indicated by K and each of these is further split by the spin interactions into ($2S + 1$) energy levels denoted by different values of J. When $S = \frac{1}{2}$ and 1 we have the so-called rotational or ρ-type doublets and triplets which can be seen in Figure 12 where we have shown for $^2\Pi$ radicals the transition from case a to case b as the spin is uncoupled from the molecular axis by the rotation. This rotational distortion of case a is in effect

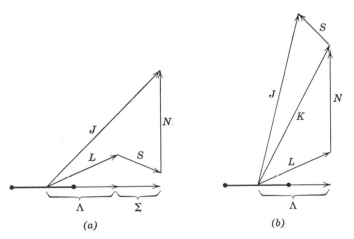

(a)   (b)

Fig. 11. Vector diagrams for Hund's coupling cases a and b.

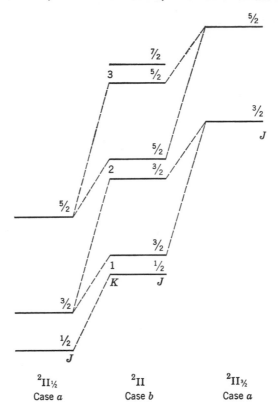

Fig. 12. Hund's case *a* and *b* energy levels and the relation between them for $^2\Pi$ radicals.

a mixing of the fine-structure states $^2\Pi_{3/2}$ and $^2\Pi_{1/2}$ so that the extent of uncoupling for a given J depends upon relative sizes of the spin-orbit coupling constant and the rotational constant, the ratio of which is called the spin-uncoupling constant. Among linear doublet-state radicals those with orbital angular momentum (e.g., $^2\Pi$, $^2\Delta$ species) usually correspond closely in their coupling to case *a*, at least for the lower rotational levels, while those without it ($^2\Sigma$) conform to case *b*.

An example of intermediate coupling is provided by very light $^2\Pi$ radicals such as OH which rotate very rapidly even in their lower rotational states. With triplet-state radicals there is the extra complexity of the inter- action between the unpaired spins. As this spin-spin coupling is equivalent to an interaction between the resultant spin and the molecular axis it tends to take $^3\Sigma$ radicals along the road from case *b* toward case *a*, although this tendency will diminish as the rotational energy increases. In addition to the angular momenta so far considered there may also be a nuclear spin angular momentum ($\mathbf{I}$) present in the radical and this may be coupled to the other angular momenta in a variety of ways (77). However, in the large magnetic fields of about 10,000 G employed in most gas-phase electron resonance experiments, the nuclear spin is usually uncoupled from the other angular momenta (the Back-Goudsmit effect). In contrast, the coupling between the other angular momenta is not usually disrupted, although this "Paschen-Back effect" is becoming apparent for the oxygen molecule in such magnetic fields (78,79).

B. g Factors

The magnetic moment of a free radical in the gas phase may have contributions from the electron spin, the electronic orbital motion, the rotation of the nuclei and the nuclear spin, and these are expressed in terms of four gyromagnetic ratios or g factors (g_s, g_i, g_r, g_n) which give the relation between a magnetic moment and the corresponding angular momentum (80):

$$\mu_s = -g_s\beta\mathbf{S}, \quad \mu_i = -g_i\beta\mathbf{L}, \quad \mu_r = -g_r\beta\mathbf{N}, \quad \mu_n = g_n\beta_n\mathbf{I}$$

If we assume that the coupling between $\mathbf{J}$ and $\mathbf{I}$ is broken by the external field, then we may write the energy of interaction with the magnetic field as $g_j\beta HM_j - g_n\beta_n HM_I$ but since electron resonance transitions involve no change in M_I we may ignore the second term in this expression. The g_j factor is a measure of the resultant magnetic moment excluding nuclear spin and its value depends on the precise details of the coupling between $\mathbf{L}$, $\mathbf{S}$, and $\mathbf{N}$.

For Russell-Saunders coupling in atoms we have:

$$g_j = g_i \frac{J(J + 1) - S(S + 1) + L(L + 1)}{2J(J + 1)}$$

$$+ g_s \frac{J(J + 1) + S(S + 1) - L(L + 1)}{2J(J + 1)}$$

but to a good approximation $g_i = 1$ and $g_s = 2$ so that this reduces to the familiar Landé formula:

$$g_j = 1 + \frac{J(J + 1) + S(S + 1) - L(L + 1)}{2J(J + 1)}$$

Thus for $^2P_{3/2}$ and $^2P_{1/2}$ states $g_j = \frac{4}{3}$ and $\frac{2}{3}$, respectively, whereas $^3P_1$ and $^3P_2$ states have the same g_j factor ($g_j = 1.5$) since $L = S$. To a better approximation $g_s = 2.002319$, because of a quantum electrodynamical correction (81), and then the above values become 1.334106, 0.665894, and 1.501160, respectively. Further small corrections (81) ranging in size from about 10^{-4} to 10^{-6} may be made to allow for the deviation of g_s from the free-spin value and g_i from unity. Variations in g_s arise from a relativistic effect due to the velocity dependence of electron mass and hence of the magnetic moment, and from diamagnetic effects caused by modification of the electron velocity by a magnetic field which alters the spin–orbit, spin–other-orbit, and orbit–orbit interactions. Variations in g_i are the result of the nucleus possessing a noninfinite mass and therefore being in motion.

Larger departures of the g_j factor from the above ideal values may be taken as a measure of the breakdown of Russell-Saunders coupling resulting from magnetic interactions involving the electron spin, namely spin–spin, spin–orbit, and spin–other-orbit interactions. For instance, the transition from Russell-Saunders to j–j coupling in the $J = \frac{3}{2}$ state of a ns^2np^3 configuration is accompanied by a change in g_j from 2 to $\frac{4}{3}$. The latter value can be seen as arising from one $p_{3/2}$ and two antiparallel $p_{1/2}$ electrons which behave like a single $p_{3/2}$ electron.

For Hund's case a radicals the g_j factor is different for each rotational state and is given by (80):

$$g_j = J(J + 1)^{-1}\{(g_i\Lambda + g_s\Sigma)\Omega + g_r[J(J + 1) - \Omega^2]\}$$

Taking $g_i = 1$, $g_s = 2$ and $g_r = 0$ we obtain:

$$g_j = \frac{(\Lambda + 2\Sigma)\Omega}{J(J + 1)}$$

Thus for the $J = \frac{3}{2}$ and $J = \frac{5}{2}$ rotational levels of a $^2\Pi_{3/2}$ state $g_j = 0.8$ and 0.34286, whereas it is zero for all the rotational levels of a $^2\Pi_{1/2}$ state. Rotational mixing of the $^2\Pi_{3/2}$ and $^2\Pi_{1/2}$ states with the same J value alters the individual g_j factors but leaves unchanged the sum $\bar{g}_j(^2\Pi_{3/2}) + \bar{g}_j(^2\Pi_{1/2}) = 3/J(J + 1)$. Rotational uncoupling of the orbital angular momentum from the internuclear axis, which lifts the $\pm\Lambda$ degeneracy, produces different g_j factors for each member of the Λ-type doublet. However, the sum of the average factors, $\bar{g}_j = \frac{1}{2}(g_j^+ + g_j^-)$, for the two states is still $3/J(J + 1)$. This is well illustrated by the $J = \frac{3}{2}$ levels for the hydroxyl radical (see Table XI). The individual values $\bar{g}_j(^2\Pi_{3/2}) = 0.93557$ and $\bar{g}_j(^2\Pi_{1/2}) = -0.13393$ are very different from the ideal values of 0.8 and 0, but the sum of 0.80164 is close to the predicted value of 0.8. The remaining discrepancy may be attributed in part to the choice of g_i and g_s as described above for atoms and to the rotation of the nuclei ($g_r \neq 0$). In addition, uncoupling of L from the axis allows the electrons to rotate with the nuclei and cancel out some of their rotational angular momentum. It is this contribution which accounts for the difference between g_j^+ and g_j^-.

For linear radicals in Σ states a small amount of orbital motion is induced by the spin–orbit and rotation–electronic interactions which mix excited Π states into the Σ ground state. This is accommodated by assuming that g_s has a small correction added to it for a magnetic field perpendicular to the internuclear axis (79). This correction is also designated g_i and should be distinguished from the true orbital g factor described above. In this case g_i is a measure of the amount of induced orbital angular momentum.

There is one further effect of the magnetic field to be considered. Because the field mixes adjacent J states, the $(2J + 1)$ sublevels into which each J level is split by a magnetic field are not equally spaced. Accordingly, the energy of each sublevel must be represented by a term in H^2 as well as one in H. This quadratic Zeeman effect has important spectral consequences, as we shall see in Section VI-D.

C. Hyperfine Coupling Constants

We now come to a consideration of the magnetic hyperfine interaction between a nuclear spin magnetic moment and magnetic moments associated with electron spin, electron orbital motion, molecular rotation, and other nuclear spins. The last two are much smaller than the others and may be neglected. The exact details of the hyperfine interaction depend upon the way in which the various angular momenta are oriented with respect to one another and to the magnetic field.

Let us start by examining the situation for Russell-Saunders coupling in atoms. The resultant hyperfine coupling in this case can be written down quite simply if the atom possesses one unpaired electron outside closed shells or subshells, or if the atom is one electron short of a closed-shell configuration (82). For an unpaired s electron the coupling is entirely of the Fermi-contact type and the corresponding coupling constant is $A = (8\pi/3)g_n\beta_n |\psi(0)|^2$ G, where g_n is the nuclear g factor, β_n the nuclear magneton, and $\psi(0)$ the value of the wave function for the s electron at the nucleus. If the unpaired electron is a p electron then the combined effect of the dipole–dipole interactions of the nucleus with the spin and with the orbital motion is $A = [L(L + 1)/J(J + 1)]g_n\beta_n < r^{-3} >$ where $< r^{-3} >$ is the average value of r^{-3} for the p orbital, r being the distance between nucleus and electron. For a positive hole in a p subshell the coupling constant is of the same magnitude but opposite in sign. In each of the above cases an extra contribution must be added to allow for spin polarization of the core s electrons (82). In general for each set of fine structure states (e.g., $^3P_{2,1,0}$) one coupling constant (written a_J) is required for each state and a second-order one $(a_{J,J-1})$ for each pair of adjacent states to allow for mixing between them (83). Analysis of these constants is difficult; suffice to say that if at least three independent coupling constants (e.g., $a_{3/2}$, $a_{1/2}$, and $a_{3/2.1/2}$ for $^2P_{3/2.1/2}$) can be determined for a given set of fine-structure states, then the contributions due to the orbital motion, the electron-spin dipole–dipole interaction and the Fermi-contact coupling can be separated and expressed in terms of $\langle r^{-3} \rangle$ and $|\psi(0)|^2$ values and in this form they provide a severe test of atomic wave functions (82,83).

The hyperfine interaction for linear radicals may be expressed in terms of four hyperfine structure constants (in gauss) (84,85):

$$a = g_n\beta_n\langle r^{-3} \rangle$$

$$b = g_n\beta_n\{(8\pi/3)|\psi(0)|^2 - \tfrac{1}{2}\langle(3\cos^2\chi - 1)/r^3\rangle\}$$

$$c = 3/2 g_n\beta_n\langle(3\cos^2\chi - 1)/r^3\rangle$$

$$d = 3/2 g_n\beta_n\langle(\sin^2\chi)/r^3\rangle$$

the last being required to accommodate Λ-type doubling. In these expressions χ is the angle between the internuclear axis and the line joining the electron to the nucleus. The constant a represents the magnetic interaction between the nucleus and the orbital motion and the average $\langle r^{-3} \rangle$ is to be taken over electrons carrying uncancelled orbital angular momentum. The other constants express the interaction with the electron spin and their averages are to be taken for electrons carrying unpaired spin. The first term in b is the Fermi-contact term arising from unpaired electron density within the nucleus and it may be provided directly by an unpaired electron in an orbital with s character or by spin polarization of bonding, lone-pair, and core electrons as explained in Section II. The second term in b and the constants c and d are dipole–dipole in origin.

For a Hund's case a species the resultant hyperfine coupling constant is $A = [a\Lambda + (b + c)\Sigma]$, G. If the spin is partially or completely uncoupled from the molecular axis by the rotational motion, then A is a more complicated function of the constants a, b, and c, the coefficients of which depend upon the spin-uncoupling constant (λ) and upon J (80,86). When Λ doubling is of importance A must be replaced by $(A_1 \pm A_2)$ where A_1 is a function of a, b, c, λ, J, and A_2 is proportional to d, the constant of proportionality also being a function of λ and J. If the spectra from a sufficient number of electronic and rotational states can be analyzed then it is possible to extract from them the values of the individual constants a, b, c, and d. Since these constants are a measure of the spatial distribution of the electrons which carry spin and orbital angular momentum, their extraction yields valuable information about electronic structure as we shall see in Section VI-F.

D. Detection and Analysis of Spectra

There are two major problems to be overcome in the study of gaseous radicals by electron magnetic resonance spectroscopy: the difficulty of establishing a sufficiently high concentration of radicals for detection and that of analyzing the spectra in terms of the many parameters involved. Short-lived free radicals are usually generated by passing a gas at low pressure through a microwave discharge but because of noise this must be done some distance from the resonance cavity. Consequently, this method is useful only for the less unstable intermediates such as SO or for radicals such as OH which are continuously regenerated by chemical reactions on their way to the cavity. Alternatively, the radicals may be produced in the cavity itself by reaction between a stable gas and a stream of atoms from a discharge and then the magnetic resonance method may be employed to study the kinetics of such a reaction.

What saves the technique from very restricted application is the possibility of inducing transitions with intensity that depends upon a large molecular electric dipole moment rather than a small magnetic one. These electric dipole transitions are induced by the oscillating *electric field* of the microwave radiation—provided that this has a component perpendicular to the applied static magnetic field—and they should be contrasted with the usual magnetic dipole transitions observed in condensed phases, which require a perpendicular microwave *magnetic* field. Roughly speaking, the intensity of an electric or magnetic dipole transition is proportional to the square of the corresponding dipole moment of the radical and in favorable cases an electric dipole transition may be 10,000 times more intense than its magnetic equivalent. Obviously, electric dipole transitions cannot be observed for monatomic and homonuclear diatomic species which have no electric dipole moment; nor do they seem to be possible for nonlinear radicals (87) (see Section VI-H).

Some of the selection rules and hence the spectra for the two types of transition are rather different. The common selection rules are $\Delta J = 0$, $\Delta M_J = \pm 1$, and $\Delta M_I = 0$, so that all transitions take place between the magnetic sublevels of a given J state, which for atoms is a fine-structure state (e.g., $^2P_{3/2}$ or $^2P_{1/2}$) and for Hund's case a radicals a rotational state (e.g., the $J = \frac{3}{2}$ state of $^2\Pi_{3/2}$). For Hund's case a radicals we must add the selection rules $+ \leftrightarrow +$ and $- \leftrightarrow -$ for magnetic dipole transitions and $+ \leftrightarrow -$ for electric dipole transitions (Fig. 13). In other words, the former transitions occur within and the latter between the two members of a Λ-type doublet. The intensity of an $M_J - 1 \rightarrow M_J$ transition for an atom or Hund's case a radical is proportional to $[J(J + 1) - M_J(M_J - 1)]$ so that for a $J = \frac{3}{2}$ state the three transitions have relative intensities $3:4:3$. For Hund's case b $\Delta K = 0$ for magnetic dipole transitions and ± 1

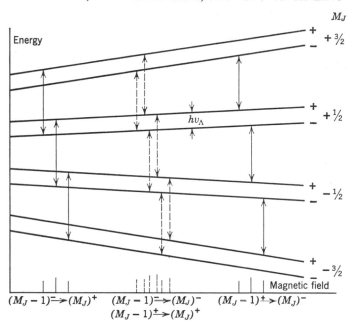

Fig. 13. Electric (————) and magnetic (— — —) dipole transitions for the $J = \frac{3}{2}$ level of a $^2\Pi_{3/2}$ state. In the presence of a magnetic nucleus each of the above sublevels and transitions would be split into $(2I + 1)$ components.

for electric ones. If the microwave electric field is parallel to the external magnetic field, then $\Delta M_J = 0$ electric dipole transitions may also be observed (Fig. 14). This time the magnetic dipole transitions take place within and the electric ones between ρ-type multiplets; that is, within or between the levels of a rotational state. The full significance of these rules will become apparent when we consider specific examples in Sections VI-E to VI-H.

Because of the many magnetic interactions involved in a gas-phase magnetic resonance transition, the extraction of structural information from the spectrum is a complicated process. The method of analysis is to assume what form the interactions will take and to calculate the resonance conditions in terms of a set of parameters (rotational constant, g factors and coupling constants) some of which are known (e.g., from microwave and optical spectra) and the others are to be determined (79,80). The unknown parameters are then varied until the closest fit is obtained between the calculated and experimental values of the magnetic field at which resonance occurs. When the number of unknowns is exceeded by the number of lines, the calculation can be checked for self-consistency.

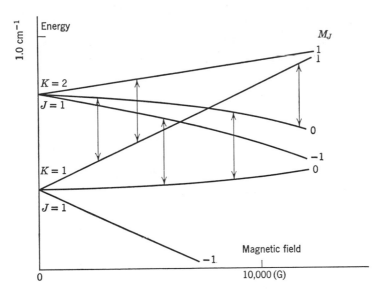

Fig. 14. Electric dipole transitions for a $^3\Sigma$ radical.

We shall now treat in more detail the spectrum expected for an atom or a Hund's case *a* radical. In the absence of all effects other than the linear Zeeman splitting, both magnetic and electric dipole spectra would consist of a set of single lines, one for each rotational state such that $h\nu = g_J\beta H$. Let us consider the splitting of one of these lines by the quadratic Zeeman effect, Λ-type doubling and hyperfine coupling. The quadratic Zeeman effect displaces each magnetic sublevel by an amount proportional to M_J^2 and to H^2 so that transitions between states differing in $|M_J|$ are displaced to high or low field according to the resonance condition for $M_J - 1 \to M_J$, which is $h\nu = g_J\beta[H + K(2M_J - 1)H^2]$. For example, the three transitions between the magnetic sublevels of a $J = \frac{3}{2}$ state are found at different fields H_1, H_2, and H_3 where $(H_2 - H_1) = 2KH_1^2$ and $(H_3 - H_2) = 2KH_3^2$, and since K is small these splittings are approximately equal. The relative intensities of these lines are $3:4:3$ as indicated above. The extent of mixing of adjacent J states by the external field depends on the separation between these states. Consequently, the rotational constant and hence the bond length may be estimated from the quadratic Zeeman splitting.

The absence of a quadratic Zeeman splitting suggests that the spectrum is either from a $J = \frac{1}{2}$ level (e.g., $^2S_{1/2}$ of hydrogen and $^2P_{1/2}$ of fluorine and chlorine) or in the case of atoms from an S state (e.g., $^4S_{3/2}$ of nitrogen and phosphorus). The spectra from $J = \frac{1}{2}$ levels exhibit no splitting because there is only one possible transition $(M_J = -\frac{1}{2} \rightarrow \frac{1}{2})$ and although atoms in S states with $J > \frac{1}{2}$ have more than two magnetic sublevels, there is only one J level, and therefore no possibility for the magnetic field to mix in adjacent ones.

In the presence of Λ-type doubling we may write the energy levels as

$$g_J^{\pm} \beta [HM_J \pm \frac{1}{2}(\bar{g}_J/g_J^{\pm})H_\Lambda]$$

where H_Λ, the Λ-doubling field, is assumed to be the same for both members of the doublet and is related to the Λ-doubling frequency by $h\nu_\Lambda = \bar{g}_J \beta H_\Lambda$. For magnetic dipole transitions we have $h\nu = g_J^{\pm} \beta H$ so that the Λ-doubling splits the resonance by only a small amount. On the other hand, electric dipole transitions are given by:

and

$$h\nu = g_J^+ \beta [H - (\bar{g}_J/g_J^+)\,H_\Lambda + \{(g_J^- - g_J^+)/g_J^+\}M_JH]$$

$$h\nu = g_J^- \beta [H + (\bar{g}_J/g_J^-)\,H_\Lambda - \{(g_J^- - g_J^+)/g_J^-\}M_JH]$$

so that to a first approximation the original line is split into two lines separated by twice the Λ-doubling field. If the Λ-doubling frequency is greater than the microwave frequency, then the low-field line cannot be observed. The third terms in the above resonance conditions lift the M_J degeneracy of each new line in roughly the same way as the quadratic Zeeman effect and when the two effects are present they oppose one another for one-half of the spectrum and add for the other, giving for $J = \frac{3}{2}$, for example, a closely spaced triplet at low field and a widely spaced one at high field.

Finally, we must treat the hyperfine coupling with a single magnetic nucleus which splits each of the above lines into a hyperfine multiplet of equally intense lines which are approximately equally spaced. The spacing is rendered unequal by second-order effects if the splitting is large and by quadrupole effects if $I > \frac{1}{2}$. For magnetic dipole transitions:

$$h\nu = g_J^{\pm} \beta [H + (A_1 \pm A_2)M_I]$$

and for electric dipole transitions:

$$h\nu = g_J^{\pm} \beta [H \mp (\bar{g}_J/g_J^{\pm})\,H_\Lambda \pm \{(g_J^- - g_J^+)/g_J^{\pm}\}M_JH + \{A_1 \\ \pm (2M_J - 1)A_2\}M_I]$$

from which it will be seen that the equal spacing for electric dipole transitions is also destroyed by the Λ doubling.

Before proceeding to our review of specific gas-phase radicals we should give a brief guide to identification. From the number of lines and their relative intensities it is usually possible to distinguish between splittings arising from hyperfine coupling, Λ doubling and the quadratic Zeeman effect. If this is not so, then the last can be identified from its strong field dependence by performing the experiment at a different microwave frequency. If the resonance as a whole moves to higher fields as the microwave frequency is reduced then it must arise from transitions between the magnetic sublevels of *different* rotational states. Increasing the gain to reveal hyperfine lines from low abundance isotopes or isotopic substitution serves to characterize the hyperfine coupling. The number of quadratic Zeeman lines gives directly the value of J for the state (number of lines = $2J$) and confirmation is obtained from the relative intensities. The information combined with the value of g_J and chemical intuition narrows the field to a few possibilities which may often be distinguished by a full analysis of the magnitudes of the above splittings.

E. Atoms

Although the g factors and hyperfine coupling constants of numerous atoms have been measured in the gas phase by atomic beam magnetic resonance and other methods, the only gaseous atoms so far studied by electron magnetic resonance are hydrogen (88), nitrogen (89), phosphorus (90), oxygen (79) sulfur (91), and the halogens (83,87,92–95). Consequently, a full discussion of the experimental data for atoms in the gas phase would take us far beyond our intention here, so we must content ourselves with a cursory examination of the spectra of these nine atoms.

The first point to note is the position of the resonance as specified by the g_J factor. On this evidence all of the atoms under consideration conform closely to Russell-Saunders coupling. The second important spectral feature is the presence or absence of quadratic Zeeman splitting. In the case of oxygen and sulfur atoms this splitting permits the spectra from the $^2P_2$ and $^2P_1$ states to be readily distinguished, despite their similar g factors as the $^2P_2$ spectrum consists of a $2:3:3:2$ quartet whereas the $^2P_1$ spectrum is a doublet (79,91). The quadratic Zeeman effect has also made possible the detection and identification of multiple quantum transitions ($\Delta M_J = \pm 2, \pm 3, \pm 4$) within the $^2P_2$ ground state of oxygen (96).

Our final concern is with hyperfine structure. If the electronic structure of atoms were accurately represented by a single electronic configuration no hyperfine splitting would be observed for nitrogen and phosphorus atoms since the interactions with the three p electrons cancel out and there are no unpaired s electrons. Consequently, the observed hyperfine splitting for these atoms (89,90,) which represents about 0.2% unpaired spin density in the $2s$ and $3s$ orbital, respectively (see Section II), can only be accommodated if allowance is made for core polarization (82). This is done either by introducing configuration interaction (e.g., $2s^2 2p^3 \rightarrow 2s 2p^3 3s$)

or by employing wave functions, such as unrestricted Hartree-Fock functions, which place electrons with the same principal and azimuthal quantum numbers but with opposite spin in orbitals with different spatial distributions (82). Often the hyperfine splitting, including a core-polarization contribution, is simply superimposed on the quadratic Zeeman splitting [e.g., ^{17}O (83) and ^{35}Cl (95)], but with ^{19}F ($I = \frac{1}{2}$) the hyperfine coupling is so large that the nuclear spin is not completely un-coupled from J by the applied magnetic field and the spectrum has a decidedly intermediate-field character (83,87,94).

F. Diatomic Doublet-State Radicals

The diatomic doublet-state radicals investigated in the gas-phase fall into three groups. First, there is the pair NO and NS which have one unpaired electron in a π^* level, and second, the pair ClO and BrO which have three electrons in this doubly degenerate level. The third group comprises the quasi-isoelectronic (i.e., same number of valence electrons) family, OH, SH, SeH, and TeH in which three electrons occupy a roughly nonbonding doubly degenerate π level located on the atom other than hydrogen. Therefore, they are all $^2\Pi$ radicals with the $^2\Pi_{1/2}$ state of lowest energy for the first group and the $^2\Pi_{3/2}$ for the other two.

The X-band magnetic dipole spectrum of $^{14}N^{16}O$ in its excited $^2\Pi_{3/2}$ electronic state consists of a major 3:4:3 triplet of 1:1:1 triplets confirm-ing that it is due to a $J = \frac{3}{2}$ state coupled with a nucleus of spin $I = 1$ (2). The hyperfine splittings are not quite equal because of quadrupole coup-ling. The assignment of the larger splitting of about 200 G to the quadratic Zeeman effect and the smaller one of about 27 G to the hyperfine coupling is vindicated by the spectrum of $^{15}N^{16}O$ which is a major 3:4:3 triplet of doublets. In the corresponding electric dipole spectra each of the above lines is split into a doublet having a separation of about 1.5 G and re-vealing a small Λ-type doubling (97). Because of the strong field depend-ence of the quadratic Zeeman effect the S-band spectra of $^{14}N^{16}O$ and $^{15}N^{16}O$ are strikingly different from those at X band, consisting of three and two equivalent 3:4:3 triplets, respectively (98). The electric dipole spectra of the $J = \frac{5}{2}$ levels have also been observed and the hyperfine splittings are almost the same as for the $J = \frac{3}{2}$ levels showing that the coupling is close to that of Hund's case a. This conclusion is supported by the g_j values (Table XI).

A full analysis of the spectra, employing the results from the microwave spectrum of the $^2\Pi_{1/2}$ ground state, has yielded the values of the hyperfine structure constants a, b, c, and d shown in Table XII. In the approximation that the molecular orbital containing the unpaired electron is a linear combination of self-consistent-field atomic orbitals, the spin density on

TABLE XI

g and A Factors for Diatomic $^2\Pi$ Radicals

Radical	$|\Omega|$	J	g_J	$(g_J^- - g_J^+)$	A_1 (G)	A_2 (G)	ν_Λ (Mc/s)	$2H_\Lambda$(G)	Ref.
$^{14}N^{16}O$	3/2	3/2	0.777246	0.000011	27.427	0.017	0.906	1.666	98
		5/2	0.316648	0.000019	28.070	0.070	3.601	16.251	98
$^{15}N^{16}O$	3/2	3/2	0.778072	0.000010	−38.463	−0.022	0.814	1.495	98
		5/2	0.317617	0.000017	−39.322	−0.090	3.224	14.505	98
$^{14}N^{32}S$	3/2	3/2			22				99
$^{35}Cl^{16}O$	3/2	3/2			40				99
^{16}OH	3/2	3/2	0.93557	0.00129	20.63	0.39	1,666.34	2,545.15	80
		5/2	0.48529	0.00188	7.94	1.00	6,033.5	17,766.2	80
		7/2	0.32561	0.00214	2.19	1.91	13,437.8	58,973.5	80
	1/2	3/2	−0.13393	0.00099	110.16	77.67			80
		5/2	−0.14113	−0.00042	76.65	45.72			80
^{16}OD	3/2	3/2	0.88945	0.00051	3.89	0.02	310.12	498.24	80
^{32}SH	3/2	3/2			5.4			190	100
^{32}SD	3/2	3/2						28	100
^{80}SeH	3/2	3/2	0.80800		1.68		14.4		101
^{130}TeH	3/2	3/2	0.80366		1.60		6.6		101

TABLE XII

Hyperfine Structure Constants (G) for $^2\Pi$ Radicals

Radical	a	b	c	d	Ref.
$^{14}N^{16}O$	30.11	14.9	−21.0	41	98
$^{15}N^{16}O$	−42.23	−21.4	29.8	−57	98
^{16}OH	30.7	−42.51	47.59	20.2	80

nitrogen is $a/42.5 = 0.71$ or $c/25.5 = 0.83$. In view of the discrepancy between these two estimates there is no point in making allowance for the small hyperfine interaction between the spin density on oxygen and the nitrogen nucleus. The average value of 0.77 is in good accord with the antibonding character of the molecular orbital and the relative electronegativities of nitrogen and oxygen. The Fermi-contact part of the hyperfine coupling, which is $b + c/3 = 8$ G, represents about 1.4% $2s$ character and arises from spin polarization of σ bonding, σ nonbonding and core electrons. The fact that a is not equal to $c + d/3$ suggests that the same electrons do not carry both the spin and the orbital motion and this is presumably because of configuration interaction (98). Unfortunately, it is not possible to compare the above analysis with that for NS as the latter has not yet been carried out (87,99).

The electric dipole spectra of ClO and BrO in the lowest $J = \frac{3}{2}$ rotational level of their $^2\Pi_{3/2}$ electronic ground states have not been analyzed in detail but they are similar to the $^{14}N^{16}O$ spectrum, except that no Λ-type splitting is resolved and that the hyperfine structure arises from two isotopes both of spin $I = \frac{3}{2}$ (87,99).

Electric dipole transitions have been observed for the hydroxyl radical in three rotational levels ($J = \frac{3}{2}, \frac{5}{2}, \frac{7}{2}$) of the $^2\Pi_{3/2}$ electronic ground state and two levels ($J = \frac{3}{2}, \frac{5}{2}$) of the $^2\Pi_{1/2}$ excited state (80). Spectra for the $^2\Pi_{3/2}$, $J = \frac{3}{2}$ rotational level have also been reported for OD, SH, SD, SeH, and TeH (80,100,101). An examination of the g_j factors for these radicals (see Table XI) reveals that, while on the one hand SeH and TeH have approximately Hund's case a coupling, the hydroxyl radical because of its very rapid rotation assumes intermediate coupling, so that its $^2\Pi_{1/2}$ excited state is also paramagnetic. The Λ doubling is also much more pronounced for the hydroxyl radical and this splits the $^2\Pi_{3/2}$ spectrum into two well-separated parts, a low-field half due to transitions of the type $(M_J - 1)^- \rightarrow (M_J)^+$ and a high-field half due to $(M_J - 1)^+ \rightarrow (M_J)^-$ transitions (see Fig. 13), although for the $J - \frac{5}{2}$ and $\frac{7}{2}$ levels one-half of the spectrum is inaccessible (80).

Only for the hydroxyl radical has the hyperfine structure been fully analyzed to give the hyperfine structure constants shown in Table XII (80). As with nitric oxide there is evidence for configuration interaction but the value of b is in excellent accord with the figure of 47.9 G calculated for an electron in a p_π orbital on oxygen (7).

G. Diatomic Triplet-State Radicals

Of the three diatomic triplet-state radicals so far investigated in the gas phase, O_2 (79) is, of course, a stable molecule and SO (87,100,102) is a moderately short-lived species, while SeO (87) has made only brief appearances between explosions. All three are members of a quasi-isoelectronic family and have $^3\Sigma^-$ ground states in which the highest occupied level, a doubly degenerate π^* level, contains two electrons with parallel spins. In the absence of orbital angular momentum the magnetic sublevels of these ground states may be described to a first approximation in terms of the Hund's case b quantum numbers K, J, M_J. We shall see later to what extent this approximation holds. Because of the symmetry requirements of the wave function K is restricted to odd integral values for $^{16}O_2$, but no such restriction exists for $^{16}O^{18}O$, SO, or SeO. Each rotational level denoted by K is split by the spin–spin and spin–rotational interactions into a ρ-type triplet for which $J = K - 1, K, K + 1$. The energies of the $(2J + 1)$ magnetic sublevels into which each J level is split by a magnetic field (see Fig. 14) may be expressed in terms of the above three quantum numbers, the rotational constant (B), the spin–spin coupling constant (λ), the spin–rotational constant (μ), the magnetic field (H), and the g factors g_j, g_i, and g_r (78,79,102). In order to fit the spectra, B and λ must be corrected for vibrational and centrifugal distortions of the nonrigid radical and for mixing of different vibrational states. Furthermore, B, λ, and μ must be modified to allow for the small amount of orbital motion induced by the spin–orbit and rotational–electronic interactions, and we may express them as a sum of first- and second-order contributions: $B = B' - B''$, $\lambda = \lambda' + \lambda''$, $\mu = \mu' + \mu''$, where B'' represents the contribution of the rotating electrons to the moment of inertia, λ'' the spin–orbit interactions between the electrons and μ'' the orbital–rotational interaction. Whereas $B'' \ll B$ and $\lambda'' \ll \lambda$, μ'' is of the same order of magnitude as μ. The usual procedure is to take the values of B, λ, and μ determined from microwave, infrared, and optical spectra and to use the electron magnetic resonance results to determine the g factors (79,103).

Since oxygen has no electric dipole moment only magnetic dipole transitions are possible (79) whereas for SO and SeO only the stronger electric dipole transitions have been detected (87,100,102,104). At ordinary temperatures many rotational levels are populated and as a result the oxygen spectrum comprises many lines arising from $\Delta J = 0$ transitions within each rotational state and also $\Delta J = \pm 2$ transitions due to a breakdown of the quantum number J which we shall discuss below. Only five main lines and five satellites have been observed for $^{32}S^{16}O$ and $^{34}S^{16}O$, respectively, and these correspond to transitions between the J levels of the $K = 1$ and $K = 2$ rotational states as indicated in Figure 14 (87,102, 104). Hyperfine splitting of about 10 G from $^{33}S^{16}O$ has been observed for one of these transitions but it awaits detailed analysis (97,104). Some additional weak lines are thought to arise from $^{32}S^{16}O$ in a vibrationally excited state (87,104). The g factors extracted from the spectra of $^{16}O_2$ and $^{32}S^{16}O$ are $g_s = 2.00200$ and 2.00197, $g_i = 0.00281$ and 0.00371, and $g_r = 0.00013$ and 0.00019, respectively (79,102). In both cases the nuclear contribution to the rotational g factor is smaller than the electronic one.

Comparison between theory and experiment for O_2 shows that, while at low magnetic fields Hund's case b is a good approximation, at fields above 8000 G the spin is becoming significantly decoupled (incipient Paschen-Back effect) and the pattern of magnetic sublevels is tending toward $(2K + 1)$ levels corresponding to each value of $M_s = 0, \pm 1$ (78,79). On the other hand, the much stronger spin-spin coupling in SO prevents this (102). Indeed so strong is this coupling of the spin to the molecular axis that it causes a considerable deviation from Hund's case b toward case a by mixing together states for which $\Delta K = \pm 2$. Thus, the $K = 2, J = 1$ state is an almost equal mixture of the pure case b states

$K = 0, J = 1$, and $K = 2, J = 1$ (102). However, the $K = 1, J = 1$ state has no such states with which to mix and remains pure, apart from a very slight intermixing of all the K,J states by the magnetic field. We may contrast the situation for O_2 with that for SO by saying that for the former J is a poor quantum number and K a fairly good one, whereas for the latter the reverse is true. In both cases the K,J description is retained for labeling purposes.

The singlet excited electronic states ($^1\Delta$) of these radicals are also paramagnetic owing to the possession of electronic orbital angular momentum and the magnetic resonance spectra from them have been observed for O_2 (103) and SO (104). The rotational state of origin may be identified with the lowest $J = 2$ state by the almost symmetric $2:3:3:2$ quartet pattern produced by the quadratic Zeeman effect. The coupling in the excited states corresponds closely to Hund's case a as evidenced by the g factors which are close to the ideal value of $\frac{2}{3}$. From the quadratic Zeeman splitting the bond length in the $^1\Delta$ state of SO, which was previously unknown, has been calculated (104).

H. Polyatomic Radicals

Under the heading of polyatomic radicals there is little to report and less hope for the future. The problem is twofold: for all but a few stable species, a spectrum is exceedingly difficult to obtain and even if it were obtained the task of unraveling it would be extremely complicated. The problem of detection is that those transitions which are field-dependent are not electric-dipole in character because there is no orbital angular momentum to couple the spin to the molecular framework (87). It is just possible that the spin–spin interaction in polyatomic triplet-state radicals may couple the spin to the molecular axis sufficiently strongly to give detectable transitions as it does for the $^3\Sigma$ state of SO. So far the only polyatomic species that have been observed are the stable triatomic radicals NO_2 and NF_2, which possess 17 and 19 valence electrons, respectively (1). The many populated rotational levels of NO_2 have produced a multitude of spectral lines that have defied analysis (3). On the other hand, the gas-phase spectrum of NF_2 consists of a very broad single line, the lack of resolution being ascribed to the equilibrium $2NF_2 \rightleftharpoons N_2F_4$ (32).

References

1. P. W. Atkins and M. C. R. Symons, *The Structure of Inorganic Radicals*, Elsevier, Amsterdam, 1967.
2. R. Beringer and J. G. Castle, *Phys. Rev.*, **78**, 581 (1950).
3. J. G. Castle and R. Beringer, *Phys. Rev.*, **80**, 114 (1950).
4. P. W. Atkins, J. A. Brivati, N. Keen, M. C. R. Symons, and P. A. Trevalion, *J. Chem. Soc.*, **1962**, 4785.

5. T. Cole, *J. Chem. Phys.*, **35**, 1169 (1961).
6. J. Cunningham, 5th International Symposium on Free Radicals, Uppsala, 1961.
7. J. A. Brivati, M. C. R. Symons, D. J. A. Tinling, H. W. Wardale, and D. O. Williams, *Chem. Commun.*, **1965**, 402.
8. P. W. Atkins, N. Keen, and M. C. R. Symons, *J. Chem. Soc.*, **1962**, 2873.
9. D. W. Ovenall and D. H. Whiffen, *Mol. Phys.*, **4**, 135 (1961).
10. M. C. R. Symons, *J. Chem. Soc.*, **1965**, 2276.
11. M. Karplus and G. Fraenkel, *J. Chem. Phys.*, **35**, 1312 (1961).
12. T. F. Hunter and M. C. R. Symons, *J. Chem. Soc.*, **1967** (in press).
13. P. W. Atkins, A. Horsfield, and M. C. R. Symons, *J. Chem. Soc.*, **1964**, 5220.
14. C. Jaccard, *Phys. Rev.*, **124**, 60 (1961).
15. H. Zeldes and R. Livingston, *J. Chem. Phys.*, **35**, 563 (1961).
16. G. W. Chantry, A. Horsfield, J. R. Morton, and D. H. Whiffen, *Mol. Phys.*, **5**, 233 (1962).
17. P. W. Atkins, M. C. R. Symons, and H. W. Wardale, *J. Chem. Soc.*, **1964**, 5215.
18. W. C. Lin and C. A. McDowell, *Mol. Phys.*, **7**, 223 (1964).
19. P. H. Kasai and E. B. Whipple, *Mol. Phys.*, **9**, 497, (1965).
20. S. N. Foner, E. L. Cochran, V. A. Bowers, and C. K. Jen, *Phys. Rev. Letters*, **1**, 91 (1958).
21. L. Shields and M. C. R. Symons, *Mol. Phys.*, **11**, 57 (1966).
22. C. J. Delbecq, W. Hayes, M. C. M. O'Brien, and P. H. Yuster, *Proc. Roy. Soc.* (*London*), *Ser. A*, **271**, 243 (1963).
23. R. Catterall, M. C. R. Symons, and J. W. Tipping, *J. Chem. Soc.*, **1966**, 1529.
24. Z. Sroubek, L. Novak, and K. Zdansky, *Solid State Phys.*, **6**, 173 (1964).
25. A. R. Reinberg, *J. Chem. Phys.*, **41**, 850 (1964).
26. W. T. Doyle and M. C. R. Symons, *Quart. Rev.*, **14**, 62 (1960).
27. P. W. Atkins, N. Keen, M. C. R. Symons, and H. W. Wardale, *J. Chem. Soc.*, **1963**, 5594.
28. T. G. Kastner and W. Kanzig, *J. Phys. Chem. Solids*, **3**, 178 (1957).
29. J. W. Wilkins and J. R. Gabriel, *Phys. Rev.*, **132**, 1950 (1963).
30. W. E. Falconer, J. R. Morton, and A. G. Streng, *J. Chem. Phys.*, **41**, 902 (1964).
31. J. R. Morton and W. E. Falconer, *Proc. Chem. Soc.*, **1963**, 95.
32. L. H. Piette, F. A. Johnson, K. A. Booman, and C. B. Colburn, *J. Chem. Phys.*, **35**, 1481 (1961).
33. J. B. Farmer, M. C. L. Gerry, and C. A. McDowell, *Mol. Phys.*, **8**, 253 (1964).
34. R. W. Fessenden and R. H. Schuler, *J. Chem. Phys.*, **44**, 434 (1966).
35. J. C. Baird, *J. Chem. Phys.*, **37**, 1879 (1962).
36. P. H. Kasai and A. D. Kirschenbaum, *J. Am. Chem. Soc.*, **87**, 3069 (1965).
37. F. Neumayr and N. Vanderkooi, *Inorg. Chem.*, **4**, 1234 (1965).
38. R. W. Fessenden and R. H. Schuler, *J. Chem. Phys.*, **43**, 2704 (1965).
39. W. T. Dixon and R. O. C. Norman, *J. Chem. Soc.*, **1963**, 3119.
40. C. J. W. Gutch and W. A. Waters, *J. Chem. Soc.*, **1965**, 751.
41. J. A. McRae and M. C. R. Symons, *Nature*, **210**, 1259 (1966).
42. F. J. Adrian, E. L. Cochran, and V. A. Bowers, *J. Chem. Phys.*, **36**, 1661 (1962).
43. F. J. Adrian, E. L. Cochran, and V. A. Bowers, *J. Chem. Phys.*, **43**, 462 (1965).
44. E. L. Cochran, F. J. Adrian, and V. A. Bowers, *J. Chem. Phys.*, **44**, 4626 (1966).
45. K. D. J. Root, M. C. R. Symons, and B. C. Weatherley, *Mol. Phys.*, **11**, 161 (1966).
46. K. D. J. Root, M. C. R. Symons, and D. J. A. Tinling, *J. Chem. Soc.*, **1967** (in press).

47. J. R. Morton, *Can. J. Chem.*, **43**, 1948 (1965).
48. A. D. Walsh, *J. Chem. Soc.*, **1953**, 2266.
49. M. C. R. Symons, *Advan. Chem. Ser.*, **36**, 76 (1962).
50. R. L. Morehouse, J. J. Christiansen, and W. Gordy, *J. Chem. Phys.*, **45**, 1751 (1966).
51. J. R. Morton, *Mol. Phys.*, **5**, 217 (1962).
52. P. W. Atkins and M. C. R. Symons, *J. Chem. Soc.*, **1964**, 4363.
53. J. R. Morton, *Can. J. Phys.*, **41**, 706 (1963).
54. R. W. Fessenden and R. H. Schuler, *J. Chem. Phys.*, **45**, 1845 (1966).
55. M. Hampton, F. Herring, W. Lin, and C. A. McDowell, *Mol. Phys.*, **10**, 565 (1966).
56. W. V. Smith, P. P. Sorokin, J. L. Gelles, and G. J. Lasher, *Phys. Rev.*, **115**, 1546 (1959).
57. J. H. N. Loubser and L. du Preez, *Brit. J. Appl. Phys.*, **16**, 457 (1965).
58. H. J. Bower and M. C. R. Symons, *Nature*, **210**, 1037 (1966).
59. J. A. Baldwin, *Phys. Rev. Letters*, **10**, 220 (1963).
60. J. Owen, in *Physical Properties of Diamond*, R. Berman, Ed., Oxford University Press, Cambridge, 1965, p. 274.
61. J. H. E. Griffiths, J. Owen, and I. M. Ward, in *Report on Defects in Crystalline Solids*, Physical Society, London, 1955, p. 81.
62. E. A. Faulkner and J. N. Lomer, *Phil. Mag.*, **7**, 1995 (1962).
63. G. Feher, *Phys. Rev.*, **114**, 1219 (1959).
64. G. D. Watkins and J. W. Corbett, *Discussions Faraday Soc.*, **31**, 86 (1961).
65. G. D. Watkins in *Effets des Rayonnement sur les Semiconducteurs*, Academic Press, Paris, 1964, p. 97.
66. G. A. Jeffrey, G. S. Parry, and R. L. Mozzi, *J. Chem. Phys.*, **25**, 1024 (1956).
67. P. H. Kasai, *J. Chem. Phys.*, **43**, 4143 (1965).
68. S. Lee and P. J. Bray, *J. Chem. Phys.*, **39**, 2863 (1963).
69. A. H. Silver and P. J. Bray, *J. Chem. Phys.*, **29**, 984 (1958).
70. Y. Nakai, *Z. Physik. Chem. (Frankfurt)*, **44**, 45 (1965).
71. G. M. Muha, *J. Phys. Chem.*, **70**, 1390 (1966).
72. R. A. Weeks, *J. Appl. Phys.*, **27**, 1376 (1956); *Phys. Rev.*, **130**, 570 (1963).
73. M. C. M. O'Brien, *Proc. Roy. Soc. (London)*, *Ser. A* **231**, 404 (1955).
74. J. H. Anderson and J. A. Weil, *J. Chem. Phys.*, **31**, 427 (1959).
75. Y. Nakai, *Bull. Chem. Soc. (Japan)*, **38**, 1308 (1965).
76. G. Herzberg, *Molecular Spectra and Molecular Structure*, Vol. 1, Van Nostrand, New York, 1950.
77. C. H. Townes and A. L. Schawlow, *Microwave Spectroscopy*, McGraw-Hill, New York, 1955.
78. M. Tinkham and M. W. P. Strandberg, *Phys. Rev.*, **97**, 937, 951 (1955).
79. K. D. Bowers, R. A. Kamper, and C. D. Lustig, *Proc. Roy. Soc. (London)*, *Ser. A*, **251**, 565 (1959).
80. H. E. Radford, *Phys. Rev.*, **122**, 114 (1961); **126**, 1035 (1962).
81. A. Abraham and J. H. Van Vleck, *Phys. Rev.*, **92**, 1448 (1953).
82. D. A. Goodings, *Phys. Rev.*, **123**, 1706 (1961).
83. J. S. M. Harvey, *Proc. Roy. Soc. (London)*, *Ser. A*, **285**, 581 (1965).
84. R. A. Frosch and H. M. Foley, *Phys. Rev.*, **88**, 1337 (1952).
85. G. C. Dousmanis, *Phys. Rev.*, **97**, 967 (1955).
86. G. C. Dousmanis, T. M. Sanders, and C. H. Townes, *Phys. Rev.*, **100**, 1735 (1955).

87. A. Carrington and D. H. Levy, *J. Phys. Chem.*, **71**, 2 (1967).
88. R. Beringer and M. A. Heald, *Phys. Rev.*, **95**, 1474 (1954).
89. M. A. Heald and R. Beringer, *Phys. Rev.*, **96**, 645 (1954).
90. H. G. Dehmelt, *Phys. Rev.*, **99**, 527 (1955).
91. R. L. Brown, *J. Chem. Phys.*, **44**, 2827 (1966).
92. K. D. Bowers, R. A. Kamper, and C. D. Lustig, *Proc. Phys. Soc.* (*London*), **B70**, 1176 (1957).
93. J. S. M. Harvey, R. A. Kamper, and K. R. Lea, *Proc. Phys. Soc.* (*London*), **76**, 979 (1960).
94. H. E. Radford, V. W. Hughes, and V. Beltran-Lopez, *Phys. Rev.*, **123**, 153 (1961).
95. V. Beltran-Lopez and H. G. Robinson, *Phys. Rev.*, **123**, 161 (1961).
96. C. C. McDonald, *J. Chem. Phys.*, **39**, 3159 (1963).
97. R. Beringer, E. B. Rawson, and A. F. Henry, *Phys. Rev.*, **94**, 343 (1954).
98. R. L. Brown and H. E. Radford, *Phys. Rev.*, **147**, 6 (1966).
99. A. Carrington and D. H. Levy, *J. Chem. Phys.*, **44**, 1298 (1966).
100. C. C. McDonald, *J. Chem. Phys.*, **39**, 2587 (1963).
101. H. E. Radford, *J. Chem. Phys.*, **40**, 2732 (1964).
102. J. M. Daniels and P. B. Dorain, *J. Chem. Phys.*, **45**, 26 (1966).
103. A. M. Falick, B. H. Mahan, and R. J. Myers, *J. Chem. Phys.*, **42**, 1837 (1965).
104. A. Carrington, D. H. Levy, and T. A. Miller, *Proc. Roy. Soc.* (*London*), *Ser. A*, **293**, 108 (1966).

CHAPTER 11

Fragments in Irradiated Ionic Solids

JOSEPH CUNNINGHAM

Chemistry Department, University College, Dublin, Ireland

I. MECHANISM DETERMINED FROM STUDIES ON FRAGMENTS

Radical ions and other fragments, when produced in ionic solids by interaction with a radiation field, carry information on the radiation-induced processes which formed them. Sections II and III of this chapter will discuss the detailed information that may be derived on energy localization or fragment distribution in irradiated ionic solids from studies on fragments "frozen in" after irradiation. By way of introduction to the utility and power of such studies to yield information on radiation-induced processes in ionic solids, this first section considers the development of a detailed mechanism for radiation decomposition of alkali metal nitrates.

A. Indirect Studies on Nitrates

Early investigations were carried out using ultraviolet light (1,2), 1 MeV electrons (3) or 45 kV x-rays (4,5). Dissolution of crystalline nitrates exposed to any of these irradiations was accompanied by formation of gas bubbles. Resultant aqueous solutions gave positive results when tested colorimetrically by a method of analysis (6) designed to detect nitrite ions in the presence of nitrate and other common anions. Ease of decomposition of nitrate ion to products varied markedly with cation as shown in Table I for various irradiations.

The hundredfold variation of efficiency for conversion of absorbed energy into decomposition of the nitrate ion in different lattices has been variously interpreted. The sequence of increasing sensitivity: $LiNO_3$ $< NaNO_3 < Sr(NO_3)_2 < AgNO_3 < Pb(NO_3)_2 < La(NO_3)_3 < Ba(NO_3)_2$ $< KNO_3 < CsNO_3$ with UV was attributed by Doigan and Davis to the influence of the cation "field strength" upon the probability of dissociation of excited ions (2). The rate-controlling step in radiolysis with x-rays or γ-rays was identified by the author as diffusion-controlled separation of reactive fragments (8). Lattices of large "free-volume" (unit cell volume minus total volume of ions in cell) facilitate the diffusion-controlled, rate-controlling process, but small free volume reduces it to low efficiency (Table I). The empirical correlation between radiolytic decomposition and free volume (4,5,7,8) is obeyed also in other ionic solids (9,10), but its basis has not yet been precisely defined. As expected for a simple "cage effect," radiolytic decomposition values fall on a smooth continuously rising curve as free volume increases for alkali-metal nitrates (5), but values for lattices having more strongly polarizing cations, e.g., $Ba(NO_3)_2$, $AgNO_3$ or $Sr(NO_3)_2$, fall off the curve (5).

According to James, the exact frequency of the ν_1 vibrational mode of the nitrate ion in different lattices reflects the extent of polarization of the anion by the cation (11). Plots of the frequency of ν_1 vs. decomposition value should therefore reveal if any correlation exists between them. Figure 1 is plotted in this way; it contains data obtained with γ-rays at low temperatures where secondary processes are minimized (8). It indicates that cation–anion interactions are important in the rate-controlling process. More direct evidence on the important role of cation–anion interaction is presented later (Section II-E).

Mass spectrometric studies of the gaseous product released from potassium nitrate upon dissolution in water after irradiation in a reactor at approximately 50°C showed the gaseous product to be more than 95% oxygen (7). A stoichiometric ratio of 2 was observed between the nitrite detected in solution and the oxygen evolved. These facts and the similarities of the *products formed* or *relative ease of decomposition* for various nitrates

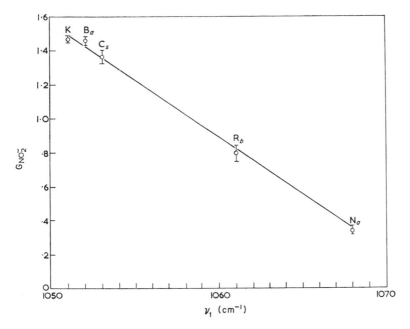

Fig. 1. Correlation between rate of radiolysis, $G_{NO_2^-}$, of the nitrate ion and frequency of the ν_1 stretching mode of NO_3^- for various ionic lattices at low temperatures. Increasing ν_1 indicates increasing polarization of the nitrate ion by near-neighbor lattice cations.

by either ultraviolet or ionizing radiation led to equation 1 to express the observed results at room temperature.

$$NO_3^- = NO_2^- + \tfrac{1}{2}O_2 \tag{1}$$

The kinetics of buildup of the decomposition fragment(s) which give rise to nitrite on dissolution of the irradiated solid have been studied in detail for irradiations with x-rays and ^{60}Co γ-rays at various temperatures (5,8). The results indicated that expression 1a represented an acceptable *mechanism* of dissociation because the kinetics of product buildup were first-order in nitrate concentration and were independent of the dose rate.

Several workers deduced evidence to support the idea that equations 1 or 1a represented the actual fragments within the solid after irradiation rather than merely the stoichiometry of products observed by the solution analysis used. Hennig, Lees, and Matheson (7) compared the radiation-induced change in magnetic susceptibility of irradiated powdered sodium and potassium nitrates with the predictions of expressions 1 or 1a.

$$NO_3^- \rightsquigarrow NO_2^- + 0 \tag{1a}$$

TABLE I

Efficiency of UV or Low LET Radiations in Decomposing Crystalline Nitrates

Radiation	Crystal	$LiNO_3$	$AgNO_3$	$NaNO_3$	$Pb(NO_3)_2$	$Sr(NO_3)_2$	$RbNO_3$	KNO_3	$CsNO_3$	$Ba(NO_3)_2$	Refs.
X-rays or γ-rays at 20 ± 10°C	$G_{NO_2^-}$ [b]	—	—	0.16	0.48	—	—	1.38	1.44	—	17
	$G_{NO_2^-}$ [b]	—	—	0.20	—	—	0.60	1.46	1.72	1.80	8
	$G_{NO_2^-}$ [b]	0.02	0.14	0.37	—	0.52	0.64	1.96	1.37	1.75	5
	$G_{NO_2^-}$ [b]	0.02	0.02	0.25	0.44	—	—	1.57	1.68	1.88	99
	$P(20°)$ [c]	—	—	70% (1b) 46% (1d)	—	—	—	18% (1b) 12% (1d)	—	—	13
X-rays at −110°c;	$G_{NO_2^-}$ [b]	—	—	0.34	—	—	0.75	1.47	1.36	1.46	8
γ-rays at −190°C	$G_{NO_2^-}$ [b]	—	—	0.40	—	—	—	1.15	—	—	13
	$P(−190°)$ [c]	—	—	100% (1d)	—	—	—	100% (1b) 66% (1d)	—	—	13
UV at 20°C	ϕ [a]	0.004	0.072	0.022	0.074	0.026	—	0.20	0.38	0.096	2
	$P(20°)$	—	—	100% (1d)	—	—	—	100% (1d)	—	—	
Crystal free volume (A^3/NO_3^-)		32.7	43.5	44.3	—	41.3	50.7	55.3	53	47.2	

[a] ϕ is the number of nitrate ions dissociated per photon absorbed—original values corrected to take into account that photolysis proceeds via equations 1b or 1d. See text.

[b] $G_{NO_2^-}$ is the number of dissociations per 100 eV absorbed if all product is assumed to form according to equations 1 or 1a.

[c] $P_{(T°)}$ values provide an approximate measure of the percentage of dissociation which must proceed via reaction 1b or 1d to produce other than nitrate during irradiation at $T°C$.

The paramagnetic contribution to the magnetic susceptibility change could be accounted for by molecular oxygen formed with the equivalence of equation 1. Critical reexamination of the data shows that they do not definitely exclude mechanisms producing other fragments with comparable combined paramagnetic susceptibility, such as dissociations 1b, 1c, or 1d.

$$NO_3^- \rightsquigarrow NO + O_2^- \tag{1b}$$

$$2NO_3^- \rightsquigarrow NO_2 + O^- \tag{1c}$$

$$2NO_3^- \rightsquigarrow N_2O_3^{2-} + \tfrac{3}{2}O_2 \tag{1d}$$

Sayre (12) noted that the absorption spectra of sodium and potassium nitrate at 77 and 4°K became diffuse below 3300 Å. Since the energy of a photon at this wavelength corresponds closely to the change of thermochemical energy in process 1a, he argued that predissociation was proceeding via process 1a at 4.2 and 77°K. This argument overlooked the fact that the poor thermochemical (13) data available on O_2^- made process 1b of equal energy with process 1a, so that both these mechanisms were consistent with the kinetic data and absorption spectra at 77°K.

Chemical solution analyses with reagents of varying oxidizing power have been used to distinguish contributions by process 1a from those by processes 1b, 1c, or 1d. It was established experimentally that an aqueous solution $2 \times 10^{-4}M$ in ceric ion and $0.4M$ in H_2SO_4 reacted with millimolar quantities of nitric oxide or nitrogen dioxide according to processes 2 or 3, respectively (13). Products of dissociation *via* processes 1b, or

$$NO + 3Ce^{4+} + H_2O = NO_3^- + 3Ce^{3+} + 4H^+ \tag{2}$$

$$NO_2 + Ce^{4+} + H_2O = NO_3^- + Ce^{3+} + 2H^+ \tag{3}$$

$$NO_2^- + 2Ce^{4+} + H_2O = NO_3^- + 2Ce^{3+} + 2H^+ \tag{4}$$

1d would reduce Ce^{4+} by reaction 2, since all produce nitric oxide on dissolution in $0.4M$ acid (14), and since reaction 2 is unaffected by dissolved oxygen (13). Products of processes 1 or 1a would react via process 4.

The reduction in Ce^{4+}, $M(-Ce^{4+})$ may readily be determined colorimetrically. In the general case in which the irradiated solid contains fragments, which give rise to $m(NO_2^-)$, $m(NO)$, and $m(NO_2)$ moles of nitrite, nitric oxide, and nitrogen dioxide, respectively, on dissolution, relation 5 describes their relative contributions to ceric reduction. An

$$M(-Ce^{4+}) = 2m(NO_2^-) + m(NO_2) + 3m(NO) + \tag{5}$$

independent method of analysis (Shinn's method) converts all nitrogen–oxygen fragments in the irradiated solid into nitrous acid with the equivalence of expression 6 (13).

Comparison of expressions 5 and 6 shows that if all product were

$$M(HNO_2) = m(NO_2^-) + \tfrac{1}{2}m(NO_2) + \tfrac{1}{2}m(NO) + \qquad (6)$$

present as NO_2^-, then plots of $\tfrac{1}{2}M(-Ce^{4+})$ vs. dose should be identical with plots of $M(HNO_2)$ vs. dose. This was observed to be true (13) for nitrate samples irradiated at 300°K and annealed at 400°K and to be approximately true for KNO_3 irradiated and analyzed at 300°K. Data for nitrates irradiated at 77°K differed sharply, in the sense that the majority of product was present as a fragment reducing more Ce^{4+} than would nitrite. Detailed consideration of reactions of all fragments, including oxygen fragments, with the solution reagents are given elsewhere (13) and enabled the proportion, P, of dissociation proceeding to nitric oxide (or other equally strongly reducing species such as $N_2O_3^{2-}$ or NO_2^{2-}) to be assigned the values shown in Table I. Indirect studies thus make it clear that although expression 1 can describe radiation-induced decomposition at room temperature, other processes such as 1b predominate at low temperatures.

B. Direct Observations on Fragments

Radiation-induced absorption attributed to nitrite ions (15), the characteristic NO_2^- fluorescence spectrum (16), and lattice spacings characteristic of crystalline potassium nitrite (5) have been observed in samples of nitrates exposed to large doses of ionizing radiation at room temperature. These results establish the presence of nitrite ions as fragments within irradiated nitrates.

Interpretations of the results of indirect studies leave the nature and role oxygen fragments in doubt. Johnson analyzed the kinetics of product buildup in irradiated $NaNO_3$ in terms of oxygen atom fragments that react with NO_3^- to produce molecular oxygen (17) whereas kinetic data of Heal and Cunningham on radiolysis of KNO_3 at various temperatures (5) indicated that molecular oxygen did not form below ca. $-40°C$. Electron spin resonance (ESR) and optical absorption studies were undertaken on irradiated single crystals of sodium and potassium nitrate to clarify the identity of the oxygen fragments within the solids. However, the results forced a complete reexamination of the ideas that the expressions 1a, 1b, 1c, and 1d adequately represented decomposition by ionizing radiation. The ESR spectra revealed the presence of at least six radical species (17–19) in potassium nitrate irradiated at 77 or 4°K. Experiments with ^{15}N-enriched potassium nitrate confirmed that in five of these radical species the principal coupling of the unpaired electron was to a nitrogen nucleus. The ESR spectra of the sixth species was observable at 4°K in crystals exposed to γ-rays at 77°K and corresponded to a single line occurring at $g_{\parallel} = 1.958$ and $g_{\perp} = 2.408$ for the magnetic field parallel or perpendicular to the crystal planes containing the nitrate ions (18). The similarity of these unusual values to those reported for O_2^- in potassium chloride crystals (20) make it highly probable that O_2^- is produced in potassium nitrate by ionizing radiation at 77°K. A similar conclusion has recently been reached for sodium nitrate (21) irradiated at 77°K. O_2^- is the only oxygen fragment directly identified in low temperature irradiated nitrates.

Different identification schemes have been advanced for the nitrogen-containing radicals observed by ESR in the irradiated nitrates (18,21–25). An excellent account will be found in the previous chapter of facts and arguments leading to acceptance or rejection of various radicals as consistent or inconsistent with observed ESR spectra. As a result of these and similar considerations several authors have recently identified the ESR signals observed in crystals irradiated at 77°K with NO_3^{2-} and NO_3. The very satisfactory measure of agreement between the magnetic parameters detected for NO_3^{2-} radicals in different crystals will be apparent from inspection of Tables II and III where these data have been collected.

Hardly less surprising than the abundance of nitrogen–oxygen fragments indicated by ESR is evidence that normal nitrite ions are not produced at low temperatures. Zeldes and Livingston used the ESR signal of NO_2 as a probe to test for the presence of nitrite ions (23). They found that if $^{15}NO_2^-$ ions were added to $K^{14}NO_3$ then irradiation produced only the ESR signal of $^{15}NO_2$. This proved that NO_2 was produced with high efficiency at 77°K from nitrite ions located on anion sites. Since short irradiations of $K^{14}NO_3$ at 77° did not produce the ESR signals of $^{14}NO_2$, they concluded that normal nitrite ions were *not* being directly produced by irradiation and thus could not act as precursors of NO_2 radicals.

This conclusion from ESR studies on crystals irradiated at low temperatures is in striking contrast to Russian work reported on the fluorescence of potassium nitrate crystals irradiated at room temperature (16). Identical fluorescence spectra of the nitrite ion were observed both from potassium nitrate doped with nitrite and from crystals γ-irradiated at room temperature. These workers concluded that nitrite ions located on normal anion sites must be present in both types of crystals (16).

The very different conclusions can be shown to have their origin in the different conditions of irradiation and temperature. The ESR studies were made on crystals which received low doses of irradiation at 77°K, whereas the fluorescence studies were carried out on crystals exposed to high dose at room temperature. Corresponding differences in kinetic behavior (5,8, 31), chemical reactivity (13,32), kinetic isotope effects (8), and the effect of applied compression (32,33) upon the rate of radiolysis have been

JOSEPH CUNNINGHAM

TABLE II

Parameters of ESR Signals Attributed to NO_3^{2-} in Nitrate Crystals Exposed to Low LET Radiations at 77°K

Crystal	KNO₃	Sr(NO₃)₂	Ba(NO₃)₂	AgNO₃	Pb(NO₃)₂	NaNO₃
Site	$NO_3^{2-}\|NO_3^-\|$	$NO_3^{2-}\|NO_3^-\|$	$NO_3^{2-}\|NO_3^-\|$	$\|AgNO_3\|-$	$NO_3^{2-}\|NO_3^-\|$	$NO_3^{2-}\|NO_3^-\|$
A_{iso}(G)	42.3	47.8	46.2	46.8	46.3	44.0
Stable to °K	<200°	<300°	<300°	<135°	<300°	<300°
g_y (in-plane)	2.0057	2.0060	2.0057	2.0020	1.9912	2.0052
g_z (in-plane)	2.0057	2.0060	2.0057	2.0070	1.9912	2.0052
g_x (⊥ plane)	2.0015	2.0019	1.9997	2.0000	1.9857	2.0011
A_y (G)	31.8	37.3	35.5	35.8	36.5	33.8
A_z (G)	31.8	37.3	35.3	37.1	36.5	33.8
A_x (G)	63.4	68.8	67.6	67.4	66.0	64.4
Ref.	22	27	29	28	27	21,31

TABLE III

Parameters of ESR Signals Attributed to NO_3^{2-}, Formed by Irradiating Nitrate-Doped Potassium Salts

Crystal	KCl/NO_3^-	KBr/NO_3^-	KI/NO_3^-	KN_3/NO_3^-	KNO_3
Site	$NO_3^{2-}\|Cl^-\|$	$NO_3^{2-}\|Br^-\|$	$NO_3^{2-}\|I^-\|$	Int:[a]	$NO_3^{2-}\|NO_3^-\|$
A_{iso}(G)	40.2[a]	40.3[a]	—	41.3	42.3
Stable to °K	273°	273°	273°	400°	<200°
g_y (in-plane)	2.0068	2.0068	2.0050	2.0039	2.0057
g_z (in-plane)	2.0068	2.0068	2.0050	2.0039	2.0057
g_x (⊥ plane)	2.0020	2.0020	—	1.9994	2.0015
A_y (G)	30.5	32	—	31	31.8
A_z (G)	30.5	32	—	31	31.8
A_y (G)	61.5	65	—	62	63.4
$W^{1/2}$ (G)	5.2 ± 4[a]	10 ± 1[a]	15 ± 2[a]	5	4 ± 1
Ref.	26	26	26	30	22

[a] Measured value assigned to NO_3^{2-} tumbling freely in anion site.

extensively documented for nitrates exposed to different doses at different temperatures. A meaningful representation of the results of these several investigations is possible only when primary, secondary, and subsequent processes are carefully distinguished from each other and from temperature effects. This distinction is made in Table IV which represents a detailed scheme for nitrate radiolysis as constructed from reported results of direct and indirect studies on fragments.

C. Consequences of Detailed Mechanism of Radiolysis

The reader may be inclined to question the need for such a complex scheme as that shown in Table IV and ask whether it represents any improvement on the simple processes 1a and 1b which appeared to account satisfactorily for the early data. Each primary, secondary, or tertiary reaction of Table IV was originally (32) based upon, and justified in terms of, results published prior to 1965. Subsequent experiments (34–36) have provided support for important features of the primary dissociations there proposed.

Table IV explains the absence of normal nitrite ions after irradiation at 77°K and their formation by irradiation at 300°K in terms of competition for low-energy electrons by lattice anions vs. parent positive holes. This explanation derived from experiments (17,18,22) which showed that the ESR signal of NO_3^{2-} appeared rapidly and with high efficiency in nitrates exposed to ionizing radiation at 77°K *but* was completely absent from nitrates similarly irradiated (18) at 300°K. In Table IV this is summarized by $k_2 > k_1$ at 77°K (the rate constant for electron attachment to nitrate ion is greater than that for electron–hole recombination) but $k_2 < k_1$ at 300°K.

Electron–hole recombination process k_1 gives rise to an optically forbidden excited state NO_3^{-}** which dissociates to nitrite ions. A corollary of this proposal was that nitrite ions should not result directly from photodissociation of nitrate ion. Experiments in the author's laboratory were designed to test whether or not nitrite ions resulted directly from optical promotion of nitrate ions to excited states via the strongly allowed $*\pi \leftarrow \pi$ transition (12) at 2000 Å or the weakly allowed $*\pi \leftarrow n$ transition at 3000 Å. Powdered crystalline nitrate samples were irradiated with UV light in an experimental arrangement which continually exposed fresh crystallites to the UV light and so minimized surface and secondary reactions. Samples were irradiated *in vacuo* and analyzed without exposure to air. Two solution analyses, reduction of Ce^{4+} and Shinn's method based on reactions 2–6 described above, were used to determine whether product was present as nitrite ions or as other fragments (e.g.,

$NO + O_2^-$, $N_2O_3^{2-}$, or NO_2). Results are presented in Figure 2 as plots of $\frac{1}{2}M(-Ce^{4+})$ or $M(HNO_2)$ vs. exposure to UV. The plots would be superimposed if nitrite ions were the direct product of the optical excitation. There is a ratio greater than two between the initial slopes of these plots for $NaNO_3$ or KNO_3 in Figure 2, as would be the case if reaction 1b and 1d described the buildup of product from optical excitation. When light in the wavelength region 2900–3700 Å only was incident on the samples, very much longer exposure times were required than when the total spectral output of the low pressure Hg lamp was used but data were otherwise identical to those presented in Figure 2. Apparently optical excitation *via* the $*\pi \leftarrow \pi$ or $*\pi \leftarrow n$ transitions does not lead to nitrite ions but to other products.

Petriconi and Papee (35) report that when *concentrated* solutions of alkali metal nitrates were irradiated with UV, oxides of nitrogen formed at acid and alkaline pH values. Other studies of interaction of radiation with nitrates in solids or concentrated solution are likewise consistent with formation of species other than nitrite ions as primary products (36,37).

A full justification of other features of the complex decomposition scheme represented by Table IV has appeared elsewhere (32) and need not be repeated in detail here. Quite apart from its value in illustrating the detailed information to be gained from the study of fragments, another point of general importance brought out by the scheme is that *mechanisms*

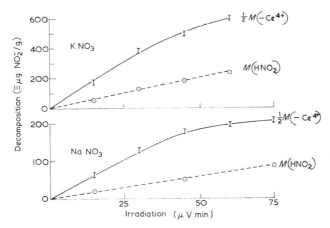

Fig. 2. Growth of product in crystalline KNO_3 and $NaNO_3$ *in vacuo* under UV irradiation at room temperature. Product measured by two solution chemical procedures: one converted nitrogen–oxygen fragments to HNO_2 and so measured them as $M(HNO_2)$; another detected fragments as $M(-Ce^4)$ through their power to reduce Ce^{4+} to Ce^{3+}. Plots of $\frac{1}{2}M(-Ce^4)$ or $M(HNO_2)$ vs. irradiation time would be superimposed if nitrite were the only product.

TABLE IV

Formation of Primary and Secondary Products in Nitrates Irradiated at 77, 300, and 400°K[a,b,c]

		Region 0 ←———————————————————————————→	Region I ←——————————————→	
Primary excited species (p.e.s.)	Reaction of p.e.s.	Primary products (p.p.) — Concn. at 77°K	Reactions of p.p.	Secondary products
$NO_3^* \xrightarrow[k_1]{+\,e} NO_3^{-**}$	$NO_3^* \xrightarrow{k_1'} NO + O_2$	$[NO]\ \sim k_1' + k_3'$	$NO + O \xrightarrow{k_1''} NO_2^*$	$[NO_2] \sim k_1''$
NO_3^{-*}	$NO_3^* \xrightarrow{k_2'} NO_3$	$[NO_3]\ \sim k_2'$		
$e + NO_3^- \xrightarrow{k_2} NO_3^{2-*}$	$NO_3^{-*} \xrightarrow{k_3'} NO + O_2^-$	$[O_2]\ \sim k_1'$		$[N_2O_4] \sim k_3''$
	$NO_3^{-*} \xrightarrow{k_4'} NO_3^-$	$[O_2^-]\ \sim k_3'$	$O + NO_3^- \xrightarrow{k_2''} NO_2^- + O_2$	$[N_2O_3^{2-}] \sim k_5''$
$k_2 > k_1$ at 77°K	$NO_3^{2-*} \xrightarrow{k_5'} NO_2^- + O$	$[NO_2^{2-}] \sim [O] \sim k_5'$	$NO_3^{2-} + O \xrightarrow{k_3''} NO_2^- + O_2^-$	$[NO_2^-] \sim k_6'' + k_4''$
At 77°K $k_2 > k_1$	$NO_3^{2-*} \xrightarrow{k_6'} NO_3^{2-}$	$[NO_3^{2-}] \sim k_6'$		

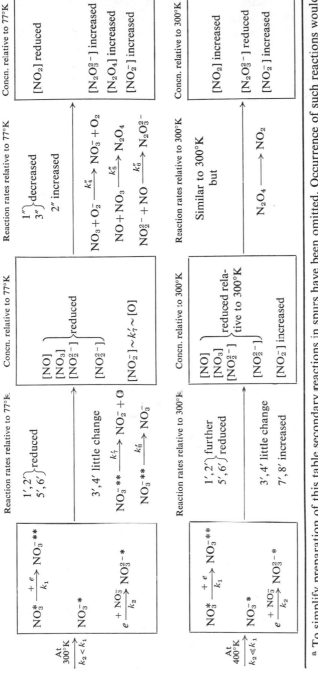

[a] To simplify preparation of this table secondary reactions in spurs have been omitted. Occurrence of such reactions would produce "secondary products" even at very low doses.

[b] The products NO, NO_2^{2-}, NO_3^{2-}, and $N_2O_3^{2-}$ would give a ratio $\geqslant 2$ for the slopes of product vs. dose plots when product was determined and plotted, respectively, as $\frac{1}{2}M(-Ce^{4+})$ or $M(HNO_2)$. For products NO_2, NO_2, N_2O_4, such plots would be superimposed.

[c] Reference 32.

and rate-controlling processes may be markedly different for various dose ranges (regions) of the radiation induced decomposition. Electron attachment or dissociative excitation are very important in determining the course and the decomposition rate *only* for primary decomposition (cf. region 0 in Table IV). This is supported by the fact that the most convincing evidence for dissociative electron attachment in condensed systems has come from studies at low dose and low temperature where secondary processes are minimized. However, as fragment concentration increases, secondary diffusion-controlled reactions can become rate determining and observable patterns of secondary products differ markedly from those of the primary products (e.g., formation at $77°K$ of NO_2 as a secondary product in nitrates by reaction k_1'' of Table IV). *Secondary* products in various irradiated ionic solids and the information they can provide on primary-fragment distribution or reactions will be discussed in Section III.

In the section immediately following, attention will be focused on the information that *primary* products convey about processes which localize energy at particular lattice positions.

II. ENERGY LOCALIZATION IN IRRADIATED CRYSTALS

A. Electron-Hole Trapping and Trapping Site Definition

Convincing arguments for an important role for electron and hole attachment in irradiated glassy and polycrystalline systems have been presented by Hamill for organic glasses (38,39) and by Kevan for frozen aqueous solutions (40). Dispersion of various solutes in different solvents facilitated studies at those authors' laboratories on "competition" between various solutes for electrons produced in the systems by ionizing radiation. Kevan found evidence that nitrate ions were among the most effective electron scavengers in frozen ices (40). Indirect evidence pointing to a similar conclusion for the nitrate ion or a related nitrogen–oxygen species in crystalline ionic solids has come from several sources.

Pringsheim observed that the well-known electron excess *F* band did *not* form in alkali halide crystals grown from a melt to which small concentrations of nitrite or nitrate were added (41). Delbecq and co-workers observed that new electron trapping centers, not present in silver-doped KCl crystals, were introduced into material doped also with potassium nitrite in the melt (42). Jones reported that irradiation of nitrate-doped alkali halide pellets yielded a dissociation product of nitrate with yields so high that energy absorbed by the alkali halide must transfer preferentially to the nitrate ion by a process such as electron localization (43). Studies of the radiation-induced optical absorption of pure and silver-doped sodium nitrate and potassium nitrate single crystals have also been interpreted in terms of efficient electron and hole attachment to various nitrogen–oxygen species in the crystals (15,19,44).

In favorable cases quite detailed information can be derived from ESR studies on the nature of the centers formed when electrons or holes become localized at a position within a crystalline lattice. Precise values describing the interaction of F-center electrons with the nuclear magnetic moments of nuclei in the first and second coordination shells around the anion vacancy is perhaps the best-known example of this (45). Similar interactions for localized holes such as Cl_2^- in irradiated KCl (46) or $(Ag\ Cl_6)^{4-}$ in silver-doped KCl (42) also give rise to super hyperfine structure (shfs) in the ESR spectra observed from these centers in irradiated crystals. Super hyperfine structure has been reported for NO_3^{2-} in strontium nitrate (27) and silver nitrate (28), for NO_2 in sodium nitrite (47), for NO_3 in lead nitrate (48), and for formate ion in sodium formate (49). Such studies are of great importance for an understanding of the process of charge localization because they make it possible to characterize and identify the trapping site.

Identification of the paramagnetic center is a prerequisite for meaningful discussion of any dissociation of polyatomic anions which may result from localization of the hole or electron at the observed site. Several recent studies on radicals trapped in ionic solids have indicated that the trapping site may greatly modify the properties of the radicals observed. Good examples are the radicals NO_3^{2-} and NO_3. The former had not been isolated, not clearly identified as an intermediate, until Jaccard (26) assigned to it an ESR signal in nitrate-doped KCl. Many subsequent workers have likewise found their observed ESR signals to be consistent with existence of NO_3^{2-} radicals in normal anion sites of the host crystal lattices. Relevant data are listed in Tables II and III where it may be seen that the radical remains stable up to or above room temperature in some cases but vanishes at temperatures well below 0°C in other systems. Apparently each host matrix stabilizes this radical ion to a different extent. It has not been observed except when trapped in a solid matrix. A complete representation of the trapped radical should also denote the trapping site. The convention to be used in this chapter will denote by $NO_3^{2-} \mid NO_3^- \mid$, an NO_3^{2-} radical trapped at a normal nitrate-ion position in nitrate crystals. This convention is used in Tables II and III. Table III contains data obtained on nitrate-doped crystals for which the normal anion site may be written as X^-, where $X^- = Cl^-, Br^-, I^-$, or N_3^-. The data represented in Table III have been interpreted by various workers as evidence for NO_3^{2-} radicals trapped at otherwise normal anion sites, i.e. $NO_3^{2-} \mid X^- \mid$.

The variation in the properties of the radical NO_3 as observed by different workers in various crystals is even more marked. Henchman and

Golding reported observing this radical in lead nitrate crystals irradiated at room temperature (48). Cunningham (18) and Livingston and Zeldes (24) observed a radical with similar g values and very similar small hyperfine splitting (hfs) in potassium nitrate crystals. The latter radical was stable at $4°K$ but decayed within a few hours at $77°K$. More recently, Addé has concluded from observations on sodium nitrate crystals that NO_3 radicals of very different stabilities may be obtained by irradiation at room temperature or at $77°K$ (50,51). Geshi and Kazumata (21) have also observed strong singlet ESR signals in sodium nitrate crystals irradiated at room temperature or at $77°K$. The g values of the singlets they assign to NO_3 in crystals irradiated at $77°K$ are quite different from those reported by any of the previous workers. There is thus no compelling reason for assigning their singlets to NO_3; in addition, they did not show nitrogen hfs. These workers considered it possible that deformation of the NO_3 radical occurred to different extents in different crystalline fields at various sites to give different g values. An equally acceptable explanation of the available data can be given in terms of electrons or holes localized on various defect sites in the crystal, such as anion or cation vacancies, i.e., $e \mid NO_3^- $ or $h \mid Na^+$. It is clear that a satisfactory account of these singlet signals in sodium nitrate crystals has yet to be developed *and* that the trapping site is important in determining their stability.

B. Factors Contributing to Charge Localization on Polyatomic Ions

As a first step in discussing different trapping sites consider the various processes which can lead to the localization of an electron-excess or electron-deficient species at a polyatomic anion position. It is convenient to use $NO_3^{2-} \mid NO_3^- \mid$ and $NO_3 \mid NO_3^- \mid$ to illustrate the various factors which may cause an electron or hole to become localized. The band theory applicable to these insulating solids requires that an electron in the conduction band, or the hole in the valence band, be delocalized over the entire crystal. A discontinuity or impurity in the lattice can introduce appropriate donor or acceptor levels localized at the impurity or discontinuity site. It follows that, if an electron or hole is to become localized on a particular nitrate ion position, then conditions at that anion site must differ from neighboring anions. Otherwise the probability for transfer of the excess electron or the hole to an identical nuclear configuration among neighboring ions would preclude trapping.

We can envisage two distinctly different models for a trapping site. First, the symmetry and nuclear positions of nitrogen and oxygen in $NO_3^{2-} \mid NO_3^- \mid$ or $NO_3 \mid NO_3^- \mid$ may be different than in neighboring nitrate ions. A configuration appropriate to the existence of $NO_3^{2-} \mid NO_3^- \mid$ as a localized acceptor level might arise from *intramolecular configuration change* when the planar form of the nitrate ion distorts towards the pyramidal form of the NO_3^{2-} radical (25). We shall denote contributions to the energy of localization from such intramolecular distortion by E_I (note that E_I would be smaller for $NO_3 \mid NO_3^- \mid$ than for $NO_3^{3-} \mid NO_3^- \mid$ because NO_3 has a more similar configuration to NO_3^-).

A second model which could establish localized acceptor levels involves a change in internuclear distances to neighboring ions in the lattice brought about by the presence at an anion site of an additional electron or hole. One method by which such *intermolecular configuration change* would produce nuclear configurations distinguished from neighboring configurations in the perfect lattice would be for neighboring cations or anions to be displaced inward or outward around the trapping site. An extreme case of this appears in the formation of the Cl_2^- radical in alkali-metal chlorides (46) or in $N_2O_4^-$ in irradiated sodium nitrite (52,53) in which the localized hole leads to a change of distance between anions and formation of a new chemical bond. Contributions by such lattice distortion to the total localization energy will be denoted by E_L.

Defect and impurity sites exist in all real crystals and differ from neighboring anion sites even before irradiation. When electrons are freed by radiation in such systems, the free energy of the system will be lowered when the electrons become localized at defect or impurity sites, provided that E_D, the electron affinity of these latter sites, is greater than that of the normal lattice positions. A corresponding situation exists for hole trapping if H_D, the hole affinity of the defect or impurity, exceeds that of lattice positions.

Up to the present time, little attention has been given to the relative importance of trapping by intermolecular lattice changes, trapping by intramolecular configuration change, and trapping at defect or impurity sites in producing radicals such as: $NO_3^{2-} \mid NO_3^- \mid$, $NO_3 \mid NO_3^- \mid$, $NO_2 \mid NO_2^- \mid$, $CO_3^{3-} \mid CO_3^{2-} \mid$, $ClO_4 \mid ClO_4^- \mid$, and $CO_3^- \mid CO_3^{2-} \mid$. These are the identifications offered by the original workers, who have not associated defect or impurity sites with the trapped radicals. To the extent that these identifications are correct, their data correspond to charge localization only by E_I and E_L and will be considered from this viewpoint in Section II-C.

C. Localization in a Perfect Lattice of Polyatomic Ions

1. Electron Trapping

In terms of a perfect lattice at low temperatures no sites distinguishable from neighboring positions and capable of localizing electrons exist before irradiation (see Fig. 3a). Electrons freed by irradiation and reduced to energies below that of the lowest excited electronic state of the cation or

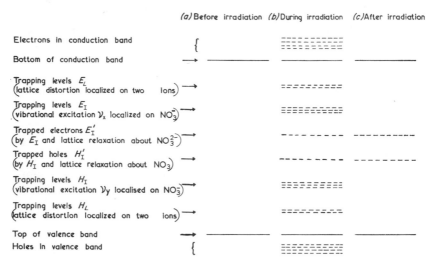

Fig. 3. Schematic representation of energy levels for electrons and holes in an ionic solid having polyatomic ions: (*a*) Before irradiation the crystal is an insulator; (*b*), (*c*) Ionizing radiation promotes electrons, to conduction band leaving holes in valence band. Inelastic "electron–polyatomic ion" interactions produce changed intramolecular and/or intermolecular configurations at specific lattice positions. The latter then represent potential electron-trapping (E_I and E_L) or hole-trapping (H_I and H_L) levels. If electrons or holes become localized, respectively, at E_I and H_I levels and relaxation of the lattice occurs about the trapping sites levels are modified to E'_I or H'_I. Such levels may persist after irradiation as shown in Figure 3c. Analogous E'_L and H'_L levels are not shown, since no evidence has been adduced for E'_L or H'_L levels persisting after irradiation.

anion can interact with molecular anions to excite vibrational or rotational motion. This introduces intramolecular configuration changes which represent potential electron-trapping levels at an energy E_I below the conduction band (see Fig. 3b). Other potential trapping sites at an energy E_L below the conduction band are produced when electrons excite lattice vibrations (electron–phonon interactions). The observable trap depths for any electrons remaining trapped *after* irradiation correspond to E_I or E_L levels modified to E'_I or E'_L by relaxation (polarization) of the lattice about the trapped electron (see Fig. 3c). Published interpretations of ESR spectra in pure ionic solids after low temperature irradiation add up to: (*1*) no evidence for stable electron trapping at E'_L levels by intermolecular configuration change only; (*2*) considerable evidence for effective trapping by intramolecular configuration change (NO_3^{2-} or CO_3^{3-}) at E'_I levels; (*3*) one example, $(AgNO_3)^-$ in $AgNO_3$, of trapping which may involve contributions by both intra- and intermolecular configuration change.

The perfect lattice is not known to trap electrons as molecular ions of the alkali metals, Na_2^+, K_2^+, etc., even in alkali halides (54) irradiated at 4°K. Point *1* is based on the absence of features attributable to such radical ions from the ESR spectra of $NaNO_3$, $NaNO_2$, $CaCO_3$, and KNO_3 (18,24) x-irradiated at low temperatures.

Point *2* is deduced from the striking contrast between the relative ease of formation (18,22,27,29,55,56) of NO_3^{2-} | NO_3^- | or CO_3^{3-} | CO_3^{2-} | and the present lack of evidence (47,57,58) for similar electron-excess situations, such as NO_2^{2-} | NO_2^- |, SO_4^{3-} | SO_4^{2-} | or ClO_4^{2-} | ClO_4^- |. The contrast is most marked for NO_3^{2-} | NO_3^- | and NO_2^{2-} | NO_2^- | because chemical evidence, such as the occurrence (59) of the salt Na_2NO_2, indicates that NO_2^{2-} would be more stable than NO_3^{2-} for which no chemical evidence had been deduced. However, irradiation of pure $NaNO_3$ and $NaNO_2$ at 77°K gives NO_3^{2-} | NO_3^- | in good yield from $NaNO_3$, but no ESR signal attributable to NO_2^{2-} | NO_2^- | appears in $NaNO_2$ even when studied at 4°K. The two main points of difference between NO_3^{2-} | NO_3^- | and hypothetical NO_2^{2-} | NO_2^- | are the greater complexity and the greater degree of intramolecular distortion of the former. The cross section Q for inelastic electron–molecule interactions increases roughly in step with the complexity and number of valence electrons of the molecule (cf. Fig. 8 of ref. 60), so $Q(NO_3^-)$ may be slightly greater than $Q(NO_2^-)$. Compound states of an electron and molecule, which in gases are thought to be important in such inelastic interactions (60) appear slightly more probable for $(NO_3^- + e^-)$ than for $(NO_2^- + e^-)$. The expected greater degree of intramolecular configuration change of NO_3^{2-} follows from placing the unpaired electron into the a_2'' orbital for NO_3^{2-} and the b_1 orbital for NO_2^{2-}. According to Walsh's correlation diagrams (61), these assignments would result in NO_3^{2-} being distorted toward a pyramidal form from the planar form of NO_3^-, but would give NO_2^{2-} a configuration very similar to the parent NO_2^-. The data on NO_3^{2-} | NO_3^- | in Table II have been interpreted (25) in terms of an O—N—O angle of 116°, implying distortion of NO_3^{2-} from planarity toward a pyramidal form. A barrier to migration of NO_3^{2-} | NO_3^- | but not to motion of NO_2^{2-} | NO_2 | therefore arises, since probability for resonant transfer of the unpaired electron of NO_3^{2-} onto a neighboring distorted NO_3^- would be low at low temperatures. The probability would be expected to increase with temperature and eventually lead to disappearance of the NO_3^{2-} | NO_3^- | radicals (see Table II). When conditions for resonant transfer *cannot* exist, as for the NO_3^{2-} | X^- | radicals listed in Table III, then NO_3^{2-} is observed to be stable to much higher temperatures.

Interpretation of radiation-induced optical absorption in single crystals of KNO_3 indicate that a 2.4 eV photon is required to excite an electron from an NO_3^{2-} | NO_3^- | center (column 2 of Table II) into the conduction band (19) of KNO_3. The dominant electron-trapping center in KCl/NO_3^-, which *may* be NO_3^{2-} | Cl^- |, requires a photon of similar energy, about 3.5 eV, to excite an electron into the conduction band (41). These energies are much too great to be accounted for only by intramolecular configuration change, E_I, and require that intermolecular interactions with lattice ions further stabilize the electron trapped on NO_3^{2-}. The theory of such interactions has been thoroughly discussed for electrons localized as *F* centers in anion vacancies and can account for trap depths of this magnitude (54). ESR data on *F* centers stress the paramount importance of the interaction of the electron with near-neighbor ions (54), and the data in Tables II and III can be similarly interpreted. Thus it will be noted that ESR data for NO_3^{2-} in Table III correspond to this radical interacting with near-neighbor potassium cations, but with different anions. The parameters in Table III show a much smaller spread of both *A* values and *g* values than those in Table II in which the radical has *different* near-neighbor cations but similar anions. The larger spread results almost entirely from changes in A_{iso} which expresses the spin density of the unpaired electron at the nitrogen nucleus. Schaafsma and Kommandeur have argued, for a similar radical NO_2 in various matrices (62), that such variations in A_{iso} reflect the extent of electron transfer between the radical and the matrix. According to this interpretation the variation in A_{iso} data in Table II reflects principally the extent of electron transfer between NO_3^{2-} and near-neighbor cations.

Support for this idea comes from the fact that additional superhyperfine splitting on each member of the $^{14}NO_3^{2-}$ triplet has been resolved in irradiated $Pb(NO_3)_2$, $AgNO_3$, and $NaNO_3$ (27,28,31). These crystal structures feature relatively short oxygen-cation distances and the observed shfs in $Pb(NO_3)_2$ has been attributed (27) to an exchange of spin density between cation(s) and oxygen orbitals of NO_3^{2-}.

2. Hole Trapping

The "perfect" lattice *does* give rise by intermolecular configuration change to localized levels which retain holes as Cl_2^-, Br_2^-, or I_2^- in alkali halides *after irradiation* at 77°K. No impurity ions or lattice defects are known to be associated with the trapped hole centers in the alkali halides (46,54). The exact mechanism for formation of these molecular ion radicals during irradiation at 77°K is not completely resolved. A probable contributing mechanism is represented schematically in Figures 3*b* and 3*c*, involving potential hole trapping sites situated at levels H_I above the valence band. These are generated when interaction with subexcitation electrons causes intramolecular or intermolecular configuration changes.

The relative thermal stabilities of species tentatively identified from ESR studies as $NO_3 | NO_3^- |$ in nitrates, $CO_3^- | CO_3^{2-} |$ in calcite, and $NO_2 | NO_2^- |$ in $NaNO_2$ are qualitatively in agreement with what would be predicted from operation of intramolecular configuration change as the dominant factor in hole trapping. For, according to Walsh's correlation diagrams (61), neither NO_3 nor CO_3^- should undergo much configuration change from the planar configuration of the parent NO_3^- or CO_3^{2-} ions. However, the O—N—O bond angle of NO_2 is wider by 20° than in parent NO_2^- ions (25) which corresponds to a significant intramolecular configuration change. The probability of this changed configuration occurring on nitrite ions adjacent to trapped $NO_2 | NO_2^- |$ would be low at 77°K. Little change would, however, be needed to cause lattice anions adjacent to $NO_3 | NO_3^- |$ or $CO_3^- | CO_3^{2-} |$ to have configurations favorable for movement of the trapped hole onto the new anion position even at 77°K. Published interpretations of ESR data show that $CO_3^- | CO_3^{2-} |$ in pure calcite (56) or $NO_3 | NO_3^- |$ in $NaNO_3$ and KNO_3 (24,51), decay within few hours of the end of irradiation at 77°K, but that $NO_2 | NO_2^- |$ resists short warmup to 200°K.

Several experimental observations indicate that trapping of electrons and holes by the mechanisms described in Figure 3 produce the first observable effects of ionizing irradiation upon pure single crystals of calcite at 77 or 4°K:

1. Immediately after irradiations $> 10^4$ rads only two intense singlet signals can be observed in the ESR spectrum (31,56). By observing very weak satellite lines which accompany these intense singlets and arise from coupling of the unpaired electrons or holes to ^{13}C occurring in 1% abundance, Marshall and Serway established that they arose from carbon-containing radicals (56). The similarities of the g values to those reported for CO_3^- in other crystals and to those assigned by other workers to the isoelectronic NO_3 or NO_3^{2-} radicals led Marshall and Serway to suggest that the intense singlets arose from CO_3^- or CO_3^{3-}, respectively.

2. Both singlet ESR signals were very intense for doses $> 10^5$ rads and had half-widths ca. 100 mG (31,56). Crude estimates (31) of the CO_3^{3-} and CO_3^- concentrations indicated both greater than 10^{18} cm^{-3}. Radiation-induced optical absorption was expected for such large concentrations. λ_{max} for the radiation-induced visible absorption appearing first under irradiation was at 6500 Å and gave the crystals a violet coloration (31). Marshall and Serway (56) have reported more intense radiation-induced absorption in the ultraviolet at 2900 and 2300 Å and another band at 4850 Å (56).

3. Hundredfold decreases in the intensity of the ESR signals of both CO_3^- and CO_3^{3-} were produced by bleaching the crystals, while immersed in liquid N_2, by the spectral output of a xenon arc lamp ($\lambda \sim 2500$–9000 Å). Rapid and efficient bleaching confirmed that the principal observable effect of radiation was the pairwise formation of trapped electrons and holes. The optical bleach also removed the radiation-induced violet coloration.

4. More selective bleaching experiments were performed by exposing irradiated calcite crystals while in the microwave ESR cavity to the output of a 35 mW neon gas laser, resonating at 6328 Å. The ESR cavity was so designed that crystals were immersed in liquid nitrogen during bleaching and during observation of the ESR spectra (31). The red laser light rapidly bleached the ESR signals of CO_3^- and the signal of CO_3^{3-} was observed to decrease in similar fashion (31). The monochromatic laser light was absorbed selectively in the violet radiation-induced optical absorption band. The fact that both ESR signals were decreased indicated that freeing the trapped hole (or electron) caused the complementary electron (or hole) signal also to disappear.

5. Calcite crystals immersed in liquid N_2 and observed in the dark immediately after irradiation showed a strong blue luminescence which was indicative of electron–hole recombination at 77°K (31). Postirradiation studies of the intensities of the ESR signals of CO_3^- and CO_3^{3-} in these crystals showed that they underwent a rapid initial decay ($t_{1/2} \sim 1$ hr) succeeded by a slower decay ($t'_{1/2} \sim 5$ hr) (31,56).

6. Evidence that these effects follow from mobility of CO_3^- at 77°K comes from the nature of a new spectrum which appears as the trapped electrons and holes decay at 77°K. Marshall and Serway have identified this with PO_4^{2-} radicals existing in six orientations at CO_3^{2-} sites (56). These could arise from hole trapping at PO_4^{3-} occurring substitutionally on anion sites.

7. The ESR spectrum of CO_3^{3-}, but not that of CO_3^-, can be observed in calcite crystals irradiated at 77°K and stored overnight at room temperature and is also produced by room temperature irradiation (56).

3. Dissociative Energy Localization

An important point emerging from the preceding discussion of charge localization by the mechanism of Figure 3 is that *effective* charge localization in solids containing polyatomic ions requires that significant configuration change accompany localization. It follows that species such as, $CO_3^{3-} \mid CO_3^{2-} \mid$, $NO_3^{2-} \mid NO_3^- \mid$, or $NO_2 \mid NO_2^- \mid$ are formed initially in vibrationally excited states.

The mechanisms of Figure 3 can be used also to describe localization of radiation-induced electronic excitation, such as $CO_3^{2-}{}^*$, $NO_3^-{}^*$, or NO_2^*, upon specific lattice sites. A vibrationally excited ion represents a potential exciton trapping site when its changed intramolecular configuration approaches that appropriate to an electronically excited state and differs appreciably from neighboring ions.

The larger the change in intramolecular configuration involved in these trapping mechanisms the more probable it is that the vibrational excitation will remain localized on the trapping site. This follows from considerations by Sun and Rice (63) of the relaxation times for vibrational excitation imparted to one of an array of molecular species. They concluded that relaxation times would be long, unless conditions favored resonance transfer of energy; this condition is unlikely to be satisfied when significant intramolecular configuration change is involved in trapping. Vibrational excitation imparted to polyatomic ions and followed by the trapping of an exciton, hole, or electron thereon may thus eventually dissociate the ion.

Evidence for dissociative electron trapping at NO_3^- ions comes from ESR studies on KNO_3 γ-irradiated at 4.2°K (18). The NO_3^{2-} radical is reported to be distorted toward a pyramidal form (25). Excitation of the out-of-plane vibration by interaction with low energy electrons could produce pyramidal-like configurations of individual NO_3^- ions appropriate to localizing an electron thereon. Evidence for the out-of-plane vibration could therefore be expected in any dissociation of NO_3^{2-} radicals formed in high vibrational levels by electron trapping. The positions and orientation dependence of nine small signals appearing in the ESR spectrum of KNO_3 after irradiation at 4.2°K can be accounted for in terms of the magnetic parameters assigned to NO_2^{2-} by Symons in the preceding chapter (18,25). Nine lines arise because the NO_2^{2-} radicals as produced at 4.2°K exist in three orientations distinguished by three orientations of the O—O direction *in the plane* of the parent NO_3^- ions. The apex of the O—N—O bonds projects *out of plane* in all three sets, as would be expected for dissociative electron attachment according to the mechanism just described. Additional studies are needed to clarify the role of other factors in determining the *probability* of dissociation following electron attachment. Although $NO_3^{2-} \mid NO_3^- \mid$ has been identified by ESR studies of several nitrates after irradiation at 77°K (Table II), ESR signals attributable to NO_2^{2-} have only been reported in KNO_3. This would be surprising if the degree of configuration change (and hence of vibrational excitation) alone determined the probability of dissociation of NO_3^{2-}. Values of A_{iso} in Table II show that $NO_3^{2-} \mid NO_3^- \mid$ is distorted *more* toward pyramidal in $Pb(NO_3)_2$, $Sr(NO_3)_2$, and $AgNO_3$, which do not show ESR signals of NO_2^{2-}, than in KNO_3. Failure to detect fragments from $CO_3^{3-} \mid CO_3^{2-} \mid$ in calcite irradiated at 77°K also points to operation of other factors (56,64). Lattice restrictions on fragment separation doubtlessly influence the probability of dissociation following electron attachment, as they do the overall rate of radiolysis (Table I).

Probable fragment radicals from dissociative attachment of holes to the anions in $NaNO_2$, $CaCO_3$, and KNO_3 would be NO | NO_2^- |, CO_2^- | CO_3^{2-} (64), and NO_2 | NO_3^- |, respectively. Although efficient hole trapping to give NO_2 | NO_3^- |, CO_3^- | CO_3^{2-} |, and NO_3 | NO_3^- | has been reported (22,50,56) in these solids after x-irradiation at 77°K, there is no evidence for the fragment radicals expected if dissociative hole attachment were important. This is not surprising for NO_3 | NO_3^- | or CO_3^- | CO_3^{2-} | in view of the small intramolecular change involved, but significant change does occur in forming NO_2 | NO_2^- | (25). The search for conclusive evidence that dissociative hole attachment is unimportant is complicated by the fact that dissociative exciton localization can also produce electron deficient radicals. Consider the nitric oxide fragment for which there is chemical evidence in irradiated nitrates (18). There is disagreement on the ESR parameters expected for this radical in solids (25,26). Even if the radicals NO | NO_3^- | and NO | NO_2^- | could definitely be identified in $NaNO_3$ and $NaNO_2$, their origin would remain indeterminate, since they could arise from dissociation of electronically excited anions, *or* be products of dissociative hole attachment.

The pattern of primary products of nitrate radiolysis at low temperatures in Table IV incorporates the features discussed in this section. Dissociative electron attachment and dissociative exciton localization are indicated as important primary steps in radiolysis, but dissociation of ground electronic state NO_3 following trapping is not included.

D. Charge Localization at Defect or Impurity Sites

1. Lattices of Monatomic Ions

Charge localization by intramolecular configuration change cannot occur for solids having only monatomic ions, such as in the alkali halides, BaO, MgO, and CaF_2, when pure or doped with monatomic impurities. Only *intermolecular* configuration changes may possibly compete with defects and impurities as trapping sites for radiation-freed electrons and holes in these solids. Data for hole trapping in alkali halides show just how effective this competition may be in certain cases (54). H centers are the sole electron deficient centers observed at 4.2°K in pure or impurity-doped alkali halides after irradiation at 4.2°K. They correspond to interstitial chlorine atoms inserted between three chlorine ions arranged linearly along the [110] direction, i.e., Cl_4^{3-} | $Cl^- \cdot Cl^- \cdot Cl^-$ |. The fact that impurities had no effect upon the efficiency of formation of these hole-trapped species at 4.2°K indicates *either* that they are produced by a defect-insensitive mechanism (such as displacement of Cl^- from lattice to interstitial positions by Auger and crowdion processes), *or* that the cross section for hole capture at radiation-induced H-center configurations is so high that it scavenges all holes and prevents their attachment to impurities. A similar intermolecular configuration change, in the form of decreased anion–anion distance along the [110] direction leading to formation of Cl_2^-, Br_2^-, and I_2^-, is the most effective hole-trapping site in pure or cation-doped alkali halides irradiated at 77°K. The concentrations of Cl_2^- ion radicals produced in KCl by a given irradiation at 77°K can be greatly enhanced by doping with silver, thallium, or lead ions. Increases by factors of 100–1000 have been reported (54).

Detailed ENDOR and ESR studies on crystals irradiated at 77°K have shown that the added impurities are not associated directly with the Cl_2^- hole traps (54). Instead, they provide new electron-trapping centers which enhance the concentrations of trapped holes by reducing electron–hole recombinations. Subsequent studies have shown that some impurity cations, particularly silver, *do* provide very stable hole traps. Upon warming KCl:Ag^+ crystals irradiated at 77°K, Cl_2^- radicals begin to migrate and become trapped as Ag^{2+} | $Ag^+ \cdot 6Cl^-$ |, i.e., a hole shared between Ag^{2+} and six coordinating anions (42). These latter centers remain stable to 373°K in some crystals (65). It may appear somewhat anomalous that hole trapping in silver-doped KCl *during* irradiation at 77°K does not lead directly to their formation. However, relative thermal stabilities, i.e., the magnitudes of the energy of localization for holes at various sites, are not simply related to ease of formation; for instance Cl_2^- centers are more stable than H centers, but the latter form in preference to Cl_2^- at 4.2°K; likewise Ag^{2+} | $Ag^+ \cdot 6Cl^-$ | is stable to higher temperatures than Cl_2^-, but irradiation produces only Cl_2^- at 77°K. These results emphasize the danger of considering only the energy of localization and the necessity for equal concern with the efficiency, or cross section, of various centers for charge localization thereon. Most of the reported data on hole trapping in pure or doped alkali halides irradiated at 77°K are fully consistent with a very high efficiency for hole trapping by intermolecular change to give Cl_2^- and it has been estimated (42) that holes produced in KCl:Ag^+ by irradiation at 77°K probably make no more than 100 jumps before capture as Cl_2^-.

By contrast, the cross section for electron trapping by configuration change is negligibly small at any irradiation temperature for alkali halides, BaO, MgO, or CaF_2. Electrons are trapped according to the outcome of competition between defect and impurity sites. This may be illustrated by radiation coloration of alkali halides at different temperatures. F centers are the only "trapped-electron" sites produced close to 4°K; the efficiency for radiation formation of anion vacancies is sufficient (66) to increase their concentration so that they capture radiation-freed electrons. In KBr only one in six radiation-produced anion vacancies contains an electron after irradiation at $4°K$. G_F, the average number of electrons trapped as F centers per 100 eV of radiation energy absorbed at $4°K$, ranges from ca. 0.08 for KCl, NaF, or KBr to ca. 10^{-4} for NaBr. Relative to pure crystals similarly irradiated, F-band intensities are markedly enhanced in crystals doped with Ca^{2+} or Pb^{2+} and irradiated at room temperature, but differences were much smaller after $77°K$ irradiation. No evidence was obtained for electron-attachment to impurity cations at $4°K$, but optical and ESR absorption attributable to electrons trapped at impurity Ag^+, Tl^+, or Sr^{2+} cations in KCl has been reported after irradiation at room temperature of $77°K$. These different temperature dependencies of the electron-capture cross sections of lattice defects vs. impurity cations contribute to the complex kinetics observed for radiation coloration at or above $77°K$.

The outcome of competition between lattice defects and impurity ions for radiation-freed electrons can be greatly modified by changing the concentration and/or cross section of defects or impurities (67). Thus, relative to alkali halides, lower efficiencies of F-center formation by ionizing radiation is expected and observed in pure MgO and BaO (54) because of greater formation energy and consequent lower equilibrium concentrations of anion vacancies. F centers have been reported in MgO exposed to neutrons to increase defect concentrations (67). The next section considers evidence of increased cross section for electron capture at polyatomic centers.

2. Lattices of Polyatomic Ions

The majority of ESR signals observed after irradiation of solids with polyatomic ions have been assigned to *radical fragments*; NH_3^+ and ClO_3 from NH_4ClO_4, ClO_2 from $KClO_4$, or NO, NO_2 and NO_2^{2-} from KNO_3. Each corresponds to charge localization at defect sites generated by radiation. As discussed in the preceding section, charge localization at defect sites is in competition with trapping by intermolecular configuration change and should not be observed when the latter has larger cross sections. Studies of holes trapped after low temperature irradiation of KCl doped with NO_2^-, NO_3^-, or OH^- show no evidence (54) for holes trapped as $NO_2 \mid Cl^- \mid$, $NO_3 \mid Cl^- \mid$, or $OH \mid Cl^- \mid$. This shows that the large cross section for capture as Cl_2^- by intermolecular configuration change still dominates hole trapping despite the presence of polyatomic impurities. The converse situation is illustrated by KNO_3 which traps holes with low efficiency when pure, so that when NO_2^- impurity ions are introduced holes are localized predominantly as $NO_2 \mid NO_3^- \mid$ (23).

The analog of $Cl_2^- \mid Cl^- \cdot Cl^- \mid$ from KCl would be $N_2O_4^- \mid NO_2^- \cdot NO_2^- \mid$ from $NaNO_2$, but γ-irradiation at $77°K$ does not produce this latter species.

Instead, it has been identified only after large gamma doses at room temperature (52,53). The only electron-deficient centers observed after irradiation of pure sodium nitrite at 77°K are NO_2 radicals (55). Recent studies of the shfs on each line of the NO_2 triplet with the magnetic field, H, parallel to the crystal b axis shows it to be different in pure and in silver-doped $NaNO_2$ (see Fig. 4). Detailed line-shape calculations for the pattern of six partially resolved shfs lines with intensity ratio ca. 1:2:3:3:2:1 observed for H parallel to the crystal b axis indicate that in pure $NaNO_2$ holes become trapped with comparable probability at *two* sites, each of which has a cation vacancy as a near neighbor. The sites may be represented by $NO_2 \mid \square \cdot NO_2^- \cdot Na^+ \mid$ and $NO_2 \mid Na^+ \cdot NO_2^- \cdot \square \mid$ and termed α and β sites, respectively. The Na^+ ion is 2.6 Å from nitrogen in the former and 2.9 Å in the latter. It appears that doping with Ag^{n+} from solution replaces cation vacancies by substitutional Ag^{n+} impurities and that hole trapping occurs at $NO_2 \mid Ag^+ \cdot NO_2^- \cdot Na^+ \mid$ and $NO_2 \mid Na^+ \cdot NO_2^- \cdot Ag^{n+} \mid$. The observed shfs arises largely from dipolar interaction with the nearest Na^+ neighbor; Ag^{n+} does not introduce measurable

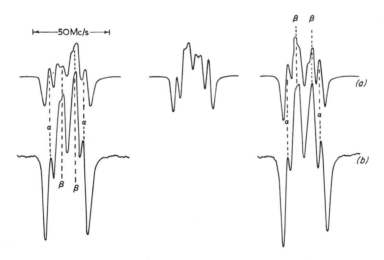

Fig. 4. ESR evidence at Q band for different hole trapping sites in pure and silver-doped $NaNO_2$ after x-irradiation at 77°K. (a) Line shapes for each member of the $^{14}NO_2$ triplet are shown for magnetic field ∥ b axis of pure $NaNO_2$. Line shapes arise from superposition of four-line patterns from two sites, each adjacent to a cation vacancy. α sites have Na^+ 2.6 Å distant along the b axis. Na^+ is 2.9 Å distant for β sites. (b) Same as a, but for silver-doped $NaNO_2$. The central region (related to β sites of a) has greater intensity than outer peaks (related to α sites of a) because holes are preferentially trapped at $\mid Ag^{n+} \xrightarrow{2.6 \text{ Å}} NO_2 \xrightarrow{2.6 \text{ Å}} Na^+ \mid$ sites.

additional splitting because of its small nuclear magnetic moment. The markedly different line shape in the silver-doped material (Fig. 4b) arises because the cross section for hole trapping is much greater for the site having Ag^{n+} only 2.6 Å from the nitrogen of the radical than for the site having Ag^{n+} 2.9 Å distant. These most recent data indicate that although intramolecular configuration change may play a significant role in the hole-trapping mechanism in pure $NaNO_2$, additional stabilization is supplied by a near-neighbor cation vacancy or substitutional impurity Ag^{n+}.

It is especially to be noted in relation to hole trapping in silver-doped KCl and $NaNO_2$ that the trapped hole is "shared" between cation and anion(s). Delbecq et al. consider in $KCl:Ag^+$ that the "total" trapping site, namely an impurity cation and six coordinated anions, undergoes a configuration change by the Jahn-Teller effect when a hole is trapped as $Ag^{2+} \mid Ag^+ \cdot 6Cl^- \mid$. Anion–impurity cation interactions thus contribute to hole trapping by sharing the trapped hole with near-neighbor ions *and* by providing intermolecular configuration change to localize the hole. Do similar effects arise for electron trapping by impurity cations in ionic solids?

Direct evidence for the effectiveness of cation–anion interaction in localizing radiation energy at anion sites adjacent to impurity Ag^{n+} cations has come from ESR studies on pure and silver-doped $NaNO_2$ (47). Irradiation with x- or γ-rays at 77°K produces only the triplet signal of NO_2 radicals in pure $NaNO_2$ with no indication of the whereabouts of an equivalent number of electrons freed from the NO_2 radicals. Studies of the line shapes and shfs on each line of the NO_2 triplet show that in silver-doped $NaNO_2$ the majority of NO_2 radicals exist at anion sites *adjacent to Ag^{n+} impurity ions*. Silver-doped $NaNO_2$ after x- or γ-irradiation at 77°K shows the complex multiline spectrum illustrated in Figure 5. It is possible to reproduce the observed multiline patterns and their intensity distributions by identifying the center as a nitrogen-containing radical located on an anion site adjacent to a substitutional Ag^{n+} and interacting with one nitrogen nucleus, one silver nucleus and five near-neighbor Na^+ ions. Values of the tensors describing the interaction of the unpaired electron with these nuclei, listed in Table V, require the total trapping site to have two different orientations in the crystal. The principal values of the hfs tensor, describing interaction of the unpaired electron with nitrogen, greatly resemble those observed by Jaccard in KCl exposed to nitric oxide vapor (26) and attributed by him to nitric oxide radicals locked in a fixed orientation in the lattice. Symons (25) has since argued that the g tensor is more appropriate to NO_2^{2-} than to nitric oxide and his interpretation is followed here for consistency with the preceding chapter. Support for assigning to NO_2 and NO_2^{2-} the two ESR signals produced in

TABLE V

Parameters of ESR Signals Produced in Crystals by Low Temperature Irradiation and Tentatively Assigned to NO_2^{2-}

Crystal: Radical orientation:	KNO_3 $x \parallel c$ axis	KCl/NO_3^- Tumbling	KCl/NO_3^- $x \parallel 110$	$NaNO_2/Ag^+$ $x \parallel a$ axis $y \parallel b$ axis	$NaNO_2/Ag^+$ $x \parallel a$ axis $y \parallel c$ axis
(a) Nitrogen hfs					
A_x (G)	31	$A_{iso} = 14.2$	30.9	46	46
A_y (G)	4.0		5.0	4.4	4.4
A_z (G)	4.0		7.0	5.6	5.6
(b)					
g_x	2.005		2.0038	2.0020	2.0020
g_y	2.010	2.0099 avg.	2.0099	2.0048	2.0074
g_z	2.008		2.0070	2.0062	2.0056
(c) Cation shfs					
A_x (G)	<3	<1	<2.8	2.2 to Na^+ / 28 to Ag^{n+}	2.2 to Na^+ / 14 to Ag^{n+}
A_y (G)	<3	<1	<2.8	2.8 to Na^+ / 14 to Ag^{n+}	2.8 to Na^+ / 28 to Ag^{n+}
A_z (G)	<3	<1	<2.8	2.6 to Na^+ / 14 to Ag^{n+}	2.6 to Na^+ / 14 to Ag^{n+}
Ref.	18[b]	26	25,26[a]	47[c]	47[c]

[a] Reference 25 assigns values to NO_2^{2-}, according to: z bisects ONO, y joins oxygens. Reference 26 assigns values to nitric oxide with x values along the N–O bond direction.

[b] Reference 18 observed three orientations of y and z in the c plane in KNO_3 irradiated at 4°K. All NO_3^- ions are coplanar in c planes. Radical rotation about x axis is possible at 77°K.

[c] Values from preliminary analysis of complex spectrum produced by x-irradiation of $NaNO_2/Ag^+$ at 77°K. All parent NO_2^- ions are coplanar and perpendicular to the crystal a axis. Crystal b axis bisects ONO in NO_2^- ions. Ag^{n+} denotes that the oxidation state of Ag in the total trapping site has not been established.

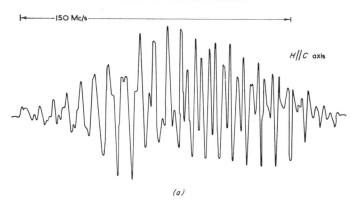

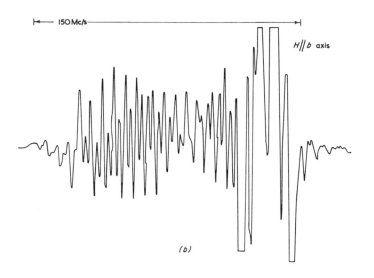

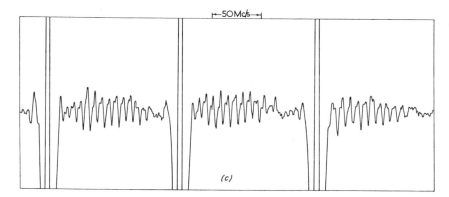

$NaNO_2:Ag^+$ by x-irradiation at 77°K comes from the fact that both signals can be simultaneously bleached by 2500–9000 Å light (47). The data in Table V confirm that the unpaired electron of NO_2^{2-} is "shared" with the adjacent impurity silver cation and that the other coordinating cations share the electron to a smaller extent. Total absence of any comparable signal from pure $NaNO_2$ similarly irradiated confirms that the "anion–impurity cation" interaction is an important factor in the electron-trapping process.

ESR data on electrons trapped as $Ag^0 \mid Ag^+ \cdot 6Cl^- \mid$ in $KCl:Ag^+$ also show evidence of interaction of the unpaired electron with surrounding lattice anions. However, it is not yet clear to what extent the intermolecular configuration of the total trapping site is distorted by the electron-trapping process in $NaNO_2:Ag^+$ or $KCl:Ag^+$. Detailed ENDOR information will be needed to resolve this point in these solids and also in the cases of efficient electron attachment to Ag^+ in silver-doped nitrates, or to Mn^{2+} impurities in natural calcite crystals (31,44).

E. Localization of Charge and Excitation by Anion–Impurity Cation Interaction

The magnitude of the cross section for charge localization at impurity sites *relative* to cross sections in the pure material has been identified as the factor which determines how impurities influence charge localization. For systems in which observable radiolysis occurs largely from charge localization, impurities with large cross sections can be expected to affect radiolysis. Doping alkali halides with nitrate ions is known to introduce traps with cross section for electron attachment larger than that of anion vacancies (41,42). Measurable chemical change (i.e., growth of metallic sodium and molecular halogen) in irradiated alkali halides results primarily from charge localization at anion vacancies. Therefore, radiolysis of nitrate-doped alkali halide should differ from the pure materials. In fact, Jones (43) has reported that irradiation of nitrate-doped alkali halides ($\sim 1\% \ NO_3^-$) produced radiolytic products of nitrate ions with

---

Fig. 5. ESR spectra at Q band of a radical produced in silver-doped $NaNO_2$ by x or γ irradiation at 77°K. The complex multiline spectrum shown in *a, b,* and *c* was *not* detected in pure $NaNO_2$ crystals similarly irradiated. It has nitrogen hfs values similar to those previously assigned to NO_2^{2-}. Additional splitting arises from interaction with near-neighbor silver and sodium ions. (*a*) Spectrum at H ∥ *c* axis. Large *g*-value differences separate the NO_2^{2-} spectrum completely from that of coexisting NO_2 radicals. (*b*) Spectrum at H ∥ *b* axis. The NO_2^{2-} spectrum overlaps with the four-line pattern of the central member of the NO_2 triplet. (*c*) Spectrum at H ∥ *a* axis. Complex multiline spectrum extends over a wider range than the total splitting of the intense triplet arising from coexisting NO_2 radicals.

such high efficiency that processes must exist for localizing radiation effects at the impurities. Trapping of radiation-freed electrons to give $NO_3^{2-} \mid Cl^- \mid$, followed by dissociation of vibrationally excited NO_3^{2-} could account for these results. Jaccard (26) has identified an electron-excess radical fragment in this system.

In the radiation-induced dissociation of polyatomic ions such as nitrates, bromates, azides, and perchlorates in crystals, the proportions of dissociation events which proceed from charge localization *or* from unimolecular decomposition of excited states are generally not known nor directly calculable. Consequently, if addition of an impurity ion to these ionic solids affects their radiolyses, careful experimentation is needed to determine whether the impurities act via charge localization at the impurity *or* by modifying certain excited state decompositions. Studies of the radiation-induced optical absorption (15,19,44), ESR spectra (18–24,47, 55), and rates of radiolysis of pure and silver-doped $NaNO_3$, KNO_3, and $NaNO_2$ provide an opportunity to examine this question for these systems.

Unipositive silver ions Ag^+ are known to provide good electron- *and* hole-trapping centers in crystals (42) and frozen solutions (68). Investigations of radiation-induced optical absorption in $NaNO_3$ and KNO_3 has confirmed that Ag^+ modifies charge localization processes (44) in these crystals at 77°K. Evidence for electron-trapping by Ag^+ is particularly clear in $NaNO_3:Ag^+$ in which an optical absorption attributable to silver atoms, Ag^0, appeared after irradiation at 77°K. Investigation of the rates of radiolysis of pure and silver-doped $NaNO_3$ and KNO_3 yielded for KNO_3 the results in Table VI. A maximum reduction of 32% in the rate of radiolysis of KNO_3 by 1% Ag^+ ions was observed at room temperature (69). However, in $NaNO_3$, under experimental conditions in which only

TABLE VI
First-Order Rate Constants for Radiolysis of KNO_3
Doped with Ag^+, Expressed Relative to Corresponding
Rate Constant for Pure KNO_3

Salt	Temp. (°K)	$\dfrac{k \text{ (doped)}}{k \text{ (pure)}}$
KNO_3 + 0.04% Ag^+	293	0.93 ± 0.002
KNO_3 + 0.1% Ag^+	293	0.83 ± 0.01
KNO_3 + 0.4% Ag^+	293	0.86 ± 0.06
KNO_3 + 1.0% Ag^+	293	0.68 ± 0.02
KNO_3 + 1.0% Ag^+	400	0.90
KNO_3 + 0.04% Ag^+	77	0.97
KNO_3 + 0.4 Ag^+	77	0.88

differences greater than 10% would be detected reliably, no difference was found between the relative rates of radiolysis of pure and silver-doped $NaNO_3$ at 300°K *or* at 77°K. For $NaNO_3$ it might be argued that the known attachment to Ag^+ at 77°K does not affect radiolysis because electron attachment is not an important part of nitrate radiolysis at 300 or 77°K, but this would not explain data in Table VI. ESR data on silver-doped $NaNO_2$ irradiated at 77°K further increase the difficulty of sustaining a consistent description solely in terms of charge localization at Ag^+. No ESR signals attributable to Ag^0 or Ag^{2+} are detected in silver-doped $NaNO_2$ although Ag^+ was clearly implicated in the radiation effect by Livingston and Zeldes' report that silver doping increased the efficiency for formation of NO_2 radicals at 77°K by tenfold (22,23).

A more consistent explanation of these phenomena can be based on the postulate that the presence of Ag^{n+} as a cation impurity perturbs anion(s) on adjacent site(s) and thus establishes conditions for preferential localization of excitons *or* charge at those anions. Nitrate ions undergoing radiation-induced decomposition at sites adjacent to an Ag^+ cation impurity experience, in part, the cation–anion interaction present in $AgNO_3$. According to information summarized in Table I, the rate of radiolysis of nitrate ions experiencing this cation–anion interaction with Ag^+ may be crudely approximated by $G_{NO_2^-} = 0.17$ observed in $AgNO_3$ at 300°K. Preferential localization of radiation energy at anions adjacent to Ag^+ impurities would therefore be expected to *decrease* the rate of radiolysis of $KNO_3:Ag^+$ relative to pure KNO_3 (since $G_{NO_2^-} = 1.5$ for pure KNO_3), but to cause little change in the rate for $NaNO_3:Ag^+$ relative to pure $NaNO_3$ (since $G_{NO_2^-} = 0.3$ for pure $NaNO_3$). This agrees with the observed results at room temperature. The ESR studies by Moulton and Mosely (28) on $AgNO_3$ irradiated at 77°K show that cation–anion interaction leading to formation of $(AgNO_3)^-$ is an effective process for charge localization. This would provide a mechanism for continued effectiveness of Ag^+ in modifying the rate of radiolysis of nitrate ions in silver-doped KNO_3 at 77°K.

III. FRAGMENT DISTRIBUTION IN IRRADIATED SOLIDS

A. Spatial Distribution of Energy Loss

1. Model for Electron Energy Loss

The spatial distribution of fragments produced in solids by irradiation may be preserved provided that the temperature after irradiation is kept sufficiently low to prevent diffusion of fragments. Evidence presented in Section II on pure and doped sodium nitrite underlined the importance of preexisting traps in determining the sites for charge localization. The NO_2 and NO_2^{2-} radicals observed after irradiation were distributed through the crystal according to the spatial distribution of defect sites. Section III considers pertinent experimental data on irradiated solids to discover if they provide reliable evidence for fragment formation according to the theoretical distribution of energy-loss events.

The spatial distribution of energy-loss events, predicted by the Bethe equation, differs sharply for various types of radiation (70–72). The differential rate of energy loss, $-dE/dx$, for fast-charged particles occurs predominantly by inducing electronic transitions (including ionization) of ions or molecules along their path. Instantaneous rates of energy loss, $-dE/dx$, have been calculated by the Bethe equation for electrons, protons, or α particles of 1 MeV energy, respectively, as 0.02, 2.8, and 26.4 eV/Å for aqueous systems (71). Such rates of energy transfer to the system along the linear path of the radiation are referred to as LET. Each primary ionization produces a positive ion and a secondary electron. Observed chemical effects of fast-charged particles arise principally from the additional ionization and excitation caused by secondary electrons. This is true also for x-ray or γ-ray irradiations. For different radiations the spatial distributions of energy-loss events involving these secondary electrons are markedly different. This can be illustrated in terms of the mean separation between electron energy-loss events for different radiations. This is approximately given by $E/(-dE/dx)$, where E is the mean energy of secondary electrons and equals ca. 60 eV for aqueous systems. For 1 MeV electrons (or γ-rays), protons and α particles, respectively, the expression predicts mean separations of 3000, 21, and 2.3 Å for aqueous systems (71).

Appropriate models are required to move from the preceding description of instantaneous energy loss in the medium to descriptions of the spatial distribution of primary ions, excited species, radicals, and finally products. Magee and co-workers have elaborated models for aqueous systems which proceed by equating the spatial distribution of primary ionized, excited, and radical species with that for energy loss by secondary electrons (73–75). According to Mozumder and Magee (75), three types of energy-loss events should be considered for electrons with initial energies greater than 5000 eV.

The first type includes resonant primary events involving small losses of energy (ca. 6–100 eV). It is characteristic of the models of Magee and co-workers for aqueous systems that electrons produced in such low energy-loss events do not escape from the coulombic field of their parent ions but recombine in 10^{-12} to 10^{-15} sec (76). Clusters of ions plus excited states (at times 10^{-12} to 10^{-15} sec after energy deposition), or of radicals plus excited states (after ion–electron recombination) occur along the main track and along branch tracks. The main track represents the path of the incident radiation. Branch tracks arise from secondary electrons which are ejected from their parent ions with energies > 5000 eV by head-on encounters. They are generally referred to as delta rays. The fact that the low energy-loss events produce nonoverlapping clusters, or spurs, of primary species distinguishes it from the other two energy-loss processes.

The second type of energy-loss events are those in which 500–5000 eV are imparted to secondary electrons. Such energy-loss events can be regarded as generating low energy delta-ray electrons, which still have sufficient energy to escape from the coulombic field of the parent ion. The distinguishing spatial characteristic of the distribution of primary species from such events is that they overlap throughout the length of the "short track." Mozumder and Magee have pointed out that the cross section for producing low energy delta rays should be much greater than for high energy delta rays. They calculated that ca. 80% of the energy of an electron of initial energy 7 keV would be deposited in such a short track.

The third type of energy-loss events are those which impart 100–500 eV to the secondary electron. The distinguishing feature of these events is that such electrons do not have sufficient energy to escape completely from the coulombic field of the parent ion. They do have sufficient energy to generate a relatively large number of ionizations and radicals in this spur. Magee and Mozumder have suggested the term "blob" for such large spurs of relatively undefined shape (75).

For aqueous systems exposed to radiations having low values of $-dE/dx$, Mozumder and Magee have estimated the following approximate separations between parent ions and delta-ray electrons of various energies: separations > 500 Å for electrons of initial energies > 5000 eV; 100–5000 Å for electrons with energies 500–5000 eV, which give rise to short tracks; initial separations < 120 Å for low energy delta-ray electrons of energies 100–500 eV, which give rise to blobs. Mean separations between thermalized electrons and their parent positive ions will be decreased or increased in other systems according to whether the rate of electron energy loss is greater or less than in water.

Studies related to mechanisms of reducing electron kinetic energies toward thermal values and to trapping such electrons as negative ions were recently reviewed by Schwarz (72). Electrical conductivity measurements on irradiated, pure hydrocarbon liquids indicate 0.09–0.2 separated ion pairs produced per 100 eV absorbed (77,78). Such low values of G_{ion} with low LET ionizing radiation correspond approximately with predicted yield of higher energy delta-ray electrons (79). After irradiation, a pure hydrocarbon system at 77°K in the glassy state has been reported to luminesce with lifetimes of the order of 10^{-3} sec (80). The long lifetimes have been variously interpreted as an entropy effect or as representing the time required for recombination at $77°K$ of widely separated (~ 5000 Å) ion–electron pairs (71,80).

2. Distribution of Primary Species at Low LET

Do the radicals [CO_3^- plus CO_3^{3-}] in calcite, or [NO_3 plus NO_3^{2-}] in irradiated nitrates represent ion pairs with the spatial distribution described initially by the model of Mozumder and Magee for low LET radiation? The experimental results present serious difficulties to such an interpretation, because the efficiency for producing these radicals is higher than calculated yields of delta rays. Thus Addé reported ten $NO_3 \mid NO_3^- \mid$ radicals produced per 100 eV deposited in $NaNO_3$ crystals at $77°K$ by 1 MeV electrons (51). Comparable yields of $CO_3^- \mid CO_3^{2-} \mid$ and $CO_3^{3-} \mid CO_3^{2-} \mid$ have been observed in pure calcite immediately after irradiation with 150 kV x-rays at $77°K$ in the dark ($G \sim 4$) (31). The yields of $NO_3 \mid NO_3^- \mid$ and $NO_3^{2-} \mid NO_3^- \mid$ measured by ESR on KNO_3 after γ-irradiation at 4.2 or $77°K$ ($G \sim 2$) (18) are also an order of magnitude greater than yields of separated ion pairs measured in irradiated liquids. For these radiations Mozumder and Magee's calculations would, for water, require that most of the energy of incident or photoelectrons be expended in formation of isolated spurs. The percentage of energy going to form spurs, blobs, and short tracks in water for a 1 MeV primary electron would be 67, 11, and 22%, respectively (75). If one assumes a similar partition of energy loss in crystalline $NaNO_3$, Addé's result can not be accounted for solely in terms of blobs and short tracks, for this would imply that ca. 33 eV so deposited generates ten separated ion pairs. Optical spectra, however, indicate an ionization potential of at least 6 eV for the nitrate ion in $NaNO_3$ (81).

The reported large yield of $NO_3 \mid NO_3^- \mid$ would not be anomalous if it included ion pairs generated from spurs. Ion-electron separations, i.e., between NO_3 and NO_3^{2-} in nitrates or CO_3^- and CO_3^{3-} in calcite, would be smallest for those produced by low energy spur events. Experiments were carried out on calcite and sodium nitrate to examine whether ion pairs were produced by low LET radiations in such close proximity that interaction occured between the hole (e.g., CO_3^-) and the trapped electron (e.g., CO_3^{3-}). Such electron–electron interactions can lead to line broadening or the appearance of new satellite spectra (82,83,87) (see Section III-A-3).

Interactions with the nuclear magnetic moments of near-neighbor lattice ions so affected the line shapes and half-widths of ESR signals in $NaNO_3$ that additional effects from electron–electron interactions were not discernible (31). Calcite, however, represented an ideal system to study such effects, because of the almost total absence of nuclei possessing magnetic moments. The line widths of ESR signals in calcite are therefore expected and observed to be extremely narrow (e.g., 30 mG for CO_2^-) (64). Use was made of this property to look for evidence for formation of ion pairs by irradiation of calcite at 77°K. First, the line widths of the ESR signal of CO_3^- and CO_3^{3-} were measured within minutes after the end of irradiation with 150 kV x-rays at 77°K. In order to eliminate instrumental line broadening arising from power saturation or modulation amplitude effects, power was progressively reduced to 3×10^{-7} W and modulation amplitude to 30 mG and effects on the line width were noted. No further decrease in line width was observed below 3×10^{-6} W power and 100 mG and the irreducible line half-width for first derivative presentation was 110 mG. Second, the line half-widths were observed after various times of storage at 77°K. It was assumed that the luminescence emitted by the crystals during storage arose from electron–hole recombination (Section II-C). If the spatial distribution of electrons and parent ions was that expected from the Mozumder-Magee model, ion pairs generated from spurs would recombine before those of blobs or short tracks. Recombination of vacancy–interstitial pairs produced in alkali halide crystals by low temperature irradiation has been interpreted in a similar fashion in which the closer pairs recombine first (84). For calcite the predicted effect of ion pair recombination upon the ESR signals would be a progressive decrease in line width, if ion pairs had initially the distribution depicted by Mozumder and Magee's model (75). No such effect was noted, although isothermal anneal reduced the signal intensity of CO_3^- and CO_3^{3-} to one-third their postirradiation values. Third, it was possible by means of selective optical bleaching in situ in the cavity with 6328 Å laser light to further reduce ESR signal intensity of CO_3^- and CO_3^{3-} by factors of 5–10. The line half-widths after this treatment were identical to those measured directly after irradiation.

The results of these line width studies on x-irradiated calcite crystals are in full agreement with an assumption generally made in interpreting ESR spectra observed in ionic crystals after low LET irradiation—namely, that radicals are produced singly at lattice positions (85). Details of the mechanisms by which this spatial distribution arises at low LET have yet to be elaborated.

3. Distribution of Primary Species at Increasing LET

As LET increases the mean separation between primary energy-loss events of the incident radiation decreases until spurs overlap and merge into a continuous track at high LET. Smith and Wyard first reported that line widths of ESR signals from radicals produced by various low temperature radiation in H_2O_2/H_2O and D_2O_2/D_2O glasses or polycrystalline ices increased as LET increased (82). Wyard later showed that line width increases in these systems at increasing dose from 6 MeV electrons arose from dipolar broadening by electron–electron interaction between radicals produced in close proximity to one another (86). In addition to this dipolar broadening, *extra* line widths of about 1 G were observed and attributed to formation of radicals in clusters containing ca. 3×10^{19} radicals cm^{-3}. Wyard has also reported preliminary results of further studies on these systems with radiations of higher LET (87). Local concentrations increased to $0.08M$ with helium ions of average LET 3.5 eV/Å and to $0.1M$ with carbon ions of LET 31 eV/Å. No differences between glassy and poly-crystalline samples were reported for these studies (86,87). Comparable studies on ionic crystals exposed to radiations of different LET at low temperature would be valuable to determine if clusters of radicals exist along high LET tracks in ordered crystalline lattices or if long-range order prevents their formation. So far as is known, ESR line-width data have not been reported for a specific radical produced in a given crystal lattice by a wide range of LET radiations at low temperatures. Attempts to measure ESR line widths of CO_3^{3-} or CO_3^- signals in calcite crystals exposed to 1 MeV protons at 77°K, for comparison with x-ray data, have thus far been unsuccessful because of small penetration and thermal heating by the proton beam (31). In an attempt to avoid these difficulties, high LET tracks have been produced *within* $NaNO_2$ crystals at 77°K by the $^{14}N(n,p)^{14}C$ nuclear transformation induced by thermal neutrons (47). The crystals were immersed in liquid N_2 and exposed to thermal neutrons plus γ-rays in a cryostatted facility at the Herald reactor at Aldermaston. If NO_2 radicals were produced in close proximity along the high LET tracks of the 0.6 MeV proton and 40 keV ^{14}C recoiling from these $^{14}N(n,p)^{14}C$ events, then ESR spectra of such radicals should differ from spectra of single NO_2 radicals at lattice sites. Spectra of the latter were produced by x-irradiation at 77°K and compared with ESR spectra measured on reactor irradiated crystals some days or weeks after irradiation. Samples were stored and handled throughout under liquid N_2. No differences in spectra or line half-widths were detected for doses < 5 Mrads total absorbed dose. Since it was probable that an intense ESR signal from single NO_2 radicals was produced by the unavoidable γ-ray component of the reactor irradiation, this signal might "mask" any ESR spectrum with different details or greater line half-widths arising from clusters of NO_2 radicals formed along the high LET tracks. Above 5 Mrads total dose the signal for single NO_2 radicals tended to a limiting intensity and additional features consisting of weak satellite lines were resolved at doses > 10 Mrads on the outsides of the high and low field members of the NO_2 triplet for $H \parallel$ crystal b axis. The satellite lines arise from interactions between close pairs of NO_2 radicals. Satellite spectra also appeared in silver-doped $NaNO_2$ irradiated only with low LET x-rays. This indicates that processes other than highly localized energy loss at high LET give rise to close pairs of NO_2 radicals at high dose. Trapping a second "hole" at hole-trapping sites existing *prior* to irradiation after all sites had been singly populated by ca. 5 Mrads of irradiation would account for the satellite spectra observed at high dose in $NaNO_2$ (47).

Studies with an electron microscope on the effects of fission fragments (LET $\sim 10^3$ eV/Å) upon metal films have provided other evidence for delocalization of the *effects* of energy imparted to electrons in systems showing long-range order (88–91). Fission fragments incident on metal films with thicknesses 50–500 Å, i.e., less than the range of fission fragments in the metal, lose energy predominantly via electronic excitations because energy loss by momentum transfer is only important toward the end of the tracks (91). Kelsch, Goland, and Paskin studied palladium films which had resistivities and regions of long-range order similar to those of bulk metal (88). They failed to find any evidence for physical changes caused in such films by fission fragment irradiation. With metal films of small grain size they reproduced the observations of earlier workers that, for film thicknesses of 25–50 Å, fission fragment irradiation produced numerous holes observable by the electron microscope (88,89). The holes have been attributed to evaporation of metal atoms from small crystallites along the high LET tracks of the fission fragments. Goland and co-workers have pointed out that energy imparted to electrons of a small crystallite may be confined to that crystallite by reflection of energetic electrons from the grain boundaries (90,91). Evaporation of metal atoms from a small crystallite follows from conversion of the electron energy into thermal motion of the atoms. The later experimental findings of Kelsch, Goland, and Paskin, showing that tracks could not be produced in films possessing a degree of long-range order, have been interpreted in terms of the electronic energy being rapidly transported away from the sites of energy deposition (88,92).

Collinson, Conlay, and Dainton concluded from their studies on organic systems doped with $FeCl_3$ and irradiated in the glassy or poly-crystalline states (93) that long-range order greatly increased migration of electronic excitation away from sites of energy deposition. However, the observed LET dependence of the radiolyses of ionic solids (e.g., Table VII), shows that energy cannot be regarded as completely delocalized. Such data require that processes occurring during migration of energy away from sites of energy deposition affect bond rupture or formation. Models used to account for the LET dependence of radiolysis, and effects

TABLE VII
Dose and LET Dependence of Radiolysis of Nitrates and NaN$_3$

Radiation			G values reported at 300°K					
			Doses^b 0.1–0.8 eV/ion pair			Doses^b > 1 eV/ion pair		
Type	$D_e/D_m{}^a$	LET (eV/Å)	NaN$_3$	NaNO$_3$	KNO$_3$	NaNO$_3$	KNO$_3$	NaN$_3$
Co^{60} γ-rays	~99	0.06	0.47	0.2	1.45	0.11	0.95	0.47
45 kV x-rays	~99	0.8	2.1	0.37	1.96	—	1.4	—
^{14}N$(n, p)^{14}$C	~14	13	—	—	—	0.33 ± 0.16	3.9 ± 0.6	0.7 ± 0.4
3.4 MeV α	~99	34	—	—	—	1.3	2.2	—
Fission fragments	~19	730	—	—	—	—	6	—
2 keV D$^+$	~ 0.2	3	—	1.8	2.0	1.3	1.5	—
10 keV He$^+$	~ 0.5	3	—	—	—	1.3	2.2	—
End of f.f. track	~ 0.2	10^3	—	—	—	—	5 (or 9)	—

^{a} D_e/D_m = ratio of energy deposited by electronic processes to that by momentum transfer.
^{b} Total dose in sample volume actually reached by radiation.

upon them of energy migration through ordered lattices, are considered in the following paragraphs.

B. Influence of Ordered Crystal Structure on LET Models

"Diffusion" models or "spike" models have been applied to explain the LET dependence of radiolysis (71,94,95). Diffusion models equate the initial spatial distribution of primary excited and ionized species with that of the spurs or tracks representing energy-loss events. Kinetic descriptions are given of reactions between these species or between radicals as they diffuse outward during expansion of the spurs or tracks (70,71,94). Spike models consider that at high LET some part of the radiation-deposited energy is converted along the track into displacements or into thermal agitation resembling heat (95). Thermal spike models consider that the "effective temperature" in regions close to the site of energy deposition are raised sufficiently to affect bond rupture or formation in that region (96). Displacement spike models, which were primarily developed to account for radiation effects in metals, consider the consequences of atoms being ejected from lattice positions close to the center of the track (97).

1. Diffusion Models

Kinetic treatments based on diffusion models have been applied to radiation-activated species, X^*, where X^* can represent primary excited (98) or ionized species, or radicals formed by bond rupture after ion–electron recombination (70,94). The LET dependence arises from increased occurrence at high LET of second-order reactions between radiation-activated species (7) at the expense of processes involving only one radiation-activated species and normal molecules or ions in the system, (8).

$$X^* + X^* \rightsquigarrow X^*\!-\!X^* \longrightarrow \text{Products} \tag{7}$$

$$X^* + M \rightsquigarrow \longrightarrow \text{Products} \tag{8}$$

Evidence presented above (Section III-A) indicated slow ion–electron recombination in ionic solids with polyatomic ions, hence it is reasonable to consider that LET effects in such solids arise from reaction 7 between primary excited species. The LET dependence of the radiolyses of crystalline nitrates are qualitatively in accord with the requirements of this diffusion model. Thus, first-order kinetics have been reported for the LET radiolyses of various nitrates and $G_{NO_2^-}$ values taken from these studies are listed in Table I. They have been interpreted (8) as representing approximately the relative efficiencies for decomposition of nitrate ions in different lattices by type 8 reactions (with M representing near-neighbor ions which modify excited state dissociation). Efficiencies of reaction 8 are thus indicated to be very low in $LiNO_3$, low in $NaNO_3$, but high in KNO_3 or $CsNO_3$; other nitrates have intermediate values. Increasing LET to 34 eV/Å by using 3.4 MeV α particles places reaction 7 between excited nitrate ions into competition with reaction 8. Greater efficiencies of type 8 processes are expected in the close-packed structures of $LiNO_3$ or $NaNO_3$ than in the more open structures of KNO_3 or $CsNO_3$. On changing from γ to α irradiation, the qualitative prediction of the diffusion model is that the overall efficiency of radiolysis, $G_{NO_2^-}$, for $LiNO_3$ and $NaNO_3$ should show a greater *increase* than for KNO_3 or $CsNO_3$. The $G_{NO_2^-}$ values obtained with 3.4 MeV α particles for $LiNO_3$, $NaNO_3$, KNO_3, and $CsNO_3$ were, respectively, 25, 6.5, 1.5, and 0.8 times the values measured with γ-rays (Table VII).

It is expected that products of type 7 second-order reactions between excited or radical species would be formed *closer* to the axis of high LET tracks than products of type 8 reactions. Radical pairs produced by reactions of type 8 appear to have been detected by ESR studies on dimethylglyoxime crystals x-irradiated at 77°K (83). Products with chemical identity and spatial distribution consistent only with process 7 appear not yet to have been detected in ionic crystals irradiated at high LET. Several factors operate against their detection by ESR techniques; these include the high probability of nonradical products and the severe broadening of the ESR spectra of any radicals formed in close proximity along high LET tracks.

2. Thermal Spike Models

Occurrence of efficient mechanisms for transport of electronic excitation away from the site of energy deposition reduces the probable importance of thermal spike effects by reducing the probability for conversion of electronic to thermal energies close to the axis of the track. Hochanadel has argued, however, that the increases in efficiency of radiolyses of several crystalline nitrates or sodium chlorate, on changing from low LET γ-rays to high LET α irradiation, may be accounted for by higher effective temperatures along α-particle tracks (99,100).

For sodium chlorate previous work showed that the yield of chloride ion in γ-ray decomposition was about doubled by postirradiation annealing for several hours at 185–210°C (101). With high LET α particles, Hochanadel measured at 25°C a chloride yield, $G(Cl^-) = 2.12$, much larger than $G(Cl^-) = 1.50$ for γ-rays at the same temperature (100). Gamma irradiation at 185°C gave $G(Cl^-) = 2.3$, and post irradiation annealing at 185°C of samples γ-irradiated at 25°C gave $G(Cl^-) = 1.92$. These chloride yields are *similar to the α-particle value at 25°C*. Hochanadel argued that the similarity indicated higher effective temperatures, i.e., thermal spikes, along the α-particle tracks. He also compared the temperature and LET dependence of the total product yield from alkali metal nitrates and again noted that similar increases could be produced by increasing LET *or* by raising the temperature during low LET irradiation. However, the temperature dependence of the γ radiolysis of nitrates at the decomposition relevant to Hochanadel's studies has its origin in the activation energy for diffusion of fragments through the lattice (102). The relevance of such diffusion with jump frequencies 10^2 to 10^{-2} sec^{-1} to thermal spike processes of duration of 10^{-10} sec is not readily apparent.

Critical examination of available experimental data on the chemical identity of product species at high LET also fail to support the thermal spike mechanism. Thus, Boyd and co-workers have investigated in great detail the decompositions of alkali and alkaline earth metal bromates at different temperatures and with radiations of varying LET (103–106). Studies with low LET γ-rays enabled these workers to establish a reasonable and self-consistent description of the distribution of the total radiolytic products between fragments containing bromine in various states of oxidation (105). Thus, radiolysis at or above 300°C gave only bromide ion and oxygen. At lower temperatures increasing amounts of "oxidizing fragments," such as hypobromite, bromite, and bromine species with higher oxidation numbers, were formed and the amounts of Br$^-$ and $O_2(g)$ were decreased. Detailed kinetic studies on the growth of the bromine–oxygen fragments established that, as the temperature of radiation was raised above room temperature, "oxidizing" fragments were either thermally decomposed to bromide ion and oxygen gas, or caused to recombine and reform bromate ions. If thermal spike mechanisms were operating during radiolysis at high LET, it would be expected that the proportion of the "oxidizing", bromine–oxygen fragments would be greatly reduced relative to the bromide ion yield. The radiolysis of lithium bromate at high LET was studied (106) by exposing material enriched in ^{6}Li to thermal neutrons to produce the nuclear transformation ^{6}Li$(n,\alpha)^3$H. The α particles recoiling from this transformation would have LET = 34.7 eV/Å and the tritons a value of 9.4 eV/Å. Initial 100 eV yields were $G(-\mathrm{BrO}_3) = 1.48$, $G(\text{"Ox"}) = 1.1$, $G(\mathrm{Br}) = 0.38$, for this high LET. Values found with γ-rays of LET ca. 0.1 eV/Å, were 0.31, 0.21, and 0.10, respectively, so that high LET did increase the total efficiency for radiolysis of the bromate ion by a factor of 5. However, the yields for the thermally sensitive "oxidizing" fragments were increased by the same factor as the thermally stable bromide ion yields.

Another result which does not appear to be consistent with a thermal spike mechanism is that no additional increase in rate of radiolysis attributable to thermal spikes is observed when the effect of an equal increase in LET is compared for thermally sensitive sodium azide and thermally more stable $NaNO_3$ (102) (cf. Table VII).

3. Displacement Spike Models

Brinkman has described a displacement spike model for the effects of high LET particles which transfer momentum to metal atoms (97). Atoms are represented as being ejected into interstitial positions some distance from the track axis. Vacancies remain concentrated close to the track axis. The effects of high LET-charged particles upon single crystals of silver chloride (107) can be interpreted in terms of such a model. Tracks are not directly visible in AgCl after passage of the charged particles but are revealed by subsequent treatments which cause photoelectrons and silver to migrate to imperfections concentrated along particle tracks.

An ordered lattice can facilitate the formation of separated vacancies and interstitials by mechanisms which have been elaborated from studies of radiation damage in metals (95). A lattice atom to which kinetic energy is imparted by irradiation can be transported through a metal lattice by dynamic crowdion and channelon mechanisms. The former produces an interstitial and vacancy separated by n lattice atoms, where n represents a number of lattice atoms each of which was moved one lattice spacing by focused replacements. A channelon denotes movement of a displaced atom along a crystallographic direction in which it suffers minimum collisional energy loss. Focused collisions can occur at low atom energies (ca. 30 eV). Channelling becomes important at higher energies. Both mechanisms should be of low efficiency in ionic lattices, especially in those consisting of ions of widely different masses.

For most types of ionizing radiation, energy is initially deposited predominantly via electronic excitation, D_e. Energy initially imparted to lattice atoms as momentum, D_m, generally represents less than 1% of the total absorbed energy (108) (see values of D_e/D_m in Table VII). The possibility of frequently displacing lattice species by radiation energy is not, however, restricted to those with a high energy loss by D_m. It has been realized in recent years that Auger processes may provide mechanisms by which D_e can be converted, in part, into kinetic energy of parent or fragment ions (109). Briefly, this results when outer-shell electrons fill a radiation-induced "hole" in an inner shell and initiate a cascade process leading to multiple ionization. Multiply ionized molecular species can dissociate into fragments with like charge which repel one another (110). Displacement of a lattice anion with high kinetic energy can also arise in ionic solids when electrostatic repulsion by near-neighbor cations ejects multiply ionized anions from their lattice sites (111,112).

Studies on alkali halides with low LET radiations have demonstrated occurrence of such displacements (54,84,112). Thus, anion vacancies (evident in appearance of α and F bands) and interstitial chlorine (evident in growth of the H-center band) form in greater numbers in KCl x-irradiated at $4.2°K$ than predicted by the low cross section for direct displacement by D_m (112). Production of close pairs of vacancies and interstitials in KBr irradiated with x-rays at temperatures below $20°K$ have also been reported (84). Itoh, Royce, and Smoluchowski have studied the recombination of Frenkel pairs in x-irradiated KBr and identified processes with activation energies of 0.015, 0.03, and 0.04 eV. These they identified with correlated recombinations of close pairs of vacancies and interstitials produced by x-irradiation with configurations strictly controlled by the crystal lattice. These results show that sites of energy deposition in ionic solids may be "marked" after irradiation by occurrence of vacancies thereon.

Probable effects of such vacancies, or clusters of vacancies, upon radiolysis are limited to provision of new electron and hole trapping sites [recall the effects in single crystals of AgCl exposed to high LET-charged particles (107)]. Energetic displacement of monatomic ions in simple ionic lattices can result in recognizable new chemical species, such as F_3^{2-} in LiF (85) or Cl_4^{3-} in KCl irradiated at $4.2°K$ (54). Lattice displacement of polyatomic ions, such as nitrate or carbonate, appears less probable than dissociation into fragments, which is the fate of multiply ionized molecular species in the gas phase (110). The chemical consequences of displacement spike models may therefore be indistinguishable from those of other models except in ionic lattices with monatomic ions.

IV. SUMMARY

The need to distinguish clearly between primary and secondary species formed by radiation is illustrated by data on radiation effects in crystalline nitrates. In studying the nature and mechanism of formation of primary radical species, it is necessary to distinguish carefully between energy localization at trapping sites existing prior to irradiation and energy localization at trapping sites generated by irradiation. Trapping at radiation-produced fragments accounts for a large proportion of the reported radiation damage in inorganic crystals. ESR signals which have been widely assigned to NO_3^{2-} radicals upon normal lattice sites pose the problem of identifying a mechanism for localizing the extra electron upon one of an array of identical nitrate ions. A mechanism based on trapping at nitrate ions temporarily distorted by radiation-induced intramolecular configuration change is discussed. It appears to be consistent with reported results for the stability of NO_3^{2-}, NO_3, CO_3^{3-}, and CO_3^{-} radicals. The mechanism must remain tentative until uncertainties in the assignments of ESR data to these radicals are finally resolved and trapping sites are unambiguously identified.

Studies of the spatial distribution of primary radicals, such as CO_3^{3-} in calcite, have failed to provide conclusive evidence that they are located according to the predictions of energy-loss models. Evidence for rapid transport of electronic energy away from the site of energy deposition in solids possessing long-range order is discussed. Rapid transport of electronic energy away from the site of energy deposition reduces the probable importance of thermal spikes in the formation of products at high LET. Diffusion models based on second-order interactions between excited ions at high LET are affected to lesser extent by long-range order. The chemical consequences of the displacement spike model are difficult to observe but this model provides the most probable mechanisms for track imaging even with low LET radiation.

References

1. L. K. Narayanswamy, *Trans. Faraday Soc.*, **31**, 1411 (1935).
2. J. Doigan and T. W. Davis, *J. Phys. Chem.*, **56**, 764 (1952).
3. A. O. Allen and P. Chormley, *J. Chem. Phys.*, **15**, 208 (1947).
4. H. G. Heal and J. Cunningham, *Nature*, **179**, 1021 (1957).
5. H. G. Heal and J. Cunningham, *Trans. Faraday Soc.*, **56**, 1355 (1958).
6. M. B. Shinn, *Ind. Eng. Chem. (Intern. Ed.)*, **13**, 33 (1941).
7. G. Hennig, R. Lees, and M. Matheson, *J. Chem. Phys.*, **21**, 664 (1953).
8. J. Cunningham, *J. Phys. Chem.*, **65**, 628 (1961).
9. G. E. Boyd, E. W. Graham, and Q. V. Larson, *J. Phys. Chem.*, **66**, 300 (1962).
10. L. A. Prince and E. R. Johnson, *J. Phys. Chem.*, **69**, 359 (1965).
11. D. W. James, in *Vibrational Spectra of Molten Salts ORN L—3413, July, 1963*.
12. E. V. Sayre, *J. Chem. Phys.*, **31**, 73 (1959).
13. J. Cunningham, *J. Phys. Chem.*, **67**, 1772 (1963).
14. H. R. Hunt, J. R. Cox, and J. D. Ray, *Inorg. Chem.*, **1**, 938 (1962).
15. P. Pringsheim, *J. Chem. Phys.*, **23**, 369 (1955).
16. Yu. A. Kulyupin and A. F. Yatsenko, *Fiz. Tver. Tela*, **5**, 3334 (1963). See also Report AD.604.341 as (TT64 71236).
17. E. R. Johnson and J. Forten, *Discussions Faraday Soc.*, **31**, 238 (1962).
18. J. Cunningham, *J. Phys. Chem.*, **66**, 779 (1962).
19. J. Cunningham, *J. Phys. Chem. Solids*, **23**, 843 (1962).
20. W. Känzig and M. H. Cohen, *Phys. Rev. Letters*, **3**, 509 (1959).
21. K. Geshi and Y. Kazumata, *Nippon Genshiryoku Kenkyusho, Shiryo Hokoku*, **1965**, 2054.
22. H. Zeldes in *Paramagnetic Resonance*, W. Low, Ed., Academic Press, New York, 1963, pp. 764–784.
23. H. Zeldes and R. Livingston, *J. Chem. Phys.*, **37**, 3017 (1962).
24. R. Livingston and H. Zeldes, *J. Chem. Phys.*, **41**, 4011 (1964).
25. M. C. R. Symons, *Advan. Chem. Ser.*, **36**, 76 (1962).
26. C. Jaccard, *Phys. Rev.*, **124**, 60 (1961).

27. K. Ždánský and Z. Šroubek, *Phys. Status Solidi (Czech.)*, **7**, 167 (1964).
28. W. C. Mosley and W. G. Moulton, *J. Chem. Phys.*, **43**, 1207 (1965).
29. T. Asada, R. Kikuchi, T. Nogaito, and K. Tagaya, *Mem. Inst. Sci. Ind. Res. Osaka Univ.*, **22**, 67, 73, 81 (1965).
30. D. Mergerian and S. A. Marshall, *Phys. Rev.*, **127**, 2015 (1962).
31. J. Cunningham, *J. Phys. Chem.*, **71**, 1967 (1967).
32. J. Cunningham, *J. Phys. Chem.*, **70**, 30 (1966).
33. T. H. Chen and E. R. Johnson, *J. Phys. Chem.*, **66**, 2068 (1962).
34. J. Cunningham, *Trans. Faraday Soc.*, **62**, 2423 (1966).
35. G. L. Petriconi and H. M. Papee, *Can. J. Chem.*, **44**, 977 (1966).
36. M. L. Hyder, *J. Phys. Chem.*, **64**, 1858 (1965).
37. H. A. Mahlman, *J. Inorg. Nucl. Chem.*, **5**, 213 (1957).
38. W. H. Hamill, J. P. Guarino, M. R. Ronayne, and J. A. Ward, *Discussions Faraday Soc.*, **36**, 169 (1964).
39. J. B. Gallivan and W. H. Hamill, *J. Chem. Phys.*, **44**, 1274 (1966).
40. L. Kevan, *Prog. Solid State Chem.*, **2**, 304 (1965).
41. E. Hutchinson and P. Pringsheim, *J. Chem. Phys.*, **23**, 1113 (1955).
42. C. J. Delbecq, W. Hayes, M. C. M. O'Brien, and P. H. Yuster, *Proc. Roy. Soc. (London), Ser. A*, **271**, 243 (1963).
43. A. R. Jones, *J. Chem. Phys.*, **35**, 751 (1961).
44. J. Cunningham, *J. Chem. Phys.*, **41**, 3522 (1964).
45. G. Feher, *Phys. Rev.*, **105**, 1122 (1957).
46. T. G. Castner, W. Känzig, and T. O. Woodruff, *Nuovo Cimento, Suppl.*, **8**, 612 (1958).
47. R. Cook and J. Cunningham *Trans. Faraday Soc.* (in press).
48. R. M. Golding and M. Henchman, *J. Chem. Phys.*, **40**, 1554 (1964).
49. R. Cook and D. Whiffen (in press).
50. R. Addé, *Compt. Rend.*, **260**, 2781 (1965).
51. R. Addé, *Compt. Rend.*, **261**, 685 (1965).
52. J. Tatero and K. Ueshi, *J. Chem. Phys.*, **40**, 1317 (1964).
53. N. M. Atherton, R. N. Dixon, and G. H. Kirby, *Nature*, **206**, 83 (1965).
54. J. H. Shulman and W. D. Compton, *Color Centers in Solids*, Pergamon Press, Oxford, 1962.
55. H. Zeldes and R. Livingston, *J. Chem. Phys.*, **35**, 563 (1961).
56. R. A. Serway, Ph.D. dissertation, Illinois Institute of Technology, 1966. See also with S. Marshall, Report IITRI-A6074 from IIT Research Institute, March, 1965.
57. J. R. Morton and V. V. Gromov, *Can. J. Chem.*, **44**, 527 (1966).
58. T. Cole, *J. Chem. Phys.*, **35**, 1169 (1961); also J. R. Morton, *J. Chem. Phys.*, **45**, 1800 (1966).
59. D. M. Yost and H. Russel, Jr., *Systematic Inorganic Chemistry*, Prentice-Hall, New York, 1944, pp. 52–58.
60. T. L. Cottrell and I. C. Walker, *Quart. Rev. (London)*, **20**, 153 (1966).
61. A. D. Walsh, *J. Chem. Soc.*, **1953**, 2266.
62. T. J. Schaafsma and J. Kommandeur, *J. Chem. Phys.*, **42**, 438 (1965).
63. H. Y. Sun and S. A. Rice, *J. Chem. Phys.*, **42**, 3826 (1965).
64. S. A. Marshall, A. R. Reinberg, R. A. Serway, and J. A. Hodges, *Mol. Phys.*, **8**, 225 (1964).
65. Y. Asano, T. Okuno, S. Uranishi, N. Takeuchi, F. Akao, and M. Ishiguro, *Mem. Inst. Sci. Ind. Res., Osaka Univ.*, **22**, 73 (1965).

66. H. Ruchardt, *Phys. Rev.*, **103**, 873 (1956).
67. J. E. Wertz, P. Auzins, R. A. Weeks, and R. A. Silsbee, *Phys. Rev.*, **107**, 1535 (1957); see also H. Schulman, *Luminescence Dosimetry*, F. H. Attix, Ed., USAEC, 1967.
68. L. Shields, *Trans. Faraday Soc.*, **62**, 1042 (1966).
69. J. Cunningham, *J. Am. Chem. Soc.*, **85**, 3716 (1963).
70. A. O. Allen, *Radiation Chemistry of Water and Aqueous Solutions*, Van Nostrand, London, 1961.
71. W. G. Burns and R. Barker, in *Progress in Reaction Kinetics*, Vol. 3, Pergamon Press, Oxford, 1965, pp. 305–365.
72. H. A. Schwarz, *Ann. Rev. Phys. Chem.*, **16**, 347 (1965).
73. A. H. Samuel and J. L. Magee, *J. Chem. Phys.*, **21**, 1080 (1953).
74. A. K. Ganguly and J. L. Magee, *J. Chem. Phys.*, **25**, 129 (1956).
75. A. Mozumder and J. L. Magee, *Radiation Res.*, **28**, 203 (1966).
76. J. L. Magee, *Discussions Faraday Soc.*, **36**, 233 (1963).
77. A. O. Allen and A. Hummel, *Discussions Faraday Soc.*, **36**, 95 (1963).
78. G. R. Freeman, *J. Chem. Phys.*, **39**, 988 (1963).
79. J. L. Magee, *Ann. Rev. Phys. Chem.*, **12**, 389 (1961).
80. M. Burton, M. Dillon, and R. Rein, *J. Chem. Phys.*, **41**, 2228 (1964).
81. K. C. McEwen, *J. Chem. Phys.*, **34**, 547 (1961).
82. R. C. Smith and S. J. Wyard, *Nature*, **191**, 897 (1961).
83. Y. Kurita and M. Kashiwagi, *J. Chem. Phys.*, **44**, 1727 (1966).
84. N. Itoh, B. S. H. Royce, and R. Smoluchowski, *Phys. Rev.*, **A137**, 1010 (1965).
85. J. R. Morton, *Chem. Rev.*, **64**, 453 (1964).
86. S. J. Wyard, *Proc. Phys. Soc. (London)*, **86**, 587 (1965).
87. S. J. Wyard, Paper presented Radiation Research Society meeting, Florida, May, 1964 (see also report UCRL 11387, 1964).
88. T. S. Noggle and J. O. Stiegler, *J. Appl. Phys.*, **33**, 1726 (1962).
89. J. J. Kelsch, A. N. Goland, and A. Paskin, *J. Phys. Chem. Solids*, **26**, 203 (1965).
90. J. J. Kelsch, O. Kammerer, A. N. Goland, and P. Bahl, *J. Appl. Phys.*, **33**, 1475 (1962).
91. J. Ozeroff, *U.S. At. Energy Comm. AECD-2973* (unpublished).
92. K. L. Merkle, *Phys. Rev. Letters*, **9**, 150 (1962).
93. E. Collinson, J. J. Conlay, and F. S. Dainton, *Discussions Faraday Soc.*, **36**, 153 (1963).
94. A. Kuppermann, in *The Chemical and Biological Action of Radiations*, M. Haissinsky, Ed., Vol. 5, Academic Press, New York, 1961, pp. 89–166.
95. L. T. Chadderton, in *Radiation Damage in Crystals*, Wiley, New York, 1965.
96. J. Y. Yang, J. D. Strong, and J. G. Burr, *Abstr. Meeting Am. Chem. Soc., 148th Chicago, 1964*; see also *J. Phys. Chem.*, **69**, 1157 (1965).
97. J. A. Brinkman, *J. Appl. Phys.*, **25**, 961 (1953).
98. W. G. Burns and J. A. Winter, *Discussions Faraday Soc.*, **36**, 124 (1963).
99. C. J. Hochanadel, *Radiation Res.*, **16**, 286 (1962).
100. C. J. Hochanadel, *J. Phys. Chem.*, **67**, 2229 (1963).
101. P. F. Patrick and K. J. McCallum, *Nature*, **194**, 776 (1962).
102. J. Cunningham, *Trans. Faraday Soc.*, **62**, 2423 (1966).
103. G. E. Boyd and Q. V. Larson, *J. Phys. Chem.*, **68**, 2627 (1964).
104. J. W. Chase and G. E. Boyd, *J. Phys. Chem.*, **70**, 1031 (1966).
105. J. W. Chase and G. E. Boyd, "Effects of High Radiation on Inorganic Substances," ASTM publication, No. 400, 1966.

106. G. E. Boyd, E. W. Graham, and Q. V. Larson, *J. Phys. Chem.*, **66**, 300 (1962).
107. C. B. Childs and L. M. Slifkin, *Rev. Sci. Instr.*, **34**, 101 (1963).
108. W. B. Price, in *Nuclear Radiation Detection*, 2nd ed., McGraw-Hill, New York, 1965.
109. J. Durup and R. L. Platzman, *Discussions Faraday Soc.*, **31**, 156 (1961).
110. T. Carlson and R. White, *Symp. Chem. Effects Associated Nucl. Reactions Radioactive Transformations, Vienna, 1964*; IAEA (CONF-773-12).
111. J. H. O. Varley, *Phys. Chem. Solids*, **23**, 985 (1962).
112. C. C. Klick, *Phys. Rev.*, **120**, 760 (1960).

CHAPTER 12

Trapped Radicals in Inorganic Glasses

A. Treinin

*Department of Physical Chemistry, The Hebrew University,
Jerusalem, Israel*

I. INTRODUCTION

A. General

The matrix isolation method has led to an extensive study of low temperature glasses. Special techniques were developed for preparing and handling frozen solutions of the appropriate compositions. Organic solvents and their mixtures have usually been employed as matrix material at 77°K.

The increasing interest in inorganic glasses for this purpose has been stimulated by (1) the convenience of using room temperature glasses which are much more simple to handle than the low temperature ones; (2) the need for polar media suitable for studying radical production from ionic systems; and (3) the recognition that solarization processes and color centers in ordinary commercial glasses often involve trapped radicals.

Low melting inorganic glasses have long been used for studying the luminescence of complex molecules. [Some references to early works are given by Kasha (1).] Boric acid glass, in particular, has been employed for this purpose; the classical work on the triplet state of fluorescein was carried out with this matrix (2). But only in 1955 did Evans (3) present the first evidence for radical formation and trapping in boric acid glass. Thin layers of the glass can be prepared sandwiched between silica disks that transmit light down to 160 mμ (4), which much extends the possibility of radical detection. The relatively low temperature required for making this glass (240°C) makes it available for studying organic compounds, which are not sensitive to thermal decomposition. It was also found to dissolve various inorganic salts and this has initiated its use for trapping inorganic radicals at room temperature (5). Since most electrolytes can withstand higher temperatures, the use of other glasses for this purpose, including ordinary ones, has also been developed.

The need for polar matrices has led to research of frozen aqueous solutions, in both the polycrystalline and the glassy states. This research was initiated by the work of Livingston, Zeldes, and Taylor (6), who detected hydrogen atoms in γ-irradiated mineral acid solutions at 77°K. An extensive study of other radicals in these matrices has been carried out by Weiss et al. and Dainton et al. (Section V). Frozen alkali matrices were introduced by the works of Schulte-Frohlinde and Eiben (7) and of Jortner and Sharf (8). Direct evidence for photoionization processes could thus be presented. From the chemical point of view these inorganic glasses are related to the ordinary oxide glasses. Thus, glassy phosphoric acid, the binary system of H_2O and P_2O_5, shows evidence for the existence of polymer chains (Section II-A-3). Moreover, on γ-irradiation it displays optical and ESR spectra which closely resemble those induced by irradiation in ordinary phosphate glasses (Section IV-B).

Radical trapping processes in ordinary glasses are commonly encountered though often not correctly interpreted. It has been known for a long time that glasses change color when subjected to sunlight. This photochemical process is called *solarization*. The history of the study on solarization until 1951 is summarized in Weyl's book *Coloured Glasses* (9), which is the most comprehensive monograph on the optical properties of glasses. (The book is somewhat out of date but still very valuable.) Weyl described solarization as a chemical oxidation–reduction equilibrium between impurity ions. In a few cases free radicals were postulated as participants in the solarization process (e.g., silver atoms in photosensitive glasses) but in many cases the chemical equations used to describe the process involved stable molecular species and changes of valence state which are not likely to occur in one stage (e.g., the conversion of Ag^{2+} to Ag^0). Improved methods of preparing glasses with controlled impurity addition provided the basis for clearer understanding of solarization, and its relation to color centers in glasses became evident.

Much work has been done on the coloration of glasses induced by high energy radiation. The theory of coloration followed closely that of color centers in crystals: trapped electrons and holes were considered to be involved. Doping the glasses with various impurities, especially transition ions, has been shown to have a remarkable effect on the coloration. The impurities were considered to act in one of the following ways: (*1*) scavenging the charge carriers and thus undergoing change in valence state; (*2*) formation of new defects in their surroundings; and (*3*) modification of existing defects, such as those responsible for the induced absorptions in the pure glasses. Investigators in this field can be divided into two schools according to their emphasizing the direct (*1*) or the indirect (*2* and *3*) effects. Much obscurity was caused by the too close analogy drawn between the centers in crystals and glasses (this led, for example, to *a priori* assignment of visible color centers to trapped electrons) and the lack of information concerning the properties of unstable valence states. It was in this connection that the works of Stroud et al. and of Baxendale et al. gave the research a strong impetus. The former developed methods for classifying the color centers in the pure base glass (Section IV-A) and the latter used pulse radiolysis technique to record the spectra of various cations in abnormal valence states (Section V). The great progress in the field of electron spin resonance had a tremendous influence on the study of color centers and trapped free radicals in glasses. The paramagnetic resonance spectra of many radicals were measured in various media and together with the corresponding optical spectra opened the way toward rationalization of basic processes which occur in either pure or doped glasses. However, much has still to be done. For the sake of illustration, it was shown that a few unstable monovalent ions (Cd^+, Ni^+, Mn^+, Zn^+, Pb^+, etc.) absorb strongly around 300 mμ (Section V). The considerable loss of UV transmission of commercial glasses in sunlight (9) may be due to the photochemical production of such radicals at tiny concentrations. The so-called regeneration of solarized glasses by heat treatment may simply involve the annihilation of these radicals.

B. Scope

Radicals trapped in inorganic glasses are the subject of this review. Low and room temperature glasses are described since many radicals have been investigated in both kinds of media. The discussion of frozen aqueous solutions also includes polycrystalline samples, because in many cases the ESR spectra of the radicals were measured in polycrystalline ice whereas the corresponding mineral acid glasses were used for recording the optical spectra. As for the term "radical," it is so used as to encompass transition group ions which are not stable in aqueous solution, e.g., Ag^{2+}.

Sections II and III deal, respectively, with the vitreous state and with production of trapped radicals and their detection. These subjects have been already reviewed at length, so only brief surveys of some pertinent topics, are given with special references to the glasses that are frequently mentioned later. (Very useful reviews on the vitreous state are included in J. D. Mackenzie, Ed., *Modern Aspects of the Vitreous State*, Volumes 1, 2, and 3, Butterworths, London, 1960, 1962, 1964.) Radical formation and trapping in the solid state is discussed by Pimentel (10) and electron spin resonance of trapped radicals by Jen (11). Section IV deals with radiation-induced color centers in pure glasses and this not only because they directly involve radicals, but because their study is closely related to that of radicals trapped in the doped glass. Thus, the suppression of one center relative to the other or the appearance of only one center (either the "electron" or "hole" center) often indicates the formation of a new radical and provides information about its identity. For example, from the suppression of the electron center in a glass doped with Cd^{2+} or Pb^{2+} one may infer the formation of Cd^+ or Pb^+. However, this reasoning may be misleading and should be supported by other pieces of evidence. The last two sections review the information obtained on inorganic (Section V) and organic (Section VI) radicals. Radicals, such as H, OH, O^-, etc., are only mentioned when necessary, since pertinent reviews are included elsewhere (12,13).

II. STRUCTURE AND PROPERTIES OF GLASSES

A glass is an isotropic material having no long-range order with viscosity greater than about 10^{14} poise (14). Liquids which have high viscosity at the liquidus temperature are expected to form a glass. The transition from the supercooled liquid to the glass resembles (and may be identical to) a second-order phase transition (15). The temperature *range* in which it occurs is called the *transformation region* or simply the transition temperature.

A. Structure

The best-known model for the structure of glasses is the *random network* model proposed by Zachariasen in 1932 (16). According to this model the glass has structural units similar to that of the corresponding crystal but with no long-range order. For example, crystalline and vitreous silica both contain SiO_4 tetrahedra, but in the glass the Si–O bond angles slightly vary, giving rise to a random network with cavities of varying size. Silicon atom is the *network former* and each oxygen atom is a so-called *bridging oxygen*, since it is linked to two silicon atoms. Incorporation of a basic oxide such as Na_2O into the glass leads to rupture of Si–O bonds and formation of *nonbridging oxygen* atoms, each with a net charge of e^-. (In the case of vitreous B_2O_3, the addition of basic oxide up to a certain concentration does not produce nonbridging oxygens, but changes the coordination from triangular to tetrahedral.) The negative charges are normally neutralized by cations (e.g., Na^+), the so-called *network modifiers*, which are situated in adjacent cavities (interstices). Altogether the structure becomes more open, Stevels and Kats (17) consider these changes as imperfections in the network of silica. The combination of nonbridging oxygens and interstitial cations, denoted by D, is the most common imperfection. (There are other kinds of imperfections which will not be considered here.) With increase in the concentration of the basic oxide, the network becomes more open and looser, the nonbridging oxygens become more separated from each other and highly irregular networks may be formed. Ordinary oxide glass contains a large concentration of such imperfections and therefore the glass can incorporate small amounts of impurities without any basic alteration of its structure. For this reason, the effects of impurities on the radiation-induced coloration are probably more of a direct nature (i.e., trapping of electrons and holes) than in crystals, where the concentration of crystal defects is relatively largely affected by doping with foreign ions.

The model of Zachariasen pictures three-dimensional *continuity* of the random network. This cannot be the case at high concentrations of the metal oxide and so the model has been severely criticized. More flexible models are now in use. They stress the relation of the glass to the liquid more than to the crystal. Various kinds of aggregates are taken into account with relative amounts being dependent on the glass composition. The differences between different types of glasses are more emphasized and different models are accordingly given. However, some of the concepts and conclusions mentioned above are still of great importance. A description of some glasses with which this review is most concerned follows.

1. Phosphate Glasses

In these glasses phosphorus is the network former and alkali or alkaline earth ions are the network modifiers. Their structure depends on the ratio M_2O (or MO)/P_2O_5, which is usually $\geqslant 1$. The present view is that phosphate glasses containing 50–60 mole % of metal oxides are mixtures of small rings and chains of varying lengths, the relative amounts being dependent on the composition. From 60 to over 70% only chains are present (14). The chief representative of this group is Graham's salt.* It is prepared from a melt of NaH_2PO_4 (mp 620°C) by quenching. Apart from the linear polyphosphate chains, Graham's salt always contains cyclic phosphates: trimeta- (6–10%), and tetrametaphosphate (up to $\sim 4\%$) and very small amounts of larger rings. The chain length distribution depends on the melting conditions. Equilibrium is attained slowly (after 24 hr at 650°C) and the mean chain length $\bar{n}$ being greater the higher the temperature used in the preparation and the lower the water vapor pressure in the surrounding atmosphere, P_w. By the following expression $\bar{n}$ (at equilibrium) may be calculated within $\pm 5\%$:

$$\bar{n} = \exp (8.87 - 5100/RT - \tfrac{1}{2} \ln P_w) \qquad (1)$$

with P_w in torr. The hydrolysis of the glass at room temperature is rather

* The following description is adapted from the review of Thilo (18).

slow so aqueous solutions can be prepared containing the same polymer units as in the glass.

The melt of Graham's salt readily dissolves various electrolytes and therefore this glass is a convenient matrix for study of trapped radicals. In routine work the melting is carried out in a platinum crucible; disks can be prepared by pressing drops of melt between two slabs of glazed porcelain until they cool down to room temperature. In the following sections the name "metaphosphate (MP) glass" will be used although the term metaphosphate is now used to denote only the cyclic phosphates.

In aluminophosphates, aluminum acts as a network former: the network is formed by interlinking of AlO_4 and PO_4 groups by bridging oxygens.

2. Boric Acid Glasses

The boric acid glass prepared by the method suggested by Kasha (1) has the composition $B_2O_3 \cdot \frac{2}{3}H_2O$, approximately. Other compositions can be obtained under properly regulated conditions (19). Milberg et al. (19,20) have examined the structure of some B_2O_3–H_2O glasses (the so-called "wet boron oxide glasses") with x-ray and infrared techniques. The results were consistent with a random network structure in which the triangular coordination of oxygen around boron, characteristic of vitreous B_2O_3, is mostly retained. However, some of the B—O—B bonds are replaced by weaker B—O—H—O—B hydrogen bonds and this brings about a loosening of the structure. The glasses of high water content (15–40 mole % H_2O) are probably heterogenous, containing disordered regions of high H-bond density of the order of 1000 Å across, embedded in a matrix very similar to B_2O_3. NMR study of these glasses (21) has revealed that the presence of H_2O produces a small percentage of tetrahedral BO_4 units. For example, about 5% of the boron atoms have a tetrahedral environment in $B_2O_3 \cdot \frac{1}{2}H_2O$. The proton resonance spectrum confirmed that water molecules, as such, do not exist in the glass. Here it is of interest to note that boric acid glass, contrary to its aqueous solution, behaves as a strong acid; its Hammett function has been estimated as $H_0 = -2.5$ (22). This is consistent with the increase in acidity which occurs when boric acid polymerizes in aqueous solution or when it is complexed to polyhydroxy compounds (23).

The remarkable solvent power of boric acid glass toward relatively large organic molecules is probably due to its loose open structure.

3. Aqueous Glasses

Water can form a glass when it is subjected to sudden cooling with liquid air. [The transformation region of water lies somewhere between

123 and 148°K (24).] However, glass formation is facilitated by the addition of substances which can form hydrogen bonds with water, since this increases the degree of disorder (25). For some solutions both glassy and polycrystalline samples can be readily prepared, depending on the concentration of solute and mode of cooling. High solute concentration and rapid freezing favor the formation of glassy samples. Solutions of $HClO_4$, H_3PO_4, and H_2SO_4 can give rise to both states of aggregation throughout considerable concentration ranges (26). Dainton and Jones (27) propose that in these solutions the formation of the ice lattice is prevented by the presence of polymer chains, which result from polymerization by addition or condensation of the acid molecules. These chains are H-bonded to water molecules. In general this view may be correct, though condensation is not likely to play a prominent role. The polymer units probably consist of acid molecules and H_2O molecules, strongly H-bonded. Regions of random three-dimensional network may also be present in these glasses.

B. Properties

1. Diffusion in Glasses

The matrix isolation method is based on the ability of the matrix to restrict the movement of the radicals. For this reason, the discussion of diffusion in glasses is very valuable. For low temperature organic glasses Pimentel (10) has proposed that diffusion becomes appreciable when the temperature exceeds half the melting point. This relation is questionable for strongly interlinked networks, where specific steric effects become of major importance. Hence diffusion in ordinary glasses will be better considered. A comprehensive review on this subject was written by Doremus (28) and the brief survey which follows is adapted from his review.

Over certain ranges of temperature the diffusion coefficient D is given by an expression typical for rate processes:

$$D = D_0 \exp\left(-Q/RT\right) \qquad (2)$$

where D_0 and Q are constants which depend both on the nature of the diffusing species and the matrix. It is convenient to group the diffusing species into three categories: (1) molecules; (2) ions (only cations have been considered. The diffusion of interstitial anions is usually rare but it is of interest for our subject); and (3) network molecules. Only the first two will be considered.

The size of the diffusing molecule has a great influence on molecular diffusion; usually Q increases and D drops as the size increases. A simple explanation for this behavior is based on the model of diffusion as involving a jump of the molecule from one cavity to another. Now, it is assumed that the activation energy Q is the elastic energy required to enlarge the orifice of the cavity enough to allow the molecule to perform this jump. If r_0 and r are the radii of the cavity and the diffusing molecule, respectively, then the energy can be estimated from the equation:

$$Q = 8\pi G r_0 (r - r_0)^2 \tag{3}$$

where G is the elastic modulus of the glass. This equation seems to be a reasonable first approximation for the case of fused silica. It is strange to note that diffusion is hindered by incorporating modifying oxides into the silica glass, although the oxides break up the network. In some way the added cations block the way of the diffusing molecule.

In general, ions interact with the glass network more strongly than neutral molecules. This is reflected in the abrupt increase of their diffusion coefficients in the transformation region. The size of the ion is not the decisive factor. A model has been proposed considering the ionic transport in glass to occur by a defect mechanism, in which the defect consists of two ions in different sites around one oxygen ion.

2. Spectra

As is well known, pure fused silica is transparent down to about 150 mμ, whereas in silicate glasses the absorption starts around 280 mμ. It was shown (29) that melting the silicate glass under reducing conditions can move the absorption to shorter wavelengths. This was ascribed to the reduction of metallic impurities (especially iron and titanium), which have strong UV absorptions in their oxidized states. This can be one of the reasons, but not the main one, since the absorption of the purest silicate glass available is still considerably red shifted relative to that of silica. The shift has been attributed to the nonbridging oxygen ions (30). The effect of composition and temperature on the UV absorption spectra of borate and silicate glasses is in complete agreement with this view (31). The electrons are less tightly bound to these oxygen atoms than to the bridging ones and therefore they are more readily excited. The excitation may lead to photoionization and production of color centers (Section IV-A).

Here it is of interest to consider the effect of the matrix on the spectra of dissolved ions or molecules. The effect on the d–d transitions of the transition metal ions was reviewed by Bates (32). The main conclusion is that most of the transition ions of the first series occur in octahedral or tetrahedral symmetries (the oxygen atoms as ligands) with distortions which are only a little larger than in crystal or solution. This excepts those ions which are inherently distorted through the Jahn-Teller effect which distortions are also somewhat larger in glasses. Thus, the ligand field theory can be readily applied to such spectra. It appears that in sodium silicate glasses the ligand field energy Δ is about 10% smaller than that for the corresponding hydrate (33). A reduction of 15% in Δ is shown by Ni^{2+} in metaphosphate glass (34). The nonbridging oxygen atoms are probably more easily polarized. This may also explain the change of Co^{2+} and Ni^{2+} from octahedral to tetrahedral symmetries on increasing the alkali content of the glass (32).

Allowed intramolecular transitions (intramolecular charge–transfer, $\pi \to \pi^*$ transitions, etc.) are little affected by environment. Thus, the spectra of I_3^- and Br_3^- in boric acid glass are nearly identical with that in solution (5). The same applies to the spectra of some aromatic polynuclear hydrocarbons which were studied in this matrix (35,36). However, 3,4-benzpyrene (35) and perylene (36) display an additional weak absorption around 600 mμ, which was attributed to some complex of the hydrocarbon with the matrix material. Some interesting information on the state of aggregation of these molecules in the glass could be obtained from studying the emission spectra. Contrary to its behavior in various solvents (37) the fluorescence spectrum of pyrene in boric acid glass does not depend on the concentration (in the range 0.02–0.14M) and is identical with that shown by $2 \times 10^{-4}M$ solution. The concentration dependence was attributed to interaction between excited and unexcited pyrene molecules. At high concentrations, when most of the emitted light is from these dimers, the emission band is structureless with $\lambda_{max} = 478$ mμ (37). A similar emission band is displayed by crystalline pyrene (38), where the molecules are arranged in pairs in the unit cell. These results suggest that the glass matrix does not favor close interaction between the pyrene molecules.

Electron transfer spectra which directly involve the medium should be sensitive to change of solvent. To this category belong the electronic spectra of the halide ions which are now generally assigned to charge-transfer-to-solvent (CTTS) type of electronic transition (39). Such transitions should lead primarily to the production of radicals and detached electrons, which may be subsequently trapped or react with the medium. CTTS spectra display a large and characteristic sensitivity to environmental changes and a special solvent scale was established for their identification (40). In boric acid glass the spectra of I^- and Br^- are similar to that in aqueous solution but considerably blue shifted (Fig. 1). The spectrum of F^- in solution is not accessible to measurement. The spectrum of Cl^- as recorded in literature appears to be in error: its λ_{max} recently measured is at ~ 175 mμ (41). In the glass only its onset could be detected.

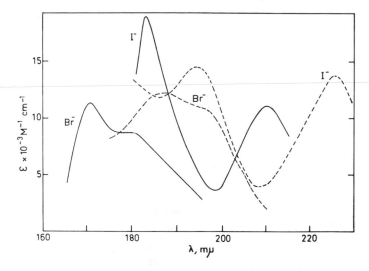

Fig. 1. The spectra of Br$^-$ and I$^-$ in aqueous solution (dashed curves) and in boric acid glass. Spectrum of I$^-$ in glass measured with Zeiss PMQ II, and the other with Perkin-Elmer Model 450 spectrophotometer. (The spectrum of Br$^-$ in glass is on an arbitrary scale.)

III. PRODUCTION OF TRAPPED RADICALS AND THEIR DETECTION

A. Production

Radical production by bond fission does not readily occur in a rigid matrix. To overcome cage recombination, either sufficient energy should be imparted to the radicals or reaction with the matrix material should occur. In some cases the course of photolysis changes when going from fluid to rigid media. From some of their observations Symons and Townsend (42) concluded that "processes which can follow both radical and nonradical paths in the fluid state seem to follow a nonradical path only in rigid media. . . . It is not clear whether or not radicals are transiently formed within the solvent cage before the formation of the nonradical products."

Radicals can be readily produced by oxidation–reduction processes, where electrons are transferred from the solute to the matrix or conversely. This occurs most easily in a polar matrix, which (1) weakens the coulomb field attracting the electron to the "hole" (the term "hole" in this context is not restricted to mobile species); and (2) provides deep enough potential wells. The electron–hole recombination is much reduced in the vitreous state, as evident from the increase in chemical yield (26). Dainton and Jones (27) pointed out that polar glasses provide high trapping opportunities, since the electron "may traverse regions in which the solvent molecules are either suitably oriented to solvate it or with little expenditure of energy may become so." Moreover, it appears that the migration of electrons in glass is more efficient than in liquid or crystal and so they can succeed in being trapped far from the "holes." The electron migration is probably facilitated by polymeric units which act as electron conducting pathways (27). However, the effect of the vitreous state on the yield of radical production does not seem to be confined to processes involving free electrons. It was observed, e.g., in the photolysis of ethyl iodide (43).

Electron or hole scavengers can suppress the back reaction. They may be supplied by the matrix itself (e.g., electron scavenging by acidic matrix) or by added materials. New radicals are thus formed and so many of them can be prepared by choosing the appropriate scavengers.

The effect of rigid media on the efficiency of photoionization and the role of the triplet state is discussed in Section VI.

B. Detection

Spectroscopic methods are usually employed for detection. The optical and ESR spectra are measured and their assignment to certain radicals is based on comparison with known spectra or on theoretical considerations. The effect of environment must be taken into account and it should be kept in mind that the radical is usually trapped in an environment which is natural to its parent molecule, but not to the radical. Thus, for example, Cd^+ formed by irradiation of Cd^{2+}-doped glass will be situated in environment natural to Cd^{2+}, since the rigidity of the glass prevents the environment from accommodating itself to the change in the valence state. This effect has been clearly shown in the case of ions with two or more stable valence states. Thus, the species obtained by photoxidation of Mn^{2+} or photoreduction of V^{3+} in silicate glasses show optical spectra somewhat different from that of normal Mn^{3+} or V^{2+} in the corresponding base glasses (44). The shift in the d–d transitions could be related to the difference in the ligand field energy Δ, which results from the difference in interionic distances. Thus, the distance Mn^{3+}–O^{2-} in the photolyzed glass is larger than that of the normal Mn^{3+} ion; the ligand field energy is smaller and the visible band of the photoxidized ion is red shifted.

The ESR spectrum usually depends on the orientation of the paramagnetic center with respect to the external magnetic field. In powders and glasses the centers are randomly oriented and the spectrum is the sum of the resonances in all orientations. This leads to anisotropy broadening and the spectrum often displays "shoulders" or "kinks." For organic radicals, with low residual spin-orbit coupling, the anisotropy of the *g* factor is rather small, but that of the hyperfine (hf) interaction may still be considerable. Different hf components in the spectrum will usually experience varying degrees of hf broadening (45). *g* Anisotropy can be readily detected by the effect of measuring frequency on the width of ESR signal. Methods have been developed for the analysis of the ESR spectra of powders and glasses. (A brief survey and the main references are given in Ref. 46.) The magnitudes of the principal components of *g* tensor are usually derived by Kneubühl's method (47).

Here we should note that a glass differs from a polycrystalline sample that in the glass the coordination sphere of each center may be different from that of another. In some cases the variation may be negligible (there is definite short-range order) but in others it may be considerable. The variation in the symmetry and intensity of the local fields is reflected in the optical and magnetic spectra of the glasses mainly as further broadening. However, in some cases there is evidence for a few distinct types of trapping sites. The broad optical bands often overlap. The resolution of the spectrum to its components is usually based on the assumption that the bands are gaussian-shaped (48).

Finally, it should be noted that in many cases the ESR spectrum of a radical may escape detection. Relaxation times which are too short or too long and, in glasses and powders, large anisotropy broadening may be responsible for undetectable signals.

IV. IRRADIATION COLORS IN GLASSES

Despite the extensive research carried out in the last 20 years (for an up-to-date bibliography see Ref. 49), the nature of the radiation-induced color centers in common oxide glasses has not yet been resolved. There are conflicting views even as to the type of trapped charge, hole or electron, which is responsible for a given absorption band. These views are based on apparently conflicting results, some of which have not yet been reconciled. Still, much of the data on silicate and phosphate glasses appear to be consistent with a simple model, which assigns the radiation-induced *visible* colors to *holes*, each trapped at a network-forming tetrahedron with one or more nonbridging oxygens (49). These two types of glasses are discussed below. Color centers in aqueous glasses have already been reviewed at length (12,13). Boric acid glass, which much concerns this review, is little affected by UV or x-ray radiation (50,51) and similar resistance is shown by vitreous B_2O_3 (52). Incorporation of basic oxides in the latter increases its response to radiation, each hole produced being primarily associated with the oxygens of one BO_4 tetrahedron (52,53). These results seem to be consistent with the above model; however, recent work has shown that the visible color of some irradiated borate glasses is mainly due to trapped electrons (49).

Much of the terminology concerning the coloration of glasses has real meaning only for periodic potential fields, such as exist in crystals. Holes, for instance, should be quite mobile. Now, there is no evidence for a comparable mobility of "holes" (electron deficient centers) in glasses. The mechanism of ionization transport in glass is probably more closely related to that of organic polymers (54) with the reservation that the oxide glasses are usually inert to chemical changes. Still, rupture of bonds may occur to some small extent; see below. Thus, migration of a hole along a polyphosphate chain may readily occur, but evidently such hole mobility is spatially confined.

General treatments of radiation-induced coloration and its kinetics are given in references 48 and 55.

A. Silicate Glasses

In an attempt to rationalize the color centers in silicate glasses, Kats, Stevels, and Van Wieringen (30,56) carried out a detailed study on their optical and paramagnetic resonance spectra, their dependence on glass composition and bleaching processes. It was shown that radiation energy above about 4.1 eV is sufficient for creating the color centers; UV radiation (254 mμ) and x-rays have nearly the same effect. Irradiated alkali silicates display at least three absorption bands, two in the visible and one peaking at about 300 mμ. The position of the latter is independent of the type of alkali ion in the glass but it depends somewhat on the alkali concentration. In contrast, the position of the central band depends on the type of alkali ion but not on its concentration. On going along the alkali series from Li$^+$ to Cs$^+$ the peak of this band gradually shifts from 415 mμ to 490 mμ, respectively. The third band peaks at about 620 mμ. Kats and Stevels assigned the UV band and the pair of visible bands to trapped-hole and trapped-electron centers, respectively. The absorbed photon was considered to eject an electron from a nonbridging oxygen ion, thus leaving a hole center designated by $\dot{Q}_+$. (With decrease of alkali concentration other hole centers are likely to occur, e.g., one or two holes trapped at two adjacent nonbridging oxygens: Q_+ and Q_{2+}, respectively. This change was considered to be responsible for the effect of alkali concentration on the position of the UV band.) The cation (the network modifier) in the vicinity of the hole center will tend to recede. It was considered to settle together with an electron in an interstice which contains no nonbridging oxygens. The central absorption band was assigned to this electron-excess center, which is designated by P_-. It may be visualized as a trapped alkali atom strongly polarized by the surrounding oxygens. This picture explains the observed dependence of the peak position on the type of alkali. However, the shifts are small in comparison with the variation in the $ns \rightarrow np$ transitions of the free alkali atoms and, furthermore, the latter transition has its maximum energy value for Na (57). The 620 mμ band was assigned to such a polarized atom trapped in the vicinity of a nonbridging oxygen *vacancy* (the so-called T center). However, it is questionable whether a 254 mμ photon is capable of disrupting the Si—O$^-$ bond. Moreover, it is not clear why this center does not display cation specificity.

The ESR spectra of the irradiated glasses show two signals, centered at about $g = 2.01$ and $g = 1.96$, respectively. The low field signal is stronger, more resistant to thermal bleaching and less susceptible to power saturation than the high field one. Both show g anisotropy. Van Wieringen and Katz (56) assigned the high field and low field signals to trapped electrons and holes, respectively. This assignment has been confirmed later and is now generally accepted. However, there have been conflicting views about the connection between the ESR signals and the optical bands. By studying the effect of glass composition on the intensities of the ESR signals and comparing with the corresponding effect on the optical bands, Van Wieringen and Katz came to connect the electron signal with the central visible band and the hole signal with the 300 mμ band. The 620 mμ band could not be connected with either of the ESR signals. This was shown by studying the effect of optical bleaching. At 77°K the 620 mμ band could be bleached by a sodium lamp much more efficiently than the other two bands. The latter bands always bleach simultaneously. In general, these conclusions are in agreement with the assignment of Katz and Stevels. However, more detailed work carried out later has shown that these connections are probably wrong (see below). As to the model of the electron center, Van Wieringen and Katz have pointed out that since the electron signal does not show evidence for hyperfine interaction, the electron is probably smeared over an appreciable volume and not localized near an alkali ion.

A different experimental approach has been developed by Stroud, Schreurs, and Tucker (the Corning group). They introduced the use of hole and electron scavengers for classifying the color centers according to the type of trapped charge. Ce^{3+}, Fe^{2+}, and Mn^{2+} act as efficient hole scavengers in glasses, whereas Eu^{3+} has been used to scavenge electrons. This method was initiated by Stroud's observation (58,59) that Ce^{3+} could suppress the visible coloration of the x-irradiated glass and that the resulting UV spectrum was nearly identical with that obtained by *photolyzing* Ce^{3+} in the same base glass. The photolysis was induced by 313 mμ light, which does not affect the pure base glass, but is strongly absorbed by Ce^{3+} (λ_{max} = 314 mμ). Both types of irradiation induce in the Ce^{3+}-doped glass an intense absorption band peaking at 250 mμ. This band resembles that of Ce^{4+} in the same base glass though the latter is somewhat blue shifted (λ_{max} = 240 mμ). From this and from simple chemical reasoning, the 250 mμ band has been assigned to Ce^{4+} ion in a site normally occupied by a Ce^{3+} ion (Section III-B). The ceric ion in this state is denoted here by (Ce^{4+}). Indeed, the peak position is shifted from 250 to 240 mμ on heating to 350°C (60). The 313 mμ photon is thus considered to photoionize the Ce^{3+} ion:

$$Ce^{3+} \xrightarrow{\ h\nu\ } (Ce^{4+}) + e_t \tag{4}$$

and the similar effect of x-irradiation is explained by the process:

$$Ce^{3+} + \text{hole} + e \longrightarrow (Ce^{4+}) + e_t \tag{5}$$

where e_t represents the trapped electron.

The above results indicate that both visible bands are due to trapped holes. The origin of the 300 mμ band has not been definitely established, since it overlaps the Ce^{3+} band. However, it may be due to trapped electrons since when total hole scavenging occurs the resulting spectrum shows a tail of a band extending from 350 to 600 mμ (59). This tail is suppressed by Ce^{4+} which acts as an electron scavenger. Furthermore, the photoionization of Ce^{3+} also leads to a "tail" in this region and both "tails" are bleached by light with $\lambda \geqslant 350$ mμ, together with some of the ceric ions.

Using probability theory, Stroud derived a simple expression for the number of charges scavenged as a function of the scavenger's concentration (59). The number of charges that *escape* scavenging and are thus trapped in the matrix is:

$$n = n_0 \exp(-vc) \tag{6}$$

where v is a characteristic capture volume of the scavenger and c its concentration. The same expression (with n and n_0 replaced by the appropriate symbols) describes the intensity of optical absorption or paramagnetic resonance of the corresponding trapped charge centers (provided only one type of center absorbs at the given wavelength or magnetic field). Any overlap should be taken into account.

Four assumptions are implicit in the above treatment and its application to experimental results (49): (1) The addition of low concentration of scavenger to glass does not alter the glass structure radically (Section II-A). (2) Melting under reducing conditions has no effect other than reducing the oxidation state of polyvalent ion. This assumption is necessary when using hole scavengers, such as Ce^{3+}, Fe^{2+}, and Mn^{2+}, and keeping the concentration of the corresponding oxidized states as low as possible since the latter act as electron scavengers. Exceptions are known to occur when strong reducing conditions are employed. (*3*) The creation of new traps by radiation is negligible. This assumption has been justified by the observation that the same color centers are produced by UV, x-ray, and γ-radiation. [γ-Radiation probably produces new traps, but the rate at which they are produced is much less than the rate at which color centers are formed by pure ionization processes (48).] (*4*) The scavenger does not interfere with the electron–hole recombination. This is the most questionable assumption. There is evidence that in some cases it is not correct (49).

The visible bands in sodium (59) and potassium silicates (49) were found to be suppressed by Ce^{3+} according to equation 6. The capture volume of Ce^{3+} is $v \sim 8 \times 10^4$ Å^3. As for the ESR spectrum only the $g = 2.01$ signal could be suppressed by hole scavengers and here also the effect follows equation 6. This was shown by using either Ce^{3+} or Fe^{2+}, the values derived for v are about 8×10^4 and 10×10^4 Å^3, respectively (61). On the other hand, only the $g = 1.96$ signal could be suppressed by Eu^{3+}. This ion has hardly any effect on the visible band (49).

Altogether the results show definitely that the visible bands and the $g = 2.01$ signal are due to trapped holes, whereas the $g = 1.96$ signal arises from trapped electrons. Other experiments (49) have proved that the $g = 2.01$ signal is directly connected with one or both of the visible bands. These experiments include the dependence of the intensities of the ESR and optical spectra on x-ray dose, on duration of thermal bleaching, and on soda-to-silica ratio. [Actually, both the $g = 2.01$ and $g = 1.96$ signals are superpositions of at least two resonances (49).]

Regarding all this body of evidence, one is inclined to accept the Corning group classification of the color centers in silicate glasses. But still some of the previous results remain unexplained, in particular, the cation specificity shown by the central band. On the other hand, this classification provides simple explanations to many other results. For example, it is known that glasses melted under mild reducing conditions are less liable to be visibly colored by radiation. Glasses usually contain polyvalent ions as impurities (ions of iron, manganese, etc.). In their reduced states, these are likely to scavenge holes and thus inhibit the visible color.

Classification experiments (i.e., studying the dependence of optical and ESR spectra on the concentration of the appropriate scavenger) have been carried out for other glasses too (see below). The precautions that should be taken in performing these experiments are described in reference 49. In principle they involve competition of two different scavengers on one reactive species. This method, which is so widely used in fluid state experiments, has recently been adapted to the study of frozen solutions (some examples are discussed in Section V).

B. Phosphate Glasses

Phosphate glasses readily turn pink on γ, x-ray, or far-UV irradiation. The color results from a broad absorption around 500 mμ which is probably a superposition of two or more bands. [In some phosphates two bands are clearly displayed, e.g., calcium metaphosphate (62).] It is always accompanied by a double-peaked ESR signal around $g = 2.01$, the two components being separated by ~ 40 G. The shapes and positions of both the visible band and the ESR doublet vary only little with the glass composition (63,64). They appear to be closely related to the PO_4 tetrahedra with little interaction with the surroundings. Thus similar spectra is induced by ionizing radiation in frozen phosphoric acid solution (65), cyclic trimetaphosphate (63), phosphate and aluminophosphate glasses. There is ample evidence that the visible band is directly connected with the ESR doublet. This has already been shown by Hensler and Kreidl (66) on grounds of their being simultaneously suppressed by doping the glass with various transition metal ions. The interaction of the unpaired electron with the ^{31}P nuclear spin has been considered to be responsible for the doublet structure of the signal. However, there have been conflicting views as to the nature of this center, whether it is an electron-excess (64,66–68) or an electron-deficient center (34,61–63). As a matter of fact, no evidence has been presented for the former assignment apart from the color being similar to that of F centers. On the other hand, there is much evidence for the hole center assignment. Thus, hole scavengers, such as Mn^{2+}, Ti^{3+} (66), and the halide ions (34), inhibit its formation. Schreurs and Tucker (62) used Mn^{2+} for a quantitative classification experiment. The intensities of both the visible absorption and the ESR signal decrease exponentially with increasing Mn^{2+} concentration with the same v (Eq. 6).

The structure of the hole resonance provides valuable information about its charge distribution. The spectrum displays small anisotropy of both g value and hf interaction. Two somewhat different models have been proposed. Both associate the hole with a single PO_4 tetrahedron which has at least one nonbridging oxygen, so that it spends only little of its time on the phosphorus atom. In one model (63) the hole is mainly trapped at a nonbridging oxygen and in the other (62) it occupies a molecular orbital which essentially involves the π orbitals of several oxygen atoms.

High energy radiation also induces an ill-defined absorption in the UV. The photolysis of I^- in the same base glass also leads to some new absorption in this region (Section V-A-1). (The photolysis was induced by

229 mμ light, which does not affect the base glass.) This suggests that the UV absorption is due to trapped electrons. Now, in addition to the strong double-peaked hole signal, the ESR spectrum of the irradiated base glass displays two weak and broad signals on the low and high magnetic field sides (Fig. 2). These were first observed by Nakai (63), who assigned them to different centers: the low field signal to a new hole center and the high field signal to trapped electrons. The latter should have $g \sim 1.85$, which means that a considerable amount of orbital angular momentum is involved. However, no change of line width with measuring frequency v could be observed. Actually, the two signals appear to be components of a doublet with $g = 2.00$ (69). They always grow and decay together with nearly identical intensities; the separation between them (~ 700 G) is hardly changed by fivefold variation of v. The new doublet (with hf splitting about 20 times large than that of the hole center) appears to be due to trapped electrons. The evidence for this is the following: (1) It shows marked power saturation. (2) The photolysis of I^- (and Br^-) leads to the same doublet (Fig. 2). (3) Electron scavengers, such as Pb^{2+} and Cd^{2+}, inhibit this but not the hole doublet. (The previously reported effect of $CdSO_4$ on the hole center (34) was probably due to some impurity.) In the case of Cd^{2+}, the inhibition is accompanied by the growth of the Cd^+ center (Section V-F-1). (4) Hole scavengers, such as Ce^{3+}, suppress the hole but not this doublet.

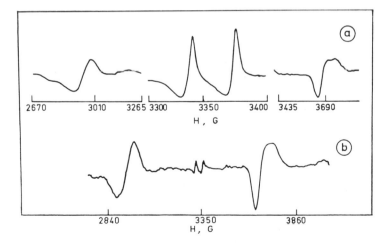

Fig. 2. The ESR spectra of x-irradiated metaphosphate glass (a) and of I^- containing glass irradiated at 229 mμ (b). (The intensity scale of the central signal in a is reduced by a factor of 30.) Spectra taken with Varian V-4502 spectrometer at 9.4 kMcps.

The large hyperfine splitting and marked power saturation suggest that the trapped electron wave function has a considerable contribution from $3s$ or $4s$ orbital of phosphorus. We consider the center to result from an electron attachment to a PO_4 unit in the phosphate chain (or ring). It is thus isoelectronic with the PF_4 radical, which shows even larger hf splitting (70).

Finally, it is interesting to compare the photochemistry of the phosphate polymer ions to that of their monomers. Halmann and Platzner (71) have shown that the absorption spectra of the initial members of the polyphosphate series contain both weak bands (above 200 mμ) and steep absorption edges (below 200 mμ). The former were assigned to internal transitions and the latter to charge-transfer-to-solvent (CTTS) type of excitation. Irradiation in the CTTS region leads to photoionization and formation of such radicals as HPO_4^- (72). Now, the spectrum of metaphosphate glass (both of the glass and in solution) seems to follow this pattern (34). The steep rise of the CTTS band is below 210 mμ and, indeed, irradiation above this wavelength does not lead to photoionization, i.e., to formation of color centers.

V. INORGANIC RADICALS

Most of the radicals discussed in this section have been investigated in liquid and frozen solutions and in room temperature glasses. Usually the optical spectra displayed in these different media are, within reasonable shifts, quite similar. [When comparing liquid to rigid media one should bear in mind the rigidity factor (Section III-B).] In the case of cation radicals this may reflect similar coordination of oxygens around the radical. The spectra of neutral atoms should not be much different than that in the gas phase, so that comparison with free atoms data is helpful. However, one must be careful in arriving at definite assignments, from mere spectroscopic evidence. Considerable shifts, on one hand, and accidental similarity in spectra may lead to wrong conclusions. ESR spectra, when available, and their resemblance to that of the radicals in single crystals add much to our confidence.

The discussion below follows the periodic table. Usually, only those radicals are included which have been identified in more than one medium and so their identification is likely to be correct.

A. Halogens

The dihalide ions X_2^-, which long ago have been postulated as intermediates in some photochemical and redox reactions, are now among the best-known inorganic radicals. The so-called V_K centers are considered to be X_2^- radicals properly aligned in the crystals. The discovery and identification of these centers by Känzig and Castner (73) is now a classical work in ESR spectroscopy. In the last ten years they have been identified and studied in solutions, crystals, and glasses. They were produced from halide and trihalide ions and from the halogen molecules by using various sources of radiation. Of great help in their identification were the selective photochemical methods, therefore this kind of work will be first reviewed.

1. Photolysis of X^-

In their pioneering work Jortner, Ottolenghi, and Stein (74) showed that the primary stage in the photochemistry of the halide ion, X^-, is the dissociation of the spectroscopically excited ion X^{-*} (the CTTS state, Section II-B-2) to yield a halogen atom X and solvated electron, e_{aq}^-. This was proved by conducting the photolysis in presence of various electron scavengers. It appears that X^{-*} dissociates with a quantum yield Φ which does not depend on the concentration of the scavenger. The latter competes only with the secondary recombination of the electron-radical pair. With increase of scavenger concentration (S) total scavenging finally occurs and the measured quantum yield φ attains a limiting value equal to Φ which is usually smaller than 1. The scavenging of the solvated electron was found to follow diffusion-controlled kinetics; φ depended on $(S)^{1/2}$ over a range of (S). The reason for this correlation is still under dispute (75). It was found that even high concentrations of salts have no effect on Φ, but it depends markedly on the nature of the solvent and also on temperature, decreasing with decrease of temperature (74a,c). The latter effect is of interest for the discussion of low temperature glasses.

Direct evidence for the formation of solvated electrons from the excited halide ions was presented by Matheson, Mulac, and Rabani (76), who used the flash-photolysis technique. Grossweiner and Matheson (77,78), who had previously carried out the same type of experiment recorded the spectra of intermediates which they identified as the dihalide ions. Their formation and decay were considered to proceed as follows:

$$X + X^- \rightleftharpoons X_2^- \tag{7}$$

$$X + X \longrightarrow X_2 \tag{8}$$

$$X + X_2^- \longrightarrow X_3^- \tag{9}$$

$$X_2^- + X_2^- \longrightarrow X_3^- + X^- \tag{10}$$

It was still left to identify the precursor of X_2^-, namely the halogen atoms. The difficulty lies in that their absorptions are in the far UV, where all solvents strongly absorb. Moreover, reaction 7 is very fast and the equilibrium constant is large (about 10^4 and 10^5 for I_2^- and Br_2^-, respectively)

(78,79). Hence, to detect the X atoms the matrix isolation technique should be used.

Frozen Aqueous Solutions. The first work on I^--doped glass was reported by Voevodsky et al. (80). [Earlier, Hilsenrod and Gehauf (81) carried out some crude experiments with iodide-metaphosphate glass in Dry Ice–acetone bath.] They photolyzed frozen solutions (77°K) of KI in highly concentrated phosphoric and sulfuric acids and observed the ESR doublet of H atoms. With D_2O the ESR triplet of D appeared. From their results they were unable to tell whether the spectroscopically excited state is *directly* involved in the production of H atoms, e.g., by a Frank-Haber mechanism (82), or whether there is some intermediate stage in which the electron is first released. That the latter is the case was shown by Moorthy and Weiss (83). They measured the quantum yield of H-atom formation as a function of the concentration of the acid present in the matrix. The curves obtained were similar in shape to those representing the effect of electron scavengers on the corresponding liquid system (74). However, the limiting yields appear to depend on the nature of acid and are much smaller. Eventually the small yield may be a temperature effect. [The value of Φ at 77°K, obtained by extrapolation from the liquid data (74c), assuming no phase effect, is practically zero.] Direct experimental support to this view will be presented later. Moorthy and Weiss compared polycrystalline with glassy specimens and found that in the latter higher concentrations of acids were required to reach total scavenging. The electron scavenging power of the acids followed the same sequence as in the radiolysis of the undoped acidic ice. Cd^{2+} and NO_3^-, which are known to scavenge electrons, suppress the yield of H atoms. I^- itself was found to inhibit the reaction and this was attributed to its deactivating interaction with I^{-*}. However, such an effect has not been detected in the liquid system.

Since trapping of electrons can be achieved in alkaline glasses, it is of interest to use such a matrix for photolysis. However, attempts to induce photoionization of I^- in alkaline glass have failed (84). Again, this may be due to a very low residual yield (i.e., the yield in absence of scavenger) at 77°K.

The aqueous glasses experiments have dealt only with the formation of hydrogen atoms (the formation of X_2^- in aqueous glasses by *γ-radiolysis* have recently been reported, to be discussed later), and thus they do not supply substantial evidence to the various photochemical stages previously postulated for the liquid phase. This was achieved by investigating the photolysis of the halides in room temperature glasses.

Boric Acid Glass. Br^- and I^- were photolyzed in boric acid glass with a considerable quantum yield (~ 0.3 for I^-) (4). By investigating the reactions in dilute I^- glass ($\sim 10^{-2}M$) all the stages postulated by Grossweiner and Matheson could be followed spectroscopically. The decay of I^- is accompanied by the growth of a new band with a broad peak at about 177 mμ (Fig. 3). This band readily undergoes thermal bleaching and is replaced by the spectra of I_2, I_3^- and I_2^- (the latter could be determined by subtracting the overlapping band of I_3^-). The intermediate absorbing at 177 mμ is thus (1) directly produced from I^- by photolysis; (2) the precursor of all the other iodine compounds formed. This indicates its identity with the iodine atom, an assignment which is in accord with the well-known absorption spectrum of I atoms in the gas phase; the two first lines are at 183 and 178.3 mμ (85). This suggests little interaction between the trapped atom and the matrix. No other report on the spectrum of iodine in solution or solid is available.

With more concentrated glasses the formation of I_2^- immediately follows irradiation, since on the average any iodine atom photochemically

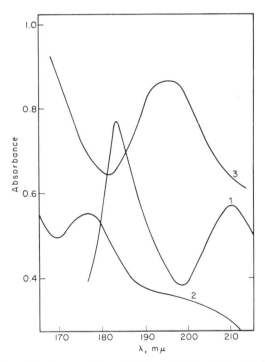

Fig. 3. The photochemistry of I^- at 185 mμ. (I^-) = 1.5 × $10^{-2}M$. Absorption curves: (1) before irradiation, (2) after irradiation for 55 min, (3) after 3 min at 120°C. (4).

produced is in the proximity of an iodide ion. With Br^--doped glass this process could not be avoided, which indicates how steeply the diffusion coefficient increases with decrease in the size of the diffusing molecule (Section II-B-1). Experiments with Cl^--doped glass (only CsCl was found to be soluble enough) failed to give any result. This is due to the low absorption of Cl^- at 185 mμ (the effective wavelength of the low pressure mercury lamp) (Section II-B-2).

The identification of the X_2^- radicals in the glass followed (*1*) from the resemblance between their spectra and those previously ascribed to the dihalide ions in liquids and crystals (Table I, Section V-A-4); (*2*) in the case of I_2^- from the identity of its spectrum with that produced by the photolysis or radiolysis of I_2-doped boric acid glass (Section V-A-3); and (*3*) from the results concerning their formation and decay. It was shown (*4*) that at room temperature X_2^- is formed and decays by reactions 7 and 9, respectively. At elevated temperatures reaction 10 takes place. From the spectral changes which accompany this reaction one can readily evaluate upper limits for ϵ_{max} of X_2^- (*5*).

There is still some uncertainty as to the fate of the photoejected electron. The photolysis has recently been carried out at 77°K (51) and the ESR doublet of H atoms (or the triplet of D in deuterated glass) could be detected. It decays on raising the temperature and at room temperature the glass shows a weak unidentified signal.

The mixed dihalide IBr^- was also identified in this glass (86). By utilizing the difference in optical absorption between I^- and Br^-, the former could be selectively photolyzed in presence of Br^- in excess. The iodine atoms thus formed combine with Br^- to yield IBr^- and then I_2Br^-. IBr^- could also be produced from Br atoms and I^-, in which case further reaction gives rise to IBr_2^-.

Attempts to obtain IBr^- in aqueous solution by flash photolysis failed though the same type of selective photolysis, with much larger excess of Br^-, was used (78). I_2^- was the sole product, probably owing to its thermodynamic stability being much larger than that of IBr^-. In such cases the matrix isolation method has a great advantage, since the glass is a metastable system and the formation of XY^- may be simply due to the encagement of X and Y^- at close proximity. In other words, the thermal decomposition of XY^- is prevented by the rigidity of the matrix.

Metaphosphate Glass. I_2^-, Br_2^-, and Cl_2^- were prepared (5,69) by subjecting the corresponding halide containing glass to 185 mμ light. (For I^- the 229 mμ Cd light is also effective. For Cl^- the mechanism probably resembles that of the corresponding radiolysis, Section V-A-2.) The ESR spectra after irradiation indicates the formation of trapped electrons

(Fig. 2, Section IV-B). Again, the production of I_2^- is the slowest and glasses could be prepared with no distinct absorption of I_2^-. In this case some optical absorption appeared in the UV but it was not identical with that of the electron center in the pure base glass. The difference may be due to small amounts of iodine compounds.

Iodide-doped glasses which were irradiated by 229 mμ light at 77°K did not produce any detectable electron signal. This result shows the large effect of temperature on a photoionization process.

Cl_2^- showed an ill-defined ESR spectrum whereas that of Br_2^- and I_2^- could not be detected. This is probably due to anisotropy broadening which smears the signals beyond detection. A similar behavior is shown by X_2^- in frozen aqueous solutions (13). As to the halogen atoms, their ESR spectra has never been observed in polycrystalline materials (11) and no signals in the glass could be assigned to them. On heating the glass to 200–300°C, the X_2^- radicals were converted to X_3^-.

2. Radiolysis of X⁻-Containing Systems

Extensive work has been done on the pulse radiolysis of aqueous Cl^- (87) and Br^- solutions (79,88); the formation and decay of Cl_2^- and Br_2^- were thus studied. The maximum extinction coefficients of their prominent absorption bands were evaluated: $\epsilon_{max}(Cl_2^-) = 12{,}500 \pm 1{,}000$ (87) and $\epsilon_{max}(Br_2^-) = 9{,}600 \pm 800$ (79). $\epsilon_{max}(I_2^-) = 15{,}600 \pm 3{,}000$ was obtained by Grossweiner and Matheson (78) from the flash photolysis of I_3^-. The precursor of X_2^- in these systems is again the X radical, which is formed by the reaction $OH + X^- \rightarrow OH^- + X$. The reaction appears to be pH dependent, especially in the case of chloride (87). This was considered by Stein (89) to reflect the effect of pH on the oxidation potential of OH. The effect may also play a role in aqueous glasses.

Frozen Aqueous Solution.   Moorthy and Weiss (13) reported that alkaline ice doped with KI on γ-irradiation does not display the resonance signal ascribed to O^-. This they attributed to I^- acting as hole scavenger. Their studies on irradiated frozen solutions of HCl, HBr, and HI suggested the formation of X_2^-, since in the case of HCl there was an ESR signal which might be assigned to Cl_2^-.

Brown and Dainton have recently studied the optical spectra developed by the γ-radiolysis of sulfuric acid glasses (77°K) containing NaCl and NaBr (90). The spectra of Cl_2^- and Br_2^- appeared on irradiation. Warming to 135–150°K enhanced their absorption and since the absorption assigned to SO_4^- (Section V-B-2) simultaneously decreased, the following reaction was considered to occur: $SO_4^- + X^- \rightarrow SO_4^{2-} + X$. At 150–155°K the spectra of X_2^- decayed and X_3^- was formed.

Metaphosphate Glass. MP glasses containing alkali halides were subjected to x-ray radiation (69). Both optical and ESR spectra showed very little of the hole center, whereas the electron center was intense. The irradiation leads to the growth of the dihalide bands. In general, the effect of x-ray irradiation closely resembles that of UV light, but its origin is not necessarily the same. This is evident from the observation that 229 mμ light, which has no effect on the base glass, is still able to photolyze I^- in the glass. Moreover, glasses doped with high concentration of X^- (to ensure a high fraction of the 185 mμ to be absorbed by X^-) still give the same results on irradiation with low pressure Hg lamp. The close resemblance between the effects of the two kinds of radiation conceals two different mechanisms (Section IV-A):

$$\text{Photolysis: } I^- \longrightarrow I_t + e_t \tag{11}$$

$$\text{Radiolysis: } I^- + \text{hole} + e \longrightarrow I_t + e_t \tag{12}$$

3. Radiolysis and Photolysis of X_2-Containing Systems

X_2^- may be formed by the direct attachment of an electron to X_2. In the gas phase the vertical attachment process is dissociative (91):

$$X_2 + e \longrightarrow X^- + X$$

In a condensed phase the cage effect should largely determine the secondary process; if the energy imparted to the two fragments is not sufficient they will subsequently recombine to yield X_2^-. The chance for escape from the cage should depend on the kinetic energy of the electron and the local viscosity around the X_2 molecule, which may not be uniform. Thus, both X_2^- and X^- may be formed with relative amounts which depend on the conditions. The attachment of electrons to I_2 molecules in aqueous solution was studied by pulse radiolysis (92). The decay of e_{aq}^- and formation of I_2^- were reported to proceed at identical rates, which means that no dissociation occurs. The value of $\epsilon_{max}(I_2^-)$ used for this comparison was not reported. Some I^- may still be formed.

The excitation of a charge-transfer complex $D \cdot X_2$ may also lead to formation of X_2^-. The photolysis of I_3^- exemplifies this case (78). Electron transfer from solvent to solute may be responsible for photochemically produced X_2^- in aqueous X_2 solutions (77). This reaction may be compared with the photochemical reduction of Ce^{4+} and Fe^{3+} by water (93).

Aqueous Glasses. Sulfuric acid glass doped with I_2 gives on γ-irradiation the spectrum of I_2^- (90).

Boric Acid Glass. I_2^- was produced by subjecting the I_2-doped glass to either x-ray or 185 mμ radiation (4). In both cases some evidence indicated simultaneous formation of I^-. The mechanism of I_2^- production by light is not clear; it may involve the interaction of the excited I_2 molecule with the matrix (see above).

The photolysis of I_3^- was tried in a glass, which might also contain I^- and I_2 (4). Fast decay of the I_3^- absorption was induced by 185 mμ light. Direct photoionization of I_3^- was suggested with the formation of the radical I_3.

4. Properties of X_2^-

The maxima of the X_2^- absorption spectra in various media are recorded in Table I. There is a gradual decrease of transition energy with increase of molecular weight. I_2^- shows a second strong band at about 700 mμ which is probably due to the $^2\Pi_{g1/2} \leftarrow {}^2\Sigma_u^+$ transition.

The relatively high stability of X_2^- radicals in room temperature glasses provides the opportunity of a convenient study of their properties. Some results were already reviewed. However, the medium effect should be always taken into consideration. This becomes clear when discussing photochemical reactions in glasses. Thus I_2^- in glass does not undergo photolysis at 365 mμ, a wavelength within its prominent absorption band. But all known excited states of I_2^- are repulsive and should lead to decomposition (91). It appears that the energy imparted to the fragments by a 365 mμ photon is not sufficient to overcome cage recombination in the matrix. There is some evidence that shorter wavelengths do lead to photolysis (4). Still, a negative result is also important. For example, it was once

TABLE I
λ_{max} (mμ) of X_2^- in Various Media[a]

Medium	Cl_2^-	Br_2^-	I_2^-	IBr^-	Ref.
Alkali halides					
(77°K)[b]	365	385	400, 800		
H_2O	340	350	370		78
Ethanol[c]			380, 750		
Glasses					
Boric acid		350	375, 680	360	4, 5, 86
Metaphosphate	330	350	375, 720		69
Sulfuric acid					
(77°K)	335	355	380		90
Alkyl halides					
(77°K)[d]		375	405, 720		

[a] Only the strong bands are recorded.
[b] C. J. Delbecq, W. Hayes, and P. H. Yuster, *Phys. Rev.*, **121**, 1043 (1961).
[c] G. Dobson and L. I. Grossweiner, *Radiation Res.*, **23**, 290 (1964).
[d] R. F. C. Claridge and J. E. Willard, *J. Am. Chem. Soc.*, **88**, 2404 (1966).

suggested that the spectra of X_2^- in the 300–400 mμ region are due to CTTS origin (77). Since electron ejection is quite efficient in the glass, this assignment is at variance with the absence of photolysis. Indeed, it is now generally accepted that the prominent X_2^- bands are due to $^2\Sigma_g^+ \leftarrow {}^2\Sigma_u^+$ electron transitions. Similar considerations may be of some help in other cases, but they must be used carefully: the yield of electrons from a CTTS state may be very small owing to competing deactivation processes.

5. Oxyhalogen Radicals

IO_4^- and IO_3^- were claimed to be unaffected by 254 mμ light in some aqueous glasses (94). On the other hand, IO_3^- could be slowly photolyzed in boric acid glass at room temperature and some new absorptions were apparent (51). Their nature has not yet been determined.

a. ClO. It was obtained in rigid solutions of sulfuric and phosphoric acids by the photolysis of ClO_2 (95) and was identified by its ESR spectrum (no optical spectrum was taken). ClO_2 is reformed in good yield on heating. It was postulated that the oxygen atom adds to the acid to give the corresponding peroxy compound and that the back reaction occurs on heating. No evidence was given for this. The O atoms may be physically trapped far enough from ClO (96).

b. ClO$_4$(?). The radical ClO_4, with Cl at $+8$ oxidation state, was claimed to be formed by γ-radiolysis of frozen $HClO_4$ solution at 77°K (65). Its ESR spectrum was considered to constitute a quartet, as expected from hyperfine interaction with ^{35}Cl and ^{37}Cl, both of which have spin $\frac{3}{2}$ and nearly equal magnetic moments. However, the ESR spectrum is very weak and considerably overlapped by that of other centers, so that its structure is still in doubt. The optical spectrum of the radical has not been measured but it is apparently in the UV region, since the irradiated sample is not visibly colored. This is in accordance with the gradual blue shift on going from HPO_4^- (Section V-C-1) to SO_4^- (Section V-B-2). Still, it was argued that the optical absorption of ClO_4 has a long tail in the visible, since the magnetic resonance assigned to it is optically bleached with visible light. The nature of this process is discussed later (Section V-B-2). However, in the case of ClO_4, the process is not reversible; heat treatment either before or after bleaching leads to irreversible changes.

B. Group VI-b

Sulfur and selenium play prominent roles in the technology of colored glasses (9). In some cases atomic or diatomic molecules of these elements were postulated as color producers. According to Weyl, the so-called blue sulfur glasses contain S_2 molecules, whereas the pink selenium glasses (which are widely used) are solutions of atomic selenium. Later work does not seem to support the first assignment, but the problem is not yet resolved (see below). This and the nature of pink selenium glasses are still open fields for research with new techniques of radicals detection.

1. Blue Sulfur Glasses

Chemical literature contains many references to the blue color of sulfur solutions and minerals. Most familiar is the blue ultramarine, the absorption spectrum of which closely resembles that of the blue sulfur glass ($\lambda_{max} \sim 575$ mμ). The former shows paramagnetic resonance with $g \sim 2.025$ (97). Similar ESR spectra is shown by some other blue sulfur solutions (98). Orgel discussed the nature of the blue sulfur in these solutions and came to identify it with S_2^-.

Some work has been done on the effect of radiation on blue sulfur glasses (67,99). On x-irradiation the blue color was found to fade and at the same time the glass developed a weak band at 340 mμ. The visible coloration of the irradiated base glass was absent. Since at that time the visible color was considered to be due to trapped electrons (Section IV-B), the bleaching of the blue color was ascribed to the reaction: $S_2 + e \rightarrow S_2^-$. Now it seems more probable that the reaction is: $S_2^- + \text{hole} \rightarrow S_2$. This has still to be confirmed.

S_2 was claimed to be trapped in the cavities of water clathrate lattice (100). These cavities are real traps which may stabilize radicals at relatively high temperatures (253°K and above). H_2S–water clathrate turned purple when photolyzed, the reflectance spectra showing two maxima: in the range 275–290 mμ and at 550 mμ. Both were ascribed to S_2, the visible band considered to arise from a normally forbidden transition which is relaxed by the matrix field. However, the mechanism proposed requires that pairs of HS radicals diffuse out of their cages and react, the resulting S_2 radical then becomes stabilized in one of the available cages. This may not be the real situation. It is interesting to note the resemblance between the color of the photolyzed H_2S–water clathrate and the blue sulfur glasses. In the case of CH_3SH water clathrate, where trapped CH_3S could be detected after photolysis, the situation is much simpler. The use of clathrates as a trapping matrix shows that the simple relationship of diffusion coefficients to melting point (10) may be misleading. For small radicals, specific sites of trapping should be considered.

2. SO_4^-

SO_4^- has been postulated as intermediate in the photolysis of SO_4^{2-} (101) and in many reactions involving $S_2O_8^{2-}$ (102). It can be produced from $S_2O_8^{2-}$ by one of the following reactions:

$$\text{Bond fission: } S_2O_8^{2-} \longrightarrow 2SO_4^- \qquad (13)$$

$$\text{Reduction: } \quad S_2O_8^{2-} + e \longrightarrow SO_4^{2-} + SO_4^- \qquad (14)$$

The radical was identified in single crystals of $K_2S_2O_8$ which were irradiated by γ or UV radiation (103); in the latter case pairwise trapping of SO_4^- seems to occur.

SO_4^- belongs to the group or oxyanion radicals (ClO_4, HPO_4^-, and SO_4^-) detected in radiolyzed frozen solutions of the corresponding acids or acid salts (65). According to Weiss et al. they result from the reaction of "holes" with the oxyanion, e.g.:

$$(H_2O)^+ + HSO_4^- \longrightarrow H_3O^+ + SO_4^- \qquad (15)$$

Hole scavengers such as Fe^{2+} were found to suppress their formation. The radicals were identified by their optical and magnetic spectra. SO_4^- shows a broad optical band with $\lambda_{max} = 445\ m\mu$ and an anisotropic ESR signal with no hyperfine structure ($g_1 = 2.0186$, $g_2 = 2.0134$, $g_3 = 2.0053$) (104).

The assignment of Weiss et al. has recently been supported by pulse radiolysis experiments (105). Deaerated $K_2S_2O_8$ solution gave a transient spectrum similar to that in the sulfuric acid glass. N_2O which scavenges electrons was found to suppress this absorption, thus indicating that reaction 14 is responsible for the formation of SO_4^-. The same absorption was also obtained by pulse-radiolyzing N_2O-saturated $1M$ Na_2SO_4 solution. N_2O is known to transform the solvated electron to OH and the latter oxidizes SO_4^{2-} to SO_4^-. In this case sodium formate (OH scavenger) was found to suppress the transient spectrum. However, Brown and Dainton consider the radical in the glass to be different from that in the liquid phase (Section II-A-3). Regarding the spectrum, this conclusion may be correct, since the degree of polymerization seems to have little effect on the spectrum of the analogous phosphate radical (Section V-C).

The radical in aqueous glass shows an interesting photochromism.* Its yellow color is bleached by visible light and it is restored in the dark slowly at 77°K and almost instantaneously at $\sim 120°K$ (65). The ESR spectrum also decays on bleaching, being replaced by a new signal at its higher field side. (This signal is weakly displayed by the radiolyzed glass even before bleaching and disappears on annealing.) Moorthy and Weiss explained this behavior as due to the following reaction:

$$SO_4^-\ H_2O \xrightarrow{\ h\nu\ } SO_4^{2-}\ (H_2O)^+ \qquad (16)$$

---

*A fine example of photochromism with trapping mechanism was discovered by Massey and Orgel (106).

The bleaching yields holes trapped in the hydration shell of the anion. The same hole center was produced from the photolysis of ClO_4, HPO_4^-, or of $Ce(ClO_4)_4$ in frozen $HClO_4$ solution. The latter process which is induced by 254 mμ light was considered to involve "hole" transfer from the ceric ion to the hydration layer of ClO_4^-.

C. Group V-b

The systems As_2O_3–As_2O_5 and Sb_2O_3–Sb_2O_5 are much used in glass technology to control the oxygen potential in the glass; they act as oxygen buffers. They have great influence on the coloration induced by radiation. Various solarization couples involving As_2O_5 are known (9) and As_2O_3 in an indispensable component in some high energy dosimeters. However, the role of arsenic in these cases is not clear. The change from As(III) to As(V) and conversely is not likely to occur in one stage; probably some intermediates are formed. As (IV) has been postulated as intermediate in a number of chemical and photochemical reactions (107).

A borate glass containing As_2O_3 and Bi_2O_3 develops on γ-irradiation an absorption band at 515 mμ (108). This glass was proposed as a dosimeter. The visible band has been attributed to bismuth atoms. The $^2P_{1/2} \leftarrow \,^4S_{3/2}$ optical transition of Bi is at 461 mμ (57), so this assignment may be correct. But it is more likely to be a Bi(II) intermediate.

1. HPO$_4^-$

This radical has been postulated for the photochemistry of HPO_4^{2-} (72). Weiss and Moorthy (65) produced the radical designated HPO_4^- by γ-radiolysis of frozen H_3PO_4 and NaH_2PO_4 solutions. The optical and ESR spectra of this radical closely resembles that of the "hole" center in metaphosphate and aluminophosphate glasses (Section IV-B): $\lambda_{max} = 525$ mμ and a doublet ESR structure with hf splitting of 35 G. The radical in ice may not be HPO_4^- but also may be some polymer chain (27); it is not likely to be the same as in metaphosphate glass if the average polymer chain is considered. This shows that the extent and nature of polymerization has little effect on the spectra of the electron-deficient phosphate radical. Still, they may differ in other properties.

The radical in aqueous glass displays photochromism similar to that of SO_4^- (Section V-B-2).

D. Lead

Pb^{2+} is a common ingredient of commercial glasses, where it usually acts as a network modifier. Only at high concentrations does it act also as a network former. When *lead silicate glass* is subjected to high energy radiation, it develops an optical absorption which can be bleached thermally or optically. By gaussian analysis, the spectrum was resolved into two bands with peaks at 370 and 490 mμ (109). X-ray irradiation of Pb^{2+} doped *metaphosphate glass* leads to some new ill-defined absorption in the UV peaking at about 290 mμ (Fig. 4); it is separate from the visible band ordinarily induced in the base glass (110). Comparing the ESR spectra of the irradiated MP glasses, with and without Pb^{2+}, shows that the electron signal has disappeared leaving the hole center (Section IV-B). Any contribution of lead to the visible color is probably masked by that of the hole center; no contribution to the ESR spectrum could be detected.

The above results suggest the Pb^{2+} affects the coloration by trapping electrons and undergoing reduction to Pb^+. This conclusion is supported by recent experiments. The spectrum of reduced Pb^{2+}, as derived from the pulse radiolysis of Pb^{2+} solution, shows a broad asymmetric band with a peak at about 310 mμ (111), very similar to that in MP. The shift in MP is rather small, whereas in the silicate glass the calculated position of the peak may be in error. This band is probably due to Pb^+, but one also should consider the possibility that it arises from Pb^0. The $^3P_1 \leftarrow {}^3P_0$ transition of free lead atoms is at 283 mμ (57). Pb^+ being its precursor should also be present in the glass.

Like most M^+ radicals in glass the 290 mμ band of lead undergoes fast optical bleaching. For further discussion of monovalent cations, see Section V-F-1.

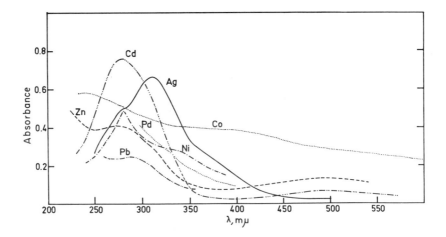

Fig. 4. The spectra of x-irradiated metaphosphate glass doped with various cations. Spectra taken with Cary-14 spectrophotometer.

E. Group III-b

1. Thallium

Tl^+ is used as an activator in various luminescent crystals and glasses, alone or in combination with other activators. For this reason much work has been done on its light absorption and fluorescence properties. (For some discussion of this see refs. 9 and 68.) Related to this are the chemical changes induced in Tl^+ systems by irradiation. Some interesting results have recently been obtained (112). The pulse radiolysis of Tl_2SO_4 in aqueous solution yields transient spectra which were assigned to Tl^{2+} and Tl_2^+. The former has an absorption peak at 260 mμ with $\epsilon_{max} = 5400 \pm 50 M^{-1} cm^{-1}$, and the latter shows a broad maximum near 400 mμ with $\epsilon_{max} = 12000 \pm 2500 M^{-1} cm^{-1}$. This assignment followed from the effect of electron scavengers and Tl^+ concentration on the transient spectra. The equilibrium $Tl^0 + Tl^+ \rightleftharpoons Tl_2^+$ was found to be well to the right with $K = 2.3 \times 10^3 M^{-1}$. The decay of these radicals proceeds according to the reaction: $Tl_2^+ + Tl^{2+} \rightarrow 3Tl^+$ and $2Tl^{2+} \rightarrow Tl^+ + Tl^{3+}$.

H_2SO_4 Glass. γ-Irradiation of sulfuric acid glass doped with Tl^+ (105) probably produces the same radicals. The visible band appears already at 77°K and its spectrum overlaps that of SO_4^- (Section V-B-2). Tl^{2+} appears only on warming to 143–145°K, when the radicals SO_4^- decay. This shows that at 77°K the holes are preferentially scavenged by HSO_4^- (or the corresponding polymer chains) and they are transferred to Tl^+ only at about 145°K. These experiments refer to the following glass composition: $5.4M$ H_2SO_4 and $6.5 \times 10^{-2}M$ Tl_2SO_4.

In the acid glass the two bands have their peaks at 417 and 267 mμ. (Apart from these, two other bands appear on warming, at 541 and 625 mμ.) In agreement with Cercek et al., the 267 mμ band was assigned to Tl^{2+}. On the other hand, the 417 mμ band was attributed to Tl^0. In the gas phase the $7^2S_{1/2} \leftarrow 6^2P_{1/2}$ transition of Tl^0 is at 377.5 mμ (57). A shift of 2500 cm^{-1} is a rather large environmental effect for a neutral atom, but is not impossible (see Section V-G-1). It appears that the radical is Tl_2^+, as proposed by Cercek et al. The increase of its absorption with Tl^+ concentration (105) can be thus readily explained. The origin of the 541 and 625 mμ bands is not clear. There is no evidence for them in the liquid phase.

2. Indium and Gallium

In x-irradiated *soda-silica glasses* these elements produce intense absorption bands in the UV at about 320 and 260 mμ for indium and gallium, respectively (113). In fused silica the radiation-induced gallium band is at 244 mμ (114). These bands were ascribed to the elements in their lower oxidation states (113). However, the result for indium seems to be at variance with that obtained from *sulfuric acid glass* (105), where the reduced ion shows a strong absorption peaking at 250 mμ. Pulse radiolysis of In^{3+} solution showed "the tail of a similar spectrum at wavelengths greater than 250 mμ" (105). The 250 mμ band was attributed to In^{2+} and the gradual blue shift in the isoelectronic series Ag^0, Cd$^+$, In^{2+} was pointed out. The results for reduced Ga^{3+} obtained by these techniques may be similar to that in silicate glass, since the former shows absorption at wavelengths less than 320 mμ (105). Indium is known to have stable monovalent compounds and so it may be present in the silicate glass in its monovalent state (at least partially) and be further reduced by radiation to atomic indium. The $^2P_{1/2,3/2} \leftarrow {}^2P_{1/2}$ transitions of the latter in the free state are at 314 and 311 mμ (57), close to that observed in the glass.

F. Group II

Cd^{2+} and Zn^{2+}, especially in combination with sulfur and selenium, are widely used in making special colored and luminiscent glasses. The effect of these ions on radiation-induced coloration is thus of special interest. Some of the "impurity centers" involved, which appear to be free radicals, will be discussed here.

1. Cadmium

Cd$^+$ has been identified in the liquid phase and in low and room temperature glasses.

The pulse radiolysis of Cd^{2+} aqueous solution gives rise to a transient absorption at about 300 mμ, which grows up simultaneously with the decay of solvated electron absorption (111,115). It was assigned to Cd$^+$. It is reoxidized either by OH (directly or by first undergoing dismutation to Cd^{2+} and Cd^0 and the latter then being oxidized) or by water. From the known extinction coefficient of e_{aq}^- at 543 mμ the value ϵ_{max}(Cd$^+$) = $7500 M^{-1}$ cm^{-1} could be determined. This value actually refers to 313 mμ, but the difference is rather small. This Laporte-allowed transition, as well as that of some other M$^+$ radicals similarly produced, has been considered to involve electron transfer from cation to water. The most puzzling property of these M$^+$ radicals is that their spectra lie so close to each other (λ_{max} at about 300 mμ). Baxendale et al. (111) attribute this to some balance between the effects of two factors determining $h\nu_{max}$: ionization potential and size of the ion. They base their view on the simple model proposed by Dainton and James (116) for the spectra of the reducing bivalent ions of the first transition group. However, in the latter case it was argued that since the band intensities are rather low, the transitions may be the Laporte-forbidden $3d^n \rightarrow 3d^{n-1} 4s$ (117). The possibility that the spectra of M^+ may also involve internal transitions, should be considered. The spin allowed $S \rightarrow P$ transitions of Cd^+ and Zn^+ in the gas phase are at 220 and 204 mμ, respectively (57) (the average of the multiplet is taken). The orbital energy difference between s and p decreases on going to solutions or complexes (Section V-G-1). This is probably due to participation of the s orbital in chemical bonding with the unpaired electron occupying an antibonding molecular orbital. Therefore, in aqueous solution the spectra of these ions may be removed to about 300 mμ. As in the case of the M^{2+} cations mentioned above, the excited states of M^+ may be highly reducing and transfer the p electron to an available acceptor.

Further support for the identification of Cd^+ and other M^+ radicals was derived from the work with frozen solutions and glasses. The paramagnetic resonance spectrum of the radicals could thus be measured.

Frozen Aqueous Solutions. Moorthy and Weiss (104) produced the radical by γ-radiolysis of polycrystalline frozen solution of $CdSO_4$ (77°K). The ESR spectrum showed, in addition to the known signals of OH, SO_4^-, and H, a new signal which was assigned to Cd^+. Its overlapping with the other signals could be prevented by using Fe^{2+} as scavenger for the holes and annealing at 110°K to bleach the OH center. At 77°K Fe^{2+} does not scavenge the OH radicals which are presumably not mobile in ice at this temperature. Electron scavengers, such as Fe^{3+} and H_2O_2, could effectively suppress the Cd^+ signal. Its g factors ($g_1 = g_2 = 1.9880$, $g_3 = 1.9989$) are typical for an electron-excess center and are in accord with the electron occupying a nearly pure s orbital. However, apart from the singlet, two weaker doublets are expected with very large hf splitting. These should result from ^{111}Cd (12.86%) and ^{113}Cd (12.34%) with spins $\frac{1}{2}$ and nuclear magnetic moments which are about five times larger than that of the silver isotopes. Since the s orbital in Cd^+ should be more confined than in Ag^0, the hf splitting expected for these isotopes is larger than 3000 G (Section V-G-1). For this reason the doublets could have escaped detection.

Working with sulfuric acid glasses, Brown and Dainton (105) were able to record the spectrum of the radical, which was found to be identical with that in the liquid phase. It is supressed by adding $ClCH_2COOH$ and NO_3^- to the glass, the latter, which is probably converted to NO_2^+, is more effecient. The decay of the radical at 150–152°K was attributed to reactions similar to those proposed by Baxendale et al. (111) with SO_4^- replacing OH. The weak band at 244 mμ, which became apparent as the main band decayed, may be due to Cd^0 atoms, which result from dismutation. The pulse radiolysis also gives rise to a band at 250 mμ with a halflife of about 5 msec (118). The strong $^1P_1 \leftarrow ^1S_0$ transition of Cd^0 in the gas phase is at

229 mμ. On further warming to 155°K the Cd atoms are probably oxidized by SO_4^- to Cd^{2+}.

Considering the formation of $M^{(n-1)+}$ as homogeneous competition between M^{n+} and the acid traps for the electrons, a simple expression was derived (105) relating the absorbance of the radical to the concentration of M^{n+}. It agrees with experiment in the case of Cd^{2+}, In^{3+}, and Ag^+.

Room Temperature Glasses. X-ray or UV irradiation of metaphosphate glass containing $CdSO_4$ leads to optical and ESR spectra which can be attributed to Cd^+ (34). This is concommitant with the suppression of the electron center (Section IV-B). The resonance signal of Cd^+ overlaps the high field component of the hole center. They could be separated by increasing the microwave frequency or the hole center could be completely suppressed by adding Br^- or I^- to the glass. The Cd^+ signal in MP has g value close to that in ice and shows marked power saturation already at room temperature. Its optical band is similar in shape to that in aqueous solution but with $\lambda_{max} \sim 280$ mμ (Fig. 4); the hole center is also apparent. In both media the cadmium band exhibits a pronounced asymmetry which suggests the occurrence of two overlapping electronic transitions originating in the same species. These may be the two components of the $^2P \leftarrow {}^2S$ transition in Cd^+, which in the gas phase are separated by about 2500 cm^{-1} (57). Both the optical and ESR spectra undergo fast bleaching by light of 254 mμ. The hole center fades simultaneously. This supports the view that the transition ultimately leads to electron transfer from the ion to the medium.

X-irradiation of Cd^{2+}-doped silicate glass leads to an absorption band at about 320 mμ, which may be assigned to Cd^+ (113). It does not appear in glasses which are prepared under strongly reducing conditions. This is probably due to the Cd^{2+} being chemically reduced to the metal under such conditions.

2. Zinc

The bimolecular rate constant for the reaction of Zn^{2+} with the solvated electron is considerably smaller than that of many electron traps, e.g., it is about 1/30 that of Cd^{2+}. For this reason the formation of Zn^+ may not be apparent in media which have marked trapping efficiency for the electrons, unless high concentrations of Zn^{2+} are employed. And indeed, in *sulfuric acid glass* there has not been evidence for the production of Zn^+ induced by irradiation (105). On the other hand, frozen polycrystalline samples of $ZnSO_4$ solution, when γ-radiolyzed, showed a weak signal which could be assigned to Zn^+ (104). *Metaphosphate glass* doped with a high concentration of Zn^{2+} (110) shows on x-irradiation a band at about

280 mμ (Fig. 4) (the hole center is also apparent). A similar spectrum with peak at 300 mμ is produced in aqueous solution by pulse radiolysis (115), with $\epsilon_{max} \sim 5200\ M^{-1}\ cm^{-1}$. In the latter case there is some evidence for the formation of Zn^0 by dismutation.

3. Magnesium

Mg^{2+} is still weaker electron scavenger. The optical spectrum of Mg^+ has not been reported. A weak ESR signal assigned to it was produced by γ-radiolysis of frozen $MgSO_4$ solution (104). A regular decrease in g factor in going from Mg^+ to Cd^+ was observed and it was attributed to the gradual increase in binding of the unpaired electron.

4. Mercury

The true monovalent mercury ion Hg^+ (to distinguish from the dimer Hg_2^+) was reported in frozen aqueous solution (13) and in sulfuric acid glass (105). In the former, the ESR of the radical was obtained, whereas in the latter—the tail of an optical band was observed with λ_{max} below 240 mμ. This may be due to the Laporte-forbidden $^2D_{3/2} \leftarrow {}^2S_{1/2}$ transition, which in the gas phase occurs at 198 mμ (57). For mercury with its pronounced j–j coupling this band may be quite strong.

G. Group I-b

Weyl contributes a substantial part of his monograph (9) to colored glasses containing copper, silver, and gold, such as the purple gold ruby, the red copper ruby, and the yellow silver glass. "The glasses owe their color to the selective light absorption of metals in a finely subdivided state. The cromophore groups in this case are very large, consisting of a crystalline arrangement of at least several hundred atoms. . . . Gold or silver can also form atomic solutions in glass but in this state of subdivision, which might be called 'frozen-in metal vapor,' the characteristic light absorption is absent." This frozen-in metal vapor is actually a system of trapped free radicals and the aggregation of these radicals to form the chromophor group is a radical annihilation process. It involves spin pairing, e.g., formation of M_2 molecules and loss of the characteristic paramagnetism of the atoms. The study of the true metal–glass solutions and the aggregation processes which they undergo on heating ("striking" as it is called in glass technology) is thus of great importance. Such solutions have been considered to be formed by rapidly chilling the liquid solution or, when the glass can be doped with the corresponding ions, by reducing the ions in the rigid matrix. Most of the research carried out in this direction concerns silver.

1. Silver

Weil proposed two methods for reducing Ag^+ to Ag^0 in the glass: (1) Treating the glass with H_2 at relatively low temperatures (between 80° and 120°C) in order to prevent the aggregation of the atoms. This method is not suitable for phosphate glasses in which Ag^+ is more tightly bound than in silicate glass. (2) Bombarding the glass with electrons by exposing it to cathode radiation. No clear-cut evidence was presented for the formation of silver atoms by these methods. Closely related to the latter method is to subject the glass to high energy radiation. But in this case, Ag^+ may also interact with the holes to produce Ag^{2+}. Since most of the works described below have used ionizing radiation (or 185 mμ light), the radicals Ag^0 and Ag^{2+} often occur together. Their identification relies much on two works: that of Delbecq et al. (119), who studied the effect of x-ray radiation on Ag^+–KCl single crystals, and the pulse-radiolysis work of Baxendale et al. (120).

Frozen Aqueous Solution. Shields (121,122) presented ESR evidence for the formation of Ag^0, Ag^{2+}, and Ag_2^+ in γ-irradiated frozen solution of $AgNO_3$. The resemblance between Ag^+ and Tl^+ (Section V-E-1) is thus illustrated again. Here are the main results of Shields' work: Ag^0 is readily produced at 77°K, but its resonance spectrum is simplified by warming to 150°K and remains so on cooling to 77°K. The warming was considered to annihilate the small proportions of Ag^0 situated in slightly different crystal fields. The simplified spectrum shows a pair of doublets with the same g values but with different hf splittings: 505 G for ^{109}Ag and 435 G for ^{107}Ag. The spectrum could be analyzed in terms of axially symmetric tensors. It is characterized by a considerable anisotropic negative g shift. This was ascribed to mixing of the 5p orbital into the ground state which is a precondition for a Jahn-Teller distortion. The relatively large reduction in the hf splitting $\Delta\nu$, compared with that of the free atom, was attributed to electronic delocalization on the ligands, $(\Delta\nu_{free} - \Delta\nu)/\Delta\nu_{free}$ was taken to measure the extent of the delocalization. It was found to be 0.28 for both Ag^0 isotopes in ice. Thus, in this case at least, the picture presented by Weyl (9) of separated single atoms slightly perturbed by the medium, does not seem to fit reality. The metal atoms appear to chemically interact with their ligands. This also explains the considerable shift in the optical spectrum (see below).

Hole scavenging by Ag^+ does not occur readily in ice. High concentration of Ag^+ ($\geqslant 10$ M) is required to produce Ag^{2+}, and this was considered to involve direct ionization of the solvated Ag^+ ion (121). If it is correct, as Moorthy and Weiss (13) propose, that electrons in ice cannot react without the holes reacting simultaneously, then we have to assume that the Ag^+ ions are reduced by H atoms. This is known to be a very fast reaction (120). As to the remaining OH radicals, they were found to display a relatively intense signal in the central part of the spectrum. Ag^{2+} could be more readily produced in sulfuric acid glass (see below). Its ESR spectrum lies in the low field side and displays an axially symmetric g anisotropy. The hf splitting is primarily isotropic and small so that the isotopes were not resolved.

KF in the frozen solution has an interesting effect on the radiation products (122). It increases the yield of Ag^0. This effect was ascribed to the enhancement of the reactivity of e_{aq}^-; however, as discussed above, this explanation may be incorrect. Above 150°K KF brings about the conversion of Ag^0 to Ag_2^+. The mechanism of this effect is not clear. Ag_2^+ was identified by its ESR spectrum which consists of a hf triplet with each component further resolved into three. In sulfuric acid or alcohol glasses Ag_2^+ could be produced in the absence of KF.

In sulfuric acid glasses the silver radicals could be followed spectrophotometrically. Very relevant here are the results obtained by the pulse radiolysis of Ag^+ aqueous solutions (120). Three transient species were claimed to be detected by this technique: (1) Ag^0 has $\lambda_{max} = 310$ mμ ($\epsilon_{max} = 2.3 \times 10^4$). The $5^2P_{1/2,3/2} \leftarrow 5^2S_{1/2}$ transitions of Ag^0 in the gas phase are at 339 and 328 mμ (57). Ag^0 always appears after the pulse and in the absence of O_2 it decays relatively slowly by a second-order process which is probably $2Ag \rightarrow Ag_2$. (2) Ag^{2+} has $\lambda_{max} = 270$ mμ. It is formed more slowly, probably from Ag^+ + OH. (3) An unidentified species has λ_{max} at about 360 mμ; it is produced by a very fast reaction which is faster than the reaction e_{aq}^- + Ag^+ and decays rapidly at a rate increasing with Ag^+ concentration. It was tentatively identified as an excited Ag^+ ion. Now, it is difficult to reconcile these results with those obtained from sulfuric acid glasses. At 77°K the radiolyzed glass shows a strong absorption peaking at 350 mμ with a rather weak shoulder at 313 mμ (105). The band is suppressed by electron scavengers. The same glass shows the ESR signals of silver atoms and a broad unidentified absorption on the low field side in addition to the signals of H and SO_4^- (122). On warming to about 146°K, the 350 mμ band decays and the 313 mμ band builds up together with a new band at about 275 mμ (105). The corresponding ESR spectra show the decay of silver atoms and the buildup of Ag_2^+ and Ag^{2+}. Other broad unidentified signals also appear (122).

The above works seem to agree only with respect to Ag^{2+}. It is formed on warming the glass by the reaction Ag^+ + $SO_4^- \rightarrow Ag^{2+}$ + SO_4^{2-}. On the other hand, the results concerning the 310 mμ band are perplexing. One may also inquire if there is any close relation between the 350 mμ band displayed by the glass and the 360 mμ band produced by pulse radiolysis. Such relation rules out the excited Ag^+ theory. One is tempted to assign this band to Ag^0 and the 310 mμ band to Ag_2^+. (The formation of Tl_2^+ is known to be very fast, being completed within 2 μsec at $5 \times 10^{-4} M$ Tl^+ (112).) This appears to be confirmed by the works with room temperature glasses.

Phosphate Glasses. The radiation-induced color centers in silver activated phosphate glasses have been extensively studied by Schulman and his co-workers (123). The absorption changes and the optically excited luminescence of these centers are utilized for high energy dosimetry. The radiophotoluminescent glass dosimeters are usually composed of $(Ag, K, Ba, Al)PO_3$ or $(Ag, Li, Mg, Al)PO_3$. X-irradiation of such glasses does not produce the ordinary pink coloration of the base glass but a new band peaking at about 320 mμ. The new center is quite stable at room temperature. It can be excited by light in its absorption band to give visible fluorescence. Schulman et al. assigned the 320 mμ band to Ag^0. Trapping of holes by Ag^+ was not taken into account; the pink coloration was ascribed to trapped electrons and its suppression by Ag^+ was considered as an electron scavenging process. Actually, this is a hole scavenging process (Section IV-B) and so Ag^{2+} should be produced.

Tucker (61) measured the x-ray induced ESR spectrum of calcium metaphosphate glass with about 2% silver added. Three distinct resonance signals were observed, two were assigned to Ag^0 (the hf doublet with about 650 G splitting) and the most intense one to Ag^{2+} ($g_{\perp} = 2.07$, the parallel features weakly displayed with $g_{\parallel} \sim 2.27$). Another weak signal appearing at the high field side was not identified. Recent investigation (69) of Ag^+-doped sodium metaphosphate supports part of this assignment and also relates the resonance signals to the optical bands. Silver ions suppress both the electron and hole centers, which characterize the irradiated base glass (Section IV-B). The new ESR spectrum shows a strong signal at the low field side with an unresolved pattern at both sides (Fig. 5). The optical spectrum shows a well-defined peak at 313 mμ and some inflections representing other concealed bands, the most prominent are near 280 and 370 mμ (Fig. 4). Electron scavengers (Pb^{2+} and Cd^{2+}) suppress the optical absorption above 300 mμ and the unresolved ESR pattern—which are thus assigned to reduced silver species—leaving the 280 mμ band and signal C together with some minor features (Fig. 6). The latter spectrum, which suggests an axially symmetric center, is suppressed by Ce^{3+} which acts as an efficient hole scavenger. Thus, the 280 mμ band and the corresponding ESR signal belong to Ag^{2+} with $g_{\perp} = 2.041$ and $g_{\parallel} \sim 2.34$. ($g_{\perp} = 2.065$ and $g_{\parallel} \sim 2.35$ are displayed in sulfuric acid glass (122); see also Section V-H-1.)

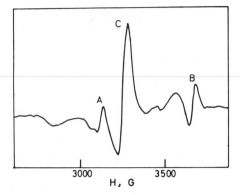

Fig. 5. The ESR spectrum of x-irradiated metaphosphate glass doped with Ag_2O, taken with Varian V-4502 spectrometer at 9.4 kMcps.

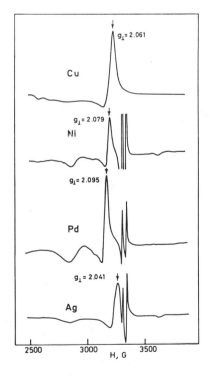

Fig. 6. The ESR spectra of various d^9 ions in metaphosphate glass. Ag^{2+}, Pd^+, and Ni^+ obtained by x-irradiation of the glass doped with Ag_2O, $PdCl_2$, and $NiSO_4$, respectively. Spectra taken with Varian V-4502 spectrometer at 9.4 kMcps.

The irradiation effects were also studied at 77°K (69). The optical spectrum could now be resolved into two prominent bands peaking at about 365 and 315 mμ, which grow up with irradiation time at constant ratio. On lowering the Ag^+ concentration the 365 mμ band is relatively enhanced and the corresponding ESR spectrum becomes close in shape to that of silver atoms in various matrices; the hf splittings are 1.65 and 1.91 kMc/sec, very close to the zero field splittings of $^{107}Ag^0$ and $^{109}Ag^0$, respectively. The 365 mμ band is selectively bleached by light of $\lambda > 300$ mμ. It also undergoes thermal bleaching, but in this case its decay is accompanied by the growth of the 315 mμ band. The characteristic ESR spectrum of Ag^0 could be correlated with the 365 mμ band by comparing their dependence on (Ag^+) and bleaching processes. These results have led to the assignment of the 365 mμ and 315 mμ bands to Ag^0 and Ag_2^+, respectively. The ESR spectrum of the glass at room temperature, when freed from the Ag^{2+} signal by Ce^{3+}, shows a smeared triplet structure, which may be due to Ag_2^+.

The $5s \to 5p$ transition of Ag^0 in metaphosphate glass is red shifted by about 2500 cm^{-1} relative to the free atom. This shift is smaller than that displayed by Ag^0 in KCl (119). It shows that the oxygen ligands in metaphosphate are less efficient in chemically interacting with Ag^0. And indeed while there is hardly any reduction in the hf splitting of Ag^0 in metaphosphate, an 8% reduction was observed in KCl (119). Further support to this relation between red shift and reduction of hf splitting is provided by the sulfuric acid glasses, where Ag^0 exhibits a red shift of 1400 cm^{-1} (105) and only 1% reduction of hf splitting (122). The sulfate and phosphate groups appear to be less efficient than Cl^- in forming complexes with silver atoms.

The pulse radiolysis work (120) remains obscure. Ionic strength effects on the decay of the various species should be studied in order to determine their charges.

H. Group VIII

Iron is the most common impurity in glass, but still little is known about its abnormal valence states. The rate constant of the hydrated electron with Fe^{2+} is relatively low (111) so other scavengers or electron traps may efficiently compete with the reduction of Fe^{2+}. Moreover, even if Fe^+ is formed, it probably escapes detection since its allowed $y^6P_{7/2} \leftarrow a^6D_{9/2}$ transition is in the far-UV region; it is at 161 mμ in the gas phase (57). Indeed its spectrum could not be observed in solution (111). Some evidence is available for the formation of unstable *coordination* states of Fe^{3+} in sulfuric acid glass, e.g., the uncomplexed ion (105).

1. Nickel

Ni^+ has been detected in *liquid solution* (111,115), *sulfuric acid glass* (105) and *metaphosphate glass* (34). In all cases it shows a relatively sharp peak at 280–290 mμ. Its maximum extinction coefficient is about 2500 M^{-1} cm^{-1} [2100 M^{-1} cm^{-1} at 313 mμ (111)]. In the two glasses it also displays another band, appearing as a "shoulder" on the long wavelength side (Fig. 4) (34,105). Since the latter has no parallel in solution and, furthermore, its intensity relative to the main peak was found to vary (34), this band is not directly related to Ni^+. The 300 mμ band of Ni^+ may be assigned to the $a^2P_{3/2} \leftarrow a^2D_{5/2}$ transition (57) which is *blue* shifted in solution by about 5000 cm^{-1}.

Further evidence pertinent to the identification of Ni^+ comes from the ESR spectrum of the radical in metaphosphate glass (Fig. 6). The formation of a d^9 radical is strongly suggested by the resemblance of its resonance signal to that of Cu^{2+} and also to that of other presumably d^9 radicals— Ag^{2+} and Pd^+. All lie on the low field side with axially symmetric g tensors, which indicate a strong tetragonal distortion of the elongated octahedron type. (In CaO crystal Ni^+ appears to be in a compressed octahedron (124).) The parallel features of these signals in glass are ill-defined.

The Ni^+ center, as with all the M^+ centers discussed here, is readily bleached by 254 mμ light

2. Palladium

Metaphosphate glass doped with Pd^{2+} gives rise on x-irradiation to a new ESR signal which can be assigned to Pd^+ (Fig. 6) (110). No distinct optical band bould be assigned to the radical. However, there is some new absorption tail in the UV (Fig. 4); a similar increase in absorption was obtained by pulse radiolysis (105).

3. Cobalt

Co^{2+} strongly suppresses the visible coloration induced by ionizing radiation in *phosphate and silicate glasses* (66,125). This is probably due to hole scavenging and formation of Co^{3+} (Section IV). At the same time, there is a general growth in the ultraviolet absorption reaching into the short-wave visible range. This absorption has been utilized for high-level dosimetry (125). It may be due to Co^+, produced by electron scavenging since Co^{3+} has no strong absorption in this region. And indeed, both pulse radiolysis (115) and *sulfuric acid glass* methods (105) suggest that Co^+ has a broad absorption extending into the visible. However, the two methods give somewhat different results. Figure 4 shows the result recently obtained (110) by x-irradiation of Co^{2+}-doped *metaphosphate glass.* The absorption shows a very broad ill-defined band at about 400 mμ which may be the analog of the 370 mμ band detected in solution (115). It may originate from the $a^3D_3 \leftarrow a^3F_4$ transition, which is at 364 mμ in the gas phase (57). There is no indication of the 300 mμ band detected in solution (115), but the general appearance shows some resemblance. Small contributions from other absorbing species may be responsible for the difference in shape.

I. Manganese

Mn$^+$ has been reported in liquid solution (115) and in *sulfuric acid glass* (105) with a peak at about 290 mμ. The rather broad band may conceal the three close transitions $(3d^54p)^7P_{2,3,4} \leftarrow (3d^54s)^7S_3$, which in the gas phase are at 268, 260, and 258 mμ (57).

J. Chromium and Tungsten

Pentavalent chromium appears to be present in Cr^{3+} containing *borate and borosilicate glasses* (126). It shows an asymmetric resonance line with $g = 1.97$. A similar signal is shown by chromia–alumina catalysts (127), by frozen solutions of $K_2Cr_2O_7$ and CrO_3 with various organic acids (128) (these solutions show some radical stability even at room temperature) and by γ-irradiated frozen solutions of CrO_4^{2-} or $Cr_2O_7^{2-}$ (13). The paramagnetic species shows axial symmetry, with $g_\perp$ either smaller or larger than $g_\parallel$. Pulse radiolysis of CrO_4^{2-} gives rise to a transient absorption (111) which may be due to CrO_4^{3-}.

Pentavalent *tungsten* was reported to be formed in *silicate and phosphate glasses*, containing WO_3, when melted under reducing conditions (129). It displays a large negative g shift. Tungsten probably enters the oxygen tetrahedra, acting as a network former.

K. Conclusions

The results described in this section show that the radiation-induced "impurity centers" in glasses are very often definite chemical species, produced by reduction or oxidation processes. Their study in glasses may thus give reliable information about their properties in the liquid phase. Some of these radicals, e.g., Pb$^+$, Cd$^+$, etc., are probably responsible for "impurity centers" in crystals (68), in the same way as the dihalide ions produce the V_k centers.

VI. ORGANIC RADICALS

Aromatic radical ions, in particular, have been studied in glasses. (For a recent review on aromatic free radicals in general see Ref. 130.) Both UV and ionizing radiations have been used for their production. The study of photoionization in rigid media was initiated by the work of Lewis and Lipkin (131) on aromatic amines and hydrazines and has developed to include aromatic hydrocarbons with relatively high ionization potentials. Much consideration has been given to the mechanism by which a photon of 3–5 eV can induce such ionization. Owing to polarization effects, the ionization potential in these media may be somewhat smaller. This effect should increase with polarity of the medium and so should be most operative in inorganic glasses. And indeed, the photoionization of a few aromatic hydrocarbons could be achieved in boric acid glass but not in vitreous glucose or various plastics (132). However, the ionization potential is not likely to be reduced to about half its value in the gas phase. Recent works (133,134) have shown that some of these reactions are actually biphotonic involving the triplet state as intermediate. (For a review of some earlier works on this subject see Ref. 135.) The effect of the rigid matrix is to increase the lifetime of the triplet state, so that a second photon can be absorbed by the triplet molecule. In some cases the excited triplet can also sensitize the dissociation of the solvent to produce free radicals and hydrogen atoms, which abstract another H atom from the solvent or the solute (134,135). The rate of such biphotonic reactions, where the excitation of the triplet competes with its decay, should be proportion to I^n, where I is the light intensity and n depends on the range of I, increasing from 1 to 2 with *decrease* of I (134).

The methods used for establishing photoionization in glass are summarized in reference 133.

The following short review describes this kind of work which has been conducted with inorganic glasses.

A. Aromatic Hydrocarbon Ions

These ions are readily produced in solution by chemical methods: the positive ions by oxidation in concentrated sulfuric acid, and the negative ions by reduction under vacuum with alkali metals in tetrahydrofuran (136).

Boric Acid Glass. Ionization of aromatic hydrocarbons in boric glass at room temperature was first demonstrated by Evans (3). *Triphenylene* showed rapid photodecomposition with the formation of a blue color and paramagnetism that remained after decay of the phosphorescence. Irradiation of *3,4-benzpyrene* in this medium was shown later to yield a residual red color (137). Such changes were ascribed to formation of free radicals (3). It was left to Bennema et al. (35) to show that the spectra of these radicals are identical with those of the monopositive ions of triphenylene and 3,4-benzpyrene, respectively. In the former case the spectrum of the positive ion was not known previously and so it was compared with that of the negative ion, which should be very similar; see later. They extended the work to other aromatic hydrocarbons: *biphenyl, phenanthrene, tetracene, pyrene, perylene,* and *coronene.* The photoproduction of radicals was also confirmed by their ESR spectra which however were not recorded. The identity of some other radicals with the corresponding positive ions was also shown; so the general conclusion was that in all these cases photoionization occurs with formation of cation radicals and electrons. The latter were assumed to be trapped in the glass.

The fate of the ejected electron was investigated by Feldmann and Jortner (36). They carried out a kinetic study of the radical production in order to shed light on the mechanism of photoionization. The hydrocarbons investigated were: *anthracene,* phenanthrene, pyrene, perylene, and 3,4-benzpyrene. This work showed:

1. The quantum yields are very low (initial values about 10^{-5} to 10^{-4}) and decrease with time of irradiation until the concentration of the product reaches some saturation value which is only a small fraction of the solute concentration. This has not been confirmed by later work (132) but if correct it suggests that the positive ions have relatively large electron capture cross sections. When considerable ionization occurs, the inner filter effect of the product may lead to apparent saturation.

2. In the range 254–365 mμ no definite ionization threshold could be observed. A probable exception is anthracene, which did not show radical production at 365 mμ. The quantum yields increase with the photon energy, but not steeply.

3. The initial quantum yields appear to be independent of the solute concentration and light intensity. However, these results are not very reliable, since the reproducibility was rather poor. It is difficult to produce duplicate glasses with exactly the same properties. This kind of work must be repeated; in particular the study of the light intensity effect should be restudied. For some of these hydrocarbons (phenanthrene and perylene) in 3-methylpentane (77°K) a biphotonic photoionization has been *kinetically* established (134), and it is of interest to check if this also applies to boric acid glass. However, the quantum yield may still be nearly independent of light intensity if the lifetime of the triplet is long enough.

4. No spectroscopic indication of trapped electrons could be detected. The electrons were thus supposed to attach to the solute molecules to produce the mononegative ions. Molecular orbital theory predicts that the optical spectra of both radical cation and anion of an alternate hydrocarbon should be very similar (138,139). Therefore, the formation of the negative ion cannot be distinguished. Still, it was shown (36) that x-ray and UV irradiation lead to the same results, and this was considered to prove that the aromatic hydrocarbons scavenge electrons in the glass. However, the x-ray effect may also be interpreted as due to hole scavenging.

5. The radicals disappear on warming by a second-order reaction with a rather large activation energy (~ 30 kcal for all the radicals). This was interpreted as due to the reaction:

$$M^+ + M^- \longrightarrow 2M$$

However, the reaction of M^+ with any reducing species of equal concentration (e.g., trapped electrons) could give the same result. In this connection, it is of interest to note that the annihilation is accompanied by phosphorescence emission of the hydrocarbon molecules (35). Such thermoluminescence is also displayed in rigid 3-methylpentane (133,134) and there it was attributed to recombination of M^+ with the electron.

Buck et al. (22) proposed that the excited molecule in its singlet state interacts with the medium. They have shown a correlation between the rates of photoionization of some aromatic hydrocarbons (*naphthalene*, anthracene, phenanthrene, pyrene, and perylene) and the basicities of their excited singlet states: the logarithm of the rate constant varies linearly with the energy required to localize an electron pair at the carbon atom at which the proton is attached. This correlation refers to the lowest excited state except for naphthalene and phenanthrene where the second excited state is involved. It was found that the first absorption band of phenanthrene and the *second* one of pyrene do not lead to photoionization.

Joussot-Dubien and Lesclaux (132,140,141) were the first to propose that these processes are actually biphotonic and involve the triplet state. By measuring the phosphorescene lifetimes of these molecules in the glass, they could show (140) that the rates of photoionization obtained by Buck et al. (22) increase with the triplet lifetime. An ionization process which occurs by two stages was illustrated by a simple experiment. Boric acid glass containing triphenylene, which has a very long triplet lifetime of about 10 sec, was irradiated with a mercury lamp, using a concentrated solution of triphenylene in alcohol as a filter. Thus the light reaching the glass could not excite the triphenylene molecules from their ground state, but could excite any triplet molecule present. The latter were produced by removing the filter every 8 sec for a few tenths of a second. The amount of radical ions thus produced was measured and compared to that obtained in a parallel experiment but with an opaque shutter instead of the filter. It was found that the yield in the first experiment, where additional excitation of the triplet occurred, was larger by a factor of ~ 2.

Magnetic susceptibility measurements were supposed to shed light on the fate of the ejected electron (132,141). Contrary to previous results (36) the following hydrocarbons were claimed to be completely photoionized in the glass: pyrene, 3,4-benzpyrene, triphenylene, and naphthalene. The magnetic susceptibilities finally obtained indicate no more than one mole of spins for one mole of hydrocarbon. This was considered to prove that the electrons are not trapped by the matrix as proposed by Bennema et al. (35). However, the evidence for complete ionization is not entirely convincing. It was proposed (132) that most of the electrons are captured by the solute molecules, so that altogether $2M \rightarrow M^+ + M^-$. Those electrons that are captured by the medium give rise to H atoms; the latter then either yield molecular hydrogen or react with the solute molecules or radicals. At 77°K the formation of H atoms could be confirmed by ESR measurements (50,132) (see also Section V-A-1). As further evidence for the formation of negative ions, a mixture of perylene and triphenylene was irradiated in the absorption band of triphenylene. This led to the growth of the perylene-radical spectrum. However, some energy transfer mechanism may be responsible for this result. Altogether, the negative ion theory, though plausible, requires more direct evidence.

Very interesting results supporting the biphotonic mechanism were obtained by studying the effect of light frequency, ν (142). The relative efficiency of photoionization was found to be practically independent of ν from the absorption onset ν_0 up to a certain critical frequency ν_c, where it increases sharply. This suggests that ν_c coincides with the ionization threshold and that in the range ν_0–ν_c the process is biphotonic.

Hughes et al. (50) carried out a detailed ESR analysis of the irradiation products. They have shown that irradiation actually leads to some addition of H atoms to the following aromatic molecules: *benzene*, *toluene*, naphthalene, and biphenyl. Unfiltered UV light, 2 MeV electrons, and x-rays gave the same radicals with relative concentrations dependent on the source of radiation. Apart from the radical ions there was evidence for radicals produced by saturation of one or more of the carbons in the ring. In the case of benzene the *cyclohexadienyl* radical was clearly identified, and it was practically the sole photochemical product. Its ESR pattern is of about 135 G extreme width. The other hydrocarbons also gave 100–140 G ESR patterns which could not be identified, but by analogy to benzene they were assigned to radicals with a —CH_2— group in the aromatic ring. In deuterated boric acid glass this pattern contracts, which suggests the formation of a —CHD— group. Moreover, deuteration appears to take place in other parts of these radicals and also in the radical ions by H and D interchange during irradiation.

It is difficult to distinguish between the ESR spectra of the positive and negative ion, especially in matrices where considerable hyperfine broadening occurs. The major difference is that the ESR pattern of the positive ion has somewhat greater extreme width (136) and its g value is somewhat smaller than that of the negative ion (143). Now, the radical ion of bi-phenyl in boric acid glass is similar to that of the negative biphenyl ion in solution but its extreme width is somewhat larger, 24 G instead of 21 G (50). This suggests that the radical ions in the glass are of the carbonium type. However, one cannot rely too much on this kind of evidence because this may be an environmental effect.

Frozen Aqueous Solutions. The UV irradiation of frozen solution of benzene in dilute sulfuric acid (77°K) gives an ESR spectrum of H atoms and a four-line pattern which was assigned to $C_6H_6^+$ (80). The intensity distribution in this pattern suggests that the unpaired electron spin inter-acts with three equivalent protons. To account for this a Frank-Haber mechanism of photochemical process was postulated, with the OH^- paired to the positive ion:

$$C_6H_6 + H_2O \xrightarrow{h\nu} C_6H_6^+ \cdots OH^- + H$$

Voevodsky et al. claimed that in this case the unpaired electron will tend to be mainly localized in the *ortho* and *para* positions, thus interacting with three protons. To support this argument it was shown that on warm-ing to 173°K the ESR spectrum of C_6H_5, the *phenyl radical*, is obtained. Proton transfer in the $C_6H_5^+ \cdots OH^-$ ion pair was assumed to occur. How-ever, this picture, though fascinating, is doubtful. The Frank-Haber mechanism has been refuted (see, e.g., Refs. 74 and 83) and, moreover, it is questionable if ion pairing can lead to these results. Altogether, the formation of $C_6H_6^+$ in this system has not been proved. Still, it was shown (80) that in nonpolar matrices the photolysis of benzene gives different results: the phenyl radical is the primary product. This may reflect the effect of polarity in inducing photoionization.

B. Phenoxyls

Aqueous Alkali Glasses. C_6H_5O was produced by photolysis of the phenolate anion in $10N$ KOH–NaOH aqueous solution at 77°K (8). The spectrum of the irradiated glass showed the strong broad absorption of trapped electrons with $\lambda_{max} = 586$ mμ, and two weak bands appearing as "shoulders" on the "electron band" at about 385 and 410 mμ. By com-parison with previous works (144) these weak bands were attributed to the phenoxy radical. Thus, clear-cut evidence is provided for the photo-ionization of the phenolate ion induced by irradiation in its $\pi \to \pi^*$ transition. Flash photolysis (144) and electron scavenging (145) methods show that this also occurs in the liquid phase.

Blandamer et al. (146), who repeated the alkali-glass experiment, ob-tained a broad ESR spectrum "almost certainly due to the phenoxy radical, but no optical or electron resonance absorption attributable to solvated electrons." The latter appears only on controlled warming after irradiation. The 185 mμ component of the light was found to be responsible for the photolysis. However, this wavelength should be completely absorbed by the hydroxide ions. We have recently confirmed the results of Jortner et al. and found that β-naphthol also gives the blue color of the trapped electron centers (147). The optical spectrum of the naphthoxyl radical ($\sim$465 mμ, ref. 144) was probably masked by this band and so could not be detected.

C. Conclusion

This review of organic radicals in inorganic glasses is not intended to be complete. It mainly emphasizes the role of the matrix in photoionization processes. Some interesting work was done in stabilizing radicals in alkali halide matrices (148). However, these are actually polycrystalline media and so they are out of the scope of this review.

References

1. M. Kasha, *J. Opt. Soc. Am.*, **38**, 1068 (1948).
2. G. N. Lewis, M. Calvin, and M. Kasha, *J. Chem. Phys.*, **17**, 804 (1949).
3. D. F. Evans, *Nature*, **176**, 777 (1955).
4. A. Zaliouk-Gitter and A. Treinin, *J. Chem. Phys.*, **42**, 2019 (1965).
5. T. Feldmann and A. Treinin, *J. Chem. Phys.*, **39**, 1352 (1963).
6. R. Livingston, H. Zeldes and E. H. Taylor, *Phys. Rev.*, **94**, 725 (1954); *Discussions Faraday Soc.*, **19**, 166 (1955).
7. D. Schulte-Frohlinde and K. Eiben, *Z. Naturforsch.*, **17a**, 445 (1962).
8. J. Jortner and B. Sharf, *J. Chem. Phys.*, **37**, 2506 (1962).
9. W. A. Weyl, *Coloured Glasses*, Dawson's of Pall Mall, London, 1959.
10. G. C. Pimentel, in *Formation and Trapping of Free Radicals*, A. M. Bass and H. P. Broida, Eds., Academic Press, 1960, p. 69.
11. C. K. Jen, in *Formation and Trapping of Free Radicals*, A. M. Bass and H. P. Broida, Eds., Academic Press, 1960, p. 213.
12. L. Kevan, in *Progress in Solid State Chemistry*, H. Reiss, Ed., Pergamon Press, 1965, p. 304.
13. P. N. Moorthy and J. J. Weiss, *Advan. Chem. Ser.*, **50**, 180 (1965).
14. J. D. Mackenzie, in *Modern Aspects of the Vitreous State*, Vol. 1, J. D. Mackenzie, Ed., Butterworths, London, 1960, p. 1.
15. J. H. Gibbs, in *Modern Aspects of the Vitreous State*, Vol. 1, J. D. Mackenzie, Ed., Butterworths, London, 1960, p. 152.
16. W. H. Zachariasen, *J. Am. Chem. Soc.*, **54**, 3841 (1932).
17. J. M. Stevels and A. Kats, *Philips Res. Rept.*, **11**, 103 (1956).
18. E. Thilo, *Advan. Inorg. Chem. Radiochem.*, **4**, 41 (1962).
19. M. E. Milberg, R. K. Belitz, and A. H. Silver, *Phys. Chem. Glasses*, **1**, 155 (1960).

20. M. E. Milberg and F. Meller, *J. Chem. Phys.*, **31**, 126 (1959); J. L. Parson and M. E. Milberg, *J. Am. Ceram. Soc.*, **43**, 326 (1960); F. Meller and M. E. Milberg, *ibid.*, **43**, 353 (1960).
21. A. H. Silver, *J. Chem. Phys.*, **32**, 959 (1960).
22. II. M. Buck, W. Th. A. M. Van der Lugt and L. J. Oosterhoff, *Tetrahedron*, **19** (Suppl. 2), 173 (1963).
23. F. A. Cotton and G. Wilkinson, *Advanced Inorganic Chemistry*, Interscience, New York, 1962.
24. J. A. Pryde and G. O. Jones, *Nature*, **170**, 685 (1952).
25. H. Krebs, *Angew. Chem. Intern. Ed.*, **5**, 544 (1966).
26. R. Livingston and J. Weinberger, *J. Chem. Phys.*, **33**, 499 (1960).
27. F. S. Dainton and F. T. Jones, *Trans. Faraday Soc.*, **61**, 1681 (1965).
28. R. H. Doremus, in *Modern Aspects of the Vitreous State*, Vol. 2, J. D. Mackenzie, Ed., Butterworths, London, 1962, p. 1.
29. H. L. Smith and A. J. Cohen, *Phys. Chem. Glasses*, **4**, 173 (1963).
30. J. M. Stevels and A. Kats, *Philips Res. Rept.*, **11**, 115 (1956).
31. B. D. McSwain, N. F. Borrelli, and G.-J. Su, *Phys. Chem. Glasses*, **4**, 1 (1963).
32. T. Bates, in *Modern Aspects of the Vitreous State*, Vol. 2, J. D. Mackenzie, Ed., Butterworths, London, 1962, p. 195.
33. C. R. Bamford, *Phys. Chem. Glasses*, **3**, 189 (1962).
34. T. Feldmann, A. Treinin, and V. Volterra, *J. Chem. Phys.*, **42**, 3366 (1965).
35. P. Bennema, G. J. Hoijtink, J. H. Lupinski, L. J. Oosterhoff, P. Selier, and J. D. W. Van Voorst, *Mol. Phys.*, **2**, 431 (1959).
36. T. Feldmann and J. Jortner, unpublished results; T. Feldmann, M.Sc. thesis, Jerusalem (1963).
37. Th. Förster and K. Kasper, *Z. Elektrochem.*, **59**, 976 (1955).
38. J. B. Birks and A. J. W. Cameron, *Proc. Roy. Soc. (London)*, Ser. A, **249**, 297 (1959).
39. M. Smith and M. C. R. Symons, *Trans. Faraday Soc.*, **54**, 338 (1958); G. Stein and A. Treinin, *ibid*, **55**, 1086 (1959).
40. I. Burak and A. Treinin, *Trans. Faraday Soc.*, **59**, 1490 (1963).
41. J. T. Shapiro, G. L. Zimmerman, and C. W. Lutz, to be published; A. Treinin, unpublished results.
42. M. C. R. Symons and M. G. Townsend, *J. Chem. Soc.*, **1959**, 269.
43. R. H. Luebbe and J. E. Willard, *J. Am. Chem. Soc.*, **81**, 761, (1959).
44. S. Kumar and P. Sen, *Phys. Chem. Glasses*, **1**, 175 (1960).
45. E. L. Cochran, F. J. Adrian, and V. A. Bowers, *J. Chem. Phys.*, **34**, 1161 (1961).
46. O. E. O'Reilly and J. H. Anderson, in *Physics and Chemistry of the Organic Solid State*, Vol. 2, D. Fox, M. Labes, and A. Weissberger, Eds., Interscience, New York, 1965, p. 121.
47. F. K. Kneubühl, *J. Chem. Phys.*, **33**, 1074 (1960).
48. P. W. Levi, *J. Am. Ceram. Soc.*, **43**, 389 (1960).
49. J. S. Stroud, J. W. H. Schreurs, and R. F. Tucker, *Intern. Congr. Glass, 7th, Brussels, 1965* (published Corning Research, 1965), pp. 7.
50. F. Hughes, R. D. Kirk, and F. W. Patten, *J. Chem. Phys.*, **40**, 872 (1964).
51. O. Haimovich and A. Treinin, unpublished results.
52. S. Lee and P. J. Bray, *J. Chem. Phys.*, **39**, 2863 (1963).
53. S. Lee and P. J. Bray, *J. Chem. Phys.*, **40**, 2982 (1964).
54. J. Weiss, *J. Polymer Sci.*, **29**, 425 (1958).
55. W. H. Croper, *J. Am. Ceram. Soc.*, **45**, 293 (1962).

56. J. S. Van Wieringen and A. Kats, *Philips Res. Rept.*, **12**, 432 (1957).
57. C. E. Moore, *Circ. Natl. Bur. Stds.*, **467**, 1958.
58. J. S. Stroud, *J. Chem. Phys.*, **35**, 844 (1961).
59. J. S. Stroud, *J. Chem. Phys.*, **37**, 836 (1962).
60. J. S. Stroud, *Phys. Chem. Glasses*, **5**, 71 (1964).
61. R. F. Tucker, *Tech. Papers Intern. Congr. Glass, 6th, Wash., D.C. 1962.*
62. J. W. H. Schreurs and R. F. Tucker, in *Physics of Noncrystalline Solids* (Proc. Intern. Conf., Delft, 1964), North-Holland Publ. Co., Amsterdam, pp. 616.
63. Y. Nakai, *Bull. Chem. Soc. Japan*, **38**, 1308 (1965).
64. G. O. Karapetyan and D. M. Yudin, *Soviet Phys.-Solid State* (*English Transl.*) **3**, 2063 (1962).
65. P. N. Moorthy and J. J. Weiss, *J. Chem. Phys.*, **42**, 3127 (1965).
66. N. J. Kreidl and J. R. Hensler, *U.S. At. Energy Comm. Rept.* NYO-3780 (1954); NYO-3784 (1956).
67. S. Basu, *Nature*, **176**, 265 (1955); *Naturwissenschaften*, **43**, 196 (1956).
68. J. H. Schulman and W. D. Compton, *Color Centers in Solids*, Pergamon Press, New York, 1963.
69. T. Feldmann and A. Treinin, *J. Chem. Phys.*, **47**, 2754 (1967).
70. J. R. Morton, *Can. J. Phys.*, **41**, 706 (1963); P. W. Atkins and M. C. R. Symons, *J. Chem. Soc.*, **1964**, 4363.
71. M. Halmann and I. Platzner, *J. Chem. Soc.*, **1965**, 1440.
72. M. Halmann and I. Platzner, *J. Phys. Chem.*, **70**, 2281 (1966).
73. T. G. Castner and W. Känzig, *J. Phys. Chem. Solids*, **3**, 178 (1957).
74a. J. Jortner, M. Ottolenghi, and G. Stein, *J. Phys. Chem.*, **66**, 2029, 2037, 2042 (1962).
74b. J. Jortner, M. Ottolenghi, and G. Stein, *J. Phys. Chem.*, **67**, 1271 (1963).
74c. J. Jortner, M. Ottolenghi, and G. Stein, *J. Phys. Chem.*, **68**, 247 (1964).
75. F. S. Dainton and S. R. Logan, *Proc. Roy. Soc.* (*London*), **287A**, 282 (1965); F. S. Dainton and P. Fowles, *ibid.*, **287A**, 312 (1965).
76. M. S. Matheson, W. A. Mulac, and J. Rabani, *J. Phys. Chem.*, **67**, 2613 (1963).
77. L. I. Grossweiner and M. S. Matheson, *J. Chem. Phys.*, **23**, 2443 (1955).
78. L. I. Grossweiner and M. S. Matheson, *J. Phys. Chem.*, **61**, 1089 (1957).
79. B. Cercek, M. Ebert, C. W. Gilbert, and A. J. Swallow, in *Pulse Radiolysis*, M. Ebert, J. P. Keene, and A. J. Swallow, Eds., Academic Press, New York, 1965, p. 83.
80. B. N. Shelimov, N. N. Bubnov, N. V. Fok, and V. V. Voevodsky, *Dokl. Akad. Nauk. SSSR*, **134**, 145 (1960); *Opt. Spectry.*, *USSR, English Transl.*, **11**, 40 (1961); V. V. Voevodsky, *Intern. Symp. Free Radicals, 5th Upsala, 1961.*
81. A. Hilsenrod and B. Gehauf, *J. Chem. Phys.*, **24**, 914 (1956).
82. J. Frank and F. Haber, *Sitzber. Math. Naturw. Akad. Wiss. Mainz*, **1931**, 250.
83. P. N. Moorthy and J. J. Weiss, *J. Chem. Phys.*, **42**, 3121 (1965); see also, L. Kevan, P. N. Moorthy, and J. J. Weiss, *J. Am. Chem. Soc.*, **86**, 771 (1964).
84. P. B. Ayscough, R. G. Collins, and F. S. Dainton, *Nature*, **205**, 965 (1965).
85. R. J. Donovan and D. Husain, *Nature*, **206**, 171 (1965).
86. A. Treinin and A. Zaliouk-Gitter, *J. Chem. Phys.*, **43**, 4181 (1965).
87. M. Anbar and J. K. Thomas, *J. Phys. Chem.*, **68**, 3829 (1964).
88. H. C. Sutton, G. E. Adams, J. W. Boag, and B. D. Michael, in *Pulse Radiolysis*, M. Ebert, J. P. Keene, and A. J. Swallow, Eds., Academic Press, New York, 1965, p. 61.
89. G. Stein, *J. Chem. Phys.*, **42**, 2986 (1965).

90. D. M. Brown and F. S. Dainton, *Nature*, **209**, 195 (1966).
91. W. B. Person, *J. Chem. Phys.*, **38**, 109 (1963).
92. J. K. Thomas, S. Gordon, and E. J. Hart, *J. Phys. Chem.*, **68**, 1524 (1964).
93. J. J. Weiss and D. Porret, *Nature*, **139**, 1019 (1937).
94. U. K. Kläning and M. C. R. Symons, *J. Chem. Soc.*, **1960**, 977.
95. P. W. Atkins, J. A. Brivati, N. Keen, M. C. R. Symons, and P. A. Trevalion, *J. Chem. Soc.*, **1962**, 4785.
96. I. Norman and G. Porter, *Proc. Roy. Soc. (London), Ser. A*, **230**, 399 (1955).
97. D. M. Gardner and G. K. Fraenkel, *J. Am. Chem. Soc.*, **77**, 6399 (1955); Y. Matsumaga, *Can. J. Chem.*, **37**, 994 (1959).
98. L. E. Orgel, unpublished work.
99. K. O. Otley and W. A. Weyl, *J. Appl. Phys.*, **23**, 499 (1952).
100. P. Goldberg, *J. Chem. Phys.*, **40**, 427 (1964).
101. J. Barrett, M. F. Fox, and A. L. Mansell, *J. Phys. Chem.*, **69**, 2996 (1965).
102. M.-S. Tsao and W. K. Wilmarth, *Discussions Faraday Soc.*, **29**, 137 (1960).
103. P. W. Atkins, M. C. R. Symons, and P. A. Trevalion, *Proc. Chem. Soc.*, **1963**, 222.
104. P. N. Moorthy and J. Weiss, *Nature*, **201**, 1317 (1964).
105. D. M. Brown and F. S. Dainton, *Trans. Faraday Soc.*, **62**, 1139 (1966).
106. A. G. Massey and L. E. Orgel, *Nature*, **191**, 1387 (1961).
107. R. Woods, *J. Phys. Chem.*, **70**, 1446 (1966).
108. A. M. Bishay, *Phys. Chem. Glasses*, **2**, 33 (1961); A. M. Bishay and S. Arfa, *ibid.*, **6**, 134 (1965).
109. R. S. Barker, E. A. G. McConkey, and D. A. Richardson, *Phys. Chem. Glasses*, **6**, 24 (1965).
110. T. Feldmann and A. Treinin, unpublished results.
111. J. H. Baxendale, E. M. Fielden, and J. P. Keene, *Proc. Roy. Soc. (London), Ser. A*, **286**, 320 (1965).
112. B. Cercek, M. Ebert, and A. J. Swallow, *J. Chem. Soc.*, **1966A**, 612.
113. H. L. Smith and A. J. Cohen, *J. Am. Ceram. Soc.*, **47**, 564 (1964).
114. E. Lell, *Phys. Chem. Glasses*, **3**, 84 (1962).
115. G. E. Adams, J. H. Baxendale, and J. W. Boag, *Proc. Chem. Soc.*, **1963**, 241, 242.
116. F. S. Dainton and D. G. L. James, *Trans. Faraday Soc.*, **54**, 649 (1958).
117. C. K. Jørgensen, in *Absorption Spectra and Chemical Bonding in Complexes*, Pergamon Press, London, 1962.
118. G. Czapski, in *Pulse Radiolysis*, M. Ebert, J. P. Keene, and A. J. Swallow, Eds., Academic Press, New York, 1965, p. 289.
119. C. J. Delbecq, W. Hayes, M. C. M. O'Brien, and P. H. Yuster, *Proc. Roy. Soc. (London), Ser. A*, **271**, 243 (1963).
120. J. H. Baxendale, E. M. Fielden, and J. P. Keene, in *Pulse Radiolysis*, M. Ebert, J. P. Keene, and A. J. Swallow, Eds., Academic Press, New York, 1965, p. 207.
121. L. Shields, *J. Chem. Phys.*, **44**, 1685 (1966).
122. L. Shields, *Trans. Faraday Soc.*, **62**, 1042 (1966).
123. J. H. Schulman, R. J. Ginther, C. C. Klick, R. S. Alger, and R. A. Levi, *J. Appl. Phys.*, **22**, 1479 (1951).
124. W. Low and T. T. Suss, *Phys. Letters*, **7**, 310 (1963).
125. N. J. Kreidl and G. E. Blair, *Nucleonics*, **14**(1), 56 (1956).
126. G. O. Karapetyan, S. G. Lunter, and D. M. Yudin, *Opt. Spectry.*, **14**, 370 (1963).

127. O. E. O'Reilly and D. S. MacIver, *J. Phys. Chem.*, **66**, 276 (1962).
128. H. Kon, *J. Inorg. Nucl. Chem.*, **25**, 933 (1963).
129. N. R. Yafaev, N. S. Garifyanov, and Yu. V. Yablokov, *Soviet Phys.-Solid State (English Transl.)*, **5**, 1216 (1963).
130. E. J. Land, *Progr. Reaction Kinetics*, **3**, 369 (1965).
131. G. N. Lewis and D. Lipkin, *J. Am. Chem. Soc.*, **64**, 2801 (1942).
132. J. Joussot-Dubien and R. Lesclaux, *J. Chim. Phys.*, **1964**, 1631.
133. W. A. Gibbons, G. Porter, and M. I. Savadatti, *Nature*, **206**, 1355 (1965).
134. B. Brocklehurst, W. A. Gibbons, F. T. Lang, G. Porter, and M. I. Savadatti, *Trans. Faraday Soc.*, **62**, 1793 (1966).
135. A. Terenin, *Recent Progress in Photobiology*, E. J. Bowen, Ed., Academic Press, New York, 1965, p. 3.
136. E. De Boer and S. I. Weissman, *J. Am. Chem. Soc.*, **80**, 4549 (1958).
137. B. Muel and M. Hubert-Habart, *J. Chim. Phys.*, **55**, 377 (1958).
138. G. J. Hoijtink, *Mol. Phys.*, **2**, 85 (1959).
139. J. N. Murrell, *The Theory of the Electronic Spectra of Organic Molecules*, Methuen, London, 1963, p. 259.
140. J. Joussot-Dubien and R. Lesclaux, *Compt. Rend.*, **258**, 4260 (1964).
141. J. Joussot-Dubien and R. Lesclaux, *Acta Phys. Polon.*, **26**, 665 (1964).
142. T. D. S. Hamilton and T. P. Ray, unpublished results, reported by J. B. Birks in discussion (ref. 141).
143. M. S. Blois, Jr., H. W. Brown, and J. E. Maling, in *Free Radicals in Biological Systems*, M. S. Blois, Jr., H. W. Brown, R. M. Lemmon, R. O. Lindblom, and M. Weissbluth, Eds., Academic Press, New York, 1961, p. 117.
144. E. J. Land, G. Porter, and E. Strachan, *Trans. Faraday Soc.*, **57**, 1885 (1961).
145. J. Jortner, M. Ottolenghi, and G. Stein, *J. Am. Chem. Soc.*, **85**, 2712 (1963).
146. M. J. Blandamer, L. Shields, and M. C. R. Symons, *J. Chem. Soc.*, **1964**, 4352.
147. M. Mautner and A. Treinin, unpublished results.
148. H. T. J. Chilton and G. Porter, *Spectrochim. Acta*, **16**, 390 (1960).

CHAPTER 13

Electron Spin Resonance of First Row Transition Metal Complex Ions

H. A. KUSKA

Department of Chemistry, University of Akron, Akron, Ohio

and

MAX T. ROGERS

Department of Chemistry, Michigan State University, East Lansing, Michigan

I. INTRODUCTION

During the past ten years our knowledge of transition metal complexes has grown considerably. Experimentally, visible, infrared, and electron spin resonance (ESR) spectroscopy have provided the data required to test old theories and formulate new ones. Theoretically, a combination of crystal field and molecular orbital theory has been developed to explain the experimental data. This new theory, called ligand field theory, is now generally accepted and is at present being refined to the point that quantitative calculations of the various observables are being made with apparent success (1,2).

The general field of transition metal chemistry is covered by several excellent books and many recent review articles. Ballhausen's book (3) gives an introduction and review of ligand field theory in general with an excellent balance of theory and chemical applications. A pair of complementary books, one by Orgel (4) and the other by Griffith (5), provide an exhaustive pre-1961 coverage of ligand field theory. Orgel's book is a concise review of the qualitative correlations of the theory with experimental data, while Griffith's book is a very complete presentation of the mathematical and physical development of ligand field theory. Figgis (6) has written a textbook which introduces the methods and applications of ligand field theory at a graduate level. Watanabe's book (7) on operator methods in ligand field theory is an advanced textbook which bridges the gap between elementary quantum mechanics and the theoretical work now being done on transition metal systems. Jørgensen has two books; one discusses the pre-1960 field of optical spectroscopy from a ligand field viewpoint (8), while the second is a pre-1964 survey of the general scientific literature of transition metal complexes (9). Jørgensen also has three comprehensive review articles. The two most interesting from the standpoint of this review are a pre-1963 review and development of the nephelauxetic series (10) and a review and further development of the application of ligand field theory to optical spectroscopy (11). The third is a more general review of the application of spectroscopy to chemical bonding (12). The applications of group theory to ligand field theory are well reviewed and explained by Cotton (13). The theory and pre-1963 applications of infrared spectroscopy to transition metal chemistry are comprehensively reviewed by Nakamoto (14). Drago (15) presents an introductory, yet sufficiently detailed, discussion of the applications of physical methods to transition metal chemistry. Ballhausen and Gray (16) have published their lecture notes on molecular orbital theory which include a discussion of the application of molecular orbital theory to transition metal compounds.

Since optical and infrared spectroscopy and ligand field theory have received comprehensive and authoritative reviews, they will not be generally covered here, and only the basic ideas needed to correlate the electron spin resonance data will be presented. A discussion of the early development of electron spin resonance (ESR) has been given by previous reviewers and will not be duplicated. There are a number of such reviews and books which adequately cover the basic fundamentals and the pre-1960 literature.

The monograph by Ingram (1055) and the early series of reviews from the group at the Clarendon Laboratory (1056) are still quite useful. A more complete compilation of data through 1965 is now available in the Landolt-Börnstein tables (1057). Bersohn and Baird (17) have written a textbook which presents the theory of ESR at an introductory level and outlines its application to chemistry and biology. Pake's book (18) is an advanced textbook covering the theory of ESR from the viewpoint of a physicist. It does not discuss experimental details or, in general, chemical applications. It is especially useful as a critical abstract of, and a reference source to, the early theoretical papers. A slightly older but extremely useful book is that of Low (19). This book is more restricted than that of Pake in that it only covers the ESR of solids, but it is extremely thorough in its coverage of this area and therefore is also useful as a source book. A textbook by Slichter (20) provides a theoretical development of ESR spectroscopy of the solid state. The book that is the nearest comparison to the comprehensive books on optical and infrared spectroscopy discussed earlier is that by Al'tshuler and Kozyrev (21). It is a translation of a 1961 book; and, therefore, its usefulness is limited to the literature and theory of that period. There are two other Russian books which have not as yet been translated (22,23). Hershenson (24) has collected in index form the references to the ESR spectra which appeared in 67 journals during the period 1958–1963 and typical spectra are reproduced in a useful new atlas of spectra (1054). The recent book by Carrington and McLachlan (843) is an excellent introduction to the theory of ESR and experimental ESR has been covered comprehensively in a new monograph by Poole (1052). To partially fill the gap between the limitations of the above books and the general literature, there are several excellent reviews. Anderson (25) has written a general review of the experimental developments with well chosen examples of experimental applications. Stevens (26) has reviewed the use of the spin Hamiltonian (the mathematical shorthand used to describe the ESR experimental observables) and provides detailed mathematical examples of the application of the spin Hamiltonian. O'Reilly and Anderson (27) have written a general textbook-type review which serves as an introduction to ESR theory of transition metal compounds. Another useful introductory article covering the application of ESR theory to transitional metal compounds is that of Carrington and Longuet-Higgins (28). Jarrett (29) has written a detailed review of the theoretical treatment of ESR on an advanced mathematical level. Robertson (30) has written an excellent review article in which he discusses in detail representative examples of the application of ESR to transition metal complexes with organic ligands. Low and Offenbacher (31) have reviewed critically the application of ESR to magnetic ions in complex oxides, such as those with the rutile, perovskite, spinel, and garnet structures. McGarvey (1038) has written an excellent review which can be recommended as a complementary review to the present one since it covers the theory in detail. There are also several concise reviews (32–35) in the annual review literature which, in general, abstract the important ESR literature of that period with a limited amount of critical comment.

As a concentrated source of experimental papers, there are a number of published proceedings of conferences which dealt with ESR (36–43). A source of comprehensive reviews of particular aspects of ESR is the recent Ph.D. thesis literature. Of particular interest are ESR studies of those transition metal ions which give narrow lines at room temperature or at liquid nitrogen temperature, 77°K. These ions normally are of the outer electronic configuration $3d^1$, $3d^5$, low spin $3d^7$, or $3d^9$. In general the theory of each of these cases is different. Faber's thesis (44) concerns the random orientation spectra of d^1, d^5, and d^9 ions absorbed on ion exchange resins. Stamires (45) has extended this type of investigation to cover the absorption behavior of Cu(II) ions in zeolite crystals. Feltham's highly diverse investigation (46) covered solution ESR spectra, optical spectra, and ligand field theory of d^1 and d^9 complexes. The theory of ESR of high spin d^5 ions is presented in the theses of Drumheller (47), Jennings (48), Perkins (49), Van Heuvelen (50), Daehler (51), Wells (52), Wait (53), Stewart (54), Chang (55), Powell (56), Wickman (57), Garth (58), and Carter (59). The ESR of d^9 Cu(II) complexes is discussed by Neiman (60), Tucker (61), Zelewsky (62), and Kokoszka (63). d^3 ESR systems are covered by the theses of Guzzo (64), Watts (65), Clark (66), and Keating (67). Garrett (68), Hinckley (69), Rannestad (70), and Hayes (71) have investigated the relaxation mechanisms of paramagnetic transition metal systems by ESR. Chen's thesis (72) covers the theory of ligand hyperfine splittings for high spin d^5, Mn(II), and d^1, V(IV), systems. Borcherts (73) studied the single crystal ESR spectra of d^1, V(IV), and d^3, V(II), ions in $Zn(NH_4)_2(SO_4)_2 \cdot 6H_2O$. Karavelas (74) utilized molecular orbital theory to interpret the ESR data for d^1, V(IV), in SnO_2, TiO_2, and GeO_2 crystals. The low spin d^5 compounds $Mn(CN)_5NO^{2-}$ and $Cr(CN)_5NO^{3-}$ were studied by Fortman (75) and by Manoharan (76), who also studied the low spin d^7 complex ion $Fe(CN)_5NO^{3-}$.

II. THEORY

A. The Spin Hamiltonian

An unpaired electron in a transition metal complex interacts with its environment in several ways which are sensitive to study by ESR. These interactions are normally written in the form of a spin Hamiltonian of the following general form:

$$H_{spin} = \beta(g_z H_z S_z + g_x H_x S_x + g_y H_y S_y) + D\{S_z^2 - \tfrac{1}{3}S(S + 1)\}$$
$$+ E(S_x^2 - S_y^2) + A_z S_z I_z + A_x S_x I_x + A_y S_y I_y \qquad (1)$$

Where g_x, g_y, and g_z are the spectroscopic splitting factors, β is the Bohr magneton (0.92731×10^{-20} erg/G); H_z, H_x, and H_y are components of the magnetic field along the z, x, and y directions, and S_z, S_x, and S_y are the components of the electronic spin operator along the z, x, and y magnetic field axes, respectively. The quantity D is a measure of the axial crystal field distortion from cubic symmetry, while E is a measure of the distortion of the crystal field from axial symmetry. D and E are known as zero field splitting parameters since even in the absence of an external magnetic field, the components of $|S|$ will be nondegenerate if there is a local magnetic field due to a crystal field of lower symmetry than cubic. D and E only affect systems with $S \geq 1$ and do not remove the sign degeneracy ($+\tfrac{3}{2}$ and $-\tfrac{3}{2}$ have the same energy). The third term contains the hyperfine interaction of the unpaired electrons with any atomic nuclei which have finite magnetic moments. A_z, A_x, and A_y are the components of the hyperfine interaction constant, and I_z, I_x, and I_y are the components of the nuclear spin. If the unpaired electron has a finite probability of being on more than one nucleus with a magnetic moment, an additional hyperfine splitting term is added to equation 1 for each magnetic nucleus involved. There are two other terms which should be included in equation 1; however, in practice they are normally small and are neglected. They are the quadrupole interaction and the interaction of the applied magnetic field with the nuclear moment (19). In writing equation 1, it was also assumed that the principal axes of the g and A tensors coincided, and if this is not the case, cross terms must be considered (73). Sometimes terms involving S, I, and H of order higher than two must be considered; these terms will be introduced for the specific ions where they have been found to be significant.

B. ESR g Values

For a free electron the g value is 2.0023; however, in transition metal complexes spin–orbit interaction mixes some excited state into the ground state. The actual g value is given by the expression

$$g = 2.0023(\delta_{ij} - \zeta\Lambda_{ij}) \tag{2}$$

where δ is equal to unity for $i = j$ and zero for $i \neq j$ (Kronecker delta), ζ is the spin–orbit coupling constant, and Λ_{ij} is defined by

$$\Lambda_{ij} = \sum_{n \neq 0} \langle\psi_0| \hat{L}_i |\psi_n\rangle\langle\psi_n| \hat{L}_j |\psi_0\rangle/(E_n - E_0) \tag{3}$$

where $E_n - E_0$ is the energy between the ground state and the nth excited state. This equation is developed by Abragam and Pryce (77). Its use is illustrated by the following example, which illustrates the calculation of g values for a low spin d^5 system with the unpaired electron in an xy ground state, $\psi_0 = (xz)^2(yz)^2(xy)$. The results of the application of the orbital angular momentum operator, $\hat{L}$, are given in Table I. For g_z, $\sum \hat{L}_z|\psi_0\rangle = -2i(xz)^2(yz)^2(x^2 - y^2)$ since $\hat{L}_z|d_{xy}\rangle = -2i\, d_{x^2-y^2}$ and since the operation of $\hat{L}_z$ on d_{xz} and d_{yz} is not allowed because the orbits to which they transform are already fully occupied. Therefore, $\hat{L}_z$ connects the B_2 ground state (t_{2g}^5) to the B_1 excited state (t_{2g}^4, e_g). Substituting this result into equations 2 and 3, one obtains

$$g_z = 2.0023\left(1 - \frac{4\zeta}{E_{x^2-y^2} - E_{xy}}\right) \tag{4}$$

For g_x and g_y the situation is more complicated, since "hole" transitions (xz and yz to xy) and transitions from xz and yz to the z^2 and $x^2 - y^2$ levels are predicted from Table I. The transition from xz (and also from yz) occurs at a different energy for the electron of positive spin (given superscript (1)) than for the electron of negative spin (given superscript (2)) due to interelectronic repulsion. Along x the contributions are:

$$g_x = 2.0023\left(1 - \frac{\zeta}{E_{xy} - E_{xz}} - \frac{3\zeta}{E_{z^2} - E_{yz}^1} + \frac{3\zeta}{E_{z^2} - E_{yz}^2}\right.$$

$$\left. - \frac{\zeta}{E_{x^2-y^2} - E_{yz}^2} + \frac{\zeta}{E_{x^2-y^2} - E_{yz}^2}\right) \tag{5}$$

Since $E_{z^2} - E_{yz}^1$ is approximately equal to $E_{z^2} - E_{yz}^2$ and $E_{x^2-y^2} - E_{yz}^1$ is approximately equal to $E_{x^2-y^2} - E_{yz}^2$, the equation can be simplified to

$$g_x = 2.0023\left(1 - \frac{\zeta}{E_{xy} - E_{xz}}\right) \tag{6}$$

g_y is similar to g_x except that E_{xz} is replaced by E_{yz}.

TABLE I

Application of the Orbital Angular Momentum Operators to the d Orbitals

$$\hat{L}_z d_{z^2} = 0$$

$$\hat{L}_z d_{x^2 - y^2} = 2i\, d_{xy}$$

$$\hat{L}_z d_{xy} = -2i\, d_{x^2 - y^2}$$

$$\hat{L}_z d_{xz} = i\, d_{yz}$$

$$\hat{L}_z d_{yz} = -i\, d_{xz}$$

$$\hat{L}_x d_{z^2} = -\sqrt{3}\, i\, d_{yz}$$

$$\hat{L}_x d_{x^2 - y^2} = -i\, d_{yz}$$

$$\hat{L}_x d_{xy} = i\, d_{xz}$$

$$\hat{L}_x d_{xz} = -i\, d_{xy}$$

$$\hat{L}_x d_{yz} = \sqrt{3}\, i\, d_{z^2} + i\, d_{x^2 - y^2}$$

$$\hat{L}_y d_{z^2} = \sqrt{3}\, i\, d_{xz}$$

$$\hat{L}_y d_{x^2 - y^2} = -i\, d_{xz}$$

$$\hat{L}_y d_{xy} = -i\, d_{yz}$$

$$\hat{L}_y d_{xz} = -\sqrt{3}\, i\, d_{z^2} + i\, d_{x^2 - y^2}$$

$$\hat{L}_y d_{yz} = i\, d_{xy}$$

C. Development of the Theory of Obtaining Covalency Parameters from the ESR g Values

1. *Theory of Owen*

Owen (78) found by utilizing optical and magnetic data that the spin-orbit coupling constant ζ in equation 2 is smaller by 20–30% than the free ion ζ value. He interpreted this reduction by saying that partial covalent bonding forces some of the unpaired electron out on the ligands.

2. *Theory of Owen Plus Screening Effects*

Murao (79) noted that the decrease in ζ is greater for metal ions of smaller atomic number and larger valency. He attributed this to screening by the additional $3d$ electron density produced by the admixture of $3d$ wave function into the bonding orbitals. The bonding orbitals are of the form

$$\phi_b = M(\psi_p + b\psi_d) \tag{7}$$

and the antibonding orbitals are of the form

$$\phi_a = N(\psi_d - c\psi_p) \tag{8}$$

where b and c are small coefficients.

Assuming that there is one electron charge in the d orbital and that the electron charge in the ϕ_a orbital is distributed among the ψ_p and ψ_d orbitals in proportion to the squares of the ψ_p and ψ_d coefficients, Murao obtained the electron distribution given in Table II.

The ϕ_b orbital having two electrons increases the d orbital electron density by Δn where

$$\Delta n = \sum_n \frac{C_n^2}{1 + C_n^2} \tag{9}$$

This increase of d orbital electron density causes a reduction in the effective nuclear charge seen by a d electron

$$Z = Z_0 - \alpha\Delta n \tag{10}$$

TABLE II
Electron Distribution in the Metal d and Ligand p Orbits Due to Metal–Ligand Overlap

	Contribution from antibonding orbital	Contribution from bonding orbital	Total electron density
Density in metal d orbital	$1/(1 + C^2)$	$2C^2/(1 + C^2)$	$(2C^2 + 1)/(1 + C^2)$
Density in ligand p orbital	$C^2/(1 + C^2)$	$2/(1 + C^2)$	$(2 + C^2)/(1 + C^2)$

where Z_0 is the effective nuclear charge for the free ion and α is the d–d screening constant. Based on a hydrogenlike model Murao determined that

$$\frac{\zeta}{\zeta_0} \propto (Z/Z_0)^4 \equiv [1 - \alpha\Delta n/Z_0]^4 \tag{11}$$

Since ζ/ζ_0 also was proportional to the probability of the unpaired d electron being found on the metal ion the final equation was found to be

$$\frac{\zeta}{\zeta_0} = N^2[1 - \alpha\Delta n/Z_0]^4 \tag{12}$$

Murao determined the values of ζ/ζ_0 given in Table III. N^2 and C were assumed constant and obtained by making the Cu^{2+} values fit the experimental value.

Several alternate procedures for considering screening effects are also being used. Kon and Sharpless (80) used the tabulated spin–orbit coupling constants of Dunn (81) for the various possible oxidation states of the metal to calculate the covalency parameters for that particular oxidation state. They then chose the set of covalency parameters which gave a spin density on the metal in closest agreement with the corresponding assumed oxidation state. However, they pointed out that a limitation of this method is that the electron density contribution from the bonding orbitals must be estimated. In one system ($VOSO_4$) (82) this contribution was calculated to be 40% of the total spin density. McGarvey (83) assumed that only the electron donation from the bonding orbitals was important for Cr(III) systems and developed an equation of the following form:

$$\zeta = 91 - 56(1 - P_d^*) \tag{13}$$

where P_d^* is the electron charge on the Cr atom when one electron occupies the antibonding $x^2 - y^2$ orbital. DeArmond, Garrett, and Gutowsky (84) observed that ζ is proportional to $\langle r^{-3} \rangle$, and, since P the anisotropic

TABLE III

Reduction of Spin Orbit Coupling Constants for Transition Metal Hydrates

	Ti^{2+}	V^{2+}	Cr^{2+}	Mn^{2+}	Fe^{2+}	Co^{2+}	Ni^{2+}	Cu^{2+}	V^{3+}	Cr^{3+}	Mn^{3+}
Δn	1.10	0.97	0.83	0.69	0.55	0.41	0.28	0.14	1.10	0.97	0.83
ζ/ζ_0 (calculated)	55	62	68	72	76	79	82	84	61	66	70
ζ/ζ_0 (experiment)	—	≈ 80	—	—	—	81[a]	83	84	62	63	—

[a] Estimated

hyperfine splitting term is also proportional to $\langle r^{-3} \rangle$, ζ can be determined from the following equation,

$$\zeta = CP \tag{14}$$

In this equation C is approximated by using available radial functions and spin–orbit coupling constants for lower oxidation states of the metal atom. In a later paper they proposed an equation relating ζ to the interelectron repulsion parameter, F_2, obtained from optical data (85).

3. Alternate Theory to Owen's Covalent Theory—The Free Ion Theory

Although Murao was able to obtain good agreement between the theoretical and experimental reductions in the spin–orbit coupling constants. Marshall and Stuart (86) felt that the amount of covalency required was too large. They proposed a theory based on an ionic model. In an ionic model there is no covalent character to the wave functions and c in equation 8 is just equal to the metal–ligand overlap integral. They postulated that the decrease in ζ is due to an overall shift of the d wave function outward due to a repulsion between the d electron density and the $2p$ electron density which overlaps the metal ion. They supported this theory by citing a neutron diffraction study which reported that the $3d$ wave function was expanded by 10% over the free ion wave function. Using 10% expanded wave functions they were able to obtain good agreement between the experimental fluorine hyperfine splittings for MnF_2 and their calculated values.

Marshall and Stuart's theory is known as the free ion theory since covalent bonding is not considered in their model. Their theory has been reviewed by Anderson (87) and by Shulman and Sugano (88).

Shulman and Sugano pointed out that the agreement of Marshall and Stuart's theory with the experimental MnF_6^{4-} data was fortuitous and could not be extended to other ions. Anderson discussed the theoretical justifications given by Marshall and Stuart in proposing their model and concluded that their interpretation is not the only possible one.

4. Present g Value Theory. Inclusion of Charge Transfer and Ligand Spin-Orbit Coupling Constant Contributions

Several investigators (80,83,89) have recently corrected the theory of Owen to include charge transfer and ligand spin–orbit coupling constant contributions. As an example, the g value equation for the high spin d^8 Ni(II) ion in an octahedral crystal field is (90,91,138)

$$g = 2.0023 - \frac{4N_\pi N_\sigma k_{\sigma\pi}}{E_\sigma^* - E_\pi^*} (\zeta_M - \tfrac{1}{2}\lambda_\sigma\lambda_\pi\zeta_L)$$
$$- \tfrac{3}{4}\delta^2 \frac{-4\zeta_M\gamma_\pi(\lambda_\pi + \tfrac{1}{2}\lambda_\sigma + \tfrac{1}{2}\lambda_s R\langle\psi_{2p,y}|\delta\psi_{2s}|\delta y\rangle)}{E_\sigma^* - E_\pi^*} \tag{15}$$

N_π and N_σ are the coefficients of the metal ion in the molecular orbitals of pi and sigma symmetry, respectively. They appear because of the modification of the spin–orbit coupling between the ground state and excited state caused by electron delocalization and the resultant use of molecular orbitals in place of atomic orbitals

$$\langle \psi_n | \zeta L \cdot S | \psi_0 \rangle = N_n N_0 \langle \phi_n | \zeta L \cdot S | \phi_0 \rangle$$

In this equation ψ_n and ψ_0 are the molecular orbitals and ϕ_n and ϕ_σ are the corresponding metal atomic orbitals. $k_{\sigma\pi}$ is the orbital reduction factor and is due to a change in the orbital angular momentum by the delocalization,

$$\langle \psi_n | L | \psi_0 \rangle = k_{n,0} \langle \phi_n | L | \phi_0 \rangle$$

The orbital reduction factor is given by

$$k_{\sigma\pi} = N_\sigma N_\pi (1 - \lambda_\sigma S_\sigma - \lambda_s S_s - \lambda_\pi S_\pi - \tfrac{1}{2}\lambda_\sigma\lambda_\pi$$
$$- \tfrac{1}{2}\lambda_\pi\lambda_s R \langle \psi_{2p,y} | \, \delta\psi_{2s} \, | \delta y \rangle) \qquad (16)$$

λ_σ and λ_π are the coefficients of the ligand orbitals in the molecular orbitals which are of the form

$$\psi_n = N_n(\phi_n - \lambda_n \phi_{\text{ligand}}) \qquad (17)$$

δ in equation 15 is the coefficient of admixture of the excited state Γ_5 $(t_{2g}^5 e_g^3)$ into the ground state. γ_π is the actual covalency in the pi orbitals and is equal to $\lambda_\pi - S_\pi$ where S_π is the metal–ligand group overlap integral. R is the distance between the metal atom and the ligand.

D. Development of the Theory of Obtaining Covalency Parameters from the Isotropic ESR Metal Nuclear Hyperfine Splittings

1. Restricted Hartree-Fock Model (Higher Orbital s Character)

In $3s^2 3d^n$ transition metal ions one would not predict an isotropic nuclear hyperfine splitting since the $3d$ orbitals have a node at the metal ion nucleus. The earliest explanation of the observed splitting is that in the ground state there is a small admixture of $3s^1 3d^n 4s^1$ character (77,92). Since an s electron has a high electron density at the nucleus, only a small percentage of $3s^1 3d^n 4s^1$ character is required to account for the observed splittings. This theory was introduced by Abragam and Pryce (77) and utilized by Van Wieringen (93) to explain the observed variations of the Mn^{2+} nuclear hyperfine splittings in a series of Mn^{2+} complexes.

2. Unrestricted Hartree-Fock Model (Spin Polarization)

Although the theory of Abragam and Pryce was able to quantitatively account for the magnitude of the splitting, subsequent investigations showed that it predicted the wrong sign for the splittings (94–96). This discrepancy was accounted for by theoretical unrestricted Hartree-Fock calculations of the exchange polarization mechanism which showed that an unpaired $3d$ electron will polarize the core s electrons to give a net spin at the nucleus of opposite sign to the unpaired electron. For example, Freeman and Watson (94) reported for vanadium metal that the contributions of the various orbitals were $+0.05$ ($1s$), -4.85 ($2s$), $+1.6$ ($3s$), and 2.74 ($4s$) to give an overall effective field at the nucleus of -0.45 au.

Matamura (97) for Mn^{2+}, and Title (98) for Fe^{3+} and Cr^{1+}, were able to interpret the A values using only spin polarization and covalency. They plotted the experimental A values vs. estimated percentage ionicity and extrapolated back to 100% ionicity. The A values at 100% were in close agreement with the calculated values of Freeman and Watson (94). McGarvey (99) has extended this correlation to the d^3 systems, V(II), Cr(III), and Mn(IV), and the d^7 system, Co(II). These systems also show a dependence of A on the percentage ionicity; however, the dependence is less pronounced for the d^3 system than for the d^5 and the d^7 systems, presumably due to the lesser variation of covalency for pi electrons than for sigma electrons.

König (100) has interpreted the isotropic A values of Cr^{1+} and V(O), both d^5 low spin cases using a combination of the spin polarization theory and the higher s-state contribution theory. He calculated the exchange polarization contributions to be $+26.4$ and -134 G for Cr^{1+} and V(O), respectively. Since the experimental values of A were $+21.8$ and -83.5 G, he calculated the $4s$ contribution to be -4.6 and $+50.5$ G by the following relationship: A(experimental) $= A$(exchange polarization) $+ A$($4s$ character). He calculated that one electron in a $4s$ orbital would cause a splitting of -422.5 and 923.1 G for Cr^{1+} and V(O), respectively. He was then able to calculate the $4s$ spin density as 0.0109 and 0.0547, respectively. Because of the uncertainties in the calculation of exchange polarization and $4s$ character and the lack of consideration of the effects of covalent bonding on the calculated parameters, the $4s$ spin densities cannot be considered as quantitatively significant. Additional experimental data are needed. For example chromium metal is $3d^5 4s^1$; since there is an unpaired electron in the $4s$ orbital, a large $4s$ contribution is expected. Childs et al. (101) report that the experimental value for chromium metal is 29.47 G (27.6 × 10^{-4}cm^{-1}). This value is only slightly larger than the Cr splittings when there are only $3d$ unpaired electrons. This result casts considerable doubt on König's estimation of -422.5 G for a $4s$ Cr^{1+} electron. Childs et al. (101) calculate -51 G (-48×10^{-4}cm^{-1}) for the $4s$ splitting, while Budick et al. (102) calculate that, for chromium metal, the $4s$ contribution is -21.8×10^{-4}cm^{-1} from their experimental data obtained by level-crossing spectroscopy and optical double resonance. As a further example of the qualitative nature of this type of treatment, Davison et al. (103) estimate the $4s$ splitting by Cr to be -1170 G.

Another illustration of the use of both the 4s contribution and the spin polarization is the published interpretation of the unusually low value (25.7×10^{-4} cm^{-1}) of the vanadium hyperfine splitting found in bis-cyclopentadienyl vanadium (104). Since proton NMR spectra of the complex rules out the possibility that the electron is predominantly localized on the ligand, the small vanadium splitting cannot be attributed to a large covalency. The small splitting was explained by partial cancellation of the negative spin polarization contribution by a positive 4s contribution.

3. Signs of Metal Ion Hyperfine Splittings

It is normally not possible to obtain the signs of the hyperfine splitting constants from electron spin resonance data. If the nuclear magnetic resonance can be detected, NMR can be used to do this; however, in general, a paramagnetic compound which gives a good ESR spectrum does not give an NMR spectrum and vice versa since a long electron relaxation time is needed in ESR and a short relaxation time is needed in NMR. It is possible to determine the correct sign using the analysis of Fortman (75). If the electron is in the orbital along the unique axis of the molecule (by convention, the z axis) and the metal nucleus has a positive nuclear magnetic moment, the anisotropic splitting component, A_p, will be positive. If the nuclear magnetic moment is negative, the anisotropic splitting component will be negative. For the case where the unpaired electron is in an orbital perpendicular to the axis of symmetry, the anisotropic splitting component, A_p, will be negative if the nuclear magnetic moment is positive and vice versa. For the isotropic splitting, A_{iso}, normally the splitting is negative if the nuclear magnetic moment is positive and vice versa. However, if the 4s contribution to the hyperfine splitting is large, it is possible to have a positive splitting for a negative nuclear magnetic moment and vice versa. This appears to happen for low spin Co(II) complexes where the ground state z^2 orbital is of the correct symmetry to mix with the 4s orbital (99). The relative signs of A_p and A_{iso} can usually be determined from the angular dependence of the ESR spectrum or from the values of A_{iso} determined in solution and A_p determined from the frozen solution with the use of the following equations:

$$A_{\parallel} = A_{iso} + 2A_p \tag{18}$$

$$A_{\perp} = A_{iso} - A_p \tag{19}$$

E. Development of the Theory of Obtaining Covalency Parameters from the ESR Ligand Hyperfine Splittings

Two early theories were proposed to account for the observed ligand hyperfine splittings. Mukherji and Das (105), Marshall and Stuart (86), and Freeman and Watson (106) utilized ionic models and were able to quantitatively account for the magnitudes of the splittings by polarization of the ligand orbitals due to overlap of the metal–ligand wave functions. However, subsequent experiments (88) which determined the sign of the hyperfine splittings and the dependence of the splittings on whether the unpaired electron was in an orbital of σ or π symmetry indicated that covalent contributions must be considered.

The covalent contribution at first was considered to arise from covalency of the antibonding unpaired electron. Using this model Shulman and Sugano (88) were able to obtain good agreement between the observed and theoretical fluorine hyperfine splittings in $KNiF_3$. However, Watson and Freeman (107) and, independently, Simanek and Sroubek (108) have reported that the model used by Shulman and Sugano is incorrect. They propose that the spin density which reaches the ligand arises from spin unpairing in the bonding molecular orbitals rather than from the unpaired electrons in antibonding molecular orbitals. The numerical parameters calculated by Watson and Freeman did not give as good agreement with the experimental parameters as did the values calculated by Shulman and Sugano. However, a more recent paper by Ellis (109) has reconsidered Watson and Freeman's theory and found additional contributions due to multicenter contributions to ligand–ligand overlap so that the theoretical and experimental values are now in approximate agreement as are the values calculated by Simanek and Sroubek. Simanek and Sroubek allowed for a limited amount of correlation (unpaired spin density in filled orbitals) by using a self-consistency treatment. Sugano and Tanabe (110) have analyzed the work of Shulman and Sugano and also conclude that the Shulman and Sugano antibonding orbital calculation is incorrect. Hubbard, Rimmer, and Hopgood (111) have calculated the covalency parameters using a configuration interaction approach rather than the linear combination of atomic orbital, unrestricted Hartree-Fock approach used by the other workers. They obtained values of the correct order of magnitude and interpreted their success as an indication of the importance of correlation effects in determining the properties of transition metal wave functions. The values of the covalency parameters calculated by the various groups are given in Table IV.

III. DISCUSSION OF THE LITERATURE

In the following sections the theoretical and experimental work for each outer orbital configuration is presented separately. In general the literature reported covers the period from 1959 through June of 1966.

TABLE IV
Spin Density in KNiF$_3$

Spin density f_i	Shulman and Sugano (88)	Watson and Freeman (107)	Ellis (109)	Hubbard et al. (111)	Experiment (88)
f_s Spin overlap	0.0022	0.0021	0.0022		—
f_s Spin covalent	0.0020	0.0010	0.0041		—
Total f_s	0.0042	0.0031	0.0063	0.0102	0.0054
$f\sigma$ Spin overlap	0.0041	0.0037	0.0041		—
$f\sigma$ Spin covalent	0.0480	0.0060	0.0148		—
Total $f\sigma$	0.0521	0.0097	0.0189	0.0123	0.0378

A. d^1 Complexes

1. *Vanadyl Complexes*

VO^{2+} complexes are especially well suited for ESR studies. VO^{2+} has one unpaired electron; the ground state is nondegenerate; and there is a large energy separation between it and the excited states. This separation between the ground state and the excited states is due to the strong axial component of the crystal field created by the short V—O internuclear distance. The nondegenerate ground state is required in order to have sharp ESR lines at room temperature. Other advantages of VO^{2+} are that ^{51}V is $\approx 100\%$ abundant, has a large nuclear spin and magnetic moment ($\mu = 5.1392$) giving a large separation (≈ 100 G) between the lines. A disadvantage of VO^{2+} is that the large nuclear moment and nuclear spin are responsible for a large line width (112–117). The large line width usually prevents a resolution of small ligand hyperfine splittings, although recently proton (73,118), nitrogen (119), carbon (120), and phosphorus (139) splittings have been reported.

The isotropic g and A values can be obtained from the liquid solution spectrum. In solution vanadyl complexes have eight line ESR spectra due to the hyperfine splitting by the vanadium nucleus with nuclear spin of $7/2$ (see Fig. 1). The A value is measured as the magnetic field separation between lines 4 and 5. To first-order the g value is equal to $h\nu/\beta H_{4,5}$ where ν is the klystron frequency in megacycles and $H_{4,5}$ is the magnetic field in gauss halfway between lines 4 and 5. The second-order correction

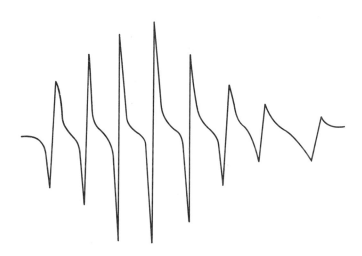

Fig. 1. ESR spectrum of VO(oxalate)$_2$ in DMSO.

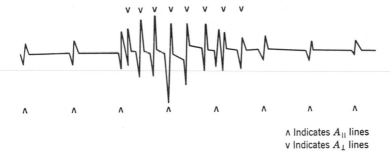

∧ Indicates $A_{||}$ lines
v Indicates $A_{\perp}$ lines

Fig. 2. Single crystal ESR spectrum of $VO(CN)_5^{-3}$ in KBr.

is significant so that the actual magnetic field that is used is:

$$H = H_{4,5} + 31A^2/4(H_{4,5})$$

The anisotropic terms can be determined from dilute powder spectra, frozen nonaqueous solutions, or dilute single crystals (see Figs. 2 and 3). $A_{||}$ and $A_{\perp}$ can be measured from the separation between their respective

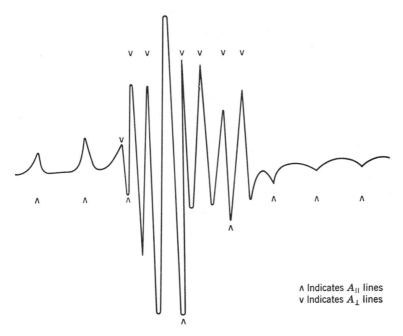

∧ Indicates $A_{||}$ lines
v Indicates $A_{\perp}$ lines

Fig. 3. ESR spectrum of $VO(NCS)_5^{-3}$ in frozen $CHCl_3$ solution.

lines 4 and 5 when resolution permits. Otherwise they are determined from the other line separations with the use of equations 27 and 28.

The experimental g values can be related to the molecular orbital coefficients by:

$$g_{\parallel} = 2.0023 - \frac{8\zeta N_{\pi_2}^2 N_{\sigma_2}^2}{\Delta b_2 \to b_1(\mathrm{I})} [1 - \tfrac{1}{2}(\lambda_{\pi_2}\lambda_{\sigma_2})T(n) - 2\lambda_{\sigma_2}S_{d,\sigma_2} - 2\lambda_{\pi_2}S_{d,\pi_2}]$$

$$- \frac{8\zeta N_{\pi_2}^2(1 - N_{\sigma_2}^2)}{\Delta b_2 \to b_1(\mathrm{II})} \quad (20)$$

$$g_{\perp} = 2.0023 - \frac{2\zeta N_{\pi_2}^2 N_{\pi_1}^2}{\Delta b_2 \to e(\mathrm{I})}$$

$$[1 - (1/2)^{1/2}\lambda_{\pi_1}^e\lambda_{\pi_2} - 2S_{d,\pi_2}\lambda_{\pi_2}^e - (1/2)^{1/2}2S_{d,\pi_2}\lambda_{\pi_1}^e - S_{d,\pi_1}\lambda_{\pi_1}^a]$$

$$- \frac{2\zeta N_{\pi_2}^2(1 - N_{\pi_1}^2)}{\Delta b_2 \to e(\mathrm{II})} \quad (21)$$

The molecular orbitals are of the form

$$\psi_{xy}^* = N_{\pi_2}(\phi_{xy} - \lambda_{\pi_2}\phi_{\text{ligand}}) \quad (22)$$

$$\psi_{x^2-y^2}^* = N_{\sigma_2}(\phi_{x^2-y^2} - \lambda_{\sigma_2}\phi_{\text{ligand}}) \quad (23)$$

$$\psi_{xz \text{ or } yz}^* = N_{\pi_1}(\phi_{xz \text{ or } yz} - \lambda_{\pi_1}^e\phi_{\text{ligand}}^e - \lambda_{\pi_1}^a\phi_{\text{ligand}}^a) \quad (24)$$

$T(n)$ is defined by Kivelson and Lee (119), S_{d,π_2} is the metal d, ligand p_{π_2} atomic overlap integral, $\lambda_{\pi_1}^e$ and $\lambda_{\pi_1}^a$ are the xz, yz molecular orbital coefficients for the equatorial and axial ligands, respectively, and ζ is the spin–orbit coupling constant. The spin–orbit coupling constant is positive if the transition is one where an unpaired electron goes from a half-filled orbital to an unoccupied orbital and is negative if the transition is from a filled orbital to a half-filled orbital. The latter type of transition is commonly called a hole transition. Transitions I and II are the d–d and the charge transfer transitions, respectively. $\Delta b_2 \to b_1$ and $\Delta b_2 \to e$ are determined from optical spectroscopy with the aid of the energy level diagram given in Figure 4. The g values are obtained from the experimental spectrum with the use of the following equations:

$$g = \frac{h\nu}{\beta H_0} \quad (25)$$

$$H_0 = H_{(m)} + A \cdot m + \frac{A^2}{2H_{(m)}}\left[I(I + 1) - m^2\right] + \frac{A^3}{4H^2_{(m)}} \quad (26)$$

For $g_{\parallel}$

$$H_0 = H_{(m)} + A_{\parallel} \cdot (m) + \frac{A_{\perp}^2[I(I + 1) - m^2]}{2H_{(m)}} \quad (27)$$

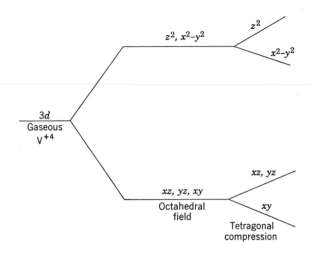

Fig. 4. Crystal field splittings for a d^1 system.

For $g_\perp$

$$H_0 = H_{(m)} + A_\perp \cdot (m) + \frac{(A_\parallel^2 + A_\perp^2)[I(I + 1) - m^2]}{4H_{(m)}} \qquad (28)$$

$H_{(m)}$ is the magnetic field position of the line corresponding to the nuclear moment m, ν is the klystron frequency in megacycles, I is the total nuclear spin, and A, $A_\parallel$, and $A_\perp$ are the nuclear hyperfine splitting constants.

The experimental metal ion nuclear hyperfine splittings are related to the molecular orbitals by the equations:

$$A_\parallel = -\tfrac{4}{7}N_{\pi_2}^2 P + A - \frac{8\zeta N_{\pi_2}^2 N_{\sigma_2}^2 P}{\Delta b_2 \rightarrow b_1(I)} - \frac{\tfrac{6}{7}\zeta N_{\pi_2}^2 N_{\pi_1}^2 P}{\Delta b_2 \rightarrow e(I)} \qquad (29)$$

$$A_\perp = \tfrac{2}{7}N_{\pi_2}^2 P + A - \frac{11\zeta N_{\pi_2}^2 N_{\pi_1}^2 P}{7\Delta b_2 \rightarrow e(I)} \qquad (30)$$

where $A = \tfrac{2}{3}A_\perp + \tfrac{1}{3}A_\parallel$ and $P = \mu_n \beta_n / I_n \langle r^{-3} \rangle$. For the $N_{\pi_2}^2$ values in Table V the value of P used in the calculations is the value for V^{2+}, 0.0128 cm^{-1}, since electron sharing by the ligands is expected to reduce the actual charge on the vanadium from the formal 4+ to somewhere around 2+.

The d_{xy} molecular orbital coefficient N_{π_2} can be determined from the anisotropic splittings with the use of the following modified form of equation 29 which removes the need for knowing the values of the optical transitions.

$$A_\parallel = -\tfrac{4}{7}N_{\pi_2}^2 P + A + \tfrac{2}{3}g_\parallel P - \tfrac{5}{21}g_\perp P - \tfrac{6}{7}P \qquad (31)$$

TABLE V
ESR Data for Vanadyl Complexes

Compound and host	g	$g_\parallel$	$g_\perp$	A $(10^4 cm^{-1})$	$A_\parallel$ $(10^4 cm^{-1})$	$A_\perp$ $(10^4 cm^{-1})$	$N^2_{\pi_2}{}^a$	$N^2_{\pi_2}{}^b$	Reference
$VOCl_2$ in $12NHCl$	1.968 ± 0.002	1.933 ± 0.002	1.978 ± 0.002	101.9 ± 0.5	182.0 ± 0.5	70.0 ± 0.5	0.876	1.025	121
		1.941 ± 0.002	1.977 ± 0.002		177.9 ± 0.5	69.5 ± 0.5		0.978	
$VO(DMSO)_5$ $(ClO_4)_2$ in DMSO	(1.962)	1.938	1.974	101.2	177	65.9	0.863	0.973	122
$VOCl_2$ in $3NH_2SO_4$	1.965 ± 0.002	1.933 ± 0.002	1.980 ± 0.002	106.2 ± 0.5	182.6 ± 0.5	71.7 ± 0.5	0.912	0.973	121
$VOCl_2$ in $3NHCl$	1.965 ± 0.002	1.932 ± 0.002	1.981 ± 0.002	106.4 ± 0.5	182.6 ± 0.5	71.8 ± 0.5	0.914	0.969	121
VO(porphyrin) in $CHCl_3$	1.979	1.961	(1.989)	88.2 ± 0.7	161.2 ± 0.6	(51.7)	0.766	0.955	119
VO^{2+} in $Zn(NH_4)_2(SO_4)_2 \cdot 6H_2O$	(1.9644)	1.9316	1.9808 1.9797	(108.3)	182.75	71.04 72.55	0.930	0.945	118
VO^{2+} in $Zn(NH_4)_2(SO_4)_2 \cdot 6H_2O$	(1.9652)	1.9331	1.9813(x) 1.9801(y)	(108.5)	182.8	71.37(x) 72.56(y)	0.932	0.944	118
VO^{2+} in $Zn(NH_4)_2(SO_4)_2 \cdot 6H_2O$	(1.9640)	1.9299	1.981	(109.8)	184.4	72.5	0.943	0.944	118
$(VOCl_5)^{3-}$ or $[VO(H_2O)Cl_4]^{2-}$ in $(NH_4)^2In[Cl_5H_2O]$	1.971	1.9450	1.9847	(100.2)	173.0	63.8	0.865	0.942	84

Compound									Ref.
$VOCl_2$ in HCl	(1.98)	1.93	2.00	(108)	182 ±10	71 ±5	0.941	0.937	123
$VO[(CF_3CO)CH(NH_4)_2$ In $[Cl_5H_2O]$ CO)]$_2$ in DMF	1.966	1.943	1.978	100.5	173	66.0	0.861	0.932	122
$VO[(CF_3CO)CH(CH_3CO)]_2$ in DMF	1.965	1.945	(1.975)	99.7	172	64.1	0.853	0.932	122
VO(tetraphyenyl-porphyrin) in H_2TPP	(1.979)	1.966 ±0.0003	1.985 ±0.0005	(90)	161 ±1	55 ±1	0.785	0.931	124
$VO[(CH_3CO)_2CH]_2$ in toluene	1.969 ±0.001	1.943 ±0.001	1.979 ±0.001(x) 1.985 ±0.001(y)	98.3	170.5	63.5(x) 59.6(y)	0.845	0.926	115
$VO[(CH_3CO)_2CH]_2$ in CH_3NH_2	1.969 ±0.001	1.944 ±0.001	(1.979)	95.5 ±0.5	(167.4 ±0.8)	59.5	0.820	0.924	119
VO(porphyrin) in THF	1.981 ±0.001	1.964 ±0.001	1.989 ±0.001	88.7 ±0.7	159.1 ±1.5	54.2 ±0.6	0.773	0.923	119
$VO[(CF_3CO)_2CH]_2$ in DMF[3]	1.9635	1.9415	1.9745	103.2	175	65.0	0.773	0.922	122
VO(phthalocyanine) in Zn (phthalo-cyanine)	(1.980)	1.966 ±0.003	1.993(x) ±0.001 1.981(y) ±0.001	(88)	158 ±1	55(x) ±1 52(y) ±1	0.766	0.922	137
$VO[(CH_3CO)_2CH]_2$ in THF	1.969 ±0.001	1.945 ±0.001	(1.980)	97.5 ±0.7	(169.0 ±0.9)	61.8	0.838	0.919	119

(continued)

TABLE V (continued)

Compound and host	g	$g_\parallel$	$g_\perp$	A ($10^4 cm^{-1}$)	$A_\parallel$ ($10^4 cm^{-1}$)	$A_\perp$ ($10^4 cm^{-1}$)	$N^2_{\pi_2}$ [a]	$N^2_{\pi_2}$ [b]	Reference
[VOCl₄]²⁻ in HAc-HCl	1.969 ±0.002	1.944 ±0.002	1.979 ±0.002	101.4 ±0.5	172.9 ±0.5	66.2 ±0.5	0.873	0.919	121
VO (etioporphyrin I) in oil	(1.974)	1.948 ±0.009	1.987 ±0.005	(88)	159	52	0.756	0.918	125
VO²⁺ in GeO₂	(1.960)	1.929 ±0.001	1.976 ±0.001	(104.0)	175.5 ±0.1	68.2 ±0.1	0.886	0.903	126
VO[(CH₃CO)₂CH]₂ in NH₃	1.968 ±0.001	1.947 ±0.001	(1.978)	95.0 ±0.3	(165.0 ±1.5)	(59.9)	0.815	0.901	119
VO(porphyrin) in CS₂	1.980 ±0.001	1.961 ±0.001	(1.988)	90.2 ±0.6	159.1 ±1.6	(55.8)	0.785	0.899	119
VO(NCS)₅³⁻ in CHCl₃	1.967	1.945	(1.978)	98.3	168	(63)	0.843	0.896	122
VO(phthalocyanine) in H₂ (phthalocyanine)	(1.981)	1.966 ±0.0003	1.989 ±0.0005	(90)	158 ±1	56 ±1	0.785	0.894	137
VO(tetraphenyl-porphine) in CHCl₃	(1.979)	1.966 ±0.0003	1.985 ±0.0005	(90)	161 ±1	55 ±1	0.786	0.892	124
VO(tetraphenyl-porphine) in CS₂	(1.982)	1.965 ±0.0003	1.990 ±0.0005	(91)	159 ±1	57 ±1	0.795	0.891	124
VO(etioporphyrin II) in castor oil	(1.975)	1.9474 ±0.001	1.9885 ±0.001	(89)	158	54	0.766	0.890	127
VO[(CH₃CO)₂CH]₂ in CHCl₃	1.970 ±0.001	1.948 ±0.001	1.980 ±0.001	97.8 ±0.3	(166.5 ±0.6)	63.5	0.843	0.883	119

VO(C$_2$O$_4$)$_2$·2H$_2$O in K$_2$TiO(C$_2$O$_4$)$_2$·2H$_2$O	1.961	1.940	1.972	(94)	163	60	0.798	0.881	128 129
VO^{2+} in IR-100 resin	(1.965)	1.93	1.983	(110)	180	75	0.946	0.881	130 44
VO(phthalocyanine) in H$_2$SO$_4$	(1.980)	1.965 ±0.0003	1.988 ±0.0005	(92)	159 ±1	59 ±1	0.799	0.880	137
VO(NCS)$_5^{3-}$ in DMF	1.969	1.9475	1.977	96.3	164	61.4	0.827	0.872	122
VO^{2+} in Dowex-50	(1.946)	1.88	1.979	(111)	184	74	0.930	0.870	130
VO(CN)$_5^{-3}$ in KBr powder	(1.981)	1.9735	1.98475	(77.6)	138.4	47.3	0.674	0.805	122
VO^{2+} in IR-4B resin	(1.97)	1.93	1.989	(93)	158	61.2	0.803	0.804	130
VO(CN)$_5^{-3}$ in KBr single crystal	(1.980)	1.9711	1.9844	(77.2)	137.1	47.2	0.669	0.789	122
VO(S$_2$CCN)$_2^{2-}$ in CHCl$_3$	1.992 ±0.005	1.975 ±0.004	2.000 ±0.004	65 ±2	122 ±2	40 ±2	0.575	0.752	131
VOSO$_4$ in H$_2$O	1.9624			108			0.926		113
VOF$_2$ in HF	1.968 ±0.002			107 ±3			0.919		123
VOSO$_4$ in H$_2$O	1.962			106.4 ±0.2			0.910		122
VOSO$_4$ in H$_2$O	1.962			106			0.909		132
VOSO$_4$ in H$_2$O	1.961 ±0.001			105.7 ±0.5			0.913		133
VOF$_5^{3-}$	1.962 ±0.002			105.2 ±0.5			0.899		121

(continued)

TABLE V (continued)

Compound and host	g	$g_{\parallel}$	$g_{\perp}$	A (10^4cm^{-1})	$A_{\parallel}$ (10^4cm^{-1})	$A_{\perp}$ (10^4cm^{-1})	$N^2_{\pi_2}$ a	$N^2_{\pi_2}$ b	Reference
VO[CF$_3$COCHCO CH$_3$]$_2$ in benzene	1.9693			101.6			0.875		134
VO[(CH$_3$CO)$_2$CH]$_2$ in benzene	1.9695			99.5			0.857		134
VO[(CH$_3$CO)$_2$CH]$_2$ in benzene	1.970 ±0.001			99.3 ±0.2			0.855		135
VO[(CH$_3$CO)$_2$CH]$_2$ in CS$_2$	1.968 ±0.001			99.5 ±0.2			0.855		119
VO(phthalic acid)$_2^{2-}$ in H$_2$O	1.963 ±0.001			99.9 ±0.5			0.853		133
VO(nitriletriacetic acid)	1.963 ±0.001			99.9 ±0.5			0.853		133
VO[CF$_3$COCHCO CH$_3$]$_2$·pyridine in benzene	1.9704			98.5			0.849		134
VO(NCS)$_n^{(2-n)+}$ in H$_2$O (pH 2.5 0.4M KNCS)	1.964 ±0.001			99.0 ±0.5			0.846		133
VO[(CH$_3$CO)$_2$CH]$_2$·2 methyl piperidine in benzene	1.9697			97.4			0.838		134
VO[(CH$_3$CO)$_2$CH]$_2$ ·piperidine in benzene	1.9699			96.9			0.834		134

VO[(CH₃CO)₂CH]₂ ·pyridine in benzene	1.9699	96.7	0.833	134
VO(nitriletriacetic acid) (OH)²⁻ in H₂O	1.963 ±0.001	97.6 ±0.5	0.833	133
VO[(CH₃CO)₂CH]₂ in acetonitrile	1.969 ±0.001	96.8 ±0.1	0.832	135
VO[(CH₃CO)₂CH]₂ in nitrobenzene	1.972 ±0.001	96.3 ±0.6	0.831	135
VO(C₂O₄)₂ in H₂O	1.964 ±0.001	97.19	0.857	133
VO(5-sulfosalicylic acid)¹⁻ in H₂O	1.963 ±0.001	97.1 ±0.5	0.828	136
VO(2-picolylimino diacetic acid) in H₂O	1.966 ±0.001	96.4 ±0.5	0.825	133
VO[(CH₃CO)₂CH]₂ in pyridine	1.971 ±0.001	95.3 ±0.6	0.821	134
VO(iminodiacetic acid) in H₂O	1.966 ±0.001	95.5 ±0.5	0.817	133
VO[(CH₃CO)₂CH]₂ in CH₃OH	1.9688	94.1	0.808	134
VO(ethylene-diaminetetra acetic acid)²⁻ in H₂O	1.967 ±0.001	94.1 ±0.5	0.806	133
VO[(CH₃CO)₂CH]₂ in CH₃OH	1.968 ±0.001	94.0 ±0.1	0.806	135

(continued)

TABLE V (continued)

Compound and host	g	$g_\parallel$	$g_\perp$	A $(10^4 cm^{-1})$	$A_\parallel$ $(10^4 cm^{-1})$	$A_\perp$ $(10^4 cm^{-1})$	$N^2_{\pi_2}$ [a]	$N^2_{\pi_2}$ [b]	Reference
VO(diethylene-triaminepenta acetic acid)$^{3-}$ (protonated complex)	1.967 ±0.001			93.7 ±0.5			0.802		133
VO(malonic acid)$_2^{2-}$ in H_2O	1.967 ±0.001			93.7 ±0.5			0.802		133
VO(tiron)$^{2-}$ in H_2O	1.966 ±0.001			93.2 ±0.5			0.796		136
VO(2-picolylimino-diacetic acid)(OH)$^{1-}$ in H_2O	1.966 ±0.001			92.2 ±0.5			0.788		133
VO(picolinic acid)$_2$ in H_2O	1.970 ±0.001			91.1 ±0.5			0.782		133
VO(5-sulfosalicylic acid)$_2^{4-}$ in H_2O	1.966 ±0.001			88.6 ±0.5			0.755		136
VO(bipyridine)$_2^{2-}$ in H_2O	1.974 ±0.001			87.5 ±0.5			0.755		133
VO(picolinic acid)$_2$ (OH)$^{1-}$	1.968 ±0.001			88.2 ±0.5			0.754		133

Numbers in parentheses indicate values calculated from $g = 1/3\, g_\parallel + 2/3\, g_\perp$ or $A = 1/3\, A_\parallel + 2/3\, A_\perp$.

N_{π_2} can also be determined from the isotropic splitting with the use of the following equation:

$$A = -N_{\pi_2}^2 PK + (g - 2.0023)P \tag{32}$$

K is the Fermi contact term and, as is discussed in Section II-C, is due to both spin polarization and unpaired $4s$ spin density. The value of K was arbitrarily chosen as 0.872 since this value gives an $N_{\pi_2}^2$ for VOSO$_4$ of ≈ 0.93.

a. **Experimental results.** Literature ESR data are given in Table V, along with the calculated values of the molecular orbital coefficients for the in-plane pi bonding, N_{π_2}. Kivelson and Lee (119) proposed that the amount of in-plane pi bonding is negligible ($N_{\pi_2}^2 \approx 1$), and that the change in the isotropic A value from complex to complex is due to a change in the Fermi contact term, K. If this is correct, the first set of $N_{\pi_2}^2$ values have no meaning since they were calculated from equation 32 with the assumption that K is constant. Kivelson and Lee's proposal appears to be supported by the linear correlation (120) between the value of A_{iso} and the ratio of the axial to equatorial crystal field (see Fig. 5). A possible explanation for this correlation is based on the assumption that the ground state contains a

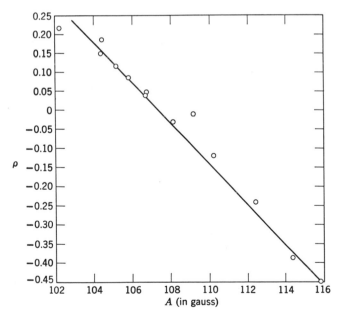

Fig. 5. Correlation of ratio of axial to equatorial crystal field, ρ, and ESR A values for a number of vanadyl complexes.

TABLE VI
Calculation of Vanadyl Nuclear Hyperfine Splittings
for Mixed Complexes from Equation 33

Complex	Coordinating groups	$A_{calculated}$	$A_{experimental}$
VO(Tiron)$^{2-}$	L_1, L_2 = Phenol groups L_3, L_4 = H_2O	100.5 G	101.5 G
VO(Sulfosalicylic acid)	L_1 = Phenol group L_2 = Aromatic carboxyl group L_3, L_4 = H_2O	106.5 G	106.0 G
VO(Sulfosalicylic acid)$^{4-}_2$	L_1, L_2 = Phenol group L_3, L_4 = Aromatic carboxyl groups	97.5 G	96.5 G
VO(Picolinic acid)$_2$	L_1, L_2 = Aromatic N L_3, L_4 = Aliphatic carboxyl groups	98.5 G	99.0 G

The following values were used by Wuethrich for the calculations: A = 86.0 G for VO(tiron)$^{6-}_2$, A = 115.5 for VOSO$_4$, A = 109.0 for VO(phthalic acid)$^{2-}_2$, A = 95.0 for VO(bipyridine)$^{2+}_2$, and A = 102.0 for VO(malonic acid)$^{2-}_2$.

small amount of $3d_{z^2}$ and $4s$ character. The change in the amount of $4s$ character as the ratio of the axial to equatorial charge changed would then account for the change in A_{iso} since, as discussed earlier, an electron in a $4s$ orbital has a hyperfine splitting contribution of opposite sign to the main polarization contribution. An alternate explanation is that the change is merely due to a covalency contribution. This is hard to reconcile with the above mentioned correlation; however, it is supported by an interesting correlation by Wuethrich (136). He found that he could predict the experimental values of A_{iso} by the following equation:

$$A_{iso} = (A_{L_1} + A_{L_2} + A_{L_3} + A_{L_4})/4 \qquad (33)$$

In this equation A_{L_1} is the A_{iso} found experimentally for a vanadyl complex that had four L_1 type atoms bonded to the VO^{2+} in the equatorial positions. His correlation is given in Table VI. Of course, it is possible (in fact probable) that both factors contribute, the amount of $4s$ character being the predominant term for the more ionic complexes used in the optical correlation given in Fig. 5.

b. **Ligand Hyperfine Splittings.** A ligand isotropic hyperfine splitting, A_s, is not expected since the ground state orbital is an orbital of π symmetry. The observed A_s values have been attributed by Kivelson and Lee (119) to configuration interaction in which an electron is promoted from a bonding orbital to an antibonding orbital. Specifically, the promotions of importance are:

$$(x^2 - y^2)\uparrow\downarrow^{(b)} \ (xy)\uparrow^{(*)} \rightarrow (x^2 - y^2)\downarrow^{(b)} \ (x^2 - y^2)\uparrow^{(*)} \ (xy)\uparrow^{(*)} \tag{34}$$

$$(z^2)\uparrow\downarrow^{(b)} \ (xy)\uparrow^{(*)} \rightarrow (z^2)\downarrow^{(b)} \ (z^2)\uparrow^{(*)} \ (xy)\uparrow^{(*)} \tag{35}$$

The superscript b indicates a bonding orbital and $*$ indicates an antibonding orbital. For the equatorial ligands the first promotion is the important one. The isotropic splitting is given by:

$$A_s = -\frac{N_{\sigma_2}^2(1 - N_{\sigma_2}^2)(d_{xy}, d_{x^2-y^2})A_s'}{2\Delta E(x^2 - y^2)^b \rightarrow (x^2 - y^2)*} \tag{36}$$

where $(d_{xy}, d_{x^2-y^2})$ is an exchange integral and the $\frac{1}{2}$ comes from the assumption that the sigma ligand orbital is an s–p hybrid. The approximations involved in equation 36 are such that molecular orbital coefficients cannot be calculated from them; however, the spin density, f_s, at the ligand can be calculated with the use of equation 38.

$$A_s' = \frac{8}{3}\frac{\mu_n\beta_n}{I_n} \ [\psi(0)_{2s}^2] \ \text{(in gauss)} \tag{37}$$

$$f_s = \frac{A_s}{A_s'} \tag{38}$$

An alternate mechanism also considered (but rejected by Kivelson and Lee) is that the A_s values are due to polarization of the ligand by unpaired spin density in the ligand π orbitals.

The experimental hyperfine splittings and the calculated f_s values are given in Table VII.

TABLE VII
Ligand Hyperfine Splittings for Vanadyl Complexes

	Ligand Nucleus	A	$A_\parallel$	$A_\perp$	f_s[a]	Reference
VO(CN)$_5^{3-}$ in H$_2$O	^{13}C	11.3 G ± 0.2	—	—	0.010	120
VOF$_5^{3-}$	F	(not observed)	—	—	—	121–123
VO(porphyrin)	N	—	2.9 G ± 0.05	2.8 G ± 0.05	0.005	119
VO(NCS)$_5^{3-}$ in CHCl$_3$	N	(not observed)	—	—	—	122,133
VOCl$_5^{3-}$	Cl	(not observed)	—	—	—	121,123
VO^{2+} in Zn(NH$_4$)$_2$(SO$_4$)·6H$_2$O	H	—	≈ 4 G	—	0.008	118
VO(S$_2$P(OC$_2$H$_5$)$_2$)$_2$ in toluene	P	50 G	50 G	50 G	0.014	139

[a] A_s' for ^{13}C = 1110 G, A_s' for N = 550 G, A_s' for H = 508 G, and A_s' for P = 3600 G.

TABLE VIII

ESR Data for d^1 Vanadium Complexes Other than Vanadyl

Compound and host	g	$g_\parallel$	$g_\perp$	A (10^4 cm^{-1})	$A_\parallel$ (10^4 cm^{-1})	$A_\perp$ (10^4 cm^{-1})	Reference
$V(OC(CH_3)_3)_4$ at 30°C in CS_2, in pure solid, and in $Ti(OC(CH_3)_3)_4$	1.964 ±0.005			64 ±2			160
$V(OC(CH_3)_3)_4$ in $Ti(OC(CH_3)_3)_4$ at −186°C	(1.969)	1.940 ±0.005	1.984 ±0.005	(65)	125 ±5	36 ±4	160
$VS_6C_6(CN)_6^{-2}$ in $CHCl_3$–DMF	1.980 ±0.001	1.974 ±0.005	(1.983)	58.5 ±0.5	92 ±2	42 ±1	103
V(IV) in SnO_2		1.943	1.903 (y) 1.939 (x)		140.1	41.78 (y) 21.1 (x)	161
V(IV) in GeO_2 (tetragonal)		1.9632 ±0.0003	1.9213 ±0.0006 1.9213 ±0.0001		134.36 0.02	36.69 ±0.01 (x) 37.54 ±0.01 (y)	126
V(IV) in TiO_2		1.9565	1.915 (x) 1.9125 (y)		142	31.5 (x) 43 (y)	162
$V(C_5H_5)_2Cl_2$ in benzene	1.99			66.1			159

System	g values	Conditions		A (G)	Reference
V(C5H5)2Cl2 in CHCl3	1.99			68.8	159
VCl3 in heptane	No signal 90°K to 300°K 8 × 10⁻⁴ to 8 × 10⁻²M				159
(C5H5)2V(C6H5) in toluene	2.13	1 × 10⁻²M 300°K	Line width ≈1000 G		159
(C5H5)2 · V(C6H4CH3) in toluene	2.13	1 × 10⁻²M 300°K	Line width ≈1000 G		159
V(IV) in Al2O3	1.97	1.97	1.97	≈132 ≈132 ≈132	163
V(S2(CN)(C2H5)2)3 in toluene	1.974 ±0.002	1.960 ±0.005	1.948 ±0.005	66 ±2 127 ±5 35 ±5	139

Additional ESR studies involving the vanadyl ion include references 140–158.

2. d^1 Vanadium Complexes Other Than Vanadyl

Some literature data are given in Table VIII. As demonstrated by the experimental work of Chien and Boss (159) an ESR signal will only be observed if the symmetry of the complex is sufficiently low such that the ground state is nondegenerate. A point of particular interest in Table VIII is that the ESR A values are in general much smaller than the A values for vanadyl complexes. This observation supports the $4s$ contribution theory since in low symmetry the ground state can include some $4s$ character. Karavelas (74) utilized molecular orbital theory to analyze the ESR data for V^{4+} in SnO_2, TiO_2, and GeO_2 and obtained the molecular orbital coefficients given in Table IX. The small amount of $4s$ character found is significant in lowering the A values.

Ligand hyperfine splittings were observed in TiO_2 and SnO_2, see Table X. In SnO_2 there are two inequivalent sets of Sn nuclei which give rise to the two sets of hyperfine constants in Table X. Chen, Kikuchi, and Watanabe (168) calculated the vanadium–tin overlap integrals and found that the ratio of the overlap integrals is the same as the ratio of the hyperfine splittings.

Although, at present, the calculation of the molecular orbital coefficients from the ESR g values for vanadyl complexes is ambiguous due to uncertainty in the assignments of the optical spectra, for the tetrahedral $V(OC(CH_3)_3)_4$ compound the $x^2 - y^2$ to xy, yz, and xz transitions are expected to be degenerate and assignable to the single observed optical

TABLE IX

Variation of the Molecular Orbital
Coefficients for the Ground State of V^{4+} in SnO_2, TiO_2, and GeO_2 (74)

Assumed vanadium charge	SnO_2			TiO_2			GeO_2		
	$4s$	z^2	x^2-y^2	$4s$	z^2	x^2-y^2	$4s$	z^2	x^2-y^2
0.65	0.073	−0.139	0.986	0.069	−0.114	0.992	0.082	−0.140	0.987
0.45	0.069	−0.133	0.989	0.058	−0.108	0.992	0.078	−0.135	0.988
0.30	0.068	−0.132	0.989	0.057	−0.107	0.993	0.076	−0.134	0.988
0.10	0.067	−0.130	0.989	0.056	−0.106	0.993	0.0749	−0.133	0.988
0.00	0.066	−0.130	0.989	0.055	−0.105	0.993	0.074	−0.132	0.988
−0.10	0.065	−0.130	0.989	0.055	−0.105	0.993	0.074	−0.132	0.988
−0.30	0.064	0.129	0.990	0.054	−0.104	0.993	0.073	−0.131	0.989
−0.40	0.064	−0.128	0.990	0.053	−0.104	0.993	0.072	−0.131	0.989
−0.50	0.063	−0.128	0.990	0.053	−0.103	0.993	0.072	−0.130	0.989

TABLE X
Ligand Hyperfine Splittings in V^{4+} Complexes, Other than Vanadyl

	Nucleus	A_x	A_y	A_z	A_s	References
TiO_2	Ti	2.0 G	2.0	2.4	2.13	164
SnO_2	Sn	166	172.6	165.2	168	161
		28	28	28	28	
VCl_4–$AlEt_3$	H					165
in toluene	or					166
or benzene	Cl?					167

peak. Kokoszka, Allen, and Gordon (160) have analyzed the data for this compound using the following relationship between the spin–orbit coupling constant and P:

$$\zeta = 1.45 \times 10^4 P \qquad (39)$$

They used an iterative program along with Murao's equation (79) for calculating ζ to obtain the following values: $\zeta = 156$ cm^{-1}, $P = 108$ 10^{-4}cm^{-1}, $N^2_{x^2-y^2} = 0.90$, $N^2_{xy} = 0.83$, and $N^2_{xz,yz} = 0.94$.

Other ESR papers covering nonvanadyl V^{4+} complexes include references 169–181.

3. ESR Of d^1 Titanium Complexes

The ESR of titanium complexes has been relatively neglected compared to the situation for vanadium complexes. This is true partly because there is not a titanium analog to the vanadyl system, and partly because many Ti^{3+} complexes are unstable and are oxidized in air to Ti^{4+} complexes. Normally only low symmetry titanium complexes will exhibit a narrow ESR spectra at room temperature. Titanium has two isotopes that have magnetic moments. ^{47}Ti is 7.75% abundant, has a nuclear spin of $5/2$, and has a magnetic moment of -0.78711. ^{49}Ti is 5.51% abundant, has a nuclear spin of $7/2$, and has a magnetic moment of -1.1022.

The ESR data are given in Table XI. Gladney and Swalen (182) have attempted to calculate the covalency parameters for Ti^{3+} in Al_2O_3, Cs $Ti(SO_4)$,·$12H_2O$, $Ti[(CH_3CO)_2CH]_2$, and $AlCl_3$. They found that the inclusion of a complete trigonal distortion Hamiltonian is necessary, but they could not determine both the trigonal distortion parameters and the covalency parameters from the available data. Waters and Maki (183) have observed a fluorine hyperfine splitting of 7.05×10^{-4} cm^{-1} for TiF_2^+ in methanol. Since anisotropic data have not been reported, one cannot say definitely what the ground state of TiF_2^+ is. But based on the relatively low fluorine hyperfine splitting value (the fluorine hyperfine

TABLE XI
ESR Data for d^1 Titanium Compounds

Compound and host	g	$g_{\parallel}$	$g_{\perp}$	A (10^4 cm^{-1})	$A_{\parallel}$ (10^4 cm^{-1})	$A_{\perp}$ (10^4 cm^{-1})	Reference
Ti[(CH₃CO)₂CH]₃ in Al[(CH₃CO)₂CH]₃		2.000 ± 0.002	1.921 ± 0.001		6.3 ± 3.0	17.5 ± 0.5	185
Water solution of TiCl₃ and CH₃COCH₂COCH₃							186
pH 1.7–2.6	1.946 ± 0.002						
Water solution of TiCl₃ and N(CH₂COOH)₃							186
pH 1.9, 8.0, 10.2	1.962 ± 0.002						
pH 2.1, 2.2, 2.5, 3.1, 4.0, 4.4, 4.9, 5.9	1.961 ± 0.002						
Water solution of TiCl₃ and N(CH₂COOH)₂CH₂CH₂OH							186
pH 1.2	1.952						
pH 5.0, 7.9	1.953						
Water solution of TiCl₃ and N(CH₂COOH)₂CH₂CH₂OH							186
pH 6.9	1.950						
pH 9.6	1.954						

Water solution of TiCl$_3$ and N(CH$_2$CH$_2$OH)$_2$CH$_2$COOH		186
pH 3.3, 3.7, 3.9	1.957	
pH 8.9, 9.2	1.954	
pH 9.6, 10.1	1.953	
Water solution of TiCl$_3$ and C$_2$H$_4$[N(CH$_2$COOH)·(CH$_2$COONa)]$_2$		186
pH 1.1, 7.1	1.958	
pH 8.0, 9.0, 9.1, 9.6	1.956	
pH 2.7, 7.3, 9.1, 9.3 (with tartaric acid)	1.957	
pH 9.5, 10.1 (with tartaric acid)	1.956	
Water solution of TiCl$_3$ and N(CH$_2$CH$_2$OH)$_3$		186
pH 7.0, 7.4, 7.6, 7.7, 7.9, 8.1, 8.2, 8.3, 8.6, 8.8, 9.0	1.970 and 1.964 (two peaks)	
Water solution of TiCl$_3$ and N(CH$_2$CH$_3$)$_3$		186
pH 6.6	1.969	
pH 7.1, 7.7, 7.9, 8.3, 8.8, 9.3	1.970 and 1.965 (two peaks)	
pH 10.4	1.970	

(continued)

TABLE XI (continued)

Compound and host	g	$g_\parallel$	$g_\perp$	A (10^{-4} cm^1)	$A_\parallel$ (10^4 cm^{-1})	$A_\perp$ (10^4 cm^{-1})	Reference
Water solution of TiCl$_3$ and NH(CH$_2$CH$_3$)$_2$ pH 7.5, 7.8, 8.0, 8.6, 9.7	1.970 and 1.964 (two peaks)						186
Water solution of TiCl$_3$ and H$_2$N(C$_4$H$_9$) pH 7.5, 8.1, 8.3, 8.9, 9.4, 9.6, 10.0	1.970 and 1.964						186
(C$_5$H$_2$)$_2$Ti(C$_2$H$_5$) in toluene	1.94						159
TiCl$_3$·6H$_2$O	1.91						188
Ti$_2$(SO$_4$)$_3$·4H$_2$O	1.91						188
				$\approx$12 G	30 G	2 G	193
TiCl$_3$·6H$_2$O in ethanol	1.9 ±0.1	2.00	1.90				187
Ti(III) in CH$_3$OH	1.9532 ±0.0005						183
TiF$_2^+$ in CH$_3$OH	1.9465 ±0.0004		16.7				183
AlCl$_3$·6H$_2$O		1.93	1.93				190
Al$_2$O$_3$		1.067	≪0.1				189

Compound					Reference
TiO₂		1.941	1.974		191
TiO₂		1.953	1.977		192
TiO₂		1.940	1.975, 1.978		164
TiCl₂⁺ in CH₃OH	1.951		1.972 (y), 1.975 (x)	18.3	183
(C₅H₅)₂TiCl₂Al(C₂H₅)₂	1.976			10.2	183
KTi(C₂O₄)₂·2H₂O		1.86	1.96		Unpublished quoted in 182
Ti³⁺ in RbAl(SO₄)₂·12H₂O		1.895 ± 0.002	1.715 (x) ± 0.002, 1.767 (y) ± 0.002		241
Ti(N(CH₂COOH)₃)₂ pH 3.5–9	1.961 ± 0.002				247
Ti(N(CH₂COOH)₂-CH₂CH₂OH) pH 1.2–5.5	1.952 ± 0.002				247
Ti(N(CH₂COOH)₂-CH₂CH₂OH) pH > 8	1.952 ± 0.002				247

splitting for $KNiF_3$ (88) where the unpaired electron is in a sigma orbital to the fluorine is $39.1 \times 10^{-4} cm^{-1}$) and on the observation that the two fluorines are equivalent, we can predict that the ground state is probably the d_{xy} orbital. The value of $7 \times 10^{-4} cm^{-1}$ is consistent with the reported hyperfine splitting values for d^3 complexes $A \approx 1.5 \times 10^{-4} cm^{-1}$ since a d^3 complex is expected to give a hyperfine splitting value one-third that of a d^1 complex. The spin density, f_s, on the fluorine is very small, 0.005. Fujiwara, Nagashima, and Codell (184) have utilized ESR and optical spectroscopy to follow the changes in equilibrium of Ti^{3+} mixed complexes with pH. They were able to determine equilibrium constants and the probable composition. This was possible because the different complexes had resolvable ESR spectra which would, of course, grow or decrease as the equilibrium was shifted. Other ESR papers which studied Ti^{3+} are listed in reference 194 through 212 and references 242 and 243.

4. *ESR of d^1 Chromium Complexes*

The ESR of Cr^{5+} complexes has been the subject of intense investigation mainly because the Cr^{5+} ion is a catalytically active species in the chromia–alumina-type catalyst systems (213–222). The principle chromium isotope does not have a nuclear magnetic moment. In order to measure the nuclear hyperfine splittings one must be able to resolve the 9.54% abundant chromium-53 splittings. ^{53}Cr has a small magnetic moment ($\mu = -0.47354$); however, its spin is relatively large ($^3/_2$) so that frequently it is possible to resolve at least the two outermost ^{53}Cr lines. The ESR data are given in Table XII. The $CrOCl_5^{2-}$ ion has been particularly interesting. It was expected to have ESR parameters similar to those found for vanadyl complexes since it has the same ground state; however, it was found that $g_\parallel > g_\perp$ rather than the expected $g_\parallel < g_\perp$ as found for vanadyl complexes. This discrepancy was explained by Kon and Sharpless (80). They pointed out that a charge-transfer optical transition from the bonding sigma orbitals of the chlorine (p_{Cl}^b) to the chromium ground state (d_{xy}) would give a positive contribution to the g value. For Cr^{5+} this transition is found at a lower energy, $\approx 18.000 cm^{-1}$, than the $d_{xy} \rightarrow p*$ Cl transition ($\approx 23.200 cm^{-1}$). Since the $g_\parallel$ value is given by an equation of the following approximate form,

$$g_\parallel \approx 2 - \frac{\zeta}{d_{xy} \rightarrow p_{Cl}^*} + \frac{\zeta}{p_{Cl} \rightarrow d_{xy}} \tag{40}$$

this assignment does give the observed increase in $g_\parallel$. Kon and Sharpless also determined the molecular orbital coefficients for the $CrOCl_5^{2-}$ ion. They found that $N_{\pi_2}^2 = 0.868$, $N_{\pi_1}^2 = 0.814$, and $N_{\pi_2}^2 = 0.818$ (see eqs. 22–24 for the form of the molecular orbital equations). A 6 G hyperfine splitting from the four equivalent fluorines in $[CrOF_5]^{2-}$ was observed by Garif'yanov (223). This gives an s electron spin density on each fluorine, f_s, of 0.004. CrO_8^{-3} is of special interest since eight coordination is rare among first-row transition metal complexes. It has been studied by Swalen and Ibers (224) and by McGarvey (225). X-ray studies indicated that there are two sets of inequivalent Cr—O bonds, and the ESR results showed that the shorter Cr—O bonds are more covalent than the longer. Additional ESR references for Cr^{5+} are 229 through 232.

B. d^2-Ti^{2+}, V^{3+}, Cr^{4+}, Mn^{5+}, and Fe^{6+} Complexes

The available literature data are given in Table XIII. The small amount of data is primarily due to two considerations. The first is the general instability of the valence states and the second is the necessity to take the experimental data at liquid helium temperatures with a high klystron frequency spectrometer. The high klystron frequency is needed so that H (magnetic field) $\gg D$. If this requirement is not satisfied and $D \gg H$, the angular dependence is given by the following equation (30,233,246):

$$h\gamma = g\beta H [\cos^2 \theta + 2.25 \sin^2 \theta]^{1/2} \qquad (41)$$

From this equation it follows that $g_\parallel$ is not affected by the choice of relative magnitude of D and H; however, $g_\perp$ (observed) will be ≈ 3 if the actual $g_\perp$ value is 2. In order to stabilize the Cr^{4+} state in Al_2O_3, Hoskins and Soffer (234) substituted some N^{3-} ions in place of the O^{2-} ions in the lattice. This technique provided the charge compensation necessary to substitute the 4+ chromium ion in place of a 3+ aluminum ion. Ray (235,248) has attempted to theoretically calculate the g values for V^{3+} in Al_2O_3. In order to satisfy the ESR data he had to use a value for the trigonal field splitting of one-half the experimental value. Other ESR papers concerned with d^2 complexes are references 249–253 and 164.

C. ESR of d^3 Complexes

Octahedral d^3 complexes normally contain the three unpaired electrons in the orbitals of correct symmetry to form pi bonds with the ligands. These orbitals are the d_{xy}, d_{xz}, and d_{yz}. The combined action of any field of lower symmetry and spin–orbit coupling produce the zero magnetic field splittings, D and E, which separate the $M = \frac{1}{2}$ states from the $M = \frac{3}{2}$ states. The application of a magnetic field removes the remaining sign degeneracy, see Figure 6. The allowed transitions are those where $M = 1$. Besides the three expected transitions, additional transitions are observed whenever the separation between two energy levels equals the applied magnetic field. Normally, the ESR data are obtained from

TABLE XII

ESR Data for Cr^{5+} d^1 Complexes

Compound and host	g	$g_\parallel$	$g_\perp$	A (10^4 cm^{-1})	$A_\parallel$ (10^4 cm^{-1})	$A_\perp$ (10^4 cm^{-1})	Reference
K_2CrOCl_5 in acetic acid	1.9877 ±0.0003	2.008_5	1.977_3	18.3	36.1	(9.7)	80
Cr^{5+} in 65% oleum room temp. 77°K	$(1.964)^a$ $(1.964)^b$	1.951^a 1.936^b	1.970^a 1.968^b				132
Cr^{5+} in 30% oleum	1.970 1.965 (Two species present)			21 21			132
Cr^{5+} in 100% H_2SO_4	1.970 1.965 (Two species present)			21 21			132
$CrOCl_4(pyridine)^{1-}$	1.9877 ±0.0003	2.000 ±0.001	1.978 ±0.001	18.5 ±0.1			226
$CrOCl_4(pyridine)^{1-}$		1.9883	1.9792				80
$CrOCl_4(quinoline)^{1-}$	1.9880 ±0.0003	1.991 ±0.001	1.991 ±0.001	18.5 ±0.1			226
$CrOCl_4(N(CH_4)_4)$	1.9875 ±0.0003	1.989 ±0.001	1.989 ±0.001	18.4 ±0.1			226
CrO_3 in 70% H_2SO_4 (probably forms $Cr_2O_3(SO_4)_2$)	1.966 ±0.002	1.969	1.976	26			223
$Cr_2O_3(SO_4)_2$ in solid H_2SO_4		1.951	1.985				223

	g	g	g	A	A	A	Ref.
K_3CrO_8 single crystal		1.95 ±0.02	1.98 ±0.01				225
CrO_3 in H_2O (probably forms CrO_8^{-3})	1.973			17.6			223
Cr^{5+} in glycerol (similar spectra in borate and silicate glasses)	1.978	1.99	1.972 ±0.002	18	34	11	227
$Cr[S_2C_2(C_6H_5)_2]_3^{1-}$ in $CHCl_3$	1.996			17.8 ±0.5			181
$Ba_3(CrO_4)_2$ in $Ba_3(PO_4)_2$	1.97						213
$Ba_5(CrO_4)_3 \cdot OH$ in $Ba(PO_4)_3 \cdot OH$	1.97						213
$(NH_4)_2CrOCl_5$ in 20% HCl	1.986 ±0.02	1.995 ±0.005	1.937 ±0.005	17.7			223
K_2CrO_8	1.944 ±0.006		1.986 ±0.001				228
CrO_3 in concentrated HCl[3] (probably forms $[CrOCl_5]^{2-}$)	1.986	1.995	1.937	17.7			223
CrO_3 in HF (probably forms $[CrOF_5]^{2-}$)	1.960						223
CrO_3 + acetic acid in acetic acid	1.9652 ±0.0003			19.3 ±0.1			226
$K_2Cr_2O_7$ + CF_3COOH in acetic acid	1.9710 ±0.0003			20.3 ±0.1			226
$K_2Cr_2O_7$ + $(COOH)_2$ in acetic acid	1.9779 ±0.0003			17.0 ±0.1			226

(continued)

TABLE XII (*continued*)

Compound and host	g	$g_{\parallel}$	$g_{\perp}$	A (10^4 cm^{-1})	$A_{\parallel}$ (10^4 cm^{-1})	$A_{\perp}$ (10^4 cm^{-1})	Reference
$K_2Cr_2O_7$ + lactic acid in acetic acid	1.9780 ±0.0003	1.968 ±0.001	1.979 ±0.001 (x) 1.975 ±0.001 (y)	17.2 ±0.1			226
$Cr[S_2C_2(CF_3)_2]_3^{1-}$ in CH_2Cl_2	1.9941 ±0.0003	1.995 ±0.002	1.995 ±0.002	14.8 ±0.5			103
$K_3CrO_8(1.8\%)$ in K_3NbO_8		1.944 ±0.005	1.982 ±0.005				225
$K_3CrO_8(0.26\%)$ in K_3NbO_8		1.9434 ±0.0004	1.9848 ±0.0004				225
K_3CrO_8		1.936 ±0.002	1.983 ±0.002				224

TABLE XIII
ESR Data for d^2 Complexes

Compound and host	g	$g_\parallel$	$g_\perp$	A $(10^{-4}\,cm^{-1})$	$A_\parallel$ $(10^{-4}\,cm^{-1})$	$A_\perp$ $(10^{-4}\,cm^{-1})$	D	E	Reference
Cr^{4+} in Al_2O_3 at 4.2°K		1.90 +0.02 −0.01					<1500 $10^{-4}\,cm^{-1}$	$0 \lesssim E$ $\lesssim 0.05\,cm^{-1}$	234
V^{3+} in CdS	1.933			65					236
Cr^{4+} in Si	1.9962			12.54					236
Mn^{5+} in Si	2.0259			63.09					236
Mn^{5+} in $Na_3VO_4\cdot 12H_2O$	2			62.5					237
V^{3+} in Al_2O_3		1.915 ±0.002	1.63 ±0.05	95.9 ±0.5			70,000 $10^{-4}\,cm^{-1}$ ±3000	<$10^{-2}\,cm^{-1}$	238
							82,900 ±200		246
V^{3+} in Al_2O_3									245
V^{3+} in ZnS	1.9433 ±0.0005			63.0 ±0.1					244

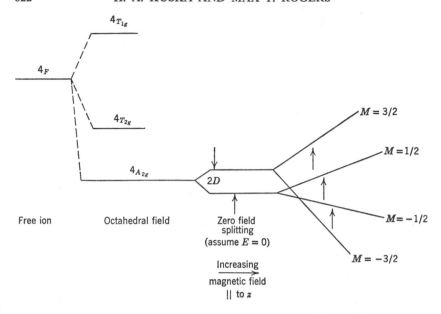

Fig. 6. Energy levels for a d^3 complex.

single-crystal experiments since the angular dependence of the transitions to first order in D are (239):

$$M = \tfrac{3}{2} \leftrightarrow \tfrac{1}{2} \qquad h\gamma = g\beta H\left[1 + (3\cos^2\phi - 1)\frac{D}{g\beta H}\right] \qquad (42)$$

$$M = \tfrac{1}{2} \leftrightarrow -\tfrac{1}{2} \qquad h\gamma = g\beta H \qquad\qquad\qquad\qquad\qquad (43)$$

$$M = -\tfrac{1}{2} \leftrightarrow -\tfrac{3}{2} \qquad h\gamma = g\beta H\left[1 - (3\cos^2\phi - 1)\frac{D}{g\beta H}\right] \qquad (44)$$

The equations complete to third order in D and E are available (239). The interpretation of the powder spectra has been investigated by Burns (240). He found that it is possible to obtain the D and g values from the powder spectrum when the compound is diluted in an isomorphic diamagnetic host. Molecular orbital analyses of the experimental g and D values have been carried out by Garrett, DeArmond, and Gutowsky (85) and by McGarvey (83). Garrett et al. studied the $[CrCl_5(H_2O)]^{2-}$ ion. They could not assign independent values to the molecular orbital coefficients but were able to determine the relative range of the parameters. They report: if D is positive, $N_{\pi_2}^2 \approx 1.12$–0.98, $N_{\sigma_2}^2 \approx 0.97$–$1.01$, $N_{\pi_2}^2 \approx 0.92$–0.97, and $N_{z^2}^2 \approx 0.98$–0.81. If D is negative, $N_{\pi_2}^2 = 1.01$, $N_{\sigma_2}^2 = 0.97$, $N_{\pi_1}^2 = 0.986$, and $N_{z^2}^2 = 0.828$ (see eqs. 22–24 for the form of the molecular orbital equations). The amount of covalency in the equatorial plane is surprisingly small. McGarvey reported considerably more covalency in the compounds that he studied. His values are given in Table XIV. For his calculations McGarvey made the assumption that there was no pi bonding. If pi bonding is significant, the $N_{\sigma_2}^2$ values would be larger than those given in Table XV. The amount of pi bonding can be determined from ligand hyperfine splittings with the use of the following equations.

$$N_\pi = (1 \pm 4\lambda_\pi S_{d,p_\pi} + \lambda_\pi^2)^{-1/2} \qquad (45)$$

$$f_\pi = \lambda_\pi^2 N_\pi^2/4 = -2SA_\sigma/A_\sigma' \qquad (46)$$

S is the total electron spin ($3/2$), and the other terms are defined in Section II-D. In writing these equations, we are assuming that the d_{xy}, d_{yz}, and d_{xz} pi orbitals are degenerate. The ESR ligand hyperfine splitting data and N_π^2 values are given in Table XVI.

Title (98) and McGarvey (99) have plotted the isotropic nuclear hyperfine splittings, x, vs. the electronegativity differences between the anion and cation for a number of d^3 complexes. The plot for Cr^{3+} is given in Figure 7. The expected trend is found; those compounds which are expected to be more covalent do have smaller nuclear hyperfine splitting values. x is related to the Fermi contact term, K, by the following equation:

$$x \text{ (in atomic units)} = -\frac{(4.7068 \times 10^2 IK)}{\mu} \qquad (47)$$

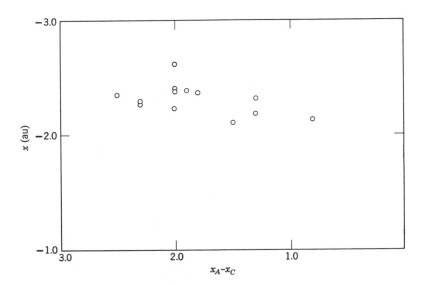

Fig. 7. Plot of isotropic nuclear hyperfine splittings for Cr^{3+} vs. the electronegativity differences between the anion and cation of the host lattice.

TABLE XIV
ESR Data for d^3 Complexes

Compound and host	g	A (10^4 cm^{-1})	D (10^4 cm^{-1})	E (10^4 cm^{-1})	Reference
$Cr[(C_2H_5O)_2PS_2]_3$	1.992 ± 0.005		143 ± 5	812 ± 5	272
$Cr[(C_2H_5O)_2PS_2]_3$	1.9903 (x) ± 0.0010 1.0014 (y) ± 0.0010 1.9901 (z) ± 0.0010		∓ 138 ± 1	∓ 814 ± 1	279
Cr^{3+} in TiO_2 (anatase)	1.973 ± 0.002	16.8 ± 0.5	373 ± 3		296
Cr^{3+} in TiO_2	1.97	15	5500	2700	281
$Cr[(CH_3CO)_2CH]_3$ in $Co[(CH_3CO)_2CH]_3$	1.9802 ± 0.0005	16.2 $(\parallel)$ ± 0.1 16.9 $(\perp)$ ± 0.1	6000 ± 10	85 ± 5	259
$Cr[(CH_3CO)_2CH]_3$ single crystal	1.983 ± 0.002		5.920 ± 20	520 ± 20	285
$Cr(NH_3)_6Cl_3$ in $Co(NH_3)_6Cl_3$	1.986 ± 0.003 1.984 ± 0.005 1.984 ± 0.007		313 ± 2 537 ± 3 688 ± 7	19 ± 1 119 ± 1 203 ± 2	239

Compound	g				Ref.
Cr^{3+} in $Co(NH_3)_6I_3$	1.9842 ±0.0005				280
$[Cr(NH_3)_6](ClO_4)_3$	1.96				283
$trans$-$CrCl_2(NH_2(CH_2)NH_2)_2$- $Cl \cdot HCl \cdot 2H_2O$	1.9765 ±0.0005	16.5 ±1.5	5040 ±10	360 ±10	83
$Cr(NH_2(CH_2)NH_2)Cl_3 \cdot 3H_2O$	1.9900 ±0.0004		360 ±30	0	83
$Cr(NH_2(CH_2)_2NH_2)_3Cl_3$ in $Cr(NH_2(CH_2)_2NH_2$- $Cl_3 \cdot NaCl \cdot 6H_2O$	1.9874 ±0.0002	16.2 ±0.7	49.5 ±0.7	0	83
$Cr(NH_2(CH_2)_2NH_2)_3Cl_3$	1.9871 ±0.0003		413 ±1	0	83
Cr^{3+} in $NH_4Co((CH_2)_2$- $(N(CH_2COOH)_2)_2) \cdot 2H_2O$	1.982 (x) ±0.002 1.982 (y) ±0.002 1.987 (z) ±0.002	17 ±3	10,690 ±20	2030 ±20	304
$K_3Cr(CN)_6$ in $K_3Co(CN)_6$	1.993 (x) ±0.001 1.991 (y) ±0.001 1.991 (z) ±0.001	14.7 ±0.5	831 ±10	108 ±10	288

(continued)

TABLE XIV (continued)

Compound and host	g	A (10^4 cm^{-1})	D (10^4 cm^{-1})	E (10^4 cm^{-1})	Reference
$K_3Cr(CN)_6$ in $K_3Mn(CN)_6$	1.992 (x) ±0.002 1.995 (y) ±0.002 1.993 (z) ±0.002		538 ±10	120 ±10	288
$K_3Cr(CN)_6$ in $K_3Co(CN)_6$	1.991$_2$ (y) 1.993$_6$ (x) (two species) 1.992$_3$ (y) 1.993$_3$ (x)		738.2	90.2$_6$	289
$[CrCl_5(H_2O)]^{2-}$ in $[(NH_4)_2$ In $Cl_5(H_2O)]$	1.9871 (∥) ±0.0005 1.9828 (⊥) ±0.0005	15.4 (∥) ±0.3 14.7 (⊥) ±0.3	786.6 594.6 ±0.3	97.3$_0$ 50.7 ±0.3	85
$CrCl_3$	2.006 ±0.007				268
$CrCl_3$	1.984 (∥) ±0.001 1.989 (⊥) ±0.001				298
Cr^{3+} in $AlCl_3 \cdot 6H_2O$	1.977 (298°K) ±0.001 1.977 (77°K) ±0.001	17.0 (77°K) ±0.1	327 (298°K) ±1 430 (77°K) ±1		190

Cr³⁺ in AlCl₃·6D₂O	1.977 (298°K) ±0.001 1.977 (77°K) ±0.001	17.2 (77°K) ±0.1	315 (298°K) ±1 327 (77°K) ±1		190
Cr³⁺ in ScF₃	1.967 ±0.001	≈12	<10		274
Cr³⁺ in ZnF₂	1.95 1.97 (two species)		7214 7114	766 916	305
Cr³⁺ in KMgF₃	1.9733 ±0.0002				286
Cr₂(SO₄)₃·6H₂O	2.007 ±0.003				268
K₂SO₄·Cr(SO₄)₃·24H₂O	1.963 ±0.004				268
Cr³⁺ in K₂Zn(SO₄)₂·6H₂O	1.977 (∥) 1.979 (⊥)	≈16	3305	102	284
Cr³⁺ in Al₂SiO₅	1.982 (∥) ±0.0005 1.977 (⊥) ±0.002		6354 6948 5322	180 4960 3470	260
Cr³⁺ in MgAl₂O₄	1.985 (∥) ±0.001		9230 ±100		264
(Natural crystal)	1.980 (⊥) ±0.002				

(continued)

TABLE XIV (continued)

Compound and host	g	A (10^4 cm^{-1})	D (10^4 cm^{-1})	E (10^4 cm^{-1})	Reference
(Synthetic crystal)	1.985 (∥) ±0.001 1.985 (⊥) ±0.005		9080 ±50		
Cr^{3+} in MgAl$_2$O$_4$	1.986 (∥) ±0.001 1.989 (⊥) ±0.002		4450		266
Cr^{3+} in Y$_3$Ga$_5$O$_{12}$	1.98 (300°K) 1.98 (77°K)		3500 3490		282
Cr^{3+} in Y$_3$Al$_5$O$_{12}$	1.98 1.98		2550 2620		282
Cr^{3+} in Y$_2$O$_3$	1.97 ±0.01		1215 ± 4 (300°K) 1211 ± 4 (77 and 4.2°K)		265
Cr^{3+} in CdWO$_4$	1.98 (z) ±0.01 1.97 (y) ±0.01 1.97 (x) ±0.01		+1430 ±2	783 ±7	267

Cr^{3+} in $MgWO_4$	1.966 (z) ±0.002 1.960 (x,y) ±0.02	18 ±1	+7940 ±20	613 ±15	273
Cr^{3+} in $ZnWO_4$	1.958 (x) ±0.002 1.962 (y) ±0.002 1.968 (z) ±0.002	17 ±1	+8487 ±2	−806 ±10	263
Cr^{3+} in SnO_2	1.975	14	+5760	2810	254
Cr^{3+} in MgO	1.9796	16.5			258
Cr^{3+} in MgO	1.9800 ±0.0003	16.3 ±0.2			270
Cr^{3+} in MgO	1.9797 1.9782	16.0	819.4		290
Cr^{3+} in CdS	1.98 (broad line)				364
Cr^{3+} in MgS	1.9874	15.3			258
Cr^{3+} in SrO	1.952 (77°K)				258
Cr^{3+} in SrO	1.9683 (77°K) 1.9683 (20°K) ±0.0006 1.9686 (4.2°K) ±0.0005	17.2 ±5 17.3 ±5			287

(continued)

TABLE XIV (continued)

Compound and host	g	A (10^4 cm^{-1})	D (10^4 cm^{-1})	E (10^4 cm^{-1})	Reference
Cr^{3+} in CaO	1.9734	16.8			258
Cr^{3+} in CaO	1.9732 ±0.0005	17.0 ±1			287
Cr^{3+} in CaO	1.9732 ±0.0005	17.0 (77°K) ±0.1			278
Cr^{3+} in SrTiO$_3$	1.978 ±0.007	15.8 ±1			275
Cr^{3+} in MgTiO$_3$	1.976 (∥) ±0.002 1.981 (⊥) ±0.002		5015 ±10		303
Cr^{3+} in LaAlO$_3$	1.9825 (291°K) ±0.0005 1.9825 (273°K) ±0.0005 1.9225 (80°K) ±0.0005	17 ±3	416 ±1 440 ±1 526 ±6		261
Cr^{3+} in Al$_2$O$_3$	1.984 (4.2°K) ±0.006	+16.2 ±0.3	−1907.8 ±1.0		294
Cr^{3+} in Al$_2$O$_3$	2.003 (∥) ±0.006 2.002 (⊥) (300°K)		1930 ±10		295

	g	A			Ref.
Cr³⁺ in β-Ga₂O₃	1.978 (x) ±0.001 1.978 (y) ±0.001 1.983 (z) ±0.001		−4668 ±1	+2047 ±2	276
V²⁺ in CdS	1.980	71.5			364
V²⁺ in CdCl₂	1.9661 (∥) ±0.0009 1.9704 (⊥) ±0.0006	76.7 ±0.6	−2077 ±2	0 ±2	297
V²⁺ in NaCl (tetragonal)	1.9704 (∥) ±0.0006 1.9754 (⊥) ±0.0006	−80.5 (∥) ±0.7 −78.8 (⊥) ±0.7	−572.4 ±0.7	±0.5 ±0.7	257
V²⁺ in NaCl (orthorhombic)	1.969 (z) ±0.001 1.970 (y) ±0.001 1.976 (x) ±0.001	−81 (z) ±1 −80 (y) ±1 −81 (x) ±1	−655 ±1	−197 ±1	257
V²⁺ in CaO	1.9683 ±0.0005	76.04 (290°K) ±0.05 76.15 (77°K) ±0.05 76.22 (20°K) ±0.05			277 278

(continued)

TABLE XIV (continued)

Compound and host	g	A (10^4 cm^{-1})	D (10^4 cm^{-1})	E (10^4 cm^{-1})	Reference
V^{2+} in MgO	1.9801 ±0.0002	−74.26			270
V^{2+} in MgO	1.9803 ±0.0002	−74.14 ±0.04	≈7		363
V^{2+} in MgO	1.9800 ±0.0005	−75.1 ±0.1			262
V^{2+} in $KMgF_3$	1.9720 ±0.0002	86.2 ±0.2			286
V^{2+} in ZnF_2	1.97	30	4245	1526	305
V^{2+} in Al_2O_3	1.991	−73.538 (A) ±0.008 −74.267 (B) ±0.03	−1601.2 ±0.3		255
V^{2+} in $K_4Fe(CN)_6 \cdot 3H_2O$	1.996 ±0.003	56 ±1	$T^{\circ}c$ −180 264 ± 15; −150 237; −120 228; −100 226; − 80 206; − 60 188; − 50 181; − 40 166	65 ± 10; 64; 60; 58; 55; 51; 41; 36	256

Compound	g				Reference
$K_4V(CN)_6 \cdot 3H_2O$ in $K_4Fe(CN)_6 \cdot 3H_2O$	1.9919 (x) ±0.0006 1.9920 (y) ±0.0006 1.9920 (z) ±0.0006	55.3 ±0.3	− 30 130 − 20 40 0 40 20 40 ± 2 264 ±4	27 0 0 0 ± 3 72 ±4	288
V^{2+} grown in $Zn(NH_4)_2(SO_4)_2 \cdot 6H_2O$	1.9717 ±0.0005 (z) 1.9733 ±0.0005 (y)	−82.63 (z) ±0.05 −82.46 (y) ±0.05	−1561.3 ±0.3	−229.0 ±0.3	118
V^{2+} produced by irradiation of V^{2+} in $Zn(NH_4)_2(SO_4)_2 \cdot 6H_2O$	1.9718 ±0.0005 (z) 1.9733 ±0.0005 (y)	−82.67 (z) ±0.05 −82.49 (y) ±0.005	−1560.9 ±0.3	−229.7 ±0.3	118
V^{2+} in $Mg(NH_4)_2(SO_4)_2 \cdot 6H_2O$	1.9720 (z) 1.9723 (y)	82.62 (z) 82.53 (y)	1579.3	245.2	118
V^{2+} in $ZnK_2(SO_4)_2 \cdot 6H_2O$	1.9722 (z) 1.9741 (y)	82.53 (z) 82.12 (y)	1524.4	274.2	118
Mn^{4+} in Al_2O_3	1.993 (4.2°K)	−69.608 (A) ±0.008 −70.480 (B) ±0.033	−1956.0 ±0.3		255

(continued)

TABLE XIV (continued)

Compound and host	g	A ($10^4\,cm^{-1}$)	D ($10^4\,cm^{-1}$)	E ($10^4\,cm^{-1}$)	Reference
Mn^{4+} in Al_2O_3	1.9937 ± 0.0007	70.0 ± 0.5	−1957 ± 1		291
Mn^{4+} in SnO_2	1.9879 (x) ± 0.0003 1.9870 (y) ± 0.0003 1.9907 (z) ± 0.0003	72.1 (x) ± 0.5 69.9 (y) ± 0.5 74.94 (z) ± 0.5	8809 ± 1	2635 ± 1	292
Mn^{4+} in TiO_2	1.995 (x) ± 0.005 1.991 (y) ± 0.0005 1.990 (z) ± 0.0005	72.3 (x) ± 1 70.3 (y) ± 0.3 72.7 (z) ± 0.3	4075 ± 12	1310.5 ± 0.5	293
Mn^{4+} in MgO	1.99 ± 0.002	72.0 ± 0.4			269
Mn^{4+} in $SrTiO_3$	1.994 ± 0.001	70 ± 1			271

TABLE XV
Values of $N_{\sigma_2}^2$ for d^3 Complexes Reported by McGarvey (83)

Complex	$N_{\sigma_2}^2$ [a]	
	δ = Constant	δ = Variable
$Cr(H_2O)_6^{3+}$	0.66	0.76
$Cr(NH_3)_6^{3+}$	0.61	0.70
$Cr(ethylenediamine)_3^{3+}$	0.59	0.67
$Cr(acetylacetonate)_3$	0.58	0.68
$Cr(CN)_6^{3-}$	0.59	0.66
CrO_6^{9-}	0.60	0.69
MnO_6^{8-}	0.45	0.48
$V(H_2O)_6^{2+}$	0.99	0.99

[a] The values given are only approximately equal to $N_{\sigma_2}^2$. They are actually equal to $N_{\sigma_2}^2 + 4N_{\sigma_2}^2\lambda_{\sigma_2}S_{d_1\sigma_2}$.

where μ is the nuclear magnetic moment and I is the nuclear spin. Ligand hyperfine splittings have been reported for a number of complexes, see Table XVI. The amount of pi bonding has been found to be small. Of particular theoretical interest is the sign of the hyperfine splittings as this information is necessary when attempting to explain the actual delocalization mechanism. ESR data only give the relative signs of A_s and A_p. NMR, however, does determine the actual sign; an NMR shift to higher magnetic field than the resonance of the nucleus in a diamagnetic environment gives a negative A value and vice versa. A positive A value means that the unpaired electron reaching the nucleus has the same sign as the original unpaired electron if the electron is sigma delocalized and the opposite sign if it is pi delocalized. The above rules are for the case of a positive nuclear magnetic moment. The negative values of A_p for the fluoride complexes are in agreement with a covalent contribution from unpaired electrons in orbitals of π symmetry. The positive value for A_p in $Cr(CN)_6^{3-}$ indicates that the dipolar (A_D) contribution to A_p is the primary contribution.

$$A_p = -A_\pi + A_D \tag{48}$$

Marshall (365) has rederived the theory for the fluorine hyperfine interactions in K_2NaCrF_6 and has found that for $g \approx 2$ the correction terms which were omitted in the earlier papers only contribute about 1% to the experimental values.

Cr^{3+} has properties which make it valuable as a maser. The requirements of a maser material have been discussed by Van Uitert (299). Some

TABLE XVI
Ligand Hyperfine Splittings for d^3 Complexes

Compound and host	Nucleus	A_s (10^{-4} cm^{-1})	A_p (10^{-4} cm^{-1})	A_D (10^{-4} cm^{-1})	f_s	$f_\sigma - f_\pi$	Reference
V^{2+} in KMgF$_3$	F	-1.0 ± 0.2	-6.1 ± 0.2	3.1	-0.00019	-0.0415	286
Cr^{3+} in KMnF$_3$	F	-1.6 ± 0.2	-7.0 ± 0.2	3.1	-0.00031	-0.0476	286
Cr^{3+} in K$_2$NaCrF$_6$	F	-1.1 ± 0.5	-7.2 ± 1.2		-0.00021	-0.0490	300
K$_3$Cr(CN)$_6$	C	-9.2	$+0.61$	0.7	-0.026		301
Cr^{3+} in K$_2$NaGaF$_6$	F	-1.1 ± 0.5	-4.5 ± 1.0				302
Mn^{4+} in Cs$_2$GeF$_6$	F	$+5.5$ ± 1.0	-9.5 ± 1.0				302
Cr^{3+} in Al$_2$O$_3$	Al	(Five inequivalent Al)					306
		0.23	0.67 (z)				
			0.00 (x)				
		1.08	-0.27 (z)				
			0.18 (x)				
		0.74	-0.05 (z)				
			0.28 (x)				
		0.79	0.02 (z)				
			0.23 (x)				

					Ref.
Mn^{4+} in SnO_2	Sn	0.44	28.3 (x) ±0.5 27.4 (y) ±0.5 31.6 (z) ±0.5	0.02 (z) 0.23 (x)	292
Cr^{3+} in SnO_2	Sn		35		254, 292
Mn^{4+} in TiO_2	Ti		<0.5 (x) <0.5 (y) 0.9 (z)		293

d^3 compounds which have been studied by ESR and are considered maser materials are Cr^{3+} in $K_3Co(CN)_6$ (288,301,362,307–321), Cr^{3+} in Al_2O_3 (65,66,233,294,295,314,322–361), and Cr^{3+} in TiO_2 (67,164,281,296,366–370).

Walsh, Jeener, and Bloembergen (427) have studied the effect of temperature on the ESR parameters of V^{2+} and Cr^{3+}. It was found that the g values decreased as the temperature increased. Consideration of the effect of the thermal expansion of the lattice was sufficient to explain the observed g shifts. The V^{2+} hyperfine splitting was found to decrease with increasing temperature according to the following equation:

$$A(T) = 0.007426(1 - 2.2 \times 10^{-8}T^{1.92}) \tag{49}$$

Additional papers which discuss d^3 complexes are references 64,71,73, 144,145,148,197,207,219, and 371–426.

D. ESR of d^4 Complexes

The amount of available data for d^4 complexes is small, see Table XVII. Gerritsen and Sabisky (428) investigated Mn^{3+} as a possible high frequency maser. They derived the equations for the possible ground states and found that the unoccupied d orbital is the $d_{x^2-y^2}$ orbital. Morigaki (429,430) and also Estle, Waters, and De Wit (433) studied Cr^{2+} in tetrahedral CdS crystals. The spectra were interpreted in terms of a Jahn-Teller distortion. Hyperfine splittings of ≈ 5 G were observed from the cadmium nuclei. The theory of Jahn-Teller distortions in d^4 systems is considered in detail in the Ph.D. thesis of Coffman (431). It is important to note that the apparent $g_\parallel$ value ($g_\parallel = h\nu/\beta H$) is around 8 for the systems studied. The actual g value is found from the following equation:

$$g_\parallel = \frac{h\nu\sqrt{1 - \nu_0^2/\nu^2}}{\beta H} \tag{50}$$

ν_0 is the zero-field splitting. Additional ESR papers of d^4 systems are references 434–436.

E. d^5 Complexes

1. *ESR of High Spin d^5 Complexes*

The ground state for d^5 high spin complexes is an orbital singlet $^6S_{5/2}$ which to first order should not interact with the crystalline electric field, However, to higher order the combined action of an electric field gradient

TABLE XVII
ESR of d^4 Complexes

Compound and host	$g_\parallel$	$g_\perp$	A $(10^4\ cm^{-1})$	D $(10^4\ cm^{-1})$	E $(10^4\ cm^{-1})$	References
Cr^{2+} in CdS	Between 2.0023 and 1.94	≈ 0				429
Cr^{2+} in CdS	Between 1.937 ± 0.001 and ≈ 1.97		12.50 ($\parallel$) ± 0.04 (assuming $g_\parallel = 1.937$)			433
Mn^{3+} in TiO_2	1.99 ± 0.01	2.00 ± 0.02	84.5 (z) ± 2 52.8 (y) ± 0.5 80.6 (z) ± 1.0	-34000 ± 1000	1160 ± 10	428
Cr^{2+} in $CrSO_4$	1.95	1.99		22400	1000	432

and the spin–spin interaction does split the energy levels (437). A typical spin Hamiltonian is (439)

$$H = g\beta H \cdot S + D[S_z^2 - \tfrac{1}{3}S(S + 1)] + E(S_x^2 - S_y^2)$$
$$+ \tfrac{1}{6}a(S_1^4 + S_2^4 + S_3^4 - {}^{707}\!/_{16}) + (7F/36)(S_z^4 - {}^{95}\!/_{14} S_z^2 + {}^{81}\!/_{16})$$
$$+ AS \cdot I - \gamma H_0 \cdot I + Q'(I_z^2 - {}^{35}\!/_{12}) \tag{51}$$

Neglecting the nuclear hyperfine splittings, five transitions corresponding to $\Delta M_s = 1$ are observed in single crystal ESR experiments. The transitions are (438)

$$\pm\tfrac{5}{2} \to \pm\tfrac{3}{2} \qquad h\nu = g\beta H \pm 2D(3\cos^2\theta - 1) \pm 2ap \tag{52}$$

$$\pm\tfrac{3}{2} \to \pm\tfrac{1}{2} \qquad h\nu = g\beta H \pm D(3\cos^2\theta - 1) \pm \tfrac{5}{2}ap \tag{53}$$

$$\tfrac{1}{2} \to -\tfrac{1}{2} \qquad h\nu = g\beta H \tag{54}$$

where $p = \tfrac{1}{8}(35\cos^4\theta - 30\cos^2\theta + 3 + 5\sin^4\theta\cos^4\theta)$. θ is the angle between the applied magnetic field and the direction of the axial distortion. For simplicity additional terms in D, in E, in F, and in Q have not been included in equations 52–54. They are available in the literature (438). Also, the quadrupole moment term has been ignored. It can be obtained from measurements of the separations of the forbidden lines.

In a powder only the $\tfrac{1}{2} \to -\tfrac{1}{2}$ transition is observed since the angular dependence of the $\pm\tfrac{5}{2} \to \pm\tfrac{3}{2}$ and $\pm\tfrac{3}{2} \to \pm\tfrac{1}{2}$ transitions broaden these peaks beyond resolvability. The $\tfrac{1}{2} \to -\tfrac{1}{2}$ transition is affected to second order by a term proportional to $D^2/g\beta H$.

If the metal nucleus has a magnetic moment, each of the $\Delta M_s = 1$ lines will be split further. An experimental powder spectrum for a Mn^{2+} compound is given in Figure 8. The six main lines are manganese hyperfine lines, μ for manganese is equal to 3.4611; I is equal to 5/2. The pair of low intensity lines between the main lines are due to simultaneous changes of both the electronic and nuclear spin by ± 1. From the intensity ratio of the forbidden lines to the allowed lines one can obtain an approximate value of D. The equation is (440)

$$IR \text{ (intensity ratio)} = \frac{8}{15}\left(\frac{3D}{4g\beta H}\right)^2\left[\frac{1 + S(S + 1)}{3M(M - 1)}\right][I(I + 1) - m^2 + m]$$

where $S = \tfrac{5}{2}$ (total electron spin), $I = \tfrac{5}{2}$ (total nuclear spin), $m = \tfrac{1}{2}$ (component of electron spin), and $M = \tfrac{1}{2}$ (component of nuclear spin). As an alternate method of determining D one can utilize the published graphs of Allen (441) which give D as a function of the relative intensities of the allowed transitions. Kunii, Tobita, and Hirahara (442) have found a linear correlation between the separation between the two forbidden transitions and the covalency parameter $r_L/\{(\sqrt{3/4})a_0 + \alpha\}$ where r_L is

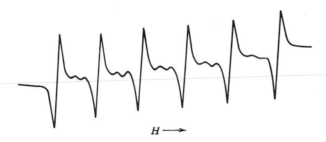

Fig. 8. ESR powder spectrum for Mn(pentamethylenetetrazole)$_6$ClO$_4$ diluted in the corresponding Fe(II) complex.

the radius of the anion, a_0 is the lattice constant and α is a correction term to take into account lattice distortion. $\alpha = -k(r_c - r_{Mn})$ where r_c is the ionic radius of the divalent host cation and r_{Mn} is the ionic radius of the divalent manganese ion. They also found a smooth but nonlinear correspondence between the relative intensity of the forbidden transition and the above parameter.

Matamura (97) and Title (98) have plotted the isotropic hyperfine splitting parameter versus the per cent ionicity of the host lattice as determined by Pauling's equation (443) for the ionic character of a bond.

$$I = 1 - \exp\left[\frac{-(x_A - x_B)^2}{4}\right] \tag{56}$$

x_A and x_B refer to the values of the electronegativity of the two atoms in the bond. The extrapolated value at 100% ionicity is in good agreement with the theoretical value.

The ESR data for high spin d^5 complexes are given in Table XVIII. In addition to the quantitative data included in the table there are in the literature a number of studies of the effects of high temperature (615,652, 665,666), viscosity (612), solvent type (604,627), and concentration (606, 609,610,612,696) on the line widths of d^5 ESR signals. From these studies the relaxation processes are determined. The D and E values reported in Table XVIII are not unique but are dependent on the choice of the symmetry axes. The per cent ionicity as determined from Title's graph indicates that most d^5 complexes are relatively ionic. Unfortunately, one cannot distinguish between the covalency contribution of the electrons while involved in sigma orbitals and while involved in pi orbitals. Title's method is only an approximate one since with it one would predict the same ionicity for Cr^{1+}, Mn^{2+}, and Fe^{3+} if they were in the same lattice. This is because for his graph he calculated the ionicity from the electronegativity

TABLE XVIII
ESR of d^5 Complexes

Compound and host lattice	g	A (10^4 cm^{-1})	D (10^4 cm^{-1})	E (10^4 cm^{-1})	a (10^4 cm^{-1})	References for data	Other references
Cr^{1+} in CdTe	1.9997 ±0.0003	+12.781 ±0.005			3.1 ±0.6	466	
Cr^{1+} in KMgF$_3$	2.0005 ±0.0005					286	
Cr^{1+} in NaCl	1.998 ±0.001	18.3 ±1.0			7.2 ±2.0	464	
Cr^{1+} in NaF	2.000 ±0.002	14.0 ±0.5			3.6 ±0.6	465	
Cr^{1+} in NaF	2.001 ±0.001				2.2 ±0.2	286	
Cr^{1+} in Si	1.9978	+10.67			+30.16	408	
Cr^{1+} in ZnS	1.9995 ±0.0005	13.4 ±0.1			3.9 ±0.1	98	474,475
Cr^{1+} in ZnSe	2.0016 ±0.0005	13.3 ±0.2			5.35 ±0.08	476	
Cr^{1+} in ZnTe	2.0023 ±0.0005	12.4 ±0.2			6.60 ±0.2	476	
FeCl$_3$ in acetone and other solvents	≈2	(Assumed due to tetrahedral FeCl$_4^-$)				477	
Fe^{3+} in AgCl	2.015 ±0.002				76 ±4	478	

(Qualitative measurements with a zero field spectrometer.)

	g	D	E	a, F	Ref.	Ref.
Fe³⁺ in Al((CH₃CO)₂CH)₃					479	
Fe³⁺ in AgCl	2.015 ±0.002			76 ±4	480	58,481
Fe³⁺ in AlCl₃·6H₂O	2.002 ±0.002	1500 +20		160 (a) ±50 310 (F) ±20	190	
Fe³⁺ in Al₂O₃	2.0026 ±0.0005	+1719.2 (4°K) +1718.2 (80°K) +1678.5 (299°K)		229.4 (a) −112.1 (F) (4°K) +236.4 (a) −101.3 (F) (80°K) 299.1 (a) −110.8 (F) (299°K)	482	366,483 484,485 486,487
Fe³⁺ in Al₂SiO₅	(Three inequivalent sites)	3552 7130 13,000	195 1380 570		488	489,490 491,510 511
Fe³⁺ in BaTiO₃	2.003	3900	1630	17 (cubic ±2 phase) 15 (tetrahedral phase)	492	493,494,495 496,497,498
Fe³⁺ in BaTi(SO₃)₃	2.0026 ±0.0005 (Ba Site)	337.9 ±0.3 (Ba Site)	119 (a–F) ±1 123 (a)		499	500

(continued)

TABLE XVIII (continued)

Compound and host lattice	g	A (10^4 cm^{-1})	D (10^4 cm^{-1})	E (10^4 cm^{-1})	a (10^4 cm^{-1})	References for data	Other references
Fe^{3+} in $BaTi(SO_3)_3$ (cont.)	1.998 +0.001 (Ti Site)		245 ±1.0 (Ti Site)		±3 (Ba Site) 127 ±1 (Ti Site)		
Fe^{3+} in $CaCO_3$	2.0030 (calcite)		+963			469	501,502,503
Fe^{3+} in CaO	2.0059 ±0.0006	10.5 ±0.5 (20°K)			+64.3 ±0.3 (77°K) +65.1 ±0.3 (20°K)	278	258,277,504
Fe^{3+} in $CaWO_4$	4.317 (effective g value)					505	506
Fe^{3+} in CdS	2.018 0.002		−49 ±2		96 (a) ±2 −3 (F) ±2	507	364,508,509
FeF_6^{3-} in $CdTe$	2.0029	10.7			+99.28 ±0.05	468	
Fe^{3+} in $CdWO_4$			7930	1140		512	

Ion	Parameters				
Fe^{3+} in C(NH$_2$)$_3$·Al(SO$_4$)$_2$·6H$_2$O	2.003 Type II, 298°K	−1760.1	205.95 (a) 1004.7 (F)	513	
	2.003 Type II, 77°K	−1890.2	539.63 (a) 1520.3 (F)	513	
	2.003 Type I, 298°K	−1850.8	219.66 (a) 1053.0 (F)	513	
	2.003 Type I, 77°K	−1950.6	593.02 (a) 1638.9 (F)	513	
Fe(NH$_4$)(SO$_4$)$_2$·12H$_2$O					416,514
Fe^{3+} in ferrichrome	4.3 (effective g value)			515	
Fe^{3+} in GaAs	2.0462 ±0.0006 1.3°K		339.7 ±0.3	471	516
	2.0453 ±0.0008 77°K		342.2 ±0.5	471	516
Fe^{3+} in glass	4.27 (effective g value)			517	

(continued)

TABLE XVIII (continued)

Compound and host lattice	g	A (10^4 cm^{-1})	D (10^4 cm^{-1})	E (10^4 cm^{-1})	a (10^4 cm^{-1})	References for data	Other references
Fe^{3+} in InAs	2.035 ±0.002				+421 ±1	518	
$FeCl_4^-$ in isopropyl ether	2.013 ±0.006	(Line width 200–400 G depending on concentration)				473	
Fe^{3+} in $KAlSi_3O_8$	2.00 ±0.1		1060 ±10	170 ±30	$\geqq 560$	519	
Fe^{3+} in $KCdF_3$	2.0027 ±0.0002				53.0 ±2.0	286	
Fe^{3+} in $KMgF_3$	2.0031 ±0.0002				51.2 ±0.5	286	
Fe^{3+} in K_2NaGaF_6					62 ±2 (G)	520,521	
Fe^{3+} in $Li_{0.5}Al_{2.5}O_4$	2.008 (∥) ±0.003		800			522	
Fe^{3+} in $Li_{0.5}Al_{2.5}O_4$	2.006 ±0.002		1040		166 (a–F)	522	
Fe^{3+} in $LiAl(SiO_3)_2$	2.0086 (x) ±0.0050 2.0100 (y) ±0.0050 2.0046 (z) ±0.0025		−1.34	−88		470	

Complex ion	g				References	
Fe^{3+} in $Lu_3Al_5O_{12}$	2.001 ±0.0005 (octahedral site)		−935 ±5	292 (a) ±5 / 64 (F) ±5	555	
	2.004 ±0.0005 (tetrahedral site)		−1249 ±5	84 (a) ±5 / −104 (F) ±5	555	
Fe^{3+} in $Lu_3Ga_5O_{12}$	2.001 ±0.0005 (octahedral site)		−1290 5	174 (a) ±5 / −33 (F) ±5	555	
	2.003 ±0.0005 (tetrahedral site)		−1131 ±5	65 (a) ±5 / −47 (F) ±5	555	
Fe^{3+} in methylamine					523	
Fe^{3+} in metmyoglobin	2.002 (∥) ±0.001 / 1.985 (⊥) ±0.002		43,800 ±6000		556	
Fe^{3+} in $MgAl_2O_4$	2.001 ±0.007		2470 ±10	720 ±6	525	524
Fe^{3+} in MgO	2.0037	11.4			258	388,391,526 527,528,529 530

(continued)

TABLE XVIII (*continued*)

Compound and host lattice	g	A (10^4 cm^{-1})	D (10^4 cm^{-1})	E (10^4 cm^{-1})	a (10^4 cm^{-1})	References for data	Other references
Fe^{3+} in $MgWO_4$						531	
Fe^{3+} in 80% $NaAlSi_3O_8$ 20% $CaAl_3Si_2O_8$						532	
Fe^{3+} in $NaCo$-$(EDTA) \cdot 4H_2O$	2.00		825 ±100	5500 ±1000		533	
F^{3+} in NH_4Al-$(SO_4)_2 \cdot 12H_2O$			≈50		≈120	534	535
Fe^{3+} in NH_4Co-$(EDTA) \cdot 2H_2O$	2.00	10.3 ±0.3	300 ±60	5000 ±1000		536	
Fe^{3+} in NH_4Cl						537	
Fe^{3+} in $PbTiO_3$	2.009 (‖) ±0.005 5.97 (⊥) ±0.02					538	
Fe^{3+} in quartz	2.0023 (α-quartz)		−681.89	1842	−9.40 (F)	539	540,541,542 543, 557
Fe^{3+} in SnO_2	2.004		1270	137		544	
Fe^{3+} in SrO						258	
Fe^{3+} in $SrTiO_3$	2.0054 (‖) ±0.0007		14,250 ±1500			545	397,546,547

Fe^{3+} in TiO_2	2.0101 ($\perp$) ±0.0008, 2.009 ($\parallel$) ∓309, 2.002 ($\perp$) (anatase)		±99 (a), ∓308 (F)	548	549,59
Fe^{3+} in $TmAl_5O_{12}$				550	
Fe^{3+} in $TmGa_5O_{12}$				550	
Fe^{3+} in xanthine oxidase	1.9			551	
Fe^{3+} in $YAlO_3$				552	
Fe^{3+} in $Y_3Al_5O_{12}$	2.0015 ±0.0005 (octahedral site)	-1053 ±5	205 (a) ±5, 27 (F) ±5	555	
	2.004 ±0.0005 (tetrahedral site)	-1028 ±5	75 (a) ±5, -110 (F)	555	
Fe^{3+} in $Y_3Ga_5O_{12}$	2.003 (octahedral site)	-1294, -880	185 (a), 26 (F)	553	554
	2.003 (tetrahedral site)	-880	62 (a), -37 (F)	553	554

(continued)

TABLE XVIII (continued)

Compound and host lattice	g	A (10^4 cm^{-1})	D (10^4 cm^{-1})	E (10^4 cm^{-1})	a (10^4 cm^{-1})	References for data	Other references
Fe^{3+} in $ZnAl_2O_4$						524	
Fe^{3+} in ZnS	2.019 ±0.001	7.69 ±0.05			127.4 ±0.5	98	474,558
Fe^{3+} in $ZnSe$	2.0464 ±0.0002	6.75 ±0.05			48.3 ±0.5	472	559
Fe^{3+} in $ZnWO_4$	2.0019	9.63 ±0.5	−6985	1644		560	394
Mn^{2+} in acetone and in other solvents	(Varied from a broad line to a six line pattern depending on solvent)					477	
Mn^{2+} in $AgCl$	2.000 ±0.002	80.4 (‖) ±0.5 84 (⊥) ±3	122 ±1		1.4 (F)	51	
Mn^{2+} in $AlCl_3 \cdot 6H_2O$						561	
Mn^{2+} in $Ag(Cl:Se)$						561 562	
Mn^{2+} in $Ag(Cl:S)$						562	
Mn^{2+} in AlF_3						563	
Mn^{2+} in Al_2O_3	2.0025 (‖) ±0.0006	−80.11 (‖) ±0.02	+220.0 ±0.4		23.1 (a–F) ±0.6	452	439,435,483 487,467

Compound	g	A			References
Mn²⁺ adsorbed on Amberlite and on other resins.	2.0010 (⊥) ±0.002	−78.24 (⊥) ±0.2			130
Mn²⁺ in As_2O_3	2.0016 ±0.0010	−81.60	115.05		564
Mn²⁺ in As–Se–Ge glass					565
Mn²⁺ in Au					566
Mn²⁺ in BaF_2	2.0009 ±0.0010 (at 298°K)	−90.6 ±1		<1	461, 580
	1.9998 ±0.0020 (at 77°K)	−94.9 ±1		<1	461
Mn²⁺ in $BaTiO_3$	2.002	−79.6	+216		451, 567,568
Mn²⁺ in Beryl					569
Mn²⁺ in $CaAl_2Si_4O_{12}\cdot 6H_2O$	1.998 (∥), 2.000 (⊥)	89.1 (∥), 89.4 (⊥)	≈93	≈0	570
Mn²⁺ in $CaB(OH)SiO_4$	2.0014 (z) ±0.0005, 2.0011 (y) ±0.0005, 2.0008 (x) ±0.0005	88.6 (∥) ±0.5, 86.7 (⊥) ±0.5	419.3 ±0.5	63.4 ±0.2	571

(continued)

TABLE XVIII (*continued*)

Compound and host lattice	g	A (10^4 cm^{-1})	D (10^4 cm^{-1})	E (10^4 cm^{-1})	a (10^4 cm^{-1})	References for data	Other references
Mn^{2+} in CaC$_4$H$_4$O$_6$· 4H$_2$O	1.992 ± 0.003	−83.3 (∥) ± 1 −89.6 (⊥) ± 1	489 ± 3	86 ± 10		572	501,53,574 575,576,577 578
Mn^{2+} in CaCO$_3$	2.001 ± 0.0005	86.4 (∥) ± 0.5 88.0 (⊥) ± 0.5	144.7			573	
Mn^{2+} in 2CaCO$_3$· MgCO$_3$·FeCO$_3$	2.003	86	140			579	
Mn^{2+} in CaF$_2$	1.9993 ± 0.0015	95 ± 5				580	563,581,582
Mn^{2+} in Ca$_5$- (F,Cl,OH)- (PO$_4$)$_3$	1.9976 (∥) ± 0.0005 1.9889 (⊥) ± 0.0005	88.6 ± 0.5 86.0 (⊥) ± 0.5	399.2 ± 0.5			583	
Mn^{2+} in CaMg(CO$_3$)$_2$	2.003 (Mg site) 2.003	87.3 (∥) 88.2 (⊥) 87.3	143.3		9.7 (a–F)	579 579	
Mn^{2+} in CaMgSi$_2$O$_8$						584	
Mn^{2+} in Ca$_2$Mg$_5$- Si$_8$O$_{22}$(OH)$_2$						585	

Mn²⁺ in CaMoO₄					586	
Mn²⁺ in CaO	2.0015 1.9931 (two species present)	81.4 72.8			258	277,278,587 588
Mn²⁺ in CaS	2.0018	76.8			258	
Mn²⁺ in CaSe	2.0037	74.05			258	
Mn²⁺ in CaWO₄	2.00006 (∥) ±0.00005 2.00079 (⊥) ±0.00006	−88.93 (∥) ±0.06 −89.60 (⊥) ±0.06	−137.6 ±0.05		455	505,590
MnF₄²⁻ in CaWO₄	1.9955 (∥) 1.9885 (⊥)	−87.5 (∥) −87.2 (⊥)	380		589	
Mn²⁺ in CdBr₂	2.001 ±0.01	78 ±1	168 ±1	13 ±1	446	460
Mn²⁺ in CdCl₂	2.066	81.6	<15		460	
Mn²⁺ in CdCO₃					591	
Mn²⁺ in CdF₂	2.0026 ±0.0006	93 ±0.2		4	592	
Mn²⁺ in CdI₂	2.002 ±0.0001	80 ±3	148 ±5	14 ±3	446	
Mn²⁺ in CdS		−64.8 ±0.9	8.2 ±0.3	3.3 ±0.4	593	364,594,595 596
Mn²⁺ in CdSe	2.003 ±0.001 (77°K)	−62.7 ±0.5	15.2 ±0.5	+14.3 (a) ±1.0 −2.0 (F) ±1.0	445 597	442,598

(continued)

TABLE XVIII (continued)

Compound and host lattice	g	A (10^4 cm^{-1})	D (10^4 cm^{-1})	E (10^4 cm^{-1})	a (10^4 cm^{-1})	References for data	Other references
Mn^{2+} in CdTe	2.0069	−57.5			27.7	442	592,594,599
Mn^{2+} in CdWO$_4$	2.001 (z) 2.003 (x) 1.997 (y)	82.0 (z) 80.6 (x) 86.3 (y)	1.717	465		600	
Mn^{2+} in CeF$_3$						563	
Mn^{2+} in CoSO$_4\cdot$7H$_2$O						601	
Mn^{2+} in Cs$_3$ZnCl$_5$						602	
Mn^{2+} in CuCl	2.0015 ± 0.0010	73.3 ± 0.3				603	
Mn(ClO$_4$)$_2$ in di-ethylformamide and in other solvents						604 68	
Mn^{2+} in GaAs	2.003 ± 0.001	52.4 ± 0.5				605	
Mn^{2+} in β-Ga$_2$O$_3$	2.002 (z) 2.007 (y)	−82.0 (z) ± 0.2 −80.0 (y) ± 0.2	509	116.2		444	
Mn^{2+} in H$_2$O							69,207,606 68,604,607

	g						
Mn^{2+} in KCl	2.005 ± 0.003	78 ± 5				463	608,609,610 611,612,613 614,615,616
Mn^{2+} in KF	2.0038 ± 0.0004	92.9 ± 0.1		−98.1	< 4	286	617,618
Mn^{2+} in KFCa$_4$-(Si$_2$O$_5$)$_4$·8H$_2$O	1.992 (z) 1.991 (y) 1.990 (x)	83.3 (z) 87.0 (y) 88.7 (x)	686			619	592,286,620 621
Mn^{2+} in KMgF$_3$	2.000 ± 0.002	−91.2 ± 0.9			8.0 ± 1	462	
Mn^{2+} in K$_2$MgF$_4$	2.000 ± 0.002	−91.5 ± 0.9			8.0 ± 1.0	462	
Mn^{2+} in KMnCl$_3$						622	
Mn^{2+} in KMnF$_3$						623	
Mn^{2+} in KN$_3^{-}$	1.9961 (∥) ± 0.0005 1.9878 (⊥) ± 0.0050	−83.8 (∥) ± 0.5 −84.5 (⊥) ± 0.5	−496 ± 3.0		9 ± 0.5	457	
Mn^{2+} in La$_2$Mg-(NO$_3$)$_{12}$·24H$_2$O						624	
Mn^{2+} in LiCl	2.003 ± 0.001	77 ± 5	102 ± 9		23 ± 9	463	48,614,52 616,615,625
Mn^{2+} in LiCl-KCl							423,615
Mn^{2+}-X^{2-} in LiCl	2.0016 ± 0.0004	−79.7 ± 2.0	−672 ± 5		12 ± 3	453, 625	463

(continued)

TABLE XVIII (continued)

Compound and host lattice	g	A (10^4 cm^{-1})	D (10^4 cm^{-1})	E (10^4 cm^{-1})	a (10^4 cm^{-1})	References for data	Other references
Mn^{2+} in LiF	2.0002 ±0.0002 (700°K)	87.7 ±0.1			≤4	286	55,52,626
Mn^{2+} in methanol and in other solvents			≈140 to 250 (temperature dependent)			441	449,627,628
Mn^{2+} in MgAl$_2$O$_4$	2.0015 ±0.0003					629	
Mn^{2+} in Mg$_2$Al$_4$Si$_5$O$_{18}$	2.001 ±0.002					630	
Mn^{2+} in MgCl$_2$	2.002 ±0.003	−82 ±4	140 ±10	≈0		458	592,631
Mn^{2+} in MgCO$_3$	2.001	85.9 (∥) 86.9 (⊥)	79.9		11.3 (a–F)	579	
Mn^{2+} in MgCO$_3$–FeCO$_3$	2.003	88	131			579	
Mn^{2+} in MgF$_2$						632	
Mn^{2+} in MgO	2.0008 ±0.0002	81.00 ±0.06			18.0 ±0.3	526	563,581,258, 388,530,529, 633,634,635, 636,637,639, 456

Mn²⁺ in Mg(OH)₂	2.0001 (∥) ±0.0005 2.0005 (⊥) ±0.0005 (295°K)	−85.7 (∥) ±0.4 −84.9 (⊥) ±0.6	−6.79 ±0.25	+10.15 ±0.45	638	
	2.0007 (∥) ±0.0010 2.0020 (⊥) ±0.0010 (90°K)	−85.9 (∥) ±1.0 −84.9 (⊥) ±0.6	−12.8 ±0.25	+12.0 ±0.25	638	
Mn²⁺ in MgS	2.0017	74.8			258	
Mn²⁺ in Mg₂Si	2.0048	−50.6 ±0.1		7.14 ±0.01	459	
Mn²⁺ in MgSO₃·6H₂O	2.0001	−89.1	+18.2	7.9 (a) −0.9 (F)	640	
Mn²⁺ in MgTiF₆·6H₂O		≈92	≈ −213	≈ +7	641	
Mn²⁺ in Mg(antipyrene)₆X₂ X = ClO₄ or I					642	
Mn²⁺ in Mn(CH₃CO₂)₂·4H₂O	2.005 ±0.01				643	644,645
Mn²⁺ in MnCl₂	2.12				645	646,647
Mn²⁺ in MnF₃					648	
Mn²⁺ in Mn(NH₃)₆Cl₂					649	

(continued)

TABLE XVIII (continued)

Compound and host lattice	g	A (10^4 cm^{-1})	D (10^4 cm^{-1})	E (10^4 cm^{-1})	a (10^4 cm^{-1})	References for data	Other references
Mn^{2+} in Mn(NH$_4$)$_2$-(SO$_4$)$_2\cdot$6H$_2$O						416	650,651
Mn^{2+} in MnS						652	
Mn^{2+} in MnSiF$_6\cdot$6H$_2$O			-250			653	
Mn^{2+} in MnSn-Cl$_6\cdot$6H$_2$O			-159			653	
Mn^{2+} in MnSO$_4\cdot$4H$_2$O	2.00					654	645,416,655
Mn^{2+} in MnTiF$_6\cdot$6H$_2$O			-205			653	
Mn^{2+} in Na$_{88}$-[(AlO$_2$)$_{88}$(SiO$_2$)$_{104}$]	2.029 ±0.001	89 ±2	237 (After heat treatment)			656	
Mn^{2+} (Na:Ca)Cl and in (Na:Cd)Cl	2.002 ±0.001	82.7 ±1				658	657,659,662, 663,668
Mn^{2+} in NaCl			≈129	≈48		661	659,54,641, 660,662,664, 665,666,667, 669,670
Mn^{2+}-F^{1-} in NaCl	1.9988 ±0.0004	-83.2 ±1.0	-420 ±1	65 ±1		453,625	

Complex	g						References
Mn^{2+}–X^{2-} in NaCl	2.0023 ±0.0006	−81.0 ±2.0	−511 ±5	25	+5		625
Mn^{2+} in NaF	2.0005 ±0.0005 (600°K)	88.6 ±0.1			+5	≤2	286
Mn^{2+} in NaMgF$_3$	2.001 ±0.002	−92.5 ±1.5					462
Mn^{2+} in NaN$_3$	2.001 ±0.002	81 ±1	−224 −248	+53			457
Mn^{2+} in (NH$_4$)$_2$Cd$_2$(SO$_4$)$_3$	2.000 to 1.995 ±0.002 (temp. dependent)		(Two species present) 140 to 158				450 671
Mn^{2+} in NH$_4$Cl	2.0012 ±0.0005	82.8 (∥) ±0.5 84.8 (⊥) ±0.5					447,448 672,673,674, 675
Mn^{2+} in NH$_4$Cl–MnCl$_2$–H$_2$O			1500			2.8	676
Mn^{2+} in NiSnCl$_6$·6H$_2$O							677
Mn^{2+} in Pd	≈1.98	≈58					679 678,566
Mn^{2+} in RbMnF$_3$							648

(continued)

TABLE XVIII (continued)

Compound and host lattice	g	A $(10^4\ cm^{-1})$	D $(10^4\ cm^{-1})$	E $(10^4\ cm^{-1})$	a $(10^4\ cm^{-1})$	References for data	Other references
Mn^{2+} in RbN_3	2.0005 ($\parallel$) ±0.0005 1.9971 ($\perp$) ±0.0050	−82.0 ($\parallel$) ±0.5 −82.9 ($\perp$) ±0.5	−260 ±3.0		8.1 ±0.5	457	
Mn^{2+} in Si	2.0066	−53.47			+19.88	408	
Mn^{2+} in silica gel						680	
Mn^{2+} in SnO_2	1.9907 (z) ±0.0003 1.9879 (x) ±0.0003 1.9870 (y) ±0.0003	74.9 (z) ±0.5 72.1 (x) ±0.5 69.8 (y) ±0.5	8809 ±25	2636 ±25		681	
Mn^{2+} in $SrCl_2$	2.004	82.7			<5	460	682,683,684
Mn^{2+} in SrF_2	1.9925	99.2				560	563,685
Mn^{2+} in SrO	2.0012 ±0.0005	78.7 ±0.2				688	587,287,687 258,686
Mn^{2+} in SrS	2.0015	76.8				258	581,689,690
Mn^{2+} in $Tl_2SeAs_2Se_3$						692	
Mn^{2+} in $Y_3Ga_5O_{12}$	2.001 ±0.001	−90.6 ±0.5	−879 ±0.1		28.3 ±0.5 (a–F)	693	
Mn^{2+} in zeolites						694	
Mn^{2+} in Zn						695	

Host	g	A	D		a		Ref.
Mn^{2+} in $ZnAl_2O_4$	2.0002	74.9			<8	266	
Mn^{2+} in $(Zn:Cd)S$						696	
Mn^{2+} in $ZnCl_2$						423	
Mn^{2+} in ZnF_2	2.002 ±0.005	−90.8 (∥) ±0.3 −92.3 (⊥) ±0.5				700	637,698,699 697
Mn^{2+} in ZnO	2.0016	−76.0	−216.9			596	592
Mn^{2+} in ZnS	2.0021	−63.73			7.97	290	595,398,98
Mn^{2+} in $Zn(SiSe)$		57 to 66	(depends on S, Se ratio)			454	696
Mn^{2+} in $ZnSe$	2.0055 ±0.0005	−61.7 ±0.1			19.7 ±0.4	445	240,438
Mn^{2+} in $ZnSiF_6 \cdot 6H_2O$						49	
Mn^{2+} in $\alpha\text{-}Zn_2SiO_4$	2.002 ±0.003 2.001 ±0.002 (two sites)	79 ±2 79 ±2	+680 ±7 +386 ±4	134 ±19 120 ±12			
Mn^{2+} in $ZnTe$	2.0107	−56.5			30.0	442	598

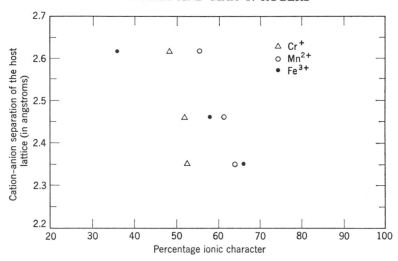

Fig. 9. Plot of cation–anion separation of the host lattice vs. % ionic character as
determined from ESR metal hyperfine splittings.

of the anion and cation of the host lattice. Dieleman (472) compared the
decrease in metal hyperfine splittings for Cr^{1+}, Mn^{2+}, and Fe^{3+} in various
lattices. His data are presented in Figure 9 as a plot of the cation–anion
separation of the host lattice vs. the percentage of the theoretical 100%
ionic value for the three ions in ZnS, ZnSe, and ZnTe. Surprisingly the
expected trend of Fe^{3+} more covalent than Mn^{2+} and Mn^{2+} more
covalent than Cr^{1+} is not found. Walsh, Jeener, and Bloembergen (427)
studied the temperature dependence of the Mn^{2+} hyperfine splitting in
MgO and found that A decreased with increasing temperature. Simanek
and Orbach (456) have proposed that this decrease is due to excited $4s$
state contributions of opposite sign to the main polarization contribution.
They were able to calculate theoretically the observed shifts from 80 to
800°K. At low temperatures a T^4 temperature dependence is predicted but
only a $T^{1.5}$ dependence is observed.

Electron-nuclear double resonance (ENDOR) has proved to be of considerable value in studying ligand hyperfine splittings. For example
Kravitz and Piper (468) utilized this method to obtain very accurate values
of the fluorine hyperfine splittings for FeF_6^{3-} in CdTe, and Garth (481)
did likewise for the chlorine splittings for $FeCl_4^{1-}$ in AgCl.

The ESR ligand hyperfine splitting data are given in Table XIX.
Hubbard, Rimmer, and Hopgood (111) have used a configuration interaction approach to calculate theoretically the fluorine hyperfine splittings
in $KMnF_3$. They found that spin up electron density was transferred from

the fluorine to the manganese $4s$ orbital and that spin down electron density was transferred from the fluorine to the $3d$ orbitals. Their theoretical values are given in Table IV. The net result of a $4s$ transfer is a smaller value of f_σ and f_s. They also found that because of the half-closed shell and small positive charge, Mn^{2+} does not tend to form covalent complexes. To illustrate this they pointed out that the binding energy of an electron to the metal ion decreases with charge: Fe^{3+} has -1.2 au, Mn^{2+} has -0.51 au, and Cr^{1+} has -0.09 au and that the binding energy of an electron to a ^4F Mn^{2+} ion is -0.71 which is greater than that found for the ^6S Mn^{2+} ion which has the half-filled shell. They concluded that the small value of $f_\sigma - f_\pi$ for Mn^{2+} ions is not due to cancellation of the two terms as had been thought previously, but is due to the small covalency and to the $4s$ contribution to f_σ. For Fe^{3+} a smaller $4s$ contribution is expected since the $3d^6$ level lies lower than the $3d^54s$ level (the two are reversed for Mn^{2+}) and the $3+$ charge results in a higher electron binding energy. For Cr^{1+} the $3d^54s$ level is very low so the large $4s$ contribution is expected to reduce f_σ and f_s as is also the low binding energy. Their explanation is consistent with the experimental data as $f_\sigma - f_\pi$ is negative for Cr^{1+} complexes ($f_\pi > f_\sigma$), near zero for Mn^{2+} (f_π and $f_\sigma \approx 0$), and positive for Fe^{3+} ($f_\sigma \gg f_\pi$).

Ogawa (462) has plotted the fluorine hyperfine splittings vs. the metal–fluorine distance of the host lattice (see Fig. 10). The exponential shape of

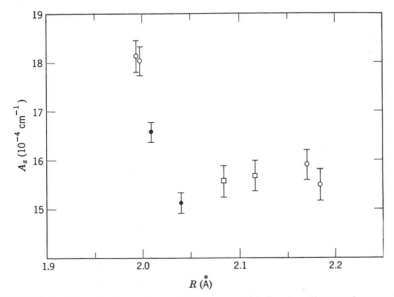

Fig. 10. Plot of fluorine hyperfine splittings vs. metal–fluorine distance for a series of manganese complexes.

TABLE XIX
ESR Data For Low Spin d^5 Complexes

Compound and host lattice	g	$g_\parallel$	$g_\perp$	A (10^4 cm^{-1})	$A_\parallel$ (10^4 cm^{-1})	$A_\perp$ (10^4 cm^{-1})	Reference
Cr(dipyridyl)$_3^{1+}$ in CH$_3$OH	1.9971 (^{52}Cr) ±0.0002 1.9973 (^{53}Cr) ±0.0002			20.3 ±0.5			100
V(dipyridyl)$_3$ in tetrahydrofuran	1.9831 ±0.0002			77.3 ±1.0			100
V(dipyridyl)$_3$ in C$_5$H$_5$N	1.9830 ±0.0005			77.8 ±0.5			103
VS$_6$C$_6$(C$_6$H$_5$)$_6$ in CH$_2$Cl$_2$	1.9900			57.1 ±0.2			103
LiTi(dipyridyl)$_3$	2.0074 ±0.0002						100
Cr(CN)$_5$NO^{3-} in K$_3$Mn(CN)$_5$NO and K$_3$Co(CN)$_6$	(1.9950)	1.9745	2.0052	(17.2)	30.0	10.8	731
Cr(CN)$_5$NO^{3-} in KBr	(1.9937) ±0.0008	1.9722 ±0.0005	2.00447 ±0.0002	(17.6) ±1.0	30.75 ±1.0	11.1 ±1.0	730
in KCl	(1.9936) ±0.0008	1.9722 ±0.0005	2.0044 ±0.0005	(17.5) ±0.5	30.75 ±0.1	10.9 ±0.5	
in NaCl	(1.9947) ±0.0008	1.9750 ±0.0010	2.0045 ±0.0005				

						Ref.
in H₂O	1.99454 ±0.00005		17.22 ±0.05			808
in KI	1.99475 ±0.0001					
Cr(NH₃)₅NO²⁺ in DMF	1.980	1.995	23.1			741
Cr(H₂O)₅NO²⁺ in H₂O	1.966	1.916	23.2			741
Mn(CN)₅NO²⁻ in Na₂Fe(CN)₅NO	(2.0141) (2.0181)	2.0265 2.0311	(74.3) (72.7)	150.5 148.8	36.2 34.7	731 738
Mn(CN)₅NO²⁻ in H₂O	2.0146 2.0144	2.0279	73.6 72.8	152.3	32.2	731 812,813
K₃Fe(CN)₆ in K₃Co(CN)₆	0.915 0.01	2.35 (x) ±0.02 2.10 (y) ±0.02				811
K₄Mn(CN)₆·3H₂O in K₄Fe(CN)₆·3H₂O	0.63 ±0.10	2.624 (x) ±0.008 2.182 (y) ±0.008		104 ±20	84.5 (x) ±0.5 46.5 (y) ±0.5	811
Cr(C₆H₈)₂I in ethanol	1.9863 ±0.002		15.8 ±0.3			735 734
V(C₆H₆)₂	1.9866 ±0.0002		58.9 ±1			733
Cr(C₆H₅–C₆H₅)₂I	1.980 ±0.001					744
Cr(C₆H₅C₆H₅)₂⁻ OC₆H₅	1.993 ±0.007					744

the curve is explained by the rapid increase in overlap contributions to the A_s value.

2. *ESR of Low Spin d^5 Complexes*

When the crystal field is larger than the interelectronic repulsion energy four of the d electrons will pair up in the lowest energy orbitals leaving the complex with a single unpaired electron. The ESR data are given in Table XIX. The low spin d^5 complexes studied so far can be divided into two groups.

The first group consists of those complexes which have a strong tetragonal crystal field. For this case the paired electrons go into the degenerate xz and yz orbitals and the unpaired electron is found in the xy orbital. This is the same orbital that the unpaired electron is found in for vanadyl complexes. Therefore equations 20, 21, 29, and 30 can be used with the appropriate changes in sign for those electronic transitions which are now hole transitions. Complexes of this type give narrow ESR lines at room temperature. Of particular interest is the $Cr(CN)_5NO^{3-}$ ion. Complete experimental ESR data have been obtained for each of the nuclei bonded to the chromium (726–732,740–743). The data have been interpreted in terms of a molecular orbital description by several groups. The following points are of particular interest.

a. **Anisotropic ^{13}C Splittings.** The equations for the angular dependence of the ^{13}C hyperfine splittings (eqs. 57–59) indicate that if there is appreciable covalency in the xy_π bond such that $|f_{\pi_2}A_p| \gg |N_{\pi_2}^2 A_D|$ the symmetry will be $A_z^C \approx A_\sigma^C \neq A^C$; but if the xy_π bond is essentially ionic, $A_z^C \approx A_\pi^C \neq A_\sigma^C$ since in this case the main contribution to the angular dependence should be $N_{\pi_2}^2 A_D$. In a KBr host Kuska and Rogers (730) were not able to determine the axis of symmetry, but in KCl it appears that the A_σ axis is the symmetry axis.

$$A_z = A_s - f_{\sigma_2}A_p' - N_{\pi_2}^2 A_D 2f_{\pi_1}A_p' - f_{\pi_2}A_p' \tag{57}$$

$$A_{\sigma_2} = A_s + 2f_{\sigma_2}A_p' + 2N_{\pi_2}^2 A_D - f_{\pi_1}A_p' - f_{\pi_2}A_p' \tag{58}$$

$$A_\pi = A_s - f_{\sigma_2}A_p' - N_{\pi_2}^2 A_D - f_{\pi_1}A_p' + 2f_{\pi_2}A_p' \tag{59}$$

$$A_p' = \frac{2\mu_n\beta_n}{5I_nR^3} \tag{60}$$

The carbon anisotropic splitting value found with this assignment, $+1.13$ G, is consistent with the value calculated for A_D, 1.06 G. This interpretation is in agreement with published work (301) on $K_3Cr(CN)_6$ where the anisotropic ^{13}C splitting is of the same magnitude as A_D. Fortman and Hayes (731), in a study of $Cr(CN)_5NO^{3-}$ in $K_3Mn(CN)_5NO$, have found that $A_\pi^C \approx A_\sigma^C \neq A_z^C$. Their analysis indicates that this is due to $f_{\pi_2} A_p$ being of comparable magnitude to $N_{\pi_2}^2 A_D$.

Using equations similar to 57–59 with the assumption that $f_{\pi_1} A_p' = f_{\sigma_2} A_p' = 0$ and Marshall's higher order equations for $N_{\pi_2}^2 A_D$ (365), Fortman and Hayes obtained a p_{xy} spin density (f_{π_2}) of ≈ 0.03. Equations 57–59 allow three separate determinations of $f_{\pi_2} A_p$. From Fortman and Hayes' analysis one obtains $f_{\pi_2} A_p' = 0.69, 0.96,$ and 1.20 G. The agreement is satisfactory considering the approximations made and the experimental errors; however, if one attempts to improve the treatment further by estimating the $f_{\sigma_2} A_p'$ contribution from the experimental $f_s A_s'$ and a model of an s–p hybrid orbital, the agreement is lost and one obtains $f_{\pi_2} A_p' = 1.55, 0,$ and 1.57 G. From theoretical self-consistent charge and configuration molecular orbital calculations Manoharan and Gray (2) obtained an f_{π_2} value of 0.032 in close agreement with Fortman and Hayes' value.

b. **Unpaired Electron Density on Nitrogen.** The observed nitrogen anisotropic splitting value of $+1.41$ is too large to be accounted for by the A_D term alone. The anisotropic splitting in excess of the dipolar (A_D) splitting is about $+1$ G (730). This can be accounted for by positive spin density in the sigma orbital or negative spin density in the π orbital or the difference between $+(-)$ spin density in the sigma orbital and $+(-)$ spin density in the π orbital if both are appreciable.

The negative spin density in the nitrogen s orbital indicates that the sigma p spin density will also be negative assuming that the sigma orbital is an sp hybrid. With this hybridization we can estimate the contribution of the p part of the sigma orbital to be -0.16 G. This value combined with the A_D value of $+0.47$ G and $N_{\pi_2}^2 = 0.83$ leaves a splitting of $+1.2$ G to be accounted for by π spin density. This is a π spin density, f_π, of -0.07. Assuming that the spin density arises from configuration interaction Fortman and Hayes have derived an equation similar to equation 36 to account for the π spin density

$$f_\pi = -\frac{4}{3} \frac{(d_{xy}, d_{xz}) N_{\pi_1}^4 (\lambda_1^N)^2}{xz \to \pi^*(NO)} \tag{61}$$

With the assignment $xz \to \pi^*(NO) = 30{,}000$ cm^{-1} and with Fortman and Hayes' estimate of $(d_{xy}, d_{xz}) = 3{,}868$ cm^{-1}, one obtains $N_{\pi_1}^4 (\lambda_1^N)^2 = 0.41$. Calculations of this type are not expected to give quantitative estimates of the molecular orbital coefficients. In this light the *qualitative* agreement between the $N_{\pi_1}^4 (\lambda_1^N)^2$ value (≈ 0.35) obtained from $g_\perp$ by the reduction of the spin–orbit coupling constant (eq. 21) and the value obtained with equation 61 $N_{\pi_1}^4 (\lambda_1^N)^2 \approx 0.41$ supports the configuration interaction model.

c. **Importance of Considering Charge Transfer Contributions.** Using the conventional d–d transition g value theory, Fortman and Hayes found that the observed g values could not be explained without using unreasonably small molecular orbital coefficients. Kuska and Rogers (730) suggested that charge-transfer contributions are important and proposed some possible optical assignments. Manoharan and Gray (2) using low temperature optical data and theoretical molecular orbital calculations were able to assign the optical transitions. The excellent agreement between their theoretical ESR parameters using charge transfer contributions and the experimental ones (see Table XX) gives considerable support to the charge transfer model.

TABLE XX

Calculated and Measured ESR Parameters for $Cr(CN)_5NO^{3-}$

	Calculated	Experimental
$g_{\parallel}$	1.9874	1.9722
$g_{\perp}$	2.0040	2.0044
$g_{\perp}/g_{\parallel}$	1.0084	1.0163
$|A_{\parallel}^{Cr}-A_{\perp}^{Cr}|$	2.0505×10^{-3} cm^{-1}	2.0085×10^{-3} cm^{-1}
f_{π_2}	0.032	~ 0.03

Bernal, Robinson, Meriwether, and Wilkinson (741,807) have studied the series $Cr(X)_5NO^n$ where $X = CN^{1-}$, NH_3, and H_2O. Surprisingly, they find that both the metal hyperfine splittings and the nitrogen hyperfine splittings increase as the X ligand becomes less basic. For $Cr(NH_3)_5NO^{2+}$ the axial and equatorial NH_3 nitrogen splittings are the same (2.36 G) (808). This gives support to a configuration interaction mechanism since a direct ligand polarization mechanism would result in the equatorial splitting being larger than the axial.

The second group consists of those complexes which have essentially an octahedral crystal field. Shulman and Sugano (809) have analyzed the $Mn(CN)_6^{4-}$ and $Fe(CN)_6^{3-}$ ESR results of Baker, Bleaney, and Bowers (288) and of Bleaney and O'Brien (811) in terms of a molecular orbital description. They found that the d^5 cyanide complexes contained only a small amount of pi covalency ($\gamma^2 \approx 0.13$) but d^6 cyanide complexes contained considerably more ($\gamma^2 \approx 0.26$).

The ligand hyperfine splittings for low spin d^5 high symmetry complexes are given in Table XXI. Of special interest is the value for the nitrogen splittings in $V(dipyridyl)_3$ (100). Based on the small nuclear vanadium hyperfine splittings and the similarity of its other ESR parameters to those for $VS_6(C_6H_5)_6$ Davison et al. (103) proposed that the unpaired electron was strongly delocalized on the ligand. The small nitrogen hyperfine splitting seems to favor the model of König (100) which accounts for the low value of the vanadium hyperfine splitting by partial cancellation of the polarization term by a $4s$ contribution of opposite sign.

A number of ESR studies of low spin d^5 sandwich compound have been reported (104,733,735,744–747). The metal nuclear hyperfine splittings are low presumably due to $4s$ mixing.

$K_3Fe(CN)_6$ has been studied extensively (70,720–725,748,749,755,810) especially in regard to the transfer of electronic energy from the Fe^{3+} ion to the lattice.

F. ESR of d^6 Complexes

As can be seen from the data in Table XXII there has been relatively little work on d^6 complexes. Liquid helium temperatures and low microwave power are required to prevent broadening and saturation, respectively. Normally three peaks are observed. The broad peak is due to $\Delta M = \pm 1$ transitions. Its width is caused by a spread of ground state splittings due to local distortions (probably dislocations). Superimposed on the broad line is a narrow line due to simultaneous absorption of two quanta between the $S_z = \pm 1$ levels. The third peak is asymmetric and due to $\Delta M = \pm 2$ transitions. The line shape has been explained by assuming a gaussian distribution for the zero-field splittings. The transitions are strictly forbidden in a cubic field, and this accounts for the sharp high field cutoff. Ham (760) and also Stevens and Persico (763) have studied the effects of Jahn-Teller distortions in d^6 system. A recent Ph.D. thesis is available; it is a study of the effects of the virtual phonon processes on the ESR of Fe^{2+} in MgO by McMahon (761). A commercial application of the ESR of Fe^{2+} in MgO has been reported by Lewis (756). He found that the spin–phonon coupling of the Fe^{2+} is so strong that the saturation of the ESR signal can be used to monitor microsecond ultrasonic pulses. Hall, Hayes, Stevenson, and Wilkens (737) observed a fluorine hyperfine splitting from Fe^{2+} in NaF. They found $A_s^F = 24.7 \pm 2.5 \times 10^{-4}$ cm^{-1}, $A_D = 3.4 \times 10^{-4}$ cm^{-1}, $A_p - B_p = 17.7 \pm 1.6 \times 10^{-4}$ cm^{-1}, $f_s = 0.0245$, and with the assumption $f_\sigma = f_\pi$, f_σ and $f_\pi = 0.0245$. A_p and B_p are given by:

$$A_p = p[f_\sigma(-\tfrac{3}{8}K + \tfrac{3}{10}) + f_\pi(-\tfrac{9}{20}K + \tfrac{16}{50})] \qquad (62)$$

$$B_p = p[f_\sigma(-\tfrac{3}{8}K - \tfrac{3}{20}) + f_\pi(-\tfrac{21}{20}K + \tfrac{21}{200})] \qquad (63)$$

K (the contact interaction) was assumed to have a value of 0.04.

G. ESR of d^7 Complexes

d^7 Complexes are of two types, high spin and low spin, depending on the strength of the crystal field. The ESR data for d^7 high spin complexes are

TABLE XXI
Ligand Hyperfine Splittings in Low Spin d^5 Complexes

Complex and host lattice	Nucleus	A_s $(10^4\ \mathrm{cm}^{-1})$	A_p $(10^4\ \mathrm{cm}^{-1})$	A_D $(10^4\ \mathrm{cm}^{-1})$	Reference
$Cr(\text{dipyridyl})_3^{1+}$ in CH_3OH	N	2.84 ±0.05			100
$V(\text{dipyridyl})_3$ in tetrahydrofuran	N	2.1 ±0.1			100
$Cr(CN)_5NO^{3-}$ in $K_3Mn(CN)_5NO$	N	−4.93	1.50	0.29	731
	equatorial C	−11.33	1.08	0.86 (x) 0.72 (y) 1.05 (z)	
and in $K_3Co(CN)_6$	axial C	−7.83	0.38	0.57	
$Cr(CN)_5NO^{3-}$	N	−5.31	1.33 +0.1	0.44	730
in KBr	equatorial C	−11.1 ±0.3	1.1 ±0.3		
	N	−5.15 ±0.1	1.5 ±0.1	0.44	
in KCl	equatorial C	−10.9 ±0.2	1.2 ±0.2		
in NaCl	N	−5.03	1.6 ±0.2	0.44	

	Nucleus			Reference
$Cr(CN)_5NO^{3-}$ in H_2O	N	-4.90 ± 0.5		742
	Equatorial carbon	-11.63 ± 0.1		
	Axial carbon	-7.84 ± 0.2	0.4	
$Mn(CN)_5NO^{2-}$ in $Na_2Fe(CN)_5NO$	N	-3.58	≈ 1.6 0.92	731 738
$Mn(CN)_5NO^{2-}$ in H_2O	N	Not observable		731
$Cr(H_2O)_5NO^{2+}$ in H_2O	N	5.92 5.0		741,808 726
$Cr(NH_3)_5NO^{2+}$ in H_2O	N	6.45 (NO) 2.18 (eq. NH_3) 2.18 (ax. NH_3)		808
$K_3Fe(CN)_6$	C	11.0 (assuming $g = 2$)		814
$V(C_6H_6)_2$	H	3.7 ± 1		733
$Cr(C_6H_6)I$ in ethanol	H	3.01 ± 0.05		735

TABLE XXII
ESR Data for d^6 Complexes

Compound and host lattice	g	Reference	Other References
Fe^{2+} in MgO	3.428	1051	760,761,756,
	6.86		763,765,757,
			759,1050
Fe^{2+} in CaO	3.30 (broad)	810	763,760
	3.298 (narrow)		
	± 0.003		
	≈ 6.58 (asymmetric)		
Mn^{1+} in Si			760
Cr^0 in Si			760
Fe^{2+} in NaF	3.420 ± 0.002	737	737
Fe^{2+} in $ZnSiF_6$	2.38 ($\parallel$)	762	762
Fe^{2+} in ZnS	2.25	1051	1050
Cr^0 and Mn^+ in diamond-type lattice			764

given in Table XXIII. When the ion is in a tetrahedral or cubic field the g and A values are nearly isotropic as discussed by Henning, van den Boom, and Dieleman (785). When the field is octahedral the ground state is an admixture of two orbital triplets the $^4P(^4T_1)$ and the $^4F(^4T_1)$. Because an additional parameter is required (the percent of admixture of the ^4P into the ^4F), a complete optical study of the complex is necessary before the ESR parameters can be utilized to obtain the molecular orbital coefficients. The ESR theory for the octathedral case has been developed by Abragam and Pryce (842), by Low (825), and by Thornley, Windsor, and Owen (852). The ligand hyperfine splittings are also difficult to interpret because of the need for knowing the admixture coefficients and also because the unpaired electrons are in orbitals of both pi and sigma symmetry. The theory has been developed by Thornley, Windsor, and Owen (852). Gladney (792) has recently utilized a computer program to analyze the experimental ESR spectra of Co^{2+} in MgF_2. He found that fourth-order perturbation contributions could not be neglected.

The experimental ligand hyperfine data are given in Table XXIV. In comparing the literature data one must consider any differences in the definitions, the extent of higher order corrections, and the values used for the physical constants. For example: Tsang's A_s value (857) is only 3/5 the A_s value as defined by Hall et al. (737); Thornley, Windsor, and Owen (852) use a more detailed theory than used by Windsor, Thornley, Griffiths, and Owen (858); and Gladney (791) used values for the physical constants that are different than those used in earlier papers. In the earlier papers it was assumed that $f_\sigma = f_\pi$; however, in a recent paper Gladney (791) reported that $f_\sigma \gg f_\pi$.

The ESR equations for the possible ground states of a low spin d^7 system are given by Maki, Edelstein, Davison, and Holm (777). In general for a tetragonal system the unpaired electron is found in the d_{z^2} orbital although for some complexes with sulfur–metal bonds the large amount of π interaction apparently leads to a large splitting of the d_{xz} and d_{yz} orbitals so that the d_{yz} orbital contains the unpaired electron (777). As pointed out by McGarvey, if the unpaired electron is in the d_{z^2} orbital a low value of the metal hyperfine splitting value does not necessarily indicate a high covalency since the d_{z^2} orbital is of the correct symmetry to mix with the $4s$ orbital. This explanation probably accounts for the large variation of ESR parameters reported for cobalt–porphine-type complexes (124,790, 805). The cobalt–phthalocyanine system is rather unique in that it is a stable square planar system with the unpaired electron in an orbital perpendicular to the plane. Assour (805) has utilized this system to study the basicity of a number of substituted pyridines since the pyridines interacted with the complex along the z axis and the magnitude of the interaction was directly measurable by observing the pyridine nitrogen ESR hyperfine interaction.

Iron nitrosyl complexes have been the subject of considerable study (730,780–783,795,812,813,1027,1029–1031). Manoharan and Gray (1028), on the basis of theoretical molecular orbital calculations, predicted that the unpaired electron in $Fe(NO)(CN)_5^{3-}$ is in a π orbital on the nitrogen while ESR studies (730,782,783,795,812,1031) indicated that the unpaired electron is in the d_{z^2} orbital. This dilemma was resolved by van Voorst and Hemmerich (1027), who showed that the unpaired electron is in a π orbital for $Fe(CN)_5NO^{3-}$ and that the species studied by the ESR workers is $Fe(CN)_5NOH^{2-}$ for which the energy levels are shifted such that the unpaired electron is now in the d_{z^2} orbital.

ESR has been utilized to study the nature of the bridges in binuclear cobalt complexes (758,784,798,1032,1033). The ESR results are best interpreted in terms of a peroxo-bridge structure of the form

$$\overset{\displaystyle \backslash\,|}{\underset{\displaystyle |\,\backslash}{-\text{Co}}}\!-\!O\!-\!O\!-\!\overset{\displaystyle |\,/}{\underset{\displaystyle /\,|}{\text{Co}}}\!-$$

for monobridged complexes and of the form

$$
\begin{array}{ccc}
 & O\!-\!O & \\
\overset{\backslash\,|}{\underset{/\,|}{\text{Co}}} & & \overset{|\,/}{\underset{|\,\backslash}{\text{Co}}} \\
 & NH_2 &
\end{array}
$$

for dibridged complexes.

TABLE XXIII
ESR Data for d^7 High Spin Complexes

Compound and host lattice	g	$g_\parallel$	$g_\perp$	A (10^4 cm^{-1})	$A_\parallel$ (10^4 cm^{-1})	$A_\perp$ (10^4 cm^{-1})	D (10^4 cm^{-1})	Reference	Other references
Fe^{1+} in MgO	4.15							778	
Co^{2+} in MgO	4.278 ±0.001			97.8 ±0.2				258	388 856
Co^{2+} in CaO	4.372 ±0.002			132.2 ±0.2				277 278	
Co^{2+} in Al$_2$O$_3$		2.929 ±0.001	4.947 ±0.003		32.4 ±0.1	97.2 ±0.5		772	800 205
		2.808 ±0.003	4.855 ±0.005 (two species)		20.8 ±0.9	151 ±1.1			774 816 820 768
Co^{2+} in Mg(CH$_2$COOH)$_2$·4H$_2$O		2.518 ±0.008	6.018 (x) ±0.018 4.046 (y) ±0.012		31 ±3	192 (x) ±4 92 (y) ±5		775	
Co^{2+} in CdS		2.269 ±0.005	2.286 ±0.008		4.7 ±0.2	10.5 ±0.6	6.700	787	801 786
Co^{2+} in Y$_3$Ga$_5$O$_{12}$		7.01 ±0.01	2.69 ±0.02		308 ±3	15 ±5		693	
Co^{2+} in ZnSe	2.2742 ±0.0005			7.7 ±0.1				785	807
Co^{2+} in CaF$_2$	2.31 ±0.02			23				803	807

Ion in host	g	g	A	A	Ref.	Ref.
Co^{2+} in CdF_2	2.278 ±0.005				803	769
Co^{2+} in $CdTe$	2.3093		23.0 ±0.6		815	803,818
Co^{2+} in TiO_2	5.860 (z) ±0.001	2.090 (x) ±0.001 3.725 (y) ±0.02	23.4	142.8 (z) ±0.6 39.1 (x) ±0.4 25.0 (y) ±0.3	773	789
Ni^{3+} in $SrTiO_3$	2.180 ±0.002 (203°K)	2.172 ±0.001 (x) 2.184 ±0.001 (at 80°K) 2.136 ±0.001 2.202 (at 20°K) 2.110 ±0.002 2.213 ±0.002 (at 4.2°K)			796	858 737
Co^{2+} in $KMgF_3$	4.369 ±0.002		104 ±2		852	858
Co^{2+} in NaF	4.391 ±0.004		110 ±2		737	737
Fe^{1+} in LiF	4.251 ±0.004				737	
Fe^{1+} in NaF	4.351 ±0.001				737	
Fe^{1+} in $KMgF_3$	4.297 ±0.001				737	
Ni^{3+} in $KMgF_3$	4.163 ±0.001				737	
Co^{2+} in MgF_2	6.027	4.240 (x) 2.296 (y)			792	
Co^{2+} in CdI_2						858

(continued)

TABLE XXIII (continued)

Compound and host lattice	g	$g_\parallel$	$g_\perp$	A (10^4 cm^{-1})	$A_\parallel$ (10^4 cm^{-1})	$A_\perp$ (10^4 cm^{-1})	D (10^4 cm^{-1})	Reference	Other references
Ni^{3+} in MgO	2.282 ±0.002								854
Ni^{3+} in CaO	2.170 ±0.002								854
Co^{2+} in $Zn[HC(pz)_3]_2(NO_3)_2$		8.534 ±0.005	0.807 ±0.005		369 ±1	<1			855
in $Zn[HB(pz)_3]_2$		8.46 ±0.01	0.97 ±0.01		362 ±3	<1			
in $Zn(B(pz)_4)_2$		8.48 ±0.01	0.94 ±0.03		365 ±2				
in $Zn[HC(pz)_3]_2SO_4$		8.06 ±0.01	1.30		338 ±2				
		8.47 ±0.01	0.83 ±0.03		363 ±2				
in $Zn[HC(pz)_3]_2I_2$		8.53 ±0.01	0.78 ±0.03		380 ±2				
in $Zn[HC(pz)_3]_2Cl_2$ (pz = 1-pyrazolyl)									
Co^{2+} in NH_4Cl									537
Co^{2+} in $CdCl_2$		3.04 ±0.02	4.95 ±0.02		36 ±6	169 ±9			799
Co^{2+} in $Bi_2Mg_3(NO_3)_{12} \cdot 24H_2O$		4.145 ±0.002	4.415 ±0.002		95 ±3	103 ±3			802
		7.20 ±0.01	2.39 ±0.002		302 ±6	<1			
(Two species present)									

Co^{2+} in CdBr$_2$	2.71 ±0.05	4.99 ±0.05	32 ±8	175 ±10		799	767 858
Co^{2+} in Co(NH$_3$)$_5$-O$_2$H(SO$_4$)$_3$·H$_2$O	2.12	1.99				770	
Co^{2+} in CoCl$_2$·2H$_2$O						806	
Co^{2+} in AgCl	5.38 ±0.30	3.87 ±0.02	233 ±3	89 ±2		804	
	3.48 ±0.02	4.70 ±0.05	55 ±10	170 ±20			
(Two species)							
Co^{2+} in Y$_3$Ga$_5$O$_{12}$	7.01 ±0.01	2.69 ±0.02	308 ±3	15 ±5		693	817
Co^{2+} in ZnS	2.248					815	
Co^{2+} in ZnTe	2.2972				17.5	815	

TABLE XXIV
Ligand Hyperfine Splittings For d^7 High Spin Complexes

Complex and host lattice	Nucleus	A_s $(10^4\ cm^{-1})$	A_D $(10^4\ cm^{-1})$	f_s	f_σ	f_π	References
Co^{2+} in MgF$_2$	Axial F			0.0061	0.039	0.009	792
	Equatorial F			0.0052	0.045	0.003	
Co^{2+} in KMgF$_3$	F		6.1	0.0054	0.029	0.019	852
Fe^{1+} in NaF	F	23.0 ±1.6	4.4	0.0029	0.0145	0.0145	737
Fe^{1+} in LiF	F	38.1 ±6.0	6.5	0.0048	0.022 assumed ($f_\sigma = f_\pi$)	0.022	737
Fe^{1+} in KMgF$_3$	F	37.0 ±6.0	5.8	0.0051	0.014 assumed ($f_\sigma = f_\pi$)	0.014	737
Co^{2+} in NaF	F	29.6 ±5.0	4.4	0.0037	0.035 assumed ($f_\sigma = f_\pi$)	0.035	737
Co^{2+} in KMgF$_3$	F	38.3 ±3.5	6.1	0.0052	0.028 assumed ($f_\sigma = f_\pi$)	0.028	737
Ni^{3+} in KMgF$_3$	F	48.7	5.8	0.0068	0.086 assumed ($f_\sigma = f_\pi$)	0.086	737
Co^{2+} in KCoF$_3$	F	(38)		0.0055			857
Co^{2+} in CdBr$_2$	Br	23	0.6	0.0057	0.053 assumed ($f_\sigma = f_\pi$)	0.053	858
Co^{2+} in CdI$_2$	I	19	0.4	0.0054	0.076 assumed ($f_\sigma = f_\pi$)	0.076	858

Co^{2+} in $CoCl_2 \cdot 2H_2O$	^{35}Cl	$+5.58$ ± 0.20	806
Co^{2+} in ZnSe	Se	16.4 ($\parallel$) ± 0.2 9.6 ($\perp$) ± 0.2	785

TABLE XXV
ESR Data for Low Spin d^7 Complexes

Compound and host lattice	g	$g_\parallel$	$g_\perp$	A (10^4 cm^{-1})	$A_\parallel$ (10^4 cm^{-1})	$A_\perp$ (10^4 cm^{-1})	Reference
Co²⁺ in α-Zn phthalocyanine		2.007 ±0.003	2.422 ±0.003		116 ±3	66 ±3	790
Co²⁺ in β-Zn phthalocyanine		1.91 ±0.01	2.92 ±0.02 (x) 2.89 ±0.02 (y)		160 ±10	270 (x) ±10 260 ±10	790
Co²⁺ in β-phthalocyanine		1.89 ±0.01	2.94 ±0.01		160 ±10	280 ±10	790
Co²⁺ in β-Ni phthalocyanine		1.89 ±0.01	2.94 ±0.01		150 ±10	280 ±10	790
Co²⁺ in tetraphenylporphine (two species present)		1.798 ±0.001 2.034 ±0.003	3.322 ±0.001 2.505 ±0.003		197 ±1 115 ±1	315 ±1 92 ±1	124
Co tetraphenylporphrine in CHCl₃ (three ⊥ spectra observed)		1.848 ±0.003	3.330 ±0.003 3.198 ±0.003 3.066 ±0.003		187 ±1	380 ±2 358 ±2 298 ±2	124
Co phthalocyanine in:							
sulfuric acid		2.029	2.546		85	96	
pyridine		2.016	2.268		78		805
pyridazine		2.018	2.308		78		
isoquinoline		2.011	2.336		84		
quinoline		2.013	2.288		79		

Complex	g	g	g	A	A	A	
Co phthalocyanine in:							
3-methylpridine		2.010	2.326		88		805
4-methylpridine		2.010	2.306		84		812, 1027
2-methylquinoline		2.007	2.317		91		783, 1027
$[Fe(CN)_5NOH]^{2-}$ in dimethylformamide	2.023∥	2.0059	2.0313	−6.73			1027
$[Fe(CN)_5NOH]^{2-}$ in $Na_2Fe(CN)_5NO\cdot2H_2O$		2.0069	2.0374		~+8.4		
$[Fe(CN)_5NO]^{3-}$ in $Na_2Fe(CN)_5NO\cdot2H_2O$		1.93	2.00 (x); 1.98 (y)	~1.4	−13.6		
$Fe(NO)[S_2C_2(CN)_2]_2$ in H_2O	2.027			8.9			780
$Fe(NO)[S_2C_6H_4]_2$ in H_2O	2.028			8.8			780
$Fe(NO)[S_2CC(CN)_2]_2$ in H_2O	2.041			8.0			780
$Fe(NO)[S_2CN\cdot(CH_3)_2]_2$ in single crystal	(2.037)	2.0277 ±0.0004	2.0461 (x) ±0.0005; 2.0379 (y) ±0.0005				821
Co^{2+} in $(Bu_4N)_2Ni\cdot[S_2C_2(CN)_2]_2$	(2.267)	1.977 ±0.003	2.789 (x) ±0.003; 2.025 (y) ±0.003	(33.7)	23 ±1	50 (x) ±1; 28 (y) ±1	777
Ni^{3+} in $(Bu_4N)_2Cu\cdot[S_2C_2(CN)_2]_2$		1.998 ±0.001	2.160 (x) ±0.001; 2.042 (y) ±0.001		<2	15 (x) ±2; 2.9 (y) ±1	777
Ni(toluene-3,4-dithiolate)$_2^{1-}$ in DMF–CHCl$_3$	2.082	2.016	2.048 (x); 2.183 (y)				1035
$Ni[S_2C_2(C_6H_5)_2]_2^{1-}$ in DMSO	2.0568 ±0.0003			4.3 ±1			779, 1037

(continued)

TABLE XXV (continued)

Compound and host lattice	g	$g_\parallel$	$g_\perp$	A $(10^4\ cm^{-1})$	$A_\parallel$ $(10^4\ cm^{-1})$	$A_\perp$ $(10^4\ cm^{-1})$	Reference
$Ni[S_2C_2(CF_3)_2]_2^{1-}$ in acetone	2.0618 ±0.0004						1037
(structure) in DMSO	2.034						1035
(structure) in DMF–CHCl₃	2.055	2.006	2.030 (x) 2.123 (y)				1035
$Ni[S_2C_2(CN)_2]_2^{1-}$ in DMF–CHCl₃	2.0633	1.996	2.043 (x) 2.140 (y)				1036
(structure) in DMF–CHCl₃	2.0042	1.975	2.005 (x) 2.026 (y)				1036

					Ref.
in DMF–CHCl₃	2.015	2.009	2.027 (x) / 2.119 (y)		
in DMF–CHCl₃	(2.052?)	2.008	2.022 (x) / 2.118 (y)		
in DMSO–CHCl₃	(2.003?)	1.978	2.005 (x) / 2.026 (y)		
in DMSO–CHCl₃	2.004?	1.980	2.004 (x) / 2.025 (y)		
in 2Me-THF	(2.004?)	1.979	2.006 (x) / 2.028 (y)		
$Fe(NO)_2(OH)_2$ in H_2O, pH = 11	2.027			14.7	780
$Fe(NO)_2(PO_4)_2^{2-}$ in H_2O pH = 7	2.033			13.8	780
$Fe(NO)_2(P_2O_5)^{2-}$ in H_2O	2.040			12.2	780
$Fe(NO)_2$ (penicillamine)$_2$ in H_2O	2.032				780
$Fe(NO)S$ in H_2O pH = 11	2.021				780
$K_5[(CN)_5CoO_2Co(CN)_5] \cdot H_2O$ in 50% H_2SO_4	2.0200			8.01	1032
$[(NH_3)_5CoO_2Co(NH_3)_5](NO_3)_5$ in 50% H_2SO_4	2.0249			10.8	1032
$K_4 \left[(CN)_4Co \begin{smallmatrix} O_2 \\ NH_2 \end{smallmatrix} Co(CN)_4 \right] \cdot 2H_2O$ in H_2O (pH < 7)	2.0244			9.6	1032
$K_3 \left[(CN)_3NH_3Co \begin{smallmatrix} O_2 \\ NH_2 \end{smallmatrix} Co(CN)_4 \right] \cdot 4H_2O$ in H_2O (pH < 7)	2.0241			9.6	1032

(continued)

TABLE XXV (continued)

Compound and host lattice	g	$g_\parallel$	$g_\perp$	A (10^4 cm^{-1})	$A_\parallel$ (10^4 cm^{-1})	$A_\perp$ (10^4 cm^{-1})	Reference
$K_2\left[(CN)_3NH_3Co \underset{NH_2}{\overset{O_2}{\diamond}} Co(CN)_3NH_3 \right] \cdot H_2O$ also				9.6			1032
$K_2\left[(CN)_4Co \underset{NH_2}{\overset{O_2}{\diamond}} Co(CN)_2(NH_3)_2 \right] \cdot H_2O$ in H_2O (pH < 7)							
$\left[(NH_3)_4Co \underset{NH_2}{\overset{O_2}{\diamond}} Co(NH_3)_4 \right](NO_3)_4$ in H_2O (pH < 7)	2.0342			11.8			1032
Fe(hexamethylbenzene)$_2^+$ in 50% H_2O–ethanol	2.08$_6$	1.86$_5$ (x) 1.99$_6$ (y)					771

For d^7 sandwich compounds the ESR results indicate that a Jahn-Teller distortion is present (771,776). Scott's Ph.D. thesis (1034) is an excellent review of the bonding in sandwich complexes.

The ESR data for low spin d^7 complexes are given in Table XXV and the ligand hyperfine splitting data are given in Table XXVI.

As an example of the use of ESR to determine the metal–ligand bond characteristics we return to the sulfur-containing ligand systems studied by Maki, Edelstein, Davison, and Holm (777). For $Ni[S_2C_2(CN)_2]_2^{-}$ and $Co[S_2C_2(CN)_2]_2^{\frac{1}{2}-}$ they found that the unpaired electron is in the d_{yz} orbital. As pointed out by Kuska and Farona (1039) the hyperfine splitting ESR equations for a d_{yz} ground state are:

$$A_x = p[(g_x-2)+A/p-(g-2)-\tfrac{4}{7}N_{yz}^2+\tfrac{3}{14}(g_z-2)+\tfrac{3}{14}(g_y-2)] \qquad (64)$$

$$A_y = p[(g_y-2)+A/p-(g-2)+\tfrac{2}{7}N_{yz}^2-\tfrac{1}{14}(g_x-2)-\tfrac{3}{14}(g_z-2)] \qquad (65)$$

$$A_z = p[(g_z-2)+A/p-(g-2)+\tfrac{2}{7}N_{yz}^2+\tfrac{1}{14}(g_x-2)-\tfrac{3}{14}(g_y-2)] \qquad (66)$$

The hyperfine splitting equations have been written in a manner such that the dependence on the Fermi contact term has been replaced by the isotropic A and g values. The g value equations are complex; terms involving spin–orbit coupling of the ligands and charge transfer terms must be considered. However, by using the experimental g values in the metal hyperfine splitting equations one eliminates the requirements that the complete g value equations be derived and that the optical assignments be correct in order to obtain the value of N_{yz}^2. N_{yz}^2 can be interpreted as the fraction of time that the unpaired electron is on the metal.

Using the value obtained by McGarvey (99) for $P(254 \times 10^{-4}\ cm^{-1})$, for Co^{2+} Kuska and Farona (1039) obtained $N_{yz}^2 = 1.12$, 1.04, and 0.964 from A_y, A_x, and A_z, respectively. For the Ni complex, using $P = 112 \times 10^{-4}\ cm^{-1}$, N_{yz}^2 is found to be 0.43. This large difference in covalency between two complexes differing only in metal ion and ionic charge points out the sensitivity of the molecular orbital distributions to the relative energy levels of the contributing atomic orbitals.

H. ESR of d^8 Complexes

High spin d^8 complexes are unique in that there is one unpaired electron in each of the two sigma orbitals and no unpaired electrons in the pi orbitals. Because of this relatively simple geometry, the d^8 configuration has been a popular one for the testing of the theoretical models proposed for the various ESR observables. The equation for the g value of a d^8 system is given by equation 15 in Section II-C. In Table IV the sigma covalencies for $KNiF_3$ as determined from several different theoretical models are compared with the experimental values. Huang and Simanek

TABLE XXVI
Ligand Hyperfine Splittings for Low Spin d^7 Complexes

Compound and host lattice	Nucleus	$A_\parallel$ $(10^4\ \mathrm{cm}^{-1})$	$A_\perp$ $(10^4\ \mathrm{cm}^{-1})$	A_s $(10^4\ \mathrm{cm}^{-1})$	A_p $(10^4\ \mathrm{cm}^{-1})$	A_D $(10^4\ \mathrm{cm}^{-1})$	f_s	f_σ	Reference
$Fe(CN)_5NOH^{2-}$ in $Na_2Fe(CN)_5NO$	N	15.28	13.47	(14.07)	0.60	0.44	0.0273	0.0100	783
$Fe(CN)_5NOH^{2-}$ in DMF	N	16.01	13.99	14.67	0.68	0.44	0.0285	0.0150	812
	Equatorial C			9.4			0.009		730
$Fe(NO)(S_2CN\cdot(CH_3)_2)_2$ in benzene	N			11			0.0214		821
$Fe(NO)_2(OH)_2$ in H_2O, pH = 11	N			2.1			0.0041		780
$Fe(NO)_2(PO_4)_2^{2-}$	N			≈1.7			0.0033		780
	P			≈2.5			0.0007		
$Fe(NO)_2(AsO_4)_2^{2-}$	N			≈2.0			0.0034		780
	As			≈2.9			0.0009		
$Fe(NO)_2(P_2O_5)^{2-}$	P			5.2			0.0015		780
$Fe(NO)_2(SCH_2\cdot CHNH_2COO)_2$	H			≈1.5 G			0.0032		780
	(from CH_2)			≈2 G			0.004		
$Fe(NO)-[S_2C_2\cdot(CN)_2]_2$	N			14.7			0.0286		780
$Fe(NO)[S_2C_6H_4]_2$	N			14.3			0.0278		780

Fe(NO)-$[S_2CC\cdot(CN)_2]_2$	N			12.2	0.0237	780
Fe(NO)S in H_2O	N	11.4?	12 8	4.7	0.0091	780
Co phthalo-cyanine in pyridine	N (from solvent)					805
in pyridazine	N (from solvent)	16.2				805
in isoquinoline	N (from solvent)	13.3				805
in quinoline	N (from solvent)	15.2				805
in 3-methyl-pyridine	N (from solvent)	15.1				805
in 4-methyl-pyridine	N (from solvent)	16.1				805
in 2-methyl-pyridine	N (from solvent)	16.1				805

TABLE XXVII

ESR Data For d^8 Complexes

Compound and host lattice	g	A (10^4 cm^{-1})	D (10^4 cm^{-1})	E (10^4 cm^{-1})	Reference	Other references
Ni^{2+} in AgBr	2.20 2.238 (Two species present)				845	
Cu^{3+} in Al$_2$O$_3$	2.0784 ($\parallel$) ±0.0005 2.0772 ($\perp$) ±0.0005	−64.296 ($\parallel$) ±0.001 −60.015 ($\perp$) ±0.01	−1883.8 ±0.4		841	
Ni^{2+} in Al$_2$O$_3$	2.1957 ($\parallel$) ±0.0013 2.1859 ($\perp$) ±0.0013		$-(1.3287 + \alpha T^2)$ $\alpha = 5.2 \times 10^{-7}(°K)^{-2}$		847	850,849 835,826 816
Co^{1+} in CaO	2.2743 (20°K) ±0.0008 2.2756 (12°K) ±0.0008	31.6 (20 and 12°K) ±0.3			828	
Ni^{2+} in CaO	2.327 ±0.001				278	
Co^{1+} in CdS	2.16 ($\parallel$) ±0.01 4.9 ($\perp$) ±0.5				844	

Ion	g	A	D		Ref.
Ni^{2+} in $CdSiF_6 \cdot 6H_2O$	2.25 ±0.1		< 150	< 150	838
Ni^{2+} in $KMgF_3$	2.2797 ±0.0004	65.9 (∥) ±0.3, 25.8 (⊥) ±0.3			286	90,138
Ni^{2+} in $La_2Zn_3(NO_3)_{12} \cdot 24H_2O$			−22,500 (x-site) +430 (77°K) (y-site) +650 (4.2°K)		827
Ni^{2+} in $Mg_3Bi_2(NO_3)_{12} \cdot 24H_2O$	2.232 (77°K) ±0.006, 2.225 (4.2°K) ±0.006		2690 (77°K) ±10, 2980 (4.2°K) ±30		832
Ni^{2+} in $Mg_3La(NO_3)_{12} \cdot 24H_2O$	2.238 (77°K) ±0.01, 2.230 (4.2°K) ±0.005		1770 (77°K), 2000 (4.2°K)		832
Co^{1+} in MgO	2.1728 ±0.0005	54.0 ±0.2			778
Ni^{2+} in MgO	2.2145 ±0.0005	8.3 ±0.4			778	822,278
Ni^{2+} in $MgSiF_6 \cdot H_2O$	2.25 ±0.1		≲200	≲200	838
Ni^{2+} in NaF	2.2933 ±0.0003	59.2 (∥) ±0.3, 18.5 (⊥) ±0.3			286

(continued)

TABLE XXVII (*continued*)

Compound and host lattice	g	A (10^4 cm^{-1})	D (10^4 cm^{-1})	E (10^4 cm^{-1})	Reference	Other references
Ni^{2+} in NH$_4$Cl					537	
Ni^{2+}					836	
in Ni(CN)$_2$NH$_3$	2.38					
in Ni(CN)$_2$NH$_3 \cdot$ C$_6$H$_6$	2.11					
in Ni(CN)$_2$NH$_3 \cdot$ C$_4$H$_5$N	2.14					
in Ni(CN)$_2$NH$_3 \cdot$ C$_4$H$_4$S	2.05					
Ni^{2+} in Ni(NH$_3$)$_6$X$_2$ X = Br, or I					649	
Ni^{2+}	2.162 (300°K)				410	649,834
in Ni(NH$_3$)$_6$Cl$_2$	2.177 (90°K)					846
Ni(NH$_4$SO$_4$)$_2 \cdot$ 6H$_2$O					830	
Ni phthalocyanine	$\approx$ 2.0036				837	
NiSiF$_6 \cdot$ 6H$_2$O	2.36 (∥) 2.29 (⊥)				839	827,851
Fe^0 in Si	2.0699	6.98			408	824
Mn^{1-} in Si	2.0104	−71.28			408	
Ni^{2+} in Sr$_2$WO$_6$	2.242				1040	
Ni^{2+} in	2.225 (77°K) ± 0.002		1280 (77°K) ± 10		832	
Zn$_3$Bi$_2$(NO$_3$)$_{12} \cdot$ 24H$_2$O	2.225 (4.2°K) ± 0.002		1640 (4.2°K)			

Compound	g				
Ni^{2+} in ZnF$_2$	2.33	4,182	2670	305	
Ni^{2+} in Zn$_3$La$_2$(NO$_3$)$_{12}$·24H$_2$O	2.235 (77°K) ±0.01 2.238 (4.2°K) ±0.05	430 (77°K) ±10 650 (4.2°K) ±10		832	
Ni^{2+} in ZnSiF$_6$·6D$_2$O	2.23 (77°K) ±0.01 2.225 (4.2°K) ±0.003	−2780 (77°K) ±30 −2180 (4.2°K) ±10		838	
Ni^{2+} in ZnSiF$_6$·6H$_2$O	2.25 (77°K) ±0.01 2.25 (4.2°K) ±0.01	−2000 (77°K) ±100 −1290 (4.2°K) ±10		838	840
Ni^{2+} in ZnSnF$_6$·6H$_2$O	2.25 ±0.1	≲|200|	≲|200|	838	
Ni^{2+} in ZnTiF$_6$·6H$_2$O	2.25 ±0.1	≲|200|	≲|200|	838	

(90) and Misetich and Watson (138) have determined the amount of pi covalency in the excited state where there is an unpaired electron in the pi orbitals. Both groups conclude that the sigma and pi covalencies are of the same order of magnitude. We would like to emphasize that the theoretical work that has been done on the d^8 complexes is perhaps the most thorough theoretical work that has yet been applied to ESR transition metal spectroscopy. Blumberg, Eisinger, and Geschwind (841) have studied the rare copper 3+ valence state. The expected trend of $\langle 1/r^3 \rangle$ for Cu^{3+} being greater than $\langle 1/r^3 \rangle$ for Cu^{2+} is found. Woodbury and Ludwig (408) appear to have been successful in observing ESR spectra from manganese ions in two different valence states in the same silicon site. The g and A values obtained for Mn^{1-} are $g = 2.0104$, $A = -71.28 \times 10^{-4}$ cm^{-1} and for Mn^{2+} they are $g = 2.0066$, $A = -53.47$. The larger absolute value of A for Mn^{1-} does not mean that it is more ionic than the Mn^{2+} since the A value is inversely proportional to S, the total electron spin. The ESR data are given in Table XXVII. Additional d^8 ESR references are 406 and 833.

I. ESR of d^9 Complexes

In octahedral symmetry the unpaired electron is expected in the degenerate $x^2 - y^2$ (or xy) and z^2 energy levels. Since these two orbitals contain three electrons an additional *net* stabilization is expected if the symmetry is lowered such that the two paired electrons go into the resulting lower energy orbital and the single unpaired electron occupies the now higher energy orbital (968,1041). The higher energy orbital is expected to be the sigma orbital to those ligands which are closest to the metal. The resulting distortion is normally tetragonal with the two axial ligands moving outward. At higher temperatures it is found that the distortion resonates along the three symmetry axes while at lower temperatures the distortion freezes in along one of the axes (868). This type of behavior can be expected for MX_6 systems. However, for MX_4Y_2 the difference in the crystal field between X and Y should lead to a tetragonal crystal field even at room temperature. Most $3d^9$ ESR work has been done on tetragonal Cu^{2+} systems. The spin Hamiltonian for a tetragonal crystal field is

$$H = g_\parallel \beta H_z S_z + g_\perp \beta (H_x S_x + H_y S_y) + A_\parallel^{Cu} I_z S_z + A_\perp^{Cu}(I_x S_x + I_y S_y)$$
$$+ A_\parallel^N (I_x S_x \text{ or } I_y S_y) + A_\perp^N (I_y S_y \text{ or } I_x S_x + I_z S_z) \quad (67)$$

where the tetragonal distortion is along the z axis. The relationships between the ligand hyperfine splittings and the molecular orbital that the unpaired electron is in are illustrated by the following equations for a nitrogen-containing copper chelate with effective D_{2h} symmetry.

TABLE XXVIII
ESR References for d^9 Complexes

Type of compound or behavior	References
Cu^{2+} in acetate-type complexes	879,917,928,931,932,964,971,1023,1024,
Cu^{2+} in acetylacetonate-type complexes	848,861,870,872,882,885,888,905,914,925,938, 939,957,994,995,
Cu^{2+} adsorbed ions	130,177,713,862,863,865,883,884,895,1022,
Cu^{2+} in AgCl	61,899,900,990,
Cu^2 in amine-type complexes	848,870,880,882,885,888,903,918,920,938,956, 957,966,973,974,979,980,983,984,985,988
Cu^{2+} in borate glasses	194,1014
Ni^{1+} in diamond	788
Cu^{2+} in CaO	1020
Ni^{1+} in CaO	1020
Cu^{2+} in $CdCl_2$	935,936
Cu^{2+} in CdS	962 (see also 952)
Ni^{1+} in CdS	844
Cu^{2+} in $CdWO_4$	1025,1026
Cu^{2+} chelate complexes (general)	860,867,869,872,873,874,877,881,888,889,893, 894,897,909,910,912,914,915,916,921,926,938, 939,941,942,944,958,959,960,961,999,1016,978
Cu^{2+} citrate complex	996
Co^{0+} in Sc, Y, Ce, Pr, Nd, Tm, Zr, and U	1001
$Co(CO)_4$	922
Cu^{2+} in Cs_2ZnCl_4	969,990
$CuCl_2 \cdot 2H_2O$	228,907
$CuF_2 \cdot 5HF \cdot 5H_2O$	986
$CuF_2 \cdot 2H_2O$	963
$Cu(NH_4)_2Cl_4 \cdot 2H_2O$	228,864,876,987
$Cu(NH_3)_4PtCl_4$	923
$Cu(NH_4)_2(SO_4)_2 \cdot 6H_2O$	886,906,908,1010,1017,1021
$CuSO_4 \cdot 5H_2O$	875,901,907,911,919,1002,1011,1018
Experimental techniques	712,919,987,1018,908,911
Cu^{2+} in $Fe(NH_4)(SO_4)_2 \cdot 12H_2O$	416
Cu^{2+} in GeO_2	853
Jahn-Teller effect	61,705,808,868,891,920,934,946,947,948,968, 991,1020,936,431,778,982,989
Cu^{2+} in $K_2Co(SO_4)_2 \cdot 6H_2O$	950
$K_2CuCl_4 \cdot 2H_2O$	929,930
$K_3Cu(NO_2)_5$	945

(continued)

TABLE XXVIII (*continued*)

Type of compound or behavior	References
$K_2Cu(SO_4)_2 \cdot 6H_2O$	1009
Cu^{2+} in $K_2Zn(SO_4)_2 \cdot 6H_2O$	950
Cu^{2+} in LiF	981
Line width and relaxation	71,197,416,862,863,870,875,876,882,885,886, 895,898,903,906,907,908,911,929,931,949,956, 959,961,963,971,990,995,1002,1005,1017,1021, 1022,1007,386
Cu^{2+} in $MgCl_2$	936
Cu^{2+} in MgO	431,778,982,989
Cu^{2+} in $MgSO_4 \cdot 7H_2O$	878,913
Cu^{2+} in $MgWO_4$	1025
Cu^{2+} in $Mn(NH_4)_2(SO_4)_2 \cdot 6H_2O$	416
Cu^{2+} in $MnSO_4 \cdot 4H_2O$	416
Cu^{2+} in $NaKC_4H_4O_6 \cdot 4H_2O$	1048
Cu^{2+} in NH_4Cl	537,674,972,976,977
Cu^{2+} porphyrin-type complexes	837,866,888,896,902,904,951,959,992,993,994, 1000,1004
Cu^{2+} pyridine-type complexes	642,705,927,933,938,943,953,955,980,1019
Cu^{2+} salicylaldehyde-type complexes	718,859,890,938,994
Cu^{2+} in $2SiO_2 \cdot B_2O_3 \cdot CaO$	967
Solvent behavior	142,477,612,867,871,887,903,907,925,954,998, 1003
Cu^{2+} complexes with sulfur-containing ligands	829,860,888,949,965,975,980,994,997,1006, 1008,1012,1013,1015
Cu^{2+} in TiO_2	924
Cu^{2+} in $Zn(HCOO)_2 \cdot 2H_2O$	940
Cu^{2+} in ZnO	892

$$A_{\parallel}^{N} = A_{s}^{N} + 2A_{p} \tag{68}$$

$$A_{\parallel} = A_{s} + \tfrac{4}{5}n^2 \frac{\mu_I \beta_I}{I} \langle 1/r^3 \rangle (\alpha')^2/4 + 2A_D \beta^2 \tag{69}$$

$$A_{\perp}^{N} = A_{s}^{N} - A_{p} \tag{70}$$

$$A_{\perp}^{N} = A_{s}^{N} - \tfrac{2}{5}n^2 \frac{\mu_I \beta_I}{I} \langle 1/r^3 \rangle (\alpha')^2/4 - A_D \beta^2 \tag{71}$$

where A_{s}^{N} is the isotropic splitting, $A_{s}^{N} = \tfrac{1}{3}A_{\parallel}^{N} + \tfrac{2}{3}A_{\perp}^{N}$, n^2 is the fraction of p character in the nitrogen sigma orbital ($n^2 = \tfrac{2}{3}$, assuming sp^2

hybridization). I is the nuclear spin of the ligand ($I = 1$ for nitrogen), β_I is the nuclear magneton, μ_I is the magnetic moment of the ligand nucleus, and A_D is the direct dipole term. For nitrogen

$$\tfrac{2}{5}\mu_I\beta_I/I \langle 1/r^3 \rangle = 17.05 \text{ G} \tag{72}$$

using $\langle 1/r^3 \rangle_{2p} = 3.10$ au (1042).

The spin density can also be determined from the A_s^N values by the following equation

$$A_s = \frac{8\pi}{3} \frac{\mu_I\beta_I}{I} (1 - n^2) \frac{\beta^2(\alpha')^2}{4} |\psi(0)|^2 \tag{73}$$

For nitrogen

$$\frac{8\pi}{3} \frac{\mu_I\beta_I}{I} |\psi(0)|^2 = 550 \text{ G} \tag{74}$$

The molecular orbitals involved are:

$$|xy> \;=\; \alpha d_{xy} - \tfrac{1}{2}\alpha'[-\sigma_{xy}^{(1)} + \sigma_{xy}^{(2)} + \sigma_{xy}^{(3)} - \sigma_{xy}^{(4)}] \tag{75}$$

$$|x^2 - y^2> \;=\; \beta d_{x^2-y^2} - \tfrac{1}{2}(1 - \beta^2)^{1/2}[-p_{xy}^{(1)} - p_{xy}^{(2)} + p_{xy}^{(3)} + p_{xy}^{(4)}] \tag{76}$$

$$|z^2> \;=\; \gamma d_{z^2} - \tfrac{1}{2}(1 - \gamma^2)^{1/2}[\sigma_{xy}^{(1)} + \sigma_{xy}^{(2)} - \sigma_{xy}^{(3)} - \sigma_{xy}^{(4)}] \tag{77}$$

$$|yz> \;=\; \delta' d_{zy} - \tfrac{1}{2}(1 - \delta'^2)^{1/2}[p_z^{(1)} + p_z^{(2)} - p_z^{(3)} - p_z^{(4)}] \tag{78}$$

$$|xz> \;=\; \delta'' d_{xz} - \tfrac{1}{2}(1 - \delta''^2)^{1/2}[p_2^{(1)} + p_2^{(4)} - p_2^{(2)} - p_2^{(3)}] \tag{79}$$

where the y axis bisects the chelate rings. The effective D_{2h} symmetry was suggested by Gersmann and Swalen (938) for copper acetylacetonate and found for bis(dipivaloylethanido) copper(II) from a recent investigation of the polarized optical spectra, ESR, and extended Hückel molecular orbital calculations (1043). The magnetic parameters as given by Gersmann and Swalen (938) are:

$$g_z = 2.0023 - \frac{8\lambda}{\Delta x^2 - y^2} |\alpha^2\beta^2 - f(\beta)| \tag{80}$$

$$f(\beta) = \alpha\alpha'\beta^2 S + \alpha\alpha'\beta(1 - \beta^2)^{1/2}T(n)/2 \tag{81}$$

$$g_x = 2.0023 - \frac{2\lambda}{\Delta xz} [\alpha^2\delta''^2 - \alpha\alpha'S\delta''^2] \tag{82}$$

$$g_y = 2.0023 - \frac{2\lambda}{\Delta yz} [\alpha^2\delta'^2 - \alpha\alpha'S\delta'^2] \tag{83}$$

$$A_z = P\left[-\alpha^2(\tfrac{4}{7} + K) - 2\lambda\alpha^2\left(\frac{4\beta^2}{\Delta_{x^2-y^2}} + \tfrac{3}{14}\frac{\delta'^2}{\Delta yz} + \tfrac{3}{14} 1/\Delta xz \right) \right] \tag{84}$$

$$A_x = P[\alpha^2(\tfrac{2}{7} - K) - \tfrac{22}{14} \lambda\alpha^2(\delta'')^2/\Delta xz] \tag{85}$$

$$A_y = P[\alpha^2(\tfrac{2}{7} - K) - \tfrac{22}{14} \lambda\alpha^2\delta'^2/\Delta yz] \tag{86}$$

S is the group overlap integral between the copper d_{xy} orbital and the assumed sp^2 hybrid ligand sigma orbitals. Its value has been determined by Kivelson and Neiman (896). They obtained $S_{oxygen} = 0.076$ and $S_{nitrogen} = 0.093$ for a copper–ligand distance of 1.9 Å. $T(n)$ is an integral over the ligand functions and is equal to 0.220 for oxygen and 0.333 for nitrogen (896). λ is the spin-orbit coupling constant for the free ion and is equal to -828 cm^{-1}. P is the free ion dipole term proportional to $1/r^3$ and is given a value of 0.036 cm^{-1}. K is the Fermi contact term and is usually given a value of 0.43. However, Kuska and Rogers (925) found that K cannot be considered a constant since the use of a single constant value of K leads to a relative ordering of covalency opposite to that obtained by other physical methods. Fortunately equations 84–86 can be rewritten in a form which permits the use of the isotropic A value in place of K. This equation is

$$\alpha^2 = {}^7\!/_4[|A_\parallel|/P - |A|/P + {}^2\!/_3 g_\parallel - {}^5\!/_{21} g_\perp - {}^6\!/_7] \tag{87}$$

The corresponding equation for obtaining α^2 from the isotropic A value is

$$\alpha^2 = +\frac{|A|}{PK} + \frac{g - 2.0023}{K} + \frac{(1 - f^2)0.0975}{PK} \tag{88}$$

f^2 is the fraction of $3d$ character in the copper $3d$-$4s$ ground state. In equation 88 an electron in a $4s$ orbital has been assigned a value of 0.0975 cm^{-1}. This is the value determined theoretically from unrestricted Hartree-Fock theory by Freeman and Watson (94).

In obtaining equations 87 and 88 we have assumed that the molecular orbital is composed of d_{xy} and $4s$ metal character. The origin of the $4s$ character has been attributed by McGarvey (99) to a configuration inter-action mechanism and by Kuska, Rogers, and Drullinger (1044) to a vibronic mechanism of the type discussed by O'Brien (968). Of course, it is possible that both mechanisms contribute. Falle and Luckhurst (939) and also Wilson and Kivelson (995) have reported a temperature dependence for the ESR parameters.

As pointed out by Kuska, Rogers, and Drullinger (1044) the model of $3d_{xy}$ and $4s$ metal character does not give consistent results for a number of complexes. This may be due to a lowering of symmetry as suggested by Wuethrich (955) to explain a marked decrease in the copper hyperfine splittings found in a series of substituted pyridine copper complexes. Bates et al. (892,894) and Dietz et al. (1045) studied Cu^{2+} ions in tetra-hedral crystal fields and found that the $4p$ copper orbital must be included in the molecular orbital description. From the above tetrahedral studies it appeared to be possible to distinguish between a tetragonal and a tetra-hedral crystal field for Cu^{2+} by comparing the ESR data with data for complexes of known symmetry; however, Kokoszka, Reimann, and

Allen (1046,1053) and Siegel and Lorenc (853) have recently studied tetrahedral copper complexes which have ESR parameters similar to those reported for tetragonal complexes. Sroubek et al. (1025,1026), Kasai et al. (1047), and Dunhill et al. (996) have recently reported Cu^{2+} complexes in which the unpaired electron is in the z^2 orbital rather than the usual xy or x^2-y^2 orbital.

Some copper complexes form dimers in the solid state resulting in an effective electronic spin of 1. For papers which have studied this behavior, see the "acetate type complexes" division in Table XXVIII. It was not possible to present experimental data in Table XXVIII due to the large number of variables present (solvent, substituent, coordination number, and temperature) and the large number of papers available. Computer programs (in FORTRAN IV) for single crystal, powder, and least squares simulation of spectra are available in the Ph.D. thesis of Venable (1049).

Acknowledgments

We would like to thank the Pittsburgh Plate Glass Foundation for its support of one of us (H.A.K) for the summer of 1965 which made this review possible. We would also like to thank Miss Lois Ann Johnson and Mr. Michael Johnson for their assistance in the literature search and in the preparation of the manuscript.

Research on ESR studies of transition metal complexes at Michigan State University has been supported by the U.S. Army Research Office (Durham) through contract ARO-D-319-DA-B-124.

References

1. R. F. Fenske, K. G. Caulton, D. D. Radtke, and C. C. Sweeney, *Inorg. Chem.*, **5**, 960 (1966). "Energy Levels, Spin Densities, and the Nephelauxetic Effect in Metal Hexafluorides."

2. P. T. Manoharan and H. B. Gray, *Inorg. Chem.*, **5**, 823 (1966). "Electronic Structures of Metal Pentacyanonitrosyls."

3. C. J. Ballhausen, *Introduction to Ligand Field Theory*, McGraw-Hill, New York, 1962.

4. L. E. Orgel, *An Introduction to Transition Metal Chemistry*, 2nd ed., Wiley, New York, 1966.

5. J. S. Griffith, *The Theory of Transition Metal Ions*, University Press, Cambridge, England, 1961.

6. B. N. Figgis, *Introduction to Ligand Fields*, Interscience, New York, 1966.

7. H. Watanabe, *Operator Methods in Ligand Field Theory*, Prentice-Hall, Englewood Cliffs, N. J., 1966.

8. C. K. Jørgensen, *Absorption Spectra and Chemical Bonding in Complexes*, Pergamon Press, New York, 1962.

9. C. K. Jørgensen, *Inorganic Complexes*, Academic Press, New York, 1963.

10. C. K. Jørgensen, *Progress in Inorganic Chemistry*, **4**, 73, Interscience, New York, 1962. "The Nephelauxetic Series."

11. C. K. Jørgensen, *Advances in Chemical Physics*, **8**, 47, Interscience, New York, 1965. "Applications of Ligand Field Theory to Complexes."

12. C. K. Jørgensen, *Advances in Chemical Physics*, **5**, 33, Interscience, New York, 1963. "Spectroscopy of Transition Metal Complexes."
13. F. A. Cotton, *Chemical Applications of Group Theory*, Interscience, New York, 1963.
14. N. Nakamoto, *Infrared Spectra of Inorganic and Coordination Compounds*, Wiley, New York, 1963.
15. R. S. Drago, *Physical Methods in Inorganic Chemistry*, Reinhold, New York, 1965.
16. C. J. Ballhausen and H. B. Gray, *Molecular Orbital Theory*, Benjamin, New York, 1965.
17. M. Bersohn and J. C. Baird, *Electron Paramagnetic Resonance*, Benjamin, New York, 1966.
18. G. E. Pake, *Paramagnetic Resonance*, Benjamin, New York, 1962.
19. W. Low, *Solid State Physics, Supplement 2, Paramagnetic Resonance in Solids*, Academic Press, New York, 1960.
20. C. P. Slichter, *Principles of Magnetic Resonance*, Harper and Row, New York, 1963.
21. S. A. Al'tshuler and B. M. Kozyrev, *Electron Paramagnetic Resonance*, Academic Press, New York, 1964.
22. L. A. Blyumenfeld, "Application of EPR in Chemistry," *Izv. Sibirsk. Otdel. Akad. Nauk SSSR*, **1962**.
23. O. B. Roitsin, "Paramagnetic Resonance" *Gostekhizdat Ukr. SSSR*, **1963**.
24. H. M. Hershenson, *Nuclear Magnetic Resonance and Electron Spin Resonance Spectra*, Academic Press, New York, 1963.
25. R. S. Anderson, *Methods Exptl. Phys.*, **3**, 441 (1962). "Electron Spin Resonance."
26. K. W. H. Stevens, *Magnetism*, **1**, 1, Academic Press, New York, 1963. "Spin Hamiltonians."
27. D. E. O'Reilly and J. H. Anderson, *Physics and Chemistry of the Organic Solid State*, **1**, 121, Wiley, New York, 1965. "Magnetic Properties."
28. A. Carrington and H. C. Longuet-Higgins, *Quart. Rev.*, **14**, 427 (1960). "Electron Resonance in Crystalline Transition-Metal Compounds."
29. H. S. Jarrett, *Solid State Physics, Advances in Research and Applications*, **14**, 215, Academic Press, New York, 1963. "EPR in Molecular Solids."
30. R. E. Robertson, *Determination of Organic Structures by Physical Methods*, **2**, 617, Academic Press, New York, 1962. "EPR of the Organometallics."
31. W. Low and E. L. Offenbacher, *Solid State Physics, Advances in Research and Applications*, **17**, 135, Academic Press, New York, 1965.
32. S. I. Weissman, *Ann. Rev. Phys. Chem.*, **12**, 151 (1961), "Nuclear And Electron Spin Resonance."
33. R. G. Shulman, *Ann. Rev. Phys. Chem.*, **13**, 325 (1962). "Electron And Nuclear Spin Resonance."
34. M. C. R. Symons, *Ann. Rept. Progr. Chem.*, **59**, 45 (1962).
35. D. H. Eargle, Jr., *Anal. Chem.*, **38**, 371R (1966).
36. W. Low, Ed., *Paramagnetic Resonance*, Vols. 1 and 2, Academic Press, New York, 1963.
37. Groupement Ampere, *Compte rendu du 9e Colloque*, Pisa, 1960.
38. Groupement Ampere, *Compte rendu du 10e Colloque*, Leipzig, 1961.
39. *Spectroscopy and Relaxation at Radiofrequencies*, Eindhoven, 1962, North-Holland Publ. Co., Amsterdam, 1962.

40. J. Smidt, Ed., *Magnetic and Electron Resonance and Relaxation*, North-Holland Publ. Co., Amsterdam, 1963; R. Servand and A. Charru, Eds., *Electronic Magnetic Relaxation and Solid Dielectrics*, North-Holland Publ. Co., Amsterdam, 1964.
41. *J. Phys. Soc. Japan*, **17**, Suppl. B-1 (1962).
42. *J. Appl. Phys.*, **33**, Suppl. 1 (1962).
43. *J. Phys. Chem.*, **71**, 109 (1967). "Symposium on Electron Spin Resonance Spectroscopy," E. Lansing, Michigan, August, 1966.
44. R. J. Faber, Ph.D. thesis, Michigan State University, 1957. "Paramagnetic Resonance of Some Adsorbed Transition Metal Ions."
45. D. N. Stamires, Ph.D. thesis, Princeton University, 1963. "Electron Spin Resonance Studies on Synthetic Crystalline Zeolites."
46. R. D. Feltham, Ph.D. thesis, University of California, Berkeley, UCRL **3867**, 1957. "Bonding and Spectra of Coordination Compounds."
47. J. E. Drumheller, Ph.D. thesis, University of Colorado, 1962. "Electron Spin Resonance of S State Ions in Barium Fluoride."
48. D. A. Jennings, Ph.D. thesis, University of Colorado, 1962. "NMR and EPR Studies of Manganese-Doped Lithium Chloride."
49. N. H. Perkins, Ph.D. thesis, Cornell University, 1965. "Electron Paramagnetic Resonance of Mn^{2+} Single Crystals of $\alpha-Zn_2SiO_4$."
50. A. Van Heuvelen, Ph.D. thesis, University of Colorado, 1964. "Electron Spin Resonance of Mn^{2+}, Eu^{2+}, and Gd^{3+} in Strontium Fluoride."
51. M. Daehler, Jr., Ph.D. thesis, University of Wisconsin, 1963. "Electron Spin Resonance of Mn^{2+} in AgCl."
52. J. S. Wells, Ph.D. thesis, University of Colorado, 1964. "Electron Magnetic Resonance of Manganese-Doped Lithium Fluoride and Lithium Chloride Polycrystalline Samples at Low Temperatures."
53. D. F. Wait, Ph.D. thesis, University of Michigan, 1963. "Hydrostatic Pressure Dependence of the EPR Spectrum of Mn^{2+} in Calcite."
54. W. H. Stewart, Jr., Ph.D. thesis, Clemson College, 1964. "An Electron Paramagnetic Resonance Study of the Diffusion of Manganese Ions in Single Crystal Sodium Chloride."
55. T.-T. Chang, Ph.D. thesis, University of Colorado, 1962. "The Nuclear Magnetic Resonance and the Electron Paramagnetic Resonance of LiF Doped with MnF_2."
56. H. D. Powell, Ph. D. thesis, Clemson University, 1965. "An Electron Paramagnetic Resonance Study of Crystalline Cuprous Chloride Containing Divalent Manganese."
57. H. H. Wickman, Ph.D. thesis, University of California, Berkeley, UCRL-**11538**, 1965. "Nuclear And Magnetic Resonance Studies In S- State Ions."
58. J. C. Garth, Ph.D. thesis, University of Illinois, 1965. "A Magnetic Resonance Study of Iron in Silver Chloride."
59. D. L. Carter, Ph.D. thesis, Columbia University, 1962. "Electron Paramagnetic Resonance and Maser Studies of Fe^{3+} in TiO_2 (Rutile)."
60. R. Neiman, Ph.D. thesis, University of California, Los Angeles, 1960.
61. R. F. Tucker, Jr., Ph.D. thesis, University of Illinois, 1958. "Paramagnetic Resonance Study of Copper-Doped Silver Chloride."
62. A. v. Zelewsky, Ph.D. thesis, Eidg. Technischen Hochschule, Zurich, 1964 (in German).
63. G. F. Kokoszka, Ph.D. thesis, University of Maryland, 1966. "Magnetic and Optical Spectra of Binuclear Copper Complexes."

64. A. V. Guzzo, Ph.D. thesis, Washington University, St. Louis, 1960. "Paramagnetic Resonance in the Hexafluorochromate (III) Ion."

65. R. K. Watts, Ph.D. thesis, Rice University, 1965. "Paramagnetic Relaxation in Very Dilute Cr^{3+}:Al_2O_3."

66. A. F. Clark, Ph.D. thesis, University of Michigan, 1964. "The Hydrostatic Pressure Effect on the EPR Spectra of Cr^{3+} and V^{2+} in Sapphire."

67. J. D. Keating, Ph.D. thesis, St. Louis University, 1962. "Electron Spin Resonance in Cr^{3+}-Doped Rutile."

68. B. B. Garrett, Ph.D. thesis, University of Texas, 1963. "Electron Spin Relaxation in Solvated Manganese(II) Ions."

69. C. C. Hinckley, Ph.D. thesis, University of Texas, 1964. "Electron Spin Resonance in Concentrated Manganese(II) Perchlorate Solutions."

70. A. Rannestad, Ph.D. thesis, Johns Hopkins University, 1963. "Paramagnetic Relaxation in Dilute Potassium Ferricyanide."

71. R. G. Hayes, Ph.D. thesis, University of California, Berkeley, UCRL 9873, 1961. "Electron Spin Resonance Line Widths of Transition Metal Ions and Complexes in Solution."

72. I. Chen, Ph.D. thesis, University of Michigan, 1964. "On the Theory of Super-hyperfine Interaction in Iron Group Ion Complexes."

73. R. H. Borcherts, Ph.D. thesis, University of Michigan, 1963. "An EPR Investigation of VO^{2+} and X-Ray Produced V^{2+} in Tutton Salt."

74. S. Karavelas, Ph.D. thesis, University of Michigan, 1964. "Molecular Orbital Theory of Vanadium in the Rutile Structure Crystals SnO_2, TiO_2, and GeO_2."

75. J. J. Fortman, Ph.D. thesis, University of Notre Dame, 1965. "An Electron Paramagnetic Resonance Study of Some Pentacyanonistrosyl Complexes."

76. P. T. Manoharan, Ph.D. thesis, Columbia University, 1965. "Electronic Structure of Metal Pentacyanonitrosyls."

77. A. Abragam and M. H. L. Pryce, Proc. Roy. Soc. (London), A205, 135 (1951). "Theory of the Nuclear Hyperfine Structure of Paramagnetic Resonance Spectra In Crystals."

78. J. Owen, Proc. Roy. Soc. (London), A227, 183 (1955). "The Colors and Magnetic Properties of Hydrated Iron Group Salts, and Evidence of Covalent Bonding."

79. T. Murao, Progr. Theoret. Phys. (Kyoto), 21, 657 (1959). "Effect of Covalency on the Spin-Orbit Coupling Constant of Transition Metal Ions."

80. H. Kon and N. E. Sharpless, J. Chem. Phys., 42, 906 (1965). "Study on the Quinquevalent Chromium Complex."

81. T. M. Dunn, Trans. Faraday Soc., 57, 1441 (1961). "Spin-Orbit Coupling in the First and Second Transition Series."

82. C. J. Ballhausen and H. B. Gray, Inorg. Chem., 1, 111 (1962). "Electronic Structure of the Vanadyl Ion."

83. B. R. McGarvey, J. Chem. Phys., 41, 3743 (1964). "Spin Hamiltonian For Cr(III) Complexes. Calculation from Crystal Field and Molecular Orbital Models and ESR Determination for Some Ethylenediammine Complexes."

84. K. DeArmond, B. B. Garrett, and H. S. Gutowsky, J. Chem. Phys., 42, 1019 (1965). "Paramagnetic Resonance Studies of Bonding in Vanadyl and Molybdenyl Metal Complexes."

85. B. B. Garrett, K. DeArmond, and H. S. Gutowsky, J. Chem. Phys., 44, 3393 (1966). "Paramagnetic Resonance Studies of Bonding in $[CrCl_5(H_2O)]^{2-}$."

86. W. Marshall and R. Stuart, Phys. Rev., 123, 2048 (1961). "Theory of Transition Ion Complexes."

87. P. W. Anderson, *Solid State Phys.*, **14**, 99 (1963). "Theory of Magnetic Exchange Interactions: Exchange in Insulators and Semiconductors."

88. R. G. Shulman and S. Sugano, *Phys. Rev.*, **130**, 506 (1963). "Covalency Effects in $KNiF_3$. I Nuclear Magnetic Resonance Studies."

89. R. Lacroix and G. Emch, *Helv. Phys. Acta*, **35**, 592 (1962). "Paramagnetic Covalency and Resonance."

90. N. L. Huang and E. Simanek, *J. Chem. Phys.*, **44**, 2524 (1966). "Covalency Parameters and the g Factor for $Ni^{2+}:KMgF_3$."

91. A. A. Misetich and T. Buch, *J. Chem. Phys.*, **41**, 2524 (1964). "Gyromagnetic Factors and Spin–Orbit Coupling in Ligand Field Theory."

92. A. Abragam, J. Horowitz, M. H. L. Pryce, and K. W. Morton, *Proc. Roy. Soc. (London).*, **A230**, 169 (1955). "The Hyperfine Structure of Paramagnetic Resonance. The s-Electron Effect."

93. J. S. Van Wieringen, *Discussions Faraday Soc.*, **19**, 118 (1955). "Paramagnetic Resonance of Bivalent Manganese Incorporated in Various Lattices."

94. A. J. Freeman and R. E. Watson, *Phys. Rev.*, **123**, 2027 (1961). "Origin of Effective Fields in Magnetic Materials."

95. J. H. Wood and G. W. Pratt, Jr., *Phys. Rev.*, **107**, 995 (1957). "Wave Functions and Energy Levels for Fe As Found by the Unrestricted Hartree-Fock Method."

96. V. Heine, *Phys. Rev.*, **107**, 1002 (1957). "Hyperfine Structure of Paramagnetic Ions."

97. O. Matamura, *J. Phys. Soc. Japan*, **14**, 108 (1959). "ESR of Manganese-Activated Phosphors."

98. R. S. Title, *Phys. Rev.*, **131**, 623 (1963). "Electron Paramagnetic Resonance Spectra of Cr^+, Mn^{2+}, and Fe^{3+} in Cubic ZnS."

99. B. R. McGarvey, *J. Phys. Chem.*, **71**, 51 (1967). "The Isotropic Hyperfine Interaction."

100. E. König, *Z. Naturforsch*, **19A**, 1139 (1964). "Untersuchungen der Paramagnetisden Elektronenresonanz an tris-2.2′-Dipyridyl-Komplexen der Konfiguration d^5 des Zentralions."

101. W. J. Childs, L. S. Goodman, and D. von Ehrenstein, *Phys. Rev.*, **132**, 2128 (1963). "Magnetic Hyperfine Interaction Of ^{53}Cr."

102. B. Budick, R. J. Goshen, S. Jacobs, and S. Marcus, *Phys. Rev.*, **144**, 103 (1966). "Core Polarization in ^{53}Cr."

103. A. Davison, N. Edelstein, R. H. Holm, and A. H. Maki, *J. Am. Chem. Soc.*, **86**, 2799 (1964). "Synthetic and Electron Spin Resonance Studies of Six-Cordinate Complexes Related by Electron-Transfer Reactions."

104. R. E. Robertson and H. M. McConnell, *J. Phys. Chem.*, **64**, 70 (1960). "The Magnetic Resonance Properties of Some Sandwich Compounds."

105. A. Mukherji and T. P. Das, *Phys. Rev.*, **111**, 1479 (1958). "^{19}F Hyperfine Interaction in the Paramagnetic Resonance Spectrum of Mn^{2+} Ions in ZnF_2."

106. A. J. Freeman and R. E. Watson, *Bull. Am. Phys. Soc.*, **6**, 234 (1961).

107. R. E. Watson and A. J. Freeman, *Phys. Rev.*, **134A**, 1526 (1964). "Covalency in Crystal Field Theory: $KNiF_3$."

108. E. Simanek and Z. Sroubek, *Physica Status Solidi*, **4**, 251 (1964). "Theory of the d-Electron Covalency in Ionic Crystals."

109. D. E. Ellis, *MIT Quart. Progr. Rept.*, **55** 58 (1965). "Solid-State and Molecular Theory Group."

110. S. Sugano and Y. Tanabe, *J. Phys. Soc. Japan*, **20**, 1155 (1965). "Covalency in Ionic Crystals: $KNiF_3$."

111. J. Hubbard, D. E. Rimmer, and F. R. A. Hopgood, *Proc. Phys. Soc.*, **88**, 13 (1966). "Weak Covalency in Transition Metal Salts."

112. R. N. Rogers, Ph.D. thesis, Stanford University, 1962. "Influence of Relaxation on Line Shapes in Paramagnetic Resonance."

113. R. N. Rogers and G. E. Pake, *J. Chem. Phys.*, **33**, 1107 (1960). "Paramagnetic Relaxation in Solutions of VO^{2+}."

114. D. Kivelson and G. Collins, "Electron Spin Resonance Line Widths in Liquids," *Paramagnetic Resonance*, Vol. 2, Academic Press, New York, 1962, p. 496.

115. R. Wilson and D. Kivelson, *J. Chem. Phys.*, **44**, 154 (1966). "Electron Spin Resonance Line Widths in Solution, I. Experiments on Anisotropic and Spin–Rotational Effects."

116. P. W. Atkins and D. Kivelson, *J. Chem. Phys.*, **44**, 169 (1966). "Electron Spin Resonance Line Widths in Solution, II. Analysis Of Spin–Rotational Relaxation Data."

117. R. Wilson and D. Kivelson, *J. Chem. Phys.*, **44**, 4440 (1966). "Electron Spin Resonance Line Widths in Solutions, III. Experimental Study of the Solvent Dependence of Anisotropic and Spin-Rotational Effects."

118. R. H. Borcherts and C. Kikuchi, *J. Chem. Phys.*, **40**, 2270 (1964). "VO^{2+} And X-Ray-Produced V^{2+} in Tutton Salt."

119. D. Kivelson and S. K. Lee, *J. Chem. Phys.*, **41**, 1896 (1964). "Electron Spin Resonance Studies and the Electronic Structure of Vanadyl Ion Complexes."

120. H. A. Kuska and M. T. Rogers, *Inorg. Chem.*, **5**, 313 (1966). "Assignment of Optical Spectra for Vanadyl Complexes."

121. H. Kon and N. E. Sharpless, *J. Phys. Chem.*, **70**, 105 (1966). "Electron Spin Resonance Study of Some Halomolybdenyl, -Tungstenyl, and Vanadyl Complexes in Solution."

122. H. A. Kuska and M. T. Rogers (unpublished).

123. N. S. Garif'yanov and S. E. Kamenev, *Soviet Phys., JETP, English Transl.*, **19**, 340 (1964). "Hyperfine Structure of the EPR Lines of the ^{50}V and ^{51}V Isotopes." Translated from *Zh. Eksperim. i Teor. Fiz.*, **46**, 501 (1964).

124. J. M. Assour, *J. Chem. Phys.*, **43**, 2477 (1965). "Electron Spin Resonance of Tetraphenylporphine Chelates."

125. D. E. O'Reilly, *J. Chem. Phys.*, **29**, 1188 (1958). "Paramagnetic Resonance Of Vanadyl Etioporphyrin I. Erratum: *J. Chem. Phys.*, **30**, 591 (1959)."

126. I. Siegel, *Phys. Rev.*, **134**, A193 (1964). "Paramagnetic Resonance of Vanadium in Amorphous and Polycrystalline GeO_2."

127. E. M. Roberts, W. S. Koski, and W. S. Caughey, *J. Chem. Phys.*, **34**, 591 (1961). "Electron Spin Resonance of Some Vanadyl Porphyrins."

128. R. M. Golding, *Mol. Phys.*, **5**, 369 (1962). "An ESR Study of a Diluted Single Crystal of Potassium Vanadyl Oxalate."

129. R. M. Golding, *Trans. Faraday Soc.*, **59**, 1513 (1963). "Anisotropic Broadening of the Hyperfine Lines in the ESR Spectrum of the Vanadyl Ion."

130. R. J. Faber and M. T. Rogers, *J. Am. Chem. Soc.*, **81**, 1849 (1959). "Paramagnetic Resonance Spectra of Adsorbed Manganese(II), Copper(II), and Oxovanadium(IV)."

131. N. M. Atherton, J. Locke, and J. A. McCleverty, *Chem. Ind. (London)*, **1965**, 1300. "A New Vanadyl Sulfur Compound."

132. H. C. Mishra and M. C. R. Symons, *J. Chem. Soc.*, **1963**, 4490. "Structure and Reactivity of the Oxyanions of Transition Metals. Part XVI. Paramagnetic Ions of Vanadium, Chromium, and Manganese in Sulfuric Acid and Oleum."

133. K. Wuethrich, *Helv. Chim. Acta*, **48**, 779 (1965). "ESR Measurements of VO^{2+} Complexes in Aqueous Solutions."

134. F. A. Walker, R. L. Carlin, and P. H. Rieger, *J. Chem. Phys.*, **45**, 4181 (1966) "ESR Studies of Coordination to the Sixth Position of Vanadyl Acetylacetonate."

135. I. Bernal and P. H. Rieger, *Inorg. Chem.*, **2**, 256 (1963). "Solvent Effects on the Optical and ESR Spectra of Vanadyl Acetylacetonate."

136. K. Wuethrich, *Helv. Chim. Acta*, **48**, 1012 (1965). "ESR Investigation of VO^{2+} Complex Compounds in Aqueous Solution."

137. J. M. Assour, J. Goldmacher, and S. E. Harrison, *J. Chem. Phys.*, **43**, 159 (1965). "The ESR of Vanadyl Phthalocyanine."

138. A. A. Misetich and R. E. Watson, *Phys. Rev.*, **143**, 335 (1966). "Gyromagnetic Factors and Covalency in Iron-Series Complexes."

139. N. S. Garif'yanov and B. M. Kozyrev, *Teor. i Eksperim. Khim., Akad. Nauk SSR*, **1**, 525 (1965). "The EPR Study of Some Organic Complexes of Vanadium (IV)."

140. L. V. Bershov and A. S. Marfunin, *Izv. Akad. Nauk SSR, Ser. Geol.*, **30**, 42 (1965). "Vanadyl Ion in Minerals and EPR of Initial Elements."

141. I. P. Lipatova, *Dokl. Akad. Nauk SSSR*, **164**, 849 (1965). "Vanadyl Chloride Solutions in Organic Solvents Investigated by Means of Infrared Absorption Spectra and ESR Spectra."

142. N. S. Garif'yanov and N. F. Usacheva, *Zh. Fiz. Khim.*, **38**, 1367 (1964). "Hyperfine Structure of Lines of EPR Spectra of Supercooled Solutions of VO^{2+} and Cu^{2+}."

143. W. Snipes and W. Gordy, *J. Chem. Phys.*, **41**, 3661 (1964). "EPR of Vanadyl Ions Trapped in RNA and DNA."

144. J. P. Meehan, *U.S. At. Energy Comm.*, TID-21946 (1965). "Crystal Field Effects in Zirconium Oxide."

145. Y.-C. Hsu and H.-M. Tseng, *K'o Hsueh T'ung Pao*, **1964**, 522. "EPR Spectra of Complex Bis(8-hydroxyquinoline) Polymers."

146. K.-C. Hsu, S.-M. Ch'en, C. Pi, and Y.-C. T'ang, *K'o Hsueh T'ung Pao*, **1964**, 157. "ESR Spectra of V_2O_5 Catalyst Systems."

147. B. Nador, *Acta Chim. Acad. Sci. Hung.*, **40**, 1, (1964). "ESR Investigations in the System Vanadium Pentoxide–Phosphorus Pentoxide."

148. C. Nicolau and E. Angelescu, *Rev. Roumaine Chim.*, **10**, 27 (1965). "EPR Studies of Some Organometallic Catalysts."

149. K. Tarama, S. Teranishi, S. Yoshida, N. Tamura, and S. Ishida, *Kogyo Kagaku Zasshi*, **68**, 1499 (1965). "ESR Absorption Study on Vanadium Oxide Catalysts."

150. A. I. Rivkind and L. P. Kuznetsova, *Dokl. Akad. Nauk. SSSR*, **164**, 860 (1965). "Destruction of the Hydration Shells of the Vanadyl Ions under the Action of the Electrostatic Field of Diamagnetic Ions. Investigation by Means of ESR Spectra."

151. G. P. Vishnevskaya, *Zh. Strukt. Khim.*, **5**, 779 (1964). "Effect of the Solvent on the Time for Electron Paramagnetic Relaxation of Vanadyl Ions in Liquids."

152. N. S. Garif'yanov, B. M. Kozyrev, R. Kh. Timerov, and N. F. Usacheva, *Zh. Eksperim. i Teor. Fiz.*, **42**, 1145 (1962). "EPR in Dilute Vanadyl [di]Chloride Solutions."

153. N. S. Garif'yanov, B. M. Kozyrev, R. Kh. Timerov, and N. F. Usacheva, *Zh. Eksperim. i Teor. Fiz.*, **41**, 1076 (1961). "EPR in Concentrated Aqueous Solutions of VO^{2+}."

154. G. P. Vishnevskaya and P. G. Tishkov, *Dokl. Akad. Nauk. SSSR*, **154**, 1149 (1964). "Paramagnetic Relaxation in Vanadyl Salt Solutions."

155. A. I. Rivkind, *Dokl. Akad. Nauk SSSR*, **145**, 1075 (1962). "Effect of Acidity on the Exchange Interaction of Electron Spins in Vanadyl Salt Solutions."

156. G. P. Vishnevskaya, B. M. Kozyrev, and P. G. Tishkov, *Dokl. Akad. Nauk SSSR*, **152**, 644 (1963). "Paramagnetic Relaxation in Concentrated Aqueous Solutions of VO^{2+}."

157. K.-C. Hsu and Y.-C. T'ang, *K'o Hsueh T'ung Pao*, **1963**, 53. "Study of EPR on the V_2O_5 Catalyst System."

158. W. A. Anderson and L. H. Piette, *J. Chem. Phys.*, **30**, 591 (1959). "Forbidden $\Delta m_s = \pm 1, \Delta m_I = \mp 1$ Transitions in a Vanadyl Chelate."

159. J. C. W. Chien and C. R. Boss, *J. Am. Chem. Soc.*, **83**, 3767 (1961). "ESR of Some Vanadium and Titanium Compounds."

160. G. F. Kokoszka, H. C. Allen, Jr., and G. Gordon, *Inorg. Chem.*, **5**, 91 (1966). "The EPR Spectrum of Tetrakis-*tert*-butoxyvanadium(IV)."

161. C. K. Kikuchi, I. Chen, W. H. From, and P. B. Dorain, *J. Chem. Phys.*, **42**, 181 (1965). "Spin Resonance of SnO_2: V and the Vanadium $3d$ Electron Orbital."

162. H. J. Gerritsen and H. R. Lewis, *Phys. Rev.*, **119**, 1010 (1960). "EPR of V^{4+} in TiO_2."

163. J. Lambe and C. Kikuchi, *Phys. Rev.*, **118**, 71 (1960). "EPR of V^{2+}, V^{3+}, V^{4+} in α-Al_2O_3."

164. E. Yamaka and R. G. Barnes, *Phys. Rev.*, **135**, A114 (1964). "Paramagnetic Resonance of Iron Group Elements in Rutile (TiO_2). I. The ^{47}Ti and ^{49}Ti Hfs Interaction."

165. S. V. Shulyndin, N. N. Tikhomirova, A. E. Shilov, and A. K. Shilova, *Zh. Strukt. Khim.*, **2**, 740 (1961). "EPR Spectra of Complexes of VCl_4 with Organo-aluminium Compounds."

166. E. Angelescu, C. Nicolau, and Z. Simon, *J. Am. Chem. Soc.*, **88**, 3910 (1966). "ESR Investigations of Some Soluble Organometallic Catalysts."

167. G. Natta, A. Zambelli, G. Lanzi, I. Pasquon, E. R. Mognaschi, A. L. Segre, and P. Centola, *Makromol. Chem.*, **81**, 161 (1965). "Polymerization of Propylene to Syndiotactic Polymer. Part I: Valence of Active Vanadium in the Catalytic Systems."

168. I. Chen, C. Kikuchi, and H. Watanabe, *J. Chem. Phys.*, **42**, 186 (1965). "Mechanism of Superhyperfine Structure in SnO_2: V^{4+}."

169. V. M. Nagiev, *Fiz. Tverd. Tela*, **7**, 2726 (1965). "EPR Study of Vanadium Phosphate Glasses."

170. G. M. Zverev, *Zh. Eksperim. i Teor. Fiz.*, **44**, 1859 (1963). "Temperature Dependence of Spin–Lattice Relaxation of the V^{4+} Ion in TiO_2."

171. D. K. Ray, *Fiz. Tverd. Tela*, **3**, 2535 (1961). "ESR Spectrum of V^{4+} Ion in Rutile (TiO_2)."

172. G. M. Zverev and A. M. Prokhorov, *Zh. Eksperim. i Teor. Fiz.*, **39**, 222 (1960). "EPR of Vanadium in Rutile (TiO_2)."

173. V. A. Ioffe and I. B. Patrina, *Fiz. Tverd. Tela*, **6**, 3045 (1964). "EPR in V_2O_5 Single Crystals."

174. D. K. Ray, *Nuovo Cimento*, **21**, 1 (1961). "Second-Order Effect of Spin–Orbit Interaction on the Paramagnetic Resonance Spectra of Ions with a Single $3d$ Electron."

175. A. Nicula, I. Ursu, and Gh. Cristea, *Studia Univ. Babes-Bolyai Ser. Math-Phys.*, **1**, 109 (1966). "ESR of V^{4+} Ion in Zeolites of X and Y Type."

176. J. L. Ragle, *J. Chem. Phys.*, **38**, 2020 (1963). "ESR Study of Partially Reduced Vanadium Pentoxide."

177. K. Hirota, Y. Kageyama, and K. Kuwata, *Bull. Chem. Soc. Japan*, **36**, 875 (1963). "Paramagnetic Chemical Species of Triphenylmethane and Diphenylamine Formed on the Surface of Several Oxides."

178. E. Boesman and E. Gillis, *Phys. Status Solidi*, **14**, 349 (1966). "EPR Studies of V_2O_5 Single Crystals. II. Defect Centers in Molybdenum-Doped Vanadium Pentoxide."

179. E. Gillis and E. Boesman, *Phys. Status Solidi*, **14**, 337 (1966). "EPR Studies of V_2O_5 Single Crystals. I. Defect Centers in Pure, Nonstoichiometric Vanadium Pentoxide."

180. P. H. Kasai, *Phys. Letters*, **7**, 5 (1963). "g Tensor of a $3d$ Electron in a Rutile Structure."

181. J. H. Waters, R. Williams, H. B. Gray, G. N. Schrauzer, and H. W. Finck, *J. Am. Chem. Soc.*, **86**, 4198 (1964). "Tris(*cis*-1,2-stilbenedithiolato) vanadium-(VI) or Tris(dithiobenzil vanadium(0). A Novel Vanadium Complex." (As can be seen from the title the actual valence state is open to question. This reference is included here primarily for bookkeeping reasons.)

182. H. M. Gladney and J. D. Swalen, *J. Chem. Phys.*, **42**, 1999 (1965). "Theory of EPR Of Ti^{3+} in Trigonal Environments."

183. E. L. Waters and A. H. Maki, *Phys. Rev.*, **125**, 233 (1962). "^{47}Ti and ^{49}Ti Hyperfine Structure in the ESR of Titanium(III) Complexes."

184. S. Fujiwara, K. Nagashima, and M. Codell, *Bull. Chem. Soc. Japan*, **37**, 773 (1964). "Mixed Chelate Compounds of Ti(III) As Studied by EPR and Spectrophotometry."

185. B. R. McGarvey, *J. Chem. Phys.*, **38**, 388 (1963). "ESR of Titanium(III) Acetylacetonate."

186. S. Fujiwara and M. Codell, *Bull. Chem. Soc. Japan*, **37**, 49 (1964). "EPR Studies of Titanium(III) Ions with Complexing Compounds."

187. V. I. Avvakumov, N. S. Garif'yanov, and E. I. Semenova, *Zh. Eksperim. i Teor. Fiz.*, **39**, 1215 (1960). "EPR and Paramagnetic Relaxation in Liquid and Supercooled Ti^{3+} Salt Solutions."

188. V. I. Avvakumov, N. S. Garif'yanov, S. G. Salikhov, and E. I. Semenova, *Fiz. Tverdogo Tela*, **3**, 2111 (1961). "Paramagnetic Resonance in $TiCl_3 \cdot 6H_2O$ And $Ti_2(SO_4)_3 \cdot 4H_2O$."

189. L. S. Kornienko and A. M. Prokhorov, *Paramagnetic Resonance, Proc. Intern. Conf., 1st, Jerusalem, 1962*, **1**, 126. "ESR and Spin-lattice Relaxation of Ti^{3+} in Corundum (Al_2O_3)."

190. E. Y. Wong, *J. Chem. Phys.*, **32**, 598 (1960). "Paramagnetic Resonance of Ti^{3+}, Cr^{3+}, and Fe^{3+} In $AlCl_3 \cdot 6H_2O$."

191. P. F. Chester, *J. Appl. Phys.*, **32**, Suppl., 2233 (1961). "ESR in Semiconducting Rutile (TiO_2)."

192. H. J. Gerritsen, *Paramagnetic Resonance, Proc. Intern. Conf., 1st, Jerusalem, 1962*, **1**, 3. "Paramagnetic Resonance of Transition Metal Ions in Rutile (TiO_2)."

193. N. S. Garif'yanov and E. I. Semenova, *Zh. Eksperim. i Teor. Fiz.*, **41**, 337 (1961). "Hyperfine Structure of the EPR Line in Supercooled Solutions of Ti^{3+} Salts."

194. S. P. Burley, *Australian J. Phys.*, **17**, 543 (1964). "Paramagnetic Resonance of Cu^{2+} and Ti^{3+} Ions in Borax Beads."

195. V. I. Avvakumov, N. S. Garif'yanov, and E. I. Semenova, *Fiz. Metal. i Metalloved., Akad. Nauk SSSR*, **12**, 624 (1961). "EPR in Halide Compounds of Trivalent Titanium."

196. H. J. M. Bartelink, H. Bos, J. Smidt, C. H. Vrinssen, and E. H. Adema, *Rec. Trav. Chim.*, **81**, 225 (1962). "EPR Studies on Ziegler Catalyst Systems. III. Some Mixtures of Al–Me Compounds and $AlCl_3$ with Dicyclopentadienyltitanium Dichloride and Dicyclopentadienylmethylchlorotitanium."

197. G. P. Vishnevskaya and B. M. Kozyrev, *Zh. Strukt. Khim.*, **6**, 667 (1965). "Paramagnetic Relaxation in Cr, Ti, and Cu Salt Solutions."

198. E. H. Adema, H. J. M. Bartelink, and J. Smidt, *Rec. Trav. Chim.*, **81**, 73 (1962). "ESR Studies on Ziegler Catalyst Systems. II. Titanium Tetrachloride-Aluminumethyl Dichloride."

199. H. J. M. Bartelink, H. Bos, W. van Raayen, and J. Smidt, *Arch. Sci. (Geneva)*, **14**, 158 (1961). "Electron and Proton Resonance Measurements on the Systems $Ti(C_5H_5)_2Cl$-$(Al(CH_3)_2Cl)_2$ and $Ti(C_5H_5)_2CH_3Cl$-$(Al(CH_3)Cl_2)_2$· at Room Temperature."

200. H. Nöth, J. Voitländer, and M. Nussbaum, *Naturwissenschaften*, **47**, 57 (1960). "Electron-Resonance Experiments on Organometallic Complexes."

201. H. K. Ostendorf, *Phys. Letters*, **13**, 295 (1964). "Relaxation of the EPR Absorption of the Titanium(III) Complex of Ethylenediaminetetraacetic Acid."

202. T.-W. Ch'iu, Y.-F. Chu, H.-M. T'ang, F.-C. Hsiung, and H.-Y. Kung, *Wu Li Hsueh Pao*, **17**, 600 (1961). "The ESR Spectra of π-$(C_5H_5)_2TiCl_2$·AlR_3 Soluble Catalyst System."

203. N. S. Garif'yanov, E. I. Semenova, and N. F. Usacheva, *Zh. Strukt. Khim.*, **3**, 596 (1962). "The Hyperfine Structure of ESR Lines In Ti^{3+} Solutions."

204. Sh. Sh. Bashkirov, *Paramagnitn. Rezonans, Kazansk. Univ., Sbornik*, **1960**, 54. "Theory of Paramagnetic Spin-Lattice Relaxation Owing to Two-Phonon Processes."

205. S. A. Al'tshuler and M. M. Zaripov, *Zh. Eksperim. i Teor. Fiz.*, **40**, 377 (1961). "Theory of the Paramagnetic Resonance of Titanium and Cobalt Ions in Corundum."

206. N. S. Garif'yanov, A. V. Danilova, and R. R. Shagidullin, *Opt. i Spektroskopiya*, **13**, 212 (1962). "EPR and the Visible Absorption Spectra of Alcoholic and Glycerol Solutions of Ti^{3+}."

207. A. Carrington and G. R. Luckhurst, *Mol. Phys.*, **8**, 117 (1964). "ESR Line Width of Transition Metal Ions in Solution. Relaxation through Zero-Field Splitting."

208. S. A. Al'tshuler, Sh. Sh. Bashkirov, and M. M. Zaripov, *Fiz. Tverd. Tela*, **4**, 3367 (1962). "Paramagnetic Resonance and Spin-Lattice Relaxation of Ti^{3+} in Corundum (Al_2O_3)."

209. V. M. Mastikhin, L. M. Kefeli, and N. P. Keier, *Kinetika i Kataliz*, **6**, 180 (1965). "EPR Spectra of Rutile (TiO_2) on Adsorption of Oxygen."

210. M. P. Votinov and N. I. Demidenko, *Fiz. Tverd. Tela*, **4**, 3277 (1962). "Temperature Variation of the Width of the EPR Spectrum in Ti—O_x System $(x = 1.5 - 2.0)$."

211. E. H. Adema, H. J. M. Bartelink, and J. Smidt, *Rec. Trav. Chim.*, **80**, 173 (1961). "ESR Studies on Ziegler Catalyst Systems. I. System Titanium Tetrachloride-Aluminum Diethyl Chloride."

212. V. Antuf'ev, Ya. V. Vasil'ev, M. P. Votinov, O. K. Kharitonova, and E. V. Kharitonov, *Fiz. Tverd. Tela*, **4**, 1496 (1962). "EPR in Titanium–Oxygen System."

213. L. L. van Reijen, P. Cossee, and H. J. van Haren, *J. Chem. Phys.*, **38**, 572 (1963). "Coordination and Spin-Lattice Relaxation of Cr^{5+}."

214. D. G. Howard and R. H. Lindquist, *J. Chem. Phys.*, **37**, 573 (1963). "ESR of Chromia on Alumina."

215. V. B. Kazanskii and Yu. I. Pecherskaya, *Kinetika i Kataliz*, **2**, 454 (1961). "Investigation of Aluminum–Chromium Catalysts by the Method of EPR."

216. C. P. Poole, Jr., and J. F. Itzel, Jr., *J. Chem. Phys.*, **41**, 287 (1964). "ESR Study of the Antiferromagnetism of Chromia Alumina."

217. C. S. Nicolau and H. G. Thom, *Actes Congr. Intern. Catalyse, 2e, Paris, 1960*, **2**, 1923. "ESR of Metal–Oxide Catalysts."

218. S. Benbenek, S. Malinowski, and S. Kosek, *Przemysl Chem.*, **43**, 317 (1964). "Study on Cr Oxide Catalysts by EPR Method. II."

219. A. Matsumoto, H. Tanaka, and N. Goto, *Bull. Chem. Soc. Japan*, **38**, 1857 (1965). "EPR Absorption of Cr Ions Dispersed on SiO_2–Al_2O_3. II. Variation in the Spectrum under Several Chemical Treatments."

220. J. Deren, J. Haber, and S. Kosek, *Bull. Acad. Polon Sci., Ser. Sci. Chim.*, **13**, 21 (1965). "The EPR of Chromium Ions in CrO_3–Al_2O_3 Catalysts."

221. D. E. O'Reilly and D. S. MacIver, *J. Phys. Chem.*, **6**, 276 (1962). "EPR Absorption of Chromia–Alumina Catalysts."

222. P. B. Ayscough, C. Eden, and H. Steiner, *J. Catalysis*, **4**, 278 (1965). "Polymerization of Ethylene over Supported Chromium Oxide Catalysts."

223. N. S. Garif'yanov, *Dokl. Akad. Nauk SSSR*, **155**, 385 (1964). "Study of Some Quinquevalent Chromium Complexes by the EPR Method."

224. J. D. Swalen and J. A. Ibers, *J. Chem. Phys.*, **37**, 17 (1962). "Chemical Bonding in the Perchromate Ion."

225. B. R. McGarvey, *J. Chem. Phys.*, **37**, 2001 (1962). "ESR and Optical Spectrum of Potassium Perchromate."

226. H. Kon, *J. Inorg. Nucl. Chem.*, **25**, 933 (1963). "Study of the Quinquevalent Chromium Compounds by ESR and Optical Spectra."

227. N. S. Garif'yanov, *Fiz. Tverd. Tela*, **4**, 2450 (1962). "EPR of Cr^{5+} in Glasses."

228. V. S. Korol'kov and A. K. Potapovich, *Opt. i Spektroskopiya*, **16**, 461 (1964). "Analysis of the Shape of the EPR Signals Containing Randomly Arranged Paramagnetic Centers."

229. V. K. Zakharov and D. M. Yudin, *Fiz. Tverd. Tela*, **7**, 1571 (1965). "EPR Study of Glasses Containing Chromium."

230. R. W. Kedzie, J. R. Shane, and M. Kestigian, *Phys. Letters*, **11**, 286 (1964). "EPR Observation of Saturation Effects Due to T_1-Limited Spin Packet Line Widths in $CaWO_4$:Cr^{5+}."

231. N. S. Garif'yanov and N. F. Usacheva, *Dokl. Akad. Nauk SSSR*, **145**, 565 (1962). "EPR in Cr^{5+} Solutions."

232. H. Kon, *Bull. Chem. Soc. Japan*, **35**, 2054 (1962). "ESR Study of Quinquevalent Cr Complexes."

233. E. O. Schulz-Du Bois, *Bell System Tech. J.*, **38**, 271 (1959). "Paramagnetic Spectra of Substituted Sapphires—Part I: Ruby."

234. R. H. Hoskins and B. H. Soffer, *Phys. Rev.*, **133**, 490 (1964). "Observation of Cr^{4+} in α–Al_2O_3."

235. D. K. Ray, *Nuovo Cimento*, **20**, 1148 (1961). "EPR Spectra of V^{3+} in Corundum (Al_2O_3)."

236. F. S. Ham and G. W. Ludwig, *Paramagnetic Resonance, Proc. Intern. Conf., 1st, Jerusalem, 1962*, **1**, 130. "Paramagnetic Properties of Iron Group Ions in Tetrahedral Coordination."

237. A. Carrington, D. J. E. Ingram, K. A. K. Lott, D. S. Schonland, and M. C. R. Symons, *Proc. Roy. Soc. (London)*, **A254**, 101 (1960). "EPR Studies of Transition Metal Oxyions. I. Experimental Results for the Manganate, Hypomanganate, and Ferrate Ions."

238. G. M. Zverev and A. M. Prokhorov, *Zh. Eksperim. i Teor. Fiz.*, **38**, 449 (1960). "Spectrum of the EPR of V^{3+} in Corundum (Al_2O_3)."

239. K. Okumura, *J. Phys. Soc. Japan*, **17**, 1341 (1962). "Paramagnetic Resonance of Diluted $[Cr(NH_3)_6]Cl_3$."

240. G. Burns, *J. Appl. Phys.*, **32**, 2048 (1961). "ESR in Powders."

241. G. F. Dionne, *Can. J. Phys.*, **42**, 2419 (1964). "EPR Experiments with Ti^{3+} Ions in $RbAl(SO_4)_2 \cdot 12H_2O$."

242. H. J. M. Bartelink, H. Bos, W. van Raayen, and J. Smidt, *Arch. Sci. (Geneva)*, **14**, 197 (1961). "Electron and Proton Resonance Measurements on the Systems $Ti(C_5H_5)_2Cl_2-(Al(CH_3)_2Cl)_2$ and $Ti(C_5H_5)_2CH_3Cl-(Al(CH_3)Cl_2)_2$ at Room Temperature."

243. P. E. M. Allen, J. K. Brown, and R. M. S. Obaid, *Trans. Faraday Soc.*, **59**, 1808 (1963). "ESR Studies of Some Complexes Derived from Dicyclopentadienyltitanium Dichloride and Trialkyl Aluminum."

244. W. C. Holton, J. Schneider, and T. L. Estle, *Phys. Rev.*, **133**, 1638 (1964). "EPR of Photosensitive Iron Transition Group Impurities in ZnS and ZnO."

245. M. Sauzade, J. Pontnau, P. Lesas, and D. Silhoutte, *Phys. Letters*, **19**, 617 (1966). "Paramagnetic Resonance of V^{3+} in Al_2O_3 with Millimeter Waves and Strong Fields."

246. G. M. Zverev and A. M. Prokhorov, *Zh. Eksperim. i Teor. Fiz.*, **40**, 1016 (1961). "The EPR of the V^{3+} Ion in Corundum (Al_2O_3)."

247. M. Codell, S. Fujiwara, K. Nagashima, and T. Seki, *Bull. Chem. Soc. Japan*, **38**, 21 (1965). "EPR and Spectrophotometric Study of Ti(III)–Chelate Compounds with Nitrilo Tricarboxylic Acid and Its Derivatives."

248. D. K. Ray, *Fiz. Tverd. Tela*, **3**, 2214 (1961). "Analysis of the Spectrum of EPR of V^{3+} Ion in Corundum (Al_2O_3)."

249. K. A. Valiev, *Fiz. Metal. i Metalloved., Akad. Nauk SSSR*, **6**, 776 (1958). "Magnetic Resonance in Ionic Crystals of Nuclei of Atoms of Elements of the Iron Group."

250. Gh. Cristea, *Studia Univ. Babes—Bolyai Ser. Math. Phys.*, **2**, 117 (1964). "ESR Spectrum of the V^{3+} Ion in Corundum (Al_2O_3).

251. D. P. Seed, *Phil. Mag.*, **7**, 1371 (1962). "An Evaluation of the Trigonal Field Parameter for Vanadium Corundum."

252. J. Schneider and A. Raeuber, *Phys. Letters*, **21**, 380 (1966). "ESR of Ti^{2+} in ZnS."

253. S. A. Al'tshuler and V. N. Yastrebov, *Zh. Eksperim. i Teor. Fiz.*, **47**, 382 (1964). "Electron Nuclear Paramagnetic Resonance on V^{3+} Ions in Corundum (Al_2O_3)."

254. W. H. From, *Phys. Rev.*, **131**, 961 (1963). "EPR of Cr^{3+} in SnO_2."

255. N. Laurance and J. Lambe, *Phys. Rev.*, **132**, 1029 (1963). "Quadrupole Interactions of Vanadium and Manganese in Corundum (Al_2O_3)."

256. D. E. O'Reilly and G. E. Schacher, *J. Chem. Phys.*, **43**, 4222 (1965). "Paramagnetic Resonance of Vanadium(II) in Ferroelectric Potassium Ferrocyanide."

257. G. Kuwabara, *Phys. Rev.*, **138**, A99 (1965). "ESR and Optical Spectra of V^{2+} in NaCl."

258. P. Auzins, J. W. Orton, and J. E. Wertz, *Paramagnetic Resonance, Proc. Intern. Conf., 1st, Jerusalem, 1962*, **1**, 90. "ESR Studies of Impurities in Groups II–VI Compounds."

259. B. R. McGarvey, *J. Chem. Phys.*, **40**, 809 (1964). "Anisotropic Hyperfine Interaction of ^{53}Cr in Chromium(III) Acetylacetonate."

260. D. R. Hutton and G. J. Troup, *Brit. J. Appl. Phys.*, **15**, 275 (1964). "Paramagnetic Resonance of Cr^{3+} in Kyanite."

261. D. Kiro, W. Low, and A. Zusman, *Paramagnetic Resonance, Proc. Intern. Conf., 1st, Jerusalem, 1962*, **1**, 44. "EPR Spectra of Cr^{3+} and Gd^{3+} in Lanthanum Aluminate."

262. J. S. van Wieringen and J. G. Rensen, *Paramagnetic Resonance, Proc. Intern. Conf., 1st, Jerusalem, 1962*, **1**, 105. "Influence of Lattice Imperfections on the Paramagnetic Resonance of V^{2+} and Cr^{3+} in MgO."

263. S. K. Kurtz and W. G. Nilson, *Phys. Rev.*, **128**, 1586 (1962). "Paramagnetic Resonance Spectra of Cr^{3+} in $ZnWO_4$."

264. V. A. Atsarkin, *Zh. Eksperim. i Teor. Fiz.*, **43**, 839 (1962). "Paramagnetic Resonance of the Cr^{3+} Ion in Spinel ($MgAl_2O_4$)."

265. J. W. Carson, D. P. Devor, and R. H. Hoskins, *Phys. Rev.*, **122**, 1141 (1961). "Paramagnetic Resonance of Cr^{3+} in Yttrium Oxide."

266. R. Stahl-Brada and W. Low, *Phys. Rev.*, **116**, 561 (1959). "Paramagnetic Resonance Spectra of Chromium and Manganese in the Spinel Structure".

267. E. V. Andreeva, N. V. Karlov, A. A. Manenkov, V. A. Milyaev, and A. V. Shirkov, *Fiz. Tverd. Tela*, **6**, 1649 (1964). "EPR of Chromium Ions in Cd Tungstate."

268. M. I. Ali, M. H. Ali, F. Rahman, A. K. Nath, and A. K. Roy, *J. Nat. Sci. Math.*, **4**, 23 (1964). "EPR in Some Iron Group Salts."

269. M. Nakada, K. Awazu, S. Ibuki, Y. Miyako, and M. Date, *J. Phys. Soc. Japan*, **19**, 781 (1964). "ESR of Mn^{4+} in MgO."

270. Cl. Declerck, *Bull. Soc. Roy. Sci. Liege*, **35**, 230 (1966). "ESR Spectrum of Cr^{3+} and V^{2+} in MgO."

271. K. A. Mueller, *Phys. Rev. Letters*, **2**, 341 (1959). "EPR of Manganese(IV) in Strontium Titanate."

272. S. Gregorio and R. Lacroix, *Proc. Colloq. Ampere*, **12** (1963), 213. "EPR of Chromium Chelates."

273. V. A. Atsarkin, E. A. Gerasimova, I. G. Matveeva, and A. V. Frantsesson, *Zh. Eksperim. i Teor. Fiz.*, **43**, 1272 (1962). "Paramagnetic Resonance of a Trivalent Chromium Ion in the Crystal Lattice of Magnesium Tungstate."

274. V. F. Koryagin and V. N. Grechushnikov, *Fiz. Tverd. Tela*, **6**, 422 (1964). "EPR Spectrum of Cr^{3+} Ion in a Pseudocrystalline Field."

275. K. A. Mueller, *Arch. Sci. (Geneva)*, **11**, Spec. No., 150 (1958). "Paramagnetic Resonance of Chromium(III) Ion in Single Crystals of Strontium Titanate."

276. H. H. Tippins, *Phys. Rev.*, **137**, A865 (1965). "Optical and Microwave Properties of Trivalent Chromium in β-Ga_2O_3."

277. W. Low and R. S. Rubins, *Phys. Letters*, **1**, 316 (1962). "ESR in the Cubic Crystalline Field of Calcium Oxide."

278. W. Low and R. S. Rubins, *Paramagnetic Resonance, Proc. Intern. Conf., 1st, Jerusalem, 1962*, **1**, 79. "Paramagnetic Resonance of Iron Group and Rare Earth Impurities in Calcium Oxide."

279. S. Gregorio, J. Weber, and R. Lacroix, *Helv. Phys. Acta*, **38**, 172 (1965). "Paramagnetic Resonance of Cr Diethyldithiophosphate."

280. B. R. McGarvey, *J. Chem. Phys.*, **37**, 3020 (1962). "Spin Hamiltonian of Chromium(III) in a Cubic Field."

281. H. J. Gerritsen, S. E. Harrison, H. R. Lewis, and J. P. Wittke, *Phys. Rev. Letters*, **2**, 153 (1959). "Fine Structure, Hyperfine Structure, and Relaxation Times of Cr^{3+} in TiO_2 (Rutile)."

282. J. W. Carson and R. L. White, *J. Appl. Phys.*, **32**, 1787 (1961). "Zero-Field Splitting of the Cr^{3+} Ground State in Y Ga and Y Al Garnet."

283. S. Mito, K. Okumura, and H. Mima, *Mem. Fac. Eng., Osaka City Univ.*, **5**, 105 (1963). "ESR of $Cr(NH_3)_6(ClO_4)_3$."

284. E. D. Arkhangel'skaya, M. M. Zaripov, Yu. E. Pol'skii, V. G. Stepanov, G. K. Chirkin, and L. Ya. Shekun, *Fiz. Tverd. Tela*, **4**, 2530 (1962). "EPR of Cr^{3+} in $K_2Zn(SO_4)_2 \cdot 6H_2O$."

285. L. S. Singer, *J. Chem. Phys.*, **23**, 379 (1955). "Paramagnetic Resonance Absorption in Some Cr^{3+} Complexes."

286. T. P. P. Hall, W. Hayes, R. W. H. Stevenson, and J. Wilkens, *J. Chem. Phys.*, **38**, 1977 (1963). "Bonding of Iron-Group Ions in Fluoride Crystals."

287. W. Low and J. T. Suss, *Phys. Letters*, **11**, 115 (1964). "Paramagnetic Resonance Spectra in Single Crystals of Strontium Oxide."

288. J. M. Baker, B. Bleaney, and K. D. Bowers, *Proc. Phys. Soc.* (*London*), **B69**, 1205 (1956). "Paramagnetic Resonance in Some Complex Cyanides of the Iron Group."

289. J. O. Artman, J. C. Murphy, J. A. Kohn, and W. D. Townes, *Phys. Rev. Letters*. **4**, 607 (1960). "Effects of Polytypism on the EPR of $K_3Co(CN)_6$ and Other Spectroscopic Implications."

290. W. M. Walsh, Jr., *Phys. Rev.*, **122**, 762 (1961). "Effects of Hydrostatic Pressure on the Paramagnetic Resonance Spectra of Several Iron-Group Ions in Cubic Crystals."

291. S. Geschwind, P. Kisliuk, M. P. Klein, J. P. Remeika, and D. L. Wood, *Phys. Rev.*, **126**, 1684 (1962). "Sharp-Line Fluorescence, Electron Paramagnetic Resonance, and Thermoluminescence of Mn^{4+} in $\alpha-Al_2O_3$."

292. W. H. From, P. B. Dorain, and C. Kikuchi, *Phys. Rev.*, **135**, A710 (1964). "Hyperfine and Superhyperfine Structure of Manganese in SnO_2."

293. H. G. Andresen, *J. Chem. Phys.*, **35**, 1090 (1961). "Hyperfine Structure and g-Tensor Anisotropy of the Paramagnetic Resonance of Manganese in TiO_2."

294. R. W. Terhune, J. Lambe, C. Kikuchi, and J. Baker, *Phys. Rev.*, **123**, 1265 (1961). "Hyperfine Spectrum of Chromium 53 in Al_2O_3."

295. J. E. Geusic, *Phys. Rev.*, **102**, 1252 (1956). "Paramagnetic Fine Structure Spectrum of Cr^{3+} in a Single Ruby Crystal."

296. T. I. Barry, *Solid State Commun.*, **4**, 123 (1966). "ESR Of Cr^{3+} in Anatase (TiO_2)."

297. I. Y. Chan, D. C. Doetschman, C. A. Hutchison, Jr., B. E. Kohler, and J. W. Stout, *J. Chem. Phys.*, **42**, 1048 (1965). "Paramagnetic Resonance by Divalent Vanadium ion in Cadmium Dichloride."

298. G. A. Egorov and Yu. V. Yablokov, *Zh. Eksperim. i Teor. Fiz.*, **39**, 265 (1960). "Paramagnetic Resonance in a Quasi-Single Crystal of $CrCl_3$."

299. L. G. Van Uitert, *Metallurgy Advan. Electron. Mater.*, **19**, 305 (1963). "Solid-State Maser Materials."

300. R. G. Shulman and K. Knox, *Phys. Rev. Letters*, **4**, 603 (1960). "Interactions of P_σ and P_π Orbitals in Transition Element Fluorides."

301. H. A. Kuska and M. T. Rogers, *J. Chem. Phys.*, **41**, 3802 (1964). "EPR Studies and Covalent Bonding of Cyanide and Fluoride Complexes of Transition Metals."

302. L. Helmholz, A. V. Guzzo, and R. N. Sanders, *J. Chem. Phys.*, **35**, 1349 (1961). "Paramagnetic Resonance Spectra of Chromium(III) and Manganese(IV) Hexafluoride Ions: CrF_6^3 and MnF_6^{2-}."

303. E. J. Schimitschek, *Phys. Rev.*, **130**, 2199 (1963). "Paramagnetic Resonance of Chromium in $MgTiO_3$."

304. R. Aasa, K. E. Falk, and S. A. Reyes L., *Arkiv. Kemi*, **25**, 309 (1966). "ESR of Cr(III) in Single Crystals of EDTA."

305. M. Peter and J. B. Mock, *Phys. Rev.*, **118**, 137 (1960). "EPR of Ni^{2+}, V^{2+}, and Cr^{3+} in ZnF_2."

306. N. Laurance, E. C. McIrvine, and J. Lambe, *J. Phys. Chem. Solids*, **23**, 515 (1962). "Aluminum Hyperfine Interactions in Ruby."

307. J. G. Castle, Jr., *Phys. Rev.*, **119**, 953 (1960). "Electron Spin-Lattice Relaxation in Dilute Potassium Chromicyanide at Helium Temperatures."

308. W. M. Walsh, Jr., *Phys. Rev.*, **114**, 1485 (1959). "Pressure Dependence of the Paramagnetic Resonance Spectra of Two Dilute Chromium Salts."

309. P. F. Chester, P. E. Wagner, and J. G. Castle, Jr., *Quantum Electron. Symp., High View, N. Y., 1959*, 359. "Relaxation Processes in Dilute Potassium Chromicyanide."

310. T. Mitsuma, *J. Phys. Soc. Japan*, **16**, 1796 (1961). "Extra Lines in the EPR Spectra of Heavily Chromium(III)-Doped $K_3Co(CN)_6$."

311. A. N. Kozlova and G. I. Subbotin, *Tr. Estestv. Nauchn. Inst. pri Permsk. Univ.*, **11**, 153 (1964). "EPR Spectra of the Polytypical Crystal $K_3Co_{(0.99)}Cr_{(0.01)}(CN)_6$ at 9340 Megacycles."

312. N. E. Ainbinder, I. N. Bazhina, V. S. Grechishkin, A. N. Kozlova, and G. I. Subbotin, *Tr. Estestv. Nauchn. Inst. pri. Permsk. Univ.*, **11**, 147 (1964). "Relative Intensities of EPR Lines in Crystals in the Case of a 3/2 Effective Spin."

313. G. Berthet, F. Blanc, J. Grangeon, and G. Raoult, *Arch. Sci. (Geneva)*, **12**, 226 (1959). "ESR Spectra of Dilute Potassium Chromic Cyanide in a Crystal of Potassium Cobaltic Cyanide."

314. B. W. Faughnan and M. W. P. Strandberg, *Phys. Chem. Solids*, **19**, 155 (1961). "The Role of Phonons in Paramagnetic Relaxation."

315. J. Vanier, *Can. J. Phys.*, **42**, 494 (1964). "Dipolar Interaction in Selected Paramagnetic Crystals."

316. B. Bolger and B. J. Robinson, *Physica*, **26**, 133 (1960). "Paramagnetic Relaxation Rates Determined by Pulsed Double Resonance Experiments."

317. G. V. Marr and P. Swarup, *Can. J. Phys.*, **38**, 495 (1960). "Spin-Lattice Relaxation Effects Observed in the Continuous Power Saturation of Paramagnetic Lines."

318. J. C. Dyment, *Can. J. Phys.*, **44**, 637 (1966). "Spectral Diffusion Studies of the Cr^{3+} Ion Using Electron Spin Echoes."

319. P. Swarup, *Can. J. Phys.*, **37**, 848 (1959). "Paramagnetic Resonance Line Shapes."

320. G. Raoult, J. C. Parouty, M. Lacombat, and A. M. Duclaux, *Arch. Sci. (Geneva)*, **14**, 165 (1961). "EPR of the Cr^{3+} Ion."

321. A. L. McWhorter and J. E. Meyer, *Phys. Rev.*, **109**, 312 (1958). "Solid-State Maser Amplifiier."

322. D. N. Klyshko, *Fiz. Tverd. Tela*, **5**, 2825 (1963). "The Second Moment of EPR Lines in Ruby."

323. R. B. Hemphill, Ph.D. thesis, Rice University, 1964. "Effect of Uniaxial Stress on the Spin Resonance of Cr^{3+} in Al_2O_3."

324. W. S. C. Chang, *Quantum Electron., Sympo., High View, N.Y., 1959*, 346. "Spin-Lattice Relaxation Via Harmonic Coupling."

325. R. J. R. Hayward, *Chem. Soc. (London), Spec. Publ.*, **20**, 173 (1966). "The Electron Spin-Lattice Relaxation of Transition-Metal Ions in Solids at Low Temperatures."

326. Yu. A. Sherstkov, V. I. Nepsha, A. E. Nikiforov, and V. I. Cherepanov, *Zh. Eksperim. i Teor. Fiz., Pis'ma v Redaktsiyu*, **3**, 401 (1966). "Effect of an Electric Field on EPR Signals of Exchange Coupled Pairs of Cr Ions in Ruby."

327. G. C. Brown, Jr., AD 602186. Avail. OTS. "Measurement of Relaxation Times of Paramagnetic Ions in Crystals: Ruby."

328. P. L. Donoho and R. B. Hemphill, *Proc. Intern. Conf. Low Temp. Phys., 8th, London, 1962*, 294. "Spin-Lattice Interaction in Ruby."

329. M. D. Sturge, *J. Chem. Phys.*, **43**, 1826 (1965). "Effect of Stress on the Level Splittings of Ruby: Origin of the Ground-State Splitting."

330. L. Rimai, R. W. Bierig, and B. D. Silverman, *Phys. Rev. Letters*, **12**, 667 (1964). "Population Inversion and Microwave-Stimulated Emission in the EPR Spectrum of Ruby after Rapid Reversal of the Magnetic Field."

331. J. C. Gill, *Nature*, **190**, 619 (1961). "Spin-Lattice Relaxation of Pairs of Chromium Ions in Ruby."

332. A. Hadni, G. Morlot, and P. Strimer, *Compt. Rend.*, **258**, 515 (1964). "Energy Levels of Low Frequency in Concentrated Ruby."

333. L. Rimai, H. Statz, M. J. Weber, G. A. DeMars, and G. F. Koster, *Phys. Rev. Letters*, **4**, 125 (1960). "Paramagnetic Resonance of Exchange-Coupled Chromium(III) Ion Pairs in Ruby."

334. Y. Nishida, *J. Phys. Soc. Japan*, **19**, 2273 (1964). "Paramagnetic Relaxation of Chromium Ion in Ruby and Potassium Alum."

335. D. S. Thompson and J. S. Waugh, *Rev. Sci. Instr.*, **36**, 552 (1965). "Adjustable Ruby Intensity Standard for ESR Spectra."

336. W. J. Grant and M. W. P. Strandberg, *Phys. Rev.*, **135A**, 727 (1964). "Line Shapes of Paramagnetic Resonance of Chromium in Ruby."

337. R. B. Hemphill, P. L. Donoho, and E. D. McDonald, *Phys. Rev.*, **146**, 329 (1966). "Spin-Lattice Interaction in Ruby Measured by ESR in Uniaxially Stressed Crystals."

338. D. N. Klyshko, V. S. Tumanov, and L. A. Ushakova, *Zh. Eksperim. i Teor. Fiz.*, **43**, 25 (1962). "Effect of Cross Relaxation on the Inversion of the Spin Level Population in Ruby."

339. T.-K. Chang, *Wu Li Hsueh Pao*, **20**, 381 (1964). "Relation of Cr^{3+} Concentration with the Peak Intensity and Width of Cr^{3+} Paramagnetic Resonance Absorption Lines in Al_2O_3."

340. H. Statz, M. J. Weber, L. Rimai, G. A. De Mars, and G. F. Koster, *J. Phys. Soc. Japan*, **17**, Suppl. B-1, 430 (1962). "Exchange in Interactions in the Paramagnetic Resonance Spectrum of Ruby."

341. W. H. Culver, R. A. Satten, and C. R. Viswanathan, *J. Chem. Phys.*, **38**, 775 (1963). "Measurement of the Spin-Lattice Relaxation Time of the $\bar{E}(^2E)$ State of Cr^{3+} in Al_2O_3 by Paramagnetic Resonance at X Band Frequency."

342. N. Bloembergen and E. B. Royce, *Paramagnetic Resonance, Proc. Intern. Conf., 1st, Jerusalem, 1962*, **2**, 607. "Electric Shift of the Cr^{3+} Magnetic Resonance in Ruby."

343. E. C. McIrvine, J. Lambe, N. Laurance, and T. Cole, *Phys. Rev. Letters*, **8**, 318 (1962). "Double Nuclear Resonance and Nuclear Relaxation."

344. R. H. Hoskins, *Phys. Rev. Letters*, **3**, 174 (1959). "Spin-Level Inversion and Spin-Temperature Mixing in Ruby."

345. A. Szabo and T. Igarashi, *Appl. Phys. Letters*, **7**, 289 (1965). "Effect of Ground-State ESR Saturation on Ruby Laser Output at 90°K."

346. J. Brossel, S. Geschwind, and A. L. Schawlow, *Phys. Rev. Letters*, **3**, 548 (1959). "Optical Detection of Paramagnetic Resonance in Crystals at Low Temperatures."

347. U. Kh. Kopvillem, R. M. Mineeva, and I. D. Morozova, *Paramagnitn. Rezonans, Kazansk. Univ., Sbornik, 1960*, 92. "Theory of the Width of the Line of Paramagnetic Resonance in Corundum-Containing Chromium."

348. A. A. Manenkov and V. B. Fedorov, *Zh. Eksperim. i Teor. Fiz.*, **38**, 1042 (1960). "Width and Shape of Cr^{3+} Ion EPR Spectral Lines in Corundum Single Crystals."

349. E. U. Schafer, H. Friedburg, H. Kuiper, J. Lipp, and E. Recknagel, *Phys. Letters*, **6**, 21 (1963). "Paramagnetic Resonant Frequency Mixing in Ruby."

350. Yu. L. Shelekhim, M. P. Votinov, and B. P. Berkovskii, *Fiz. Tverd. Tela*, **8**, 589 (1966). "Exchange Interaction of Pairs of Cr^{3+} Paramagnetic Ions in a Corundum Lattice."

351. H. Statz, L. Rimai, M. J. Weber, G. A. De Mars, and G. F. Koster, *J. Appl. Phys.*, **32**, Suppl. 3, 218 (1961). "Chromium Ion Pair Interactions in the Paramagnetic Resonance Spectrum of Ruby."

352. J. C. Gill, *Quantum Electron. Symp., High View, N.Y., 1959*, 333. "Some Measurements of the Decay of Paramagnetic Saturation in Synthetic Ruby."

353. E. B. Royce and N. B. Bloembergen, *Phys. Rev.*, **131**, 1912 (1963). "Linear Electric Shifts in the Paramagnetic Resonance of Al_2O_3:Cr and MgO:Cr."

354. R. D. Mattuck and M. W. P. Strandberg, *Phys. Rev. Letters*, **3**, 550 (1959). "Saturation of Paramagnetic Spin by 13 Mc./Sec. Ultrasonic Phonons."

355. N. S. Shiren and E. B. Tucker, *Phys. Rev. Letters*, **6**, 105 (1961). "Selection Rule for the Interaction of Microwave Ultrasonics with Spins."

356. A. E. Nikiforov, *Fiz. Tverd. Tela*, **7**, 1248 (1965). "The Effect of Electric Field on EPR Spectrum of Cr Pairs in Corundum."

357. A. E. Nikiforov and V. I. Cherepanov, *Fiz. Tverd. Tela*, **7**, 1162 (1965). "The Theory of EPR Spectrum of Exchange-Coupled Paramagnetic Ion Pairs in Crystals."

358. S. Geschwind, *Proc. Colloq. Ampere*, **11**, 548 (1962). "Optical Detection of Paramagnetic Resonance in the Excited $E(^2E)$ State of Cr^{3+} in Al_2O_3."

359. S. Geschwind, R. J. Collins, and A. L. Schawlow, *Phys. Rev. Letters*, **3**, 545 (1959). "Optical Excitation of Paramagnetic Resonance in an Excited State of Cr^{3+} in Aluminum Oxide."

360. A. F. Clark, R. H. Sands, and C. Kikuchi, AD 601961. Avail. OTS. "The Hydrostatic Pressure Effect on the EPR Spectra of Cr^{3+} and V^{2+} in Sapphire."

361. U. Kh. Kopvillem, *Fiz. Tverd. Tela*, **2**, 1829 (1960). "Theory of Cross Relaxation on Magneto-Diluted Crystals."

362. A. N. Kozlova, *Izv. Vysshikh Uchebn. Zavedenii, Fiz.*, **9**, 129 (1966). "Determination of the Spin Hamiltonian Constants of the ESR by Using the Energy Levels Intersection Points."

363. J. E. Drumheller and D. H. Dickey, *Bull. Am. Phys. Soc.*, **11**, 719 (1966). "Axial Field Splitting of V^{2+} in MgO."

364. D. R. Locker, K. A. Gale, B. A. Kulp and P. B. Dorain, *Bull. Am. Phys. Soc.*, **11**, 719 (1966). "EPR Study of Mn^{2+}, V^{2+}, Cr^{3+}, and Fe^{3+}, in the NaCl Structure of Cadmium Sulfide."

365. W. Marshall, *Paramagnetic Resonance, Proc. Intern. Conf., 1st, Jerusalem, 1962*, **1**, 347. "Hyperfine Interactions with Ligand Nuclei in Transition Ion Complexes."

366. J. H. Pace, D. F. Sampson, and J. S. Thorp, *Proc. Phys. Soc.*, **77**, 257 (1961). "Spin-Lattice Relaxation Times in Sapphire and Chromium Doped Rutile at 34.6×10^3 Mc/Sec."

367. B. I. Tsukerman and M. A. Vinetskaya, *Fiz. Tverd. Tela*, **5**, 129 (1963). "The Interpretation of Paramagnetic Resonance Spectra in Crystals."

368. D. R. Lampe and P. E. Wagner, *J. Chem. Phys.*, **45**, 1405 (1966). "Paramagnetic Relaxation and Crystal-Field Theory for the Ground Manifold of Chromium in Rutile."

369. J. Sierro, R. Lacroix, and K. A. Mueller, *Helv. Phys. Acta*, **32**, 286 (1959). "Hyperfine Structure of the Magnetic Resonance Spectrum of Chromium in Rutile."

370. J. Sierro, K. A. Mueller, and R. Lacroix, *Arch. Sci. (Geneva)*, **12**, 122 (1959). "Paramagnetic Resonance of Chromium in a Monocrystal of Rutile."

371. E. Brun, S. Hafner, H. Loeliger, and F. Waldner, *Helv. Phys. Acta*, **33**, 966 (1960). "EPR of Cr^{3+} in Spinel ($MgAl_2O_4$)."

372. L. N. Ansel'm, G. L. Bir, I. E. Myl'nikova, and M. P. Petrov, *Fiz. Tverd. Tela*, **8**, 1013 (1966). "EPR of Cr^{3+} Ions in Li-Al Spinel."

373. J. E. Geusic, M. Peter, and E. O. Schulz-Du Bois, *Bell System Tech. J.*, **38**, 291 (1959). "Paramagnetic Resonance Spectrum of Cr^{3+} in Emerald."

374. G. F. Imbusch and S. Geschwind, *Phys. Letters*, **18**, 109 (1965). "Optical Detection of Paramagnetic Resonance in the Excited $\bar{E}(^2E)$ State of Mn^{4+} in Al_2O_3."

375. M. Browne, *U. S. Dept. Com., Office Tech. Serv., P B Repts.*, *147, 366* (1960). "Effects of Applied Electric Fields on Paramagnetic Resonance in Chrome Alums."

376. A. M. Vasil'ev, *Fiz. Tverd. Tela*, **2**, 2252 (1960). "Fine Structure of the Paramagnetic Resonance Spectrum of the Chromium Ion in Chrome Alum with Allowance for Higher Terms."

377. Y. W. Kim and D. D. Hearn, *Appl. Phys. Letters*, **2**, 36 (1963). "EPR Absorption of Thermally Annealed Cr_2O_3 below the Curie Temperature."

378. A. A. Slinkin and E. A. Fedorovskaya, *Dokl. Akad. Nauk SSSR*, **159**, 904 (1964). "The Appearance of Fine Structure of the ESR Spectra of Chromium Oxide Alloyed with Li^+ Ions."

379. A. Knappwost and W. Gunsser, *Z. Physik. Chem. (Frankfurt)*, **21**, 305 (1959). "Magnetic Resonance Absorption in Mixed Crystal $\alpha-Al_2O_3-Cr_2O_3$ by Aid of a Modified Reflection Method."

380. R. F. Wenzel and Y. W. Kim, *Phys. Rev.*, **140**, 1592 (1965). "Line Width of the EPR of $(Al_2O_3)_{1-x}(Cr_2O_3)_x$."

381. T. V. Rode, V. B. Kazanskii, and Yu. I. Pecherskaya, *Zh. Fiz. Khim.*, **35**, 2370 (1961). "EPR Study of Chromium Oxides."

382. D. E. O'Reilly and D. S. MacIver, *J. Phys. Chem.*, **66**, 276 (1962). "EPR Absorption of Chromia–Alumina Catalysts."

383. Yu. I. Pecherskaya, V. B. Kazanskii, and V. V. Voevodskii, *Actes Congr. Intern. Catalyse, 2ᵉ, Paris, 1960*, **2**, 2121. "Use of the ESR Method in the Investigation of an Oxide Catalyst."

384. R. G. Meisenheimer and J. D. Swalen, *Phys. Rev.*, **123**, 831 (1961). "Magnetic Properties of $HCrO_2$ and $DCrO_2$."
385. A. A. Slinkin and E. A. Fedorovskaya, *Dokl. Akad. Nauk SSSR*, **150**, 328 (1963). "ESR Spectra of Products Obtained from High-Temperature Interaction of CrO_3 with $K_2Cr_2O_7$, K_2CrO_4, K_2CO_3, KCl, and KOH."
386. J. B. Spencer, *U.S. At. Energy Comm.* UCRL-16175(1965). "ESR Studies of Transition Metal Ion Complexes."
387. S. A. Marshall, J. A. Hodges, and R. A. Serway, *Phys. Rev.*, **136**, 1024 (1964). "Isotopic Shift in the ESR Absorption Spectrum of Cr^{3+} in Magnesium Oxide."
388. M. Weger and E. Feher, *Paramagnetic Resonance, Proc. Intern. Conf., 1st, Jerusalem, 1962*, **2**, 628. "Second-Order Effect of Applied Electric Fields on the ESR of Impurity Ions in MgO."
389. J. G. Castle, Jr., and D. W. Feldman, *Phys. Rev.*, **121**, 1349 (1961). "Electron Spin-Lattice Relaxation of Chromium in MgO."
390. J. L. Kolopus, L. V. Holroyd, and K. E. Mann, *Phys. Status Solidi*, **9**, K95 (1965). "EPR Spectra of Gd^{3+} and V^{2+} in SrO."
391. J. H. E. Griffiths and J. W. Orton, *Proc. Phys. Soc. (London)*, **73**, 948 (1959). "Some Weak Lines in the EPR Spectrum of Impure MgO Crystals."
392. L. P. Lipovkina, M. L. Meil'man, V. G. Adrianov, and N. I. Sergeeva, *Zh. Strukt. Khim.*, **6**, 643 (1965). "EPR of the Cr^{3+} Ions in Magnesium Molybdate Single Crystals."
393. J. W. Orton, A. S. Fruin, and J. C. Walling, *Proc. Phys. Soc. (London)*, **87**, 703 (1966). "Spin-Lattice Relaxation of Cr^{3+} in Single Crystals of Zinc Tungstate."
394. E. N. Emel'yanova, N. V. Karlov, A. A. Manenkov, V. A. Milyaev, A. M. Prokhorov, S. P. Smirnov, and A. V. Shirkov, *Zh. Eksperim. i Teor. Fiz.*, **44**, 868 (1963). "EPR Spectrum and Spin-Lattice Relaxation of Chromium and Ferric Ions in Zinc Tungstate Single Crystals."
395. A. A. Bugai, P. T. Levkovskii, V. M. Maksimenko, M. V. Pashkovskii, and O. B. Roitsin, *Zh. Eksperim. i Teor. Fiz.*, **50**, 1510 (1966). "Splitting of EPR Lines of Cr^{3+} in $ZnWO_4$ by an External Electric Field."
396. V. A. Atsarkin, M. E. Zhabotinskii, and A. V. Frantsesson, IAA Accession No. A 64-23432, (1964) "ESR of Trivalent Chromium Ion in Spinel and Magnesium Tungstate Crystals."
397. L. Rimai, T. Deutsch, and B. D. Silverman, *Phys. Rev.*, **133**, 1123 (1964). "Effect of Temperature and Pressure on the EPR Spectra of Substitutional Impurities in Cubic $SrTiO_3$."
398. K. A. Mueller, *Helv. Phys. Acta*, **33**, 497 (1960). "Forbidden $\Delta(M + m) = 0$ Transitions in the Paramagnetic Resonance Spectrum of Mn^{4+} in $SrTiO_3$ and Mn^{2+} in ZnS."
399. K. A. Mueller, *Paramagnetic Resonance, Proc. Intern. Conf., 1st, Jerusalem, 1962*, **1**, 17. "Paramagnetic Resonance and Optical Absorption of Transition Element Ions in $SrTiO_3$ and $LaAlO_3$."
400. H. J. Gerritsen, S. E. Harrison, and H. R. Lewis, *J. Appl. Phys.*, **31**, 1566 (1960). "Chromium-Doped Titania as a Maser Material."
401. W. Low, *Phys. Rev. Letters*, **1**, 51 (1958). "ESR in Single Crystals of Barium Titanate."
402. N. S. Garif'yanov and M. M. Zaripov, *Itogi. Nauchn. Konf. Kazansk. Univ. za, 1963, g., Sekts. Paramagnitn. Rezonansa, Spektroskopii, i Fiz. Polimerov., Radiofiz. Astron., Bion., Kazan., Sb.*, **6** (1964). "EPR of Trivalent Chromium and Trivalent Gadolinium at Low Frequencies."

403. G. Emch and R. Lacroix, *Helv. Phys. Acta*, **33**, 1021 (1960). "Paramagnetic Resonance of the Cr^{3+} Ion in a Single Crystal of $AlCl_3 \cdot 6H_2O$."

404. O. B. Roitsin, *Fiz. Tverd. Tela*, **4**, 2948 (1962). "The Role of Electric Fields in Paramagnetic Resonance."

405. M. M. Zaripov, *Fiz. Tverd. Tela*, **7**, 3666 (1965). "EPR Study of Glasses with Cr."

406. S. A. Al'tshuler, A. M. Leushin, and A. K. Morocha, *Paramagnitn. Rezonans, Kazansk. Univ., Sbornik, 1960*, 57. "Theory of Spin-Lattice Interaction in Ionic Crystals Containing Cr^{3+} and Ni^{2+}."

407. H. M. McConnell, W. W. Porterfield, and R. E. Robertson, *J. Chem. Phys.*, **30**, 442 (1959). "Paramagnetic Resonance of Biscyclopentadienyl Vanadium."

408. H. H. Woodbury and G. W. Ludwig, *Phys. Rev.*, **117**, 102 (1960). "Spin Resonance of Transition Metals in Silicon."

409. B. I. Tsukerman, *Zh. Strukt. Khim.*, **4**, 625 (1963). "Paramagnetic Spectrum of Cr^{3+} in Aluminum Nitrate."

410. M. Santangelo, *Atti Accad. Sci., Lettere Arti Palermo P. I*, **18**, 123 (1957/58). "Electronic and Optical Spin Transitions in Magnetic Complex [Ions]."

411. K. M. Sancier and J. S. Mills, *J. Phys. Chem.*, **67**, 1438 (1963). "The ESR of Chromium(III) Complexes in Aqueous Solution."

412. N. F. Usacheva, *Zh. Eksperim. i Teor. Fiz.*, **41**, 1771 (1961). "Paramagnetic Resonance in Solutions of Cr^{3+} Salts."

413. N. S. Garif'yanov, *Dokl. Akad. Nauk SSSR*, **138**, 612 (1961). "The Hyperfine Structure of the EPR Line in Aqueous Solutions of V^{2+} Salts."

414. W. Wojciechowski and B. Jezowska-Trzebiatowska, *Bull. Acad. Polon. Sci., Ser. Sci. Chim.*, **11**, 79 (1963). "ESR in Binuclear Chromium(III) Complexes."

415. M. Constantinescu, O. Constantinescu, and I. Pascaru, *Acad. Rep. Populare Romine Studii Cercetari Fiz.*, **13**, 631 (1962). "Study of Ions Adsorbed on Ion Exchangers by EPR. I. EPR Spectra of Cr Adsorbed on Ion Exchangers."

416. T. I. Volokhova, *Izv. Vysshikh Uchebn. Zavedenii, Fiz.*, **8**, 153 (1965). "Paramagnetic Relaxation in Single Crystals of Mn^{2+}, Cr^{3+}, Fe^{3+}, and Cu^{2+} Salts as a Function of Their Orientation in a Constant Parallel Magnetic Field at Room Temperature."

417. G. Emch and R. Lacroix, *Arch. Sci. (Geneva)*, **13**, 157 (1960). "Paramagnetic Resonance of the Complex $Cr(H_2O)_6^{3+}$ in a Single Crystal of $Al(H_2O)_6^{3+}$."

418. R. Clad and J. Wucher, *Compt. Rend., Ser. A.,B.*, **262B**, 113 (1966). "EPR of Aqueous Solutions of the Complex Acetate $Cr_3(CH_3CO_2)_6(OH)_2Cl \cdot 8H_2O$, between 20 and 100°."

419. R. Clad and J. Wucher, *Compt. Rend., Ser. A.,B.*, **262B**, 795 (1966). "EPR of the Mixed Complex Acetate $(Cr_2Fe(CH_3COO)_6(OH)_2Cl \cdot 6H_2O$, between 4 and 290°K."

420. R. Clad and J. Wucher, *Compt. Rend.*, **260**, 4318 (1965). "EPR of the Complex Acetate $[Cr_3(CH_3COO)_6(OH)_2]Cl \cdot 8H_2O$ between 4 and 290°K."

421. J. F. Dillon, Jr., and J. P. Remeika, *Proc. Colloq. Ampere*, **11**, 480 (1962). "Ferromagnetic and Paramagnetic Resonance Line Widths in $CrCl_3$ and $CrBr_3$."

422. Z. Sroubek, K. Zdansky, and M. Vichr, *Phys. Letters*, **21**, 264 (1966). "Effects of Cr^{3+}–Eu^{3+} Interaction on the Paramagnetic Resonance of Cr^{3+} in Europium Gallium Garnets."

423. J. Brown, *J. Phys. Chem.*, **67**, 2524 (1963). "ESR in Solid and Liquid Salt Mixtures."

424. H. H. Dearman, W. W. Porterfield, and H. H. McConnell, *J. Chem. Phys.*, **34**, 696 (1961). "EPR of Dicyclopentadienyl Vanadium in Ferrocene."

425. M. Konstantinescu, O. Konstantinescu, and J. Pascaru, *Rev. Phys. Acad. Rep. Populaire Roumaine*, **7**, 367 (1962). "EPR Investigation of Ions Absorbed on Ion Exchangers. I. EPR Spectra of Cr Absorbed on Ionites."

426. M. Nussbaum and J. Voitländer, *Z. Naturforsch.*, **20a**, 1411 (1965). "EPR of Organometallic Sandwich Compounds, Part I."

427. W. M. Walsh, Jr., J. Jeener, and N. Bloembergen, *Phys. Rev.*, **139A**, 1338 (1965). "Temperature Dependent Crystal Field and Hyperfine Interactions."

428. H. J. Gerritsen and E. S. Sabisky, *Phys. Rev.*, **132**, 1507 (1963). "Paramagnetic Resonance of Trivalent Manganese in Rutile (TiO_2)."

429. K. Morigaki, *J. Phys. Soc. Japan*, **19**, 187 (1964). "ESR of Cr^{2+} in Cadmium Sulfide Single Crystals."

430. K. Morigaki, *J. Phys. Soc. Japan*, **18**, 733 (1963). "ESR Of Cr^{2+} in CdS."

431. R. E. Coffman, Ph.D. thesis, University of Minnesota, 1965. "The Eg Ground States of Cr(II) and Cu(II) in MgO by the Method of Paramagnetic Resonance."

432. K. Ono and H. Abe, *Phys. Rev.*, **96**, 38 (1954). "Paramagnetic Resonance in Chromous Sulfate Pentahydrates."

433. T. L. Estle, G. K. Walters, and M. De Wit, *Paramagnetic Resonance, Proc. Intern. Conf., 1st, Jerusalem, 1962*, **1**, 144. "Paramagnetic Resonance of Cr in CdS."

434. P. B. Dorain and D. Locker, *Rev. Sci. Instr.*, **34**, 359 (1963). "Angular Modulation of the Magnetic Field in EPR Experiments."

435. J. J. Krebs, *Bull. Am. Phys. Soc.*, **8**, 259 (1963). "Electric Field Broadening of ESR Lines in Mn^{2+} and Fe^{2+} and Fe^{2+} Doped Al_2O_3."

436. R. S. Rubins, *U.S. Gov. Res. Rep.*, **38**, 76 (1963). AD 293848. "Paramagnetic Resonance Spectrum of Divalent Iron in Zinc Fluosilicate."

437. A. S. Chakravarty, *J. Chem. Phys.*, **39**, 1004 (1963). "Zero-Field Splitting in $3d^5$ Ions."

438. E. Friedman and W. Low, *Phys. Rev.*, **120**, 408 (1960). "Paramagnetic Resonance Spectrum of Mn^{2+} in $ZnSiF_6:6H_2O$, $\Delta m = \pm 1$ Transition."

439. W. Low and J. T. Suss, *Phys. Rev.*, **119**, 132 (1960). "Paramagnetic Resonance Spectrum of Manganese in Corundum."

440. B. Bleaney and R. S. Rubins, *Proc. Phys. Soc. (London)*, **77**, 103 (1961). "Explanation of Some Forbidden Transitions in Paramagnetic Resonance."

441. B. T. Allen, *J. Chem. Phys.*, **43**, 3820 (1965). "Zero-Field Splitting Parameter of the Mn^{2+} Ion in Glassy and in Polycrystalline Media."

442. S. Kunii, S. Tobita, and E. Hirahara, *J. Phys. Soc. Japan*, **21**, 479 (1966). "Intensities and Doublet Separations of Forbidden Transitions in the Paramagnetic Resonance of Mn^{2+} in the Group II–VI Compounds."

443. L. Pauling, *The Nature of the Chemical Bond*, 3rd Ed., Cornell University Press, Ithaca, New York, 1960, p. 98.

444. V. J. Folen, *Phys. Rev.*, **139**, A1961 (1965). "ESR Spectrum of Mn^{2+} in β–Ga_2O_3."

445. R. S. Title, *Phys. Rev.*, **131**, 2503 (1963). "EPR Detection of Lattice Distortion in Mn^{2+} Doped II–VI Compounds."

446. C. G. Windsor, J. H. E. Griffiths, and J. Owen, *Proc. Phys. Soc.*, **81**, 373 (1963). "Bonding in Manganese Complexes."

447. A. Forman and J. A. van Wyk, *J. Chem. Phys.*, **44**, 73 (1966). "EPR of Divalent Manganese in Ammonium Chloride."

448. M. M. Zaripov and G. K. Chirkin, *Zh. Strukt. Khim.*, **5**, 36 (1964). "The EPR of Mn^{2+} in NH_4Cl."

449. B. T. Allen and D. W. Nebert, *J. Chem. Phys.*, **41**, 1983 (1964). "Hyperfine Structure in the EPR Spectra of the Manganous Ion in Frozen Solutions."
450. I. Tatsuzaki, *J. Phys. Soc. Japan*, **17**, 1312 (1962). "Temperature Dependence of EPR of $(NH_4)_2Cd_2(SO_4)_3-Mn^{2+}$."
451. H. Ikushima and S. Hayakawa, *J. Phys. Soc. Japan*, **20**, 1517 (1965). "Forbidden Transitions in the ESR of Mn^{2+} in a $BaTiO_3$ Single Crystal."
452. J. J. Krebs, J. Lambe, and N. Laurance, *Phys. Rev.*, **141**, 425 (1966). "Electron Nuclear Double Resonance of Mn^{2+} in Al_2O_3."
453. Y. Yokozawa, *J. Phys. Soc. Japan*, **15**, 1131 (1960). "Paramagnetic Resonance of $Mn^{2+}-F^-$ Pair in Sodium Chloride."
454. S. Asano, Y. Nakao, and K. Omori, *J. Phys. Soc. Japan*, **20**, 1120 (1965). "Paramagnetic Resonance of Mn^{2+} in $Zn(S:Se)$ Powder Phosphors."
455. D. H. Lyons and R. W. Kedzie, *Phys. Rev.*, **145**, 148 (1966). "Paramagnetic Resonance Determination of a Nuclear Quadrupole Interaction by Means of Forbidden Hyperfine Transitions: $CaWO_4:Mn^{2+}$."
456. E. Simanek and R. Orbach, *Phys. Rev.*, **145**, 191 (1966). "Temperature Dependence of Hyperfine Coupling of S-State Ions in Cubic Environment."
457. G. J. King and B. S. Miller, *J. Chem. Phys.*, **41**, 28 (1964). "Paramagnetic Resonance of Mn^{2+} in NaN_3, KN_3, and RbN_3."
458. K. Fukuda, H. Matsumoto, T. Takagi, and Y. Uchida, *J. Phys. Soc. Japan*, **16**, 1256 (1961). "EPR of Manganese in $MgCl_2$."
459. H. B. Nudelman, S. H. Johnson, and R. G. Barnes, *J. Phys. Chem. Solids*, **26**, 1035 (1965). "ESR of Mn^{2+} in Mg_2Si."
460. H. Koga, K. Horai, and O. Matsumura, *J. Phys. Soc. Japan*, **15**, 1340 (1960). "ESR of Mn^{2+} in $SrCl_2$, $CdCl_2$, and $CdBr_2$."
461. J. E. Drumheller, *J. Chem. Phys.*, **38**, 970 (1963). "ESR of S-State Ions in Barium Fluoride."
462. S. Ogawa, *J. Phys. Soc. Japan*, **15**, 1475 (1960). "The EPR of Mn^{2+} Ions Surrounded by an Octahedron of Fluorine Ions."
463. H. Yoshimura, *J. Phys. Soc. Japan*, **15**, 435 (1960). "EPR of Mn in Alkali Chlorides."
464. B. Welber, *Phys. Rev.*, **138**, 1481 (1965). "ESR of Chromium Ions in NaCl."
465. W. Hayes and D. A. Jones, *Proc. Phys. (London)*, **71**, 503 (1958).
466. G. W. Ludwig and M. R. Lorenz, *Phys. Rev.*, **131**, 601 (1963). "Paramagnetic Resonance of Chromium in CdTe."
467. V. J. Folen, *Phys. Rev.*, **125**, 1581 (1962). "'Forbidden' Transitions in the Paramagnetic Resonance of Mn^{2+} in Al_2O_3."
468. L. C. Kravitz and W. W. Piper, *Phys. Rev.*, **146**, 322 (1966). "Complex Hyperfine Structure in the EPR Spectrum of $(FeF_6)^{3-}$ in CdTe."
469. S. A. Marshall and A. R. Reinberg, *Phys. Rev.*, **132**, 134 (1963). "Paramagnetic Absorption Spectrum of Trivalent Iron in Single Crystal Calcite."
470. A. Manoogian, F. Holuj, and J. W. Carswell, *Can. J. Phys.*, **43**, 2262 (1965). "The ESR of Fe^{3+} in Single Crystals of Spodumene $LiAl(SiO_3)_2$."
471. M. De Wit and T. L. Estle, *Phys. Rev.*, **132**, 195 (1963). "EPR of Iron in Gallium Arsenide."
472. J. Dieleman, *Philips Res. Repts.*, **20**, 206 (1965). "Effect of ^{77}Se Superhyperfine Structure on the EPR of Fe^{3+} ($3d^5$) in Cubic Zinc Selenide."
473. G. R. Hertel and H. M. Clark, *J. Phys. Chem.*, **65**, 1930 (1961). "Paramagnetic Resonance Behavior of Tetrachloroferrate Ion in Isopropyl Ether."
474. F. Matossi, A. Raeuber, and F. W. Kuepper, *Z. Naturforsch.*, **18a**, 819 (1963). "Charge Conversion in ZnS and Its Analytical Evaluation by ESR."

475. J. Dieleman, R. S. Title, and W. V. Smith, *Phys. Letters*, **1**, 334 (1962). "Paramagnetic Resonance Studies of Cr^{1+} in Cubic and Hexagonal ZnS."

476. R. S. Title, *Phys. Rev.*, **133**, 1613 (1964). "Paramagnetic Resonance Spectra of the $3d^5$ Configuration of Chromium in ZnSe and ZnTe."

477. W. Lohmann, C. F. Fowler, W. H. Perkins, and J. L. Sanders, *Nature*, **209**, 908 (1966). "Complex Formation between Transition Metal Ions and Organic Solvents."

478. K. Hennig, *Phys. Status Solidi*, **7**, 885 (1964). "Paramagnetic Resonance Examination of Silver Halides Doped with Fe."

479. G. S. Bogle, H. F. Symmons, V. R. Burgess, and J. V. Sierins, *Proc. Phys. Soc. (London)*, **77**, 561 (1961). "Paramagnetic Resonance Spectroscopy at Zero Magnetic Field"; *Proc. Phys. Soc. (London)*, **82**, 412 (1963).

480. K. Hennig, *Phys. Status Solidi*, **3**, K458 (1963). "ESR Studies of Silver Chloride Doped with Fe."

481. J. C. Garth, *Phys. Rev.*, **140**, 656 (1965). "Magnetic Resonance Study of Iron in Silver Chloride."

482. H. F. Symmons and G. S. Bogle, *Proc. Phys. Soc. (London)*, **79**, 468 (1962). "Exactness of the Spin Hamiltonian Description of Fe^{3+} in Sapphire."

483. J. J. Krebs, *Phys. Rev.*, **135**, 396 (1964). "Effect of Applied Electric Fields on the ESR of Fe^{3+} and Mn^{2+} in α-Al_2O_3."

484. L. S. Kornienko and A. M. Prokhorov, *Zh. Eksperim. i Theor. Fiz.*, **40**, 1594 (1961). "EPR of the Fe^{3+} Ions in Corundum (Al_2O_3)."

485. V. M. Vinokurov, M. M. Zaripov, and N. R. Yafaev, *Zh. Eksperim. i Teor. Fiz.*, **37**, 312 (1959). "Fine Structure of the Paramagnetic Resonance Spectrum of Natural Sapphire (Al_2O_3)."

486. G. A. Siulina and G. A. Feshchenko, *Radiotekh. i Elektron.*, **6**, 806 (1961). "The Fe^{3+} Spin Levels in Corundum (Al_2O_3)."

487. Y. Nakai, *Nippon Kagaku Zasshi*, **82**, 1428 (1961). "Paramagnetic Resonance Spectra of Manganese(II)–Alumina and Iron(III)–Alumina Catalysts Saturated with Ammonia or Formic Acid."

488. G. J. Troup and D. R. Hutton, *J. Appl. Phys.*, **15**, 1493 (1964). "Paramagnetic Resonance of Fe^{3+} in Kyanite (Al_2SiO_5)."

489. F. Holuj, J. R. Thyer, and N. E. Hedgecock, *Can. J. Phys.*, **44**, 509 (1966). "ESR Spectra of Fe^{3+} in Single Crystals of Andalusite (Al_2SiO_5)."

490. F. Holuj, *Can. J. Phys.*, **43**, 726 (1965). "Paramagnetic Resonance Absorption Spectrum of Trivalent Iron in a Single Crystal of Andalusite (Al_2SiO_5)."

491. E. Boesman and D. Schoemaker, *Compt. Rend.*, **252**, 1931 (1961). "EPR of the Fe^{3+} Ion in Kaolinite (Al_2SiO_5)."

492. A. W. Hornig, R. C. Rempel, and H. E. Weaver, *Phys. and Chem. Solids*, **10**, 1 (1959). "EPR in Single Crystals of $BaTiO_3$."

493. T. Sakudo and H. Unoki, *J. Phys. Soc. Japan*, **19**, 2109 (1964). "ESR of Fe^{3+} in $BaTiO_3$ in the Rhombohedral and the Cubic Phases."

494. T. Sakudo, *J. Phys. Soc. Japan*, **18**, 1626 (1963). "ESR of Fe^{3+} in $BaTiO_3$ at Low Temperatures."

495. D. J. A. Gainon, *J. Appl. Phys.*, **36**, 2325 (1965). "EPR Observation of Oxygen Vacancies in Iron-Doped $BaTiO_3$."

496. K. Sakakibara, H. Unoki, and T. Sakudo, *Denki Shikensho Iho*, **28**, 801 (1964). "ESR of Fe^{3+} in $BaTiO_3$. II. Its Numerical Calculation and the Forbidden Transition Lines."

497. W. Low and D. Shaltiel, *Phys. Rev. Letters*, **1**, 286 (1958). "EPR in Barium Titanate."

498. A. W. Hornig, R. C. Rempel, and H. E. Weaver, *Phys. Rev. Letters*, **1**, 284 (1958). "Interpretation of EPR in Barium Titanate."

499. S. P. Burley and G. J. Troup, *Brit. J. Appl. Phys.*, **16**, 315 (1965). "Paramagnetic Resonance of Fe^{3+} in Benitoite ($BaTi(SO_3)_3$)."

500. V. M. Vinokurov, M. M. Zaripov, V. G. Stepanov, G. K. Chirkin, and L. Ya. Shekun, *Zh. Strukt. Khim.*, **5**, 49 (1964). "EPR of Iron(III) in Benitoite ($BaTi(SO_3)_3$)."

501. J. G. Constantine, AD 609185. Avail. CFSTI (1964). "Paramagnetic Resonance Absorption Spectra of Bivalent Manganese and Trivalent Iron in Calcite ($CaCO_3$)."

502. J. Wakabayashi, *J. Chem. Phys.*, **38**, 1910 (1963). "Paramagnetic Resonance Spectrum of Fe^{3+} in Calcite ($CaCO_3$)."

503. V. A. Atsarkin, V. G. Lushnikov, and L. P. Sorokina, *Fiz. Tverd. Tela*, **7**, 2367 (1965). "EPR of Gd and Fe Trivalent Ions in Synthetic Calcite."

504. A. J. Shuskus, *Phys. Rev.*, **127**, 1529 (1962). "ESR of Fe^{3+} and Mn^{2+} in Single Crystals of CaO."

505. R. W. Kedzie and M. Kestigian, *Appl. Phys. Letters*, **3**, 86 (1963). "EPR Determination of Transition Metal Ion Sites and Multiplicity of Rare Earth Ion Sites in $CaWO_4$."

506. R. W. Kedzie and D. H. Lyons, *Phys. Rev. Letters*, **15**, 632 (1965). "Simultaneous Observation of Absorption and Dispersion Signals and Low-Power Saturation Effects in the Paramagnetic Resonance of $CaWO_4$–Fe^{3+}."

507. K. Morigaki and T. Hoshina, *J. Phys. Soc. Japan*, **21**, 842 (1966). "Photosensitive Spin Resonance of Fe^{3+} in CdS."

508. K. Morigaki and T. Hoshina, *Phys. Letters*, **17**, 85 (1965). "ESR of Fe^{3+} in CdS."

509. J. Lambe, J. Baker, and C. Kikuchi, *Phys. Rev. Letters*, **3**, 270 (1959). "Photosensitive Spin Resonance in Cadmium Sulfide."

510. A. L. Bil'dyukevich, V. M. Vinokurov, M. M. Zaripov, Yu. E. Pol'skiĭ, V. G. Stepanov, G. K. Chirkin, and L. Ya. Shekun, *Zh. Eksperim. i Teor. Fiz.*, **39**, 1548 (1960). "EPR in Andalusite (Al_2SiO_5)."

511. G. J. Troup and D. R. Hutton, *Brit. J. Appl. Phys.*, **15**, 1493 (1964). "Paramagnetic Resonance of Fe^{3+} in Kyanite (Triclinic Al_2SiO_5)."

512. Z. Sroubek and K. Zdansky, *Czech. J. Phys.*, **12**, 784 (1962). "Paramagnetic Resonance of Fe^{3+} Ion in a $CdWO_4$ Single Crystal."

513. E. G. Brock, D. Stirpe, and E. I. Hormats, *J. Chem. Phys.*, **37**, 2735 (1962). "Paramagnetic Resonance Spectrum of Fe^{3+} in Guanidinium Aluminum Sulfate Hexahydrate."

514. A. Narasimhamurty, *Indian J. Pure Appl. Phys.*, **1**, 140–4 (1963). "EPR in Single Crystals. I. Anisotrophy Studies on Ferric Ammonium Sulfate."

515. H. H. Wichman, M. P. Klein, and D. A. Shirley, *J. Chem. Phys.*, **42** (6), 2113–17 (1965). "Paramagnetic Resonance of Fe^{3+} in Polycrystalline Ferrichrome."

516. R. B. Krode, J. Dieleman, and H. J. Vegter, *Philips Res. Repts.*, **17**, 513 (1962). "ESR of Iron in Gallium Arsenide."

517. T. G. Castner, Jr., G. S. Newell, W. C. Holton, and C. P. Slichter, *J. Chem. Phys.*, **32**, 668 (1960). "The Paramagnetic Resonance of Iron in Glass."

518. T. L. Estle, *Phys. Rev.*, **136**, 1702 (1964). "EPR of Iron in Indium Arsenide."

519. U. Hochli, *Proc. Colloq. Ampere*, **12**, 191 (1963). "ESR of Fe^{3+} in Feldspar ($KAlSi_3O_8$)."

520. L. Helmholz, *J. Chem. Phys.*, **31**, 172 (1959). "Paramagnetic Resonance Spectrum of the Fluoroferrate Ion FeF_6^{3-}."

521. L. Helmholz and A. V. Guzzo, *J. Chem. Phys.*, **32**, 302 (1960). "The Paramagnetic Resonance Spectrum of the Fluoroferrate Ion in FeF_6^{3-}."

522. V. J. Folen, *Paramagnetic Resonance, Proc. Intern. Conf., 1st, Jerusalem*, **1**, 68 (1961). "Paramagnetic Resonance of Fe^{3+} in Spinel-Type Single Crystals."

523. G. S. Bogle and H. F. Symmons, *Proc. Phys. Soc. (London)*, **78**, 812 (1961). "Zero-Field Paramagnetic Resonance of Fe(III) in Methylamine."

524. Y. Sugiura, *J. Phys. Soc. Japan*, **16**, 1786 (1961). "Iron(III) Ions in Spinel Structure."

525. E. Brun, H. Loeliger, and F. Waldner, *Arch. Sci. (Geneva)*, **14**, 167 (1961).

526. J. Toussaint and C. Declerck, *Bull. Soc. Roy. Sci. Liege*, **35**, 93 (1966). "ESR Analysis of MgO Doped with Fe^{3+} and Mn^{2+}."

527. J. L. Kolopus and L. V. Holroyd, *Phys. Status Solidi*, **8**, 711 (1965). "Higher-Order Transitions in the EPR Spectrum of Fe^{3+} in MgO."

528. J. H. Lundsford, *J. Chem. Phys.*, **42**, 2617 (1965). "Polycrystalline EPR Spectrum of Fe^{3+} Ions in MgO."

529. E. R. Feher, *Phys. Rev.*, **136**, 145 (1964). "Effect of Uniaxial Stresses on the Paramagnetic Spectra of Mn^{2+} and Fe^{3+} in MgO."

530. A. M. Leushin, *Fiz. Tverd. Tela*, **5**, 605 (1963). "The Theory of Paramagnetic Spin-Lattice Relaxation in Crystals with Ions in the S State."

531. M. Peter, *Phys. Rev.*, **113**, 801 (1959). "Millimeter Wave Paramagnetic Resonance of ^6S State Impurity (Fe^{3+}) in $MgWO_4$."

532. A. S. Marfunin and J. Michoulier, *Compt. Rend., Ser. A.,B.*, **262B**, 1543 (1966). "EPR of Fe^{3+} Ion in an Oligoclase Single Crystal."

533. R. Aasa and T. Vanngard, *Arkiv Kemi*, **24**, 331 (1965). "ESR Single Crystal Study of Fe^{3+} with Large Rhombic Fine Structure Splitting."

534. S. Maekawa, *J. Phys. Soc. Japan*, **16**, 2337 (1961). "EPR of Diluted (NH_4)-$Fe(SO_4)_2 \cdot 12H_2O$."

535. S. Maekawa, *J. Phys. Soc. Japan*, **17**, 1208 (1962). "Crystalline Field Anomalies of Diluted $(NH_4)Fe(SO_4)_2 \cdot 12H_2O$ at Low Temperatures."

536. R. Aasa, K. E. Carlsson, S. A. Reyes, and T. Vanngard, *Arkiv Kemi*, **25**, 285 (1966). "Fine and Hyperfine Structure in the ESR Spectrum of Fe^{3+} in Ethylenediaminetetraacetic Acid (EDTA)."

537. M. M. Zaripov and G. K. Chirkin, *Fiz. Tverd. Tela*, **7**, 100 (1965). "EPR of Iron Group Ions in Ammonium Chloride Single Crystals."

538. D. J. A. Gainon, *Phys. Rev.*, **134**, 1300 (1964). "EPR of Fe^{3+} in the Strong Axial Field of $PbTiO_3$ Host."

539. T. I. Barry, P. McNamara, and W. J. Moore, *J. Chem. Phys.*, **42**, 2599 (1965). "Paramagnetic Resonance and Optical Properties of Amethyst (α–Quartz)."

540. G. Lehmann and W. J. Moore, *J. Chem. Phys.*, **44**, 1741 (1966). "Optical and Paramagnetic Properties of Iron Centers in Quartz."

541. G. Lehmann and W. J. Moore, *Science*, **152**, 1061 (1966). "Color Center in Amethyst Quartz."

542. D. R. Hutton, *Phys. Letters*, **12**, 310 (1964). "Paramagnetic Resonance of Fe^{3+} in Amethyst and Citrine Quartz."

543. L. G. Chentsova, L. I. Tsinober, and M. I. Samoilovich, *Kristallografiya*, **11**, 236 (1966). "Quartz of Amethyst Color."

544. R. Nakada, A. Ebina, and T. Takahashi, *J. Phys. Soc. Japan*, **21**, 188 (1966). "ESR of Fe^{3+} in SnO_2."

545. E. S. Kirkpatrick, K. A. Mueller, and R. S. Rubins, *Phys. Rev.*, **135**, 86 (1964). "Strong Axial EPR Spectrum of Fe^{3+} in $SrTiO_3$ due to Nearest-Neighbor Charge Compensation."

546. W. Dobrov, R. F. Vieth, and M. E. Browne, *Phys. Rev.*, **115**, 79 (1959). "EPR in Strontium Metatitanate."

547. K. A. Mueller, *Helv. Phys. Acta*, **31**, 173 (1958). "Paramagnetic Resonance of Iron(III) in Single Crystals of $SrTiO_3$."

548. D. Gainon and R. Lacroix, *Proc. Phys. Soc.* (*London*), **79**, 658 (1962). "EPR of Fe^{3+} Ion in Anatase (TiO_2)."

549. A. Okaya, D. Carter, and F. Nash, *Quantum Electron. Symp., High View, New York, 1959*, 389. "EPR Spectrum of Fe^{3+} in TiO_2 (Rutile)."

550. L. Rimai and R. W. Bierig, *Phys. Rev. Letters*, **12**, 284 (1964). "Effect of the $Fe^{3+}-Tm^{3+}$ Exchange Interactions on the Paramagnetic Resonance and Relaxation of Fe Impurities in the Thulium Garnets."

551. A. Ehrenberg and R. C. Bray, *Arch. Biochem. Biophys.*, **109**, 199 (1965). "Magnetic Susceptibility Changes and ESR Signals Related to the Iron of Xanthine Oxidase."

552. R. L. White, G. F. Herrmann, J. W. Carson, and M. Mandel, *Phys. Rev.*, **136**, 231 (1964). "Paramagnetic Resonance of Fe^{3+} and Gd^{3+} in Yttrium Orthoaluminate ($YAlO_3$)."

553. S. Geschwind, *Phys. Rev.*, **121**, 363 (1961). "EPR of Fe^{3+} in Octahedral and Tetrahedral Sites in Yttrium Gallium Garnet and Anisotropy of Yttrium Iron Garnet."

554. S. Geschwind, *Phys. Rev. Letters*, **3**, 207 (1959). "Sign of the Ground State Cubic Crystal Field Splitting Parameter in Fe^{3+}."

555. L. Rimai and T. Kushida, *Phys. Rev.*, **143**, 160 (1966). "Paramagnetic Resonance of Fe^{3+} in Yttrium Aluminium, Lutetium Aluminum, and Lutetium Gallium Garnets."

556. P. Eisenberger and P. S. Pershan, *J. Chem. Phys.*, **45**, 2832 (1966). "ESR of Metmyoglobin: Field Dependence of $g_\perp^{eff}$."

557. D. R. Hutton and G. J. Troup, *Nature*, **211**, 621 (1966). "Paramagnetic Resonance Centers in Amethyst and Citrine Quartz."

558. A. Raeuber and J. Schneider, *Phys. Letters*, **3**, 230 (1963). "ESR of a Luminescent Center in Al Activated Cubic ZnS Single Crystals."

559. G. G. Wepfer, *Bull. Am. Phys. Soc.*, **11**, 719 (1966). "EPR Spectrum of Fe^{3+} in a Strong Axial Field in ZnSe."

560. W. G. Nilson and S. K. Kurtz, *Phys. Rev.*, **136**, 262 (1964). "Paramagnetic Resonance of Fe^{3+} in $ZnWO_4$."

561. V. F. Koryagin and V. N. Grechushnikov, *Fiz. Tverd. Tela*, **8**, 565 (1966). "Superhyperfine Structure in EPR Spectrum of Mn^{2+} in $AlCl_3 \cdot 6H_2O$ Crystals."

562. K. Hennig, *Phys. Status Solidi*, **11**, 795 (1965). "Paramagnetic Resonance of Mn^{2+} in S- or Se-Containing Silver Halides."

563. A. Cunliffe, G. F. J. Garlick, and M. N. Jones, *Paramagnetic Resonance, Proc. Intern. Conf., 1st, Jerusalem, 1962*, **2**, 755. "Correlation of ESR Spectra and Luminescence Properties of Some Manganese Activated Phosphors."

564. I. Ursu and V. Lupei, *Rev. Roumaine Phys.*, **11**, 165 (1966). "ESR of Mn^{2+} Ion in Polycrystalline As_2S_3."

565. L. D. Bogomolova, V. N. Lazukin, I. V. Chepeleva, and L. A. Bal'skaya, *Dokl. Akad. Nauk SSSR*, **165**, 1336 (1965). "EPR of Manganese Ions in the Glasslike System As–Se–Ge."

566. D. Shaltiel and J. W. Wernick, *Phys. Rev.*, **136**, 245 (1964). "Magnetic Resonance Spectra of Mn in Au and Pd."

567. J. Vesela, Z. Sroubek, and K. Zdansky, *Phys. Status Solidi*, **10**, K99 (1965). "Temperature Dependence of the Forbidden Transitions of the EPR of Mn^{2+} in $BaTiO_3$ Single Crystals."

568. H. Ikushima and S. Hayakawa, *J. Phys. Soc. Japan*, **19**, 1986 (1964). "ESR of Mn^{2+} in $BaTiO_3$."

569. V. M. Vinokurov, M. M. Zaripov, V. S. Kropotov, and V. G. Stepanov, *Geokhimiya*, **1965**, 104. "Study of Isomorphism of Mn^{2+} in Beryls by the EPR Method."

570. J. Michoulier and P. Ducros, *Proc. Colloq. Ampere*, **12**, 215 (1964). "EPR of Mn^{2+} in the Random Crystalline Field of a Zeolite."

571. L. V. Bershov, V. M. Vinokurov, M. M. Zaripov, V. S. Kropotov, and V. G. Stepanov, *Geokhimiya*, **1966**, 122. "Paramagnetic Resonance of Mn^{2+} in Natural Datolite Crystals."

572. F. G. Wakim, H. K. Henisch, and H. A. Atwater, *J. Chem. Phys.*, **42**, 2619 (1965). "EPR of Mn^{2+} in Calcium Tartrate."

573. V. M. Vinokurov, M. M. Zaripov, and V. G. Stepanov, *Fiz. Tverd. Tela*, **6**, 1125 (1964). "EPR of Mn^{2+} in Apatite."

574. M. M. Zaripov, S. F. Murtazin, and V. G. Stepanov, *Opt. i Spektroskopiya*, **14**, 421 (1963). "Calculation of the Paramagnetic Resonance of Mn^{2+}."

575. S. Fujiwara, *Anal. Chem.*, **36**, 2259 (1964). "Investigation of Trace Impurities in Solids by EPR. Distribution of Manganese in Calcium Carbonate."

576. D. F. Wait, *Phys. Rev.*, **132**, 601 (1963). "Hydrostatic Pressure Dependence of the Paramagnetic Resonance of an S-State Ion in a Noncubic Lattice Mn^{2+} in Calcite."

577. C Kikuchi and L. M. Matarrese, *J. Chem. Phys.*, **33**, 601 (1960). "EPR Absorption of Ions with Spin 5/2: Mn^{2+} in Calcite."

578. L. M. Matarrese, *J. Chem. Phys.*, **34**, 336 (1961). "Comments on the EPR Spectrum of Mn^{2+} in Calcite."

579. V. M. Vinokurov, M. M. Zaripov, and V. G. Stepanov, *Kristallografiya*, **6**, 104 (1961). "Study of Some Manganese Containing Carbonates by the Method of Paramagnetic Resonance."

580. M. Sumita, *Japan. J. Appl. Phys.*, **5**, 453 (1966). "Mn Ions in Fluorite Structure Crystals."

581. A. A. Manenkov and V. A. Milyaev, *Paramagnetic Resonance, Proc. Intern. Conf., 1st, Jerusalem, 1962*, **2**, 419. "Spin Lattice Relaxation of S State Ions."

582. R. L. Hickok, J. A. Parodi, and W. G. Segelken, *J. Phys. Chem.*, **66**, 2715 (1962). "The EPR of Manganous Ion in Ca Pyrophosphate and Ca Fluoride."

583. Y. Okubo, *J. Phys. Soc. Japan*, **18**, 916 (1963). "ESR Spectra of Bivalent Manganese Ions in Natural Apatite Single Crystals."

584. V. M. Vinokurov, M. M. Zaripov, and V. G. Stepanov, *Fiz. Tverd. Tela*, **6**, 1130 (1964). "EPR of Mn^{2+} in Diopside Crystals."

585. L. V. Bershov, A. S. Marfunin, and R. M. Mineeva, *Geokhimiya*, **1966**, 464. "EPR of Mn^{2+} in Tremolite."

586. M. I. Samoilovich, A. I. Novozhilov, V. F. Dernov-Pegarev, and L. I. Potkin, *Zh. Strukt. Khim.*, **7**, 109 (1966). "EPR of Mn^{2+} in Molybdates with a Scheelite Structure."

587. D. H. Tanimoto and J. C. Kemp, *J. Phys. Chem. Solids*, **27**, 887 (1966). "Forbidden Hyperfine Transitions in the ESR of Mn^{2+} in CaO and SrO Crystals."

588. J. E. Drumheller, *Helv. Phys. Acta*, **37**, 689 (1964). "Forbidden Hyperfine Transitions in the Paramagnetic Resonance of Mn^{2+} in Cubic CaO."

589. L. Bershov, A. S. Marfunin, and R. M. Mineeva, *Zh. Eksperim. i Teor. Fiz.*, **49**, 743 (1965). "EPR of the Tetrahedral Complex $[MnF_4]^{2-}$ in Scheelite."

590. C. F. Hempstead and K. D. Bowers, *Phys. Rev.*, **118**, 131 (1960). "EPR of Impurities in $CaWO_4$."

591. V. N. Grechushnikov, and V. F. Koryagin, *Fiz. Tverd. Tela*, **7**, 3123 (1965). "Paramagnetic Resonance of Mn(II) Ion in Synthetic $CdCo_3$."

592. T. P. P. Hall, W. Hayes, and F. I. B. Williams, *Proc. Phys. Soc. (London)*, **78**, 883 (1961). "Paramagnetic Resonance of Mn."

593. M. F. Diegen, V. M. Maevskii, V. Y. Zevin, and N. I. Vitrikhovskii, *Fiz. Tverd. Tela*, **6**, 2756 (1964). "EPR of Mn^{2+} in CdS."

594. J. Lambe and C. Kikuchi, *Phys. Rev.*, **119**, 1256 (1960). "EPR of CdTe: Mn and CdS."

595. Y. Ishikawa, *J. Phys. Soc. Japan*, **21**, 1473 (1966). "ESR Spectra of Exchange Coupled Mn^{2+} Ions in ZnS and CdS."

596. P. B. Dorain, *Phys. Rev.*, **112**, 1058 (1958). "EPR of Manganese(II) in Hexagonal Zinc Oxide and Cadmium Sulfide Single Crystals."

597. R. S. Title, *Phys. Rev.*, **130**, 17 (1963). "Covalency and the Paramagnetic Resonance of Mn^{2+} in CdSe."

598. C. Kikuchi and G. H. Azarbayejani, *J. Phys. Soc. Japan*, **17**, Suppl. B-1, 453 (1962). "Spin Resonance Properties of ZnTe: Mn and of Other $A_{II}B_{VI}$ Compounds."

599. I. Chen, C. Kikuchi, and H. Watanabe, *J. Chem. Phys.*, **42**, 189 (1965). "Superhyperfine Structures in ESR and ENDOR of Cubic CdTe: Mn^{2+}."

600. R. E. Donovan and A. A. Vuylsteke, *Phys. Rev.*, **127**, 76 (1962). "Paramagnetic Resonance Spectrum of Manganese in $CdWO_4$."

601. M. Date, *J. Phys. Soc. Japan*, **18**, 912 (1963). "Shift of Impurity Paramagnetic Resonance in Paramagnetic Crystals."

602. J. C. M. Henning and P. F. Bongers, *J. Phys. Chem. Solids*, **27**, 745 (1966). "ESR of Mn^{2+} in Cs_3ZnCl_5."

603. H. D. Powell, Ph.D. Thesis, Clemson University, 1965. "An ESR Study of Crystalline Cuprous Chloride Containing Divalent Manganese."

604. B. B. Garrett and L. O. Morgan, *J. Chem. Phys.*, **44**, 890 (1966). "Electron Spin Relaxation in Solvated Manganese(II) Ion Solutions."

605. R. Bleekrode, J. Dieleman, and H. J. Vegter, *Phys. Letters*, **2**, 355 (1962) "ESR on Manganese in GaAs."

606. A. M. Vasil'ev, *Zh. Fiz. Khim.*, **38**, 845 (1964). "Dependence of the Width of the EPR Lines of Mn^{2+} Ions in Aqueous Solutions on Concentration."

607. F. G. Wakim and A. W. Nolle, *J. Chem. Phys.*, **37**, 3000 (1962). "Paramagnetic Resonance of Glassy $Mn(H_2O)_6^{2+}$."

608. R. G. Hayes and R. J. Myers, *J. Chem. Phys.*, **40**, 877 (1964). "Effect of Cl^- and SO_4^{2-} on the Paramagnetic Resonance Line Width of Mn^{2+} in Aqueous Solution and the Rates of Formation of the Complex Ions."

609. R. T. Ross, *J. Chem. Phys.*, **42**, 3919 (1965). "Dipolar Broadening of EPR Spectra Due to Solute Segregation in Frozen Aqueous Solutions."

610. C. C. Hinckley and L. O. Morgan, *J. Chem. Phys.*, **44**, 898 (1966). "ESR Line Widths of Manganese(II) Ions in Concentrated Aqueous Solutions."

611. J. Kondo, *Progr. Theoret. Phys.*, **23**, 106 (1960). "ESR of Mn^{2+} Ion in Ionic Crystals."

612. D. Bösnecker and E. Lutze, *Z. Angew. Phys.*, **12**, 354 (1960). "EPR in Solutions."

613. A. W. Nolle and L. O. Morgan, *J. Chem. Phys.*, **36**, 378 (1962). "ESR Line Widths in Dilute Hexaaquomanganese(II) Solutions at 9.4 and 24 kMc."

614. G. D. Watkins, *Phys. Rev.*, **113**, 79 (1959). "ESR of Manganous Ions in Alkali Chlorides: Association with Vacancies and Impurities."

615. L. Yarmus, M. Kukk, and B. R. Sundheim, *J. Chem. Phys.*, **40**, 33 (1964). "Paramagnetic Resonance Spectrum of $MnCl_2$ in Molten Alkali Halides."

616. K. Fukuda, Y. Uchida, and H. Yoshimura, *J. Phys. Soc. Japan*, **13**, 971 (1958). "Paramagnetic Resonance Spectrum of Manganese in Single Crystals of Alkali Halide Grown from the Melt."

617. W. J. Veigele and W. H. Tanttila, *J. Chem. Phys.*, **41**, 274 (1964). "Paramagnetic Resonance of Mn^{2+} in KF."

618. W. J. Veigele, *Appl. Spectry.*, **20**, 113 (1966). "EPR Spectroscopy of Vacancies in $KF:Mb^{2+}$."

619. L. V. Bershov, A. S. Marfunin, and R. M. Mineeva, *Dokl. Akad. Nauk SSSR* **164**, 1141 (1965). "EPR of Mn^{2+} in Apophyllite."

620. S. Ogawa and Y. Yokozawa, *J. Phys. Soc. Japan*, **14**, 1116 (1959). "Paramagnetic Resonance of Manganese in $KMgF_3$."

621. K. Horai and K. Saiki, *J. Phys. Soc. Japan*, **21**, 397 (1966). "ESR of $(KMnF_3)_x \cdot (KMgF_3)_{1-x}$."

622. K. Zdansky, E. Simanek, and Z. Sroubek, *Phys. Status Solidi*, **3**, K277 (1963). "Paramagnetic Resonance and Antiferromagnetism in $KMnCl_3$."

623. V. Minkiewicz and A. Nakamura, *Phys. Rev.*, **143**, 356 (1966). "Magnetic Properties of $KMnF_3$. III. Nuclear and ESR."

624. B. M. M. Brandt, D. van Ormondt, and T. Thalhammer, *Phys. Letters*, **19**, 549 (1965). "The EPR Spectrum of Mn^{2+} in $La_2Mg_3(NO_3)_{12} \cdot 24H_2O$."

625. Y. Yokozawa and Y. Kazumata, *J. Phys. Soc. Japan*, **16**, 694 (1961). "Paramagnetic Resonance of Mn^{2+} Associated with Impurities in Alkali Chlorides."

626. T.-T. Chang and W. H. Tanttila, *J. Chem. Phys.*, **38**, 571 (1963). "Paramagnetic Resonance of Mn^{2+} in LiF."

627. D. W. Nebert and B. T. Allen, *Biophys. J.*, **6**, 189 (1966). "Environmental Factors Influencing the Hyperfine Structure of Manganous Low Temperature EPR Spectra."

628. N. S. Garif'yanov, R. K. Timerov, and N. Γ. Usacheva, *Fiz. Tverd. Tela*, **4** 3344 (1962). "Paramagnetic Electron Resonance in Supercooled Solutions Containing Mn^{2+} and Gd^{3+}."

629. F. Waldner, *Helv. Phys. Acta*, **35**, 756 (1962). "EPR Spectrum of Mn^{2+} in Natural $MgAl_2O_4$ Spinel."

630. V. M. Vinokurov, M. M. Zaripov, V. S. Kropotov, and V. G. Stepanov, *Geokhimiya*, **1965**, 1486. "EPR of Mn^{2+} Ions in Cordierite."

631. H. Matsumoto, K. Fukuda, M. Takeshima, and Y. Uchida, *J. Phys. Soc. Japan*, **16**, 1791 (1961). "Cubic Contribution to EPR of Manganous Ion in Magnesium(II) Chloride."

632. M. M. Zaripov, V. S. Kropotov, and L. D. Livanova, *Fiz. Tverd. Tela*, **8**, 231 (1966). "EPR of Mn^{2+} in MgF_2."

633. G. J. Wolga and R. Tseng, *Phys. Rev.*, **133**, 1563 (1964). "Forbidden Transitions in the Paramagnetic Resonance Spectrum of Mn^{2+} in Cubic MgO."

634. B. A. Coles, J. W. Orton, and J. Owen, *Phys. Rev. Letters*, **4**, 116 (1960). "Antiferromagnetic Exchange Interactions Between Manganese(III) Ions in Magnesium Oxide."

635. J. Kondo, *Progr. Theoret. Phys.*, **28**, 1026 (1962). "Spin Lattice Interaction of a Mn^{2+} Ion in MgO."

636. J. E. Drumheller, *Phys. Rev.*, **133**, 1099 (1964). "Forbidden Hyperfine Transitions in the EPR of Mn^{2+} in Cubic MgO."

637. J. Owen, *J. Appl. Phys.*, **33**, 355 (1962). "Spin Resonance of Ion Pairs in Crystal Lattices."

638. W. A. Pieczonka, H. E. Petch, and A. B. McLay, *Can. J. Phys.*, **39**, 145 (1961). "An ESR Study of Manganese Impurity in Brucite."

639. Y. Miyako and M. Date, *J. Phys. Soc. Japan*, **19**, 784 (1964). "Hyperfine Fields of Mn^{2+} and Mn^{4+} Ions in MgO."

640. P. Fontana and R. Lacroix, *Helv. Phys. Acta*, **39**, 164 (1966). "Paramagnetic Resonance of Manganese in Magnesium Sulfite."

641. T. Arakawa, *J. Phys. Soc. Japan*, **17**, 706 (1962). "Paramagnetic Resonance of Mn^{2+} in $MgTiF_6 \cdot 6H_2O$."

642. R. Srinivasan and C. K. Subramanian, *Proc. Nucl. Phys. Solid State Phys. Symp.*, *Calcutta, 1965* (*P. A*), 22. "ESR Study of Antipyrene Complexes of Iron Group Ions."

643. H. Abe and H. Morigaki, *Paramagnetic Resonance, Proc. Intern. Conf., 1st, Jerusalem, 1962*, **2**, 567. "Paramagnetic Resonance in Manganese Acetate Tetrahydrate."

644. J. A. Cowen, G. T. Johnston, and H. Van Till, *J. Chem. Phys.*, **45**, 644 (1966). "Ferrimagnetic Resonance in Manganese Acetate Tetrahydrate."

645. A. Narasimhamurty, *J. Sci. Ind. Research* (*India*), **17B**, 470 (1958). "Resonance Absorption in Paramagnetic Salts."

646. V. A. Kutuzov, *Paramagnitn. Rezonans, Kazansk. Univ., Sbornik, 1960*, 123. "Paramagnetic Absorption in Solid Solutions of $MnCl_2 \cdot 4H_2O$."

647. A. I. Kurushin, *Zh. Eksperim. i Teor. Fiz.*, **37**, 297 (1959). "Paramagnetic Absorption and the Rotation of the Plane of Polarization of Some Salts in the Microwave Range."

648. V. S. L'vov and M. P. Petrov, *Phys. Status Solidi*, **13**, K65 (1966). "Distribution of Spin Density in Paramagnetic Perovskite Crystals."

649. T. Garofano, M. B. Palma-Vittorelli, M. U. Palma, and F. Persico, *Paramagnetic Resonance, Proc. Intern. Cong., 1st, Jerusalem, 1962*, **2**, 582. "Motional And Exchange Effects in the ESR Behavior of Ni^{2+} and Mn^{2+} Hexammine Cubic Crystals."

650. V. A. Kutuzov, *Izv. Akad. Nauk SSSR, Ser. Fiz.*, **27**, 81 (1963). "Paramagnetic Absorption in Parallel Fields in Potassium Chromium Alums and Ammonium Manganese Sulfate."

651. I. N. Bakhina, G. V. Korobeinikova, and A. I. Kurushin, *Tr. Estestv.-Nauchn. Inst. pri permsk, Univ.*, **11**, 51 (1962). "Paramagnetic Absorption in Parallel Fields in $Mn(NH_4)_2(SO_4) \cdot 6H_2O$ at Ultrahigh Frequencies."

652. V. V. Panfilov and L. F. Vereshchagin, *Dokl. Akad. Nauk SSSR*, **154**, 819 (1964). "Paramagnetic Resonance of MnS over a Wide Temperature Range."

653. T. Arakawa, *J. Phys. Soc. Japan*, **17**, 703 (1962). "Axial Field Splitting Parameter for Mn^{2+} in $MnSiF_6 \cdot 6H_2O$, $MnTiF_6 \cdot 6H_2O$ and $MnSnCl_6 \cdot 6H_2O$."

654. Y. Servant, *Compt. Rend.*, **258**, 1455 (1964). "Rotation of the EPR of Manganese Sulfate Monohydrate in the 3000-Mc Band."

655. J. Herve, *Ann. Phys.*, **5**, 321 (1960). "The Shapes of the Paramagnetic Resonance Lines and the Direct Measurement of Momenta."

656. I. Ursu and A. Nicula, *Rev. Roumaine Phys.*, **9**, 343 (1964). "ESR of the Mn(II) Ion in Zeolites."

657. V. Laizans and A. Vitols, *Latvijas PSR Zinatnu Akad. Vestis*, **1963**, 57. "Peculiarities of EPR Spectra of Mn^{2+} in NaCl Crystals with Ca^{2+} and Cd^{2+} Impurities."

658. V. Laizans and A. Vitols, *Radiats. Fiz., Akad. Nauk Latv. SSR, Inst. Fiz.*, **1**, 105 (1964). "EPR of Manganese in Sodium Chloride Crystals Containing Cadmium and Calcium Impurities."

659. K. Svares, V. Laizans, and A. F. Lyushina, *Radiats. Fiz., Akad. Nauk Latv. SSR, Inst. Fiz.*, **1**, 93 (1964). "EPR and Luminescence of Solid Solutions of Sodium Chloride and Manganese Chloride."

660. K. N. Shrivastava and P. Venkateswarlu, *Proc. Indian Acad. Sci., A*, **63**, 284 (1966). "ESR of Mn^{2+} in NaCl Single Crystals and Lattice Defects."

661. K. Morigaki, M. Fujimoto, and J. Itoh, *J. Phys. Soc. Japan*, **13**, 1174 (1958). "Paramagnetic Resonance Spectrum of Mn^{2+} in Sodium Chloride Single Crystal."

662. K. Svares, V. B. Laizans, and A. F. Lyushina, *Rost. Kristallov, Akad. Nauk SSSR, Inst. Kristallogr.*, **5**, 361 (1965). "Effect of Impurities on the Optical and Paramagnetic Properties of Bivalent Manganese in NaCl."

663. V. Laizans, K. Svares, and A. Vitols, *Radiats. Fiz., Akad. Nauk Latv. SSR, Inst. Fiz.*, **3**, 103 (1965). "Effect of γ–Radiation on the Process for the Decomposition of the Paramagnetic Manganese Centers in Sodium Chloride."

664. G. Alzetta, P. R. Crippa, and S. Santucci, *Phys. Status Solidi*, **12**, K81 (1965). "Effect of Plastic Deformation on the Spectrum of NaCl: Mn."

665. J. S. van Wieringen and J. G. Rensen, *Philips Res. Rept.*, **20**, 659 (1965). "Paramagnetic Resonance of Mn(II) in Sodium Chloride between 300 and 803°."

666. G. Alzetta, P. R. Crippa, and S. Santucci, *Nuovo Cimento*, **B42**, 100 (1966). "Relaxation of Manganese Paramagnetic Centers in NaCl."

667. H. F. Symmons and R. C. Kemp, *Brit. J. Appl. Phys.*, **17**, 607 (1966). "The Early Stages of Aggregation of Mn^{2+} in NaCl."

668. A. Vitols, J. Krumins, and V. Laizans, *Radiats. Fiz., Akad. Nauk Latv. SSR, Inst. Fiz.*, **3**, 95 (1965). "Ionic Conductivity and the EPR of NaCl Crystals with Mn^{2+} and Cd^{2+} Impurities."

669. H. Kawamura and Y. Okubo, *J. Appl. Phys.*, **33**, 367 (1962). "ESR Study of Trapping of Mn Ions along Dislocation Lines in NaCl."

670. C. N. Owston, *Proc. Phys. Soc. (London)*, **88**, 205 (1966). "ESR Spectrum of Manganese Impurities in Single Crystals of NaCl."

671. I. Tatsuzaki, *J. Phys. Soc. Japan*, **17**, 582 (1962). "EPR of $(NH_4)_2 Cd_2 (SO_4)_3^-$ Mn^{2+}."

672. H. Abe and H. Shirai, *J. Phys. Soc. Japan*, **15**, 1711 (1960). "ESR of Manganese in Ammonium Chloride."

673. D. H. Goode, *J. Chem. Phys.*, **45**, 1366 (1966). "EPR of Divalent Manganese in Ammonium Chloride."

674. M. M. Zaripov and G. K. Chirkin, *Fiz. Tverd. Tela*, **7**, 2947 (1965). "EPR Spectra and Structure of Nearest Environment of Paramagnetic Ions in NH_4Cl."

675. M. M. Zaripov and G. K. Chirkin, *Fiz., Tverd. Tela*, **7**, 3409 (1965). "EPR and Second-Order Phase Transitions in NH_4Cl."

676. T. J. Seed, *J. Chem. Phys.*, **41**, 1486 (1964). "ESR of Mn^{2+} in the Ternary System $NH_4Cl–MnCl_2–H_2O$."

677. T. Arakawa, *J. Phys. Soc. Japan*, **17**, 705 (1962). "Axial Field Splitting Parameter for Mn in Fluorosilicate-Type Crystals."

678. S. Ehara and Y. Tomono, *J. Phys. Soc. Japan*, **18**, 745 (1963). "Hyperfine Structure in Paramagnetic Resonance of Mn in Pd Metal."

679. S. Ehara and Y. Tomono, *J. Phys. Soc. Japan*, **18**, 309 (1963). "Hyperfine Structure in Paramagnetic Resonance of Manganese Palladium Metal."

680. I. V. Nikolaeva and N. N. Tikhomirova, *Zh. Strukt. Khim.*, **7**, 351 (1966). "EPR Study of Mn Ions Adsorbed on Silica Gel."

681. W. H. From, P. B. Dorain, and C. Kikuchi, *Phys. Rev.*, **135** (3A), 710 (1964). "Hyperfine and Superhyperfine Structure of Manganese in SnO_2."

682. W. Low and U. Rosenberger, *Phys. Rev.*, **116**, 621 (1959). "Paramagnetic Resonance of S-State Ions in Strontium Chloride."

683. G. L. Bir and L. S. Sochava, *Fiz. Tverd. Tela*, **5**, 3594 (1963). "Intensity of Allowed and Forbidden Lines of Mn^2 Paramagnetic Resonance Spectrum in $SrCl_2$."

684. M. I. Kornfel'd and L. S. Sochava, *Fiz. Tverd. Tela*, **5**, 2232 (1963). "Complexes of Impurity Ions in $SrCl_2$ Crystals."

685. V. M. Vinokurov and V. G. Stepanov, *Fiz. Tverd. Tela*, **6**, 380 (1964). "Mn^{2+} EPR in SrF_2 Single Crystals."

686. A. J. Shuskus, *J. Chem. Phys.*, **41**, 1885 (1964). "Paramagnetic Resonance of Some S-State Ions in Single Crystals of Strontium Oxide."

687. J. Rosenthal and L. Yarmus, *Rev. Sci. Instr.*, **37**, 381 (1966). "SrO: Mn as EPR Marker and Intensity Standard."

688. L. V. Holroyd and J. L. Kolopus, *Phys. Status Solidi*, **3**, K456 (1963). "Paramagnetic Resonance of Mn^{2+} in Single Crystals of SrO."

689. A. A. Manenkov and V. A. Milyaev, *Zh. Eksperim. i Teor. Fiz.*, **41**, 100 (1961). "Relaxation Phenomena in the Paramagnetic Resonance of Mn^{2+} Ions in the Cubic Crystal Field of SrS."

690. A. A. Manenkov and A. M. Prokhorov, *Zh. Eksperim. i Teor. Fiz.*, **40**, 1606 (1961). "EPR of Mn in SrS."

691. H. G. Andresen, *J. Chem. Phys.*, **35**, 1090 (1961). "Hyperfine Structure and g-Tensor Anisotropy of the EPR of Manganese in TiO_2."

692. L. D. Bogomolova, V. N. Lazukin, and I. V. Chepeleva, *Dokl. Akad. Nauk SSSR*, **168**, 59 (1966). "ESR of Mn^{2+} Ions in $Ti_2SeAs_2Se_3$."

693. J. R. Chamberlain and R. W. Cooper, *Proc. Phys. Soc. (London)*, **87**, 967 (1966). "EPR in Yttrium Gallium Garnet: Co^{2+} and Mn^{2+}."

694. A. Nicula, I. Ursu, and S. Nistor, *Rev. Roumaine Phys.*, **10**, 229 (1965). "Forbidden Transitions in the ESR Spectrum of Mn in Zeolites."

695. E. W. Collings, F. T. Hedgock, and W. R. Muir, *Proc. Intern. Conf. Low Temp. Phys., 8th, London, 1962*, 253. "Influence of Spin Ordering on the Low-Temperature Magnetic and Electrical Properties of the Zn–Mn System."

696. G. Burns, *Phys. Rev.*, **135**, 479 (1964). "Concentration-Dependent ESR."

697. M. R. Brown, B. A. Coles, J. Owen, and R. W. H. Stevenson, *Phys. Rev. Letters*, **7**, 246 (1961). "Ferromagnetic Exchange Interaction between Mn^{2+} Ions in $(Mn,Zn)F_2$."

698. A. Mukherji and T. P. Das, *Phys. Rev.*, **111**, 1479 (1958). "Fluorine-19 Hyperfine Interaction in the EPR Spectrum of Mn Ions in Zinc Fuoride."

699. J. Owen, M. R. Brown, B. A. Coles, and R. W. H. Stevenson, *J. Phys. Soc. Japan, Suppl. B-I*, **17**, 428 (1962). "EPR from Pairs of Mn^{2+} Ions in ZnF_2, Mn."

700. A. M. Clogston, J. P. Gordon, V. Jaccarino, M. Peter, and L. R. Walker, *Phys. Rev.*, **117**, 1222 (1960). "Hfs of ^{19}F in the EPR of Mn: ZnF_2."

701. V. F. Dernov-Pegarev, M. M. Zapirov, M. I. Samoilovich, and V. G. Stepanov, *Fiz. Tverd. Tela*, **7**, 3688 (1965). "EPR of Mn^{2+} Ions in $ZnMoO_4$ Crystals."

702. J. Schneider and S. R. Sircar, *Z. Naturforsch*, **17a**, 651–4 (1962). "Paramagnetic Resonance of Mn^{2+} Ions in Synthetic and Natural ZnO Crystals. II. Analysis of the Forbidden Transitions $\Delta M = \pm 1, \Delta m = \pm 1$."

703. J. Schneider and S. R. Sircar, *Z. Naturforsch.*, **17a**, 570 (1962). "Paramagnetic Resonance of Mn^{2+} Ions in Synthetic and Natural ZnO Crystals. I. Allowed Transitions $\Delta m = \pm 1, \Delta m = \pm 0$."

704. N. I. Kuntsevich, A. L. Poznyak, and V. V. Sviridov, *Vestsi Akad. Navuk Belarusk. SSR, Ser. Khim. Navuk*, **1965**, 41. "Electron Paramagnetic Resonance of Mn^{2+} Ions in Polycrystalline Zinc Oxide."

705. H. A. Kuska, F. M. D'Itri, and A. I. Popov, *Inorg. Chem.*, **5**, 7, 1272 (1966). "ESR of Pentamethylenetetrazole Manganese(II) and Copper(II) Complexes."

706. G. E. Arkhangel'skii, *Opt. i Spektroskopiya*, **20**, 30. 513 (1966). "Two-Quantum Absorption Observed in EPR of the Mn^{2+} Ion in ZnS–Mn Phosphors."

707. J. Toussaint and C. Declerck, *Bull. Soc. Roy. Sci. Liege*, **35**, 87 (1966). "ESR Spectrum of Mn^{2+} in (Zinc) Blende."

708. G. D. Watkins, *Phys. Rev.*, **110**, 786 (1958). "Sign of the Cubic Field Splitting for Mn^{2+} in Zinc Sulfide."

709. J. Schneider, S. R. Sircar, and A. Raeuber, *Z. Naturforsch.*, **18a**, 980 (1963). "ESR of Mn^{2+} Ions in Cubic and Hexagonal Crystal Fields of ZnS."

710. B. C. Cavenett, *Proc. Phys. Soc. (London)*, **84**, 1 (1964). "The Allowed and Forbidden Transitions in the Paramagnetic Resonance of the Manganese Ion in Cubic Zinc Selenide."

711. E. E. Schneider and P. A. Forrester, *Arch. Sci. (Geneva)*, **11**, Spec. No., 143 (1958). "Effects of Resonance Exchange of Manganese in Alkali Halides."

712. F. Koch, *Studia Univ. Babes-Bolyai Ser. Math. Phys.*, **1**, 139 (1964). "Some Aspects of the Resonance of DPPH, Cu^{2+}, and Mn^{2+} in Weak Fields."

713. A. Nicula, *Studii Cercetari Fiz.*, **17**, 257 (1965). "ESR of Copper(II) and Manganese(II) Ions in Polycrystalline Substances."

714. F. Holuj, *Can. J. Phys.*, **44**, 503 (1966). "The Spin Hamiltonian and Intensities of the ESR Spectra Originating from Large Zero-Field Effects on ^6S States."

715. B. R. Cooper and F. Keffer, *Phys. Rev.*, **125**, 896 (1962). "Paramagnetic Resonance Width in Iron and Nickel."

716. Sh. Sh. Bashkirov, *Fiz. Metal. i Metalloved., Akad. Nauk SSSR.*, **6**, 577 (1958). "Paramagnetic Lattice Relaxation Times in Salts of Paramagnetic Ions in the S-State."

717. A. M. Clogston, *Phys. and Chem. Solids*, **7**, 201 (1958). "Structure of the Metastable State of Mn^{2+} and Fe^{3+}."

718. N. K. Bel'skii and V. N. Tsikunov, *Dokl. Akad. Nauk SSSR*, **142**, 380 (1962). "EPR Phenomena in Chelate Polymers."

719. H. H. Wickman, AEC Accession No. **44426**, Rept. No. UCRL-**11538**. Avail. OTS, 1964. "Nuclear and Magnetic Resonance Studies in S-State Ions."

720. I. T. M. Bray, G. C. Brown, Jr., and A. Kiel, *U.S. Dept. Com., Office Tech. Serv.*, **A D 267**, 423, 33 (1961). "Relaxation Phenomena in Dilute Potassium Ferrocyanide."

721. A. M. Prokhorov and V. B. Fedorov, *Zh. Eksperim. i Teor. Fiz.*, **46**, 1937 (1964). "Paramagnetic Relaxation in $K_3(Fe,Co)(CN)_6$ at Temperatures from 0.1 to 4.2°K."

722. T. Ohtsuka, *J. Phys. Soc. Japan*, **16**, 1549 (1961). "Interaction Effects in Potassium Ferricyanide."

723. D. H. Paxman, *Proc. Phys. Soc.* (*London*), **78**, 180 (1961). "Spin-Lattice Relaxation-Time Measurements in Dilute Potassium Ferricyanide."

724. A. Rannestad and P. E. Wagner, *Phys. Rev.*, **131**, 1953 (1963). "Paramagnetic Relaxation in Dilute Potassium Ferricyanide."

725. N. S. Garif'ynov and E. G. Kharakhash'yan, *Fiz. Tverd. Tela*, **7**, 1274 (1965). "EPR in Supercooled Solutions of Fe(III), Ru(III), and Os(III)."

726. J. Danon, H. Panepucci, and A. A. Misetich, *J. Chem. Phys.*, **44**, 4154 (1966). "ESR Studies of Chromium Nitrosyl Complexes."

727. J. G. Kenworthy, G. F. Longster, and R. E. Richards, *Trans. Faraday Soc.*, **62**, 534 (1966). "Measurement by ESR of Free Radical Concentrations, and Electron Exchange Kinetics in Solutions of Potassium Pentacyanotriosochromate."

728. I. Bernal and S. E. Harrison, *J. Chem. Phys.*, **38**, 2581 (1963). "The Paramagnetic Resonance Spectrum of the $Cr(CN)_5NO^{3-}$ Ion."

729. R. G. Hayes, *J. Chem. Phys.*, **38**, 2580 (1963). "The EPR Spectrum of the $Cr(CN)_5NO^{3-}$ Ion."

730. H. A. Kuska and M. T. Rogers, *J. Chem. Phys.*, **42**, 3034 (1965). "Single-Crystal ESR Spectra and Covalent Bonding in $Cr(CN)_5NO^{3-}$ Ion."

731. J. J. Fortman and R. G. Hayes, *J. Chem. Phys.*, **43**, 15 (1965). "EPR Studies of $Mn(CN)_5NO^{2-}$ and $Cr(CN)_5NO^{3-}$ in Dilute Single Crystals."

732. J. B. Spencer and R. J. Myers, *J. Am. Chem. Soc.*, **86**, 522 (1964). "Hyperfine Coupling Constants and Rates of Exchange for $^{13}CN^-$ with the Axial Equatorial Positions in $Cr(CN)_5NO^{3-}$."

733. K. H. Hausser, *Z. Naturforsch.*, **16a**, 1190 (1961). "ESR of Dibenzene Vanadium."

734. K. H. Hausser, *Naturwissenschaften*, **48**, 666 (1961). "^{53}Cr Hyperfine Structure of the ESR of Dibenzenechromium Iodide."

735. K. H. Hausser, *Naturwissenschaften*, **48**, 426 (1961). "ESR of the Dibenzene Complexes of the 6th Group Metals."

736. N. N. Bubnov, Yu. A. Sorokin, S. P. Solodovnikov, and V. M. Chibrikin. *Izvest. Akad. Nauk SSSR.*, *Ser. Fiz.*, **23**, 1263 (1959). "Investigation of Dibenzylchromium Derivatives with Electronic Paramagnetic Resonance."

737. E. Koenig, *Z. Naturforsch.*, **19a**, 1139 (1964). "The EPR of Tris-2,2'-Dipyridyl-Complexes with d^5 Configuration for the Central Ion."

738. P. T. Manoharan and H. B. Gray, *Chem. Commun.*, **1965**, 14, 324–5. "ESR Study of $Mn(CN)_5NO^{2-}$ in a Single Crystal."

739. I. Bernal and S. E. Harrison, *J. Chem. Phys.*, **34**, 102 (1961). "EPR and Optical Absorption of $K_3Cr(CN)_5NO \cdot H_2O$."

740. B. A. Goodman, J. B. Raynor, and M. C. R. Symons, *J. Chem. Soc.*, *A. Inorg.*, *Phys.*, *Theoret.*, **1966**, 8, 994–7. "Structure and Reactivity of Transition-Metal Complexes with Polyatomic Ligands. II. ESR Spectrum and Structure of $Cr(CN)_5NO^{3-}$."

741. I. Bernal, S. D. Robinson, L. S. Meriwether, and G. Wilkinson, *Chem. Commun.*, **22**, 571 (1965). "ESR Studies of Some Chromium(I) Nitrosyl Complexes."

742. H. A. Kuska and M. T. Rogers, *J. Chem. Phys.*, **40**, 910 (1964). "Hyperfine Splittings in the Paramagnetic Resonance Spectrum of the $Cr(CN)_5NO^{3-}$ Ion."

743. K. Heuer, R. Neubert, and H. D. Sonneck, *Exptl. Tech. Physik*, **13**, 231 (1965). "Hyperfine Structure of Electron Resonance Spectra of Molecules with Several Magnetic Nuclei in a Weak Magnetic Field. Spectrum of $K_3(Cr(CN)_5NO)$."

744. Yu. D. Tsvetkov, V. V. Voevodskii, G. A. Razuvaev, Yu. V. Sorokin, and G. A. Domrachev, *Dokl. Akad. Nauk SSSR.*, **115**, 118 (1957). "Paramagnetic Electron Resonance in Some Chromiumaromatic Compounds with 'Sandwich' Structure."

745. R. D. Feltham, *J. Inorg. Nuclear Chem.*, **16**, 197 (1961). "EPR and Optical Spectra of Chromium 'Sandwich' Compounds."

746. K. H. Hausser, *Z. Elektrochem.*, **65**, 636 (1961). "Paramagnetic Relaxation in Liquids."

747. N. N. Bubnov and V. M. Chibrikin, cf. *Opt. i Spektroskopiya*, **5**, 90 (1958). "The Width of the Hyperfine Structure in Electron Paramagnetic Resonance Spectra at Different Temperatures."

748. T. Ohtsuka, *J. Phys. Soc. Japan.*, **15**, 939 (1960). "Interaction Effects in Potassium Ferricyanide."

749. R. F. David and P. E. Wagner, *Phys. Rev.*, **150**, 192 (1966). "Angular Dependence of Paramagnetic Relaxation for $^2T_2$ States in Rhombic Symmetry General Theory and Application to $K_3(Co,Fe)(CN)_6$."

750. J. F. Gibson, D. J. E. Ingram, and D. Schonland, *Discussions Faraday Soc.*, **26**, 72 (1958). "Magnetic Resonance of Different Ferric Complexes."

751. J. A. MacKinnon and G. F. Dionne, *Can. J. Phys.*, **44**, 2329 (1966). "EPR of Ti^{3+} Ions in $TlAl(SO_4)_2 \cdot 12H_2O$."

752. J. Deren, J. Haber, and S. Kosek, *Bull. Acad. Polon. Sci., Ser. Sci. Chim.*, **14**, 185 (1966). "A New EPR Absorption Line in the System $CrO_3–Al_2O_3$."

753. M. L. Meil'man and I. A. Torchinskii, *Zh. Strukt. Khim.*, **7**, 617 (1966). "Chromium Isomorphism in Diaspore."

754. B. Jezowska-Trzebiatowska and W. Wojciechowski, *Theory Struct. Complex Compds., Papers Symp. Wroclaw, Poland, 1962*, 375. "The ESR as Proof of Electronic Structure of Binuclear Chromium(III) Complexes."

755. P. P. Pashinin and A. M. Prokhorov, *Zh. Eksperim. i Teor. Fiz.*, **40**, 49 (1961). "Measurement of the Spin-Lattice Relaxation Time in Compounds with Strong Covalent Bonds."

756. M. F. Lewis, *Phys. Letters*, **17**, 183 (1965). "Detection of Microwave Ultrasound by Paramagnetic Saturation."

757. D. H. McMahon and R. H. Silsbee, *Phys. Rev.*, **135**, 1AO, 91 (1964). "Virtual Phonon Effects in the Paramagnetic Resonance of $MgO:Fe^{2+}$."

758. J. A. Weil, G. L. Goodman, and H. G. Hecht, *Paramagnetic Resonance, Proc. Intern. Conf., 1st, Jerusalem*, **2**, 880 (1962). "Paramagnetic Resonance Absorption in Peroxo-Dicobalt Complexes: Single-Crystal Studies."

759. M. F. Lewis. *Phys. Letters*, **19**, 459 (1965). "Orientation Dependence of Hypersonic Saturation of Fe^{2+} Centers in MgO."

760. F. S. Ham, *Phys. Rev.*, **138**, 1727 (1965). "Dynamical Jahn-Teller Effect in Paramagnetic Resonance Spectra: Orbital Reduction Factor and Partial Quenching of Spin-Orbit Interaction."

761. D. H. McMahon, *Univ. Microfilms.*, Order No. **64-8750**, 175 pp.; *Dissertation Abstr.*, **26**, 2830 (1965). "The Effects of Virtual Phonon Processes on the Paramagnetic Resonance of Fe^{2+} in MgO."

762. R. S. Rubins, *Proc. Phys. Soc. (London)*, **80**, 244 (1962). "Paramagnetic Resonance Spectrum of Bivalent Iron in Zinc Fluosilicate."

763. K. W. H. Stevens and F. Persico, *Nuovo Cimento*, **41B**, 37 (1966). "Jahn-Teller Effects in the ESR Spectra of Ions with Spin 1."

764. O. B. Roitsin, *Fiz. Tverd. Tela*, **5**, 151 (1963). "The Role of Electric Fields in Paramagnetic Resonance."

765. D. H. McMahon, *Phys. Rev.*, **134**, 128 (1964). "Paramagnetic Resonance Line Shapes of Fe^{2+} in MgO."

766. A. G. Muftakhov, A. S. Sadykov, and V. B. Leont'ev, *Uzbeksk. Khim. Zh.*, **6**, No. 5, 61 (1962). "Absorption Electron Spectra of Tetra-Centered Complexes of Cobalt Chloride with Heterocyclic Compounds in Acetone."

767. T. E. Murray and G. K. Wessel, *J. Appl. Phys.*, **37**, 2196 (1966). "Antiferromagnetic Spin Resonance of $CoBr_2 \cdot 6H_2O$."

768. D. K. Ray, *Fiz. Tverd. Tela*, **3**, 2223 (1961). "Covalent Bond Theory for Cobalt Salts and Analysis of Co^{2+} Paramagnetic Resonance Spectrum in Corundum."

769. V. Jaccarino, *J. Chem. Phys.*, **30**, 1627 (1959). "Effects of the Cobalt-59 Hyperfine Structure on the Fluorine-19 High-Frequency Nuclear Magnetic Resonance in Antiferromagnetic CoF_2."

770. E. E. Schneider and J. Weiss, *Arch. Sci.*, **11**, Spec. No., 153 (1958). "Electron Resonance in a Cobalt Complex."

771. H. Brintzinger, G. Palmer, and R. H. Sands, *J. Am. Chem. Soc.*, **88**, 623 (1966). "EPR Study of Metal-Aromatic Bonding in Bis(hexamethylbenzene)Iron(I)."

772. G. M. Zverev and N. G. Petelina, *Zh. Eksperim. i Teor. Fiz*, **42**, 1186 (1962). "EPR of Co^{2+} Ions in Corundum."

773. G. M. Zverev and A. M. Prokhorov, *Zh. Eksperim. i Teor. Fiz*, **43**, 422(1962). "EPR of Rutile-Containing Cobalt."

774. G. M. Zverev and A. M. Prokhorov, *Zh. Eksperim. i Teor. Fiz*, **36**, 647 (1959). "EPR of Cobalt(II) Ion in Corundum."

775. J. A. Cowen and G. T. Johnston, *J. Chem. Phys.*, **44**, 2217 (1966). "EPR of Co^{2+} in Magnesium Acetate $\cdot 4H_2O$."

776. M. Nussbaum and J. Voitländer, *Z. Naturforsch.*, **20a**, 1417 (1965). "EPR in Organometallic Sandwich Compounds. II."

777. A. H. Maki, N. Edelstein, A. Davison, and R. H. Holm, *J. Am. Chem. Soc.*, **86**, 4580 (1964). "EPR Studies of the Electronic Structures of Bis(Maleonitriledithiolato)Copper(II),-Nickel(III),-Cobalt(II), and -Rhodium(II) Complexes."

778. J. W. Orton, P. Auzins, J. H. E. Griffiths, and J. E. Wertz, *Proc. Phys. Soc. (London)*, **78**, 554 (1961). "ESR Studies of Impurity Ions in Magnesium Oxide."

779. A. Davison, N. Edelstein, R. H. Holm, and A. H. Maki, *J. Am. Chem. Soc.*, **85**, 2029 (1963). "ESR Studies of Four-Coordinate Complexes of Nickel, Palladium, and Platinum Related by Electron Transfer Reactions."

780. C. C. McDonald, W. D. Phillips, and H. F. Mower, *J. Am. Chem. Soc.*, **87**, 3319 (1965). "An ESR Study of Some Complexes of Iron, Nitric Oxide, and Anionic Ligands."

781. K. M. Sancier, G. Freeman, and J. S. Mills, *Science*, **137**, 752 (1962). "ESR of Nitric Oxide-Hemoglobin Complexes in Solution."

782. J. B. Raynor, *Nature*, **201**, 1216 (1964). "ESR Spectrum of the Pentacyanonitrosylferrate(I) Anion."

783. J. Danon, R. P. A. Muniz, and H. Panepucci, *J. Chem. Phys.*, **41**, 3651 (1964). "ESR of Trapped Electrons in Irradiated Sodium Nitroprusside."

784. E. E. Schneider and J. Weiss, *Proc. Chem. Soc.*, **1959**, 130. "ESR in Crystals of the Amminoperoxydicobalt Complexes."

785. J. C. M. Henning, H. van den Boom, and J. Dieleman, *Philips Res. Rept.*, **21**, 16 (1966). "ESR of Co(II) in Cubic Zinc Selenide."

786. K. Morigaki, *J. Phys. Soc. Japan.*, **18**, 1558 (1963). "ESR of Co^{2+} in CdS."

787. K. Morigaki, *J. Phys. Soc. Japan.*, **19**, 2064 (1964). "ESR of Co^{2+} in CdS."

788. J. H. N. Loubser and W. P. van Ryneveld, *Nature*, **211**, 517 (1966). "ESR of Nickel in Synthetic Diamonds."

789. M. Date and Y. Miyako, *Paramagnetic Resonance, Proc. Intern. Conf., 1st, Jerusalem*, **2**, 665 (1962). "ESR of Some Magnetic Ions in TiO_2 under an External Stress."

790. J. M. Assour and W. K. Kahn, *J. Am. Chem. Soc.*, **87**, 207 (1965). "ESR of α- and β- Cobalt Phthalocyanine."

791. H. M. Gladney, *Phys. Rev.*, **146**, 253 (1966). "Electronic Structure of $MgF_2:Co^{2+}$."

792. H. M. Gladney, *Phys. Rev.*, **143**, 198 (1966). "Hyperfine Structure of ^{19}F in the EPR of $MgF_2:Co^{2+}$."

793. G. Asch, *Compt. Rend.*, **248**, 781 (1959). "Magnetic Resonance of Polycrystalline Cobalt at 35,000 Mc as a Function of Temperature."

794. J. P. Jesson, *J. Chem. Phys.*, **45**, 1049 (1966). "Optical and Paramagnetic Resonance Spectra of Some Trigonal Co(II) Chelates."

795. D. A. C. McNeil, J. B. Raynor, and M. C. R. Symons, *Mol. Phys.*, **10**, 297 (1966). "Pairwise Trapping in Irradiated Sodium Nitroprusside."

796. R. S. Rubins and W. Low, *Paramagnetic Resonance, Proc. Intern. Conf., 1st, Jerusalem*, **1**, 59 (1962). "Paramagnetic Resonance Spectra of Some Rare Earth and Iron-Group Impurities in Strontium Titanate."

797. A. H. Maki and T. E. Berry, *J. Am. Chem. Soc.*, **87**, 4437 (1965). "Paramagnetic Resonance of Some Carborane Analogs of Ferriccnium Cation."

798. I. Bernal, E. A. V. Ebsworth, and J. A. Weil, *Proc. Chem. Soc.*, **1959**, 57. "Paramagnetic Resonance Absorption in Peroxydicobalt Complexes."

799. K. Morigaki, *J. Phys. Soc. Japan.*, **16**, 1639 (1961). "Paramagnetic Resonance of Cobalt in Cadmium Chloride and Cadmium Bromide."

800. G. M. Zverev and A. M. Prokhorov, *Zh. Eksperim. i Teor. Fiz.*, **39**, 57 (1960). "Paramagnetic Resonance and Spin Lattice Relaxation of the Co^{2+} Ion in Corundum."

801. P. H. Kasai and Y. Otomo, *Phys. Rev. Letters*, **7**, 17 (1961). "Paramagnetic Resonance Detection of Luminescent Centers and Traps in Self-Activated Zinc Sulfide Phosphors."

802. W. B. Gager, P. S. Jastram, and J. G. Daunt, *Phys. Rev.*, **111**, 803 (1958). "Paramagnetic Resonance Spectrum of Cobalt in Cerium Magnesium Nitrate at $4°K$."

803. T. P. P. Hall and W. Hayes, *J. Chem. Phys.*, **32**, 1871 (1960). "Paramagnetic Resonance of Co^{2+} with Four- and Eightfold Coordination."

804. T. R. Sliker, *Phys. Rev.*, **130**, 1749 (1963). "Properties of Bivalent Cobalt and Nickel as Impurities in Silver Chloride Single Crystals."

805. J. M. Assour, *J. Am. Chem. Soc.*, **87**, 4701 (1965). "Solvent Effects on the Spin Resonance Spectra of Cobalt Phthalocyanine."

806. M. Date and M. Motokawa, *Phys. Rev. Letters*, **16**, 1111 (1966). "Spin Cluster Resonance in $CoCl_2 \cdot 2H_2O$."

807. L. S. Meriwether, S. D. Robinson, and G. Wilkinson, *J. Chem. Soc.*, **A1966**, 1488. "ESR Spectra of $Cr(CN)_5NO^{3-}$, $Cr(NO)(NH_3)_5^{2+}$, and $Cr(NO(H_2O)_5^{2+}$."

808. P. T. Manoharan, H. A. Kuska, and M. T. Rogers, *J. Am. Chem. Soc.*, **89**, 4564 (1967).

809. R. G. Shulman and S. Sugano, *J. Chem. Phys.*, **42**, 39 (1965). "Molecular Orbital Analysis of Iron Group Cyanides."

810. A. J. Shuskus, *J. Chem. Phys.*, **40**, 1602 (1964). "Paramagnetic Resonance of Divalent Iron in CaO."

811. B. Bleaney and M. C. M. O'Brien, *Proc. Phys. Soc. (London)*, **B69**, 1216 (1956). "Paramagnetic Resonance in Some Complex Cyanides of the Iron Group II Theory."

812. D. A. C. McNeil, J. B. Raynor, and M. C. R. Symons, *J. Chem. Soc.*, **1965**, 410. "Structure and Reactivity of Transition-Metal Complexes with Polyatomic Ligands, Part I, ESR of $Mn(CN)_5NO^{2-}$ and $Fe(CN)_5NO^{3-}$."

813. D. A. C. McNeil, J. B. Raynor, and M. C. R. Symons, *Proc. Chem. Soc.*, **1964**, 364. "Structure of Some Transition Metal Nitrosyl Complexes."

814. M. Shporer, G. Ron, A. Loewenstein, and G. Navon, *Inorg. Chem.*, **4**, 358 (1965). "Study of Some Cyano-Metal Complexes by NMR."

815. F. S. Ham, G. W. Ludwig, G. D. Watkins, and H. H. Woodbury, *Phys. Rev. Letters*, **5**, 468 (1960). "Spin Hamiltonian of Co^{2+}."

816. S. Geschwind and J. P. Remeika, *J. Appl. Phys.*, **33**, 370 (1962). "Spin Resonance of Transition Metal Ions in Corundum."

817. M. D. Sturge, F. R. Merritt, and J. P. Remeika, *Appl. Phys. Letters*, **9**, 63 (1966). "Spin Resonance of Co^{2+} in Yttrium Gallium Garnet."

818. S. H. Christensen, *U.S. At. Energy Comm. TID-21549*, 122 (1965). "Stark Effects in Paramagnetic Resonance."

819. H. C. Longuet-Higgins and A. J. Stone, *Mol. Phys.*, **5**, 417 (1962). "The Electronic Structure and Electronic Spin Resonance of Tricyclopentadienyl Trinickel Dicarbonyl."

820. S. A. Al'tshuler and M. M. Zaripov, *Fiz. Probl. Spektr., Akad. Nauk SSSR, Materialy 13-go Trinadtsatogo Sovesch. Leningrad*, **2**, 87 (1960). "The Theory of Paramagnetic Resonance of Co^{2+} in Corundum."

821. J. F. Gibson, *Nature*, **196**, 64 (1962). "Unpaired Electron in Nitrosobis(dimethyldithiocarbamato)Iron(II)."

822. R. Guermeur, J. Joffrin, A. Levelut, and J. Penne, *Compt. Rend.*, **260**, 108 (1965). "Ultrasonic Absorption and Scattering Spectra Obtained during an Acoustic Paramagnetic Resonance Experiment."

823. T. L. Estle and W. C. Holton, *Phys. Rev.*, **150**, 159 (1966). "EPR Investigation of the Superhyperfine Structure of Iron-Group Impurities in II–VI Compounds."

824. G. W. Ludwig and H. H. Woodbury, *Phys. Rev.*, **117**, 1286 (1960). "Magnetic Moment of ^{57}Fe."

825. W. Low, *Phys. Rev.*, **109**, 256 (1958). "Paramagnetic and Optical Spectra of Divalent Cobalt in Cubic Crystalline Fields."

826. S. A. Marshall, T. T. Kikuchi, and A. R. Reinberg, *J. Phys. Soc. Japan.*, **17**, Suppl. B-1, 450 (1962). "Paramagnetic Resonance Absorption of Bivalent Nickel in Sapphire."

827. J. W. Culvahouse, *J. Chem. Phys.*, **36**, 2720 (1962). "Paramagnetic Resonance of Nickel Ions in Double-Nitrate Crystals."

828. W. Low and J. T. Suss, *Phys. Rev. Letters*, **15**, 519 (1965). "Paramagnetic-Resonance Spectrum of Co^+ in Single Crystals of Calcium Oxide."

829. E. Billig, R. Williams, I. Bernal, J. H. Waters, and H. B. Gray, *Inorg. Chem.*, **3**, 663 (1964). "Electronic Structures of Square-Planar Metal Complexes. II Complexes of Maleonitriledithiolate with Copper(II), Nickel(II), Palladium(II), and Platinum(II)."

830. A. Bose, R. Chatterjee, and A. S. Chakraborty, *Paramagnetic Resonance, Proc. Intern. Conf., 1st, Jerusalem*, **1**, 155 (1962). "Optical and Magnetic Behaviors of $Ni^{2+} \cdot 6H_2O$ Complex in Crystalline Salts."

831. S. A. Al'tshuler, A. M. Leushin, and A. K. Morocha, *Paramagnitn. Rezonans, Kazansk. Univ., Sbornik*, 57 (1960). "Theory of Spin-Lattice Interaction in Ionic Crystals Containing Cr^{3+} and Ni^{2+}."

832. R. H. Hoskins, R. C. Pastor, and K. R. Trigger, *J. Chem. Phys.*, **30**, 1630 (1959). "Crystal Constituent Effects. II. Paramagnetic Resonance of Ni^{2+} in Double Nitrates."

833. K. Sugihara, *J. Phys. Soc. Japan*, **14**, 1231 (1959). "Spin–Spin Interaction in Paramagnetic Salts."

834. M. B. Palma-Vittorelli, M. U. Palma, and F. Persico, *J. Phys. Soc. Japan*, **17**, Suppl. B-1, **1962**, 475. "EPR Line Widths of Face-Centered-Cubic Ni^{2+} Crystals."

835. S. A. Marshall and A. R. Reinberg, *J. Appl. Phys.*, **31**, 336S (1960). "EPR Absorption of Nickel in Sapphire."

836. V. M. Bhatnagar and S. Frijiwarer, *Chem. Ind.* (*London*), **1962**, 1471. "EPR Studies on Clathrate Compounds."

837. N. N. Tikhomirova and D. M. Chernikova, *Zh. Strukt. Khim.*, **3**, 335 (1962). "EPR of Solid Phthalocyanines."

838. R. H. Hoskins, R. C. Pastor, and K. R. Trigger, *J. Chem. Phys.*, **30**, 601 (1959). "Crystal Constituent Effects. I. Paramagnetic Resonance of $NiM^{IV}F_6 \cdot 6H_2O$."

839. M. McMillan and W. Opechowski, *Can. J. Phys.*, **38**, 1168 (1960). "The Temperature Dependence of the Shape of Paramagnetic Resonance Lines."

840. S. A. Al'tshuler and R. M. Valishev, *Zh. Eksperim. i Teor. Fiz.*, **48**, 464 (1965). "A Study of Weak Exchange Interactions by the Paramagnetic Resonance Method."

841. W. E. Blumberg, J. Eisinger, and S. Geschwind, *Phys. Rev.*, **130**, 900 (1963). "Cu^{3+} Ion in Corundum."

842. A. Abragam and M. H. L. Pryce, *Proc. Roy. Soc.* (*London*), **A206**, 173 (1951). "Theory of Paramagnetic Resonance in Hydrated Cobalt Salts."

843. A. Carrington and A. D. McLachlan, *Introduction to Magnetic Resonance*, Harper and Row, New York, 1967.

844. K. Morigaki, *J. Phys. Soc. Japan.*, **19**, 1485 (1964). "Spin Resonance Detection of Trapping and Transfer of Electrons in Co- and Ni-Doped CdS."

845. J. Busse, *Phys. Status Solidi*, **3**, 1892 (1963). "Paramagnetic Resonance of Ni in Silver Bromide."

846. M. Date, *J. Phys. Soc. Japan.*, **15**, 2115 (1960). "Anomalous EPR in $Ni(NH_3)_6Cl_2$."

847. S. A. Marshall, T. T. Kikuchi, and A. R. Reinberg, *Phys. Rev.*, **125**, 453 (1962). "Paramagnetic Resonance Absorption of Divalent Nickel in α-Al_2O_3 Single Crystal."

848. H. P. Fritz, B. Golla, and H. J. Keller, *Z. Naturforsch.*, **b21**, 97 (1965). "EPR Measurements on Bis-acetylacetone–Ethylenediimine Complexes."

849. G. Raoult, A. M. Duclaux, and M. T. Chenon, *Proc. Colloq., Ampere*, **11**, 456 (1962). "EPR of Nickel Ion in a Single Crystal of Alumina."

850. P. R. Locher and S. Geschwind, *Phys. Rev. Letters*, **11**, 333 (1963). "Electron Nuclear Double Resonance (ENDOR) of ^{61}Ni in Al_2O_3 and Variation of Hyperfine Structure through an Inhomogeneous Line due to Random Crystal Fields."

851. W. M. Walsh, Jr., *Phys. Rev.*, **114**, 1473 (1959). "Stress and Temperature Dependence of the Paramagnetic Resonance Spectrum of Nickel Fluosilicate."

852. J. H. M. Thornley, C. G. Windsor, and J. Owen, *Proc. Roy. Soc.* (*London*), **A284**, 252 (1965). "Concerning the Magnetic Properties of Covalent Octahedral Cobalt Complexes."

853. I. Siegel and J. A. Lorenc, *J. Chem. Phys.*, **45**, 2315 (1966). "Paramagnetic Resonance of Copper in Amorphous and Polycrystalline GeO_2."
854. U. Hochli, K. A. Mueller, and P. Wysling, *Phys. Letters*, **15**, 5 (1965). "Paramagnetic Resonance and Relaxation of Cu^{2+} and N^{3+} In MgO and CaO: The Determination of Jahn-Teller Energy Splittings."
855. J. P. Jesson, *J. Chem. Phys.*, **45**, 1049 (1966). "Optical and Paramagnetic Resonance Spectra of Some Trigonal Co(II) Chelates."
856. M. H. L. Pryce, *Proc. Roy. Soc. (London)*, **A283** (1965). "Resonance and Relaxation in Cobalt Doped Magnesium Oxide."
857. T. Tsang, *J. Chem. Phys.*, **40**, 729 (1964). "NMR and Molecular Field Approximation in $KCoF_3$."
858. C. G. Windsor, J. H. M. Thornley, J. H. E. Griffiths, and J. Owen, *Proc. Phys. Soc. (London)*, **80**, 803 (1962). "Bonding in Octahedral Cobalt Complexes."
859. A. J. Marriage, *Australian J. Chem.*, **18**, 463 (1965). "The Hyperfine ESR Spectrum of Copper(II) N-(n-alkyl)Salicylidenimine Chelate in Solution."
860. A. I. Rivkind and Yu. V. Yablokov, *Dokl. Akad. Nauk SSSR*, **158**, 1401 (1964). "Effect of the Transition of the Spin Density from the Paramagnetic Complex to the Splitting-Off Ligands."
861. A. H. Maki and B. R. McGarvey, *J. Chem. Phys.*, **29**, 31 (1958). "Electron Spin Resonance in Transition Metal Chelates. I. Copper(II) Bisacetylacetonate."
862. A. Nicula, *Studia Univ. Babes-Bolyai Ser. Math. Phys.*, **1**, 111 (1964). "Determination of the Relaxation Times T_1 and T_2 of the Ion Cu(II) in Y-Type Zeolites.
863. A. Nicula and Gh. Cristea, *Studia Univ. Babes-Bolyai Ser. Math. Phys.*, **2**, 111 (1964). "Temperature Dependence of the ESR Spectrum of the Cu(II) Ion in Zeolites."
864. A. Narasimhamurty and D. Premaswarup, *Proc. Phys. Soc. (London)*, **83**, 199 (1964). "Structure of Copper Ammonium Chloride Dihydrate from Electron Paramagnetic Resonance Studies."
865. A. Ozols, *Fiz. Metody Issled. Osda. Porod. i Mineralov, Akad. Nauk SSSR*, **1962**, 178. "Absorption from Solutions by Clay Colloids of Heavy Metals Studied by the Method of Electron Paramagnetic Resonance."
866. A. MacCragh, C. B. Storm, and W. S. Koski, *J. Am. Chem. Soc.*, **87**, 1470 (1965). "Solvent and Substituent Effects on the Spin Resonance Spectra of Metalloporphyrins."
867. A. K. Piskunov, D. N. Shigorin, and B. I. Stepanov, *Fiz. Probl. Spektr. Akad. Nauk SSSR, Materialy, 13-go [Trinadtsatogo] Soveshch., Leningrad*, **2**, 119 (1960). "Investigation of EPR in Intercomplexes of Copper."
868. A. Hudson, *Mol. Phys.*, **10**, 575 (1966). "The Effect of Dynamic Exchange on the Electron Resonance Line Shapes of Octahedral Copper Complexes."
869. A. K. Piskunov, D. N. Shigorin, B. I. Stepanov, and E. R. Klinshpont, *Dokl. Akad. Nauk SSSR.*, **136**, 871 (1961). "Study of EPR in Solutions of Some Oxyazo-Compounds of Copper."
870. A. I. Rivkind, *Paramagnitn. Rezonans, Kazansk. Univ., Sbornik*, **1960**, 50. "Effect of the Solvent on the Paramagnetic Resonance of Complex Copper Ions."
871. A. Nicula, *Studia Univ. Babes-Bolyai Ser. Math. Phys.*, **2**, 133 (1964). "ESR of Copper(II) Ions in Different Solutions."
872. A. K. Piskunov, D. N. Shigorin, V. I. Smirnova, and B. I. Stepanov, *Dokl. Akad. Nauk SSSR.*, **130** 1284 (1960). "EPR Spectra of Some Inner Complex Compounds of Copper."

873. A. P. Terent'ev, G. V. Panova, D. N. Shigorin, and E. G. Rukhadze, *Dokl. Akad. Nauk SSSR*, **156**, 1174 (1964). "EPR Spectra of Optically Active Chelated Compounds of Copper with Hydroxy Aldimines and Hydroxy Ketimines."

874. A. S. Brill and J. H. Venable, Jr., *Nature*, **203**, 752 (1964). "EPR in a Single Crystal of Cupric Insulin."

875. A. Narasimhamurty, *Indian J. Pure Appl. Phys.*, **1**, 275 (1963). "EPR in Single Crystals: III. Copper Sulfate Pentahydrate."

876. A. Narasimhamurty, *Indian J. Pure Appl. Phys.*, **2**, 37 (1964). "EPR in Single Crystals. IV. Copper Ammonium Chloride Dihydrate."

877. A. K. Wiersema and J. J. Windle, *J. Phys. Chem.*, **1964**, 2316. "EPR of Some Nitrogen-Bonded Copper Chelates."

878. A. M. Duclaux and G. Raoult, *Compt. Rend.*, **250**, 3983 (1960). "EPR Study of the Cu^{2+} Ion of Copper Sulfate Diluted Magnetically in a monocrystal of Magnesium Sulfate Heptahydrate."

879. A. Dall'Olio, G. Dascola, and V. Varacca, *Nuovo Cimento*, **B43**, 192 (1966). "EPR of Antiferromagnetic Interactions Inside Pairs of Cupric Ions in Copper Monochloroacetate Pentahydrate."

880. A. L. Poznyak, V. N. Tadeush, and L. Λ. Il'yukevich, *Zh. Strukt. Khim.*, **6**, 779 (1965). "EPR of Some Cu Complexes at 8 mm Wavelength."

881. A. Loesche and W. Windsch, *Phys. Status Solidi*, **11**, K55 (1965). "EPR Study of Copper-Doped Triglycine Sulfate Single Crystals."

882. A. I. Rivkind, *Zh. Fiz. Khim.*, **35**, 2099 (1961). "Paramagnetic Resonance in Solutions of Complex Copper Salts and the Frequency of Brownian Rotation of the Complexes."

883. A. Nicula, D. Stamires, and J. Turkevich, *Rev. Roumaine Phys.*, **9**, 613 (1964). "Paramagnetic Resonance of Copper Ions in Porous Crystals."

884. A. Nicula, D. Stamires, and J. Turkevich, *J. Chem. Phys.*, **42**, 3684 (1965). "Paramagnetic Resonance Absorption of Copper Ions in Porous Crystals."

885. B. M. Kozyrev and A. I. Rivkind, *Dokl. Akad. Nauk SSSR*, **127**, 1044 (1959). "Paramagnetic Resonance in Solutions of the Complex Salts of Copper."

886. B. Bolger, J. M. Noothoven van Goor, and C. J. Gorter, *Physica*, **27**, 277 (1961). "Power Transfer between Paramagnetic Spins and the Crystal Lattice. III."

887. B. I. Stepanov and B. A. Korolev, *Tr. Vses. Mezhvuz. Nauchn.-Tekhn. Konf. po Vopr. Sinteza i Primeneniya Organ. Krasitelei*, 57 (1961). "Study of the Copper Complexes of Some Azocompounds by the Techniques of EPR and Polarography."

888. Bo G. Malmstrom and T. Vanngard, *J. Mol. Biol.*, **2**, 118 (1960). "ESR of Copper Proteins and Some Model Complexes."

889. Bo G. Malmstrom, R. Mosbach, and T. Vanngard, *Nature*, **183**, 321 (1959). "An ESR Study of the State of Copper in Fungal Laccase."

890. B. V. Lokshin, A. K. Piskunov, L. A. Kazitsyna, and D. N. Shigorin, *Izv. Akad. Nauk SSSR, Ser. Fiz.*, **27**, No. 1, 75 (1963). "Investigation of the Structure of Some Intercomplex Compounds by the Method of EPR."

891. B. M. Kozyrev and A. I. Rivkind, *Zh. Strukt. Khim.*, **3**, 95 (1962). "Broadening of the Fine-Structure Components in EPR Spectra of Paramagnetic Solutions."

892. C. A. Bates, *Proc. Phys. Soc. (London)*, **83**, 465 (1964). "Effects of Distortion on the Spectra of a Cu^{2+} Ion in a Tetrahedral Crystal Field."

893. C. W. Reimann, G. F. Kokoszka, and H. C. Allen, Jr., *J. Res. Natl. Bur. Stds.*, **A70**, 1 (1966). "Optical and of Magnetic Spectra Bis(*N*-Propylsalicyladiminato)Copper(II)."

894. C. A. Bates, W. S. Moore, K. J. Standley, and K. W. H. Stevens, *Proc. Phys. Soc.* (*London*), **79**, 73 (1962). "Paramagnetic Resonance of a Cu^{2+} Ion in a Tetrahedral Crystal Field."

895. D. N. Stamires, Ph.D. thesis, *Princeton University*, 1963. "ESR Studies on Synthetic Crystalline Zeolites."

896. D. Kivelson and R. Neiman, *J. Chem. Phys.*, **35**, 149 (1961). "ESR Studies on the Bonding in Copper Complexes."

897. D. B. Russel and S. J. Wyard, *Nature*, **191**, 65 (1961). "ESR of Adenosine Triphosphate."

898. D. Kivelson, *J. Chem. Phys.*, **45**, 1324 (1966). "Electric-Field Fluctuations and Spin Relaxation in Liquids."

899. D. C. Burnham and F. Moser, *Phys. Status Solidi*, **15**, 129 (1966). "Light-Induced Dispersal of Cu^{2+} Precipitates in AgCl Crystals."

900. D. C. Burnham and F. Moser, *Phys. Rev.*, **136**, 744 (1964). "ESR and Optical Studies on Copper-Doped AgCl."

901. E. A. Zamotrinskaya, *Izv. Vysshikh Uchebn. Zavedenii, Fiz.*, **1963**, 2, 178. "Effect of γ-Radiation on the ESR in $CuSO_4 \cdot 5H_2O$."

902. E. M. Roberts and W. S. Koski, *J. Am. Chem. Soc.*, **83**, 1865 (1961). "ESR of Copper Phthalocyanine."

903. E. Lutze and D. Bosnecker, *Z. Naturforsch.*, **14a**, 755 (1959). "Hyperfine Structure of Dissolved Copper Ions in Paramagnetic Resonance."

904. E. M. Roberts and W. S. Koski, *J. Am. Chem. Soc.*, **82**, 3006 (1960). "An ESR Study of Copper Etioporphrin II."

905. E. V. Kavalerova, V. B. Golubev, and V. B. Evdokimov, *Zh. Fiz. Khim.*, **37**, 226 (1963). "EPR of Copper Acetylacetate."

906. F. R. Nash and E. Rosenwasser, *Quantum Electron. Symp., High View, New York, 1959*, 302. "Cross Relaxation and Maser Action in $Cu(NH_4)_2(SO_4)_2 \cdot 6H_2O$."

907. F. K. Kneubühl, *J. Chem. Phys.*, **33**, 1074 (1960). "Line Shapes of EPR Signals Produced by Powders, Glasses, and Viscous Liquids."

908. F. R. Nash, *Phys. Rev.*, **138**, 1500 (1965). "Electron Spin Relaxation in Copper Tutton Salts at Low Temperatures."

909. G. M. Larin, *Zh. Strukt. Khim.*, **6**, 548 (1965). "EPR of Some Chelate Copper Complexes. II. Study of Glasses."

910. G. M. Larin, V. M. Dziomko, K. A. Dunaevskaya, and Ya, K. Syrkin, *Zh. Strukt. Khim.*, **6**, 391 (1965). "EPR of Some Chelate Copper(II) Compounds."

911. G. A. Candela, *J. Chem. Phys.*, **42**, 113 (1965). "Influence of Paramagnetic Resonance on the Static Susceptibility. Spin-Lattice Relaxation Time of Cupric Sulfate Pentahydrate."

912. G. M. Larin, G. V. Panova, and E. G. Rukhadze, *Zh. Strukt. Khim.*, **6**, 699 (1965). "EPR of the Compounds of Copper with *o*-Hydroxybenzaldimines."

913. G. Raonet and A. M. Duclaux, *Arch. Sci.*, **13**, Spec. No., 199 (1961). "EPR of $Cu^{2+}(CuSO_4)$ Diluted in Epsomite($MgSO_4$)."

914. G. Schoffa, O. Ristau, and B. E. Wahler, *Z. Physik. Chem.*, **215**, 203 (1960). "ESR of Copper(II) Chelates."

915. G. M. Larin, V. M. Dziomko, and K. A. Dunaevskaya, *Zh. Strukt. Khim.*, **5**, 783 (1964). "EPR of Copper 2-[2-(2-Hydroxy-1-Naphthylazo)Phenylazoxy]-4-Methylphenolate."

916. G. F. Kokoszka, H. C. Allen, Jr., and G. Gordon, *J. Chem. Phys.*, **42**, 3730 (1965). "EPR Spectrum of Bis(8-Hydroxyquinolate)Copper(II)Dihydrate."

917. G. F. Kokoszka, H. C. Allen, Jr., and G. Gordon, *J. Chem. Phys.*, **42**, 3693 (1965). "EPR Spectra of Zinc-Doped Copper Acetate Monohydrate."

918. G. S. Vozdvizhenskii, N. V. Gudin, M. S. Shapnik, N. S. Garif'yanov, and A. V. Il'yasov, *Zh. Fiz. Khim.*, **38**, 1682 (1964). "EPR Investigation of Electrode Processes in Aqueous Solutions of Copper Complexes with Organic Amino Derivatives."

919. G. Dascola, D. C. Giori, and V. Varacca, *Nuovo Cimento*, **37**, 382 (1965). "Cotton-Mouton Effect, Associated with EPR, in a Birefringent Medium."

920. H. Elliott and B. J. Hathaway, *Inorg. Chem.*, **5**, 885 (1966). "The Hexaammine Complexes of the Copper(II) Ion."

921. H. Elliott, B. J. Hathaway, and R. C. Slade, *J. Chem. Soc., A. Inorg., Phys. Theoret.*, **1966**, 10, 443. "The Electronic Properties of Monohalogenobisbipyridylcopper(II) Complexes."

922. H. J. Keller and H. Wawersik, *Z. Naturforsch.*, **20b**, 938 (1965). "Spectroscopic Investigations of Complex Compounds. II. EPR Spectra of Monomeric Cobalt Tetracarbonyl."

923. H. P. Fritz and H. J. Keller, *Z. Naturforsch.*, **b20**, 1145 (1965). "Spectroscopic Investigation of Complexes. I. EPR Spectrum of $Cu(NH_3)_4[PtCl_4]$."

924. H. J. Gerritsen and A. Starr, *Arkiv Fysik*, **25**, 13 (1963). "Theory and Experiments of Cu^{2+} in an Octahedral Surrounding."

925. H. A. Kuska and M. T. Rogers, *J. Chem. Phys.*, **43**, 1744 (1965). "Effect of Substituents on the ESR Hyperfine Splittings in Copper Acetylacetonates."

926. H. S. Jarrett, *J. Chem. Phys.*, **28**, 1260 (1958). "Paramagnetic Resonance in Copper Dimethylglyoxime."

927. H. G. Hecht and J. P. Frazier, *J. Chem. Phys.*, **44**, 1718 (1966). "Paramagnetic Resonance Absorption in Tetrakis(Pyridine)copper(II) Peroxydisulfate."

928. H. Abe and H. Shirai, *J. Phys. Soc. Japan*, **16**, 118 (1961). "EPR Study in Some Copper Salts."

929. H. Abe, *J. Phys. Soc. Japan*, **16**, 836 (1961). "Temperature Dependence of Paramagnetic Resonance Line Width in $K_2CuCl_4 \cdot 2H_2O$."

930. H. Abe, H. Morigaki, and K. Koga, *Paramagnetic Resonance, Proc. Intern. Conf., 1st, Jerusalem*, **2**, 557 (1962). "Structures in Low-Temperature Paramagnetic Resonance Line of Copper Potassium Chloride."

931. H. Abe and H. Morigaki, *Paramagnetic Resonance, Proc. Intern. Conf., 1st, Jerusalem*, **2**, 587 (1962). "Temperature Dependence of Line Width in Copper Trichloroacetate Monohydrate."

932. H. Abe, *J. Phys. Soc. Japan*, **13**, 987 (1958). "Paramagnetic Resonance in Copper Propionate Monohydrate."

933. H. Rein, O. Ristau, and F. Jung, *Z. Physik. Chem.*, **221**, 197 (1962). "ESR Investigations on a Homologous Series of Copper(II) Complexes."

934. H. C. Allen, Jr., G. F. Kokoszka, and R. G. Inskeep, *J. Am. Chem. Soc.*, **86**, 1023 (1964). "EPR Spectrum of Some Tris Complexes of Cu^{2+}."

935. H. Matsumoto and T. Miyanaga, *Bull. Inst. Chem. Res., Kyoto Univ.*, **44**, 1 (1966). "EPR Studies on γ-Ray-Irradiated $CdCl_2$:Ag and $CdCl_2$:Cu Crystals."

936. H. Matsumoto, *J. Phys. Soc. Japan*, **20**, 1579 (1965). "EPR and Optical Studies of Cupric Ions in $MgCl_2$ and $CdCl_2$."

937. H. D. Powell, *Univ. Microfilms*, **26**, 7407 (1966). "An Electron Paramagnetic Resonance Study of Crystalline Cuprous Chloride Containing Divalent Manganese."

938. H. R. Gersmann and J. D. Swalen, *J. Chem. Phys.*, **36**, 3221 (1962). "EPR Spectra of Copper Complexes."

939. H. R. Falle and G. R. Luckhurst, *Mol. Phys.*, **10**, 597 (1966). "Temperature Dependence of the ESR of Copper Acetylacetonate."

940. G. R. Wagner, R. T. Schumacher, and S. A. Friedberg, *Phys. Rev.*, **150**, 226 (1966). "ESR of Cu^{2+} in $Zn(HCOO)_2 \cdot 2H_2O$: Isolated Ions and Exchange-Coupled Pairs."

941. I. V. Miroshnichenko, G. M. Larin, B. I. Stepanov, and B. A. Korolev, *Teor. i Eksperim. Khim., Akad. Nauk Ukr. SSR*, **2**, 131 (1966). "Electron Paramagnetic Study of the Internal Complexes of Cu(II) with Derivatives of Plenylazo-β-Naphthol."

942. I. V. Miroshnichenko and G. M. Larin, *Teor. i Eksperim. Khim., Akad. Nauk Ukr. SSR*, **1**, 545 (1965). "EPR Study of Copper Bis(Benzeneazo-*p*-Cresol)."

943. I. V. Miroshnichenko, G. M. Larin, E. G. Rukhadze, and M. A. Litvinyuk, *Zh. Neorgan, Khim.*, **11**, 331 (1966). "Copper(II) Complexes of Pyridine Homologs and Their Electron Paramagnetic Resonance Spectra."

944. I. V. Miroshnichenko, G. M. Larin, B. I. Stepanov, and B. A. Korolev, *Teor. i Eksperim. Khim., Akad. Nauk Ukr. SSR*, **2**, 405 (1966). "EPR Study of Some Azo Compounds of Cu(II)."

945. I. Bernal, *Inorg. Chem.*, **3**, 1465 (1964). "Electronic and Magnetic Properties of $K_3Cu(NO_2)_5$."

946. I. B. Bersuker, S. S. Budnikov, B. G. Vekhter, and B. I. Chinik, *Fiz. Tverd. Tela*, **6**, 2583 (1964); *Zh. Eksperim. i Teor. Fiz.*, **44**, 1239 (1963). "Hyperfine Structure of the EPR Spectra for Copper Complexes with Inversion Splitting."

947. I. B. Bersuker, *Zh. Eksperim. i Teor. Fiz.*, **44**, 1239 (1963). "Spin-Inversion Levels in Magnetic Fields and the EPR Spectrum of Octahedral Cu^{2+} Ion Complexes."

948. I. B. Bersuker, *Fiz. Tverd. Tela*, **6**, 436 (1964). "'Inverse' Sound Absorption by Hydrated Cu Salt Single Crystals in a Magnetic Field."

949. J. F. Gibson, *Trans. Faraday Soc.*, **60**, 2105 (1964). "Variation in Copper ESR Hyperfine Linewidths with Orientation of the Nuclear Spin."

950. J. M. Daniels and H. A. Farach, *Can. J. Phys.*, **38**, 151 (1960). "'Spin-flip Narrowing' in Paramagnetic Resonance Lines."

951. J. M. Assour and S. E. Harrison, *Phys. Rev.*, **136**, 1368 (1964). "ESR of Concentrated Copper Phthalocyanine Crystals."

952. J. Dieleman, *Proc. Colloq. Ampere*, **11**, 409 (1962). "Paramagnetic Resonance of a Photosensitive Center in CdS:Cu, Ga."

953. J. A. McMillan and B. Smaller, *J. Chem. Phys.*, **35**, 763 (1961). "Paramagnetic Resonance of Some Copper Complex Compounds."

954. K. A. Valiev and M. M. Zaripov, *Opt. i Spektroskopiya*, **20**, 108 (1966). "Theory of the Line Width of the EPR of Cu^{2+} Ions in Aqueous Solutions."

955. K. Wuethrich, *Helv. Chim. Acta*, **49**, 1400 (1966). "ESR Spectra of Various Cu^{2+} Complexes in Aqueous Solution."

956. K. I. Zamaraev and V. V. Voevodskii, *Dokl. Akad. Nauk SSSR*, **169**, 385 (1966). "Electron Spin Exchange in Solutions of Divalent Cu Complexes with *N*-Containing Ligands."

957. K. I. Zamaraev and N. N. Tikhomirova, *Zh. Strukt. Khim.*, **5**, 621 (1964). "Effect of the Dipole–Dipole Hyperfine Interactions on the Electron Paramagnetic Resonance Spectra of the Paramagnetic Ion in Solution."

958. K. Wuethrich, H. Loeliger, and S. Fallab, *Experientia*, **20**, 599 (1964). "ESR Measurements for the Investigation of the Kinetics and Mechanism of the Cu^{2+} Catalyzed Reactions."

959. K. J. Standley and J. K. Wright, *Proc. Phys. Soc. (London)*, **83**, 361 (1964). "Spin-Lattice Relaxation in Two Organic Copper Complexes."

960. K. Toyoda and K. Ochiai, *Proc. Intern. Symp. Mol. Struct. Spectry., Tokyo, 1962*, 4. "ESR Spectra of Some Copper(II) Complexes."

961. K. J. Standley and J. K. Wright, *Phys. Letters*, **3**, No. 2, 101 (1962). "Phonon Heating Effects during Spin-Lattice Relaxation in Copper Dipyrromethene."

962. K. Morigaki, *J. Phys. Soc. Japan*, **19**, 1240 (1964). "ESR of a Photosensitive Center in Cu-Doped CdS."

963. K. Nagata and M. Date, *J. Phys. Soc. Japan*, **19**, 1823 (1964). "Short-Range Order Effect on Paramagnetic Resonance Line Width of $CuF_2 \cdot 2H_2O$."

964. L. S. Kravchuk, A. L. Poznyak, and B. V. Erofeev, *Zh. Strukt. Khim.*, **6**, 645 (1965). "The EPR Signal in a Bright-Blue Modification of Anhydrous Copper Formate."

965. L. S. Degtyarev and L. N. Ganyuk, *Vysokomolekul. Soedin.*, **6**, 28 (1964). "EPR Spectra of Tetramethylthiuram Disulfide and Its Copper Complex."

966. L. A. Il'yukevich, A. L. Poznyak, and G. A. Shagisultanova, *Zh. Strukt. Khim.*, **4**, 919 (1963). "EPR in Several Compounds of Copper."

967. L. V. Bershov and A. S. Marfunin, *Geokhimiya*, **1965**, 10, 1259. "EPR of Cu^{2+} in Danburite."

968. M. C. M. O'Brien, *Paramagnetic Resonance, Proc. Intern. Conf., 1st, Jerusalem*, **1**, 322 (1962). "ESR Spectrum of a d^9 Ion in an Octahedral Environment."

969. M. Sharnoff, *J. Chem. Phys.*, **42**, 3383 (1965). "EPR and the Primarily $3d$ Wave Functions of the Tetrachlorocuprate Ion."

970. M. Sharnoff, *J. Chem. Phys.*, **41**, 2203 (1964). "EPR in Tetrahedrally Coordinated Cu^{2+}, Tetrachlorocuprate Ion."

971. M. Date, M. Motokawa, and H. Yamazaki, *J. Phys. Soc. Japan*, **18**, 911 (1963). "Temperature Dependence of Paramagnetic Resonance Line Width in Copper Benzoate."

972. M. M. Zaripov and G. K. Chirkin, *Fiz. Tverd. Tela*, **6**, 1645 (1964). "EPR Spectrum of Cu^{2+} in NH_4Cl."

973. N. N. Tikhomirova and K. I. Zamaraev, *Zh. Strukt. Khim.*, **4**, 224 (1963). "Investigation of the Nitrogen-Containing Complexes of Copper by the EPR Method."

974. N. N. Tikhomirova, K. I. Zamaraev, and V. M. Berdnikov, *Zh. Strukt. Khim.*, **4**, 449 (1963). "Study of Copper-Ammonia Solutions by the EPR Method."

975. N. S. Garif'yanov and B. M. Kozyrev, *Zh. Strukt. Khim.*, **6**, 773 (1965). "EPR Spectra in Solutions of Bivalent Copper Diethyldithiophosphate."

976. N. J. Trappeniers and S. H. Hagen, *Physica*, **31**, 122 (1965). "The EPR Spectrum of Cu^{2+} in Ammonium Chloride."

977. N. J. Trappeniers and S. H. Hagen, *Physica*, **31**, 251 (1965). "Influence of the λ Point on the EPR Spectrum of Cu^{2+} in Ammonium Chloride."

978. P. Spacu, M. Brezeanu, C. Gheorghiu, O. Constantinescu, and I. Pascaru, *Rev. Roumaine Chim*, **9**, 801 (1964), *Studii Cercetari Chim*, **13**, 851 (1964). "EPR Spectra of Some Complex Cu(II) Compounds."

979. P. Spacu, O. Constantinescu, I. Pascaru, C. Gheorghiu, and M. Brezeanu, *Rev. Roumaine Chim.*, **11**, 161 (1966). "EPR Study of Coordination Compounds of Cu(II) With Benzidine."

980. P. Spacu, V. Voicu, and I. Pascaru, *J. Chim. Phys.*, **60**, 368 (1963). "Paramagnetic Resonance of Some Copper(II) Complexes."

981. P. B. Dorain, NASA Doc. N63-22497, 41 (1963). "EPR of Impurities of Single Crystals and of Sulfur Monoxide."

982. R. E. Coffman, *Phys. Letters*, **19**, 475 (1965). "A Third Type of Jahn Teller EPR Spectrum in Octahedrally Coordinated Cu^{2+}."

983. R. Rajan, *Indian J. Pure Appl. Phys.*, **1**, No. 3, 121 (1963). "ESR in Monomethylammonium Copper(II) Chloride."

984. R. Rajan, *Physica*, **29**, 1191 (1963). "ESR in Copper(II) Monoethylenediamine Chloride."

985. R. Rajan, *J. Chem. Phys.*, **37**, 1901 (1962). "ESR in Ethylenediamine Copper(II) Nitrate."

986. R. Rajan, *Physica*, **28**, 1329 (1962). "ESR in Cupric Acid Fluoride."

987. R. Rajan, *J. Sci. Ind. Res.*, **21B**, 445 (1962). "Absolute Intensity of ESR Absorption of Cupric Ammonium Chloride Single Crystals."

988. R. Rajan and T. R. Reddy, *J. Chem. Phys.*, **39**, 1140 (1963). "ESR in Ethylenediamine Complexes of Copper(II) Sulfate."

989. R. E. Coffman, *Phys. Letters*, **21**, 381 (1966). "Paramagnetic Resonances of Cu^{2+} : MgO at 1.2°K."

990. R. F. Tucker, Jr., *Phys. Rev.*, **112**, 725 (1958). "Paramagnetic Resonance Study of Copper-Doped Silver Chloride."

991. R. Englman and D. Horn, *Paramagnetic Resonance, Proc. Intern. Conf., 1st, Jerusalem*, **1**, 329 (1962). "Anomalies of g Factor Due to Vibrational Coupling."

992. R. Neiman and D. Kivelson, *J. Chem. Phys.*, **35**, 156 (1961). "ESR Line Shapes in Glasses of Copper Complexes."

993. R. Neiman and D. Kivelson, *J. Chem. Phys.*, **35**, 162 (1961). "ESR Spectra of Solid Phthalocyanines."

994. R. Srinivasan, *Proc. Nucl. Phys. Solid State Phys. Symp., Calcutta, 1965*, 41 "Covalency Effects in the ESR of Transition Ion Complexes."

995. R. Wilson and D. Kivelson, *J. Chem. Phys.*, **44**, 4445 (1966). "ESR Line Widths in Solution. IV. Experimental Studies of Anisotropic and Spin-Rotational Effects in Copper Complexes."

996. R. H. Dunhill, J. R. Pilbrow, and T. D. Smith, *J. Chem. Phys.*, **45**, 1474 (1966). "ESR of Copper(II) Citrate Chelates."

997. R. Pettersson and T. Vaenngard, *Arkiv Kemi*, **17**, 249 (1961). "ESR of Cu(II) and Ag(II) Dithiocarbamates."

998. R. A. Zhitnikov and N. V. Kolesnikov, *Fiz. Tverd. Tela*, **7**, 1710 (1965). "Hyperfine Structure in Paramagnetic Resonance Spectra of Ag, Au, and Cu Free Atoms Stabilized in a Benzene Matrix at Liquid Nitrogen Temperatures."

999. R. Kh. Timerov, Yu. V. Yablokov, and A. V. Ablov, *Dokl. Akad. Nauk SSSR*, **152**, 160 (1963). "Study of Cupric Bisdimethylglyoximate by the EPR Method."

1000. R. M. Deal, D. J. E. Ingram, and R. Srinivasan, *Proc. Colloq. Ampere*, **12**, 239 (1963). "Electron Resonance of Phthalocyanine Complexes."

1001. R. G. Barnes, D. A. Cornell, and D. R. Trogeson, *Phys. Rev. Letters*, **16**, 233 (1966). "Paramagnetic Resonance of Cobalt in Intermetallic Compounds."

1002. Sh. Sh. Bashkirov, *Zh. Eksperim. i Teor. Fiz.*, **34**, 1465 (1958). "Paramagnetic Lattice Relaxation in Hydrated Salts of Bivalent Copper."

1003. S. J. T. Owen, K. J. Standley, and A. Walker, *J. Chem. Phys.*, **40**, 183 (1964). "ESR in Anhydrous Copper Nitrate."

1004. S. E. Harrison and J. M. Assour, *Paramagnetic Resonance, Proc. Intern. Conf., 1st, Jerusalem*, **2**, 855 (1962). "ESR of Copper Phthalocyanine."

1005. S. Fujiwara and H. Hayashi, *J. Chem. Phys.*, **43**, 23 (1965). "ESR of Cu^{2+} Ions in Aqueous Solution."

1006. T. Vanngard and S. Akerstrom, *Nature*, **184**, Suppl. No. 4, 183 (1959). "ESR and Bivalency of Some Dithiocarbamates of the Coinage Metals (Cu, Ag, Au)."

1007. T. I. Volokhova, *Paramagnitn. Rezonans, Kazansk, Univ., Sbornik*, **1960**, 120. "Paramagnetic Relaxation on Certain Copper Salts."

1008. T. R. Reddy and R. Srinivasan, *J. Chem. Phys.*, **43**, 1404 (1965). "ESR and Optical Absorption Studies in Copper Diethyldithiocarbamate."

1009. U. S. Ghosh and A. K. Pal, *Indian J. Pure Appl. Phys.*, **2**, 332 (1964). "Application of EPR Technique to Find the Orthorhombic g Values of the Magnetic Complex and Their Orientations in Monoclinic Paramagnetic Crystals."

1010. U. S. Ghosh, A. K. Pal, and R. N. Bagchi, *J. Phys. Chem. Solids*, **26**, 2041 (1965). "Investigations on the Orthorhombic g Tensors in $Cu(KSeO_4)_2 \cdot 6H_2O$ and $Cu(NH_4SeO_4)_2 6H_2O$ Crystals by EPR."

1011. U. S. Ghosh, R. N. Bagchi, and A. K. Pal, *Indian J. Phys.*, **37**, 555 (1963). "A 1.2 cm. EPR Spectrometer and Paramagnetic Resonance in Some Copper Salts."

1012. V. F. Anufrienko, E. K. Mamaeva, and N. P. Keier, *Dokl. Akad. Nauk SSSR*, **168**, 116 (1966). "EPR Spectra of Catalytically Active Chelated Copper Complexes."

1013. V. F. Anufrienko, E. K. Mamacva, N. P. Keier, L. M. Kefeli, A. P. Terent'ev, and E. G. Rukhadze, *Dokl. Akad. Nauk SSSR*, **159**, 1059 (1964). "ESR Spectra of Cupric α-Thiopicolineanilide."

1014. V. M. Nagiev, *Izv. Akad. Nauk Azerb. SSR, Ser. Fiz.-Tekhn, i Mat. Nauk*, **1965**, 92. "EPR of Cu^{2+} in Borate Glasses."

1015. V. F. Anufrienko and A. P. Zeif, *Opt. i Spektroskopiya*, **20**, 652 (1966). "Covalent Bond in Cu^{2+} α-Thiopicolinanilide by the EPR Method."

1016. W. Schuebel and E. Lutze, *Z. Angew. Phys.*, **17**, 332 (1964). "EPR from Copper Complexes in Solution."

1017. W. J. Caspers, *Physica*, **26**, 778 (1960). "Theory of Spin–Spin Relaxation."

1018. W. Berger and H. J. Kossler, *Naturwissenschaften*, **47**, 424 (1960). "Directional Dependence of Paramagnetic Resonance in Copper Sulfate, $CuSO_4 \cdot 5H_2O$."

1019. W. Schneider and A. v. Zelewsky, *Helv. Chim. Acta*, **48**, 1529 (1965). "ESR Spectra of CuN_4 Chromophores. Complexes of Copper(II) with Pyridine and Pyridine Derivatives."

1020. W. Low and J. T. Suss, *Phys. Letters*, **7**, 310 (1963). "Jahn-Teller Effect of Ni^+ and Cu^{2+} in Single Crystals of Calcium Oxide."

1021. Y. Nagaoka, *J. Phys. Soc. Japan*, **13**, 1328 (1958). "Paramagnetic Relaxation of Copper Tutton Salt."

1022. Y. Matsunaga, *Bull. Chem. Soc. Japan*, **34**, 1291 (1961). "ESR of Cupric Oxide–Alumina Catalysts."

1023. Yu. V. Yablokov and A. V. Ablov, *Dokl. Akad. Nauk SSSR*, **144**, 173 (1962). "EPR·of Anhydrous Cu Salts of Monocarboxylic Acids."

1024. Yu. V. Yablokov, *Zh. Strukt. Khim.*, **5**, 222 (1964). "Determination of the Parameters of the Spin Hamiltonian for Copper Salts with $S = 1$ from the EPR Spectra of Polycrysts."

1025. Z. Sroubek and K. Zdansky, *J. Chem. Phys.*, **44**, 3078 (1966). "ESR of Cu^{2+} Ion in $CdWO_4$, $ZnWO_4$, and $MgWO_4$ Single Crystals."

1026. Z. Sroubek, K. Zdansky, and E. Simanek, *Phys. Status Solidi*, **6**, K149 (1964). "Paramagnetic Resonance of Cu^{2+} in $CdWO_4$."

1027. J. D. W. van Voorst and P. Hemmerich, *J. Chem. Phys.*, **45**, 3914 (1966). "ESR of $Fe(CN)_5NO^{3-}$ and $Fe(CN)_5NOH^{2-}$."

1028. P. T. Manoharan and H. B. Gray, *J. Am. Chem. Soc.*, **87**, 3340 (1965). "Electronic Structure of Nitroprusside Ion."

1029. I. Bernal and E. F. Hockings, *Proc. Chem. Soc.*, **1961**, 361. "The Pentacyanonitrosylferrate(II) Anion."

1030. E. F. Hockings and I. Bernal, *J. Chem. Soc.*, **1964**, 5029. "Properties of Pentacyanonitrosylferrates."

1031. B. A. Goodman, D. A. C. McNeil, J. B. Raynor, and M. C. R. Symons, *J. Chem. Soc.*, **1966A**, 1547. "ESR of γ-Irradiated Sodium Nitroprusside."

1032. M. Mori, J. A. Weil, and J. K. Kinnaird, *J. Phys. Chem.* (to be published). "Preparation and EPR Spectroscopy of Dicobalt-Peroxo Anions."

1033. J. H. Bayston, F. D. Looney, and M. E. Winfield, *Australian J. Chem.*, **16**, 557 (1963). "Paramagnetic Products of the Oxidation of Cyanocobaltate(II)."

1034. D. R. Scott, Ph.D. thesis, University of Houston, 1965. "Electronic Spectra and Bonding of Transition Metal Sandwich Complexes."

1035. E. I. Stiefel, J. H. Waters, E. Billig, and H. B. Gray, *J. Am. Chem. Soc.*, **87**, 3016 (1965). "The Myth of Nickel(III) and Nickel(IV) in Planar Complexes."

1036. A. H. Maki, T. E. Berry, A. Davison, R. H. Holm, and A. L. Balch, *J. Am. Chem. Soc.*, **88**, 1080 (1966). "Concerning Cation-Stabilized Anion Free Radicals."

1037. A. Davison, N. Edelstein, R. H. Holm, and A. H. Maki, *Inorg. Chem.*, **2**, 1227 (1963). "The Preparation and Characterization of Four Coordinate Complexes Related by Electron Transfer Reactions."

1038. B. R. McGarvey, "ESR of Transition Metal Complexes," *Transition Metal Chemistry*, Vol. 3, R. L. Carlin, Ed., Marcel Dekker, New York, 1966, p. 89.

1039. H. A. Kuska and M. F. Farona, *Paper 159, Phys. Chem. Div., Am. Chem. Soc., 152nd Meeting, New York, 1966.*

1040. S. Nomura and T. Nakagawa, *J. Phys. Soc. Japan.*, **21**, 1679 (1966). "Magnetic Properties and Optical and Paramagnetic Spectra of Divalent Nickel in $Sr_2(NiW)O_6$."

1041. H. A. Jahn and E. Teller, *Proc. Roy. Soc. (London)*, **A164**, 117 (1938).

1042. A. Horsfield, J. R. Morton, J. R. Rowlands, and D. H. Whiffen, *Mol. Phys.*, **5**, 248 (1962).

1043. J. J. Wise, Ph.D. thesis, Chemistry Department, Massachusetts Institute of Technology, 1965. "Assignment of Spectral Transitions in Bis(Dipivaloylmethanido)copper(II)."

1044. R. E. Drullinger, H. A. Kuska, and M. T. Rogers, *J. Phys. Chem.*, **71**, 109 (1967). "Effect of Substituents on the Anisotropic ESR Parameters in Copper Acetylacetonates."

1045. R. E. Dietz, H. Kamimura, M. D. Sturge, and A. Yariv, *Phys. Rev.*, **4**, 1559, (1963). "Electronic Structure of Copper Impurities in ZnO."

1046. H. C. Allen, G. F. Kokoszka, and C. W. Reimann, *Phys. Rev.*, **4** (1963). "The Optical and Magnetic Spectra of Copper-Doped Dichloro-(1,10-Phenanthroline) Zinc."

1047. P. H. Kasai, E. B. Whipple, and W. Weltner, Jr., *J. Chem. Phys.*, **44**, 2581 (1966). "ESR of $Cu(NO_3)_2$ and CuF_2 Molecules Oriented in Neon and Argon Matrices at 4°K."

1048. G. Voelkel and W. Windsch, *Phys. Status Solidi*, **17**, K75 (1966). "EPR Investigation of Cu-Doped Seignette Salt Single Crystals."

1049. J. H. Venable, Ph.D. thesis, Yale University, 1965. "Magnetic Methods for Protein Single Crystals: Metal Binding to Insulin."

1050. W. Low and M. Weger, *Phys. Rev.*, **118**, 1119 (1960). "Paramagnetic Resonance and Optical Spectra of Divalent Iron in Cubic Fields. I. Theory."

1051. W. Low and M. Weger, *Phys. Rev.*, **118**, 1130 (1960). "Paramagnetic Resonance and Optical Spectra of Divalent Iron in Cubic Fields. II. Experimental Results."

1052. C. P. Poole, Jr., *Electron Spin Resonance*, Interscience, New York, 1967.

1053. G. F. Kokoszka, C. W. Reimann, and H. C. Allen, Jr., *J. Chem. Phys.*, **71**, 121 (1967). "Optical and Magnetic Spectra of Copper-doped Dichloro-(1,10-phenanthroline) Zinc."

1054. B. H. J. Bielski and J. M. Gebicki, *Atlas of ESR Spectra*, Academic Press, New York, 1967.

1055. D. J. E. Ingram, *Spectroscopy at Radio and Microwave Frequencies*, 2nd ed., Plenum Press, New York, 1967.

1056. B. Bleaney and K. W. H. Stevens, *Rept. Progr. Phys.*, **16**, 108 (1953). "Paramagnetic Resonance"; K. D. Bowers and J. Owen, *Rept. Progr. Phys.*, **18**, 304 (1955). "Paramagnetic Resonance II"; J. W. Orton, *Rept. Progr. Phys.*, **22**, 204 (1959). "Paramagnetic Resonance Data."

1057. Landolt-Börnstein, Group II, Vol. II, *Magnetic Properties of Coordination and Organometallic Transition Metal Compounds*, Springer-Verlag, New York, 1966.

Author Index

Numbers in parentheses are reference numbers and show that an author's work is referred to although his name is not mentioned in the text.   Numbers in *italics* indicate the pages on which the full references appear.

A

Aalbersberg, W. I., 153(10), 202(10,191), *204*, *209*, 398(48), *416*
Aasa, R., 625(304), 648(533,536), *711*, *721*
Abakumov, G. A., 188(128), *207*
Abe, H., 639(432), 657(643), 659(672), 693(928–932), 694(929,931), *717*, *726*, *727*, *739*
Ablov, A. V., 693(999,1023), *742*, *743*
Abragam, A., 29, *33*, 584, 589, 672, *700*, *735*
Abraham, A., 457(81), *472*
Adam, F. C., 21(64), *32*, 76, *85*, 254(191, 192), 259(281), *269*, *272*
Adams, G. E., 549(88), 558(115), 561 (115), 567(115), 568(115), *576*, *577*
Adams, J. Q., 20(55), *32*, 187, 203(196), *207*, *209*, 251(138), *268*
Adams, M., 94(41), 95(41), 148(41), *149*
Adams, R. N., 153(21), 182(120), 185 (114,116,117,120), 200(114,117), 202 (21,117), *205*, *207*, 232(13), *243*, 251 (116,118,121,125), 260 (297,298,305, 311), 261, 264, *268*, *272*, *273*
Addé, R., 490, 498(50), 510, *521*
Adema, E. H., 616(196,198,211), *706*
Adrian, F. J., 437(42–44), 438(42–44), 439, 440, *471*, 537(45), *575*
Adrianov, V. G., 638(392), *715*
Ainbinder, N. E., 638(312), *711*
Akamatu, H., 190(144), 191(144), *208*
Akao, F., 499(65), *521*
Akerstrom, S., 694(1006), *743*
Albrecht, A. C., 333(11), 336(17), 382, 396(11), *415*
Alexander, S., 75(100), *85*
Alger, R. S., 347, 410(25), *415*, 564(123), *577*
Ali, M. A., 252, *269*

Ali, M. H., 626(268), 627(268), *709*
Ali, M. I., 626(268), 627(628), *709*
Allara, D. L., 178(94), 187, 195(94), 202(94), *207*
Allen, A. O., 476(3), 508(70), 509(77), 515(70), *520*, *522*
Allen, B. T., 252(163), 254(203), *269*, *270*, 640, 641(627), 656(441,449,627), *717*, *718*, *725*
Allen, H. C., Jr., 608(160), 611, 693(893, 916,917,934), 697, *704*, *737–739*, *744*, *745*
Allen, P. E. M., 616(243), *708*
Allendoerfer, R. D., 251(129), *268*
Allinger, N. L., 118
Allred, A. L., 249(89), *267*, 291–295, *298*
Al'tshuler, S. A., 581, 616(205,208), 617 (253), 638(406), 674(205,820), 691 (840), 692(406), *698*, *706*, *708*, *716*, *735*
Alzotta, G., 641(666), 658(664,666), *721*
Amos, T., 14, 17(42), *32*, 154(28), 155 (28), 157, 159, 160(28), *205*, 258, 259, *271*, *272*
Anbar, M., 549(87), *576*
Anderson, D. H., 9(16), *31*, 185(115), *207*, 246(7,8), 247(7,8), *265*
Anderson, J. H., 453(74), *472*, 537(46), *575*, 581, *698*
Anderson, M. E., 246 (9–11), 247 (9–11), *265*
Anderson, P. W., 75(96), *85*, 588, *701*
Anderson, R. S., 581, *698*
Anderson, T. H., 347, 410(25), *415*
Anderson, W. A., 75(95), *85*, 610 (158), *704*
Andreeva, E. V., 628(267), *709*
Andresen, H. G., 634(293), 637(293), *710*, *728*
Angelescu, E., 610(148), 611(166), 638 (148), *703*, *704*
Angyal, S. J., 118

747

W

Subject Index

A

Acenaphthenequinone, 44, 77, 80
Acetoin, 104, 105
  di-*t*-butyl semidione, 105
  diisopropyl semidione, 105
Acetonitrile, 224
Acetophenone, 98
  electrolytic reduction, 98
  1-phenylpropane-1,2-semidione, 98
2-Acetoxycyclobutanone, 108
Acetoxyethanal, 100
  glyoxal radical anion, 100
Acetyl group, 214
Acyclic semidiones, 100
Acylil, 89
Acyloin, 89
Acyloin condensation, 98
Acylyl, 89
Alkali atoms, 539
Alkylcyclohexane-1,2-semidiones, 117
Alkyl radicals, 9
Alloxan, 95, 147
  ninhydrin semitrione, 95
  reduction of, 147
Alloxantin, 147
  dissociation of, 147
  phenylglyoxal radical anion, 100
Allyl radical, 4, 11
  experimental spin densities in, 11
  spin density matrix, 4
Alternant aromatic hydrocarbons, 12, 570
  radical ions, 12
Aluminophosphate glasses, 531, 542, 555
Analysis, 476, 479, 480
  for nitric oxide, 479
  for nitrite, 476
  for nitrogen dioxide, 479
  for $NO_2{}^{2-}$, 480
  for $N_2O_3{}^{2-}$, 480
5α-Androstan-17β-ol-2-one, 132
  oxidation of, 132
  semidiones derived from, 132
5α-Androstan-17β-ol-3-one, 132
  oxidation of, 132
  semidiones derived from, 132

5α-Androstan-17-one, 137
  oxidation of, 137
p-Anisaldehyde, 235
Anisole, 213, 232–238, 242
Anisotropic hyperfine energy, 27
Anthracene, 12, 38, 81, 570, 571
  negative ion, 12
  positive ion, 12
  Q_{CH}^{H} in, 12
Anthracene positive and negative ions, 12, 23
  calculated and experimental ^{13}C splittings and spin densities in, 23
  [13]C hyperfine splittings in, 12
Anthracenide ion, 78
Antimony, 555
  in glasses, 555
Aqueous glasses, 531
  See also Ices.
Aromatic radical ions, 568, 569
  in boric acid glass, 569
  in glasses, 568
Arsenic, 527, 555
  As^0, 527
  As(IV), 555
  in glasses, 555
1-Aryl-2-alkyl semidiones, 101
Aryl ethers, 232
Arylthiosemiquinone radicals, 302
Ascorbic acid, 88
As (OH)₄ radical, 443
Atom exchange reactions, 76, 78, 83
Atomic orbital-spin density, 3
Atomic solutions, 561
Atom transfer reactions. *See* Atom exchange reactions.
A values, 118
p,p'-Azoanisole, 239, 241

B

Benzaldehyde, 45
Benzene, 9, 14, 211–213, 233, 243, 334, 572, 573
Benzenes, 224

785